Jerusalem Interlude

Books by Brock and Bodie Thoene

The Zion Covenant

Vienna Prelude
Prague Counterpoint
Munich Signature
Jerusalem Interlude
Danzig Passage
Warsaw Requiem

The Zion Chronicles

The Gates of Zion
A Daughter of Zion
The Return to Zion
A Light in Zion
The Key to Zion

The Shiloh Legacy

In My Father's House
A Thousand Shall Fall
Say to This Mountain

Saga of the Sierras

The Man From Shadow Ridge
Riders of the Silver Rim
Gold Rush Prodigal
Sequoia Scout
Cannons of the Comstock
The Year of the Grizzly
Shooting Star

Non-Fiction

Protecting Your Income and Your Family's Future
Writer to Writer

Jerusalem Interlude

Bodie Thoene

Research and Development By
Brock Thoene

BETHANY HOUSE PUBLISHERS
MINNEAPOLIS, MINNESOTA 55438

Cover illustration by Dan Thornberg,
Bethany House Publishers staff artist.

Published by Bethany House Publishers
A Ministry of Bethany Fellowship, Inc.
6820 Auto Club Road, Minneapolis, Minnesota 55438

Printed in the United States of America

Library of Congress Cataloging-in-Publication Data

Thoene, Bodie, 1951–
    Jerusalem interlude / Bodie Thoene.
        p. cm. — (The Zion covenant) ; 4)

    1. Holocaust, Jewish (1939–1945)—Fiction.
2. Jews—History—20th century—Fiction.
I. Title. II. Series: Thoene, Bodie, 1951–   Zion covenant ; bk. 4.
PS3570.H46J47   1990
813'.54—dc20   90-1283
ISBN 1-55661-080-7   CIP

With much love
we dedicate this story
to Luke,
who has a heart for God
and a talent
which just might create
a second generation
of Thoene writers!

The Authors

BODIE THOENE (Tay-nee) began her writing career as a teen journalist for her local newspaper. Eventually her byline appeared in prestigious periodicals such as *U.S. News and World Report*, *The American West*, and *The Saturday Evening Post*. After leaving an established career as a writer and researcher for John Wayne, she began work on her first historical fiction series, The Zion Chronicles. From the beginning her husband, BROCK, has been deeply involved in the development of each book. His degrees in history and education have added a vital dimension to the accuracy, authenticity, and plot structure of the Zion books. The Thoenes' unusual but very effective writing collaboration has also produced two non-fiction books, *Writer to Writer* and *Protecting Your Income and Your Family's Future*, as well as a new frontier fiction series, The Saga of the Sierras. Along with their prolific writing schedule, Brock and Bodie make a home for their teenagers in the California Sierras.

Acknowledgment

Our special thanks to Joseph Samuels, whose extensive knowledge and experience earns him the title of our honorary Rebbe! After a lifetime of building great synagogues across America, Joe has brought the same dedication to the monumental task of helping with the research of this series.

We thank the Lord daily for bringing you into our lives and work...

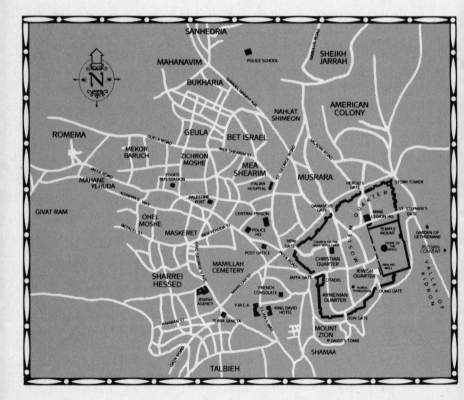

Contents

Prologue

SAN FRANCISCO
1984

Outside the ornate facade of the Far East Cafe, the neon lights of San Francisco's Chinatown blinked and shimmered a bright reflection on the rain-slick street.

Dr. Charles Kronenberger loved this street. Ever since Murphy and Elisa had brought him and Louis here as children, the place had reminded him of a set for a Charlie Chan mystery movie. He had never shed the little-kid excitement of those days, and tonight he felt it again, stronger than ever. He hefted Tikvah Thurston's cello case and pulled her beneath the awning as rain pelted from the sky.

It was almost midnight, yet a few souvenir shops remained open. Through plate-glass windows, Charles and Tikvah could see round-faced clerks reading Chinese newspapers behind cluttered counters.

A clique of diehard tourists shouted and laughed as they trudged from one shop to the next in search of some elusive bargain.

A yellow cab splashed by, and Tikvah looked up at Charles. Her eyes were warm, happy—familiar to Charles, although he had never met her before tonight.

"What is it?" he asked, sensing that there was something this beautiful woman wanted to say.

Her smile became shy. She looked away at the pools of color and light mirrored on windshields and hoods and bumpers. "I . . . I love . . . San Francisco. That's all."

He felt an urge to stoop and kiss her, but he did not. Instead, he brushed a damp strand of hair from her forehead. Even that small touch seemed to startle her. "Yes." He looked quickly away, glad he had not followed his first impulse. "Me, too. I love this place. It doesn't matter if it's midnight. Chinatown is on Hong Kong time. It's lunchtime in Hong Kong. Are you hungry?"

She nodded and smiled, moving toward the doorway of the restaurant. She seemed to have recovered from his too-familiar touch. A diminutive and ancient Oriental man in a headwaiter's tuxedo shuffled toward them, worn menus cradled in his arm. He bowed slightly and gestured toward a carved teakwood arch. Beyond lay a long corridor lined with private dining rooms with curtains across the doors.

Tikvah craned her neck upward as she gazed in astonishment at enormous bronze chandeliers suspended above them. Several decades of dust coated the massive fixtures. She grinned back over her shoulder at Charles. "I hope this is not the night the big quake happens!" She laughed, and Charles knew she felt in this place the sense of mystery that had always captivated him. Even if he had not been sent to find her, even if he were not carrying the letters he must deliver to her, he would have wanted to be here with her.

The waiter paused halfway down the corridor and pulled back a curtain to reveal a round table in the center of a small cherry-paneled room. Tikvah entered, and Charles followed. Before they could turn around, the curtain was drawn and they were alone.

Tikvah did not meet his eyes as she unbuttoned her coat. Charles propped the precious cello in the corner. Strange. Never had he thought of this wonderfully sinister place as *romantic*—until now!

"All these years in Frisco, and I've never been here." Tikvah's voice betrayed her excitement. "Private dining rooms; perfect for musicians. It's the same size as a practice room, so I won't have withdrawal being away from the concert hall."

The clatter of dishes drifted over the partition. "A bit noisier than the practice room. Maybe next time we can order take-out and eat back at the hall."

Next time! He could not believe he had said that. *Too quick. Too sure. Too hopeful.*

He had not felt this way about any woman since Edith had died. He had not wanted to see anyone. He had almost forgotten what it was like to have a woman smile at him.

Once again the urge to kiss her swept over him. He fumbled with the buttons of his overcoat, then frowned as he reached into the deep inside pockets to retrieve two bound packets of letters. He placed the packets on the table between them. He had meant to give them to her after dinner, but he needed the distraction from this unexpected jumble of emotions.

Her smile was curious as she reached out to touch one packet of yellowed envelopes. In faded ink, the address read:

Mrs. Elisa Murphy
#36 Red Lion Square
London, England

The postage stamp bore the emblem of the British Mandate of Palestine and the postmark of Jerusalem, dated October 1938.

Tikvah's smile faded as realization flooded her. She looked from the packets into Charles's eyes.

He answered the unspoken question. "A gift for you. From my mother. From Elisa."

"From . . ." Tikvah swallowed hard; she had difficulty finding her voice. Her fingers trembled as she picked up a packet and turned it to reveal the return address written in delicate hand:

Leah Feldstein
Post Office Box 679
Jerusalem,
British Mandate Palestine

She gasped and held the packet against her cheek as if Charles had presented her with a priceless treasure. Indeed, he had. "Elisa," she managed to say. "My mother wrote her . . ."

"Of course. They were friends. Best friends. Elisa kept these in a shoe box. Sometimes she would take them out and read them over and over again. Especially aloud. And she would tell Murphy that some-day the story must be published—you know, all the early struggles in Jerusalem. What it was really like. Leah was a wonderful writer. She recorded all of it."

Tikvah's tears spilled over, and she carefully wiped the drops from the frail envelopes lest the ink run.

"There was nothing left, you know," she whispered. "After the Arab Legion captured the Jewish Quarter of Jerusalem where she lived, everything was destroyed. Everything. It was a miracle that the cello survived. And then for nineteen years the Arabs would not let any Jew come home. No one to visit her grave." She faltered. "Or my father's."

"Elisa knew you would want her letters."

"All my life I have longed for some word from my mother. All . . . no matter how wonderful others may be . . ." She touched her hand to her heart. "*I never stopped wishing for her!* Sometimes in the music I heard her voice. In the music I thought I could *almost* feel her holding me." Tikvah brushed away her tears and shrugged, embarrassed by her emotion. "I never told anyone that before. Silly. I am older now than she was when she died. But still—*I long for her!*"

Charles nodded, saddened at the years that were lost to Tikvah. "Elisa and Murphy were told your mother died in the siege. Elisa knew Leah was expecting a child, but no mention was made of the baby . . . of your survival. As soon as she found out, we traced you. Traced you here to San Francisco." He shrugged and paused awkwardly as a waiter slipped in with a steaming pot of tea. Tikvah looked away, hiding her emotion in silence until the man left the room. Then the emotion returned with a rush. She grasped Charles's hand.

"If only I had known!"

Charles nodded. "Yes. My real father was a journalist in Germany. When I grew up I made my way back to Hamburg and dug up everything he had written that had not been destroyed by the Nazis . . . Every word . . . a gift." His eyes lingered on the packets of letters, then rose to meet hers. "Everything you heard in her music, Tikvah—it's all there. So full. From the day she arrived in the Holy Land with your father. Ah, such a story she told! It is *your* story, Tikvah! Maybe she sensed that one day you would need to know."

Tikvah carefully unwrapped the first packet, fanning dozens of letters out on the table before her. Here and there was an envelope addressed to Charles and Louis as well. She glanced up at him as she let her fingers rest on his name. The name her own mother had penned! "I have never even seen her handwriting before now. And you were growing up in the same house where these letters were sent." A tone of awe filled her voice. "She loved you, Charles. Do you think she would have . . . how would she have felt about *me*?"

His reply was a gentle laugh. The question was so poignant, so filled with longing and self-doubt. Charles knew the certain answer to her query, but he would let the living words of Leah Feldstein answer a question that had lingered for thirty-seven years.

"We watched for the postman every day. We waited for her letters. Laughed and cried with Elisa over the news of this and that." Charles pressed his lips together in thought. "There was so much happening then. I can tell you our side of it. But Leah alone must answer your questions. Read the letters and *know her*, Tikvah! Then you will know how she would have loved you. How proud she would have been."

Charles leaned forward and kissed her softly. She did not resist his gentle hand against her cheek.

1

The Parting

Goodbye.

Was there a more painful word in any language? Today, in the ache of their parting, Elisa Murphy and Leah Feldstein could not remember any word that had ever cut deeper.

The beauty of the afternoon somehow made it harder. Warm sunlight bathed the ancient houses of Marseilles. Browns and yellows, soft blues and rusty oranges; the pastel facades glowed like a patchwork quilt on a clothesline. Windows of the houses were shining squares within the squares that reflected the vivid blue of the sky and the movement of the clouds.

Such beauty was meant to be shared over coffee at a sidewalk cafe. Such a day should have been savored leisurely with laughter and conversation. Today all that was ending forever.

The two friends clung tightly to each other as the ship's whistle split the air above Marseilles. Their final words were drowned in the commotion of boarding passengers and shouting dock workers.

Leah kissed Elisa lightly on the cheek. *More than sisters ...* Warm brown eyes held the gaze of deep blue eyes. All was spoken in that long last look: *I will miss you. Thank you for everything. Be careful. I will pray for you. Please write ... I love you!*

These silent words were heard by both hearts and answered by a nod. Elisa shook her head and brushed away the tears on Leah's cheek. Leah managed a smile and did the same for Elisa. *One more hug ...* The whistle again! *Lord, why must it be so hard to leave her now?*

Shimon and Murphy looked on self-consciously. There was no way to make this easier. They had spent a week longer together on the crossing from New York to France, thanks to Murphy. He had found some excuse to stop over in France instead of traveling directly to

London with Elisa and the boys. The extra week had been a time of peace and elegance, like the old days in Vienna. The women had learned to laugh again. The heartache of the recent months had at least receded from the center stage of their lives. Little Charles and Louis had explored every corner of the ship while Murphy and Shimon had played chess and talked politics and watched the friendship of their wives with a sort of envy. Such friendship was rare, and yet they made it look so *easy*—that is, until now.

Now it suddenly became hard. Painful. Almost cruel to know that the daily familiarity must stop at the edge of the Marseilles quay.

The whistle. Insistent, unforgiving, calling Leah to leave for Palestine, while Elisa must travel to London.

Shimon cleared his throat. He touched Leah's shoulder. Elisa turned and hugged him too. More tears.

"Take care of her, Shimon!" Elisa cried as she thumped his arm and stepped back.

Shimon nodded and shook Murphy's hand. Leah hugged Murphy hard, then patted his cheek. "Take care of her, Murphy," she likewise admonished the tall, handsome American.

Elisa handed her a handkerchief. "Blow your nose," she instructed.

Leah laughed and obeyed. Then it was time to gather up belongings. Handbag. Cello case. Always the cello . . .

Elisa captured the picture in her mind like the after-image of a bright light: *Clouds of confetti fluttering down from the decks of the ship. Shimon and Leah together at the rail on the last leg of their journey to Zion. And beside Leah, leaning against her like a well-loved child, was the cello.*

Leah tossed down a long red streamer to Elisa. The two friends held each end as the mooring lines were cast off.

"Next month in Jerusalem!" Elisa called.

Leah heard her. Or at least she read the message on her lips. Leah nodded and tossed loose her end of the streamer, which floated down like a final embrace.

The air of Jerusalem smelled of rain. As if the population sensed a coming downpour, most of its residents had taken shelter indoors. The Arabs gathered in the gloomy coffeehouses of the Old City to smoke their water pipes and sip thick Turkish coffee. Jews of all sects gathered beneath the domes of their synagogues for Sabbath services. Armenian shopkeepers stood in the doorways of their empty shops and stared bleakly up at the clouds that kept the tourists away.

Here and there, small groups of British soldiers hurried through the crooked lanes of the Old City. Some would stop and browse, looking for a memento to send home to England. A few would bargain and buy today, but most would return empty-handed to the Allenby barracks to play cards and bemoan the fact that they had been stationed in such a godforsaken place as Jerusalem. In India, at least there were brothels. In Jerusalem there were only pious Jews and fanatic Muslims and shy Armenian girls who attended convent school.

A truly brave and desperate Englishman might find a female companion among the veiled women in the Arab Quarter. But lately the Arabs had been killing as many British soldiers as Jews. It was not wise to seek solace beyond the Damascus Gate. Many a man had met his end on the curved blade of a Muslim dagger.

On this gloomy day, only a handful of the twenty thousand British soldiers in Palestine passed through Jaffa Gate into the souks and bazaars where Doktor Hockman walked. They passed him without noticing the scuffed leather briefcase beneath his arm. Homesick guardians of the great British Empire, they never suspected that this tall, stoop-shouldered man carried within that case what was perhaps their own death warrants. Certainly it was the death warrant of the British Mandate in Palestine, and the command for the destruction of every Jew who lived there.

Hockman observed these sad-faced young men with the same emotion with which he examined the piles of oranges in the produce market. If these were the best England had to offer, he thought, then certainly the Führer was right in his predictions about the destruction of the British Empire.

He opened a shopping bag and counted out six oranges, oranges grown on the trees of the Zionists. Planting fruit trees was one thing the Jews had done for Palestine. But soon not even a trace of their trees would remain. At that thought, Hockman picked out another half-dozen oranges, and after a moment of discussion paid the wizened old fruit vendor half his asking price.

Two young soldiers joined him at the booth. A short man wearing the stripes of a corporal grinned. "It took me two months to figure out you don't pay what they ask. Not like a shop in Liverpool!" he exclaimed.

"Jerusalem has no equal," Hockman responded in flawless English, "either in the quality of oranges or the number of bargains struck in a day." He smiled and bowed slightly as the soldier proceeded to haggle noisily with the merchant. Oranges. The British were mad for oranges. Hockman sometimes thought that orange marmalade was the sole reason England clung so tenaciously to Palestine.

It made little difference what their purpose was, however. Doktor Hockman was dedicated to setting a different course for Palestine. For two years he had been pursuing a goal, and now it was about to become a reality.

By the clearest of German logic, the Führer had chosen Hockman to guide the Muslim religious leadership of Jerusalem. As a Nazi archaeologist, Hockman, like Hitler and Himmler, believed without question that the Aryan race was the original race created by God. All other peoples and tribes were the result of inbreeding between man and the subhuman creatures who occupied the world in the distant past.

The race of Jews, and those of darker color, were marked as *Untermenschen*, subhumans, destined for service as slave labor to the Aryan race until they were no longer of use. Hitler himself would decide when these races were no longer of use, and even now he was planning an alternate solution for that moment.

For the present, however, the *Untermenschen* Jews were performing the greatest of services for the Third Reich. They were the issue upon which the passions of men could come together in a mutual goal. In every land on earth the hearts of men had united in their hatred of the Jews.

This same hatred had built Hitler's personal army of Brownshirts, and then the S.S. This hatred had been fundamental in the collapse of Austria and the darkness that presently consumed the land in violence. And now, in the autumn of 1938, it had rolled up and over the mountains of the Sudetenland and left Czechoslovakia broken and without defense.

All these things the Führer had predicted. He was the prophet and high priest of the Aryan race. Hockman made the writings of the Führer his own bible. He lived to serve the prophecies. There was much, *much* yet to fulfill, and so he had been selected to come to Jerusalem where other disciples of Hitler's hatred had reasons of their own to see the Jews destroyed and the British government driven from Palestine.

Today that purpose drew him from the vaulted souks of the Old City and propelled him with single-minded intensity down the street toward the gate of Bab es-Silsileh. The name meant "Street of the Chain." One legend told that a chain had ascended into heaven from the site of the Dome of the Rock where the street ended. Yet another legend spoke of a Crusader king from Austria who had been hung there by a chain. The second tale made more sense to Hockman. If legends about Jerusalem taught anything, it was that this was a city of darkness and intrigue and slaughter. Nothing had changed. Nothing at all.

Spice merchants, weary of waiting for customers who would not come, closed the iron grills of their tiny shops. The scent of peppercorns and cinnamon sticks and precious saffron mingled with the cool air. Hockman inhaled deeply and remembered that great wars had been fought over such items as pepper and cinnamon. Religion had been used as an excuse to stir up the ignorant masses of Europe, but the real reason for quests and crusades had been economics—to capture the trade routes.

Hitler himself had discussed this fact with Hockman over a late supper in Berchtesgaden. *You see, Doktor Hockman,* Hitler had said, fixing his blue eyes on him and leaning forward, *this is the lesson I have learned from history. Men will do for religion what they would not do for mere economics! Clothe one's purpose in the robes of a religious cause, and they will gladly die for you. Ah—* He shook his finger and chuckled. *But tell them they are dying for the sake of cinnamon and peppercorns, and they will turn and kill you instead!*

For this very reason, the Führer had first sent his greetings and sympathy to Haj Amin el Husseini, the Muslim Grand Mufti of Jerusalem. Haj Amin had the piercing blue eyes of his distant Crusader forebears, and he possessed a hatred for the Jews that was as great as that of Hitler himself. Blue eyes and hatred of Jews was quite enough for the Führer to decide that Haj Amin must become an ally of the Reich. From that first meeting had come a promise of financial support for armed attacks against the Jewish settlers and the British armed forces. For two years men from the small terrorist bands recruited by Haj Amin had been trained in Germany by S.S. officers. The results had been splendid, just as they had been in Austria, Czechoslovakia, and Spain.

Hitler was certain that the English would soon throw up their hands in despair and turn all of Palestine over to Haj Amin Husseini. He would become king and do as Hitler wished with the Jews. Hitler would keep Haj Amin on his throne for as long as it suited the Reich, and then . . . there were other plans in the works for Palestine. They did not include *untermenschen* Arabs or puppet thrones.

For the moment, however, Haj Amin was most useful. He had recruited a band of five thousand guerrillas from Syria and Iraq and Lebanon—paid mercenaries who were also promised that the cause they fought for was a holy one. Drive the infidels from the holy places! *Jihad!* Holy War! And if you should die in such a cause? *Allah in His mercy will instantly welcome you to paradise!* This was the promise of the Grand Mufti as his men were paid with German money and armed with German-made weapons for the fight.

These holy strugglers fought against the British. They killed Jews. They assassinated members of the Palestinian Arab community who opposed the madness of this cause. Over five thousand Arab Palestinians had died for speaking out against the tactics of Haj Amin or for working with the Zionists. Those labeled as *friend of the Jews* were marked for death.

Under the tutelage of his friend and mentor Hitler, Haj Amin had placed his own followers in positions of leadership throughout Palestine. From the lowliest clerk to the muhqtar of a large village, all were indebted to Haj Amin. As it had been in Germany, so it was now in the British Mandate of Palestine. When Haj Amin called for a general strike, no Arab dared to work on pain of death. When he shouted for vengeance and called for demonstrations in the villages and towns, it was as he willed.

The blueprint of conquest was the same here as it had been up to this moment in Europe. And that blueprint was being carried to the study of Haj Amin in Hockman's scuffed leather briefcase.

Beneath the vaults Hockman walked, past the ornate Mameluke buildings that bordered the Western Wall road. Always ahead of him was the great compound of the Dome of the Rock where the temple of the Jews had once stood. Halfway down the vaulted section, two Jews entered a small doorway on the right. Above the doorway was a Star of David in the grillwork of the arch.

Hockman moved to the left, as though the very air would be poisoned by their breath. This was one of the Jewish soup kitchens that remained open in spite of its nearness to the Muslim Quarter. He mentally marked it as a possible target for the coming activities. The southern exposure of the soup kitchen overlooked the Wailing Wall, and there was talk that the Jews wished to make the building a shortcut to the Jewish holy site that lay in the center of the Muslim Quarter. Yes. The Führer would approve. They would make even daily prayer difficult for the Jews.

It was all so amusing, Hockman thought as the scent of cabbage soup and the sound of Jewish voices mingled to assault his senses. The Jews of Germany longed for nothing so much as they longed for Palestine! "Next year in Jerusalem!" they cried. America would not have them. That hope had died with the sinking of the coffin ship *Darien*. And so it had to be Palestine. So much the better. Round them up in one desolate corner of the world and eliminate them there by stirring up the passions of the Arabs. The Muslim fanatics would save the Reich the trouble.

As was fitting the Grand Mufti of Jerusalem, Haj Amin lived in the most important building on the street. A few drops of rain splashed Hockman's cheek as he entered the small square at the end of the lane. Suddenly he was no longer alone. A dozen Arabs huddled beneath the high arched portal of Tankiziyya, the residence of the Mufti. They had come, no doubt, as petitioners for one favor or another. Haj Amin would see them in due time. If he granted their favors, he would expect them, sooner or later, to return his favor with something much greater.

At the sight of Hockman, two tall black Sudanese bodyguards shoved the petitioners out of the shelter of the portals and barked orders that the doctor must be let through immediately.

Men stepped aside and watched him with a mixture of fear and awe. The question was evident in their dark eyes: *Who could this man be who gains such immediate access to the Mufti?*

Many watched him enter the house of Haj Amin. They whispered their knowledge of his importance to one another, but no one seemed to know what his audience was all about. And certainly no one would inform the British. If he was ever questioned by the British authorities,

Haj Amin had agreed to say that the meetings had been to discuss the possibility of research in the Muslim-held area of the Dome of the Rock.

Another black bodyguard bowed in deep *salaam* as Hockman entered the foyer.

"He is expecting you," said the man in Arabic.

Doktor Hockman replied curtly, "Good. The message I bring is most urgent. I have not had tea this afternoon."

The servant bowed again and then knocked on a massive carved door. The indolent voice of Haj Amin answered through the wood. "Enter."

The door was opened to reveal the small red-haired figure of the Grand Mufti. He was staring out the window as the rain began to pelt the glass. He did not look up, but waved a hand for Hockman to seat himself in one of the two massive leather chairs before the desk. "Doktor Hockman," the voice intoned disinterestedly, "my men saw you enter Jaffa Gate. I expected you some time ago. There is no need for you to purchase oranges like a peasant. Such action delays you. Which delays me."

This Arab intelligence network was as effective as the Gestapo. Hockman tried to guess which of the few faces he had seen on the street might have passed the word along that he was coming.

"I rather enjoy bargaining in the souks," he said lightly as he sat down.

Haj Amin spoke in perfect German, learned from the Germans who had held sway in Palestine in the Ottoman-Turkish Empire before it had been lost to Britain in 1917. "As I said, such delays also affect my schedule." He turned to face Hockman. His blue eyes seemed faded, and he pulled his thin red beard in thought as he sat down in a chair behind his desk.

"Then I offer my humble apology, Your Excellency."

Haj Amin waved an effeminate hand in disregard. "I have been waiting. My friend the Führer has kept me waiting while he bargains in the souks of the world and walks away with everything for nothing. I have waited patiently for some word . . . for more than words. And now I grow impatient as Jews still manage to straggle into Palestine from Europe. What word have you brought me from the Führer?" He raised an eyebrow expectantly.

Hockman smiled. He picked up the briefcase from beside his chair. Placing it on his lap, he held it for a moment. Haj Amin leaned forward, his gaze on the latch. "Here is the reply from the Führer, Your Excellency." With a flourish, he opened the case and pulled out a manila file folder, which he placed on the desk. Then, still smiling, he removed bound stacks of bills. "Eight thousand. Nine thousand. Ten thousand pounds. It is enough to equip and train a thousand additional mercenaries." He paused. "The Führer himself is selecting a group leader for the task of training and leading your men."

Haj Amin silently contemplated the figures on the page Hockman slid across the desk. "This is a fraction of what we need to accomplish our goal. There are British officials to bribe. Equipment and food must be provided."

"Just as the British provided all that to the Bedouin tribes who fought against us and the Turks in the last war?" Hockman laughed at the thought. The British had provided these Arab bands with military leadership under Lawrence and then had given them the weapons that the Arabs now turned back into the face of Britain. "Hitler will not be so foolish as the English have been with you, Haj Amin. You cannot imagine that he would give you everything all at once? Hardly. One favor deserves another." He motioned toward the file. "Read it. The Führer has done you a favor, and now he expects one from you in return. After that, of course, there will always be enough to meet the needs at hand."

Haj Amin lifted his eyes from the stack of bills and the lists of German-made arms and ammunition. He frowned as he picked up the folder. So here he was. Trapped in the same way he trapped the peasants who came to petition him. He did not like it.

2

The Meeting

Eli Sachar sat with his back against the rounded dome of the rooftop. He pretended to watch the haze-shrouded sun as it dropped like a coin into some giant slot beyond Jerusalem.

The trapdoor from the apartment opened and Eli's mother called up. "What are you doing, Eli? Come wash for dinner."

She did not really want to know what he was doing, so the question was followed by a command.

He answered the question but refused the command. "I am praying, Mama. I am fasting tonight."

This was followed by a long pause. "Oy! *Oy!* Fast and pray! Pray and fast! You will be a skinny rabbi, Eli Sachar!"

"The Torah sustains me, Mama," he said, giving an answer that satisfied her, even though it left a gaping hole in his own soul.

In one more year Eli would be a rabbi, graduated from the Yeshiva with honors. It was a dream his parents had carried all the days of his life. But the Torah did not sustain him. His heart was hungry, his mind ravenous. His Jewish soul was torn in two as he listened to the cry of the Muslim muezzin.

The plaintive call to evening prayer echoed over all Jerusalem. It was so common that Jews and Christians paid no attention when the Muslims stopped to bow and pray toward Mecca. The sound of the muezzin was like birds in the trees. It was not meant to awaken the conscience of those who were not Muslims. Eli had lived his lifetime honoring the song. But now it had come to pierce his heart each time he heard it.

The trapdoor banged shut. Eli was alone again with his thoughts and with the melody from the minaret. He closed his eyes and let himself imagine. *She will hear it now as she passes by her window.*

She will stop and look out and think of me. She will know that I am listening, that I am thinking of her. And then she will bow. She will pray. She will ask Allah if someday we might be together just as I ask ...

Emotion flooded him as he pictured the willowy form and dark shining eyes of Victoria Hassan. This was his nourishment: The thought of her as she had smiled at him and told him that her heart would meet his at the call to evening prayer! And yet this nourishment made him more hungry.

"Victoria!" he whispered. Longing for her surged up and made it hard for him to breathe. "Victoria! My love!" And yet, how could this be? How could Eli Sachar be in love with an Arab? With a girl he had grown up with? Just like the cry of the muezzin, he had never really noticed her beauty. He had grown up playing on these rooftops with her brother Ibrahim. Arab and Jew, the two boys had barely noticed the gap between them. But always, Eli had known that the sister of Ibrahim was as far beyond his reach as the moon. It was forbidden. Muslim woman. Jewish man. It could never be. *Never!*

And yet here he was, waiting on the roof as he had promised. Waiting for Ibrahim to come for him again and lead him to her. That which was most forbidden had now become that which Eli desired more than anything else in his life. His body ached with wanting her. His mind reeled with the forbidden possibilities.

The voice of the muezzin died away, leaving a thousand echoes to swirl around Eli. Darkness came too slowly over Jerusalem. Silence crept in, startled by the occasional clang of a shop grate or the barking of a dog. The air became cool, but Eli was sweating in his white shirt and black trousers. His sandy brown hair was damp with perspiration. He clenched and unclenched his fists as he stared out at the broadening swirl of stars above him. "Forgive me, O Eternal! I love her! More than the Law. More than my life! More than—"

"More than your Arab brother, Ibrahim?" The voice of Ibrahim Hassan laughed from behind him.

Eli leaped to his feet. "I did not hear you!"

"You never were as good as I in hide-and-seek."

"You're late."

"I am *early,* Eli."

"It feels late."

"They tell me that is as it should be when a man is in love."

"Then it feels *very* late!"

"*That* is why I allow you to see her, my Jewish brother. Such awareness of time is not the way an Arab man looks at his woman." He stepped across the division between the close-packed housetops. "My sweet little sister deserves better in her life."

Like a drowning man in need of breath, Eli needed Victoria. "Where is she?" he asked.

Ibrahim smiled and his white teeth glinted. It was good that the brother of his heart loved the sister of his blood. Somehow even that which was forbidden must work out sooner or later.

Ibrahim stepped back across the roof and easily jumped over a three-foot crevice that dropped forty feet to the stones below. Eli followed without speaking. The two young men moved effortlessly across this rooftop terrain that had once been their childhood playground. Over the vaulted souks. Above the Christian Quarter. Over the shops and homes of the shoemakers and tinsmiths and spice merchants. Finally, they crossed an unmarked boundary into the Muslim Quarter.

Even in the gloom of night Eli could see the outline of the Old City wall. Ahead and to the right was the rooftop of Tankiziyya where the Muslim Grand Mufti lived. A presence of evil seemed to hover above that place, but Eli was not afraid. He was with Ibrahim, so there was no reason to fear. Beyond the Mufti's residence was the great rounded mass of the Temple Mount and the Dome of the Rock. All this seemed so peaceful in the darkness and starlight of Jerusalem. Christian, Jew, Arab—all rested quietly beneath the roofs, which looked like a field of round caps scattered on the ground. Unless a man knew the borders that marked each religious group, it would be impossible to tell where Jew ended and Arab began. But the chasms were real. Invisible barriers were the most difficult walls to surmount.

"She is there." Ibrahim pointed to the high walls of the stone house belonging to a wealthy spice merchant. "You must climb the courtyard wall. Be careful; there are bits of glass embedded in the top of the wall. She stays there tonight with a friend who also works as a secretary for the British."

Eli studied the stones of the garden wall. Suddenly he was reminded of the gulf between his love for Victoria and the reality of his life as a Jewish rabbinical student. For one instant he almost turned back, but his doubt was smaller by far than his love for her.

"How will I find her?" he asked, choosing a place beside a tall carob tree where he might cross over.

"Inside the courtyard there is a room with a small balcony beside an apricot tree. She will not expect you so soon. You must wait until you are certain she is alone."

Eli nodded. "It feels so late," he said again, and Ibrahim laughed.

"I will wait here for you." Then his voice became solemn. "I trust you with the honor of my sister. Words cannot harm her."

"Of course." Eli was wounded by Ibrahim's hint that nothing immoral must pass between Victoria and him. "By my life, Ibrahim . . . I would not."

"Yes. I believe you. You are a better man than I." He slapped him on the back and sent him the last fifty feet alone.

Eli reached for the thick limb of the carob tree and swung out, linking his legs around the branch. He knew this place. Twelve years ago he and Ibrahim had climbed this very wall to steal oranges. They had been caught and taken home in disgrace. That was the last time Eli had stolen anything. It was also the last time he had trespassed into an Arab courtyard.

The leather of his shoes slipped on the slick bark. The drop to the cobblestones was twenty-five feet. Cautiously, he made his way through the tangle of branches. He wondered if Ibrahim remembered the last time they were here together and if the memory made him smile. Eli remembered well the bits of glass in the top of the wall. As a ten-year-old, the barrier had not seemed as formidable as it did now.

And we climbed down through the branches of an orange tree on the other side.

Reaching the wall, Eli could easily see the dark balcony with the tree beside it. He was disappointed that she was not there waiting for him. He searched the garden for a place to hide until the appointed time. *How long it seems! But how much better to wait here where I can breathe the air she breathes. So close!*

He tore his trouser leg on the glass as he searched for a sturdy old branch of the orange tree. It was heavy with nearly ripe fruit, but tonight Eli had sweeter things in mind. He groped his way through the tangle of waxy green leaves and sharp stems, then dropped the last eight feet to the ground. *Can she sense that I am here?* He sat down beneath the orange tree, his eyes never leaving the balcony window. Like a watchman waiting for dawn, he waited for her. The anticipation of seeing her again made him feel a little drunk. He forgot he was a Jew. Forgot she was an Arab. He was simply Eli and she was Victoria.

Nearly an hour passed before there was light in the window. He leaned forward, ready to call to her, and then he remembered Ibrahim's sharp warning. He must wait until he was sure. If he was caught here they would do much more to him than send him home in disgrace.

A shadow moved back and forth before the light, a delicate shadow. The sight of it made Eli's heart beat faster. He wanted to toss a pebble or run across the courtyard and stand beneath her balcony and call her name. But he dared not move until he was certain.

The French doors opened slowly. Victoria stood for a moment, framed in the doorway, silhouetted by the light. Her dark hair was loose and tumbled down over her shoulders. She wore a long white cotton shift that moved slightly in the soft autumn breeze and seemed to caress her body. *Have I ever seen beauty before tonight?* Eli ached at the sight of her. Still, he dared not move. Perhaps her friend was in the room behind her.

She leaned her cheek against the frame and looked out on the dark and desolate garden. Her eyes were filled with sadness, with longing. *Ah, she feels the pain of it too.*

She sighed. It was not the wind in the leaves. He heard it. He *felt* it. Her face seemed to speak, although she said nothing after the sigh. Was she alone? Eli started forward only one step and then he heard her voice—gentle, a whisper, filled with hope.

"Who has made this rule? Is this the way it must be in Jerusalem? The English gentlemen are always off to this cafe or that with Arab girls. Why must it be *so hard* for us?"

Eli sank back to his place beneath the tree. She was speaking her heart to someone—to her friend, perhaps? She stepped out onto the balcony. The breeze made the cotton shift cling to her and ruffled her hair.

If only I could be the wind. To caress her so ... Eli drew a long breath. *Be patient, Eli. Do not be a fool or she will be the last thing of beauty your eyes will ever see.*

She leaned against the railing. Her eyes still searched the garden. Was she alone? Did she speak to herself? Eli had to be sure.

Again she whispered, "Are not all women built the same by Allah? Breasts for nursing children? A body for the pleasure of a man? I see no difference between me and the English girls or the Jewish girls—"

Eli stood suddenly and called, "Except you are more beautiful!"

Victoria gasped. She looked around fearfully. "Shhhhh! You will be heard!"

"I could not help it." He stumbled from the overgrown path.

"Shhhhh!" she said again. "They will kill you if they catch you!" She leaned far over the banister.

"And I will die if I do not speak to you now."

"But if you die, then I will die, dear Eli ... *please!*"

"If we both die, then perhaps the Eternal will have mercy on us and let us have some small corner of Paradise where there are no garden walls to climb. Where I can love you." He moved to the trunk of the apricot tree and whispered as he climbed up toward her. "And where everyone has forgotten the names of Arab and Jew."

She glanced nervously around. "Ibrahim has brought you too early."

"It felt very late." The climb up was easy. Her face was framed through the branches: sweet and perfect. He reached out, and she reached down. Their fingertips touched.

"Then tell me what time you would have it be, Eli. The hour strikes when our fingers touch. It would be merciful if we could die together." Her voice was a whisper—soft, like the breeze.

He was near enough to lean over the balcony. She wrapped her arms around his neck and kissed him eagerly. "We must stop the clock. Let the night stay forever and I will perch here in this apricot tree to taste the sweetness of your lips."

Her hair brushed his face. Her breath was like flowers. With every kiss he inched nearer along the branch until the balcony was an easy step. He started to climb over, forgetting his promise to Ibrahim. Suddenly, Victoria pushed him away and stepped back out of his reach. Breathless, but in control, she smoothed her hair and managed a smile. Her teeth were as perfect and white as the cotton shift. He reached for her in a gesture that begged for mercy.

She took yet another step back. Her hand rose to touch her collar as if she might quiet the racing of her heart. "You will think I have . . . that I have given you my heart too fast, Eli," she breathed.

He still reached out for her, but he did not step onto the balcony. "Come. Put your hand on my heart and feel how fast it beats for you."

She did not move toward him. She knew the danger, felt the power that might sweep them both away. "My heart answers yours, but from a distance. Please. Let our hearts beat slower so we can decide what must be done so that our hearts are not broken."

"To look at you and not hold you . . . that breaks my heart."

"A lifetime of holding me will mend it again, Eli. I . . . cannot . . . give you satisfaction tonight."

"Then satisfy me with this promise, my love. Victoria, come away with me. Be my wife. Come unto my people, and I swear to you by the stars . . ."

"Romeo!" she laughed. "You fit the part well, my Romeo. And I, your Juliet, await you on the balcony."

She drew close to him as she spoke. She reached out and put a finger to his lips. "Do not swear by the stars. They are so cold and their brightness fades with morning. So might your love—"

"Never!" He embraced her again, kissing her face and her throat until once more she pushed away from him.

"And . . . if your people will not accept an Arab as the wife of a learned rabbi?" Fear filled her eyes.

"But you will no longer be an Arab, don't you see? It will not matter. I will teach you what you do not know. I will teach you . . . everything . . . you need to make me a good wife."

She closed her eyes a moment as the meaning of his words sank in. To go to him would mean denial of her people and her own faith. And yet, how could she live without him? When her heart beat slower she would think. Not now. Not tonight in the dark with only a step between her and surrender.

"A good wife is a woman of self-control. So my mother has taught me. And someday I hope to teach my daughters the same." She managed a smile and blew a kiss good night to him.

"But when?" Pain welled up in his eyes and crept into his voice.

"I will find a way. I will send Ibrahim for you." She placed her hand on the door latch as if it might hold her back from him. "And now . . . good night, sweet Eli. We have so much to think about. So many things.

We cannot be like other couples in love. Be careful on your way back to the Jewish Quarter."

"Send for me soon. The nights are a torment to me without you," he pleaded.

"Then sleep well tonight, Eli. You take my heart with you."

With those words, she slipped into her room and closed the door behind her. For a fraction of an instant, Eli considered following. But only for an instant.

He shinnied down the apricot tree and crept back across the garden. He heard the urgent whisper of Ibrahim as he climbed back up the orange tree. "Pssssst! Hurry, you idiot! The moon is rising! You will be seen!"

"It is worth it for even a moment more with her."

Ibrahim grabbed his friend by the shirt and tugged him upward the last few inches over the wall. "You will not think anything is worth it if we are caught! You are late!" he scowled.

"It feels early," Eli said.

"I was watching from the wall. It is a good thing you did not go any further, or I would have killed you myself!"

"Then did you hear?"

"I heard nothing but the endless smacking of lips." Ibrahim was half angry.

"I asked Victoria to marry me."

The anger melted. Ibrahim stopped beneath the carob tree and embraced him with a laugh. "Brother! I knew it must be! Always my heart has known it was so! My father will have a place for you. Employment. We will work side by side."

"I asked her to come with me to the Jewish Quarter. I had no thought of leaving my people. My family. My training."

The words stung Ibrahim. Then he shook it off. "Ah, you will come to your senses. You cannot live without Victoria. I am certain of it."

Eli did not reply. A heaviness filled him again. He pointed toward the light of the rising moon. "We must hurry," he said. "They will kill me if they find me in the Muslim Quarter."

———

At the sound of footsteps on his roof, Rabbi Shlomo Lebowitz turned his eyes to the ceiling and whispered, "An angel you have sent to this old man tonight, Lord?"

He waited as the footsteps scurried from south to north, scrambling on to yet another room. The old rabbi shrugged. "So. Maybe not an angel. Or maybe an angel who landed on the wrong roof." He sniffed slightly in disappointment. He would have liked an angelic visit tonight to brighten the cloud of loneliness that had enveloped him. "You couldn't stay here a while? Keep an old rabbi company, Lord?"

He lowered his eyes to the photographs laid out on his bed like cards in a game of solitaire. The silent faces of his family smiled up at him. "Tonight, my angels, I am thinking of you once again." He lifted each photograph to the light of his kerosene lamp. He recited each name like a hallowed prayer.

"Etta." He gazed lovingly at the face of his daughter. "Listen to the wind tonight. Your papa sends you blessings." He closed his eyes and held the picture against his heart as he recited a prayer for little Etta as if she were still a child and not grown up with a family of her own.

It was only a photograph, to be sure, but her clear blue eyes radiated warmth and happiness into his tiny apartment. A kiss, and then he replaced Etta on the quilt and picked up the wedding picture of Etta and Aaron. How young they were, and how very much in love they had been that evening in Jerusalem when they had stood beneath the canopy!

"A long time ago," the old man mused. His wife, Etta's mother, had been alive to rejoice on that day. They had not known then how little time she had left on this earth. "My Rachel," Rabbi Lebowitz caressed the name as he spoke it. "Perhaps you in heaven are nearer to Etta and Aaron and the children than I am here in Jerusalem, nu?" He sighed. "Can you travel anytime you like to Warsaw, Rachel? Have you leaned over the cradle of the little girl they named for you? Have you watched her grow into a beauty like her mother? Yes? Oy! How I envy you that. You have seen the grandsons? You have heard their voices and watched them wrestle on the floor while Aaron laughs above them?" Tears came to his eyes. He pictured his wife there with them all. They were all together while he remained here in Jerusalem. Here in the shadow of Solomon's Wall.

He paused and listened, wishing that the footsteps would return. Or wishing that he, too, could leave his frail body and fly up to catch a wind to Warsaw.

"Can you hear me, my love?" He spoke louder and the loneliness threatened to choke him. "You must help me. Please, you must help me bring Etta and Aaron and the little ones here to Jerusalem! Whisper to them, my angel! Tell them Grandfather longs to hold them once more." He lowered his head. "Before I am gone. Ahhhhh. Lord? Are you listening also? Then just a small request, nu? My family, you see. Bring them here from Warsaw."

3

Watchmen on the Walls

Tonight it was as it had always been. There were watchmen on the walls of Zion.

British soldiers, rifles slung over their shoulders, patrolled the ramparts of the citadel. From the Tower of David, eyes scanned the light and shadow of the city for some sign of unnatural movement in the streets.

October 1938 in Jerusalem represented only a few more nights among three thousand years. Again, as long ago, watchmen stood lonely vigil against the Unnamed Darkness that desired to possess Zion above any other city on earth.

Two thousand years before, the Darkness had whispered from the pinnacle of a crenelated tower: *"All this will I give to you if you will bow down and worship me!"*

Before that time and since, the kings and princes of this world had coveted Jerusalem from far away. They had listened to the whisper. They had believed the lie, and they had bowed down and worshiped the Darkness.

The ramparts of Jerusalem had fallen again and again throughout the centuries until now; these watchmen paced their stations on a wall rebuilt countless times. The stones were hewn by a hundred different generations of stone cutters.

From Assyria and Babylon and Rome, generals and kings had encircled the wall and heeded the whisper of Darkness: *"All this will I give to you if you will bow down and worship me..."*

From the north, Christian knights and pilgrims had come to slaughter and rape and profane the name of the One they claimed to follow. *"Bow down! Bow down and worship me and Jerusalem will be yours!"*

The Turks had joined the butchery for seven hundred years. *"Bow down and worship me!"*

The kaiser of Germany had entered through the gates on a white steed. *"All this will I give to you if you will..."*

Centuries of time had blown over these walls of Zion, turning watchmen and kings alike to dust. *"All this will I give to you,"* the Darkness had promised. The dust remained and the stones remained, and tonight there were British watchmen on the walls.

Jerusalem, City of the Covenant, was a desolate reminder of a battle more ancient than the ramparts where these shadows now paced.

Within and above and below these stones, the Prince of Darkness and the King of Light still clashed. And the watchmen on the ramparts heard the whispers: *"Bow down! Bow down and worship me!"*

Tonight the voice of Darkness called out to the people in a new way. Over the wireless radio the president of the Arab Council in Cairo announced resolutions that amounted to a call to war in the British Mandate of Palestine. *"We demand the immediate ceasing of all Jewish immigration! We pronounce the Balfour Declaration to the Jewish people as null and void in the eyes of all Muslims!"*

Captain Samuel Orde picked up his Bible from beside the radio and left the small stone room that served as his office in the city wall.

"We pledge resistance to the British Palestinian Partition scheme by all means available to Arabs!"

Orde took his jacket from the hook beside the door and locked the massive wooden door behind him.

"We demand a general amnesty of all Arab political prisoners and to those living in exile!"

"Where you goin', Captain?" asked Wendell Terry from behind the duty desk.

"Up on the wall. Take a look around."

"The natives are restless after the broadcast, eh, Captain?"

"We further state that these resolutions constitute the only solution of the..."

"Restless?" Orde smiled grimly as he took a rifle from rack. "Prime Minister Chamberlain has given them lessons on how to get whatever they want from the English, Terry. Point a gun. Throw a bomb or two. Blame it on the other chap and then make a threat. That's all it takes. Look what Hitler's got." His words were bitter. "Yes. Chamberlain has given the Arabs lessons."

Terry blinked at him in amazement. The captain had never been so blunt about His Majesty's government before. The young soldier pulled his earlobe nervously. "Yes sir, Cap'n Orde. Except this ain't Czechoslovakia."

Orde pocketed his Bible and pushed the door open, looking to the right and left inside the dark area that led to the steps of the wall. His men were at their stations. He could make each one of them out even in the dim light. He inhaled slowly, drinking in the cool night air of Jerusalem. No scent of gunpowder. Not yet, anyway. He looked back over his shoulder at Terry. "Not Czechoslovakia, eh?" he grinned. "You would be surprised how close it is."

He slipped out and stood a moment beneath the star-filled sky. Crickets still chirped in the tall grass on the other side of the wall. Back home in England the crickets would all be silent this time of year. October. It would be cold at home. Here in Jerusalem Orde did not need the coat he brought along as a cushion to sit on along the walkway.

Orde hailed each of his men as he climbed the steps. He climbed to the top of the wall, not so much to watch as to pray. The world had turned upside down. Once again prophets were being stoned because the truth was too uncomfortable to hear. *Meshugge,* the Old City Jews would say. *Crazy.*

"HALT! WHO GOES THERE?"

"Captain Orde." Orde emerged onto the wall and stepped past the young guard who searched the rooftops for some sign of unusual movement. "Anything?" Orde asked.

"Quiet night, Cap'n. They've all gone to bed with their camels." The words were brave, but the voice trembled.

Orde did not want to add to the nervous boy's tension, but he knew. If ever there was a night for trouble, this was the night.

"I'm glad. That's fine. Two more hours and you're off, eh?" Orde had come up to chat with the boy nearly every night since he and Palmer had been ambushed in Ramle. Palmer had not made it. Wilson had been saved by the sheer luck of a passing half-track. Guard duty on the wall seemed to be the easiest position for the lad to handle since then. No patrols. No emergency calls. Just the wall. The stars. And sleeping Jerusalem.

Orde hoped that it would remain so tonight.

"Sir? I read that verse you told me the other night. I memorized it, like you said," the boy blurted out, grateful that his captain stood the watch with him again. "You want me to—"

"Let's hear it." Orde crossed his arms and looked out over the blue light of the Jerusalem houses. His eyes never stopped searching.

Wilson stood beside him. He also scanned the shadows and light for movement. "My mouth shall praise thee with joyful lips: When I remember thee upon my bed, and meditate on thee in the night watches. Because thou hast been my help . . ."

Orde nodded broadly. "Memorized the Bible so I could quote it during the watches when I was in India. Kept me from being so afraid."

"You? Afraid?" Wilson could not believe it. He laughed, and in the instant of his laughter a single shot rang out from the roof of the Petra Hotel. Orde saw the flash from the corner of his eye, but it was too late. Wilson was flung forward as the bullet slammed into his back. Orde called out the warning to the other troops stationed in the citadel and along both sides of the wall. The popcorn-rattle of returning gunfire drowned out his voice as he shouted, "PETRA! PETRA HOTEL!"

Bullets began to slam the stations from other areas of the Old City as well. Where had they come from?

Orde dragged the wounded boy toward the steps. He called for help from Johnson as a bullet struck the stone above his head, splintering the chips across his face. The rattle of British gunfire by far overpowered the Arab attackers. Minutes passed: one, two, then three. As Orde and Johnson reached the safety of the enclosure with Wilson, the gunfire ceased altogether. Only echoes and silence and the labored breathing of the boy remained.

Yes, Orde was afraid. Tonight he was afraid for himself, for this bleeding soldier, and for what surely must come to Jerusalem once again as the Darkness whispered in the hearts of men.

———

There could be no question any longer that the German High Command would follow Hitler. The Czech-Sudetenland was secure. German tanks were poised at the very edge of the border as they awaited the next command.

The Führer paced before his generals as he spoke. Eyes flicked from him to the large painting hanging on the wall behind him. It was a bizarre image, new to the staff room, although everyone had heard that it had been stored somewhere in the Chancellery. After his victory of will over the English prime minister, the Führer had chosen to hang the painting in the open.

Disembodied spirits swirled with wailing demons around the likeness of the German god of Creation and Destruction, *Wotan*. The painting had been created by the artist Franz von Stuck in the year 1889, but the face of the glowering god was nevertheless the face of Hitler. Strangely, it was the same pose he had used on posters and handbills distributed to the German people.

"Frightening," Canaris whispered to Halder.

Hitler stopped his speech about the Slavic pygmies. He looked directly at Canaris. Like a schoolmaster who has been interrupted, the Führer demanded an explanation of the whisper.

Canaris was not intimidated. He returned the Führer's fierce gaze with steady blue eyes. "I was just remarking how much like the god Wotan you are, mein Führer." Although the words half gagged him, Canaris managed to smile with his flattery. Such ability had saved him more than once when dealing with Hitler.

"Painted the year of the Führer's birth," the obese Field Marshal Hermann Göring remarked, as if everyone in the room did not already know of the eerie coincidence.

Himmler, whose Gestapo rivaled Canaris's Abwehr, smiled and inclined his head as he spoke. "Remarkable. No coincidence, mein Führer."

There were men in the staff room who might have privately argued that point with Himmler in an earlier day. But the power of Adolf Hitler had indeed somehow proved that his rule over the German people was godlike.

Admiral Canaris managed to maintain his look of contentment although a sense of darkness pressed around him. He thought of Thomas von Kleistmann and hoped the Abwehr would find him first. Or that Thomas would have the good sense to kill himself before the Gestapo caught up with him. They had ways of making a man beg to tell everything. And Thomas knew enough to hang half the generals in this room.

Hitler's voice raised and lowered in a monologue. "Of course, President Beneš has not given us everything we requested. The extradition of certain criminals, for instance." A flicker of anger crossed his face. "The Jew Theo Lindheim is now in England with Beneš. No doubt he will continue to do all he can do for our defeat." He raised a finger to make a point. "You see what I have been saying! How true it is! Even one Jew can ruin everything! It is no doubt that Theo Lindheim is the cause of Thomas von Kleistmann's ruin."

Himmler spoke again. "We shall know soon enough. Commander Vargen has traced von Kleistmann to Holland. Amsterdam."

"A country of Jew-lovers," Hitler scoffed. "We could easily rid ourselves of Lindheim, but it is best if we use legal means if possible. We must be above suspicion in the eyes of the world. We must do everything *legally* . . ." The Führer smiled, and the men laughed obligingly, as was expected. "Of course, it is possible to do *anything* legally." More laughter. Yes. He had proven *that* in Czechoslovakia. There would be no stopping him now. Laws would topple to be remade for him. The German god had come to stand before them, to point the way, to laugh with them and berate them as a father might berate errant children. He would also forgive their former doubts because now they belonged to him entirely.

"You also have Abwehr agents involved in the von Kleistmann matter, Admiral Canaris?" Hitler asked.

"Also in Amsterdam." Canaris did not tell Hitler that his men had orders to shoot Thomas on sight. There must be no opportunity for even a hint of the conspiracy to escape his lips.

"Yes. On the job." Hitler stood in silent thought for a moment. Behind him the face of Wotan glared in evil menace from the canvas.

"We have men enough to watch them all. It is wise, however, in the case of Theo Lindheim and the daughter who was so involved with the illegal immigrants . . . We may wait until they are no longer in England, unless opportunity arises. The British have a sense of propriety about these things. They are upset by blood. The French do not mind blood as long as it is not related to them." More laughter. The mighty French Army was looking smaller each day. "Only Germans seem to be able to tolerate the sight of blood." He turned and gestured toward the red, sulfuric vapors that rose within the painting. "For creation of the pure race, there must be blood spilled." He snapped his fingers and a map lowered, covering the portrait of Wotan. Canaris sighed inwardly with relief.

The map was arranged showing the new boundaries of the Reich. Just beyond the red boundaries was a second, yellow line, which encompassed all of Czechoslovakia, Poland, and part of Russia. "There, you see. Soon those lines will also be red." He moved his hand down toward Palestine and the oil-rich Middle East. "Watch Palestine, gentlemen. You will observe that it is also outlined in yellow. What we do in Europe will be mirrored there. My plan is very clear." He lifted his hand in a fist, then raised his index finger and his little finger. "Two claws on the same beast. Poland and Palestine. I will work them in the same way."

He picked up a leather-bound folder and flipped it open. Scanning the pages for a moment, he smiled at what he was about to reveal. "The Polish government has issued an edict regarding Jewish passport holders who are out of the country. Within two weeks, all passports must be stamped with an additional seal or they become invalid. This will make those persons stateless, which means that Poland will not have to allow their Jews back into the country." He scanned the folder again. "This edict will leave the Reich with twelve thousand Polish-born Jews still living here within our borders. This we cannot tolerate!" He slammed his fist down on the table as though someone was arguing. "We will not keep their Polish Jews within the Reich! Such an edict is an affront to Germany and the German people!" Suddenly the voice dropped low again. "We can use such an affront quite effectively to move us toward our goal. It seems a small thing, this matter of passports. But we will use it, and when it is finished we will march into Warsaw just as we will soon overtake the remainder of Czechoslovakia."

Admiral Canaris listened wearily. Britain had proved how little it cared about the plans of Adolf Hitler. There would be no more approaches to their secret service. Thomas von Kleistmann was a doomed man because they had not listened. His old friend Theo Lindheim was doomed. Ah, well. They were small matters compared to what the god Wotan now planned for Europe.

Perched on the window seat, Elisa hugged her knees and gazed out over the dark houses of Red Lion Square in London. Murphy lay sound asleep in the huge Victorian bed he called "the Parade Ground."

Elisa pulled back the curtain a bit farther so the soft light from the streetlamp fell on his face. Such a wonderful face, even with his mouth open and the shadow of a beard on his cheek. He was handsome even with his hair tousled and his arm reaching for her. From his deepest slumber he called her name and patted the empty mattress while she looked on with tender amusement.

There was a sense of magic about this old house. Anna and Theo had found it for them while they had been in America. According to tradition, Charles Dickens had once lived here. It was a lovely place to raise two little boys like Charles and Louis, Anna had reasoned, and so, the house was purchased complete with two rooms of furnishings as a belated wedding gift for Murphy and Elisa.

They had lived in the house for only a short time, but already it felt like home. There was an old-fashioned dreaminess about Red Lion Square—stately houses and ancient trees, even a fifteenth-century church!

The fact that Charles Dickens had once written in these rooms had awakened a sense of awe in Murphy. He touched the banisters and the doorknobs with reverence. He promised Charles and Louis that when they learned English properly, he would read them *Great Expectations* and *Oliver Twist*. At Christmas they would burn a yule log in the enormous fireplace and read *A Christmas Carol* together in the very house where it had been written.

Anna had beamed when her son-in-law had stooped to kiss her cheek. "You did not find us a house; you have given us England!"

"Hard to believe this is the very heart of London," Theo had remarked. "And only a seven-minute walk from here to Covent Garden for Elisa!"

It was, indeed, just a short walk to Elisa's new position with the London Philharmonic Orchestra. Two minutes farther, in Bloomsbury, was the house where Theo and Anna lived with Dieter and Wilhelm. Murphy's offices as head of Trump European News Agency were only a short commute to Fleet Street.

Elisa could not imagine any place more perfect. At last, it seemed, through months of heartache, they had come to a place of tranquillity.

She quietly hummed a bar from the Bach piece, "What God Has Done Is Rightly Done!" At the sound of her voice, Murphy stirred and patted the mattress again. She loved the fact that he looked for her in his sleep, and she was amazed at the ease with which they had settled in. Husband. Wife. The two boys who would soon be legally adopted as their own. It all seemed perfect.

The first floor of the house had been used for storage by the former tenant. Elisa had already decided that she would convert it into a studio where she would give violin lessons when she was not playing for Sir Thomas Beecham and the Philharmonic. Her first two pupils would be Charles and Louis, who still favored the cello but agreed to try the violin and the piano since Aunt Leah had gone to Palestine.

Lovely old Georgian paneling extended up the staircase to the rooms above. The woodwork, painted a mellow ivory, gave the house a feeling of brightness. On the second floor, a short hall led from the foyer to a large, airy room with three windows facing the Square. Here, where the light of morning flooded in to warm the rich oak-planked floors, she and Murphy shared their morning coffee. He spoke of all the things he had in mind for the news service; she told him about the reported quirks of her new conductor and the dozen musicians she had known in Germany and Austria who now played for him.

And when Murphy left for work with his briefcase tucked under his arm, she lingered over her coffee and imagined evenings of chamber music in this room with old friends and happy memories.

Next to this room was a smaller room with low, heavy rafters that reminded her of the ceilings of the Wattenbarger farmhouse. For some reason the room gave her a sense of sadness; she willingly turned it over to Murphy for a study. Three days earlier she and Anna had found a wonderful old rolltop desk for him. It had to be hoisted up through the window and now was against the wall opposite the fireplace. *Like Dickens,* she had told him as he explored the maze of cubbyholes and drawers. Too large to move twice, the desk was proof of Murphy's determination to remain in England for a long time.

The desk was Murphy's toy. Charles and Louis, on the other hand, had filled their room with crates and boxes of toys that Mr. Trump had purchased for them at Macy's in New York and then shipped to England. Train sets and ranks of tin soldiers cluttered the floor until Elisa had rolled her eyes in despair at the thought of ever sweeping the planks. The newspaper magnate had left no shelf at Macy's untouched. Baseball gloves and bats like the one Babe Ruth used cluttered one corner. Murphy promised his chief that he would see to it the boys knew how to swing a bat American style, in spite of the fact they lived in London. Mr. Trump had also provided the funds to hire a special American tutor for Charles and Louis, and a speech therapist from Boston who happened to be doing doctoral work in London. It would not be long before Murphy would be able to make good on his pledge to read the works of Dickens to the boys.

Up one more flight of stairs was the bedroom where Elisa and Murphy slept. It was a large room, paneled in the same Georgian style as the rest of the house. There was room enough for the four-poster "Parade Ground" and an overstuffed sofa in front of an oak-manteled fireplace. Double French doors opened onto a roof garden where the view was the entire panorama of London, including the spires of St. Paul's Cathedral. It was too cold to sit outside for very long, but Elisa could easily imagine what the world would look like when spring came again to Red Lion Square. Beautiful. Perfect. She could not let herself dwell on all the tragic reasons why they had come here. She would not let herself contemplate for long the suffering of those who had been betrayed by peaceful England. For a time, anyway, she longed to rest her heart and mind. She longed to pretend that everything was just as it seemed to be.

Murphy was merciful to her. He did not tell her all the things that flooded the wire service. And she did not ask. She did not read his dispatches or open the newspaper. She kept her schedule for BBC broadcasts close at hand. Music was all she longed for now. When Murphy needed to hear the news, he retreated into his study and closed the heavy walnut door behind him. There were some things her heart could not bear to know. Not now. Not yet. Not while she carried Murphy's child within her.

Elisa turned her eyes back out onto the dreamy old square. Her breath was a vapor on the windowpane as she whispered her thanks. "What you have done is rightly done. . . ."

4

One Alone Survived

For Shimon Feldstein, sleep brought no rest or peace. It had been the same each night. The room he shared with Leah on the luxury liner was a suite, but it made no difference that they were surrounded by soft-spoken stewards in white coats. In the daylight hours, Shimon could look around the cruise ship and reason that this was a lifetime away from the cramped, rusty freighter that had carried him from Germany. Each morning in a new, sun-washed port of call, he would look out across the waters and imagine the *Darien*. He would see again for a moment the bright, upturned faces of five little girls as they brought him paper lilies and told him stories from the day's Torah-school lesson.

When breakfast was served in the liner's dining room, he could manage to shake off those images. Through hours of wandering the lanes of some small Greek island with Leah, he could replace those dear, lost faces with her face, her smile.

But when the SS *Hildebrand* lifted its anchor to sail on; when the darkness descended and Shimon lay down to sleep, it all came back with crushing grief and horror.

Throbbing engines boomed out the too-familiar rhythm he had known for months on board the *Darien*. Sometimes the cadence blended into dreams of a symphony he had performed in Vienna. Sometimes the thrumming heartbeat of the great ship intruded on his dreams as the slap of Nazi jackboots on the cobblestones beneath their apartment window, a giant hammer clanging against glowing metal in the steel mill of Hamburg. In the end, the dream was always the same for Shimon: *The roar of thunder as lightning split the wind. Green water above the mast of the Darien. The groaning of metal as the hand of the deep twisted the freighter like a toy ship. The tiny white coffin of Ada-*

Marie Holbein bobbing to the surface. The lapping of waves. His own gasping breath. A disembodied voice calling out to God for help. And the silence.

The silence finally awakened him. The engines of the liner slowed and stopped. Chains rattled; the anchor slid beneath the water of yet another Mediterranean port. And Shimon Feldstein sat up in his sweat-soaked berth and gasped from the terror of the nightmare that had all been true. No figment of his imagination. *All of it. True!*

As Leah slept beside him unaware, Shimon climbed from the bed and groped his way toward the morning light streaming through the porthole. He leaned his cheek against the cool glass and breathed deeply as he tried to shake himself free from the images. He forced himself to focus on the stone houses that clung to the slopes of this rocky Greek island. In the half-light they seemed to be a soft pastel blue in color. In the daylight they would be white. On the pebble-strewn beach a fisherman gathered his nets. *Is he the only living being in the silent village? No. He is not like me. There are others sleeping in the blue houses. He is not the only one . . .*

Each morning Shimon eased himself back to sanity in this way. But the question never left him. Why had he, alone of all those on board the *Darien,* survived?

The London residence of Theo and Anna Lindheim was a tall, narrow brownstone, identical to every other house on their street.

It was tiny indeed, compared with the great Berlin house on Wilhelmstrasse that Hitler had just ordered destroyed. It was even smaller than the Mala Strana house in Prague.

Anna had chosen it for its brightness and for its close proximity to the house of Elisa and Murphy. . . . *Just a short walk, and we can have tea together. Around the corner from Covent Garden! No room for even a baby grand piano? Ah, well, I can still play Chopin and Schubert on an upright!*

A nice little upright had been found in a dusty second-hand shop down the street. Anna had entertained the shopkeeper and a half dozen awed customers by playing the yellowed ivory keys as if they were attached to a concert grand. After a moving performance of Chopin's Nocturnes, Anna was able to say, truthfully, that she had purchased the instrument *for a song.* The price included delivery up a flight of narrow stairs.

Theo was content with a massive walnut desk that filled half the floor space of a tiny room he called *the study.* The room was a far cry from the enormous library of first-edition volumes he had enjoyed in Germany's better days. Opposite his desk were two nearly empty bookshelves.

Theo had talked of visits to London's book shops in the thought that he might gradually fill those shelves. But now there was no time for a leisurely stroll through the booksellers' stalls of St. Paul's. It might be months before Theo could consider reading a book for pleasure.

He had all the reading material one man could handle. Theo raised his eyes over his glasses and shook his head in wonder at the over-flowing mailbags that flanked his desk. The British postman had esti-mated that nearly two thousand letters had come addressed to Theo in the last two weeks. As many as fifty a day were still pouring in—letters from Berlin and Hamburg and Munich; letters from Vienna and Salzburg; postmarks from the mutilated Republic of Czechoslovakia and from faraway Warsaw.

Dear Herr Lindheim, as a young man I worked for the great Lind-heim's department store in Berlin....

Dear Herr Lindheim, we saw your photograph with much amaze-ment here in Germany. It was thought that you were dead....

Dear ... since my mother was a long-time employee, we were hop-ing you could....

The consulate decrees that we must have a sponsor before we can have a visa....

By a miracle we saw your photograph and once again we have hope that you might help us. Our father worked in the haberdasher department from 1925 until....

It is with much hope that we write you....

Two thousand letters. All different, yet all the same. Desperate. Hopeful. Terrified. The letters asked Theo for help in acquiring a spon-sor so that immigration might be allowed.

Ironically, the Nazi press was responsible for the flood of commu-nication Theo faced. A photograph showing Theo with former Czech President Beneš as they had arrived in England had only rated a back-page space in the London *Times*. The Nazis, however, had splashed the "traitor-Jew" Lindheim's face across the front page of every official propaganda sheet in the Reich.

Along with Theo's photograph with Beneš, *Der Stürmer* devoted an entire page to a violent attack on the Lindheims. The story described how the famous Berlin department store had grown from a little ped-dler's shop through typically Jewish trickery and fraud. Theo was de-scribed as a "Jewish extortioner" who "exploited his Gentile employees and seduced young Aryan salesgirls." A picture of the famous store facade was shown with its closing sales signs in the windows. "This is how the Jew sucks profits from the Aryan public," the caption cried. Beneath that, the address of the British consulate was given so that letters might be written to extradite this Jewish criminal back to the justice of the Reich from where he lived regally in London on the stolen money of the German workers he had exploited!

The response to the Nazi request for justice had been overwhelming. The letters had come by the tens and by the hundreds to the British consulate. But along with Nazi indignation, two thousand pleas for help had also managed to reach Theo Lindheim in this little house in London.

Herr Lindheim . . . Perhaps you will not remember me. I have managed to escape Berlin and now I am in Warsaw. Life is very difficult. . . .

We fear for our lives here in Hamburg. Each day it grows more violent. . . .

They broke my mother's nose in the market. . . .

My father and brother have been arrested. . . .

If only you could send a letter on our behalf. . . .

We pray that we might go to Palestine. Not to be a burden but only to. . . .

Might you use your connections to help me, Herr Lindheim? Once I worked in the shoe department and if you remember. . . .

The German Reich had not expected such a response. The British consulate forwarded the mail faithfully to Theo even as it considered the fierceness of Nazi wrath against him in the letters that poured in.

Theo Lindheim had never been a man to straddle a fence. Now, it seemed, that attribute carried over into public attitudes about him as well. Theo was a much-hated man in Germany. He was also a man much loved and trusted. Whatever was England supposed to do with such an enigma?

Theo Lindheim worked far into the night. A pool of light from his desk lamp encircled piles of correspondence, newspaper clippings, and Theo's open Bible.

Anna did not knock as she entered her husband's study with a tray of cookies and a kettle of steaming tea.

"Almost finished, Theo?" she asked quietly, mindful that their sons slept in the next room.

He shook his head slowly, then removed his reading glasses and rubbed his tired eyes. "Not finished. Probably will never finish." He spoke in short, choppy sentences as if the effort of speaking was too great at such an hour. "It will not end, Anna. We are at war. At war, you see." He laid his hand over the Bible.

Anna placed the tray on a coffee table laden with books and files of correspondence. The rim of light touched the letter from America that Elisa herself had delivered to Theo. The letter was from Trudence Rosenfelt. Bubbe. Anna picked it up and began to read softly. *"I am an old woman. I have no delusions that my life will go on forever. Indeed, I pray that when my usefulness is at an end, my life will also come to an end. That moment has not yet come to relieve me of the grief I feel over the loss of my dear ones. And so I continue to work, to live, so that their precious lives might also have meaning. So that their deaths might somehow awaken the consciences of good people in every nation. For this reason I ask for your help. . . ."*

Anna lowered the page. Her eyes met Theo's. He spread his hands in a gesture of helplessness. "They are only numbers. Meaningless numbers among the millions, Anna. And the nations say there are too many to help. So it seems they are expendable." He lowered his eyes. "But each life is precious. As precious and beautiful as the family that old woman lost. Ah, Anna, *what can we do?"* He held up yet another letter. This one bore the official seal of the British colonial office. Within its neatly typed lines was the request, the *order,* that Theo and Anna Lindheim, as guests of the British government, restrain themselves from any activities on behalf of illegal immigrants.

"They have tied our hands," Theo concluded. Ignoring this "request" would no doubt result in their expulsion from Great Britain, possibly even a deportation to Germany. "We have Wilhelm and Dieter to think about. Our own family. We cannot share this burden with Elisa. Not now. She deserves some time of happiness before . . ." His voice faded. He wanted to say *before war comes,* but he did not. "She needs this time," he finished simply.

Anna poured two cups of tea. Her eyes were full of sympathy for Theo's feeling of helplessness. Had she not felt the same impotence in Prague? Had God not given her a vision, a way to reach out in the midst of such darkness?

"Theo . . ." She managed a sad smile. "Those people, the numbers you speak of, they are each precious in the sight of God. The very hairs of our heads are numbered—so it is written. We must only be willing to dedicate our hands to the service of God's love. Then He will assign our tasks to us. We must not be overwhelmed by the vastness of the problem, sweet husband."

A touch of sugar. A drop of cream. Theo sipped his tea and considered the truth of Anna's words for a long time. This was the Covenant. *God would not refuse the prayer of a willing heart!* Theo had learned this much in the hell of Dachau where men became numbers— still loved by God, yet mere numbers to the Nazis.

"I alone survived that place," Theo whispered. Anna understood his words. "Like Bubbe Rosenfelt, I alone survived. There must be some reason. Some reason why I am here to sip tea with you in London, Anna, while the rest of our world suffers so needlessly."

"The Lord will untie your hands, Theo, when your hands are ready. Rested. Strong again. Until then we will watch and pray together that we will make a difference even to one among the millions."

———

Ernst vom Rath felt the presence of danger at his back as he boarded the Paris subway nearest the German Embassy in Paris. He tried not to look over his shoulder. What would he see, anyway? The faces of a thousand weary Parisians traveling home after work. If he was being followed by Gestapo—and he was almost certain of the fact—his pursuer would wear the face of a Frenchman. Frayed coat. Black beret. Shoes run down at the heels. Everyone on the crowded train felt like the enemy. Ernst disciplined himself not to look, not to guess who it might be.

He held the leather strap as the buzzer shrilled its warning. Doors slid shut with a loud crash. Wheels clacked against the tracks, and lights in the tunnel passed with a strobe effect over the faces of the commuters.

Ernst did not even know where he was going. Had he even bothered to look at the marquee? He had not thought beyond leaving the embassy building for a few hours; escaping the tortured reminders of how Thomas had killed Georg Wand. Ernst was just as guilty as Thomas. They had whispered their treason together before the votive candles of Notre Dame. They had gazed out over Paris from the observation platform of the Eiffel Tower. They had not spoken of Paris, however. Their thoughts had been directed to Berlin. Their hopes had taken the shape of plans for an end of the Nazi stranglehold over their people and their land.

A voice crackled over the speaker. "Metro l'Opéra." Doors popped and slid open even before the train came to a full stop. Ernst pushed through the crowd and stepped from the train. He had no reason for disembarking here. He felt himself flush with the memory that here, at the opera, Thomas had killed Georg Wand. *Why have I come here?* He backed up a step as crowds surged around him. He turned as if to reboard. Too late! The doors slammed in his face. He spun around again and followed the hundreds up the steep stairs to the diminishing light of dusk and the bustle of the broad avenue that faced the ornate opera building.

Vom Rath mopped his brow. Here in the cool of the autumn evening there was no physical reason for the beads of perspiration on his brow. He stopped at a newsstand and pretended to look over the racks of postcards, pretended that he was not drawn with morbid fascination to the place where Thomas had killed Georg Wand.

"You would like a picture postcard, monsieur?" asked an aging, stoop-shouldered vendor as Ernst passed his fingers absently over a card bearing the image of the Eiffel Tower. *We stood just here, Thomas and I. We talked of hope for Germany without Hitler. He told me about the girl he had loved.*

"Monsieur?" the vendor asked again. "Three for the price of two."

Ernst dug in his pocket, paid the man, and slipped the postcards into his coat. He raised his eyes to the building where the greatest musicians of Europe played, regardless of their race. And he remem-

bered the reason Thomas had killed Georg Wand. He raised his chin
slightly as the cold breeze stung his cheeks. Taking a place at a dusty
outdoor table in a nearly deserted cafe, Ernst pulled out his pen and
began to write. He prayed that if he must also die, death would come
quickly; that he would not have a chance to betray anyone. *A postcard
to mother. One to my sister. They must know I love them. I think of
them.* The last postcard he addressed to another opera house, this one
in London.

"Friday again, Rebbe Lebowitz," Hannah Cohen hailed the old rabbi
as he hurried past the steps of Tipat Chalev. "Any word about your
daughter Etta in Warsaw? You are a grandfather again yet?" Hannah
swept the steps, although there was no sign of even a speck of dust.

The old man shrugged. "The child will be two months old and
reciting Torah before I hear any word," he replied with a grimace.
"Still—" He held up his weekly offering to the mailbox. "You see I have
a letter to mail, nu? Every week it is the same—I beg them to come
home to Jerusalem, and they send me clippings about how terrible it
is here!"

"Things are better in Warsaw, I ask you?" Hannah leaned on her
broom as Rebbe Lebowitz paused a moment to consider.

"At least here it is not so cold in the autumn."

"Give me a nice Muslim neighbor any day. Compared to those Catholic anti-Semites in Warsaw the Muslims are saints!" The old woman
raised her eyes toward heaven and for a moment looked as though she
could visualize Muslim saints flying above her. Then suddenly her
expression changed from benevolence to one of disapproval. "Oy! Gottenyu! Rebbe Lebowitz," she cried and pointed the broom skyward.
"They're burning rubber tires *again*!"

The old man's gaze followed the upraised broom to where a dense
cloud of black smoke billowed up from Allenby Square. "So much for
Muslim saints." He scratched his head and grimaced down at his envelope. "The mailing will have to wait, I suppose, until the British
soldiers put the fire out. But then again, it's only a little smoke. Better
to mail it."

"Phui! Such a stink! Oy gevalt! Why don't these Arabs burn something else beside old tires for a change?" She waved her hand in front
of her nose and then rushed into Tipat Chalev to slam down the windows.

The old man stared up at the first cloud of smoke and then looked
back to where another and yet another rose up to blacken the bright
morning sky above the city. He clucked his tongue in disappointment
and coughed at the terrible stench that now pervaded everything.

He resented this. He resented this more than the closing of Arab shops in the marketplace. More than Muslim chants from the Haram. These stinking black clouds would soil the wash on every clothesline, make every bite of food unpalatable, spread a film of coarse black residue on every roof and step and stick of furniture in Jerusalem.

Will these Arab children never run out of old tires to burn? Rabbi Lebowitz wondered.

Hannah poked her head out of the door. Black ash was falling. "All over my steps!" she cried. And then, "You had better not mail your letter today, Rebbe Lebowitz. Looks like the biggest fire is just in Allenby Square."

The old man waved away her warning with a gnarled hand. These tire burnings presented little chance of danger. With such a stink in the air, even the most militant Arab also was forced to retreat indoors to wait until the fires died.

Rebbe Lebowitz covered his head and face with his coat and trudged on as shop grates slammed around him and furious Armenian shopkeepers rescued their displays of merchandise from the street.

Every native of Jerusalem knew that this murky display was for the benefit of the pristine English lords who traveled to Palestine with their notebooks open. Of everything they would see, nothing would make an impression on them as profound as these heaping mounds of burning rubber. Smoke and fire. This was the image they would take home with them to England. *Such foolishness, Lord. True? Of course true.*

Just so no one missed the point, flaming tire bonfires would also blacken the skies of other cities in Palestine. Haifa, Jaffa—anywhere there were English eyes to see and English noses to smell.

Rebbe Lebowitz ducked down a side street that led to the Armenian Patriarchate Road. He walked close to the facades of the buildings as the smoke darkened the sun. The street was nearly deserted. British soldiers on the wall put on gas masks as they stood their watch. They looked like giant insects perched on the stone ramparts. Swathed in smoke and shifting degrees of darkness, they seemed like strange, unearthly creatures, the stuff that nightmares and visions are made of.

5

The Hiding Place

Today the Grand Mufti spoke to his flock with the help of a loud-speaker. Rebbe Lebowitz could hear his voice as it floated over the walls that surround the Dome of the Rock. The voice of Haj Amin Husseini crossed boundaries, violated every tradition of Jerusalem. It called for rebellion and commanded hatred. It stirred the passions of ten thousand Muslims as no voice had done since the time of Saladin.

The roar of cheering worshipers erupted at the end of a sentence. Haj Amin Husseini was certainly one example of English foolishness. The British government had put him firmly in place as Grand Mufti, and since that day there had been no real peace in Jerusalem.

Another roar rose up. The faithful liked whatever Haj Amin told them. It was hard to make out the words exactly. The voice crackled amid static from the P.A. system powered by British electricity.

The old man shrugged and walked quickly through the winding streets. Everywhere Jewish shopkeepers had stepped from their stalls to stand in small groups and strain their ears to understand what Haj Amin was up to now. No one seemed to notice the rabbi as he made his way past familiar faces of friends and neighbors. He knew that Haj Amin would continue to shout his Friday sermon for at least another hour. That was certainly time enough for him to get to the post office in Allenby Square and back. It was the best time for him to leave the Quarter, he reasoned. After all, the Arab populace was crammed into the Haram instead of out on the streets.

Like a wave, Muslim voices rolled over the entire Old City. To his right and left along Rehov Habad, the stalls of Jewish and Armenian merchants began to close. Beneath the domed roof of the souk, men and women stared up at the vaulted ceiling as if it might fall on them. The religious rallies of Haj Amin always had that effect on Christians,

Armenians, and Jews alike. It was hard to say what might follow these fanatic tirades. The last twelve years had borne witness to what the twisted hatred of one man in power could accomplish.

"Rebbe Lebowitz!" shouted Memel the basketmaker. "Where are you going?" He had his entire display moved indoors and was just locking the metal grate.

"To the post office to mail a letter to Etta and the children!" he answered without slowing.

"Better wait! You can't hear that crazy man? He is in a very bad mood today!"

"It is Friday," he explained. There was no need for further explanation. Everyone knew that on Friday Rabbi Lebowitz mailed a letter to his daughter in Warsaw. It was the last thing he did before Shabbat services began—his way of sending a blessing to his only child and the grandchildren.

"Shabbat shalom," Memel called nervously. The words meant "Sabbath peace," but from the sound of things there would be little peace this Sabbath.

"Shabbat shalom!" He returned the greeting, which was lost beneath a resounding cry of *"ALLAH AKHBAR! GOD IS GREAT! GOD IS GREAT!"*

He quickened his pace. The back of his neck prickled with an uneasy sense of what could happen in Jerusalem after such a sermon. The graveyards were full of reminders of what had happened before. He fingered the letter in his pocket. Nothing would happen. The Muslims always ended their Fridays with this tumult of shouts and chants. Why should today be different? This was the safest time for a Jew to walk out of Jaffa Gate. The safest time. When all of them were—

"And Allah has promised the faithful that the time is near when the Holy City will no longer be occupied by infidels! The end is near for them!" Suddenly the words sounded clearly along the Street of the Chain. Had someone turned a speaker this direction from the wall of the mosque? Did the Mufti mean for everyone in the Old City to hear these threatening words?

Not one shop remained open. The Suq el-Bazaar was shuttered tight. David Street was empty except for two Copt priests hurrying away in their flowing black robes. The towers on either side of Jaffa Gate were lined with British soldiers who looked pensively toward the shiny Dome of the Rock.

Omar Square, usually a picture-postcard of activity, was deserted. The old man stopped and gazed a moment toward the New City beyond the gate. It was only a short walk to Allenby Square from here, but his uneasiness escalated into a fresh and wild sense of fear. A soldier cupped his hand and shouted down, "Old man! What are you doing? Get indoors!"

Foolish. He saw how foolish he had been. He should have turned around the first time he heard the roaring passion of Haj Amin's followers! Things were not as they had been—they were getting worse every day, every minute! He should have known. Armenians do not shut their shops for no reason. How many times had the people of the Old City witnessed as violence erupted like a storm? It had come without warning. Was this such a day?

"Old man!" shouted the soldier in Yiddish. "Get to your house!"

The rabbi's eyes widened as the rattle of gunfire sounded from behind. The dam had broken. A sea of violence swept suddenly toward him. Shouts and screams drowned out the warning of the soldier. The crackling sound of bullets aimed at nothing, yet meant to kill everything!

Rebbe Lebowitz turned to see where he might run. Everywhere the shops were shut. It was half a block to the closest side street. He could not run back now. Instead, he ran forward toward Jaffa Gate. He glanced up toward the soldier who had shouted, but the man had disappeared.

"ALLAH AKHBAR! FOR ALLAH AND THE PROPHET!" voices called out.

The rabbi ran as fast as he could. He hugged the face of the shops, searching for some opening, praying for some crevice to hide in until the storm swept past. He was old. He *felt* old. As never before, he felt years hanging on his legs, holding him back from the road of the Armenians.

Breath came hard, yet he managed to breathe the name of God. He cried for help! English guns took aim over the heads of the mob. Fire and smoke burst from their rifles. Shrieks of alarm wailed at his back. Had any Arab rioters fallen in that volley?

Bullets whined above the old man's head, and he dashed toward the corner where he imagined safety to be. There was lead in his shoes. The nightmare of a body that would not respond became reality. He stumbled and fell, tearing his trousers and bloodying his knees. *Get up, old man, or you will die!* And then he was on his feet, half running, half crawling toward the corner. A slim dark crack was visible between two shops. With his last ounce of strength, the rabbi clutched the edge of the hard stone and pulled himself forward into the tiny space.

Within seconds the mob swarmed past. Women, their hair loose and wild, shrieked with the same venom as the men. Those docile followers who had entered the holy gates of the Dome of the Rock this morning now tore their clothes, hurled stones, and shot their British-made rifles into the air and through the windows of the shops and houses.

In the shadow of his hiding place, Rebbe Lebowitz clutched at the pain in his chest. He fought to breathe, and used his breath to pray that no Muslim would discover him while they shouted, *"DEATH TO JEWS! DEATH TO ZIONISTS! DEATH TO THE BRITISH OPPRESSORS!"*

He could not guess how many thousands surged by. How many passed through Jaffa Gate and Damascus Gate into the New City? He did not look at their faces anymore. But there was one thing he noticed, one sign that marked the depth of their frenzy—the rioters were all *barefoot*! Not one had stopped to put on shoes before the hysteria had pushed them into the streets. Bare feet. Empty shoes and empty prayer rugs on the stones of the Temple Mount.

The last of the rioters straggled past. Old men and old women. Their faces reflected the same bitter hatred as the young who had gone before them. And then there was silence. Stifling heat. The hum of flies and the distant crackle of gunfire.

Rabbi Lebowitz dared not move from his hiding place.

The Promised Land. Holy Land. Zion. All these phrases that had once seemed so near to the heart of Leah Feldstein did not reflect the truth of those first moments when dreams, at last, became reality.

From the harbor, the flat, drab skyline of Tel Aviv was a shabby comparison to the Ringstrasse of Vienna. The sun beat down unmercifully on the heads of passengers on board the SS *Hildebrand* as they hung against the rails to absorb first impressions of their new homeland.

At the far end of the docks the rusting hulk of a cattle boat was moored beside a small British gunboat. British soldiers roamed the decks in search of hidden refugees.

"Tried to get past the British Navy," observed a passenger who stood next to Leah. "Poor fools. What do they think will become of them now?"

Leah turned her eyes away from the captured vessel. She tried to smile at the pitiful collection of buildings lining the docks. This was Zion. The Jewish homeland. She should feel joy, but she could not. She felt nothing but a dull ache for Shimon as he stared at the cattle boat and remembered another ship, other pilgrims.

Shimon's arm was still immobilized in a plaster cast. Sweat trickled down between the cast and his skin. It was so hot, even in October, when the trees of the Vienna woods would be turning a thousand shades of red and gold. They had talked about the heat of Zion, discussed the aridness of the land and the malarial swamps of Galilee. Yes, they had dreamed of the glorious sunlight on this land when the rain had kept them indoors with their fiddles and pots of hot coffee. Yes, they had dreamed. But they could not have imagined what it was *really* like.

"Well, here we are, Shimon!" Leah tried to sound cheerful, but the brightness of her voice quavered slightly, and Shimon heard what she was really thinking.

Tugboats nudged the ship against the dock. Thick ropes were thrown down to men who shouted and cursed in a strange language. All along the waterfront were stacks of crates and swarms of flies and dogs and beggars and urchins and donkeys and muck.

Shimon's eyes were filled with the filth of it. "You are not really going to do it, are you?" he asked grimly.

"Do what?"

"You said that as soon as you stepped on the soil of Palestine, you would kneel and kiss the earth."

Leah shook her head slowly. No. That was one vow she would not keep. In the photographs there had been no flies, rotting fish guts, camel droppings. The photographs had been clean and perfect. They had not been hot. They had not beat against their backs like hammers. They had not smelled. Black and white photos had been studied with the adoration of paintings by Monet or Renoir. Now that the waterfront was a fact before their eyes, Leah could see that nearly everything was still black and white and varying shades of gray. The sky was blue, of course, and the water was blue. She had guessed that, but she had never dreamed that Tel Aviv could be so entirely drab.

A long metal shed stretched along the wharf. A white sign with blue lettering spelled *H. M. CUSTOMS AND IMMIGRATION.* This was written first in English, then in the fluid script of Arabic, then in the blocky alphabet of Hebrew. Half a dozen British officials stood outside the building and watched the docking of the *Hildebrand* from beneath their shadowed visors. They, too, seemed to be a part of the sameness of the scene—all dressed in khaki, all with the same tight expression of disgust on their faces, waiting for this latest load of European Jews to pass beneath the tin roof of His Majesty's customs house before they emerged into the life of Zionist Palestine. Like a troop of warriors they waited, daring anyone to try to get past their stations with forged papers or smuggled weapons or some undeclared taxable item.

The last matter was really of little concern lately. With the passage of time and the tightening of Reich regulations, the Jews had come through the shed with less and less. Still, there were always a few who thought they could sneak by.

Bullhorns shouted directions in a dozen languages. All luggage was piled into one net on the deck of the ship and then lowered like a catch of fresh herring onto the dock.

Leah had been forced to argue hotly that her cello could not be treated so casually. This discussion took place with a fellow who had never heard of Bach, never seen a cello. What did he care?

Tearful appeals were made to the captain, who was mercifully sober for the second time on the journey. Yes, he would radio the customs authorities. The instrument—what was it again?—could be hand-carried off the ship, but must be immediately handed over to a British official for inspection.

A splintered wooden gangplank crashed into place and the final crossing into the Promised Land took place single file and very cautiously. There were actually some displays of emotion when Jewish soles touched hallowed ground. One Orthodox-looking fellow from Latvia actually did drop to his knees and kiss the ground, such as it was. Leah clung tightly to the cello and to Shimon's big hand. She tried not to step in anything unpleasant. She tried not to think of Vienna— its beauty and elegance. Of course, there was no more Vienna. Vienna had died, almost taking her and Shimon with it. No, Leah would not let herself think back and remember the golden days. She must turn her eyes to the land of their future and their hope.

Her chin quivered slightly. Why hadn't Moses wandered farther north? It seemed that a forty-year odyssey could have brought the children of Israel someplace more picturesque—like Italy, or the southern coast of France.

FORM LINES HERE! This sign was written in several languages besides Hebrew and Arabic and English. These British fellows were catching on—most of the people in their lines read languages like German and Polish and Czech . . . especially Czech, these days.

A grim-faced customs agent marched up to where Leah and Shimon stood. He scowled and postured as he looked at the cello case.

"Who said you could carry that off the ship?" he demanded, extending his hand to take it from her. "*Against* regulations!"

"Very valuable instrument . . ." Leah sputtered. "Centuries old. *Please* be careful."

The man muttered, *"Regulations!"* and turned his back on her.

With a little cry, Leah put her hand against her aching head. "Whatever did Moses see in this place? I *ask* you!" Her indignation caused slight smiles on faces around her. All except for one sad-eyed little man who was sweating profusely in his European-made wool suit. He tapped her lightly on the shoulder and then pointed a hundred yards down the waterfront where several hundred illegal refugees from the captured cattle boat were caged behind a wire fence. They were guarded by soldiers with guns. Men. Women. Children. Ragged, haunted-looking people like the ones Leah had seen at every turn in Europe, like those who had perished aboard the *Darien*.

Shimon drew his breath in sharply at the sight of them. Crates of oranges were stacked just beyond their reach outside the fence. Only the flies of Palestine passed freely through the wire.

"At least they are alive," Shimon managed.

Suddenly Leah felt ashamed. Why was her heart not thankful that they had arrived here with legal documents when there were so very many who tried to come but were kept out? How could she forget *so soon* after Austria? After all that Shimon had told her?

The people behind the wire began to sing a mournful dirge. *"Vi aheen zoll ich gain?—Wherever shall I go?"* This was the anthem of the coffin ships. Shimon had once sung this song with those who had not found any harbor in this life. He stopped in the slowly moving line and watched and listened. So many longed for this place. How many would not make it? How many would do anything to stand in this line and brush away the flies and bless the heat of the sun?

Leah tugged his sleeve. "Come along, Shimon. Come, love. We cannot help them now, but we can live for them, nu? Come along, Shimon."

Inside the immigration shed Leah found a bench and sat beside Shimon as they waited for their names to be called. Shimon sat silent and preoccupied as she took out her pen and began to write the letter she had promised Elisa. *Dearest Elisa, I did not kiss the ground of Palestine, but I am glad we are here all the same . . .*

Outside on the Tel Aviv dock, half a dozen distinguished-looking Englishmen chatted among themselves as their luggage was unloaded from a British naval launch. Diesel fumes rose from the sputtering engine, adding another element of unpleasantness to their first stifling moments in the Promised Land.

Captain Samuel Orde looked on as lordly glances were cast in the direction of the caged refugees.

"What are the Jews singing about?" asked one of the men with a hint of irritation.

Orde had heard the song before. "They are asking where they will go," he explained, concealing his own emotion at the sad refrain.

"Where they should go?" a member of the group bellowed. The disdain on his face was evident. "What business is it of His Majesty's government *where* they go? That's the trouble with these Jewish beggars. They expect us to provide for them after they've got themselves into a corner."

"Quite right," agreed a second member of this latest British commission. He mopped his brow and then adjusted the brim of his Panama hat lower against the sun. "Things have changed in Palestine over the last year, and not for the better, that is obvious. We'll have to review this partition and immigration question very carefully again."

Captain Orde looked away and tugged the brim of his own cap lower so these eminent British politicians would not read the anger in his eyes. He held his tongue as he had a thousand times before. *Woodhead,* he thought. *An appropriate name for this group. When they see thousands of acres of Zionist citrus orchards destroyed by Arab marauders, I suppose they'll ask what appeasement they might make for the Arabs to settle down.* Spain was in the midst of a civil war, after

all, so the British Mandate of Palestine had become the chief source
of oranges. Now that was being interrupted. What would hasten the
return of order? *Cut Jewish immigration?* Orde thought bitterly. Limit
the land sales to Jewish settlers? Give the Arab leadership what they
wanted? Forget about the 1917 British promise of a Jewish homeland?

The Jewish refugees inside the cage let their dark eyes linger on
the group of officials. Hostile glances were returned by the British in
reply to such impudence. *Did these Jews dare to sing their little song
to the government of England?*

"There are procedures for immigration," remarked yet another commission member. His aristocratic face was unmoved. "If *they* want to
get into the British Mandate, *they* should have followed the procedures." The man looked at Orde. "Isn't that right, Captain Orde?"

Orde hesitated a moment, resisting the impulse to shove the entire
lot of these haughty gentlemen into the water. "Hitler at their backs
with clubs . . ." His voice cracked. He was having difficulty finding
words. "What choice have they—"

The man in the Panama hat interrupted. He was irritated. "None of
our business," he sniffed, turning his back on the captain.

———————

"FELDSTEIN! LEAH AND SHIMON FELDSTEIN!" The harsh voice of
the British immigrations officer echoed through the enormous tin building.

The sound of her own name amid the din of a thousand voices
startled Leah. Shimon nudged her slightly, urging her back to the reality
of the moment.

She nodded and tucked her pen back into the thin writing case.
She would finish the letter later. There was so much she wanted to
share with Elisa. Paper would not hold the myriad thoughts and emotions that assaulted her with every passing moment.

The long lines of immigrants at the ten desks had diminished. One
by one the holders of legal documents were passing from one side of
the shed to the other, where representatives of the Jewish Agency gathered them into groups for transportation to tent cities where they would
be initiated into the life of a Zionist in Palestine.

"Feldstein!" the Englishman roared impatiently.

"Hurry, Leah." Shimon was nervous. He had not recovered from the
thought that these British immigration fellows had the authority to
throw them behind wire for deportation. Such power *must not* be kept
waiting!

"Yes. Shimon and Leah Feldstein." Shimon presented passports
with visas to the tight-lipped officer who barely glanced up as he
checked the official seals against the names on his clipboard.

"You have family in Jerusalem," he said flatly.

"My great aunt," Shimon answered softly.

"All the same, with the Arab demonstrations, you are required to stay at one of the refugee centers." He shrugged and stamped the papers.

Shimon and Leah exchanged looks of relief at the thump of the rubber stamp on their documents. So. It was official. They could pass through to the other side of the desk. Only two desks to the right, a young couple with two children had been escorted into a private office. Such a procedure did not bode well for the little family.

"How long will we be delayed from entering Jerusalem?" Shimon asked, almost bowing. Beads of perspiration stood out on his forehead.

"Out of my hands." The officer slapped the documents into Shimon's palm. "Up to the colonial office. They'll decide when it's safe enough. Quite common, these delays. A little welcome from the Arabs for the Woodhead Commission from England."

"That is all?" Leah laughed. How very different this was, compared to the brutality they had witnessed toward illegal immigrants. Once again her heart measured out the vastness of their good fortune. The contrast was amazing. How could they mind a slight delay?

Luggage, including Leah's precious cello, was stacked in giant piles in the center of the concrete floor. Each item was marked with blue chalk to indicate that it had passed inspection for contraband.

Leah stood for a long moment in front of the jumbled heap looking for her cello case. They had already informed her that all luggage would be hauled separately to the induction center, but she could hardly imagine traveling without her instrument.

Holding Shimon's uninjured hand, she slowly circled the pyramid until at last she spotted the case near the top.

Only then could she turn her attention toward the groups of immigrants gathered beneath signs that named their countries of origin. GERMANY. AUSTRIA. HUNGARY. POLAND. FRANCE. ENGLAND.

A babble of European languages filled the room. A thousand questions were being hurled at the Jewish Agency representatives all at the same moment. Answers to panicked voices were always calm, always polite—always meant to quell the fears of those who had come from the verdant beauty of Europe to this forbidding place.

"Tents? Nu! We are going to live in tents?"

"Will the tents have floors?"

"Can I stay with my husband?"

"Do we stay together by families?"

"You mean we have left Warsaw to come live in *tents*? OY!"

Within each language group, smaller cliques of Orthodox Jews stood beside angry young students who were eager and ready to take their places in the wilderness settlements. All had reasons why they should not be confined to the indoctrination center. The Hasidim were eager to pray in Jerusalem. The socialists had already studied farming and the principles of Zionism. *How brave those Jewish Agency representatives were to come here and take on such a group of disillusioned pilgrims,* Leah thought as she and Shimon made their way through the confusion.

Shimon squeezed her hand. He had seen this before. On board the *Darien*, he had learned that the title *Jew* had a thousand variations and nuances. On board the *Darien* they had somehow ironed out their differences. They had become one working unit that had lived together in relative peace and had finally died together. It would be so for these would-be Zionists. It *must* be so if they were to survive!

Leah had never imagined so many different kinds of Chosen People all trying to be heard at the same moment. *Moses had it easy compared to this,* she thought, making a mental note that she must write Elisa about the odd assortment of people who all called themselves Jews.

As if he had read her thoughts, Shimon leaned down and whispered in Leah's ear. "Like an orchestra tuning up. That is all. You will see, Leah. We will all find the same note eventually."

6

Watchdogs

Only the occasional crack of rifle fire broke the utter stillness of the Jerusalem streets. Wedged tightly into his refuge, Rabbi Lebowitz wondered how it was possible that a city the size of Jerusalem could be so silent, as if a giant hand had reached down to scoop up every living creature. Only he remained, and ten feet farther back in the space, a calico cat nursed five kittens.

The old man was grateful for the mother cat, who seemed unperturbed either by his presence or by the events unfolding beyond this shelter. When the rattle of guns erupted and his heart began to pound like a hammer, he looked at the cat. The cat looked back and blinked pleasantly at the intruder.

Three kittens were gray. One was calico, a duplicate of the mother, and one kitten was purest white with wide blue eyes. Certainly this was an ecumenical group; all shared equally in the bounty of the mother cat. They tumbled blissfully over one another and occasionally toddled forward in a coy attack on the rabbi's cuffs.

A burst of machine-gun fire rattled in the street. The rabbi gasped and instinctively covered his head as a bullet whistled by the opening. There was not enough room for him to crouch down between the buildings. He could only stand and lean against the cool hewn stone of the souvenir shop wall. His legs and back ached in this position, but there was no help for that. He felt lucky to be alive.

The kittens purred and meowed. They arched their backs and hopped about in mock warfare. The old man watched them. Amazingly he was able to smile. *Who would believe this?* he wondered. *An old man caught between two buildings in the middle of a cross fire, and I can smile!* If he lived through this day he must make a prayer of blessing for the cats of Jerusalem who kept him from going crazy!

Machine guns again. Closer. A block away. A scream of someone who must be dying. English? Arab? Jew? Was it someone like him who only wanted to go home?

The old man blinked and forced himself to look at the kittens. The white wide-eyed piece of fluff moved cautiously toward the big strange thing that shivered at the door of their den. Paws danced sideways toward him, then stopped and backed and started forward again more slowly. The kittens had seen thousands of human feet pass by, but none had ever stopped and stayed so long!

"Come, little one," the old man whispered as he extended a foot toward it. His own whisper sounded too loud. More bullets whistled by. He had not heard the report of a gun, but the bullets seemed to be flying up the street all the same. He dared not stretch his head out for even a quick look.

The white kitten was attacked from the rear by a gray brother, and the two tumbled over and over in a clawless battle.

Rabbi Lebowitz heard the engines of a vehicle—the grinding of gears just beyond Jaffa Gate. His heart lifted. *British! It must be British soldiers!*

Did he dare run to them? He imagined himself slipping from the hiding place and crouching to run toward the British vehicle. Across Omar Square? Every gun must be trained on the Square. Snipers would have their rifles aimed at Jaffa Gate where he must pass.

The end of the imagined sprint to the English side of the lines left the old man certain that he would be dead before he took two steps from this place.

Sweat dripped from his gray hair. He was thirsty. His tongue felt swollen and parched like leather. The kittens nursed happily again as the old man watched. It would be a long time until he could drink again, if ever, God willing. Maybe tonight he could sneak out and somehow make it through the Armenian Quarter that bordered his own neighborhood. Maybe.

The engine of the vehicle roared away down Jaffa Road. The city fell silent again. Not even the birds dared to sing. The pigeons roosting on the spires of the minarets and the domes of churches and syn-agogues alike remained in their nests as if to see which of their hosts would be victorious. The bells of the great churches did not ring out the hours.

There was only one certain sign that time passed. Afternoon shad-ows lengthened across the cobblestone of Omar Square like the finger of a sundial. The old man guessed that it was nearly four o'clock. The others would be frantic with worry, and somehow this knowledge was a comfort to Rabbi Shlomo Lebowitz.

God had sent the kittens to help him get through the ordeal. He would personally see to it that this mother cat was fed scraps every day . . . that is, if he could only get back to Tipat Chalev alive!

More gunfire rattled clearly from the rooftops not a block away, answered from David's Tower. Another scream . . .

The old man groaned and closed his eyes. Death was a near and tangible presence. Eighteen inches from him, the street was alive with fresh volleys!

He whispered the Shema: "Hear, O Israel! The Lord our God is one Lord!" This he said for the sake of the dying even though he could not know if they were Christian or Muslim or Jew. Death was turning its hollow black eyes slowly around Omar Square to see whom it might devour. The old man's breath was shallow as he felt death probe this small space between the souvenir shop and tourist information building. *Yes!* Death had noticed that someone might be hiding there! Had it seen the old rabbi?

He trembled. He turned his head away and again looked at the frolicking little family. He forced himself to study the colors and markings. White paws on the littlest gray kitten. White snip on the nose of another. The last, strutting, brazen, gray kitten was without even a dash of white. The little calico was shy and sweet. She nestled beneath the chin of her mother while the white kitten batted at the mother cat's tail.

I thank you, O Eternal, for kittens and cats! The rabbi's prayer was silent. He did not want to tempt the ominous darkness that strolled the streets. It might hear and stop to look.

The London morning was filled with the scents of imminent rain, damp wool coats, and the diesel fumes of the unwieldy double-decker buses that roared past.

Elisa inhaled deeply. It seemed like months since she had felt such freedom. *To work again! To play in an orchestra conducted by the great Sir Thomas Beecham!* How Elisa had admired the man at the Bayreuth festivals as he had conducted the works of Wagner! He was, like Toscanini, one of the maestros of Europe who was beyond politics, but not beyond honor. Elisa heard that he had made room for at least thirty Jewish musicians who had been expelled from Germany's orchestras over the last four years. Elisa was number thirty-one.

A raindrop landed on her cheek and then another and another. So many tears had been shed, the London rain seemed to wash those memories away.

She put up her umbrella, but only for the sake of the precious Guarnerius violin. She did not mind the downpour that followed a few seconds later. No morning had ever seemed as perfect as this one.

Elisa's Friday rehearsal had been a day to look forward to for Charles and Louis. Theo had promised he and Anna would take them to the zoo.

But the London rain poured down, sending lions and tigers scurrying to the shelter of their caves. American grizzly bears shook themselves and peered out at the empty bars where normally thousands of spectators stood. This was a day when all sensible creatures remained indoors.

"I'd rather be drinking a cup of tea before a fire," Anna said as Theo took Charles and Louis by the hand and dashed through the puddled sidewalk to the subway station.

"I should have known when my leg began to complain last night." Theo paid the fare as Anna shook the water from their umbrella. "Ah, well. We will be the only tourists in London today! Probably the only ones in the entire British Museum."

This thought was exciting to the boys, who had heard tales of treasures from Egyptian pyramids and golden coffins with mummies inside. For such a sight they would gladly forego seeing dripping elephants and slimy reptiles.

Bubbe Rosenfelt had taken Charles to three museums in New York. None of them had mummies, so this excursion might surpass any other for the two Kronenberger boys. Louis had never been to a museum; he could not imagine the vastness with which the British Museum was described by Theo. And when he first laid eyes on the huge building with its Ionic portico, he could not imagine that *all this* had been built just for a place to store old mummies.

Only a handful of diehard tourists stood at the ticket kiosk. All were older people, Charles observed—American, mostly. He could tell by their comparatively stylish clothes and conversations in the peculiar dialect that Murphy used. There were no children. English children were all in school today. Perhaps there would be tours of school children later, but such a possibility made Charles hope that the rain would never stop. He still did not enjoy the thought of meeting other children.

The marbled entrance of the British Museum went up and up. The rain from the boys' slickers made puddles on the floor while they craned their necks backward and Theo studied the map in search of the Egyptian antiquities sections.

"Books and manuscripts to the right. Roman sculptures to the left. Upper floor . . . medieval . . . glass and ceramics . . . Ha! North wing!" he cried and set off across the foyer with his peculiar limp, looking like a wounded explorer.

They followed arrows and signs up the broad staircases, through rooms with ancient bronze statues and golden masks, past shining armor and cases displaying weapons that might well have killed Spanish conquistadors in an Aztec temple. Onward marched the four solitary tourists; onward toward the Egyptian antiquities department.

Charles first noticed that they were not alone. In each room, along each corridor, another tourist followed at a discreet distance. When Theo paused to read and explain a sign, the small man in the English tweed jacket and trousers also paused, leaned forward to examine something, cast a look toward the little group, then resumed walking when Theo progressed to another display.

Perhaps it was a lifetime of being followed, stared at and pursued, that made Charles finally tug at Theo's sleeve and nod toward the man. Theo was also attuned to being tailed. But here in London? He had hoped it would not be the case.

From ceramics to prints, from Etruscan artifacts to Phoenician antiquities, the little man did not deviate from their path. He did not attempt to conceal the fact that he was tailing them. If anything, his routine—pause, look, glance sideways, and walk on—was so obvious that at last Theo exchanged unhappy looks with Anna, turned, and walked directly toward the man.

The little man smiled as Theo spoke to him in an impatient whisper. The man inclined his head slightly and looked toward Anna and the boys, who stared back openly. His smile broadened. He nodded as if to greet them. He gestured with an open hand toward the entrance to the extensive collection of mummies. Theo bowed slightly as if to thank him and then returned to their little party.

"Well?" Anna asked softly.

"Polite people, these English," Theo answered.

"Well?" she asked again, this time in French so that the boys would not understand Theo's reply.

He answered in French. "Yes. We are being followed. Watched. This fellow makes it sound as if it is all for my own good."

"Perhaps it is. The Nazis have not stopped raving about you, Theo. Perhaps it is not a bad thing to have the British government take an interest."

Theo took her hand. He nudged Charles gently and encouraged them to run ahead into the hall where the mummies were displayed. Then he led her back alone to where the Englishman had remained at a discreet distance.

"Mr. Beckham," Theo said, not unkindly. "Please, explain to my wife the purpose of your assignment."

Mr. Beckham was as pleasant as a shopkeeper—polite, soft-spoken, and straightforward. "Your connections with the immigration of Jewish illegals is quite well known. You are guests in our country. My superiors hope you will be respectful of our laws. It would be a pity it you were approached by some underground organization and because of a misunderstanding violated our laws. I am simply a reminder to you, as I understand it. You are a public figure, after all, Mr. Lindheim."

Theo smiled a thin-lipped smile. "So you see, Anna. The government of Great Britain has set a watchdog over us. Not a snarling mastiff like the Gestapo in Germany, but rather a terrier who will bark if someone undesirable comes to the door."

The voices of Charles and Louis echoed excitement from the north gallery. Anna glanced nervously toward the entrance. "Have we not all been through *enough*, Mr. Beckham?"

Beckham was sympathetic. "I have my assignment, Mrs. Lindheim."

"Then must you be *so obvious*? These children . . . might we at least have the illusion of freedom?"

Mr. Beckham nodded his long, thin head. "Certainly. It is enough that you know we are watching. Henceforth, you may have your illusions, and we will remain . . . invisible." He backed up a step. "It is enough that you know. Good day, Mr. Lindheim. Mrs. Lindheim."

With that, he turned and walked briskly across the floor. His heels clicked and clacked, receding down a corridor until they diminished to nothing and they were alone. At least, they *seemed* alone.

Anna looked up at Theo. "Why does this not make me feel better?"

The playful banter of members of the London Philharmonic Orchestra was a tonic for Elisa. She was the new kid on the block, as Murphy said, but the block was filled with the familiar faces of old friends who had played with her in Austria and even faraway Berlin.

Backstage conversations were in English now instead of German, but the subjects seemed remarkably unchanged from the carefree days of Vienna. Names of conductors like Toscanini and Fuchwanger were mentioned along with discussion of the music festivals that would continue to be held in Austria in spite of the Nazi takeover. It was still undecided if the London orchestra would be traveling to the Reich for the Wagner festival or the Mozart festival. Thought of such a journey back into the land of their persecution made many of the newest members of the London Philharmonic nervous in spite of the assurances of Sir Thomas Beecham, the London conductor.

This very issue clouded Elisa's first days with Sir Thomas and the orchestra. Now that she carried Murphy's child, she had more to think about than just her own safety. And she had to consider Charles and Louis, as well. She did not feel free to perform in Germany for the same people who had persecuted even these little ones.

For this reason, Elisa had made an appointment to speak with the great conductor this morning. The eyes of Frieda Hillman, Beecham's Jewish secretary, were full of understanding as Elisa explained her concerns as unemotionally as possible.

Frieda, a heavy-set woman with a doctoral degree in music, had come to London from the Berlin orchestra of Maestro Fuchwanger after the Nazi purges of 1935. Her obviously Semitic features had made it impossible for the brilliant and capable woman to show her face around the Berlin concert hall even though she arranged all the daily details of the orchestra. She had remained poised on the brink of the Nazi inferno in Berlin until Sir Thomas had asked her to join his staff. Her mother still remained in Germany as a hostage to guarantee that Frieda would not speak ill of her former persecutors. Many like Frieda carried such a burden with them. And yet, faces did not seem to reflect openly the pain that must certainly be felt in private moments.

As Frieda led Elisa through the backstage maze of the Royal Opera House, she introduced every stagehand and technician on a first-name basis. Elisa's mind was reeling as Frieda spliced in questions about Anna and Theo, both of whom she had known well in Berlin. Elisa answered rapid-fire between introductions and the hail of business questions being shot at Frieda from the right and left.

The return to such wonderful chaos was like a warm bath on a frosty day for Elisa. How long had it been since she had hurried through the corridors of a concert hall? How long since those blissful days in Vienna when she had looked through such innocent eyes at a condemned world?

"Sir Thomas may seem gruff at times, but you will see . . . in spite of the bark, there are no teeth in the bite!" Frieda had been around long enough to adapt English cliches to her own style.

The two women paused before the impressive mahogany door marked with a brass nameplate: Sir Thomas Beecham. Frieda patted Elisa. She must not be nervous in the presence of this man. Then she knocked.

"It is open" came the mellow voice of the conductor.

Frieda opened the door then stepped aside, allowing Elisa to enter the office first. Sir Thomas was lounging on an overstuffed sofa. Music scores were spread on a low table before him. He puffed on a cigarette in a long ivory cigarette holder. Barely glancing at Elisa from beneath his bushy eyebrows, he waved a hand for her to be seated.

Elisa's calmness evaporated. In spite of Frieda's assurances, Sir Thomas, with his precisely groomed goatee, was an imposing figure in his silk smoking jacket.

"Elisa Murphy, Sir Thomas," Frieda volunteered. She was still standing, uncertain if she should remain for the talk.

"The new first violinist," he said gruffly, like a general discussing a private. "Your concerts with the BBC were quite nice. But what is this nonsense that you may not be able to travel with my orchestra to Bayreuth? To Salzburg?" Then he glared at Frieda. "Sit down," he commanded. "I may need you to explain a thing or two."

Elisa hesitated. As Sir Thomas turned his piercing eyes on her, she swallowed hard. He had a way of making her feel like a music student again. "My family . . ." she began. "We are quite . . . out of favor with the Nazis."

Sir Thomas cleared his throat impatiently. "Just as it should be. If that were not the case, you would still be there instead of here. Correct?"

"Yes . . . I . . . as a matter of principle . . . cannot imagine playing there again. For the Nazis."

"As a matter of principle, you *must* consider it. They have managed to disrupt the life of one of Germany's most promising young violinists. But you must not allow them to imagine that they have destroyed your career with their silly racial nonsense." He looked to Frieda. "Tell her, Frieda!"

"Last year I traveled to Bayreuth. When I was with the Berlin Orchestra, I could not have done so. But the Nazis did not act as though my presence there was anything unusual because I am under the protection of Sir Thomas, you see . . ."

The great conductor's chin lifted regally. "You see?"

"Well . . . I traveled to Germany from Vienna . . . before the Anschluss. I . . . worked to aid refugees to escape without the knowledge of the Reich." Elisa added another dimension to the story.

"Good heavens!" Sir Thomas brushed away her objections. "Do you think we have not? Take a look at the faces in this orchestra, Elisa." His voice became more gentle. "You have been through an ordeal. But *here* we think of *music*! We perform where we are called to perform. We are above politics in many ways, although our perfection as musicians may make a political statement. They are fools, these Nazis, with their lunacy about German culture and this and that." He puffed on his cigarette as he chose his words carefully. "I attended the 1936 Olympics in Berlin. It gave me great pleasure to see the black American Jesse Owens demolish the Aryan supermen on the track field." He smiled smugly. "It also gives me great pleasure to out-perform Hitler's pure-bred albino musicians. The Nazis have banished the very best musicians in Europe. And *I have inherited them*! That includes you, Elisa. I would have hired your friend Leah Feldstein and her husband in a moment as well, but alas! They are in Palestine," he shrugged. "At any rate, I wired the High Commissioner that they were coming. He will see to it they perform there as well."

Elisa drew a deep breath. Sir Thomas was telling her that she had no choice but to travel with the orchestra even into Germany if it was arranged. The thought made her feel sick. "I . . . there is something else . . . I am expecting a child."

Sir Thomas drew himself upright, surprised. "Congratulations." Then he brushed over the news as though it had nothing to do with the subject at hand. "Such things seldom affect the quality of one's music. We encourage families to teach their children to play well—

providing me with another generation of musicians, as it were."

"Sir Thomas, I . . . fear for my safety in Germany." She tried to emphasize the danger.

He was gentle again, remarkably so. "I can understand that. Frieda and a dozen others have felt the same. But they have learned, and so must you, that while you are a member of my orchestra, no one would dare to harm or threaten you, my dear. To do so would cause an incident of world proportions." He sat back. He was finished. Clapping his hands he dismissed them. "You will learn to trust," he said. "And now . . . to work!"

7

No Sabbath Peace

There had been no sound within the walls of Old City Jerusalem for two hours. The gunfire had ceased, and the only audible noise now was the purring of cats and the old rabbi's own labored breath.

Soon the evening would come and it would be Shabbat. He wondered if there would be services tonight. Who would lead the congregation in prayers for peace?

Every muscle in his body ached, and he could find no position that offered relief. He fingered the envelope in his pocket. The weekly letter to Etta and Aaron and the children. In it he had told them how peaceful things had been the last few weeks. Once again he had begged them to return to Jerusalem after the baby was born. There was room here. And how the old man longed to see his grandchildren!

Rabbi Lebowitz determined that he would not mail the letter. How could he ask Etta and Aaron to bring the children here when a new wave of violence had erupted? No, he would not ask Etta and Aaron again. They had almost come back once before, but that had been before the riots had squeezed off Jewish immigration to a trickle. Life was good for them in Poland, Etta wrote. Certainly anything was better than this. Three million Jews together in Poland were certainly safer than this rag-tag little remnant who clung to the scarred earth of Zion and scratched out a living in the hills of Galilee.

"Oy!" Rebbe Lebowitz moaned in spite of his pledge to keep silent. Thirst had become almost unbearable. Were the battles over in the Old City now? Did the lengthy silence mean an end to the clash between the Arab rebels and the British?

The thought tempted him to step from the hiding place but he did not. Soon it would be evening, and he could walk home under cover of darkness. As the congregation prayed in the synagogue, he would come through the doors and proclaim that the Eternal had been merciful.

Such a thought this was! It almost made him smile to imagine such a thing, but his lips were so dry that they cracked when his mouth turned up. He would save his smiles until he was safe at home with a cool glass of water drawn from the cistern.

Creeping shadows offered the only movement in the Square. The sun dipped lower in the sky beyond Jaffa Gate. The old man shifted his weight from one foot to another. He wondered if he would be able to make his still body move when he left the shelter. Certainly he would make an easy target if there were snipers still in the minarets or on the rooftops. But perhaps they had all gotten weary and gone home.

How easy it would be to step out into the Square right now. Why would anyone wish to shoot an old man? Did he have a gun or a uniform? Only one letter. They should kill him for that?

He inched nearer the opening. It would be so easy. Such a relief.

As he moved, the mother cat stood.

"So you have had enough too, little Mama-leh?"

The cat purred and walked easily toward the aching legs of the rabbi. The kittens laid back their ears and remained behind in their nest of rags. The mother cat brushed against the old man's legs and then moved with calm elegance toward the opening.

He decided he would follow the cat. Both of them had had enough of this nonsense for one day.

"After you, cat." The rabbi was careful not to step on the little calico just ahead of him. The cat was unconcerned. This was not her war, after all. Her tail was erect, like a flag of neutrality. She meowed and stepped from between the two buildings onto the cobbles of Omar Square. From both directions a dozen guns erupted! The old man stifled a cry as he fell back and bullets tore through the calico cat and shattered the stones where he had stood a moment before!

The only sign of life on the street had just been shot to pieces. The kittens blinked in bewilderment. Where had their mother gone?

The rabbi moaned softly into his hands. Death was very near. *Very near!* Shabbat was coming to Jerusalem, but there would be no Shabbat peace tonight.

Rabbi Lebowitz wondered if Death would be placated by something as innocent and unconcerned as the calico cat? Or must it also reach in and take him as well?

———

The trees of the English countryside had shed their leaves, leaving tattered, barren branches to point at a somber sky. While Prime Minister Chamberlain congratulated himself and hailed the betrayal of Czechoslovakia as "peace in our time," the realists knew that hoping for peace now with Germany was like hoping that the trees would bloom in December.

Among those realists was Winston Churchill. At his side stood men like Anthony Eden and Duff Cooper, who had resigned their cabinet positions rather than support the fiasco that Prime Minister Chamberlain was bringing upon a slumbering England. Publicly these men had stood against the cheering members of Parliament and declared that the Munich Agreement was a fraud, a sham, a delusion that was, in fact, the worst defeat ever suffered by England. Churchill endured the boos and catcalls of his fellow M.P.s when he took the floor of Parliament and spoke the truth: *"I will begin by saying the most unpopular and unwelcome thing, what everybody would like to ignore . . . we have sustained a total and unmitigated defeat."*

His voice was nearly drowned out by angry shouts. Indeed, the truth was most unpopular in England during the days following Munich.

That being the case in England, it was also true in faraway America. One of the exceptions was Trump Publishing, whose publisher insisted that the truth would be printed. The first cabled orders this morning from Mr. Trump to his editor-in-chief of Trump European News Services (TENS) had been a confirmation of Murphy's instincts.

MURPHY RE: TROUBLE IN HOLY LAND STOP GET YOUR TAIL TO CHARTWELL FOR IMMEDIATE INTERVIEW WITH CHURCHILL STOP GOT TO GET CHAMBERLAIN AND HIS UMBRELLA OFF AMERICAN FRONT PAGES STOP SIGNED TRUMP

This was an assignment Murphy welcomed. While other newsmen with Hearst, INS, McCormick, and Craine publications were being forced to print the fairy tale of appeasement politics, Murphy was already driving the narrow rutted lanes toward the Churchill estate.

Through the barren trees, he could see the steep gables of the ancient brick country house. The lush green ivy of summer had also deserted Churchill, leaving the facade of the house naked and forlorn. *Gloomy* was the word for Chartwell these days. Murphy had heard that the master of the house was also gloomy. He had reason to be.

Gravel crunched beneath the tires as Murphy stopped in front of the house. Someone pulled back a curtain, then let it fall. The pudgy, somber-faced housekeeper Murphy had met last summer opened the door. In a whisper, she asked for his hat and coat. She led him quietly from the foyer and to the closed door of Churchill's study. Murphy could smell the reek of cigar smoke through the panel. The maid looked almost fearful as she raised her fist to knock. The master was obviously in a black mood!

The soft tapping was followed by a bellow from within.

"Who the devil is it now?"

Murphy answered for himself. "Murphy."

The door flew open. Churchill stood in his dressing gown, glaring at Murphy. "You mean they haven't tarred and feathered you yet?" He took Murphy by the arm and slammed the door in the housekeeper's face.

The room was hazy with smoke from a dozen cigars Churchill had fired in his battle against depression. The strain of knowing the truth and losing to lies showed on the face of the old prophet-politician. He jerked his head at a chair piled with newspapers. Murphy took this as a signal to sit. He moved the papers and obeyed. He did not open the conversation. After all, what was there to say? *You're really looking bad. Hitler got away with everything in spite of you, didn't he?*

Churchill stood facing the window. A gray and dreary day, somber and funereal like the cemetery scene in *Our Town,* Murphy thought.

Murphy cleared his throat lest Churchill forget he was in the room. Apparently the great statesman had forgotten about the interview.

Churchill growled, "I know you're there."

"Is this a bad time?"

"There are no good times left, I fear. If you wish to interview me while I am a member of Parliament, you will have to do so now."

"You are . . . resigning your seat?"

"I heard this morning there is an organized opposition within my own constituency; it has come to this for me at last."

If there were no good times to interview Churchill, Murphy could not imagine that he could have picked any time worse than this! For his outspoken stand against Munich, Winston Churchill was being punished by the Conservative party machine. The affairs of Palestine would be far from Churchill's mind.

Murphy stumbled over words. "But you . . . you are one of the few who *sees*!"

Churchill exhaled. He turned away from the window, and in the dim light Murphy could see that the man had not shaved today. "Matters in my own constituency have come to such a pass that I have made it clear—" He raised his cigar for emphasis. "If a resolution of censure is carried out against me, I shall immediately resign my seat and fight a by-election!" He shook his head and sank down in an overstuffed chair. "And yet I would give everything if only I could believe that this terrible folly in Munich could truly bring peace—*everything*."

"Would it be better . . . the interview . . . another day?"

Churchill almost smiled. "There is nothing that I may say which will bring down additional brimstone on my head, Murphy. Indeed, if I am silent now of all times, I might burst, and what a mess that would be to clean up, eh? Of course it might give the Nazis another reason to celebrate." He flicked ashes from the arm of his chair. "At least I am not paying for my opinion with my life, as some brave Germans may well be doing right now."

"You know of German opposition to what has just happened?" Murphy leaned forward.

"Not everyone in Germany is mad, Murphy, although those who are not mad may soon be dead. Hitler has managed through us—through the prime minister of Great Britain—to crush all opposition against him in Germany. Who would dare oppose him now? He has taken the Rhineland without a shot. Rebuilt his armies without a protest. Marched into Austria . . . and now carved up Czechoslovakia like a roast duck." There was deep bitterness in Churchill's voice. "And all of this with the blessings of our government and that of France. Hitler pointed a gun at our heads and demanded one pound. When that was given, two pounds were demanded. Finally the dictator consented to take one pound, seventeen shillings and six pence, and the rest in our promises of goodwill for the future."

He laughed a short, bitter laugh. "Left to themselves and told they would get no help from the Central Powers, the Czechs and President Beneš would have been able to make better terms than they have got after all this! Now we have lost the support of thirty-five Czech army divisions. All has come to nothing with the stroke of a pen. What remains of Czechoslovakia will be swallowed up soon enough. There is hardly a way this fiasco could be worse for us . . ."

"And for the refugees?" Murphy led him slightly as he took notes.

"Refugees." Churchill puffed his cigar. "They continue to shipwreck on the shoals of politics. The best interest of nations is not the best interest of individual human life, I'm afraid."

"You have heard about the violence in Palestine?"

Churchill shook his massive head in disgust. He had heard. "Chaim Weizmann called me just after you, wanting some reassurance of my support for a Jewish national home. What use is my support at this hour? I am the pariah of Parliament. I stand by my commitment to the Zionists. I stand by the promise given to world Jewry for a national home in Palestine. This seems to me a matter of honor—" He spread his hands in frustration. "But what value have we put on honor these days?" The great man closed his eyes in a private grief. "And what value, Murphy, have we put on human life?"

Silence. Murphy cleared his throat. Churchill looked as if he had seen some terrible vision. "You believe Britain will yield to the demands of the Arab Council?"

"The Arab Council simply mimics the words of Adolf Hitler. Britain has not failed to yield to his demands yet."

"Palestine will be closed to Jewish immigration." Murphy spoke these words as if the announcement had already come from the colonial office. He felt queasy at the realization. He had seen the crowds gathered outside the embassies of Prague—and that had been before the Munich agreement. How desperate were those thousands now?

Churchill nodded. "The same claw that cut the heart from Czech-oslovakia now digs into Palestine. The same." He sighed. "I cannot imagine what is to become of all those people trapped in the middle. Chased out of the Reich. Kept out of Palestine for the sake of appeasing a hoodlum."

Murphy jotted a few lines, then looked inquiringly at Churchill. "You know, I can quote you . . . or you can write it yourself. A column for an American chain of newspapers?"

At this cautious suggestion, the old lion eyed Murphy with a new interest. He rubbed a hand over his stubbled chin. "My mother was American, you know. You may call my agent, Murphy."

With this last comment, Murphy knew that, literary agent notwith-standing, he had somehow struck a very unexpected bargain with Win-ston Churchill. The old lion had begun his public career as a journalist in the Boer Wars of Africa. Writing political commentary for the land of his mother's birth seemed a natural extension of his talents as orator and writer.

Churchill lifted his chin slightly. "In spite of my current unpopular-ity, Murphy, I am convinced that history will one day be kind to me," he chuckled, "because I intend to write it myself."

So the matter was settled. Churchill called Murphy to the window and pointed to where a large, swarthy gardener labored pruning rose bushes. "Since I am unpopular now, however," Churchill continued, "I have engaged a bodyguard."

"Unnecessary, I hope." Murphy studied the man who snipped at brown branches even while he gazed toward Churchill and Murphy.

"That is my hope as well." Churchill paused. "But even so, for the sake of my health and that of my family I keep this muscular insurance policy nearby at all times." He cocked an eyebrow at Murphy. "You would be wise to do the same."

A chill of fear prickled the hair on Murphy's neck. He looked at the bodyguard and then at Churchill to see if he was serious. There was no amusement in the statesman's eyes. "Is there . . . some reason . . ." His voice faltered.

"Over the past months, I had some contact with a certain young German officer. I received a wire from him in code that he was coming to England seeking political asylum. The day of his scheduled arrival came and went, and he did not come. I fear the worst."

"But what has that got to do with me? With us?"

"The officer in question is an old friend of Elisa's . . . Thomas von Kleistmann."

———

For weeks Thomas von Kleistmann had been dodging his Gestapo pursuers, and now it had come to this.

Behind him, the shrill whistle of the train screamed in alarm as he ran through the crowds on the dock. A hundred yards away was the ship that he had prayed would carry him to England. To safety. To his right, three men pushed through porters and passengers moving slowly toward the gangplank of the Channel ferry. To the left, just ahead, three more Gestapo agents moved to intercept him.

The ship's horn bellowed. Thomas pressed on. He shoved a woman from his path. She shouted an indignant protest at him. The Gestapo agents moved without taking their eyes from Thomas, who stood a head taller than nearly everyone in the crowd.

It was cold in the morning air, but beads of perspiration mingled with the mist on Thomas's forehead. Twice he had managed to evade Leo Vargen, the S.S. commander in charge of his capture. Perhaps he would be lucky a third time. Anything else would mean a certain and terrible end.

The line of passengers moved slowly past the customs clerk. Thomas managed to pull out his passport and visa. False documents, of course. He glanced to his left. Vargen and his men were making steady and rapid progress. There would be no time to show papers to anyone. He crammed them back in his pocket and stopped.

His pursuers straightened and shouted an alarm as he turned to push back the way he had come. Escape by ship was hopeless now. Hopeless. He would have to make it to the warehouses. Hide in the labyrinth of crates and cargo boxes until it was safe to come out. He could not be taken—he knew too much. Too many names, dates, plans. Elisa's face swam before his eyes, then the image of Ernst vom Rath, Admiral Canaris, and the others. The Gestapo could make a man betray everyone and everything! No, he must not fall into their hands!

"Get out of the way!" He heard the angry voice of Vargen. Thomas pushed and struck at those who blocked his path. The engine of a train hissed as passengers departing the quay boarded for Amsterdam.

Thomas fought the panic that threatened to rob him of his ability to think. Green train cars blocked the path of his escape to the warehouse complex. Vargen and the others made better progress than he was making. If only he were not so tall!

He looked back again at the Gestapo agents. Their faces registered determination, but they seemed to have no fear of losing their quarry. Vargen smiled. He raised his hand and pointed toward Thomas. The train screamed again as two more men stepped from the high step of a green passenger car.

Now the path was blocked three ways. He could only hope to turn back. He might make it to the ship—or perhaps dive into the water!

He spun around. And then he saw them. Unmistakable in their department-issue trench coats, two more agents waited a mere ten paces behind him, their Lugers drawn . . .

"France, yes. Poland? Yes, of course. Maybe even Prague," Murphy paced the length of his study and back. "But you are *not* going back to Berlin. Or Salzburg or Vienna!" he declared to Elisa.

"Then perhaps Sir Thomas will ask my resignation from the orchestra," she said quietly. This was not an argument, but a regret.

"We will cross that bridge when we come to it. But you are *not* crossing the border of the German Reich! Not again, *ever!*" He exhaled loudly as if the very thought of it terrified him. "I am having difficulty even letting you out of my sight in London, let alone thinking of you going back *there!*"

"We still have months before the festivals." Her voice was soft, full of hope. *Was it still possible that Hitler could be taken from power between now and then? Hadn't Thomas believed?* "But of course . . . you are right, Murphy. I won't risk anything. Not myself . . ."

"For my sake, Elisa. For my peace of mind."

"And for the sake of our little one."

"Within a few months all Europe may be at war. I don't want to frighten you, but festivals at Bayreuth won't mean much compared to that. And if things happen as some are saying . . ." He did not discuss Churchill's prophecy. "Then I am sending you and the boys and the baby back to the States to sit this one out. You understand me?"

She shook her head in disagreement. "Tell me I cannot perform in Salzburg or Bayreuth, but do not make me leave you, Murphy. Not ever." Tears filled her eyes. The day had begun so perfectly. Why must this shadow hover over them still?

She put up her arms to him and he knelt beside her, laying his head in her lap. "Maybe I'll go home with you. Write a sports column. Brooklyn Dodgers. Yankees . . ."

She stroked his hair and knew with a certainty that such a life could never be for them. "Are we supposed to fiddle, Murphy, while the whole world burns down around us?" Both of them knew it would be impossible. "If darkness defeats us by simply wearing us out, then where is there any hope for the light?"

"Listen." Murphy raised his head. "Right now I just want you to be okay. Promise me that for a while, anyway, you will just fiddle, huh? Sir Thomas is right about that much at least. Just play your Guarnerius and let that baby have a little peace and quiet in there. There isn't anything you can do now that will stop whatever is coming. You have done your bit. Lay low. Take it easy for a while? Promise me, Elisa—"

"An easy promise to make," she whispered. "As long as you do not bring me the front page, Murphy!" She said the words with a sad smile, but both of them knew they were true.

8

Rescue

Plumes of smoke rose up from the port of Jaffa as the heavily guarded refugee buses moved toward a vast, unnamed refugee center on the outskirts of Tel Aviv.

The distant sounds of gunfire could be heard clearly. Shimon squeezed Leah's hand as he stared bleakly out the window of the bus.

"They have not told us everything, these Englishmen," he said.

"Only disturbances," Leah murmured, arguing inwardly with the same awareness that Shimon felt. Things were indeed much more serious than the authorities were letting on. A demonstration to show the English politicians the extent of Arab dissatisfaction.

"If it sounds like war, and looks like war—" He raised his chin and sniffed the faint scent of gunpowder on the air. "And smells like war . . ." His voice trailed off.

Ahead lay an immense city of tents, surrounded by tall barbed wire fences.

"This must be home," remarked a young man bitterly.

"At least it is not Dachau! I have seen that place!" Shimon blurted out defensively. "Here the guards have their eyes turned out. Their guns away from us. The wire is to protect us, not keep us prisoner."

"Wire is wire," argued the young man angrily. "Guards are guards."

"You would not think so if you had been to Dachau," Shimon muttered.

Only Leah heard him. Somehow his words lessened her renewed disappointment with the Promised Land. Drab green army tents on a barren plain. This was not going to be a pleasant camp-out in a lovely Alpine setting. When members of the halutz had described *hardship* at the Zionist meetings, Leah had imagined *adventure*. *How did I ever manage to confuse the two?* she wondered.

The caravan slowed. Armed escorts sped past on their motorcycles. Inside the compound, additional British soldiers peered out from behind sandbags.

Leah craned her neck to look back where the plume of smoke thickened and broadened. A distant explosion sent up yet another billowing black cloud.

"They've hit the fuel depot!" shouted a British soldier, and all heads pivoted to watch.

Only Shimon could imagine what such an inferno was like at close range.

"What is happening?" shouted a woman out the window. "Is it war?"

The soldier throttled back and glared resentfully at the frightened faces on the bus. "Not a war. Just a little welcoming demonstration in your honor. In honor of the Jewish refugees, see?"

Without waiting for reply, he revved his motor and sped off.

Those who understood English interpreted for those who did not. A heavy silence lay over the men and women on board. *So. The English soldiers were being forced to fight because of this Jewish dream of a homeland. Good boys from Brighton and Blackpool were going to die today because an English politician named Balfour said that there would be a homeland for the Jews. Arabs attacked because these buses were filled with people who hoped the promise was true.* The accusation in the young soldier's words was unmistakable.

Suddenly Shimon clapped his hands together and cleared his throat. "Yes! I knew there had to be some connection between me and all this messy business! Everywhere I go, things start blowing up!"

An uneasy laughter followed his remark.

"So it's *you!*" bellowed a man who had been a lawyer in Weimar. "All the time I thought it was me! Every place I went in Germany windows got smashed. Stones thrown! You must have been close by!"

The laughter came with an easy relief as others joined in the game. *"It was Shimon Feldstein all the time!"*

"That was my business!" Shimon half stood for a bow. He raised his cast above his head. "What do you expect from a man who plays kettle drums for a living?"

One by one the convoy of buses passed through the heavy gates into the compound. Seventh in the long line, the bus that carried Shimon and Leah was filled with laughter and jokes by the time it entered. Even the bitter young Zionist who had protested against the barbed wire joined in.

The five kittens huddled together miserably in the gathering gloom. Wide eyes blinked up at the rabbi from a patchwork ball of fur.

He knew how foolish he was to worry about kittens when his own life hung by a thread. Still, he could not help it. *If the mother cat had not stepped out, I would have done so, and it would be me in pieces now instead of her! Oy! And now they will starve while I go home, God willing, and try to forget about this day! Or they will be eaten by dogs or trampled underfoot. And all because God did not want me shot! Oy! God, you could not have sent out a tomcat to get shot instead? It had to be a mother?*

The Eternal, blessed be His name, had left the old man with no choice. When night came—and that would be soon—he would slip out from this place and take the kittens with him. *If* he could catch them. And, when he got home, he would say kaddish for the mama cat who saved him from certain death.

He clucked his tongue. Little ears perked up in curiosity. The kittens were several feet away. In the narrow crevices he could not stoop to pick them up. This operation must be coordinated carefully with the coming of night.

Two stars appeared in the darkening sky. There was little time. The Arabs would feel freer to wander the streets under cover of night. They would shoot whomever they found. They would search the cracks for stray Jews and stray cats, and they would shoot. Rabbi Lebowitz had no doubt of that.

He clucked his tongue again in hopes that the kittens would wander toward him. No luck. He could not tell where one kitten began and another ended.

He wagged his toe at the ball of fluff. It seemed to roll backward, farther from reach. He meowed, without effect. He did not meow like a mother cat and deserved no respect or attention.

Troubled, the old man stared at them. They stared back. Resigning himself to the fact that he was an old meshuggener after all, and that they would have to be left to their fate, he remembered that a failed mitzvah is still honored by the Eternal. He had tried. The kittens would not be saved.

As the minutes ticked by, the old man clucked and meowed again. Futile. Soon the night would fall. Sudden darkness would come to Jerusalem, and then the violence would be renewed. If he ran fast enough, he could make it to the Armenian Quarter, and from there to the Jewish Quarter a hundred yards down the street. *If. If. If . . .*

If these old legs can move, after such a day. And if the Arabs do not shoot me from behind and the British from the front. And if the Armenians will let me through the barricade! Oy! You have enough to trouble you!

Still, that furry heap against the wall plagued him—innocent creatures who could not fathom the fact that they were going to die or the reason for it.

Wedged into the tight space, he struggled to remove his coat—one arm scraping against the wall, then the other. The kittens jumped and climbed over one another in fear.

He looked up at the sky and asked the Eternal to be patient with such a foolish old man. Slowly, he dangled the sleeve of the coat down along his leg. He wriggled it up and down, like bait on the end of a fishing line.

Ears perked up again. Here was something of interest, much like the tail of mama cat. The tough little gray swaggered out of his heap of brothers and sister first. He paused. He crouched. He pounced toward the elusive sleeve.

The rabbi rolled his eyes upward and thanked the Eternal. The white kitten bounced up, arching its back in warning of battle. The two remaining grays followed in a charge as the white leaped to snag the fabric with sharp little claws. He hung there for a moment. The old man pulled him up and unhooked the claws, then slid him into the roomy pocket of his baggy trousers. *Yes!*

Down went the sleeve again, and up came the blustery little gray. He scratched and hissed unhappily as the rabbi dropped him in on top of the white.

Darkness descended. The old man waved the sleeve while the two captives in his pocket fought. The tiny calico did not move forward to join her brothers in the game. At last little paws scampered over the rabbi's aching feet. Another attack on the fabric netted the second gray.

Shouts began to ring out across the domed rooftops of the Old City.

"Hey, Jews! You think you will live through this night?"

The old man was uncertain. Perhaps they would find his body in the morning and stop to wonder why the old rabbi's pockets were full of kittens.

He dared to speak, "Come on, little one! I will take you to Tipat Chalev for a drop of milk, nu?"

The last gray kitten snagged claws and fangs on the fabric. The rabbi swung him up and dropped him into the other pocket. That left the last calico. The sweet one. The shy one.

There was no time. Back toward the Haram, a single shot was fired—a call to arms for the bandits in the Old City.

Rabbi Lebowitz drew a deep breath. He could wait no longer. "Sorry, little one," he whispered as he slid out of his hiding place and plastered himself against the wall. "May the Eternal keep you safe in His pocket."

More shots. The old man could plainly see the fire leap from the guns. Five shots. Five different guns on the roofs of the Old City. They fired up into the air. Flashes momentarily illuminated the ghostly forms of men in Arab dress.

He hesitated, thinking which would be the safest path. He had thought of it a thousand times throughout the day, but confronted with the need to run, he could not remember *where* to run! His heart pounded as it had during the riot. His breath grew short, as if he had already run ten miles. But he had only taken one step!

The kittens wrestled in the deep pockets. Little needle-sharp claws penetrated the fabric and stuck his thighs as if to wake him up from a stupor.

Angry Arab voices advanced. The old man looked toward the Square. Two blocks, and then the Armenian Quarter! Yes—now he remembered!

He tried to find breath. And then, from the hiding place came a tiny voice. The old man peered down. A small shadow moved. *Be patient with me, God! The calico!*

He stooped and gathered the little one up, and then he ran, kittens bouncing against him. He held the calico in his right hand and dragged himself forward along the stone facades with his left.

Gunfire cracked like a whip. He had not run like this since he had been a young man. Uneven stones jarred his old bones. Kittens clawed him through his pockets. The calico dug into his arm until he bled.

At last, the outline of the jagged wall loomed up. Would British soldiers mistake him for the enemy? No time to think! Under his breath, he muttered the name of his daughter. "Etta! Etta!" It was Shabbat in Poland. Peaceful Shabbat. Etta must never come back to Jerusalem, never come home to this!

The corner was a few yards from him. *Merciful God!* The eyes of Death turned toward him.

"Someone is moving down there!"

"Shoot! Shoot him!"

More gunfire rang out behind. He did not stop. He did not turn to look.

"Shoot! He is getting away!" Boots ran toward him from the Armenian barricade.

"Don't shoot! I am a rabbi! Gevalt! Don't shoot!"

———

The floors of the tents were wooden slats, salvaged from packing crates discarded by the British military.

The entire camp was asleep now. Or at least the confusion had died down into a stupor of exhaustion. A dim light still burned in the cubicle next to that of Leah and Shimon. Beyond the thin canvas partition, a family of six from Württemberg occupied two small spaces. The children slept more soundly than the parents, who groaned like the springs on their bunks.

From the top bunk of their allotted space, Leah studied the letters of shipping labels that remained on the slat floor.

B-L-A . . . Perhaps the word had been blankets? Blankets for the

British soldiers? Or maybe "Black boots"? On the slat at the head of the bunks the initials *H.M.* were stenciled in red paint. That must stand for "His Majesty." The floor was courtesy of His Majesty King George of England. She wondered if the English king in his palace could imagine that the discarded rubbish of the government in Palestine would be put to such good use by the Jewish Agency on behalf of the new immigrants. And if it was discovered that the Jewish Agency had created floors out of His Majesty's wooden slats, would the English demand the crates be returned?

Shimon slept soundly in the bunk beneath her. He had hardly touched his supper after reading the sheet of precautions that had come with the issued bed linens: CAUTION: ALL LINENS SHOULD BE CHECKED NIGHTLY BEFORE RETIRING.

"Checked for what?" he had asked a man who looked as if he might know.

"Scorpions. And bedbugs. They come up through the slats and climb the legs of the bunks. You will notice that each leg is set in a tin can half filled with water. When the creatures climb up the side of the can they fall in and drown. You will be saved by this device mostly. Except for the ones that come up the inside of the canvas and drop down from above . . ."

This had been meant to comfort, somehow, but it had left Leah sleepless and searching the cracks between the planks. Tonight she was more terrified of *things* than she was of the Arabs who seemed to be tearing up all of Palestine at once.

CAUTION: UPON RISING, BE CERTAIN TO CHECK BOOTS AND ALL ARTICLES OF CLOTHING BEFORE WEARING.

What sort of place is this? she asked herself again. Why had the Zionist lecturers not spoken about bedbugs and scorpions and . . .

CAUTION: USE OF WASHING FACILITIES SHOULD BE RESTRICTED TO DAYLIGHT HOURS WHENEVER POSSIBLE.

The same fellow who had told them about bedbugs explained how snakes liked to curl up beneath the washbasins. It was not so bad this time of year, but one could not be too cautious. And now with the Arabs on the rampage, it was not at all safe to leave shelter after dark.

With trembling hand Leah had added this information to the letter addressed to Number 36 Red Lion Square in London. She told Elisa that such things did not distract from the joy of being here in the Holy Land. But Elisa knew her well enough to know the truth. She would close her eyes and picture Leah lying sleepless and terrified in a sandy tent while Arab bands slaughtered whoever crossed their paths and scorpions tried to find ways around the tin cans on the legs of the bed.

"Oh, Lord," Leah whispered, "at last I am here, and I am afraid. This does not feel like home. No place feels like home."

Shimon's sleepy voice drifted up. "If we were not so desperate we would let the Arabs have it, eh?"

"You're awake?"

"I keep imagining little things trying to get into bed with me."

"Me, too."

"Then why don't *you* come down and get into bed with me?" He was laughing at her, but she didn't care.

"We will break the bed."

"We will frighten away the enemy. Two of us together. Come down, will you? I need something sweet and soft tonight."

"Oh, Shimon," she chided him, but before the words passed her lips she was climbing down to slip between the sheets. The lower bunk complained loudly and sagged down another three inches. Leah snuggled close to Shimon. Her head against his chest, her arms and legs tangled with his, somehow she felt much safer.

"There now," he stroked her hair and then held up his cast. "If anything tries to get you, I will squish it with my plaster arm!"

"Much better," she sighed. "Much more . . . comfortable . . . down . . ." Her voice trailed away as sleep at last came to her.

Shimon lay awake beside her for a long time before his own troubled thoughts finally let him sleep.

———

Shabbat night at Tipat Chalev, they had hardly noticed that Rebbe Lebowitz had been gone all day. No one was worried much. No one asked where he had been or if he was stuck in a crack between two buildings. And they were not happy about the kittens, either. He had broken a Shabbat commandment by carrying them.

Hannah Cohen faced off with Rabbi Lebowitz on the back step of Tipat Chalev as the orphan kittens scampered over his scuffed shoes.

"Kittens make cats!" said Hannah. "And cats make other kittens! And kittens make other cats!"

"And all of them kill Old City mice and rats!" the old man argued.

"Not in the kitchen of Tipat Chalev, they don't!"

"Not in the *kitchen*! Here in the *alleyway*!"

"We do not wish to listen to the endless bawling of a chorus of cats!" Hannah stamped her foot and the kittens jumped straight up and then took refuge to peer out from behind the legs of their protector rabbi.

"The mother of these five kittens saved my life! And so I made a vow—"

"Not in my kitchen!"

"So! I *told* you, already! Not in the kitchen . . . in the alley. Maybe in the basement! They will kill the rats, and now, as head of the charitable distribution of food in the Jewish Quarter of the Old City—"

"No females!" Hannah shouted. "Oy! Sort them out! *No females!*"

At the sound of shouting, half a dozen round, wide-eyed faces peered into the kitchen. Hannah Cohen and Rebbe Lebowitz were arguing. So? That was nothing unusual. But they were arguing about kittens, which was unusual. The children whispered to themselves in amazement as the learned rabbi picked up each kitten in turn, lifted its tail, and scrutinized each backside as if he were searching for a message. "There!" he cried, thrusting the gray into the arms of Hannah. "A boy!" Then again, "A boy! A boy! A boy!" The calico was the last to be examined. He picked it up. The kitten meowed sweetly and batted his beard. The old man scowled at Hannah Cohen angrily and then slipped the calico into his pocket. "This one will be mine. She almost got me killed saving her, and so I am responsible for her now, nu?"

Four kittens purred in the arms of Hannah Cohen. She looked away haughtily and then looked down at them. Her expression changed briefly to one of pleasure, but she caught herself before the rabbi could see it. "All right, then! They will grow up to be big man cats and they will fight all day, and you will be sorry." The kittens purred louder. "What will we name them?" Her voice was alarmingly gentle.

The rabbi reached out to scratch the chin of the white kitten. "I thought . . . Genesis. Exodus. Leviticus. Numbers." He smiled and lifted up the calico. "And she will be Psalms."

"Just keep her away from my boys." Hannah's eyes narrowed in threat. "That is all we need around here! More cats!"

9

Sabbath Travel

It was Saturday in Catholic Warsaw.

A low-flying biplane rattled noisily over the roofs of the city. To the south and east and west a forest of red-brick chimneys belched smoke and soot into the cold autumn air. These were the Catholic chimneys of Warsaw. During the cold Polish winters this dark mist rose up from Catholic hearths seven days a week without stopping. Like the incense of Mass or the light of votive candles before a saint, the smoke was a sign that clearly showed which chimney belonged to a Catholic.

It was Sabbath in Jewish Warsaw.

In the northeast quarter of the city, ten thousand red-brick chimneys pointed heavenward. Not even one wisp of smoke drifted up from Jewish hearths. On this holy day of rest, work was forbidden for the Chosen. Adding even a handful of coal to the fire was considered labor; the grates had been stoked with fuel in the last moments before the evening star signaled the beginning of the Sabbath. Hour by hour the coal had been consumed as the soft, mellow chants of prayer and blessing had risen up.

Lights are shining, hymns outpouring,
Welcome, holy day of rest!
Now the soul, unfettered soaring,
Holds with God communion blest.

The fervor of Sabbath greetings warmed the homes in Jewish Warsaw even as coals glowed and cooled and finally tumbled to ash.

Those who bargained and bartered and shoveled coal in Catholic Warsaw viewed the cold Sabbath chimneys of their neighbors with suspicion, even hatred. The peddler would not stop to sell where such a chimney stood. The milkman made his route blocks around the smokeless chimneys, lest his milk sour on the stoop of a customer who would not carry it indoors. A shrug and a shake of the head was the Polish answer to the clear blue sky above Jewish Warsaw. *Strange creatures, these Jews!*

From the high viewpoint of a clattering biplane, Warsaw was easily divided. And from this perspective, the sight of one lone plume of smoke rising from the Jewish district caused the pilot to turn his head and look again.

The thick double chimney on the corner of Muranow Square and Nalewki Street spewed a column of gray into the air. This tall three-story house was not the house of a Catholic in the midst of the Jewish residential district. It was too near the rounded dome of the syn-agogue—almost within the shadow of the great iron Star of David. It was a large house, square like a box, with three windows on each floor facing the Square below. The brick construction had been faced over with stucco and painted pale yellow. The cornice work was cast with scrolls of leaves and flowers. This house on Muranow Square was the house of a well-to-do Jew. *Perhaps,* the pilot thought, *the owner hired a Gentile to build his Sabbath fire for him. A Shabbes goy, as Jews call their Gentile help.*

At the moment of his thought, the stately mahogany door burst open and a young woman ran down the steps—dark hair, bouncing curls, dark blue dress with a dropped waist, high-button shoes. Even from this distance he could see that this must be the daughter of a wealthy Jew. A pretty thing. Perhaps she was in her early teens. She did not look up at the biplane as children usually did. Instead, she stopped at the bottom of the steps and turned her face upward toward the second story where the window swung back and a bearded Jewish man leaned out to shout instructions. His words were indistinguishable, drowned by the roar of the engine. But something was up. The man was in his shirt sleeves—open collar, suspenders off. His face seemed pale, almost angry behind the thick black beard. The girl nodded, and with a fearful look on her face, she began to run across Muranow Square, past the sleeping facades of Pokorna Street where the traffic gradually thickened and Jewish Warsaw melted into the bustle of Catholic Warsaw.

The pilot caught one final glimpse of the girl before her figure became only one among ten thousand in the streets. Then other children looked up and pointed at the biplane. They shouted and chased its shadow. The pilot dipped his wings in salute and laughed and forgot all about the one chimney in the Jewish district that smoked even on the Sabbath.

———

The chill wind cut through the fabric of the young woman's blue

Sabbath dress. She had forgotten all about her coat when her father had sent her on this urgent errand. In spite of the wind, the note in her hand was damp from perspiration. Her fair skin was even paler than usual from the exertion of running.

Ahead, the rail tracks ended at the *Umschlagplatz*. Great locomotives puffed and hissed, impatient to be gone from Warsaw. The girl was only halfway to the doctor's house. Her lungs burned and her legs ached. For an instant she considered slowing to a walk. *Why did Papa not send Daniel? He is younger, yes, but he runs faster than I.* She stumbled and almost fell at the feet of a group of broad-faced Polish railway workers. A man in a black wool cap reached out to break her fall.

"Careful, pretty one! Hurry too much, and you will miss your train because your head will be broken!"

She tried to thank him. There was no time to explain that she was not running to catch a train at the *Umschlagplatz*. She had no breath to explain. Willing her legs to move, she broke away and called an apology over her shoulder.

Her Polish was tinged with a heavy accent, causing the workers to joke that they had caught a little Jew running on the Sabbath. They would watch and see if the Jewish God would hurl a bolt of lightning down on the *Umschlagplatz* when He noticed the violation!

Such a joke brought a round of laughter that gave the girl a new strength born of fear. She would not speak to one of *them* again. It was forbidden by Papa to speak to the goyim. *They* were dangerous; she knew that. She had not meant to speak. Had not meant to stumble. Had not meant to be caught by one of *them*!

A strange sense of guilt dogged her. She forgot her lungs, forgot her aching legs. Before her was the picture of Mama's strained face and the soft apology she had whispered to Papa. "So sorry, Aaron. I had not meant to begin this on Sabbath."

Papa had touched her forehead as another pain came. "I tried to call Dr. Letzno. They have cut the phone wires again. I will send a note to fetch him."

Mama had blinked back tears and bit her lip as she nodded. "Yes. Dr. Letzno . . ."

The girl clutched the note tightly. She was afraid she might drop it and it would be trampled beneath the shoes of Saturday Warsaw. *Grandmothers pulling their apple-cheeked grandsons to the barbershop. Cliques of young women gathered outside the theaters. Couples crowding into the cafes of Warsaw for long talks over coffee and fresh pastry. Shop windows displaying the latest Paris fashions. Brightly colored dresses and pert little hats and silk stockings with high heels . . .*

This was a foreign world to the girl. Only blocks away from her home on Muranow, within sight of the cupola of the synagogue, the world seemed to mock the peaceful Sabbath. Did *they* not know of the commandment? The girl had never been beyond the borders of her own neighborhood on Sabbath. She had not realized, could not imagine, how *they* spent the holy day. She felt ill. Was it from running so far, or from passing through the streets where certainly every one of the 613 commandments were being broken all at the same moment—and on the Sabbath?

In her mind she recited the prayer for Sabbath evening as Papa had taught her. It did little to comfort her. Ahead was the street sign: *Dzika Street.* Her heart lifted. Only five more blocks to the home of Dr. Letzno!

The doctor was a friend of the family, a Jew who had also once lived near Muranow Square. He had grown up there within the safety and security of that society, yet when he had reached manhood he had gone out to study at the University in Prague. He had become a physician—quite renowned, Papa said. When he returned to Poland, he moved into the world of Saturday Warsaw. It was difficult to tell that he was not one of *them.* On Dzika Street he spoke Polish without a trace of Yiddish accent. Only when he returned to Muranow did he use such words as *Gottenyu,* and *oy!* He seemed a Jew again, even though he did not wear a yarmulke or worship any longer at shul. Papa loved Dr. Letzno—loved him like a brother. Papa forgave Dr. Letzno for moving away from Muranow Square and turning his back on his heritage.

But at this moment, the girl could *not* forgive the doctor for living a world away in Saturday Warsaw. Because he had turned away, now she must run coatless through the streets of the Catholic Poles! She must violate the Sabbath and dodge the children playing hopscotch and the women hefting their groceries and the men smoking on the street corners.

"Is someone chasing you?"

"Where is such a little beauty running without her coat?"

She did not answer. She would not. Her accent would be taunted, her identity revealed.

Only one block more. The beautiful house of Dr. Letzno loomed ahead. Shining automobiles were parked along the curb of the towering three-story structure. It was built much like the houses at home on the Square, but although this house had two chimneys, both of which emitted smoke today, everyone knew that Dr. Letzno had not moved away to find a better house.

A tall wrought-iron fence surrounded the house—not a fence to keep people out, but only an ornament. The girl stumbled again and reached out to grab the bars of the fence for support until she could find her breath again. Papa's note was crumpled in her hand. She exhaled with a little cry of pain when each breath did not fill her tortured lungs.

Inside the grand house, a string quartet played. She could hear the music and see a crowd of people in the parlor. Pulling herself hand-over-hand along the fence, she stumbled toward the front steps. There was a party inside. The house was full of Saturday people, and Dr. Letzno was their host. She would be brave. She would not cry as she faced them.

The stairs reared back, daring her to climb. Clutching the wide banister, she struggled toward the massive front door until at last she leaned against the wood and reached up to grasp the brass knocker. She let the metal slam down and then slam down again. The music continued. She could hear laughter and voices through the door, then footsteps and the rattle of a hand on the doorknob. The door was opened in sudden and violent welcome. They had not expected a girl to tumble panting into the foyer.

The delicate white hand raised the crumpled note to a black-coated butler. "For . . . Doctor . . . Letzno! Please . . . urgent!"

"My God, how far have you run? And without your coat on such a day! Herr Doctor! Dr. Letzno!"

Her task completed, the girl buried her face in her hands and sobbed in spite of her vow not to. There were rapid footsteps. The music did not stop, but the laughter died away.

"Who . . . well! It is Rachel Lubetkin! *Rachel!* Without your coat! You ran? Why did your father not telephone?"

Rachel could not speak. She could not tell the doctor that *they* had cut the telephone lines into the old Jewish section of Warsaw. Perhaps even one of those who sipped champagne in this very house had done the mischief!

The doctor put his arms around her and helped her across the black and white tiled floor. He guided her into a paneled room with green velvet curtains and walls of books, placed her on a leather sofa, and poured a glass of water, which he held to her lips.

"Easy, now . . . you are blue with cold."

"Please . . . it is Mama . . . she is . . ."

Dr. Letzno tore open the envelope and read the message in a glance. He chuckled to himself. "Some kinds of labor will not wait, Rachel—not even until Sabbath is over."

———

Sabbath came to every town in Germany, but this night there was no Sabbath rest. The streets of every city teemed with people shouting, *"Send the Jews to Palestine!"*

In Berlin, in Leipzig, in Cologne, it was the same: *"Send the Jews to Palestine!"*

In Hamburg and Hanover and Essen people raised their fists and roared: *"Send the Jews to Palestine!"*

In Dusseldorf and Bremen and Munich the fires of a million torches lit angry faces: *"Send the Jews to Palestine!"*

Tonight the Jews who had come to Germany from Poland a lifetime ago were rounded up and placed under guard in police stations and concert houses and abandoned buildings. Twelve thousand men, women, and children huddled beneath the weight of those shouts: *"Send the Jews to Palestine!"*

In every Jewish mind was the thought, the *hope,* that they might by some miracle be sent to Palestine! *Jerusalem!* Zion—a homeland where they might live where the air was not so thick with hatred!

But it was not Palestine that the Nazis had in mind for these twelve thousand. The British would not allow more Jews into that land for fear of Arab reprisals. And so, magically, the raging mobs changed their cry to, *"Send the Jews back to Poland!"*

Every Jew arrested in Germany that night had some former connection to Poland. The Führer, led by the will of his people, decided that, indeed, these Jews *would* be returned to Poland!

The Gestapo agents began to scream, "Sign here! You are being deported!"

Those who protested that they had brought nothing with them for a cold autumn journey were told, "You had nothing with you when you came to Germany and you will take nothing out!"

All over Germany that night, groups of twenty were led from their places of confinement. Men. Old men. Women. Old women. All sizes of children. They were led through the streets, through mobs who spit and threw paper sacks of excrement onto these twelve thousand. *"Send the Jews to Poland!"* Dozens of locomotives leading hundreds of cattle cars were jammed full of Jews who longed for Palestine.

Trains clattered along the tracks of Germany throughout that long and terrible night. The German people left the streets of their cities and went home to sleep a deep and satisfying sleep. Germany was safe from these twelve thousand Jews *at last*!

———

Lazer Grynspan was having trouble breathing. His wife Rifka and daughter Berta leaned heavily against him. Others in their cattle car leaned against them until Lazer was crushed against the wooden slats. He drew his breath in short, shallow jerks. It was just enough to keep him alive.

Throughout the night he thanked God that his son Herschel was in Paris. How wise they had been to send him to Paris, where he was safe and free! Lazer asked himself why they had not done the same for Berta after the Nazis had forced him to give up his tailor shop. Why had they not moved faster so they would not have been trapped in the Nazi cauldron?

Lazer had a hundred reasons why, but now those reasons seemed small and foolish. He could not so much as draw a breath to whisper a prayer, but he prayed all the same. Again and again he thought of Herschel. He thought of Theo Lindheim, who had barely managed to escape. He wondered where those Jews who had left Germany of their own will had gone? Theo, Anna, Elisa and the two sons—they had money. That is why *they* could go. Lazer was only a poor tailor, and now he was leaving Germany, anyway. Strange how Nazi hatred had leaned down to look at someone as small as a tailor. Why should the Germans care if a Jew stitched their buttons and hemmed their cuffs?

The clack of the train wheels lulled many into a stupor that was not true sleep but semiconsciousness. People had long since stopped weeping. There was no strength for that. This nightmare had begun Thursday night, and it was almost Saturday morning! There was only strength to breathe and only energy to pray for help—as long as the prayers were silent.

The morning sun hovered just below the German horizon. Leaves on the trees were red and gold and the sky took on the hues of burnished copper rimmed with pink and blue.

Lazer Grynspan looked through the slats of the cattle car and knew the real reason he had not left Germany before. *Was there any land on earth so beautiful?* Any other time he might have said that the beauty of Germany took his breath away, but this morning it was the barbarity of the German people that left him breathless.

Outside in a wide green field a farmer led his herd of milk cows to pasture. Did he know what cargo rode behind the slats of the cattle car that passed him now? The farmer did not look up. Peaceful morning. Beautiful morning. Lazer hoped the farmer did not know.

It was almost six in the morning. The tick of the wheels began to slow. Someone moaned; then someone else, and suddenly the entire train began to moan as the brakes squealed a protest.

A green sign with white lettering said: *Neu Bentschen.* Lazer knew this place. It was the German border station on the frontier between Germany and Poland. Lazer had crossed into Germany through this very station in 1911. His wife had been a beautiful bride then. They had fled Polish Russia as a wave of violence against Jews had engulfed the land. Thousands of Jews had died that year beneath the clubs of the Ukrainians and Russians and Persians. Lazer and Rifka had imagined they would be safe in Germany. Such a civilized land. They could raise their children in peace if they fled to Germany. It had *felt* true in 1911!

As if Rifka read her husband's mind, she moaned and managed to straighten her neck. "Here we are . . . again," she croaked. There was no humor in her voice. They were returning to a land of anti-Semitism. Brutality toward Jews. Centuries of pogroms.

But perhaps it is better than Germany, Lazer dared to think as the train finally jerked and shuddered and slid into place beside another train.

The groans of the passengers continued, punctuated by shouts of German S.S. who waited at the station. Metal rattled. Bolts and chains crashed back. The doors were opened to the shouts of, "Out! Out, you filthy swine!"

For a moment no one moved. Inside the cattle cars the bodies had been molded into one mass of human flesh that must break apart carefully, lest parts of it collapse and be trampled.

Rubber truncheons landed on the legs of those who moved too slowly. The sun burst up and long shadows reached across the border into Poland.

10

Night Sounds

Herschel Grynspan was only seventeen years old. Somehow he knew he would not live to see his eighteenth birthday.

It was raining in Paris. Not a hard rain, not the sort of downpour that washes away the dust and leaves the air clean and transparent. This rain was a gray drizzle, obscuring the view from Herschel's attic window and mingling with the smoke from the chimneys to coat everything with a dirty, wet film.

At least the attic air was cool now. Herschel had hidden here for five months since Le Morthomme had stepped between his gun and Thomas von Kleistmann. As the old bookseller had crumpled to the ground, Herschel had run back along the narrow lanes of the Left Bank until he had come to the home of Hans Schumann. Hans had secreted him in the attic and there Herschel had remained through the Paris spring, the stifling humidity of summer, and into the autumn.

Hans had brought him food each day and news of each succeeding Nazi outrage. Hans provided him with German newspapers that carried the latest speeches by the Führer. Hans kept his spirits up. He promised that the hour would come when Herschel would fulfill his vow to teach the Nazis a lesson.

When Herschel had openly spoken of suicide, Hans had taken Grynspan's gun away and reminded him that there was only one way left for a Jew to die—*for the cause!*

So it was that on this drizzly day, Hans carried a radio up the steep steps to the attic. A long cord trailed behind and music played as Hans emerged, smiling, through the trapdoor.

"Herschel!" the swarthy young man hailed the captive. "See what I have brought for you!"

Herschel could not manage a smile of gratitude. "Not a visa to Palestine."

Hans looked hurt. He held up the blaring box. "A radio. Music and news for you so you will not have to wait for me to come before you know what is happening in the world!" He set the radio on an upturned crate.

"I would rather have a visa to Palestine." Herschel hated his own ingratitude, but he could not help it. Although he owed everything to Hans, he still felt like a prisoner.

"We are trying. Such things take time. Perhaps they are still looking for the one who killed the old bookseller. Perhaps you would be arrested before you had a chance to improve your aim and kill a Nazi, Herschel." The hurt look was replaced by determination as Hans fiddled with the tuning dial.

"If I were in Palestine, I would not have to kill a Nazi." Herschel lay back on his groaning metal cot. *Why am I not more grateful for the radio?* he wondered.

"In Palestine you could kill Arabs and English—" He stopped midsentence as the dulcet tones of a French broadcaster came through the speaker.

"Following the action, the German Minister of Propaganda issued a statement assuring the world that those Jews deported from the Reich all held Polish passports..."

Herschel's breath caught in his chest. He sat bolt upright and leaned forward with both hands raised to silence any words from Hans. "My family!" he whispered. "They hold Polish passports!"

"Nearly twelve thousand Jews of Polish origin have been rounded up throughout the Reich, and as the German people demanded their immediate expulsion, they are being shipped by train toward the frontier between Germany and Poland...."

Hans looked first at the radio and then at Herschel. He clucked his tongue in sympathy and shook his head. "Been going on since Thursday, I hear. No doubt your family is among them."

Herschel cried out. He cradled his head in his hands as Hans punctuated the reports of violence with the certainty that Herschel's parents must be among the thousands of victims.

"Papa . . . my mother and sister!"

"I thought you would want to hear," Hans frowned. "Something to keep up your resolve, eh, Herschel? A man must be brave in times like these. I was afraid you might be slipping. But you were born for braver things." Hans shrugged and adjusted the tuner to eliminate the faint crackle in the reception as the broadcast shifted to live coverage of the chanting Germans in Munich. *"Jews to Poland! No more Jewish swine in Germany! Jews to Poland!"*

Night fell over Warsaw with a brittle coldness. Sabbath was ended, and once again smoke from the Jewish section of Warsaw mingled with the smoke from Catholic chimneys.

Aaron Lubetkin sat at his massive desk and tried to concentrate on passages of the Mishnah. A green-globed desk lamp cast a ring of light on stacks of books and papers, but increasingly, Aaron found his eyes wandering to the lighted hallway and the banister of the stairs that led up to the bedroom.

The children had long since been put to bed by Frau Rosen. Rachel had not stopped shivering until she soaked in a warm bath. Aaron felt badly that he had sent his daughter on her errand without so much as a thin sweater. Etta would not be happy if she knew. She would have sharp words for him if she ever found out.

The house had been silent since Dr. Eduard Letzno had arrived with his black bag in one hand and Rachel at his side. Etta was always silent at times like this. She did not cry out as some women did in childbirth. Her labor had begun nearly four weeks early. Eduard's face betrayed the seriousness of premature delivery. Etta understood the danger, and she did not wish to frighten Rachel with a display. After all, perhaps one day Rachel would give them grandchildren and it would not be good to fill her young mind with a terror of childbirth.

Etta was able to think of such things even when the contractions were four minutes apart.

Practical, beautiful Etta.

The thought of her made Aaron's throat tighten with emotion. How could he live without her if something went wrong? He wiped his eyes with the back of his hand. He had not turned a page in his book for nearly three hours. After Dr. Letzno had come and expelled him from the room, he had gone through the motions of normalcy with the children; then he had retreated here, just beneath the room where Etta labored.

The floorboards creaked above his head—Eduard's footsteps. The encouraging voice of Frau Rosen penetrated into the study, then the voice of Eduard: "That's it, Etta!" Muffled, but understandable. "Once again!" Still no sound from Etta.

Aaron stared up at the ceiling as if his gaze could pierce the rafters that separated him from her agony. His own breath was heavy with the exertion of his thoughts. "That's it, Etta," he whispered. "That's it, darling . . ."

Suddenly her silence was broken with one explosive cry, *"Aaron!"*

Aaron felt the blood drain from his face. He jumped from his chair; it toppled backward, spilling a stack of books onto the floor. Taking the stairs two at a time, he reached the landing within seconds. He threw open the bedroom door, then stopped.

Etta lay on the bed, draped in a sheet and quilt. Her hands grasped cords tied to the bedposts. Her head was thrown back, and her teeth gritted with the strain of her effort. Mrs. Rosen supported her shoulders. The doctor was reaching out to guide a tiny, crumpled form from her womb.

No one noticed Aaron as he stood panting and ashen in the doorway.

"Once again, Etta! He's almost—"

"She called me," Aaron blurted out.

"Close the door, Aaron." The doctor's words were clipped, preoccupied.

Aaron continued to gaze wide-eyed at Etta. Damp hair clung to her face. Her eyes were squeezed tight. Aaron breathed with her. He clenched his fists and moaned softly. Tears stung his eyes. He had never seen her like this, never witnessed—

"Close the door, Rebbe Lubetkin!" Frau Rosen barked her command. "The draft."

Aaron swallowed hard and obeyed. Etta did not look at him. Her knuckles were white as she strained against the cords and sat halfway up in the bed as she bore down.

"Beautiful Etta! Another son!" Eduard held the slippery gray child gently as he wiped away mucous and blood. "So tiny, and yet *alive*!"

"The Eternal be praised!" Frau Rosen helped lower her to the heap of pillows. She wiped Etta's forehead with a damp cloth.

"A boy!" Etta wept happily, raising her head to look.

"Ah!" Aaron tried to speak, but the words became garbled in his throat. Etta's face swam before his eyes.

"Sit down, Aaron," Eduard commanded. "You will fall down."

Suspended upside down, the four-pound infant bleated his first angry protest against the world. Then he squalled louder and spread his fingers at the end of flailing arms as his father sank to the floor at the bedside.

———

The gentle touch of Elisa's hands pulled Murphy from his sleep. It did not matter; he had been dreaming of her anyway. He answered her urgent kisses with a slow and drowsy response, and when at last she fell asleep in his arms, he lay wide awake for an hour still dreaming of her.

Downstairs the mantel clock chimed two o'clock. She stirred and moved closer to him. Her skin smelled like a flower garden. Her breath smelled like toothpaste. Murphy had come to love those scents, come to look forward to sliding between the sheets and inhaling her. Just the thought of it made him want her again. He wished she would wake up and lift her face to him and say his name in that funny way of hers, *"Murrrrf . . ."* Nobody but Elisa called him that. And she only called him that when she whispered his name between kisses.

Somewhere on a distant London street a siren wailed. It seemed impossible to Murphy that anything unpleasant could be happening tonight when his own world seemed so perfect. The thought made him frown. Of course, it was his job to report the news of this terribly imperfect world. But for now, he wanted to protect Elisa from it. She seemed fragile since the *Darien* had sunk. She left the room when the BBC announced the latest. She did not ask him what news had flashed across the wires. It was just as well. She had done her part. Nobody deserved a rest more than Elisa, except maybe Anna and Theo.

He smiled at the irony of that. Already Anna and Theo had joined Bubbe Rosenfelt in her work with the F.A.T.E. group. Murphy had sent the story to Trump News Service himself. *Theo Lindheim, former department store owner in Berlin, escaped Dachau to head the Fair Anglo Treatment of Emigres. The organization seeks aid to thousands of homeless as well as fair laws for those attempting to flee the tyranny of Hitler's Germany. . . .*

Some people never stopped. Murphy had married into just such a family. And were it not for the fact that a new little Murphy was on the way, Elisa would have also jumped right back into the thick of it.

Murphy slid his hand over her abdomen. Not even a bulge yet, but he smiled all the same. *Thank you, little guy. Now maybe we can stop long enough to listen to the music.*

All Murphy wanted to do was protect her, hold her, keep her safe. The doctor figured the baby would come along nine months to the day after their second wedding at the cottage in New Forest. The legal wedding. Short version. Murphy chuckled out loud in spite of himself.

"What, Murrrf?" Elisa asked dreamily.

"Just thinking about the night in New Forest. Snow White's Cottage—remember?"

"Hmmmm?"

"What a night."

"A good thing I made you marry me," she said, and Murphy breathed in the scent of toothpaste.

He raised up on his elbow and bent to kiss her. She smiled through his kiss and said his name.

He pressed his cheek against hers. "You think we'll ever sleep the whole night through again?"

"I hope not."

He caught the flash of her smile in the darkness. He was glad she was awake. "Tell me what you want," he asked.

She thought for a moment. "It doesn't matter. As long as it's healthy."

The moment was perfect. Delicious. And then the phone rang. Once. Twice. Three times.

Murphy had come to hate telephones. He groaned and reached

across her to the night table, finally yanking the receiver off the table and pulling it toward him while Elisa muffled a giggle.

It was Harvey Terrill from the office. His voice sounded unhappy and desperate even before he managed to explain the reason for the call. Elisa moved away from Murphy. She turned over as if to cover her ears lest anything reach her. When at last Murphy replaced the receiver and switched on the light, she was looking at him with eyes filled with memory.

He shrugged and sat up. "Sorry. This is worse than being married to a doctor." He tried to smile, but somehow he could not find the lightness even for that.

"Germany?" she asked, running her hands through her hair.

He attempted to pass it off. "Nazi demonstration. You know how that goes."

She nodded slowly. Yes. Elisa knew.

———————

The burled-walnut grandfather clock at the foot of the stairs chimed. Etta rested peacefully with the new baby in a cradle beside her.

Aaron took two glasses and a bottle of cognac from the cupboard behind his desk. Dr. Eduard Letzno sat down heavily in the wing-backed chair across from his boyhood friend. He leaned his head back against the brown leather and sighed.

Aaron glanced up as he poured. His friend was wearing suit trousers and a white shirt open at the collar. His stethoscope dangled from his neck like a tie. His thick brown hair was tousled, as it had been after a hard game of stickball when they were children. Eduard had grown up, but he had aged very little—except for his gray eyes. His eyes somehow looked ancient and weary.

"You have been working too hard, my friend." The glasses clinked as Aaron passed one to Eduard.

"You fathers are all the same," Eduard sipped and grimaced. "You think delivering babies is work. All we doctors do is wait and act as if the process could not happen without us." He raised his glass in a tired toast. "But don't tell anyone."

"L'Chaim," Aaron returned the toast.

"L'Chaim," Eduard replied. "To life. A new little Lubetkin. An arrow in the quiver of Aaron and Etta Lubetkin." He drank, and this time did not grimace. Aaron sprawled in the chair across from Eduard. *I do not look like a rabbi should look,* he mused. *Sitting in my study with a clean-shaven fellow who looks as much like a Gentile as any Catholic.* "Thank you for coming," he said, feeling a bit guilty that he looked at Eduard and thought such things. "Rachel told me you were having some sort of party."

Eduard sniffed and stared into his cognac. "Raising money. You know. For the Zionist settlement in Palestine. Just what we must not speak of among the Jews of this neighborhood, yes? 'There can be no homeland without Messiah,' they will say. And then they will throw me out on my ear."

"Well, it is just you and me, Eduard. I will not throw you out." He tried to joke. "Until you present your bill."

"You are certainly the only one of my old friends who welcomes me. The *apikoros*. The apostate, the traitor Zionist who no longer believes in your Jewish God."

The last was spoken with such bitterness that Aaron dared not reply. All of what Eduard said was true, down to the word *apostate*. A thousand times Aaron had asked how it had happened. And *why?* As boys they had shared the same bench at Torah school. They had discussed the Baal Shem Tov with the same enthusiasm, dreamed of becoming rabbi and cantor in the same congregation. But Aaron had gone to study in Jerusalem and Eduard to the University in Prague. When Aaron at last returned to Poland, Eduard had changed.

There was pain in this change, for both men.

"Perhaps one day you will find yourself again. And find the One who makes a Jew a Jew. In the meantime, you are Dr. Eduard Letzno. You deliver the children of your friend the rabbi . . ."

Eduard did not smile. His own words had killed the tired joy of this moment. He swirled his cognac. "And is my friend the rabbi leaving Warsaw? Leaving Poland, as I have hoped?"

Aaron tugged his beard thoughtfully. This was a matter they had discussed with unfailing regularity. "You were at Evian. I only listened to the nations of the world as they denied us. You were there, Eduard. So tell me, *Vi aheen zoll ich gain?*" He asked the question in Yiddish. "Wherever shall I go?"

Eduard leaned forward. His gray eyes smoldered with intensity. *"Palestine!* Zion! There is still time, Aaron! Take Etta and the children to her father in Jerusalem."

Aaron smiled sadly. "We have thought much about it. Jerusalem, where the Jews of the Old City live on the charity of the Jews of Warsaw. If all of *us* leave for Jerusalem, then who will be left to send money to Jerusalem?"

"Have you still not seen it, Aaron? The ground is burning beneath our feet! The one thing Poland has in common with Germany is a hatred of Jews."

"We are three million Jews here in Poland. Three million and one, as of tonight. What can they do to us? We have been here for centuries, and we will be here centuries from now. Etta and I have talked. Things will get better. People are civilized now. What can they do to us here in Poland?"

Eduard Letzno fiddled with the end of his stethoscope.

"You know what they did to the Jews of Austria, and what is being done in Czechoslovakia since the Germans entered the Sudetenland."

"This is Warsaw. The Germans are not here."

"Yet."

"They will not come here." Aaron raised his chin as if he were trying to comfort a frightened child. He had been frightened himself. But now he was confident. There would be no war. Hitler said that the Sudetenland was his last territorial claim in Europe. "There are more of us *here* than anywhere in the world. Safety in numbers, Eduard."

"I pray you will leave this place before it is too late."

"How can I set any hope in Palestine when every day the Arabs are blowing up the Zionists? There is as much violence in Jerusalem as there is in Vienna. We have the letters to prove it, letters from Etta's father. Do you think I would take my children to such a place?" He exhaled loudly. It was too late for such a talk. "New York, America. That is where I wanted to go. I *tried*! You know I did. And now they have closed those doors. Quotas filled for two years."

"Then get your name on the list for the day *after* those two years are up, Aaron! Get out of Warsaw. Those two years must pass, and who knows what is ahead for us."

"And what about you? Where are you going?"

"Palestine. Next week."

Aaron placed his glass on the blotter. "So soon?"

"Palestine is in desperate need of doctors. I have an assignment with the Jewish Agency for work in a clinic in Jerusalem."

"Can you not stay long enough—" Concern filled Aaron's eyes. "The child is so small and fragile."

Eduard hesitated a moment. "There is another matter." He swirled the cognac in his glass. "I have been questioned by the police here in Warsaw."

"Questioned?"

"It seems Poland is also listening to the broadcasts of Herr Hitler, Aaron. All Jews are subversives, he says. Bent on the overthrow of every government and the domination of the world." There was bitter amusement in his eyes. "My Zionist connections are suspect, of course." He frowned. "I have been . . . requested by the Poles . . . to leave."

"But you are no threat!" Aaron argued for Eduard as if the argument would make a difference. "Not a Communist."

Eduard stood and stepped to the window. He pulled back the heavy brocade drapery and scanned the Square beyond as he spoke. "Russia is at the back of Poland. The Nazis stand at the front door. Hitler raves that the Russians will overrun Poland to attack Germany. He says that the Bolshevik Jews who live within Poland are even now preparing the way for Russia. Do you think this government is not listening? Looking for subversives who might be playing out this scenario?"

"But *you,* Eduard! You are a humanitarian, not a politician!"

Eduard looked out the window. "Humanitarians are the enemies of politicians, Aaron. Have you not learned that here in Warsaw?" He turned from probing the dark street. There was a strange smile on his face, as though he saw Death and yet was not afraid. "Come here."

Aaron joined him at the window. He did not want to know what Eduard knew. Did not wish to see the apparition Eduard must somehow see in the streets of the Warsaw ghetto. And yet he searched the dark Square, the empty cobbles of Muranow Square. There was no one there. "What is it?" he whispered.

"Across the Square on the corner you will see his cigarette." Eduard answered hollowly, confident in his knowledge.

Aaron turned his eyes toward the corner of the street that led to the *Umschlagplatz,* the train station. The distant, shrill whistle of a train penetrated the glass. And then the small orange glow of a match flashed for an instant, illuminating a man. "You are being watched."

Eduard let the curtain fall. He nodded. "We are all being watched, Aaron. The eyes of Darkness have turned east. Again they linger on us." He sat down slowly while Aaron remained beside the window, stunned.

"Then you must leave for Palestine. But I am no Zionist. I am a rabbi only."

There was silence in the room except for the ticking of the clock. Again the shrill whistle of a train pierced the night. *A call to leave Warsaw? A warning to those who slept peacefully through this night?*

Eduard looked away from the shadow that crossed Aaron's face. He felt sorry that it must be this way. He frowned and sipped his cognac thoughtfully. "Sit down, Aaron. Sit. I will stay in Warsaw until after the baby is circumcised. Perhaps by then you will be convinced—"

A sharp knock interrupted them. Eduard raised his finger as if to hold his place. The knock sounded again, this time more urgently.

"Herr Doktor Letzno," the housekeeper's voice penetrated the door. "A gentleman has come looking for you. The Nazis, Herr Doktor! They have deported twelve thousand Jews from the Reich!"

11

God Is an Optimist

It was two kilometers from the German border station of Neu Bentschen to the Polish crossing. Most of the twelve thousand Jews under guard at the place had not eaten since Thursday.

Lazer felt weak, as if his legs would not carry him. He was not as old as some of the deportees; he could only guess how they must feel after such a journey.

On one end of the platform a young man was being beaten by two S.S. officers as a group of soldiers laughed and looked on. There were many Nazi Blackshirts strutting up and down the long lines of prisoners. Lazer wondered why so many soldiers had been called to drive the Jews out of Germany.

Everyone had been searched—men, women; it made no difference that there were no female guards to search the women. These S.S. soldiers enjoyed their work. To humiliate a Jewess was to make their comrades roll with laughter. They would carry stories of this day back to the barracks, and they would laugh again and again.

It began to rain, a hard, ruthless downpour. Lazer removed his torn jacket in an attempt to shelter Rifka and Berta. Others who stood waiting along the tracks also tried to shield themselves from the drenching rain. There were no umbrellas. No offer of shelter was made by the Nazis. Some mothers with small children begged to be allowed to get back into the cattle cars just for a while. Permission was refused. The doors slid closed to punctuate the German hope that even very small Jews would perish from pneumonia.

"Sensible of the gods to drown these vermin," laughed the S.S. commander beneath his hooded black rain slicker.

Lazer thought how much these S.S. men looked like executioners in their wet-weather gear. All of them were strong and tall. They had been chosen for their physical prowess. Ah, yes, Germany was a land of beauty until a man looked into the hard, cold eyes of one of these magnificent beasts. Lips twisted in cruel enjoyment of the misery of twelve thousand. Such power there was in making these rotten Jews stand for hours in the rain!

Young Berta's eyes were filled with a haunting fear that added centuries to her fifteen years. She had seen such brutality before, but now it was directed at her!

Lazer wrapped his arm around his daughter's shoulders and pulled her close against him. She was shivering with the cold and with the spectacle.

"I am thirsty, Papa," she said.

Lazer held his hand out and caught the rain. He held the cupped hand to her lips, and she drank. She smiled.

"Better?" he asked.

"I did not want to drink water that has touched this German soil," she said. "It is good that we have rain."

That was Berta. Always she looked for the best. The rain had become a fountain from which she could drink. "We will arrive in Poland free from German dust," Rifka added through chattering teeth. "A blessing, this rain. It washes us clean from the past." Her words were brave for the sake of their daughter, but Lazer could clearly see the pain in his wife's eyes. *Where will we go? What will become of us?*

A little before noon the soldiers came with the dogs. They stood beneath the roof of the platform and looked out at their conquered thousands. Black-muzzled German shepherds sat serene and proud beside their handlers. Beautiful, perfectly disciplined animals, these German dogs. Five hundred S.S. against twelve thousand Jews. It was more than enough.

By noon, the dogs were hungry. The colonel beneath the black slicker shouted his command: "Only two kilometers across the frontier to Poland! Let's see how fast these Jewish pigs can run!"

Suddenly, as if they understood the colonel's words, the dogs leaped to their feet, snarling. They strained against their short leather leads, lunging again and again toward the long line of Jews.

Guards began to shout, "Run! Run! Run!"

The S.S. moved from beneath the shelter of the station and laid their truncheons on the backs of their quarry. Jewish blood mingled with the rain until the road was dark red.

Lazer grasped Rifka's hand and Berta's hand. He began to run blindly as the screaming, panicked mass pressed around them. Hands reached out toward Poland, as if the reaching could bring the border closer.

The soldiers and dogs followed after. They flanked the Jews, herding them like cattle. Whips raised and crashed down on the heads of anyone in the way. It did not matter how fast they ran; it was not fast enough. Mothers and fathers carried shrieking children, but the blows fell on them as readily as they landed on the young men of the group.

The dogs' teeth tore open the legs of men and women alike. That blood mingled in rivers on the road.

Everywhere people fell into the mud and were beaten for their failure. Others who tried to help them up were also beaten for their efforts. "Run faster, Papa!" Rifka shouted as a snarling Blackshirt slashed at a woman beside him.

Lazer willed himself to go forward. Rifka tugged his arm. Two kilometers to the Polish border! How his lungs ached!

"Run, run, you filthy Jewish pigs! Out of Germany, and don't come back!"

Lazer stumbled and fell in the mud. An old man fell on top of him and took the brunt of blows that came down with the rain. Rifka screamed. Berta wept and begged the German to stop. When the old man's arms went limp, the soldier lost interest and turned to yet another victim.

Lazer pushed the dead body from him and struggled to stand. Berta clutched his hand and pulled him. "Get up, Papa! Hurry! Get up! Run, or they will kill us, too!"

The Polish border was in sight when the Nazis began to fire on stragglers. "WOMEN FIRST!" shouted a bloodied man. "WOMEN THROUGH THE CHECKPOINT FIRST! WOMEN AND CHILDREN . . ."

Lazer pushed Rifka and Berta away from him. Berta reached out for her father, but he denied her stark terror and urged the two women forward as gunfire crackled over their heads.

On the Polish side of the line, border guards stood gaping at the terrified mass.

"Open the gates! Open the gates!" The shouts were indeed in Polish, but how could the guards check so many at once?

From behind, the gunfire continued, the smell of gunpowder an acrid contrast to the rain. In the front, women were pressed painfully against the wire of the gates as those in the rear surged forward.

"Open the gates! *Please!* We will be crushed, and our children with us!"

Lazer lost sight of Berta and Rifka. He prayed that he would not lose his footing. To fall meant certain death. *How many have been trampled?* he wondered. *What would the Germans do with the Jewish dead who lined the road these last two kilometers?*

"Open the gates!" he heard himself cry. "We are Polish! We are *Polish*! Can't you hear? That is why they beat us! *We are Polish!*"

There was a space of only twelve feet between the Western Wall and the shabby houses of the Moroccan neighborhood. The houses of the Muslims of Morocco always stood at the backs of praying Jews like Rebbe Lebowitz. Some of the Chosen were ill at ease as they prayed before these stones. After all, more than one rabbi had been killed as he raised his hands to the Holy Wall and lifted prayers to heaven.

But Rebbe Lebowitz was not nervous. He decided long ago that there was no better way for a Jew to die than in the posture of fervent prayer.

For this reason, he breathed easily as he lifted his prayer shawl over his head and let the soft wind rustle the pages of his Siddur. Before these individual stones of the Holy Wall, Rebbe Lebowitz lifted his heart to the Lord of heaven.

Today, the narrow space before the Wailing Wall was almost empty. There were a few worshipers, who like Rebbe Lebowitz had come with their petitions written out to slide between the chinks in the wall. Some sat on a wooden bench to pray. Others leaned against the cool of the stones that were tarnished from the hands of two thousand years of loving touches. A soft wind whispered down the alleyway to twirl the fringes of prayer shawls and tug at aged beards. On such a day the old man lifted his eyes to the crisp blue slit of the sky and imagined the winds were stirred by the wings of the angels who hovered above this place. Ah, there were always angels here, everyone knew that. It was said that this part of the wall had been built by the beggars of Solomon's time, and that on the day of the Temple's destruction the angels had linked their wings around the Wall and the command had been given: *This, the work of the poor, shall never be destroyed!*

The Shekinah glory of God remained here, and at certain times the very stones wept for the destruction of the Temple.

Was there a better place, then, for Rabbi Shlomo Lebowitz to bring his request before the Lord? Was not this sheer face of hewn rock the one place on earth where a small chink remained open to the throne room of the Almighty?

Into that small opening, then, the old man urged his request. Perhaps the wings of the angels fluttered when they heard it. Perhaps their stirring carried the prayer of the old man near to the ear of the Almighty. Perhaps they smiled at such an old fool who came every day, rain or shine, with the same prayer on his lips.

More plaintive than the call of the ram's horn seemed the words of this prayer: "With your mighty hand, reach down and carry your children home to this place, this small piece of earth. For the sake of your name, for the sake of your promise, call out to the north and bring them home that the kingdom of your Messiah may be established, and His throne forever in Jerusalem!"

Could the Lord ignore such a prayer? And always there was a small postscript to this faithful request: "And while you are at it, Lord, if you don't mind too much, bring Etta and Aaron home along with the rest of your scattered children, nu? No matter what you may have heard me think, this is still our home. Just between you and this old rabbi, such a small thing. And I would be eternally grateful for the favor. . . ."

———

By the time the Western Union messenger raised his hand to knock on the door of Rabbi Shlomo Lebowitz, a small crowd had gathered around to hear the bad news. Telegrams did not come to the residents of Old City Jerusalem unless someone had died. Everyone knew that last night as Arab rebels attacked outposts in Palestine, the Nazis had rioted in the Reich and expelled twelve thousand Jews to Poland. No doubt there had been many deaths during that brutal pogrom.

Rebbe Lebowitz wiped his hands on a dishtowel and opened the door. He looked first at the grim-faced young Arab messenger who propped his bicycle against the wall and then doffed his Western Union cap as he presented the telegram.

From the small group of onlookers, Eli Sachar called, "Sit down, Rabbi! *Sit down* before you read it!"

The ladies auxiliary of Tipat Chalev all chimed in with agreement. Young boys from Torah school urged their venerated rabbi to sit. *"Sit! Nu?"*

The rabbi took the yellow envelope and paid the Arab messenger a shilling. Then he left the door to his tiny flat open and motioned for his friends and neighbors to join him inside.

A man did not wish to open a telegram all alone, after all.

He muttered a prayer as he sat slowly at the table. His friends stood around him. His students. His neighbors. They whispered, "Who could it be?"

"Maybe Etta?"

"Maybe it did not go well for her. She *was expecting*."

The phrase *was expecting* was certainly ominous. It had the sound of words that are said over the departed: "She *was* a good person. She *was* liked by everyone. She *was* expecting . . ."

"Maybe it isn't her. It could also be his brother in Chicago, America, nu?"

Rabbi Lebowitz had thought of nothing else since news had come of the violence on the German border last night. Could there be any connection between that and this terrible yellow envelope?

"Be brave, Rebbe Lebowitz."

"Remember, the Lord giveth and the Lord taketh away."

The old man nodded. His eyebrows knit together in a solid black line as he opened the envelope. Carefully, he unfolded the paper. The address read: *WARSAW POLAND*.

"Warsaw," he said.

A shocked sigh passed through the room. So it had to be *her. His only daughter!*

He opened the next fold and began to read. His head moved back and forth. He opened his mouth and cried, "Oy! Etta! *Etta!*"

Sad shakes of each head. So it *was* her! "When did it happen, Rebbe Lebowitz?" Hannah Cohen moved through the crowd.

"Oy! The Eternal . . . be *praised*! It is a baby boy! They will call him Yacov!"

Good news in a telegram was hard to understand. Did this mean that Etta had died but the baby had lived? Half a blessing. Or had Etta lived and the baby also? If this was so, then why send a telegram and give everyone a heart attack already?

"Is Etta. . . ?" Hannah broached the subject.

"Fine! *Fine!*" Rebbe Lebowitz wiped away tears of joy. "They sent the wire so I should not worry with all that is going on. My son-in-law has gone to aid the Jewish refugees at the border. They ask that we might help with a relief fund of some sort. OY!" He raised his eyes to heaven. "They are all *fine*! We have a new little Lubetkin! A new grandson! He is named Yacov! In the midst of such a terrible night for Jews, still . . . God proves He is an optimist, nu? He sends another Jewish baby into the world!"

The damp stone walls of the little apartment now echoed with applause and cries of *Mazel Tov!* So. At least there was some good news from God this morning for Jews, nu?

What had begun as a morning filled with fear and foreboding was transformed into a day of energetic joy. News of the baby passed from mouth to mouth. Word of the request from Warsaw for help in aiding the refugees gave everyone a new purpose—money to collect from those few who had it, socks to knit, clothing to collect and mend and package. The Jews of Jerusalem were poor, but they were not so poor that they could not help their unfortunate brothers and sisters in the border camps of Poland.

The telegram was posted on the wall of Tipat Chalev for everyone to see. Beneath it was a list of items needed for the refugees. And scrawled across the yellow paper were the Rabbi's words: GOD IS AN OPTIMIST!

Everyone understood the meaning.

12

"And Yet I Must Believe"

Somehow the numbers of people deported from Germany had not been translated into the reality of human misery that now unfolded before Rabbi Aaron Lubetkin.

Twelve thousand huddled together in the abandoned stables. The sky spit rain until the earth was a quagmire and each footprint filled with water. No heat. No blankets. No food. Only twelve thousand shivering people. Haunted eyes. Bloodied faces. Tears hidden by the rain that seeped through the broken shingles on the roof.

"So *many*!" Aaron managed a whisper as he and Eduard entered the largest of three stables. Family groups had claimed stalls as dwelling places. Never mind that everything they owned had been confiscated.

Eduard's face was flushed with rage at the sight of such needless suffering.

From within the unlit stalls, no one looked up at the two men framed in the entrance to the stables. Aaron and Eduard were just two more bodies among the thousands.

"Where do we begin?" Aaron asked.

An answer was not required; a plaintive voice called out from a stall where the door hung askew on its hinges. A woman called in anguish.

"Herr Doktor? Are you a doktor, there? You with the bag! Bitte! *Please!* It is my husband Lazer! *Mein Gott!* He is . . . *please!*"

In three steps, Eduard entered the stall with Aaron at his heels. A small, thin man lay unconscious on the damp dirt floor. A woman and a girl of fifteen or sixteen huddled over him. The unconscious man was almost a luminous white, and Aaron thought for a moment that it was too late for him. Eduard took off his overcoat and threw it over the man as he grabbed up the limp arm and felt for a faint pulse.

The woman was weeping. The girl seemed dulled with the shock of what had come upon them.

"He is alive," Eduard said. He began to ask the sobbing woman questions. "When did you last eat?"

"Days ago. They came for us at suppertime. Berta and I had at least a bite . . . but not Lazer."

"Was he beaten?" Eduard probed the man's abdomen.

"Crushed. The train. Cattle cars. And then at the border, he fell. Someone kicked him, and . . ."

Aaron studied the girl, the daughter of the fallen man. She was pretty, her features fine-chiseled and her brown eyes large and round. But her face showed no expression at the words of her mother. She squatted in the dirt near his feet and simply stared with glazed eyes at the green paint that flaked from the boards of the stall.

Aaron said the girl's name. "Berta."

The mother did not notice as she talked on about their ordeal. The eyes of the young girl did not flicker recognition at her name.

Again Aaron said the name. "Berta? You are safe now. Safe in Poland."

Still no sign of comprehension. Eduard looked up from the father toward the girl. "Your father will recover," he said without hesitation. "He is exhausted. Do you hear me, girl? He is sleeping. Soon there will be food."

The mother turned toward Berta. "Berta? Did you hear? God be thanked! Papa will live! And there will be food."

At last the young woman blinked. Her faded eyes focused, then moved to the face of her father and then to the black bag that marked Eduard as a doctor. The girl began to weep silently. She reached out to touch her mother, who then enfolded her in her arms and wept with her.

Eduard stood slowly. "Keep him warm," he instructed, leaving his own coat over the frail body of Lazer Grynspan as fulfillment of that instruction. "Berta, when the trucks come with food, you must be the one to stand in line, yes?"

The young woman nodded. Tears still streamed down her cheeks. "Yes," she sobbed. "When . . . food . . . comes . . ."

———

Mercifully, the rain had stopped by the time the bread trucks arrived at the stables where the refugees had taken shelter.

The lines consisted of thousands like Berta Grynspan who waited for a ration on behalf of thousands more inside the stables.

Rabbi Aaron Lubetkin and Dr. Eduard Letzno had spent eighteen unbroken hours among the refugees before volunteers came to take their places—groups of ten at first, then hundreds. Blankets and clothing were distributed with the food. Enormous kettles of soup simmered over open fires in the stable courtyard.

Miraculously, there had been only seven deaths throughout that long first day. Most of the victims were old—unable to survive the ordeal of the journey and cold and hunger and grief. One little boy had died only moments before Eduard entered the stalls. He had fallen and been trampled. There had been little chance of survival under the best of conditions, but here, it had been hopeless.

Aaron did his best to comfort the family, who were among the Catholics in the group. They asked for a priest to attend them in their grief, and so Aaron had sent for one to come from the village six miles to the east. Some hours later he had passed the stall and paused only for a moment to listen to the words of the Polish priest: "You are welcome in my parish . . . gather up your things."

"We have nothing."

The priest wrapped the dead child in his cloak and stood. "Come with me . . ."

Aaron turned away and fought to control his own emotion at the sight of the black-garbed man leading his tiny flock out of the suffering. The lifeless form of the child made certain that the family took all their suffering along with them. There would be no joy in the warmth of a fire or in clean beds to sleep in. They had lost a son.

Aaron felt a light tapping on his back. He looked down to see the still-grieved face of young Berta Grynspan gazing up at him. "How is your father?" he asked.

"Better. Sitting up. He ate some soup and bread." She extended an envelope to him. "The nurse found me some paper, Rabbi Lubetkin. I have written a letter to my brother. His name is Herschel. He is in Paris. Safe in Paris. But he will be frantic with worry. Would you—" She looked hopefully at the envelope. "I have no stamp, you see, and . . ."

Aaron took the letter from her. He slipped it into his pocket. "You have given a return address?" he asked. "Where he may write?"

Berta nodded. "The authorities say we will be here for some time." She pointed as yet another truck caravan brought supplies into the compound. "At least we will be fed. Someone said they will bring stoves and coal to heat the buildings with. At least we have a roof." The young woman uttered these words with a tone of such hopelessness that Aaron found it difficult to respond.

He tried to smile. "Perhaps it will not be long and you will be in real houses, eh?" He patted the pocket that held the letter. "Your brother will be relieved that you are all right."

Berta shrugged and looked down the long row of stalls. "Paris," she mumbled. "Maybe we will . . ." Her voice trailed off and she walked away from the rabbi without saying goodbye.

It was a short walk from the headquarters of the Gestapo on Albertstrasse to the Chancellery building where Adolf Hitler awaited word from Commander Leo Vargen.

The Führer had his suspicions about the possible involvement of certain military leaders in a conspiracy against the Nazi government. With the capture and interrogation of Thomas von Kleistmann, no doubt those suspicions would be resolved.

Beneath his arm, Commander Vargen carried a leather file case containing all the information gleaned from the records and from von Kleistmann himself over the past few days.

Vargen looked up at the great eagle of the Third Reich that spread its granite wings over the entrance to the marble reception hall. The heels of S.S. guards clicked as he entered. Inside the doors, a hundred black-uniformed S.S. men stood at rigid attention the entire length of the vast hall. Their clean, proud reflections shone on the polished black marble floor.

The hall was said to be longer than that of the Palace of Versailles. The Führer himself had ordered its huge dimensions so that foreign representatives and heads of state might be intimidated by the glory of the Reich. The floors were waxed until they were slick, so that, according to the Führer's reasoning, foreigners were forced to watch their step lest they fall before the leader of the German people.

Vargen did not doubt these little stories that contained evidence of the Führer's wit. Adolf Hitler left nothing to chance, not even the choice of floor wax for the Chancellery. Leo Vargen knew that he also must watch his step in the presence of the great man.

Bronze double doors swung back, revealing a sitting room with an enormous fireplace. The mantel was crowned with an eagle clutching a swastika in its claws. The Führer stood with his back to the roaring blaze. As Vargen entered and saluted, it seemed to him as if Hitler had just emerged from the fire. *Was this appearance also thought out beforehand?*

To his right, Gestapo Chief Heinrich Himmler sat in a comfortable overstuffed chair. When Vargen hesitated a moment too long, Himmler motioned impatiently for him to come into the circle of sofas and chairs in front of the fire.

"Well? What news do you have for us from von Kleistmann?" Himmler asked. The Führer did not speak. He did not turn his gaze on Vargen. He rubbed his hands as if to wash them in flame.

Vargen held out the leather case. He clicked his heels and bowed slightly. Still, the Führer did not seem to notice him.

"We captured him quite easily as he attempted to board ship in Holland."

"That ship was bound for?" Himmler asked.

"England."

At the word *England,* the face of the Führer darkened. His eyes narrowed as if this confirmed his suspicions. Yet still he did not speak.

"And who did von Kleistmann name as his conspirators?" Himmler leafed through the pages without reading them.

Vargen felt his face grow red with embarrassment. "He . . . admits to nothing . . . no one else involved, he said."

"You believe him?" A peculiar smile played on Himmler's lips.

"I cannot see that a man could lie under such . . . circumstances." Vargen shrugged. He had tried everything. What else was there to do short of killing von Kleistmann?

Himmler studied the photograph of Thomas. "A handsome man, was he not? Strong."

"It is his strength that keeps him silent . . . that is, if there is any more to tell."

The Führer's face was unmoved, dark and angry. He wanted answers from the traitorous young Abwehr officer, not examples of Aryan endurance!

"Exactly what does he admit to?"

"Nothing," Vargen said.

"Not even the murder of Georg Wand?" Himmler leaned forward.

"Not even that. He says he had a personal hatred for Wand. A distaste for worms such as Wand who soiled the German people. And he admits to secretly disliking . . . our party."

Hitler's face contorted. "Traitor!" he cried. "*That is enough!* He admits his guilt! Have I not said that he who is not for me is against me? *There!* We have a verdict on this arrogant aristocrat! And mark my words! He is not alone in his conspiracy! I want *names!*"

Both Himmler and Vargen drew back at the outburst. Vargen stuttered a reply, an apology that he had been unable to extract the desired information from von Kleistmann.

"But . . . what if he *is* alone? What if there are no others, mein Führer?" Himmler managed to ask.

"Are you saying he is *innocent?*" Hitler shrieked. "Innocent? Then do what is always done with the innocent! *Crucify him!*"

Vargen and Himmler exchanged looks. Could the Führer mean such a thing?

"Crucify him!" Hitler screamed again. "He would destroy me! Did he think I would not see? *Crucify him!*"

Vargen swallowed hard. "Yes, mein Führer. But . . . if he still does not speak?"

"*He is against me!*" A black lock of hair had fallen across Hitler's eye, completing the picture of madness. "He has slept with a Jewish whore! That is *enough! Kill him!*" Hitler took a step toward Vargen. For an instant it seemed as if he might strike him. Then, abruptly, Hitler turned on his heel and faced the fire.

Awkward minutes of silence ticked by. Vargen dared not move. Himmler dared not speak. The Führer was once again deep in thought. It was often like this. Great passion, then silence as the mind of Germany's leader moved on to other matters.

Vargen was sweating. He mopped his bald head and waited until the Führer's inspired thoughts would take the form of words. Logs crackled in the heat of the flames. At last the Führer spoke again.

"*Palestine . . .*" He turned and faced the two men. He was smiling as if the rage over Thomas von Kleistmann had been a dream. He rose up slightly on his toes and beamed. "Yes. *Palestine!*"

He gestured for Vargen to be seated and he also took a chair across from Himmler. Pleasant. Charming. An answer had come to him, and now he would share it.

Vargen was only barely able to make the jump from von Kleistmann to Palestine. Himmler, on the other hand, shifted gears smoothly.

"So, mein Führer," Himmler smiled and polished his glasses. "An answer has come to you at last?"

"It took the presence of Commander Vargen for me to see clearly," Hitler was almost jovial now. He turned to Vargen who was still perspiring, still inwardly contemplating the rage of this now reasonable man.

"Me?" Vargen ventured.

Hitler fixed his piercing blue eyes on Vargen. "You served with the Turks during the Great War against the English, did you not?"

"Yes." Vargen still failed to see where this was leading.

"Then you know how essential the territory of Palestine is to our aims, especially now."

Vargen nodded as though he understood, but he did not. "Of course."

Hitler slapped his knee. "The Arabs do us the greatest service in their rebellion against England and the Zionists. You see? There are nearly twenty thousand British troops in Palestine trying to keep the peace. *Twenty thousand!* More men deployed there than anywhere else in the British Empire. More in Palestine than are pledged to support France when war comes."

Not *if*, but *when . . .*

"How might Commander Vargen be of service, mein Führer?" Himmler asked earnestly.

"We have been training the Mufti's men here in Germany for some time. I propose that Commander Vargen return to Palestine where once he knew defeat at the hands of the English! Yes! That he train the men on location. Fight and train in Palestine and Jerusalem beneath the noses of the English while we continue to fortify our western defenses."

Vargen could not think of a more distasteful task. Perhaps this was some sort of banishment from Germany since he had failed to crack through the wall of von Kleistmann's silence. He had no choice but to accept the assignment. "An honor."

"You must engage the British, you see. Keep them tied up. Occupied by their own problems." Hitler stared thoughtfully at the ceiling. "I will send orders by courier this afternoon. We have an agent in Jerusalem now who has contact with the Mufti. It will be all arranged." He waved a hand absently. "First you may finish this unpleasantness with Thomas von Kleistmann, of course." He smiled again, as if he were discussing a favor, a gift.

Vargen was taken completely off guard. He had no chance to express opposition to duty in Palestine. Perhaps this had all been planned, like the wax on the polished floors of the Chancellery, to keep him off balance.

Himmler picked up Hitler's enthusiasm. "Of course, all of this will also serve to demonstrate the hypocrisy of the Western nations in dealing with the Jewish problem, ja?"

Hitler appraised Vargen for a moment. "If the matter is handled well, then yes. We will see that even a self-righteous race of governesses like the English will be part of the final solution to the Jewish question." The gaze lingered on Vargen like that of a snake on a bird. Then the smile reappeared. "There are great cosmic forces behind all this, Commander Vargen. Do you believe that?"

Vargen had never thought of any force greater than the man seated before him. "If that is so, then you are their prophet."

This answer pleased Hitler. "Ah. So some say." He relaxed again. "And now I will share a secret with you, Commander. Men like us are chosen to serve. We must be willing to serve in this battle . . ." He lifted his hands and eyes upward. "There are spiritual forces at work here, Commander Vargen. We are their tools. Their weapons. Like the Crusaders of old you will return to Jerusalem, and there you will fight against the Jews until our side is victorious."

There was no escaping the news; horror and dismay filled the faces of the orchestra members. This morning the halls buzzed with word of the brutal deportations of Polish Jews from Germany.

For Elisa, the mention of cattle cars heading east to the Polish border was a stark reminder of an old nightmare. Some among the orchestra members knew people in Germany who had come from Poland. Names and faces came to mind. Questions were unspoken and unanswerable. Elisa thought of the old tailor Grynspan and wondered if he was with the thousands in the cattle cars.

The orchestra played badly throughout the morning rehearsal. Horns came in late. First violins were hesitant and preoccupied. Woodwinds squawked like an amateur orchestra until Sir Thomas bellowed and barked and at last threw his baton to the stage in frustration.

"All right, children! And what can we do to change the headlines in this morning's *Times*?" he asked his silent and shamed musicians. "Do you think it will help those people if we play like the Ladies Home Auxiliary Band?" Without explanation, Sir Thomas turned his steely gaze on Elisa as though she had personally caused the disruption. She felt herself color as other members of the orchestra glanced nervously in her direction. "Any suggestions?" He seemed to direct the question to her.

Elisa stared self-consciously at the fine old instrument in her hands. She was fiddling while the world beyond was burning.

She closed her eyes and prayed for an answer. Some small thing. Something to give her prayers hands to work with. An instrument to play for the sake of mercy in an unmerciful world.

"A benefit performance!" she blurted. Her own words surprised her. She blinked in amazement that she had dared to reply.

Sir Thomas drew back as if the words had struck him. He frowned and continued to glare at Elisa. Finally his eyes shifted to the baton on the boards of the stage. He pointed at it and addressed the gray-haired concertmaster. "If you would be so kind . . ."

The concertmaster retrieved the baton and bowed slightly as he presented it to the maestro. Sir Thomas twirled the stick in his fingers. "A benefit," he remarked at last. "Yes. An excellent suggestion." He almost smiled at Elisa. "And now may I have your attention, ladies and gentlemen. We will begin again at the eighth bar, please."

———

It seemed natural that Theo, as head of the F.A.T.E. organization in England, would be chosen by Sir Thomas Beecham to travel to Poland with funds collected by the orchestra for the Jewish deportees. The request gave Theo hope that not everyone in England was asleep.

Theo's limp took on a purposeful and resolute strength as he made his way to the British colonial office. He intended to travel to Poland to see to the condition of the Jews recently deported from Germany and discuss their options.

The clerk in the visa office looked like a stork. Theo half expected the tall, thin man to be standing on one leg over a nest behind his counter. The fellow peered down his long nose at Theo's papers. His eyebrows arched as if in permanent surprise and disdain.

"Mr. Lindheim," he sniffed. "If you leave for Poland, of course, His Majesty's government can make no guarantee for your safety, nor can we guarantee your readmittance to England."

Theo stared at the clerk in disbelief. He was being told that he and Anna were veritable prisoners on the little isle of Great Britain. To travel elsewhere might mean the revocation of their residence papers. Could it be that their hands were still cruelly tied by the British bureaucracy when they wanted so desperately to help?

"Is there no appeal?" Theo asked wearily.

"Your residence papers were issued under certain conditions, Mr. Lindheim. We simply follow the regulations as stated. And you did sign the forms. You agreed to the terms. Travel outside Great Britain is limited." The man began a countdown of the conditions of Theo's residence permit.

Theo cut him short. With a curt nod, a *thank you,* and a *good day,* he left the office and limped, less resolutely, out the door.

What was the use of pretending any longer? The Reich had marked Theo as a criminal and a traitor in Germany. His extradition had been sought while he was in Prague. England had accepted him conditionally—the condition being that he do nothing which might offend Germany while he was in England. This meant that his physical presence among those spurned and persecuted by the Nazi Reich might well be misunderstood by the Führer and used as anti-British propaganda.

Anna met him as he descended the steps of Whitehall. The look on his face told her everything. She took his arm as he jammed his fedora down on his head and tugged angrily at the brim. "In a word," he said gruffly, "I am an offense to the Reich. And we must not offend the Führer by assisting those whom the Führer has singled out to destroy."

"They will not let you travel to Poland to the refugee camp." This was not a question, but a statement.

"My hands are tied."

"Your heart is willing, Theo," Anna chided her husband gently, "and so God has some other task for your hands." She intertwined her fingers with his and squeezed his hand in encouragement. "He will show you, my darling. And if you stop and think for only a moment, you will remember that you also believe this."

Theo stopped walking. He looked out across the vast city of London where he was now a prisoner of the politics of appeasement. He shook his head, then lowered his eyes a moment in acknowledgment of Anna's words. In that moment he again accepted God's sovereignty in his life—and hers. The anger melted from his heart and his face. "How hard it is for an old warrior not to want to fight the battle in his own strength," he said. "The doors slam shut. And yet I must believe."

13

Wise as Serpents

Murphy scanned Trump's latest wire from New York. In America, news of the deportations had gone unnoticed by the vast majority of the public. The horrible reality of the latest Nazi persecutions had been obscured by, of all things, the Halloween radio broadcast of Orson Welles, *War of the Worlds*. Thousands had actually believed that aliens were invading the nation and the world with the intent of destroying human life. American roads had been jammed with fleeing automobiles. Men and women had committed suicide in the belief that the performance was real. In the face of this, the fate of a few thousand Jews deported to Poland from the Reich was relegated to the back page of every newspaper except those of Trump Publications.

Murphy studied the reports of the American panic with the feeling that perhaps Orson Welles had not been far off in his make-believe story. Perhaps there was some sort of unseen power attacking the world with the intent of destroying human souls. Somehow, reports of Nazi brutality seemed to fit very easily into such a plot line.

The thought made him shudder, and with that came the realization that even as the British threatened Jewish immigration to Palestine, Hitler was turning up the flame to a white-hot intensity.

Trump in New York, along with Bubbe Rosenfelt and thirty Christian and Jewish leaders, was bombarding Congress and President Roosevelt with requests that he personally intercede with the British government on behalf of the British pledge for a Jewish homeland.

At the same time, Theo and Anna had continued with Britain's Zionist leaders to fight against what was whispered to be inevitable in the face of Arab protests in Palestine.

Murphy's repeated phone calls to the British colonial secretary in hopes of getting the straight scoop on the matter had been curtly refused. *What business was it of the United States if Britain did close off Jewish immigration to appease the Arab Council? Had not America closed her doors to the Jewish paupers as well?*

The failure of each nation had in turn become an excuse to other nations for more failure. Today's editorial in the *Manchester Guardian* expressed world sentiment about the homeless refugees who now huddled in stables at Poland's border:

> *Can Germany expect the rest of the world to receive and settle thousands of paupers in the next few years? This is carrying international cooperation to the limits of lunacy!*

Thus the matter finally became clear as Murphy pointed out the column to Theo over lunch. This was not an issue of what was morally right. It was not a matter of saving lives. It was a matter of *money*.

If England's rulers were suspicious of Theo, there were many other men who were not. This afternoon half a dozen of those men gathered in Theo's little study to plan what must be done since the utter failure of the Evian Conference. Surely *something* must be done, after all. Were the persecuted thousands of the Reich expected to be offered up as a sacrifice to apathy? The possibility seemed unthinkable to these few.

Dr. Chaim Weizmann lit his pipe and considered the flame of his match for a moment. "Perhaps we have been wrong in appealing to human decency then, Theo?" he asked.

Theo nodded slowly. He gazed sadly at the lined face of the great British scientist who had played such a vital part in Britain's first promises of a Jewish homeland. "The Nazis have proved that appeals to humanity fall on deaf ears. The failure of Evian confirms that this is true for others besides the Nazis."

"So what do you propose?" Weizmann asked, shaking out the match.

"The refugee problem is an economic problem to the leaders of world governments." Theo let out his breath slowly. He had read and reread the transcripts of Evian. Money. Cold, hard cash was always a central issue. "Germany intends that every Jew within its borders be driven out. Not one nation has disputed that intent seriously. And not one nation is willing to accept paupers as immigrants." Theo spread his hands. "So here is the dilemma: The Reich will not allow Jews to leave with any money. Nations will not take in those who are penniless."

Heads nodded in agreement. "There is not money enough that we can raise which will solve the problem," said Weizmann as a wreath of smoke encircled his head.

Theo smiled. "I was a businessman in Germany. I know what turns the hearts of these men. And also the key that will open the doors of the Reich and the doors of other nations to refugees."

"Please," Weizmann urged him on.

"If the Reich will allow its Jewish population to leave with, say, one-third of their assets, this would satisfy the countries who refuse to take paupers."

"And how do we convince Hitler and Himmler and Goebbels of the value of such a scheme?" Weizmann expressed the question in every man's mind.

"If we manage to lift the boycott on German exports, if the nations of the West pledge to purchase large quantities of German exports . . . You see? This would then be a matter of simple economics."

"Ah." Weizmann frowned at the simplicity of the idea. "The Nazis have attempted to sell Jewish hostages without success. The only profit they have found is in looting Jewish homes and businesses. But . . . if we can make it more profitable for the Reich to allow the refugees to leave with even a fraction of savings in exchange for larger purchases of German goods . . ."

"Then we manage to appeal to the *bank account* rather than the decency of Hitler's Reich. There is no other way."

The men in the room exchanged startled glances. Why had they not thought of such a plan before Evian? And where would they begin, now that doors seemed to be closing around the world?

Theo also had the answer to that question. "Perhaps it would be sensible to propose a meeting with the British foreign secretary. And another with the colonial secretary?" He again directed his proposal to Weizmann. "You know them both well."

Weizmann nodded his head in agreement. It would take a businessman to match wits with the Nazis, all right. "What is the saying?" Weizmann pondered a moment. "We must be wise as serpents and as gentle as doves."

So. Just like that, the Old City was open for business again. Had anyone been shot on the wall? You could not tell it from the way the merchants argued over the prices of fresh vegetables in the souks. Back to normal, they said this morning among the minyon of Rabbi Shlomo Lebowitz.

"Maybe the English have given the screaming Arab child his lollipop under the table, nu?" Something had quieted the racket, at any rate.

Rabbi Lebowitz carefully penned a note to the Eternal and headed through the narrow lanes of the Old City toward the ancient stones of the Western Wall. Once there, prayer shawl over his head, he raised his hands in blessing to God and placed the folded slip of paper into a crack between the stones. The prayer of eighteen blessings rose in a whisper before the Eternal, who hears the hearts and secret desires of the righteous. "And grant, O Eternal, that I many live to see my grandson here in the land of Zion, that we may worship you together in this place where our fathers worshiped you in days of old. A blessing upon Yacov, son of the Covenant."

—————

The black smoke of Muslim bonfires was replaced this morning by a cool breeze and rain clouds that promised some relief to all of Palestine.

Still in Shimon's arms, Leah was awakened by a crisp knocking against the wooden tent frame. A cheery British voice called out their names. "Shimon and Leah Feldstein in here, are they?"

Shimon wrapped a rough army-issued blanket around himself and pulled back the tent flap a fraction. A smiling British officer with a broad handlebar mustache touched the brim of his hat in greeting. "Mr. Feldstein?"

"I am Shimon Feldstein."

"Yes. They told me you were here. You have friends in high places, eh?" He presented Shimon with a folded yellow slip of paper. "From the British high commissioner himself. Permission for you and your wife to continue ahead to Jerusalem without the usual stay here in the camp."

Shimon studied the message. "But the demonstrations . . ."

"Nothing more than demonstrations," shrugged the cheerful officer. "No danger. A few burning tires is all. Little show from the Muslims for the benefit of the Woodhead Commission. Quite effective. I heard they were trembling in their shoes. Thought the ground was exploding around them."

The fellow peered around Shimon to where Leah gazed back with sleepy curiosity. "Mrs. Feldstein," he said. "Leah Feldstein." He touched his cap again nervously. "I heard you perform once in London. Several years ago. Stunning."

He motioned toward the slip of paper in Shimon's hands. "The high commissioner heard you had arrived. He is quite hopeful you might perform for the troops in Jerusalem. A bit of civilization from Europe, as it were. There is an important British committee visiting from London. It would be . . . *helpful* . . . for their impression of the Mandate."

"Perform?" Leah and Shimon exchanged looks. "Where? When?"

"Tonight. The mess hall at Allenby barracks in Jerusalem. Members of the Jewish Agency would also be invited. Your recordings are quite popular with the high commissioner, I understand. After yesterday's demonstration, a little music to calm the savage beasts, eh?"

"And then?" Shimon asked wonderingly. They had never dreamed they would be allowed into Jerusalem so soon.

"Well, then, I suppose you may go where you like. You have relatives in the Old City, we were told."

"One relative. A great-aunt. I have never met her," Shimon explained. "But we have corresponded. Our things were shipped to her address in Jerusalem."

"Well, then." The officer seemed quite pleased. "It is all settled. Tonight you sleep in Jerusalem. Your bus leaves in twenty-five minutes."

With the promise he would phone the high commissioner with the good news, the officer hurried off across the tent-studded compound.

Haj Amin gestured with a sweep of his hand at the dozen sullen Arab warriors who now gathered to meet with Doktor Hockman. Beneath their keffiyehs, black eyes burned, impatient for news from the Führer of Germany.

Hockman had memorized each name, each country of origin. Most of those within the crowded room were not from Palestine. They had been sent from neighboring Arab states to express complete Arab solidarity in the fight against the hated British and the Jews.

Hockman knew that Adolf Hitler was admired and now emulated by many of those in Muslim leadership. After all, the Führer had managed to defeat the decadent Western powers on the issue of Czechoslovakia without even a shot being fired. Britain's leadership cowered before Hitler's demands, and increasingly the Czech industrial territory was being devoured by the Reich. Every demand was being met. Every expectation was being exceeded. Hitler had only to speak and Britain and France obeyed, even at the expense of their allies. Perhaps it would be the same in Palestine. Even here the Führer would prevail!

The same thought filled the mind of every man in the room as Hockman opened his mouth to speak.

"What you have seen in Czechoslovakia will also be accomplished here, my friends. Our armies marched over the Czech fortifications, and all the enemies of the Reich fled to Prague in hopes of shelter." Hockman smiled at the irony of anyone running to Prague for safety. "The Führer has demanded that those enemies be returned to the Reich for proper punishment. Thousands are already on their way to German prisons for the punishment they deserve. The Czechs now tremble at the Führer's words, just as England and France trembled. Nothing is refused."

A surly, grim-faced young man from Iraq lifted his chin defiantly. "Why does the Führer let the Jews go? Why does he let them come here to Palestine? Why does he simply not settle the Jewish problem on German soil instead of letting them go free for the nations of Islam to deal with?"

Heads nodded in agreement to this troublesome point. Haj Amin raised a hand to silence the muttering. "Have you forgotten?" he asked with a righteous smile. "Our holy prophet Mohammed tells us that when the Jews of the world are gathered east of the river, we will destroy them there. These refugees, these Jews, show us that this day is coming soon. The German Führer is the hand of Allah, as the prophet foretold. He drives the Jews toward destruction."

Hockman smiled as well. "The Führer wishes you all to know that he has chosen a messenger of that destruction to come here to Jerusalem soon. Very soon you will meet him face-to-face, and he will teach you what you need to know to make the words of the Prophet come true."

———————

A soft autumn mist drifted across the face of the Mount of Olives. Gray wisps snagged on the onion-domed spires of the Russian Convent that bordered the Garden of Gethsemane.

Samuel Orde slowly climbed the narrow path that wound upward toward the ancient olive trees. He came here often—to pray, to think, to find some shred of hope in the fury that was wrapped around Jerusalem as the mist swirled among the olive trees.

This morning Orde's heart was heavy. He knew the purpose of the Woodhead Commission's visit to Palestine. The words and faces of these English aristocrats betrayed their intentions even before the inquiry had begun. And Orde had been commanded to keep his personal beliefs in check, or else.

He raised his eyes as a white-robed shadow moved beneath the branch of a gnarled olive tree. Stopping, he waited for a moment as the figure knelt on the hard ground—not to pray, but to pull weeds.

He smiled as he watched her. The Mother Superior of the Russian Convent pulled weeds with the same concentration as she might have exhibited saying her Rosary.

Glancing up at him, the old woman smiled and waved, her fist full of grass. "Good morning, Samuel."

"Morning prayers again, Mother?" he asked.

"A task that reminds me of the shortness of this life, Samuel." The old woman placed the weeds in a heap beside her and gestured for him to sit down. "We are like the new grass of the morning," she said quietly. " 'In the morning it flourisheth . . . in the evening it is cut down and withereth.' " The old woman raised an eyebrow and considered the troubled expression of her companion.

"A depressing thought, Mother," he said glumly.

"On the contrary, Samuel." She brushed the soil from her hands and sat back on her heels. "It is a thought of great comfort for those who love God and do His will. Life is short. Our trials in this life will pass quickly. 'Teach us to number our days, so that we may apply our hearts unto wisdom. . . .' "

"Psalm 90, verse 12," Orde responded, but his voice was not light as he spoke. He looked away from the old woman's sparkling eyes. She was the daughter of a Russian aristocrat in Moscow. Once, before the revolution, she had been young and beautiful and courted by many men. But she had never been happy until she came to Jerusalem as a penniless refugee. She had lost everything she had loved, but here, she had found true life.

"You are troubled today, my friend." The old woman patted his hand.

He nodded slowly, grateful she was here for him to share his thoughts. "Things are . . ." He faltered, wondering how much he could say. "I am afraid a great injustice is about to be done."

She raised her chin slightly. "I am certain you are right."

"And I am unable to speak up. To do anything about it."

"Ah." She nodded. She was remembering *something* . . . something very far away, and yet still very fresh and near to her. "Perhaps you do not yet see how you may help, Samuel. It is not always clear until the Lord puts it right in front of you."

"These are great matters. Dealing with many innocent lives." He spoke carefully, reasoning his way through the frustration he felt. "Men from England who will decide . . ."

"I have read about their arrival. About the matters of the refugees." She picked up a spindly weed and sighed. "These great men. They forget that they are grass, do they not, Samuel? I pray their decisions are wise. Merciful. Because great men are also grass." She tossed away the stem and sat in silence for a moment, then closed her eyes and whispered, "But you, O Lord, sit enthroned forever. You will arise and have compassion on Zion, for it is time to show favor to her. The appointed time has come. The nations will fear the name of the Lord. The Lord will rebuild Zion and appear in His glory." A soft smile crept across her lips. She opened her eyes. "It is written, Samuel. Do not be afraid. Men are unjust. But God is still God."

That was all true, yet Orde could not rid himself of this sense of hopelessness, helplessness in the face of such twisted political power. He did not want to wait until the Lord himself returned to this peaceful mount in order for things to be put right! He longed for a righteous world *now*!

Orde looked around at the garden where Jesus had prayed until drops of holy blood had dripped onto the ground—this ground, where the weeds grew and an aged nun knelt to pray while she worked in peace. He felt a twinge of resentment that the old woman could manage to lump the wicked and the innocent into the same pile and say that God alone would sort them out.

"I do not doubt God's future justice, Mother," he said with a frown. "I only wish it would come now. Today."

She returned to her work, gathering another handful of weeds from between the thick roots of a tree. "We mortals have a small and troubled view of time, Samuel. If the wicked could have one glimpse of their eternal future, perhaps they would repent." She shrugged. "And if the righteous could have one glimpse of their eternity with God, they would no longer fear what evil men might do to them in this life. No. I think we might pity the wicked man for the price he will pay for his sin."

The old woman dumped another handful of grass onto the pile and then began to hum softly to herself. It was usually this way. She was right in what she said, yet Orde found very little comfort in that truth. He longed to *do* something! *Anything* to help ease the suffering of Jerusalem! But all he could do now was pray.

14

Gentle as Doves

Great heaps of luggage were piled on the roof of the Jerusalem bus. Ashen-faced, Leah gasped as her precious cello was tossed from one man to another and then up to the very top of the pile. She watched with horror as the case was wedged between two large wooden crates of chickens bound for the poultry market of Old City Jerusalem.

"Be *careful* with it," Leah called up to the scruffy young man threading rope through luggage handles and wood slats until everything on top of the bus was connected. Shimon squeezed Leah's hand.

"I would bribe him so the cello could ride inside with us, but we may need our last few shillings for lunch."

Leah pressed her lips together in disgust. She looked up at the threatening sky. "Welcome to the Promised Land," she said dryly. "Come perform for us in Jerusalem if your cello is not ruined in a rainstorm or pierced by a stray bullet." She closed her eyes and sighed. "My whole life is up there tied onto a chicken crate."

Shimon's brow furrowed as he looked at the bus tickets. He handed them to Leah and kissed her cheek. "Not your whole life, darling. Not yet." Then he began to climb up the metal rungs fastened to the back of the bus.

"Shimon! What are you doing!" She knew what he was doing. He was going to ride on top with the luggage while Vitorio rode inside in his precious seat. No one could protest the cello case if it had a proper ticket just like every other passenger. "Shimon! Come down!" she cried, her heart beating fast at the thought of Shimon riding up the pass of Bab el Wad in such an exposed place as sullen Arab eyes watched him and Arab fingers stroked hair-triggers.

Shimon did not listen. He untied Vitorio and passed it down ever so gently to a luggage handler who shrugged at this meshugge fellow and handed the instrument to Leah. "Vitorio is our ticket to Jerusalem," Shimon said stubbornly as he took a seat beside the chicken crate. "If it rains, I will dry out. Me and the chickens, nu? Get on the bus!" he demanded.

"But they might shoot you!" Leah protested as the other passengers gaped out the bus windows.

"Pray they do not," he instructed, turning his eyes forward and lifting his chin. "Or the world will lose a great percussionist, and you will lose a great lover."

At these words, the men on the bus cheered out the window for Shimon. The engine coughed and sputtered to life. And it began to rain. Just a few drops, but definitely rain.

Leah looked at the cello, then up at Shimon.

"Get on the bus!" he ordered, covering his plaster cast with the corner of a wicker basket.

More raindrops. It had been so clear and hot yesterday. Why had it chosen *this moment* to rain?

The bus driver shouted at her. "Are you coming, lady?"

Shimon gave her a gentle look. *Go on. I will be fine. We have no choice.* "I will be the first to see Zion," he called. "The earthly Zion, of course." He motioned her away.

She backed toward the bus door. Clutching the cello, she reluctantly climbed the steps. The other passengers cheered as she and the cello took their seats.

Rain suddenly burst from the clouds, falling on the bus like the pounding of drums.

————

Ram Kadar inhaled deeply the smoke of the water pipe. His words came forth with the smoke on his breath. "I am speaking of your sister. Of Victoria." He smiled and inclined his head. A black keffiyeh framed his darkly handsome face.

Ibrahim wiped his mouth nervously. He felt the curious eyes of his half brothers on him. For Victoria to marry a man like Kadar would be a great honor. It would also guarantee the safety and position of the family of Hassan within the Mufti's council.

"She is . . . not ready for marriage." He smiled and lifted the cup of thick Turkish coffee to his lips.

"She is too old not to be married," Kadar shrugged off the answer. "My own mother had three children by the time she was Victoria's age."

"Times are different now," Ibrahim shrugged. "You know, since the Mandate. She has her job."

"A job that will be helpful to our cause." Kadar narrowed his eyes. "She will obey a husband. She will help us once she is in my bed. Beneath my protection."

His words brought laughter from the six men in the back room of the coffeehouse. Every man but Ibrahim.

"My father is in Iran on business," Ibrahim persisted, attempting to put off the discussion. "It is my father who will have the final word in such a matter as her marriage."

"I am not asking permission." Kadar seemed amused. "Marriage is a business proposition. I am prepared to pay well. I can promise your father all the things and more that would give Victoria a satisfactory life. I ask only that you support me in this. Stand with me as I make my proposition. This will strengthen my stand with him. *Inshallah!* May Allah will it!"

Ibrahim nodded with a single jerk of his head. "I must think. She is a jewel in the crown of the Prophet, and . . . I must think."

Kadar leaned forward. There was a hint of impatience in his dark, brooding eyes. He pulled the tasseled hem of his keffiyeh over his shoulder. "What is there to think about? She is a woman of marriage-able age. I am a suitor who meets the requirements of the Koran. I can pay the price your father asks." The smile reappeared and he considered Ibrahim carefully. "Unless you know of another suitor. But my offer will still surpass that of any man in Jerusalem."

"A generous offer. I . . . my sister is . . . she thinks like the English. She thinks of things like . . . love." He was embarrassed to admit such a thing in the company of men.

Kadar seemed relieved. "Is that all?" He looked amused as he glanced around the circle of men. "A much easier matter to deal with than her price. A problem I intend to solve on the night of our wedding, Ibrahim," he laughed. Genuine relief radiated from his eyes. "I will make her beg for me to keep her beneath my protection." He lifted the hem of his black robe as if it were a blanket to spread over her. No one missed his meaning. More laughter rippled through the circle. Checkered keffiyehs bobbed with approval of Kadar's words and wisdom about women.

"Perhaps my father will let her make her own choice."

The laughter died. "Then he will be thinking too much like the English himself, and no doubt Haj Amin will wish to instruct him on what the Koran says about women." This last sounded suspiciously like a threat. The family of Hassan lived on the very edge of approval. To fall off that precarious edge at this time could mean a swift death with a dagger between the ribs.

"I did not mean to offend, Ram Kadar. Allah knows . . ." Ibrahim spread his hands in innocence. He was not handling this problem well. He was angry that Eli was taking so much time in his decision to cross the Street of the Chain. If he and Victoria were married, if Eli were already a follower of the Prophet, this discussion would be settled.

Kadar nodded slowly, deliberately. He was set on his goal. He had seen the face of Victoria Hassan and liked what he saw. She was single. She was of a social class equal to that of Kadar's. Seldom had there been so much talk about such a simple matter as the marriage of a girl to a man like Kadar! He could afford more than one wife. He was a wealthy man in his own right, but he remained unmarried. He wanted Victoria as his first wife; then he would have others. He would marry her as soon as the contract was negotiated and signed. Kadar had consulted Ibrahim only to gain some idea of what to anticipate from Victoria's father. He had not expected talk of love at such a time.

"Give your sister my regards." He touched fingers to forehead. "Tell her I have seen her. That I consider her . . . a worthy woman."

Ibrahim acknowledged the request. He would tell Victoria. *Yes!* He would tell her that there was no more time to play games in the matter of Eli's conversion! Even now, things had become too dangerous for secret rendezvous. "It will be as you ask, my friend."

"My *brother*," Kadar said, leaning back and resting his hand on the gleaming silver hilt of his dagger. In his mind it was settled. Victoria Hassan would be his wife. The thought pleased him. The image of her face and body pleased him also—perhaps even to the degree the English might call love. But this last was not a matter he would speak of openly. When the business arrangement was complete and the wedding finished, then he would show her *without words* how he perceived her. That would be enough.

From his bedroom window, Eli could easily see the Dome of the Rock. He could also see the corner of the home where Victoria and Ibrahim lived with their parents and three younger brothers.

Every day that week, Eli had run home from Yeshiva and bounded up the steep steps to the apartment above the Cohen's grocery store.

"What is wrong with him?" his brother Moshe would ask when Eli charged through the front room with hardly a greeting. His mother would shrug and roll her eyes.

"Too much fasting." She would tap her temple. "It affects the mind, nu? I'm telling you, I will talk to the rabbi about him!"

But it was not fasting that affected Eli. Each afternoon, he sat at the window and waited. At 5:35, Victoria would return from her secretarial job. She would pass within his vision for the barest instant as she rounded the corner on the Street of the Chain. He would see her in her English-cut suit as she hurried home after a busy day of typing reports for the English government now housed at the King David Hotel.

Eli lived each hour looking forward to that fraction of a second when he would glimpse Victoria. It had been seven long nights since he had held her. His heart had not stopped racing since that night. Victoria had not sent for him as she had promised. She walked quickly past the corner and cast a look over her shoulder toward Eli's house. Then she walked on without a break in stride.

The frustration of it nearly drove him mad. He could not study. He growled irritably whenever Moshe tried to talk to him about things happening at Hebrew University. He ignored his mother's pleas to *eat, eat, eat!*

Why had Victoria not sent word? Yes, things were tense in the Old City just now, but the only tension Eli felt was from not speaking with her. Not touching her. Did she not understand what he was feeling? Had she decided against his proposal of marriage? Perhaps the call of the muezzin each day had drawn her away from his love, after all.

This morning, Eli rose early. He sat at his window in hopes of catching a glimpse of her as she left for work. Moshe, twenty-three years old, was determined to figure out the mystery of his brother's behavior. He lay quietly on the bed, studying Eli's back. Perhaps Moshe would miss the bus to Hebrew University, but after a week of Eli's strange actions, Moshe was willing to miss his class on Canaanite pottery.

Eli squinted and looked at his watch. The bus would be leaving from Jaffa Gate in ten minutes. She would walk past the corner . . . *right now!*

His sense of timing was impeccable. Dressed in a powder blue dress, Victoria walked by. Not breaking stride, she looked up toward the Sachar apartment. Her hair was piled onto her head and glistened like the black wing of a raven.

At the sight of her, he whispered her name. *"Victoria!"* It was only a whisper, but he sensed his mistake. *Too late to call it back!* He stiffened, feeling the eyes of Moshe on him. He turned slowly to see his brother grinning from his pillow.

"So that's it!" Moshe crowed, raising up on one elbow. "My brother the rabbi is in love! So *that's* it!" Dark brown eyes radiated a delicious glee. "Ha! All this praying and fasting up on the roof. Have you got a telescope up there to watch her?"

Eli's face hardened. He decided to deny it. "I am sure I don't know what you are talking about."

"You said her name!"

"You were dreaming."

"No! You were dreaming! Of Victoria Hassan, no less. There is only one girl I know in the Old City with a British name, and that girl does not go to synagogue!" Moshe was enjoying himself.

Eli wanted to strike him. Moshe was mocking him as if this did not matter. She was not just any girl! "You are *meshugge*! Crazy!"

"I am not the crazy one, dear brother! I am not the one running home each day and rising up in the morning for one peek at a girl! Especially not an Arab girl!"

"Shut up!" Eli warned. He stood slowly and pretended to rummage through his chest of drawers.

"Although I must admit you have good taste. Even at the university I have not come across anything as gorgeous as Victoria Hassan." He would not be silenced.

"You talk like a goy!" Eli said angrily as he still attempted to disarm Moshe.

"Yes? Well, that is what happens when a good little Orthodox boy grows up and goes to the university, nu? We should all become rabbis just like you, eh, Eli? Stick to all the old ways. Do not consider looking at a woman unless she is a Jewess who also grew up in the Old City."

"You are mocking . . ."

Moshe laughed sarcastically and climbed from the bed. "No. I am not the one in love with an Arab. I am not the one who mocks."

Moshe was still grinning when Eli's fist struck him square in the face. He had not expected the blow. Eli had not expected it either. Moshe flew back onto the bed and lay there with a startled look on his face. He rubbed his chin as he eyed his brother with a new concern.

Eli stood sweating in his underwear. Bare feet. He blinked and looked at his fist as though the thing had a mind of its own. "I . . . I . . . I am . . . I," he stammered, not knowing what to say.

"I am sorry," Moshe said at last. "I did not know." He sat up. "This is . . . you really are . . . serious."

Eli cried out. He ran his hands through his hair and sank down on the bed opposite Moshe. He cradled his head in his hands and moaned, "May the Eternal forgive me. May He . . . I love her. Oy! Moshe. I . . . I . . . I . . ." He trailed off.

There was a silence. Misery. Unquenchable fire inside Eli.

"How long?" Moshe spoke gently now. He was convinced of his brother's agony. This was not a light fantasy, and the implications were terrible to consider.

"Six months. No. Seven. I had not seen her in a while. Then I saw her in the souk. Buying vegetables. Cabbages. Oy! So beautiful."

Moshe refrained from the urge to joke about such a less-than-romantic meeting. "Yes. Victoria is beautiful."

"You noticed."

"Uh-hmmm. You have good taste, brother." He pounded Eli's shoulder, hoping to lighten this moment of discovery. Eli would not be lifted up.

"I tried not to notice."

Moshe believed that. Eli was the type of man who would try very hard not to notice. "Does she feel the same?"

"Yes. I mean . . . yes!"

"You see her?"

"Yes."

"Often?"

"I have . . . we have met once a week. Sometimes more."

This news startled Moshe. "Where? Does Ibrahim know?"

"It was he who helped me. You know . . . he is still like a brother to me in spite of . . ."

"In spite of the fact that his brothers are all supporters of the Mufti. And now anti-Semites, I hear."

"That has nothing to do with Ibrahim. Or Victoria," Eli defended.

"It will have something to do with you if you are caught with their sister! You *know* all this!" Now it was Moshe who was gripped with fear. "They are friends with assassins, Eli. In a moment they could have you killed and then melt away. No one would know why. Just another Jewish Yeshiva student murdered in the Old City."

"We are careful." Eli rubbed his hand over his sandy-colored beard.

"How can you be careful? I could pass for an Arab, but *you!* Look at you. Practically a goy! Almost a Gentile with your light hair." He frowned and shuddered as he pictured Eli walking through the Arab Quarter on his way to a secret meeting with the sister of young Arab thugs. "Where do you meet her?"

"Different places." He sighed. "Ibrahim is always with us. He knows how we love each other."

There was almost an accusation in Eli's words. After all, this had been going on for six months and Eli had not told Moshe about it. Only Ibrahim.

"So what now?" Moshe asked, looking toward the window.

"I asked her to marry me."

"You . . . what?"

"To convert. She could do it."

Moshe stood and went to the window. He looked out at the corner where Victoria passed each day. She was an Arab. She would never convert. To do so would mean the end of her relationship with her family. Possibly the assassin's knife might be unsheathed for her pretty throat as well. Muslim fanaticism had risen to a fevered pitch recently. Such things were becoming more frequent.

"And when you asked her to convert to Judaism, what did she say?"

"That we needed to think. A little distance." Eli looked up. His eyes were tortured, pleading for help. "I have to see her. You could . . . Moshe, would you carry a message to her for me? She is in the office of transportation. First floor in the British wing of the King David Hotel." All these words came in a rush. Of course Moshe could more easily go into the hotel and drop by the desk of an Arab woman on some pretext. Moshe was clean shaven. He wore the clothes of the present day, instead of the garb of an Orthodox Jewish rabbinical student.

Moshe looked from the haunted eyes of his brother, then out to the corner again. He was definitely going to miss his class this morning.

The hotel was only a short way out of his way, however.

"Sure. Yes. I will take her a note."

———————

This first rain of the season moved like a gray curtain preceding the Egged bus up the pass of Bab el Wad. A deluge to compare with the days of Noah, it drove the Jihad warriors indoors lest their weapons rust. It came in waves from the skies above Jerusalem. Drops chased drops until torrents filled the barren ravines and scrambled over ancient rocks.

Inside the bus, the Jerusalem travelers rejoiced. The first rain had been late this year and so the season of revolt and violence had gone on longer than usual. The cisterns of Jerusalem were nearly empty and now they would again be full. There would be celebration in the Jewish sections of the city tonight.

"Your husband has brought the rain, madame," laughed a beady-eyed little man across the aisle from Leah. He sliced a hunk of salami and offered it to her in a gesture of goodwill.

She shook her head and mouthed the words *no thank you.* How heartless and unfeeling all these laughing people seemed!

"You should be grateful! Not even the devil himself would stay out in this! Not even for such a fine big target as your husband makes!"

This was supposed to make her feel better?

"He may be wet, but he will be alive!" cheered the man with the salami. "Yesterday I would not have said so. Yesterday they were sniping at buses all along the pass."

Leah's eyes widened as she looked out the window at the steep, rocky slopes. In places the road seemed to double back on itself. The water had no chance to rest; no rocks or plants to cling to. No wonder half of Palestine had been malarial swamps before the Zionists came. They had drained the swamps, but what could they ever do to the barren hillsides?

This was misery. What sort of homeland was this, anyway? What kind of bus company that made a woman choose between her cello and her husband?

Leah took out her pen and notepaper and began to write as the reek of greasy salami filled her nostrils and the lurching bus made her stomach rebel.

Dear Elisa,

Maybe I am not so glad to be here, after all. If ever on this earth there was a place more desolate, more forsaken by God than Palestine, I cannot imagine it! Why, I ask myself, WHY would anyone want to come to such a place? The English have England. The Muslims have most of the Middle East. And so that leaves US. Raised in the shadow of the glorious Alps and the green farmland of Austria. Oh, Elisa! If there was any place else on earth but this place . . .

Her pen trembled as she wrote. The bus lurched around a particularly sharp corner and Leah's stomach finally rebelled.

"Stop the bus!" she shouted. "I am ill!"

The driver smirked. Nothing doing. "Open a window."

Retching out the window of a moving bus in a rainstorm, Leah got her first glimpse of Jerusalem. A jumble of white stone houses set among the white stones of a boulder-strewn hill. A few buildings of size and substance were in the panorama, but Jerusalem was far from glorious. Ah yes, there was the Dome of the Rock. The Muslim shrine in all the postcards. Nobody had mentioned that the man in charge of that place wanted every Jew in Palestine dead. Somehow, that thought detracted from the first thrill of seeing a postcard picture come to life.

Leah let the rain wash over her face and hair while passengers in the seats behind her complained that she should finish her business and close the window.

She ignored their indignant jibes and breathed deeply of air without the scent of garlic and greasy salami. Maybe Shimon had not had such a bad trip, after all. She called up to him, "Shimon! Are you all right? Shimon!"

Either he had fallen off or he did not hear her. If he had fallen off, the driver would not have stopped the bus, Leah was convinced. Such a place this was! And such people!

She and Shimon had been idealistic fools. It had taken her less than twenty-four hours in the Holy Land to figure that out.

She wiped her face and opened her mouth to catch a few raindrops before she ducked back into the stuffy bus. She closed the window halfway and let her fingers dangle out through the opening.

The bus moved past a few low houses, and the salami man asked, "So. Your first trip to Jerusalem, eh? How do you like it so far?"

Leah simply smiled a reply. She had left her opinion of Palestine beside the road a mile or so back.

The Old City of Jerusalem bristled with expectation of the arrival of the Woodhead Royal Commission of Inquiry. Samuel Orde inspected the ranks of his soldiers. Bayonets were fixed. Gas masks hung within easy reach. Heads were helmeted against a stray stone or roof tile. Faces were grim and ready.

This morning's march would cover every back street and alleyway within the circle of the city wall. It was meant to be a display of British might. Arab, Jew and Christian were meant to tremble at the sight of such force. At the sound of tramping boots and bagpipes, they would stop their work for a moment and consider that such a show demanded that every citizen of the city remain on his best behavior.

From the citadel the men marched to stand in impressive columns in the very center of Omar Square. The voices of red-faced sergeants accompanied the precise crashing of boots against the stones. The company divided into four groups of soldiers who then swiveled to face in four different directions. At the command of Captain Orde the skirl of bagpipes commenced anew and the soldiers tramped off to scour the Old City for any sign of threat.

Today, Captain Orde served double-duty. He was not only the protector of the members of the Woodhead Committee, he was also, regretfully, their tour director.

"No one knows the place like you do, Orde!" his commanding officer had shouted. "You and your articles for the *Geographic*! By thunder, Sir John Woodhead has asked for you by name! Keep your Zionist nonsense to yourself, or you'll find yourself back in England guarding coastal defenses!" A finger in Orde's face had emphasized this last point. Then the instructions had continued: "No repeating of biblical verses unless they have a direct bearing on some historical point of interest. No comments about the biblical prophecies regarding the return of the Messiah and the Jewish people to the land of Israel. No religious drivel. No comments that might influence the commission on behalf of the Jewish population over the Muslims. Fairness and impartiality must be observed by you at all times—or else!"

The *or else* had put Captain Orde in a particularly nasty mood. His men whispered among themselves. Their normally personable and gentle captain was looking for heads to roll. A half-shined shoe was reason for confinement to quarters. A misplaced gas mask was offense enough for a stay in the brig.

Wide-eyed, the Old City residents gathered before their shops and stalls in the souks to watch the mighty display of precision. Here was the law of the land in evidence for any who might doubt its weakness. The display was comforting for many; frightening for some; enraging for a handful.

This visit of the English lords of the commission was supposed to be impromptu, an example of daily life in the Old City—how the Jews and the Muslims mixed freely in the souks with all the Christian sects that warred against one another in a different kind of battle. But not one footstep went unplanned for these honored gentlemen. Not one word unrehearsed.

In the Arab Quarter, school children who usually begged from the English for a living put on their finest clothes. In the Armenian Quarter, the bearded patriarch wore his ceremonial best. In the Christian Quarter, Greeks and Copts and Ethiopians and Catholics glared at one another from across invisible boundaries in the various shrines. They silently competed for the greatest glory of each of their sects before the lofty Englishmen.

In the ragged Jewish Quarter, the steps of synagogues and apartments were swept. The shelves of shops were put in order. The dung of sheep on the way to slaughter was cleaned from the streets. Chicken crates were moved out of sight into an alley behind the kosher butcher shop. Yeshiva students cleaned the windows of Nissan Bek, while ancient rabbis prayed for a favorable impression and admonished the school children of the significance of this visit.

15

Great Performances

The little kitten Psalms was such a comfort to Rabbi Lebowitz. She had lost any vestige of her original timidity, and now she claimed his one-room flat as her own.

The old man, mindful of the four boy cats at Tipat Chalev, carried her in his pocket to a vacant lot where she tended to her basic needs twice a day. The rest of the time she strutted languidly about the room, staking claims on the table and the bed. At night she slept on the old man's chest just beneath his beard, where she purred happily until he fell asleep.

He filled his most recent letter to Etta and the children with all the news about the little creature—about her brothers who now followed Hannah Cohen everywhere as if she were a mother cat. He told how Hannah Cohen seemed to act as if *she* had rescued them from a pack of wolves. Ah, well. They would maybe grow up to kill rats. In the meantime, they had their own special plates, a warm bed in the basement, and another beneath the steps in the alley.

"My little Psalms sends greetings to the children," wrote the old rabbi. "Since Hannah has stolen her brothers, she hopes she will soon have children from Warsaw to come play with her here in Jerusalem!"

"Today is an important day," Rabbi Shlomo Lebowitz addressed the serious group of five-year-old boys in the classroom where Eli taught at the Torah school.

Eli looked first at the sturdy old man with his lined face and gnarled hands, then at the collection of miniature Orthodox students in their black coats and earlocks and yarmulkes perched on shorn heads. The old man shook a finger at them in warning. "Today the English gentlemen are coming with Captain Samuel Orde from the British Army. They are coming to see if Jewish boys are *good* boys and if more Jewish children should be allowed to come to Palestine!" There was a long pause. Rabbi Lebowitz let the weight of responsibility rest heavily on the shoulders of Eli's pupils. The entire fate of Jewish immigration depended on their behavior during the visit from the Englishmen!

A small hand moved tentatively into the air. The rabbi jabbed a finger toward it in response. The tiny brown-eyed child stood beside his desk to speak. "And if we are not good, will the Englishmen not let your daughter and grandchildren come here? Mama says that you want them to come very badly."

The old man glanced toward Eli. Perhaps it was wise to make this a personal issue. "That is correct, Yosef. If you chatter or squirm, or misbehave, the Englishmen will notice. They will say, 'Well, we want no more of that in Palestine!' Then they will send me a letter saying that my own grandchildren cannot come to Jerusalem. And there are many thousands more just like my own family who will wish to come, but will not be allowed."

This was effective. Yosef took his seat. Brows furrowed in consternation at the thought of one errant spitball on the back of an English head. The consequences were great and terrible!

Rabbi Lebowitz turned the classroom back over to Eli. Eli walked to the lectern. Today was indeed an important day in the Old City Jewish Quarter, but he could think of nothing but the fact that it had been over a week since he had seen Victoria. This was going to be the longest day of his life. *Carry on,* he told himself as he thanked Rabbi Lebowitz.

"And so, students, you can see that each of us is a representative of *all* our people, nu?"

Little heads bobbed in silent agreement.

Eli continued. "Perhaps some of you have family in Germany or elsewhere who want very badly to come here, just as Rabbi Lebowitz wishes his grandchildren to join him."

Again, nods of assent. Rabbi Lebowitz seemed pleased. He crossed his arms in satisfaction and stepped back against the chalkboard. This classroom would behave well for Captain Orde and his group of politicians. They would go home to England and tell their committees how polite Jewish children are in Jerusalem, that such politeness should be considered when they decide on how many more should be allowed through the Mandate.

Eli looked at the clock. His morning teaching assignment would end in thirty minutes. The English commission was scheduled to pass through in five minutes. After that, he would have to dismiss his pupils and return to his own studies.

He turned toward the rabbi, who was smiling pleasantly through his beard. "Would you care to remain with our classroom while the Englishmen are here? Then you can see for yourself that my students will be the best behaved of anyone in the Torah school."

"It will be a pleasure."

The old man took a seat at a desk near the back of the crowded room. Eyes glanced furtively in his direction. Determination was on every young face. They would not let him down or disgrace all Jewish children by their behavior.

Eli resumed instruction of the Hebrew alphabet. Rote memorization was the method of teaching. When he had been given this assignment as part of his training as a rabbi, Eli had hated the monotony of it. Now it was a relief. While his mouth taught the alphabet, his mind could wander easily to Victoria.

The British delegation arrived. Even though the school had been planning for this visit for weeks, all the teachers were warned that everything must appear normal.

Rabbi Lebowitz went smiling to the doorway. The suntanned face of Captain Samuel Orde appeared. Behind him came six men in British suits, varying in age from forty to sixty. They peered around the room as if they were looking for a speck of dust or a desk out of line with the others.

"This," Rabbi Lebowitz said with pride, "is our class of five-year-olds." He extended a hand toward Eli. "Eli Sachar is their teacher. He himself was once a student in this very classroom, and now he studies to become a rabbi."

Eli stepped forward. He extended his hand and smiled. What a nuisance this was, performing for a collection of English bigwigs when he could have been daydreaming about Victoria!

"How do you do?" He applied his most perfect accent and was immediately assaulted with half a dozen how-do-you-dos in reply.

Rabbi Lebowitz motioned for the men to come farther into the room. The boys looked like little clay figures. They sat rigidly with their hands clasped on their desks. It was almost their time to perform!

"Our children learn several languages," Rabbi Lebowitz said. "Including English, of course."

Eli raised his hand like a conductor. Little mouths opened to draw breath. Out came the much rehearsed words that must appear unrehearsed and spontaneous: *HOW DO YOU DO-O-O!* The class recited this in unison. It was perfect. There was not a single straggler in the lot. Eli nodded his approval, and a little boy sighed with relief. They had not failed their people!

And then it was over. *En masse,* the Woodhead Committee turned and proceeded to the next classroom where the same little drama was repeated.

Rabbi Lebowitz seemed pleased. He smiled. "Very good! And tonight at dinner you will have a special treat for dessert! Hannah and Shoshanna have made cookies for you in honor of what good boys you are!"

A delighted *A-h-h-h-h* followed him from the room.

This was good. Now the old man would go back to the soup kitchen where he supervised charity meals. The boys would recite the alphabet and think of cookies. Eli would drill them and dream of Victoria.

————

Against Theo's better judgment, he accompanied Dr. Chaim Weizmann to the offices of the British colonial secretary, Malcolm MacDonald. Since the afternoon at the British Museum, Theo had regretted his request that the officer who tailed him remain out of sight. The illusion of freedom was always tainted with the awareness that somewhere on the street a man named Beckham watched his every move.

Today, with a sort of bitter amusement, Theo considered that agent Beckham was probably walking into his own headquarters.

Weizmann and Theo were five minutes early. Secretary MacDonald kept them waiting for ten minutes later than their scheduled appointment. When they entered his large, opulent office, he was warm and friendly to Weizmann and yet cool to Theo Lindheim. No doubt he had read the Nazi accounts of Theo's "crimes" in Germany.

Half an hour passed as Weizmann patiently explained Theo's plan to the colonial secretary. He concluded with a wave of his hand. "I am a scientist and a humanitarian. Born and raised in England. I thought it best if you have any questions that you would be able to address them to a former businessman from Germany." He gestured toward Theo, who had not offered to speak during the entire meeting.

MacDonald appraised him with an indifferent gaze. "So, Dr. Weizmann." He refused to address Theo. "You propose that we increase our purchase of German goods in exchange for German Jews released from the Reich with some assets. I fail to see how this benefits Great Britain." He smiled a quick, unfriendly smile.

Weizmann did not reply. He looked at Theo for a response. For a moment an uneasy silence hung in the room. Weizmann cleared his throat expectantly and at last Theo spoke.

"It would seem," Theo said deliberately, "that the successful placement of German Jews among the Western democracies should be a major goal of this government."

"Oh?" MacDonald was almost rude in his strained propriety. "And why would you think that?"

Theo shifted in his chair. "Palestine is currently the only haven for Jewish refugees, is it not?"

"Both legal and illegal, Herr Lindheim. We have heard that you know well enough about the illegal sort."

Theo ignored the jibe. He would not defend himself or his actions in financing underground immigration from the Reich. That was not the issue here. "It would be better . . . for England . . . for everyone if all immigrants were legal. If other nations were willing to cooperate in a trade agreement with Germany, as Dr. Weizmann has explained, then perhaps there would no longer be such a flood of those attempting to flee to Palestine. Perhaps the pressure would be taken off the British Mandate."

The pure logic of Theo's explanation took the colonial secretary by surprise. He frowned, then opened his mouth in some attempt to argue, but he could not find an argument. "All very well and good, Herr Lindheim," he sniffed. "But will the German Chancellor go for the idea?"

Theo smiled knowingly. "I would ask your British ambassador. Mr. Henderson, is it?"

"Henderson. Berlin. Yes."

"I would suggest that Hermann Göring be approached with this idea first. He is, after all, in charge of the plan to improve the German economy."

"Göring. The fat one?"

"Yes. That is Hermann Göring. The one with all the medals," Theo prompted. "We were pilots together in the last war. Hermann Göring has always been a man with his mind on money. He agrees with the Führer about German Jewry mostly because he sees Jewish wealth as something he would like to have in his own account. He is a practical man."

Theo's bluntness surprised MacDonald. "He was a friend of yours, you say?"

"Of a sort. After he had me thrown into Dachau, I heard my paintings were on the walls of his home. He also confiscated my library of rare books in the name of the Reich. I am certain he enjoys the volumes almost as much as I did when they were mine."

MacDonald smoothed his eyebrows as he considered the practicality of Theo Lindheim's statements and insight. It was no wonder the Nazis wanted the man bound hand and foot and extradited back to Germany in a brown paper wrapper!

A cautious respect filled MacDonald's eyes now as he offered his hand to Theo and then to Weizmann with the assurance he would bring up the matter in tomorrow's cabinet meeting.

He inclined his head slightly and said in a lofty attempt at pleasantness, "It was quite . . . interesting to meet you after all this time. Perhaps we shall talk again."

———

Victoria raised her eyes from her typewriter as Parker, the British supervisor, entered the office and called for attention from the two dozen typists.

Frail and nervous on the best of days, today Mr. Parker mopped his brow and grimaced behind his round spectacles as he waved a piece of paper over the heads of his all-Arab staff.

"Attention, girls!" he cried a second time when Tasha had not stopped her furious typing. "An important assignment has come our way."

There was silence in the room. Victoria was grateful for the break. She looked past the harried supervisor to where the rain tapped against the window.

The high, effeminate voice of Mr. Parker began again. "For reasons known only to God and the British Mandate, an assignment has been passed down the chain to me. Unfortunately I have no one else to pass it to." His statement was thick with irritation. Parker, as the lowest man on the British administration's roster of command, was often handed the unwanted chores.

"The high commissioner has arranged some sort of concert for tonight. Not that I am invited," he added under his breath. "Someone needs to meet this musician at Egged Terminal. This musician is, I am told, from Germany or Austria or some such non-English-speaking place. I haven't the foggiest idea about the language of the Huns past *Guten Tag*—" He shoved his glasses up on the bridge of his long nose. "Pray God," he said dramatically, "that someone among you has a rudimentary grasp of that language?"

Victoria and Tasha exchanged looks. Had Allah ever made a bigger fool than their supervisor? Victoria shook her head imperceptibly and smiled as she raised her hand. German was one of several languages spoken by her father in his business as purveyor of Persian and Oriental carpets. An easy language. Much like English. Victoria understood and spoke it quite easily.

Mr. Parker slapped his chest in relief and rolled his eyes like a pilgrim overcome with ecstasy. His red polka-dot bow tie trembled under his bobbing Adam's apple.

"Miss Hassan! Thank *God*! Divide your file between Miss Habashi and Miss Aman and come along quickly then! We just have time to motor to the terminal before they arrive."

Victoria grinned happily as she deposited her day's stack of transcription onto the desks of her glowering co-workers. "You just did not volunteer fast enough," she whispered to Tasha in Arabic.

———

The rain had become a cloudburst by the time Moshe ducked beneath the awning of the King David Hotel where the administration office of the British Mandate was housed.

Following the example of the English hotel patrons around him, he greeted the doorman with a cheery greeting: "Quite a storm, eh wot?"

Shaking the water from his slicker he entered the lobby of the King David Hotel as if he belonged there. The plush red oriental carpets were damp from the feet of British officers and faithful British civil servants and the Arab staff who served them. Today there were more uniforms than usual in the lobby, owing to the visit of the Royal British Commission of Inquiry headed by Sir John Woodhead. Everyone in Jerusalem knew of the important visitors from London, and so, it seemed that the British high commissioner was taking extra precautions against any sort of potential dangers.

There were guards at the doors of the elevators. Guards at the foot of the grand staircase. Guards beside the men's room. Guards flanking the doors of the administrative wing of the hotel where Victoria labored over the endless paperwork required to run such an operation as the British mandatory government in Palestine. Eli had told Moshe that Victoria typed requisitions for everything from tea and cigarettes to toilet paper. *How small are the cogs of great government.*

The question was, how could Moshe, who was not in any way related to this grand operation, slip by the guards and reach Victoria? Even the most proper-looking Englishmen were being halted at the portals and checked for identification, as if a company of eunuchs had been set in place to guard the harem of secretaries.

Moshe looked at his rumpled khaki clothes—perfectly acceptable among the archaeologists of Britain who came to the digs of Palestine. But dripping on the red carpets of the lobby, he looked like a potsherd among Royal Worcester china.

He gazed up nonchalantly at the gilded ceiling. He looked down at the potted plants, then searched for an empty chair where he might consider the problem. *Too late!* He had been spotted by an elevator eunuch. The fellow strolled purposefully toward Moshe, who glanced at his watch and tried to look impatient.

"Looking for someone?" asked the guard.

"Waiting." Moshe displayed his most precise mastery of Oxford English. "For Professor Hrachabad. Professor of ancient Syrian ethnology, you know. We have a meeting scheduled, and he is quite late. Quite."

The guard looked doubtful, even though Moshe spoke the King's English better than Sir John Woodhead.

"Professor . . ."

"Hrachabad." Moshe scoured the lobby in search of the imaginary professor as the soldier peered doubtfully at him.

And then, miracle of miracles, Victoria Hassan emerged from the administrative offices at the side of a man who could quite easily be a professor of Syrian ethnology! "There he is now!" Moshe strode happily toward Victoria, who looked at him with a combination of muted astonishment and fear.

Moshe took no chances. He hailed the fellow in the polka-dot tie in the Arabic street language of the Old City. Pumping the confused man's hand, he did not look at Victoria as he smiled and chatted to the non-comprehending Mr. Parker.

"Eli is frantic with worry," Moshe said with a broad smile.

"I dare say!" Mr. Parker was flustered. "Can't understand a word. Do I know you?"

Moshe continued in Arabic. "Eli languishes and must meet with you before his heart breaks with the pain of his love. I am sent as a messenger."

"Please!" Mr. Parker remained blinking in confusion as Moshe pumped his hand. "Miss Hassan, can you understand this blighter?"

"Indeed," Victoria nodded graciously, then through gritted teeth she smiled and answered in Arabic as well. "You are insane to come here."

Mr. Parker managed to free himself from Moshe's handshake. "Whatever does he want? Doesn't he speak English?"

"He wants an address," Victoria replied, calmly pulling pen and paper from her handbag and scribbling a note. After a minute she handed the note to Moshe with a slight bow. "Tell Eli I love him," she whispered softly in her own tongue. Then with the grace of a duchess she swept past him and out through the doors of the lobby entrance.

Victoria recognized the musician by the cello that rested on the floor of the Egged bus station beside a large wet man with a broken arm.

Both Leah and Shimon Feldstein appeared to be wet—he more so than she, however. There was not one dry inch on the body of the big man.

"Good heavens," muttered Parker as he spotted them across the lobby. "They must have run behind the bus all the way from Tel Aviv."

The couple looked quite miserable and lost. The wide brown eyes of the cellist held an almost childlike expression of worry, like a little girl lost in the souks of the Old City.

Victoria said her name, "Leah Feldstein?" She walked toward her, and the lost expression changed to one of immediate relief.

"Tell her I said good day," mouthed Parker, exaggerating each word. "*Guten Tag!*" he said loudly as he extended his hand.

Leah accepted the handshake doubtfully; then as the strange little man likewise took Shimon's good hand, she said in German, "Should we tell him we speak English? His German is remarkably bad!"

Victoria laughed at the comment, immediately deciding she liked Leah Feldstein. She replied in German, "My name is Victoria Hassan.

I have been brought along as your interpreter."

"Your accent is much better." Leah was smiling warmly as she glanced up at Shimon. "What do you say, Shimon, shall we keep it among us three?"

Parker's mouth enunciated broadly as he relayed his message through Victoria to the musicians. "Tell them we wel-come them in the name of His Maj-es-ty's Man-da-tory Gov-ern-ment!"

"Is he just learning to speak English also?" Shimon quipped.

"Just barely," Victoria replied. "And tonight you are performing for the British Army, yes?"

"For free bus tickets to Jerusalem for me and my cello," Leah said. "Shimon was forced to ride on the top of the bus with the chickens, which may have been a blessing compared to what I rode with inside."

Victoria shook her head in sympathy. "I hear they hire these bus drivers at an insane asylum in Hebron. They stop for no one."

"I have heard that as well," Leah laughed. "And now, where are you taking us?"

As Mr. Parker continued to relay messages through Victoria, the car arrived at the King David Hotel. Arrangements had been made for Leah and Shimon to stay here the first night, if they wished, as guests of the government. If not, a taxi would take them anywhere they wished to go after the performance this evening.

Leah squeezed Shimon's hand as the doorman walked from beneath the awning of the King David to open their door. The gracious stones of the hotel seemed to Leah to mirror some of the elegance they had left behind in Europe. One night in such a place! The thought of it comforted her.

"Last night we slept in a packing crate," she said to Victoria. "Just tell me there are no scorpions or snakes here."

"None that I have seen," said the dark-eyed beauty with a laugh. "Except the two-legged kind."

"And is there hot water with which I might thaw out my husband?"

"That will take an hour at least," Shimon quipped through chattering teeth.

"And European-made tubs are big enough even for a man his size," Victoria nodded. "And it is free. If you like, I will help you find your way to your great-aunt's flat in the Old City tomorrow."

"Consider the request made," Shimon said.

This, Victoria relayed to the blissfully ignorant Mr. Parker. Ah yes, he supposed he could spare Victoria for half a day tomorrow. The government would expect such a courtesy, no doubt.

Thus, the matter was settled. Leah and Shimon were shown their suite by a white-gloved bellhop who led them through the lobby and past the stiff-backed guards flanking the ornate brass elevator doors. For just a moment, Leah felt as though Jerusalem was not the end of the world, after all. Strange that her first friendly conversation had been with an Arab woman. It was not at all what Leah had expected.

16

A Land of Milk and Honey

"Now I know how Joshua and Caleb felt when they came across the Jordan to spy!" Moshe grinned down at Eli as he presented the note from Victoria.

Eli held the folded slip of paper as if it contained news of life or a sentence of death for him. He did not open it. "Is she . . . all right?"

"She is a land of milk and honey, brother!" Moshe sat down on the ledge of the roof and crossed his arms with self-satisfaction. The mission into enemy territory had been a complete success. "So? Why don't you open it?"

Eli did not want to open such a personal note in front of Moshe. What if Victoria had rejected his love? Then it occurred to him that Moshe had probably read the note. He probably knew its contents backward and forward. *Why did she not seal it in an envelope?* He looked at Moshe, then asked, "Did you read it?" He knew the answer by the Cheshire-cat smile on Moshe's face.

"I had to know what it said." Moshe touched the bruise on his chin as the memory of Eli's fist came to mind. "What if the wind had torn it from my hand? It would have blown away and then you would not have known." He saluted. "Sergeant Joshua reporting as ordered, sir!"

Perhaps Moshe was smiling because the affair was finally over. Perhaps . . .

The trapdoor raised slightly and the irritated voice of Ida Sachar called up, "Eli? Have you seen Moshe?"

"He is here with me, Mama." Eli tucked the paper behind him.

Silence. "What are you boys doing up here?"

Moshe answered, "Praying and fasting, Mama."

"Oy! Oy!" She poked her head up and looked as if she could not believe her ears. She shook her finger at Moshe. "You could use a little praying, Moshe Sachar! You teach him, Eli. He is practically one of the goyim with all this archaeology nonsense!" She narrowed her eyes threateningly. "But if I hear another word about fasting tonight!" She shook a fist, then growled. "We *eat* in ten minutes!" She disappeared like a squirrel down a hole and let the door slam shut.

Eli sat rigid for a moment, his smile frozen, his eyes wide with false nonchalance. This was the sort of look his mother would have recognized as caught-in-the-act-innocence if she had stopped long enough to notice. Neither brother breathed as the sound of her footsteps died away.

Seconds ticked by. At last Eli wiped his brow and, with a shaking hand, pulled out the crumpled note.

"So read it, already!" Moshe whispered. Mama had frightened the cocky smirk from his face.

With a jerky nod, Eli opened the paper and scanned the neatly written note. "She wrote in English!" he protested, thrusting the paper into Moshe's hands.

"She knows Mama and Papa do not read English all that well." The grin returned.

"Neither do I," Eli protested. "Speaking is one thing. *Hallo, ald chap! Cheery-bye! Can you show me the way to the W.C.?* These Englishmen. Nonsense! Read the note!"

"I knew you would need me, dear brother."

"Just read!" he said this too loud and instantly ducked at the thought of his impatient voice carrying through the window to Mama's ear. Or down to the street to a customer at Cohen's. "But read quietly," he whispered.

Moshe cleared his throat and in a whisper he translated into Arabic what Victoria had written.

> Dearest Love, Not a moment passes without thoughts of you . . .

Moshe paused and glanced up. He expected a blush of embarrassment on Eli's face. Instead, Eli had melted like a lump of butter in the sun, his eyes dreamy. Truly he was meshugge for this girl!

Eli sighed happily as he digested the first sweet words. He rolled his hand as a sign for Moshe that he was ready for the next delicious bite.

> There are reasons I could not send for you or meet with you. The torment is terrible without you. Please, please, my dearest heart, say you will meet me at one o'clock on Friday in the chapel of Christ Church. I will be there waiting for you! I am your beloved. V.

Moshe handed the note back to Eli who scanned it over again. Had

Moshe translated correctly? *Meet her in the chapel of a Christian church?*

"Why Christ Church?" Eli pondered out loud. "She a Muslim and me a Jew. And she wants to meet in Christ Church?"

"She is smart," Moshe interjected. "Friday is the Muslim holy day. Her brothers will all be gathered in the courtyard of the mosque to hear the Mufti's sermon. Muslim shops will be closed. None of her people will be around to recognize her."

Eli raised his eyebrows slightly at the sensible plan. "And none of my people would set foot in Christ Church. Yes. She has been thinking."

Moshe reached out and tapped the round black yarmulke on Eli's head. "You will have to take that off. No one wears a hat in these goyim houses of worship. And you should wear my clothes. Comb your hair back. They will think you are an Englishman, Eli."

"Yes, and our people will be preparing for Shabbat. Everyone will be busy. Friday is a good day. The best day. I am not sure why we did not think of it before."

"There is less chance you will be killed in a Christian church than sneaking around after dark in the Muslim Quarter." Moshe was still smiling, but there was relief in his words. "Although there is less chance that you will kiss her with much satisfaction in the pew at Christ Church with the rector looking on, nu?"

Eli nodded. That much was inconvenient, to be sure. But seeing her again, just sitting beside her, seemed as urgent to him now as breathing. "I will be content," he said, counting off the days and the hours until Friday. "One o'clock at Christ Church." The thought would sustain him.

Below them, a shrill voice penetrated the trapdoor. "Enough prayers, already! Eli and Moshe, come eat! And wash your hands well after being up there with the pigeons!"

News of Roosevelt's latest appeal on behalf of a Jewish homeland had just clattered off the London wires. Murphy scanned it briefly. He was certain that the American response to the Woodhead Commission's purpose in Palestine would evoke a spate of indignant replies on British editorial pages in the morning. After all, the young soldier killed on the wall of Jerusalem had not been American, but English. It was not an American family who was receiving home the body of their son, but an English mother!

Beyond the glass cubicle of Murphy's office, the typewriters of a dozen reporters pecked out the latest news from around the continent of Europe. The arrival of the body of this soldier killed on the Old City wall had sparked a greater response than the brutality against twelve thousand Jews in Germany.

The phone on his desk rang insistently, pulling him from his bitter reverie. He picked up the receiver, uncertain of the voice on the other end of the line.

"Mr. Murphy? John Murphy?" asked the precise English accent of a man.

"Speaking."

"You are the husband of Elisa Murphy?"

The question made Murphy stir in a moment of dread. "Yes. What is it?"

There was a moment of uneasy silence on the other end of the line. "This is Sir Thomas Beecham," the conductor began. "I assure you that I am not normally in the habit of reading other people's mail, but the secretary brought me something quite disturbing a few moments ago . . ."

Now Murphy's stomach churned. "Okay, concerning Elisa?"

"A card addressed to her from Paris. I did not want to alarm her or frighten her considering her . . . delicate condition. But the message is one word. Written in German. It says, simply, *GEFAHR*. You understand German, Mr. Murphy?"

Murphy nodded before he repeated the word in English. "Danger . . ."

It was the look in Murphy's eyes that frightened Elisa most. She cradled her violin in her arms and glanced first at Murphy, then back to the towering hulk of a man who stood grinning down at her.

"Freddie has worked at the loading dock of *The Times* for years." Murphy thumped the giant on his back. Freddie tipped his ragged tweed cap and continued to smile benignly. His face was pleasant but deeply lined, and his nose took a slight bend to the right. His chin jutted forward as if daring some invisible adversary to take a poke. Large ears protruded on either side of the lumpy face. The ears were the most interesting aspect of Freddie's physical appearance. They seemed to have been inflated like helium balloons. Normal folds and indentations were the very image of cauliflowers.

"Freddie was once one of the greatest Rugby players in Great Britain." Murphy thumped the giant again and then tugged on his own earlobe as if to explain the man's battered appearance.

Elisa smiled politely. She had not yet guessed the reason Murphy had brought this kind ox home. At six feet five and three hundred pounds, Fred Frutschy was a man to reckon with; that much was undeniable. But why?

Freddie shuffled his feet slightly. He doffed his cap, revealing a nearly bald head. He smiled broadly, displaying a gap where his four front teeth should have been. "Missus Murphy," he said in a gentle voice, the voice of a man much smaller, "real pleased to meet you, Missus."

"You are working for Trump News now?" Elisa tried to guess why the dock worker from the London *Times* now stood wringing his cap in her front room.

Murphy and Freddie exchanged glances. Murphy cleared his throat and raised his chin authoritatively. "Elisa," he began, faltered, and began again. "Freddie is working for me . . . for *us*."

Freddie was nodding enthusiastically and looking eagerly at his new boss to explain his position as an employee.

"How . . . very nice." Elisa was confused. There were no stacks of newspapers to load like at the news service. *Janitor? Messenger?*

"Bodyguard." Murphy dropped the title like a boulder in a clear pond.

Elisa worked her mouth open and closed. Open again. "But *why*? Mr. Tedrick said there was . . . *no threat!*"

"You don't trust that government goon, and neither do I," Murphy scowled. He thumped Freddie for the third time, as if demonstrating the muscle of a fine horse. "Nobody's gonna get past Freddie here. Not Tedrick, or Tedrick's men, or . . . *anyone*."

Elisa found herself nodding. Yes. The very fact that Murphy could think there was need for a bodyguard made her tremble inside.

"We got me a uniform, Missus." Freddie's head bobbed vigorously.

"Uniform?" Elisa squeaked.

"Chauffeur." Murphy was more confident, relieved that she had not protested.

"But we don't have an auto," she protested.

Murphy jerked a thumb toward the front window. He stepped aside as she went to look. A gleaming black car was parked at the curb. It seemed to stretch the width of the house. "A 1932 Duesenberg," Murphy said sheepishly. "I got a deal on it."

"Used to drive a taxi, Missus," Freddie volunteered. "An' I can carry packages for you as well." He waved a big paw toward her violin case. "I likes children. Me an' the missus have seven of our own. Mostly grown now. An' twenty-two grandchildren as well."

"He says he'll teach Charles and Louis to play Rugby," Murphy exhaled with loud relief. Elisa accepted this rather large addition to their household with astonishment, but little evidence of resentment.

Elisa glanced at the man's ears. She inwardly winced and gently suggested, "Perhaps you could start them with soccer?"

"Ah, 'tis a woman's game compared to Rugby." Freddie's lumpy face scowled. "But as you wish, Missus."

Murphy mouthed the words *thank you* to Elisa. She shook her head slightly in disbelief. A car. A chauffeur. And a bodyguard who could carry packages and teach the boys to play Rugby.

"All this," she said, "and a performance tonight." She extended her hand to Freddie. He shook it heartily, then tugged the violin from her arms.

"I'll carry this, Missus." Then he screwed up his face in an expression that displayed deep pondering. "Of course, first I'll have to put on me uniform. Them tall black boots." He thrust the violin case back into her arms and bowed slightly at the waist before he turned and clumped down the stairs to the Duesenberg.

———

As Leah considered what to wear and what to play and what to say to several thousand British soldiers and the Woodhead Commission at tonight's performance, Shimon penned a note to his great-aunt, announcing that they had at last arrived in Jerusalem and would come to the Old City tomorrow. At the suggestion of Victoria he sent the note by way of a hotel errand boy with the instructions that if he returned with a note from the old woman, he would receive another shilling for his efforts.

Thirty minutes before the scheduled departure to the Allenby barracks, the messenger returned to the hotel room. Shimon opened the door to a boy who stood wringing his hands and panting as if he had run all the way without stopping. The look on his face betrayed that something was definitely wrong.

"I am sorry, Mister. I am very sorry, but I could not give your letter to your aunt in the Old City!"

"Why not?"

"I knocked and knocked on the door, Mister. I knocked until the lady in the flat downstairs yelled at me that I should quit knocking." The boy's hands were trembling as he pulled out the original note.

"But did she say where my great-aunt was?"

"Yes, Mister." Curly hair bobbed as the boy nodded his head. He looked as if he might cry. "That woman, she says the old lady was eighty-seven and nobody was surprised except now maybe you. They sent a letter to Vienna, where the boxes came from."

"Where is she? Is she ill?"

"No. She is dead this one month past, Mister. She left you with four months lease on her flat but not a farthing besides, and you can get the key from the woman in the flat downstairs."

Shimon's lips formed a round, soundless *OH* of surprise. "Ah. I was not expecting. She was very old." He winced and opened and closed his note to her.

"I am sorry, Mister," croaked the boy. "But . . . I came back with a message and . . . so . . . my other shilling?"

Shimon blinked uncomprehendingly at him for a moment. Dressed in her black concert dress, Leah reached around Shimon and paid the nearly frantic boy, dismissing him with a curt nod as he thanked her and thanked her again. She shut the door and pulled Shimon to the bed.

"Sit down, darling."

He nodded blankly and obeyed. "I did not know her. I . . . I am sorry . . ." He put his hand to his forehead. "I am made of stone. Of stone. All I can think is that she left us with four months free rent on her flat. And . . . I am relieved."

Leah sat down beside him. She put her arm around his broad shoulders and leaned her head against his. She sighed.

"Why are you relieved, darling?"

Shimon looked wonderingly at Leah. "I wrote her and told her that you and I . . . that we are *Christians*." He whispered the word and looked over his shoulder as if someone might hear. "I thought perhaps the news killed her. That she opened the letter and died of a heart attack. But then I counted. She could not have gotten my letter before she . . . *died*! She would have left the lease to someone else . . ."

"Wrong, Shimon," Leah grimaced. "I wrote her the news from Paris. Before I knew you were safe, I told her I believed God would deliver you. That we would be here together in Jerusalem, and that I had found the Messiah of Israel."

"And she still left us the apartment?"

Leah nodded and patted his leg. "You should say kaddish for her, Shimon. She would have liked that."

17

In Concert

Victoria held two handwritten invitations from Leah Feldstein to the performance tonight at Allenby barracks. *A way of saying thank you in advance for helping us our first day here....*

Two passes. Not just one. Any one of the girls in the secretarial pool would have given a week's wages for the chance to attend the concert. Every important official in the government would be among the audience.

Victoria felt rich. She would not give the extra pass to Mr. Parker, nor to a friend among the secretaries. She looked out across the lobby of the King David Hotel and thought of the brave and foolish Moshe Sachar meeting her this morning. Eli must be desperate!

She smiled and called to a passing messenger. She hastily scribbled a note and slipped the pass into a white envelope with Eli's address on it.

"A shilling if you are back within thirty minutes," she promised the boy. "I will wait here in the lobby for you."

The delicious scents of fresh baked bread and chicken soup with dumplings filled the house. "And apple strudel for dessert," Ida Sachar said, opening the door. The breathless young Armenian boy on the step wore the uniform of a page from the King David Hotel. He bowed briefly and presented the note. He did not withdraw his hand, as it was customary for a tip to be given at both ends of the line.

"She wishes me to wait for a reply," said the boy.

Ida's eyes widened. The message was to Eli. And it was from a *she*? "Eli! Eli! Eli! A message for you from a *she* at the King David Hotel!"

Eli and Moshe descended the stairs together. Both looked strangely pale, but calm. Ida knew this look. *Guilt. The guilt of boys who have been into the cookie jar. The guilt of boys who knew whose ball went through Mrs. Schlemeker's window but would not tell.*

"A message for you, Eli, and *she* wants a reply, whoever *she* is." Ida tapped her foot and watched as Eli opened the note. He frowned, and then his eyebrows practically raised up over his head. Something was up. Moshe clearly knew about it, too. Ah, well. It was time for Eli to notice girls maybe. As long as *she* was a nice Jewish girl from a good family!

"So?" Ida asked.

"It is not signed." Eli handed his mother the strange invitation.

Ida's eyebrows went up and down. "Tonight. A personal invitation from—oy! Is this the wife of old Idela Feldstein's grandnephew? The one she was talking about? The cellist! Oy! Hulda said she thought a messenger had gone to the flat. And now my Eli is invited to the . . ." She paused, puzzled. "*Why?* How does she know *you*?"

Moshe spoke up. "I think he should go, Mama. Maybe the British drew names or something. Yeshiva students. To . . . uh . . . to represent every aspect of Jewish life in the Old City and New." He scratched his chin. "I bet that is it!" He clapped Eli on the back. "Lucky fellow. He should go. It is an honor."

Ida forgot about the guilty look. An honor? Of all the Yeshiva students, her Eli was chosen? *And the bigwigs from England will be there and also those from the Jewish Agency!*

"Yes! He should go." She tipped the messenger. "Yes! Tell them my Eli will attend! Hurry now!" she instructed her son. "You have just time for supper before you go."

———————

From over her music stand, Elisa could see the huge frame of Freddie Frutschy watching the performance from the wings of the stage. Properly dressed in a dark gray uniform and tall, shining black boots, he looked like an enlarged version of the chauffeurs of the British lords and ladies who had flocked to this evening's performance of Mendelssohn's Scottish Symphony.

Unknown to her, Murphy had placed a telephone call to Sir Thomas Beecham, conductor of the London Philharmonic Orchestra. Murphy had managed to prepare the maestro for the fact that the orchestra's newest violinist would be watched over by a toothless giant in a chauffeur's uniform.

Knowing of the cryptic warning and a fraction of Elisa's history, first in Vienna and then in the saving of the former president of Czechoslovakia, Sir Thomas was not the least bit surprised. "Splendid idea," he had declared, as if he had thought of it himself.

And so tonight Murphy once again watched Elisa play from row ten, aisle seat in the Royal Opera House in Covent Garden, just as he had in better days in Vienna. Louis and Charles sat quietly beside him. After the first number, Louis poked Charles and whispered, "I wish Leah was here playing Vitorio." Charles did not answer, but kept his eyes straight ahead. A single tear rolled down his cheek; he brushed it aside fiercely and fixed his gaze on Elisa.

All the while, vigilant Freddie Frutschy stood just offstage and tapped the shiny toe of his enormous new boot to the rhythm of music he had never heard before. *A wonder and a marvel!*

His lumpy face revealed his determination that no one would get within ten feet of the beautiful young Missus Murphy! She smiled at him and nodded slightly when he put his huge hands together to applaud with the same enthusiasm as Murphy and the boys.

When the audience rose to its feet and shouted *Bravo!*, Freddie seconded the shout and tossed his cap into the air. Such a job sure beat tossing stacks of *The Times* into the back of a delivery truck.

The mess hall of the Allenby barracks in Jerusalem had no real stage. Sheets of wood were laid across supports, providing a platform three feet above the concrete floor. Three thousand British soldiers talked and laughed with the steady uproar that always preceded concerts everywhere. Above their heads, the rain drummed on the corrugated tin roof, adding to the noise.

Members of the Woodhead Commission were seated in a section of folding chairs reserved for British officers and the British high commissioner. These civilians were dressed in black dinner jackets as they would have dressed for a concert in London's Royal Opera House.

The sight of them, and that thought, made Leah suddenly homesick for Elisa. She held tightly to Shimon's hand.

"Close your eyes and listen, Shimon," she said. "Where are we?"

Eyes closed, they stood very close to each other. *Once again the audience of the Musikverein waited in red velvet seats. Behind the closed curtain, Leah and Shimon took their places. Rudy Dorbransky swung the bow of his fiddle like a sword as he strutted onto the stage. Elisa . . . dear Elisa, laughed and rolled her eyes as an unspoken message passed between her and Leah. The orchestra tuned up with a cacophony of noise that blended into the clamor of expectant voices in the audience. And then, as the oboe sounded the A, Rudy found the note and everyone suddenly came to attention.* Vienna. The Musikverein. What days those had been! How far they had come to reach this night!

At the sound of thunderous applause, Leah opened her eyes. Stacks of long dining tables lined the walls of the room. Chairs were folded and stacked in rows along the back wall, where an opening showed huge black stoves and racks of tin plates.

Leah looked up at Shimon. His eyes were still closed. *Yes. He saw it. He was there. Vienna.* She squeezed his hand as the British high commissioner climbed onto the makeshift stage and nervously grasped the neck of a microphone. The clamor fell silent except for the still-drumming raindrops on the roof.

The distinguished Englishman spoke, retelling the story of Leah and Shimon's flight from Germany. He had heard the story, he said, in a wire sent from Sir Thomas Beecham, conductor of the London Philharmonic Orchestra. How fortunate Palestine was to have stolen Leah Feldstein from the great orchestras of Europe.

Leah was not listening to the man's empty flattery. He could not know the pain and struggles and endless miracles that had brought Leah and Shimon to this place. For the first time since their arrival, Leah knew somehow that they had come home. She knew that the elegant British official on the stage and the thousands of men crowded on the floor would someday leave Jerusalem, but Leah and Shimon would not leave. They would stand on the shores of a Jewish homeland and wave goodbye to the men who made it so difficult to come here; to the men who welcomed her onto the stage. She prayed silently, asking God to shine through her first performance tonight.

" . . . And so we wish to greet virtuoso cellist Leah Feldstein. We welcome her now to the British Mandate of Palestine and to Jerusalem."

Shimon helped her up to the platform. Victoria stepped forward and handed her the cello. The applause and the rain were one continuous roar.

Victoria watched as Leah crossed the crude stage. Someone had rigged a spotlight and it shone on the bobbed hair of the petite musician. Her hands and face were a bright, animated contrast to the black of her long concert dress. The deep red wood of her instrument seemed alive, radiating with an existence all its own. The wood caught the light and sent it out, then turned in her hands to capture the light again. There was applause and more applause as she bowed slightly, turning toward David Ben-Gurion and Golda Meir and a dozen other proud Jewish faces among the members of the Jewish Agency. And then a slight bow to those men who had come to Palestine as judges—the Woodhead Committee.

This is not a beautiful woman, as men define beauty, Victoria thought as she watched Leah capture the audience with a smile. *But there is an elegance, a poise and confidence about her that is deeply beautiful.*

Victoria glanced up at the face of Shimon. He was smiling and weeping at the same time. He was so proud and so in love. The look in his eyes made Victoria search the crowd again for Eli. He was somewhere among these cheering men. *Somewhere.* She scanned the rows.

Column on column of English faces. Uniforms and civil servants. Very few women among them. She still had not found Eli when the cheering faded to expectancy.

Leah stepped up to the microphone. The drumming of the rain competed with her first words, and then, suddenly, even the rain fell silent as she spoke.

"I have played in all the great concert halls of Europe. But this is my first performance in a mess hall." Much laughter. She smiled. Waited for silence again. "This is also my first performance in my new, yet very old, homeland. And for the first time in my life—" She glanced at Shimon. "In *our* lives, we feel that we are finally home indeed." She paused. Victoria saw the emotion behind her words, and yet Leah was in control. "There is a saying in the Talmud: if a jug falls upon a stone, woe to the jug. And if a stone falls upon a jug, woe to the jug also." A small wave of laughter. "It has been this way for the People of the Book for two thousand years. We have fallen on the stones. The stones of every nation and people have fallen on us. And yet, here is a miracle far greater than any I can think of . . . still we remain. And still we are here. As the prophets have foretold, we return now to Zion from the four corners of the world. And when we are returned, so will our Messiah also return, as it is written: 'To Jerusalem Thy city, return with compassion, and dwell within it as Thou promised: Rebuild it soon in our days—an everlasting structure. . . .' "

The silence was thick in the hall. This message had not been expected! And then Victoria saw Eli. He stood across from her, half obscured by a stack of tables. His eyes were bright, on fire, as he listened to Leah Feldstein.

"The one you call Jesus, the One we call *Messiah*—He will return when the People of the Book come home to Zion! That is written. It is promised. And that is the reason the Darkness fights so hard to keep us out of this, our homeland! And that is why behind us the whole world burns and rages to destroy us!"

She looked directly at the stony faces of those honored gentlemen from London. "It is a miracle, you see, that even one of us has survived to come home. It is proof that God exists and that He does not lie! He has not forgotten His Covenant with Israel. Though men may forget, *God has not forgotten us.*"

She lowered her head for a moment, and Victoria thought perhaps she was praying. The words had stirred something inside Victoria. Leah had somehow interpreted a mystery for her tonight while she awakened a thousand questions. *Who is Light and who is Darkness?*

Leah Feldstein spoke no more with her lips. She backed up and took the chair set in place for her. The men and women were silent. The rains were silent. And Leah Feldstein said again in music what her heart had told them all a moment before.

Dressed in his black suit, Eli felt strangely out of place among the press of British uniforms that surrounded him. He pushed his way slowly through the throng, ignoring the comments that followed him.

"What's the Yid doin' here? Thought this was just for us."

"This is Jerusalem, after all. He must know somebody . . ."

Eli knew Victoria. And for that reason he had come to the concert. He could see the head of Shimon Feldstein over the crowd. Victoria had stood near the big man throughout the performance. Would she still be there? He prayed as he moved closer. Through a small crack in the dam of admirers, he glimpsed the upturned face of Leah Feldstein as she smiled and chatted with David Ben-Gurion. And there, just beyond them, was Victoria in conversation with an elegantly dressed woman. The wife of an Englishman, no doubt. Victoria was smiling, too. Eli stopped for a moment just to watch her. He had never seen her in such a setting—so beautiful, so light and at ease. Life should always be this way for her.

And then she glanced toward him. She had not been looking for him, but her eyes caught his and held him there. The Englishwoman continued to speak, "How wonderful! How wonderful the music was! Oh, my . . . she should be playing in London! And you know her . . . you are her interpreter! Oh, my dear!"

Victoria was not listening any longer, although her head nodded in feigned attention as she touched Eli with a look.

He did not come closer. In this crowd it would not be wise. To hold her in his mind was enough. She smiled at the Englishwoman and then turned toward Eli. The smile was for him.

He mouthed the words *Christ Church,* then nodded. Her smile broadened before someone stepped between them, and the connection was lost.

Hans Schumann smiled to himself as he ascended the steep stairway to Herschel Grynspan's attic room. In his arms he carried a basket of bread and two different kinds of cheese, as well as a bar of Dutch chocolate.

Herschel sat up on his cot and wordlessly watched his friend. The radio played sad French love songs as the rain drummed on the roofs of Paris overhead.

"As I promised," Hans said happily. "I have been to the home of your uncle."

Even this news did not cheer Herschel. "And?"

"He is well. He sends his greetings. He also sends this—" He tossed an envelope to Herschel. It tumbled onto the floorboards face up. Herschel leaned forward and stared at the Polish stamp and postmark. The name *Berta Grynspan* was on the return address. "They are—" Herschel swallowed hard and fought to regain his breath. "In Poland." He picked up the envelope. It had been opened. Herschel looked sharply at Hans. "What does it say?"

Hans shrugged. "I did not read it. Your uncle . . ."

As if the paper were holy, Herschel pulled it gingerly from the torn envelope. He looked up at the high window and the gray patch of sky beyond. He tried to imagine himself in Poland, with his parents and his sister. Tears of longing stung his eyes as he began to read:

Dear Herschel,

By now you must have heard what happened—we have been deported back to Poland. Papa was hurt, and I have been so frightened! On Thursday evening, rumors were circulating that Polish Jews in our city were being expelled, but none of us believed it. At nine o'clock that evening a policeman came to our house to tell us to report to the police station with our passports. When we got to the station, practically the whole neighborhood was already there. Almost immediately we were all taken to the town hall. No one told us what was happening, but we realized this was going to be the end. They shoved an expulsion order into our hands, saying that we had to leave Germany before October 29. We were not allowed to go home, so we have nothing—not a penny. Could you send something to us?

Love from us all,
Berta

Hans had not taken his eyes from the face of Herschel as he read the letter. The young man's olive skin blanched as Hans looked on.

"What is it?" Hans urged. "Are they all right?"

"They . . . want me to send them . . . something. I have nothing to send!" Herschel lay down on his bed and stared at the dark rafters of the attic. "What can I do? Oh, Hans! How can I help them? . . . I cannot. I cannot!"

———

The hands of Ernst vom Rath trembled only slightly as he held the tip of his cigarette to the flame of the match. He should not have been smoking, he knew, but something about these Gestapo men reawakened the old urge . . . *the need* . . . for tobacco.

He inhaled deeply, and then tried to gaze steadily into the face of the Gestapo agent who had called him to Berlin from Paris for the express purpose of investigating the death of agent Georg Wand.

" . . . a tragic loss to the force. Georg was quite effective. Too effective, some said." The man rubbed his bald head and smiled gently. "Perhaps it was his effectiveness that got him killed, eh?"

Ernst shrugged. He flicked the ash of his cigarette with practiced nonchalance. "This business of espionage is far beyond me, Herr Vargen." Did his nervousness show? Inside, he seethed with anger toward Thomas von Kleistmann. Why had Thomas not been content to slip away in the night? Why had he killed Georg Wand and left Ernst alone to answer these questions?

"Espionage, beyond you?" Leo Vargen laced the question with amusement. He studied Ernst and waited for him to react. Was he frightened? Did he have something to hide?

"In the embassy we call it by another name. *Politics*." Ernst played the game well.

Vargen did not accept the lightness of his tone. "But you and Thomas von Kleistmann were friends."

"Acquaintances. Two single German men in the Paris Embassy. We had an occasional drink."

"How is it that you did not know he was against the Führer?" Vargen bore down.

"He never told me," Ernst shrugged.

Incredulous, Vargen's eyes widened in disbelief. "Are you saying that he never expressed his feelings about our Führer and the goals of the Reich?"

"Why should he tell me? Would *you* tell someone if you were a traitor, Herr Vargen?" Ernst inhaled again. The cigarette helped. He was doing well.

Vargen tried a different approach to the inner workings of the young aristocratic diplomat. "Who do you think might have let him out of his quarters that night? Who among the embassy staff?"

"Thomas had a way with women. Have you interrogated the French maid?"

"She was not working that night."

Ernst smiled a knowing smile. "What has that got to do with it?"

Vargen would not be pulled from the scent. "We are almost certain that a member of the German staff unlocked the door."

Ernst no longer trembled. "I still say that the guard did not lock it in the first place. Those of us who remained in the dining room would have noticed if anyone had sneaked up to let him out." Ernst played the role of one who was also curious about the miraculous escape of Thomas. He was almost enjoying himself now. *Almost*.

"Friedrich Wanger expressed the thought that you might have let the prisoner go free." A direct assault.

Ernst deflected the blow with a laugh. "The French maid is still a better guess than that!" He leaned forward. "Believe me, Herr Vargen, had I known what von Kleistmann was up to, I would have killed him myself."

Vargen's eyebrows raised in a sort of satisfaction. "Ah. Yes." He rubbed his bald pate again and took a step toward the door. "Come on, then," he said lightly.

Was the interview over? Ernst rose from his chair and followed. He snubbed out his cigarette in the ashtray as Vargen crossed the foyer, and then jerked his head toward the stairs that led to the basement offices and storerooms below the Ministry of Information.

Ernst grinned quizzically as the two men descended the steps in silence. Vargen closed the door firmly behind them and then walked quickly down a long corridor with unoccupied rooms on either side.

"You espionage types," Ernst quipped, wishing he had another cigarette. "I did not even know there was such a maze down here. What is—"

Vargen was smiling broadly now, enjoying his own game. His look stopped Ernst mid-sentence. The weight of foreboding washed over him. Vargen unlocked a steel door and opened it slowly before he switched on the light.

The scene before him made Ernst gasp and choke back the bile that rose in his throat. The room was spattered with blood. On the concrete floor, the body of a man lay stretched out on two wooden planks fastened together like a cross. Railroad spikes protruded from his hands and feet. The face was battered beyond recognition, but Ernst knew instantly who it was.

"Thomas—?" He felt the chamber spin around him.

Vargen had an almost cheerful look. He kicked the steel door shut, and Thomas turned his head toward the two men. *He was still alive!*

"We caught him in Holland. Boarding a ship to England. Thought he would escape, no doubt. Traitor. Convicted, sentenced, and duly executed."

Ernst felt his stomach churn. He could not lean against the wall. *The blood . . .* He must not faint. *What had Thomas told them? He must not have told them everything. How could a man endure this and not beg to tell all?*

Ernst looked in horror on the smiling face of the Gestapo executioner. "Then *why* have you not . . . *executed* him? For the mercy of God, why *this*?"

"You politicians," Vargen laughed. "You like things clean." He shrugged. He walked over to Thomas and placed the toe of his boot on the head of the spike in his hand. "He is not dead because he has not told us what we want to know."

Thomas coughed, cried out in agony. "Nothing . . . to . . . tell. *God!* Let me die."

Ernst turned away and retched on the floor. "Kill him," he breathed. "Please. Get it over with. *Kill him!*"

Ernst did not look at Thomas, but everywhere he looked was proof of his friend's courage.

Vargen pulled his Luger from its holster and extended it to Ernst. "But Herr vom Rath, you said you would have killed him yourself . . ." Vargen shook his head in amusement. These diplomats could talk, but when it came to the actual matter of one's duty, they were less capable than a woman. "*Well?*"

Ernst stared at the pistol. Thomas groaned. "I cannot—" Ernst gasped. "Cannot kill . . ."

"Ah, well." Vargen was still smiling. "He will die eventually anyway . . ." He started to put away the gun. "Perhaps before I leave for Palestine tomorrow, or after you return to Paris?"

"*Please!*" Thomas moaned. "*For God's sake . . .*"

Ernst snatched the weapon from the hand of the Gestapo agent. Sweat poured from his brow, nearly blinding him. He took a step toward Thomas. His hands trembled until he feared that he would drop the gun.

Thomas gazed at him pleadingly, forgiving him for what he must now do.

Vargen looked on with the satisfaction of the master of the Hunt. He was always pleased to blood a young hound for the sake of the Reich.

He continued to smile even as the shots rang out. Four of them. One after another.

18

Beg, Buy, or Steal

Göring studied the proposal presented by the British ambassador. He immediately called the Chancellery to speak with Hitler. Now he was sorry he had done so.

Hitler's invitation to Hermann Göring to join him at the Chancellery for an evening meal was more an order than a request.

Göring hung up the telephone and scowled at his servant. "So. I am to have dinner at the Merry Chancellor's Restaurant," he quipped dryly. "To tell you the truth, the food there is too rotten for my taste. And then, those party dullards from Munich! Unbearable!" Göring patted the broad expanse of his belly. "Tell the cook to have my meal prepared beforehand. I will eat here before I go to dinner at the Chancellery."

After a dinner of veal topped with asparagus and washed down with a fine white wine, Göring felt that perhaps he could face the Führer's simple vegetarian fare and mineral water.

The Führer said nothing of his purpose to Göring as he led an entourage of thirty guests into the large dining room, forty feet square. In the center was a large round table ringed by fifteen simple chairs with dark red leather seats. Here the most honored guests were seated with Hitler. There were four smaller tables in each corner of the room for the less important sycophants and toadies of the Führer's intimate group.

Göring faced three glass doors that led out into the garden. Trees were leafless and desolate in the autumn twilight of Berlin. In spite of Hitler's great diplomatic triumphs over Great Britain and France in Munich, he was as moody as the weather these days.

"I did not listen to my Voice," he was telling his astrologer, who sat to his left. "You see, we might have had all of Czechoslovakia if only I had heeded the whisper of the Voice. Instead, I listened to statesmen and generals . . ." He inclined his head to Göring, for Göring had not been among the army staff who had urged the Führer to over-caution in the matter of Czechoslovakia.

The astrologer, a thin, pale man with a fringe of gray hair like a laurel crown around his head, seemed quite sympathetic. "It is not too late for that, perhaps, mein Führer. We will consult the charts in the matter of what remains of Czechoslovakia. Call in your medium, and we will pursue the question."

Hitler raised a finger. "But not tonight." Again he looked at Göring. "I have pressing business after dinner."

Göring pretended to eat the same poor meal that Hitler ate—meatless, tasteless dishes with cabbage soup. This sort of simplicity gained Hitler respect among the folk of the Reich. Plain china plates. Plain, smoothly plastered walls painted ivory. The seeming austerity of Hitler's Merry Restaurant, as he called his dining room, was an example of his own modesty.

Within this setting, the gaudy uniform of Göring seemed more tasteless than the vegetarian main dish. Hitler, however, did not resent Göring's outlandish uniform or ostentatious lifestyle. When the meal was finished Göring alone accompanied the Führer through yet another set of glass doors, through a salon, and back into a living room that was about a thousand square feet in area. In this room nothing about the furnishings was austere. A fireplace illuminated the beamed ceiling with dancing shadows. Wood wainscoting circled the room filled with leather furniture and marble tables.

The medals across the broad expanse of Reichsführer Hermann Göring's uniform glistened when he walked into the Führer's private quarters at the Chancellery. His flabby cheeks were red with the rouge he applied to his waxy skin. His face was ecstatic with the news he brought to Hitler today—almost as bright as Hitler's look was dark.

"We have had an interesting question posed to us from British Ambassador Henderson, mein Führer," Göring began.

Hitler glared at him. "Well?"

"It involves a sale of sorts of the Jews . . . modified slightly from what we discussed earlier. It may well be a benefit to the Reich economy."

Hitler nodded. "I am aware of this plan. Composed by Theo Lindheim in London and presented to the British government by the Jewwarmonger Weizmann."

Göring was startled by this detail. He had not known. He had heard only that the plan had been discussed by Chamberlain's cabinet as a humanitarian possibility for relief of the Jewish problem. "Theo? *Lindheim?*"

"Close your mouth, Hermann!" Hitler snapped. "The man was al-

ways clever. You cannot expect him to be otherwise until he is dead."
Hitler gazed thoughtfully at the eagle on the mantel of his fireplace.
"But that is only a matter of time."

Göring became apologetic. How could he have thought the plan to
export German products in exchange for Jewish lives was a good one?
How could he have been so foolish to assume that this plan might
work? His face was flushed in earnest by the time he finished.

"It is a good idea," Hitler replied. "If Satan himself appears at my
bed with a plan to benefit the German people, I listen. Perhaps as we
turn up the flame on the Jews, we should also reconsider how we
might profit from their pain and cause the other nations of the world
to suffer as well." He stood and warmed his hands by the fire. "Tell
Foreign Secretary von Ribbentrop to refuse all approaches of the British
in this matter. And then *you* negotiate privately with them, Hermann.
Your own little arrangement, as it were. We cannot allow the English
to think that they have any power over us in the matter of trade or our
treatment of Jews, can we? *No!* And so I delegate this to you!"

The lamps of Hermann Göring's vast Karinhall estate were all
dimmed, except for the one that burned on his desk.

His field marshal's uniform was slung carelessly over the back of
an oversized leather armchair. Like the uniform and the mansion, the
furnishings had been specially constructed so that the bulk of Göring
could sit anywhere comfortably.

Tonight he worked on some solution to this Jewish economic problem, as Hitler had instructed him. As supreme head of the Ministry of
Economy and commissioner of the Four-Year Plan for making Germany
independent from other countries, the Jewish element suddenly added
another dimension to the unsteady situation. Simply confiscating the
personal belongings and assets of the Jews had not paid off over the
years, as he had originally expected. The Reichsbank had benefited in
only a small way compared to the loss of trade experienced from foreign boycotts of German goods.

How strange it seemed that it was Theo Lindheim who had conceived the plan—Theo, who had lost everything he had in Germany,
and then had almost lost his life in the bargain.

Göring lifted his massive head from the pool of light and stared at
the wall of bookshelves that held the rare books once owned by Theo.
Göring had saved them from the Nazi book burnings, not because he
was as well-read as Theo, but because they had value. Economic value.
One day, when this fanatical reaction against literature had burned
itself out, no doubt Theo's first editions would be worth even more.
This was also the case with the Lindheim collection of Monet paintings
that now graced the bedroom of Göring's wife. *Decadent art,* the Führer

called it. But Göring himself had chosen it; it would certainly appreciate in value when things settled down again in Germany.

He yawned and rubbed the back of his neck with weariness. A slight smile crossed his lips. He owed a lot to Theo Lindheim. Books. Art. A few pieces of Louis XIV furniture, and . . . the piano in the ballroom. The Jew had been an excellent judge of value. A shrewd and clever businessman indeed. Göring almost liked him. At least he respected him for his financial judgments and his ability as a pilot.

Göring groaned slightly as he lifted his bulk from the desk chair and walked in his stocking feet toward the green leather sofa where he collapsed. His blue eyes were red-rimmed with exhaustion. He stared at the books, then glanced at the light that glinted on the medals of his uniform. He remembered the words of his Führer, and whispered a dark prayer in hopes of an answer to this economic problem—an answer that would give him praise from his master and another Reich medal. "Satan himself . . . by my bed . . ." he murmured. His words drifted off and his heavy eyelids closed of their own will.

The vision came clearly to Hermann Göring. Outside in the starlit night he could hear the hounds of Germany baying in the depths of the great forest. The hunt was on.

He opened his eyes and a swirl of sound and color filled the room. He had seen these colors somewhere . . . somewhere. Trying to focus his eyes, he looked toward his uniform. It was splattered with the red blood of a stag. Behind it he saw the shrouded image of the painting of the German god Wotan that hung in Hitler's quarters. The colors emanated; the howl of the hounds sounded from this canvas, from within its brushstrokes. The eyes of Wotan were the eyes of Adolf Hitler. Göring tried to comment on the remarkable likeness, the beauty of the color and the excitement of the sounds of the hunt, but his voice failed him.

The lips of the image moved. The painting spoke. "Hermann . . ." The eyes of the German god turned to him. He was ashamed he was not wearing his uniform. But then he remembered the blood. "Hermann," the voice called again, and Göring was filled with amazement—the voice of the god was that of the Führer!

He opened his mouth. His voice returned to answer the apparition as yet another burst of red pulsed from the undulating canvas. "Yes! mein Führer!" Göring sat up, leaving his sleeping form on the sofa. He turned to see the fat, middle-aged man and then looked at himself. Slim. Young again. He wore the green uniform of a Jäger, a huntsman. He smiled, and the eyes of the god seemed pleased.

"Go to the window," the god ordered.

Göring obeyed. Outside on the lawn a bonfire of pine branches burned brightly. A row of dead stags lay on the grass nearby. A man dressed in the green of the head forester stepped from the shadows

*into the light of the bonfire. He held up a slip of paper and began to
read the names of the hunters and the names of the fallen.*

*"Shot through the heart by Field Marshal Hermann Göring ... Theo
Lindheim." The man swept a hand toward the stag, but the animal had
taken on a different form. Before the startled eyes of Göring, the stag
transformed into the body of Theo Lindheim. There was only a moment
to marvel as the death of the stag was sounded on the horns of invisible
Jägers. With a sweep of the hand, the forester caught the flame of the
fire and threw it onto the dead body. The brightness of that fire outshone
all others. Göring looked down at his chest; the medals on his uniform
sparkled like new jewels in the light.*

*He clapped his hands together in delight and turned to show the
god what he had done. The colors swirled around him, embracing him
with warmth. "Well done," the Führer said.*

Göring raised his hand to salute. His mouth formed the words *Heil
Hitler!* and in that instant he was once again on the sofa, once more
trapped inside the heavy body of the middle-aged field marshal.

Hermann Göring opened his eyes, expecting to see the painting. It
was gone. The colors were gone. The face of the German god was not
there. No light shown in through the window.

Göring inhaled deeply and sat up. There was no blood on his uniform. His medals were still metal. The air was not filled with the sound
of horns or baying hounds. Yet one thing seemed clear in his mind:
the broken body of Theo Lindheim consumed with the flame of the
bonfire.

————

True to her promise, Victoria Hassan was waiting in the lobby of
the King David Hotel when Leah and Shimon stepped off the elevator
at 8 A.M. According to her instructions, they left their luggage in the
room to be retrieved later in the day by the porter. The cello was locked
in the hotel vault with the assurance that even if the place was blown
up, the instrument would be safe from harm.

This was to be a trip of exploration—which buses to take where,
how much to pay for what. Never, never must Leah look directly into
the eyes of a man in the Old City! Nor should she smile or giggle or
allow too-familiar conversation. A stern look and a sharp tongue was
the safest policy when shopping the Old City souks. That is, of course,
unless Shimon was also along. Then Leah could be pleasant and no
one would dare bother her.

Leah felt a sense of magic as the bus arrived just outside Jaffa Gate.
The towering walls reflected the morning light in a hundred variegated
shades of pink and rust and cream.

Everywhere children seemed to be waiting for the arrival of the
tourists, with feet bare and clothes ragged even in the cooling of au-

tumn. The children were beggars by profession, Victoria explained. They were astute business people, and could spot a kind face like that of Shimon before the bus even stopped. "You will have to look angry and tell them you are German. Then they will leave you alone."

This proved impossible for Shimon as dirty hands reached up to him, and so Victoria clapped her hands at the troop and told them this fellow was a very mean German whom they must not trouble. In an instant they were gone, crowding around a less wary British pilgrim who stood in the center of the mob looking very unhappy.

Victoria leaned in close. "The children are fed, you know. You must not worry. There are soup kitchens and medical clinics now." She pointed to the bell tower of the church just beyond the square. "Christ Church," she said simply, as if that explained everything.

During the next two hours, Victoria walked between them, showing them her city as only a native could. "Here you may buy orange juice. *Mitz tapuzim*. The vendor will squeeze it before your eyes. It is wise to bring your own cup. And there you may find boiled eggs and *ka'ak*, like a roll. Ask for *za'atar*, which is a salt and cumin mixture. A very cheap breakfast, and you will be respected in the Old City for knowing what to ask for!" She nudged them. "You have not had breakfast. I had mine already this morning. Go on . . . this is a good time to learn!"

Munching the *ka'ak*, which tasted suspiciously like a bagel, Leah and Shimon followed her through the teeming souk of el-Dabbagha, past the Church of the Holy Sepulcher and through the Triple Bazaar where everything needed for existence in the Old City was sold.

Within the crowded souks and vaulted bazaars of the Old City, a flood of humanity threatened to overflow the narrow boundaries of shops and stalls. Like rivulets, the tiny alleyways emptied their human current into side streets, which then poured men of every nation into the teeming bay of the marketplace.

Wide-eyed, Leah clung to Victoria's hand in front and Shimon's hand behind as they wove through the traffic like little ships maneuvering through a great port. She bumped into a Copt priest. Jumping back with an apology, she stepped on the toes of a giant Armenian priest, who glared at her from beneath the pointed hood of his cowl. Arab porters groaned beneath the burdens on their backs, like the little donkeys who seemed to carry their own weight of the merchandise that filled the shops. Rolled carpets extended fore and aft of one heavily laden animal. Sheepskins were piled high atop another. Bolts of bright cloth were stacked onto the back of one donkey, who seemed to disappear beneath the load.

Within the open booths that lined each street, Muslim merchants sold Christian crucifixes alongside Jewish menorahs. There were whole streets crammed with brass candlesticks and urns and ashtrays. Other streets had olive-wood carvings packed on every shelf, and each member of the Holy Family was said to be carved in genuine olive wood from the Garden of Gethsemane. Leah made a mental note that they must visit Gethsemane to see if there were any olive trees remaining after such a harvest of timber!

There were Bibles for every language and every sect, covered in carved mother-of-pearl. Leah considered this merchandise to be the one great treasure in the Old City souks. Stacked up like all the other wares and hawked and bargained over like so much cabbage, the Bibles, nonetheless, contained precious treasures between the carved mother-of-pearl covers.

As Victoria looked on with benevolent patience, Leah purchased a Bible printed in the beautiful fluid script of Arabic. She bargained for it herself, without the assistance of Victoria, and when she asked Victoria's opinion of how she had done, their lovely guide informed her that she had paid twice too much, but she would learn.

Leah slipped the purchase into her pocket and determined that she would give it to Victoria as a thank you on another day—perhaps when Victoria was not thinking of the price Leah had paid.

The beggars were everywhere, the spidery-legged children whom Victoria promised were actually well fed. Large, liquid brown eyes stared up at them. Hands reached out to these wealthy-looking European "tourists," and all the while Victoria warned that Leah must not pay attention to them; must not give them anything.

"Please, lady! Hey, lady! Something. Just a little change!"

At last, Leah removed her newly purchased Bible from her pocket and placed it into the hand of a ragged little boy whose right arm was just a stub protruding from his torn shirt. He looked up at her as if she were crazy. *A Christian Bible?* He could not eat it. He could not read it. The souks were overflowing with such merchandise.

Leah took his dirty face in her hands. His black eyes considered her with puzzlement. "It is the prettiest one," she said, sorry now that she had nothing else to give him. "You can sell it after you read it if you like."

"I cannot read, lady."

"Then sell it today, and remember the Word of God has fed you. I wish I had something else for you."

The boy's face brightened. Yes, he would sell the Bible. Eventually someone would buy it from him, and he would earn in one moment what it took an entire day to make in begging.

"Thank you, lady!" he cried as he ran off to join his sobered friends. Their looks at Leah betrayed their new conviction that maybe she was not so rich, after all.

Victoria looked at her disapprovingly. "Why did you do that? His father probably sells Bibles in the souks."

Shimon squeezed her hand and winked with relief. He had been wanting to do something like that all morning long.

"I will buy another Bible sometime and will not pay twice the price," Leah said brightly. "And I will pray that he sells it for twice what I paid for it."

Victoria walked on. "Be careful. He might sell it back to you!"

Leah knew she looked foolish in Victoria'a eyes, but it didn't matter. The truth was evident within the walls of the Old City that poverty and want pervaded Jerusalem. This place, which drew the hearts and love of people from all nations, was also harsh and brutal to her own citizens. Even the faces of the children seemed old, hungry, and desperate.

Leah looked over the undulating human current and suddenly knew why Jesus had wept over Jerusalem. She watched the little beggar run up to an English soldier and hold up the Bible for sale. The soldier brushed the boy aside, and for a moment Leah thought she might weep as well. She silently prayed that one day she and Shimon might be able to offer these little ones bread in the name of the Lord, and that then the children might beg for the bread of God's Word. She looked up into Shimon's pained face. He felt it, too. They could not speak of it in front of Victoria, who seemed not to see, but Leah loved Shimon for the wordless depth of his compassion. Their souls and the desires of their hearts were one.

She tugged on Shimon's arm and he bent for her to whisper, "I love you."

He smiled and nodded as they pressed on after Victoria.

"Now will we go to the Jewish Quarter?" Leah asked, her head spinning from the sights and smells of the Old City Christian Quarter.

Victoria's smile faded. "I cannot take you there. I am an Arab. A Muslim. The Christian Quarter is a sort of neutral ground for us these days. I can walk with you here. Show you the shops, greet the merchants. But a Muslim woman cannot go into the Jewish Quarter, and you will not be safe in my neighborhood at any time either." She frowned. "Not in these times."

Shimon and Leah exchanged glances. They had just lost their guide, it seemed. And the rules of the Old City still seemed obscure to both of them. They had seen every Christian vegetable merchant and every shoemaker's store with the help of Victoria's mastery of Arabic. But now they were to be cut adrift in the land of beggars and unscrupulous merchants who expected that anyone sensible should know how to dicker over prices. The unwary, on the other hand, deserved to be cheated.

"Well, then," Leah extended her hand in farewell. "Does this mean I cannot invite you home for tea?"

"It means I will take you to Christ Church and Reverend Robbins will guide you the rest of the journey home." Her eyes were apologetic.

"And I will meet you for tea sometime outside these walls. Perhaps at the King David."

"Tomorrow, if you like." Leah tried to press a coin into her hand. "When I fetch my cello? Four o'clock?"

Victoria recoiled from the attempted payment. The concert last night had been payment enough and then some. "A cup of tea with you would be an honor. But tomorrow is Friday—our day of worship. Next Tuesday, perhaps?" The young woman looked momentarily distant and thoughtful. "I spoke with Reverend Robbins about you last night. You are expected."

Leah sensed that she had somehow insulted Victoria in a way she could not understand. Victoria's warm personality cooled noticeably as she cut across Omar Square and led the way down the Armenian Patriarchate Road toward Christ Church. Her conversation was less than friendly, almost terse.

She entered the iron gates of Christ Church like one who had been there before. Greeting the British pastor with a proper, yet preoccupied, hello, she did not meet his gaze when she introduced her charges and passed them into his care. And when conversation turned to the concert of the night before, Victoria slipped away without another word.

19

Strangers in Paradise

There were beggars here, too, in the Jewish Quarter of the Old City. But the beggars were not children. Here and there, old men sat shaded by an alcove as they put their cups out in hope of reward from Leah and Shimon. "A blessing for a coin," called one feeble old man from his street corner.

Children ran everywhere, playing in the lanes. Yarmulkes perched atop shaved heads, and earlocks bobbed as they called out to one another in Yiddish. These children had shoes, at least.

Leah looked up to the arch of the great Hurva Synagogue. Although the residences of the Jewish Quarter were mostly poor and shabby, the synagogues were mighty reflections of the synagogues of Europe. The cupola of this temple had been donated by the Emperor Franz Josef of Austria. Two blocks beyond, an entire complex had been built with money donated by the Jewish citizens of Warsaw. Indeed, Leah thought as she laid eyes on her new neighborhood for the first time, the faces that peered out at them from the shops and houses were faces she had seen a thousand times before. In Vienna. In Prague. In Warsaw. Some small fragment of the broken Jewish homeland had always remained here in Jerusalem in the shadow of the Western Wall.

The lack of even the barest luxuries within the tiny shoe box apartments did not seem to be a matter of personal concern. As long as their houses of worship reflected the glory of God and Zion, then what did it matter if water must be fetched from a cistern? Who was concerned if the toilets were down the stairs and to the right behind the building? Tenacious poverty was a way of life.

Knowledge of the Torah was the only wealth here. The young faces of children and the ancient faces of the learned rabbis who taught them . . . this beauty Leah saw as they entered the Quarter.

Most streets were unpaved. Squealing with delight, a dozen small boys dashed through the puddles, then stopped to stare at Shimon and Leah as they trailed after the resolute Reverend Robbins. Dressed in their New York clothing, the couple looked as if they had dropped in from another century.

Childish whispers followed them. Their high, urgent voices found Leah's ears and made her smile at the excitement their arrival seemed to be causing. Wide Orthodox eyes followed their progress down the street toward Tipat Chalev, and then the tide of children turned to follow after at a safe distance. There had been rumors that the great-nephew of the recently deceased Idela Feldstein would be coming to claim his inheritance—such as it was. Perhaps he would sublet the flat and then leave. The thought was intriguing. Two members of the black-coated coterie peeled off to find their mothers.

"They do not look like us . . ."

"Are they goyim, you think? Maybe Mrs. Feldstein's great-nephew from Europe is one of them! Oy! You think they'll stay here?"

"Mama says people in Europe do not even keep a kosher kitchen, let alone believe in the Eternal! Look at the big man. A goy, surely. He does not even have a beard!"

At this, Shimon self-consciously put a hand to his cheek. He wished he had not shaved. Leah looked at him in mock dismay. He would have to grow it back, and she liked his kisses so much better without the whiskers.

Two mothers, guided by the hands of their determined children, emerged from a side street. Heads were covered in scarves. Their dresses were as plain and drab as the coats of their tiny future rabbis. Shimon tugged his sleeve in a signal that none of the clothes Elisa and Leah had purchased at Macy's were made for the streets of the Jewish Quarter.

"We might as well leave our bags at the King David," Leah said quietly to Shimon as she smiled and nodded back at the unsmiling eyes and suspicious faces that studied her openly.

"Shiksa," hissed one woman to another. "Shaygets."

"If Idela Feldstein were alive to see this, it would kill her!"

"A goy for a great-nephew! Oy gevalt!"

"Such nerve. They bring their priest with them."

"Maybe they will sublet Idela's flat, nu? Poor Hayim and Judith are living with her parents. Maybe these goyim relations of Idela Feldstein's will sublet the flat to them, nu? Go get the rabbi. He can ask them. They probably do not even speak mama-loshen, the mother tongue."

Reverend Robbins turned one last corner and then stopped before a white house that stood like an upturned rectangle listing slightly to the left. He smiled good-naturedly. "This is it."

The Orthodox chorus stood a few yards away, waiting for the re-

action of these Jews who were not Jewish at all. Leah drew in a deep
breath. Rickety stairs led up from a mud puddle to a door covered with
peeling white paint. Two windows looked down on the unpaved lane
where the crowd grew by the minute. There were bars on the windows,
giving the stark little place the feeling of a jail—a very small and impoverished jail, at that.

The pastor pushed his canvas hat back on his head a bit. He lowered his voice. "Victoria told me the address. Last night I advised her
you might not want to bring your luggage until you saw it. Perhaps we
should hire a porter in the souk to help you carry away the things you
had sent from Vienna."

The eyes of the audience bored into Leah's back. Shimon had singled out two husky, apple-cheeked youngsters and was grinning at
them—to no avail. Dark and solemn looks were returned. Shimon preferred the Arab beggars to this.

The shutters of the downstairs flat opened a bit, then flew open
with a crash. A thick-featured woman of about fifty, wearing a polka-
dot scarf to frame her leathery face, scowled at the newcomers. "Oy,"
she said under her breath. "If Idela were alive this would kill her." She
rubbed her cheek, looked at the crowd behind the three newcomers
and shrugged. *What can you do? He doesn't even have a beard like a
man,* the shrug seemed to say. She disappeared from the window and
then reappeared a second later at the door. On her arm she carried an
iron ring with a single key on it.

"You must be the great-nephew of Idela Feldstein, God rest her
soul."

"Omaine," said a voice behind Leah. "And may she not be spinning
now."

The woman with the key pronounced her name. "I am Shoshanna
Reingolt. Downstairs' neighbor to Idela Feldstein for twenty years." The
woman's eyes widened and then narrowed as she scanned Leah's
plum-colored dress and matching shoes. "Idela told me you were coming." She shook her head as if she could not believe it. "She told me
when you came you should have the flat. She had a little money, but
that was gone with the funeral, and so . . ." She pushed past them and
started up the creaking stairs.

Leah looked pleadingly at the kind Reverend Robbins, but he whispered, "You're in enough trouble already without inviting a Christian
pastor up for tea. I'll wait here. Keep the party lively."

Shimon eyed the crazily leaning steps and tested the banister. It
wobbled. He wondered if it would hold his weight.

"Well, come on!" snorted the unamused Shoshanna as she inserted
the key and leaned against the door until it opened with a reluctant
groan.

Leah and Shimon smiled in a frozen, fearful sort of way as they climbed the stairs and entered the dark and musty little space. Leah stepped in a puddle of water just inside the door. Shimon blinked as a drop hit his face. Together, in one unified motion, they looked up at a ceiling stained from water leaks.

"Well, you'll have to fix that!" snapped Shoshanna. "But there is a primus stove for cooking. A bed for sleeping." She reconsidered the last comment as she compared Shimon's size to the narrow iron cot against the wall. "You can take turns sleeping, anyway," she sniffed. "And a rocking chair." She pointed to a small wooden rocking chair beside the barred window.

Leah eyed the rocker—one small luxury in this room, which was more like a cell than an apartment. "How lovely," she remarked, noting the deep patina of the wood. "It is a very fine rocking chair."

"Yes," barked Shoshanna. "I found your great-aunt right in that very chair. Sitting frozen in death. She was staring out the window. Oy, what a shock! A woman of her health to die like that!"

"Ah . . ." Leah quickly looked away from the chair. *Relief!* There were the shipping crates they had sent from Vienna! Some spark of elegance and beauty! The weight of disappointment was lessened a tiny bit by those friendly boxes. Elisa had helped her pack them in the days before the Nazis had come. How perfect life had been then! *Oh, God!* Leah prayed her unhappiness did not show on her face. All her emotion and every brave word she had uttered last night now seemed to mock her.

"Well, are you staying?" demanded the woman. "Or subletting? There is a line of people who would take a nice apartment like this, you know."

Shimon stepped forward and took the key. "We are staying," he said firmly. There was no chance for Leah to protest. "At least for now." He bowed slightly at the waist. "My great-aunt wrote to me of your kindness to her." Shimon was smiling—a miraculous smile! Did he not see the hovel they had come to? No! He was winning this horrid, iron-eyed woman over with lies about how kind she had been!

Leah turned away and stared at the box containing her china. They had china plates, but there was no table to set.

"We had to sell a few things to pay her debts. The table. It was quite nice. It sold quickly . . ."

Leah squeezed her eyes shut tight at the words. A bed for one. A kerosene stove and a rocker. *The very rocker . . .* She felt the room spin around her. "Shimon . . ." She reached out for his hand. "I . . . am . . . I feel . . ."

There was a flurry of activity around her. Shoshanna's voice expressed dismay. "Gottenyu! Sit down in the chair!"

"No," Leah breathed, as she groped for the bed. Helped by Shimon, she lay down on the groaning cot and closed her eyes as she fought to control a wave of nausea. The harsh voice of Shoshanna became instantly sympathetic. "I'll make tea," she promised, patting Leah's hand. "You're expecting, maybe? Such a pale little thing. I'll tell them you are staying."

Shafts of dusty light beamed down through the high windows of the Yeshiva school classroom where Eli studied with forty other students. He sat on the end of a long bench shared by a dozen young men. Books and papers were piled high on desktops. Bookshelves rose twelve feet high on every wall of the room where Rabbi Shlomo Lebowitz led the discussion, which was of great interest to each student.

"Marriage!" declared the old man as he paced across the front of the classroom. "Who has the reference that is reflected in the Jewish wedding ceremony?"

A forest of hands sprouted up. Eli did not raise his hand. The subject made him uncomfortable, unhappy.

"Yes, Yagil!" The rabbi paused as a beam of light fell on his face like a spotlight.

Yagil, with his stooped shoulders and eyes that looked in different directions through thick spectacles, seemed the least likely to speak of marriage, but he rose to his feet. His smile blinked on and off through his straggly beard. He began to quote the law. " 'No man without a wife. Neither a woman without a husband. Nor both of them without God.' Genesis Rabbah 8:9." He was pleased with himself. He had said it correctly. Even a fellow as odd-looking as Yagil must have a wife. And somewhere there must be an odd-looking woman who would love to stand with him beneath the chuppa! Perhaps one day Yagil would be a father of a flock of little Yagils with eyes looking this way and that. As long as it was a *proper Jewish ceremony*!

Eli found himself feeling ill. He thought about Victoria. He knew what the Law said about marriage. This reminder frightened him for their future.

"Very good, Yagil," intoned Rebbe Lebowitz. "Now sit." Yagil obeyed, shrinking back to his position behind his books. "It is easier for us to prepare for a wedding ceremony than it is for us to prepare for marriage, nu?" The rabbi paused as the weight of this penetrated the minds of the students. "What is the basis for a sanctified relationship in accordance with the Law of Moses?"

Again hands shot up. "Emile, please."

Emile, big and hairy, with a frame like an ox, stood and began to speak in his surprisingly high voice. "This is a union between a man and a woman where the precepts of the Lord are fulfilled and where the children will be raised in the atmosphere of religious faith. Marriage is not merely a legal bond. Or a bond for the gratification of physical desire or emotional. . . ."

Eli could not hear the rest of the recitation. He knew the answers. In an examination about marriage he would not miss even one. In a mixed marriage, the foundations of a Jewish marriage were absent. He knew this. The awareness of it kept him awake each night. It followed him into the Yeshiva and plagued his every waking thought. There were deeper matters that he had not even shared with Victoria when he spoke to her of marriage. He longed to be outside right now. He looked at the swirling flecks of dust in the light and wished that he could be caught up and swept out the window of the room.

The harsh voice of Rabbi Lebowitz interrupted his thoughts. "Eli! Eli Sachar! Are you dreaming?"

"Huh?"

"Would you answer the question for us?"

"Am I dreaming? I . . . uh . . ."

"No. The question regarding marriages that are forbidden to you as a kohen."

The question was like a slap in the face. The eyes of every man in the room were on him. He drew in a ragged breath. He began, "By Torah law . . ."

"Reference?"

"Leviticus 21:6–7."

"Correct. Not bad for a sleeping man. Continue."

" . . . a kohen is forbidden to marry a divorced woman."

"Go on."

"One who is known to be promiscuous . . ."

"Yes, yes."

"A proselyte . . ." Eli swallowed hard.

"There! Nu! You see how very narrow the way must be for you!" The rabbi swept a gnarled hand over the group, but Eli felt he had pointed only at him. "You may not marry a woman who converts. And who will answer why that must be?"

Eli sank down into his seat. He did not hear the rest of the day's lesson and discussion. At the end of class when Rebbe Lebowitz asked him if he was feeling ill, Eli answered that he had not felt well in days. This seemed to satisfy Rebbe Lebowitz, who wished him a speedy recovery. But Eli knew he would never recover from his heart sickness. There was no answer to this dilemma. Victoria could convert, but Eli would never be a rabbi if he married her. He would not tell her, lest she turn from him and think she did him a kindness. His heart had made his choice for him. But he simply could not think what to do next.

Victoria did not know what drew her through the gates of the Haram into the courtyard of the Dome of the Rock. She had simply come. Like a child searching for a lost toy, she had come here to the perfect octagon of the shrine. She paused in her steps and looked up at the turquoise, greens, and golds of the tile-encrusted facade.

Above the south entrance to the Dome, *God, the Eternal* could be read in the mosaic. In the shadows beneath the arch, the words of the prophet were gracefully inscribed: *He who clings to this life will lose the next one . . .*

She gazed over the vast and empty place where thousands of the faithful came each week to bow and worship toward Mecca. Strange how very empty it seemed. Devoid of the shouts and exhortations of the Mufti; devoid of the faithful followers, the place also seemed devoid of God. She did not move forward, but lingered at the gate, lost in her thoughts. This site, the jewel of Jerusalem, no longer felt like a place she belonged. She viewed it as a tourist might. A sense of amazement touched her briefly as she scanned the green and brown marble columns and the mosaics surrounding the arched windows, but the reality of an Eternal God seemed very remote to her. She was without fear of that fierce Eternal One. Without awe, she considered the faith she was leaving.

Perhaps she had always been irreverent and faithless. Had she ever really spoken to God when she touched her forehead to the ground in obedience? She had said words, but her heart had never uttered a single prayer to the Allah whose name was intertwined with the gold-leaf and mosaic of the holy place.

She shook her head at her own coldness. She did not believe. Gold and filigreed turquoise could not impress her heart. She saw here only beauty made by man.

She leaned against a column for a moment and was startled to hear a voice behind her.

"Victoria Hassan?"

She turned to see the smiling, sun-darkened face of Ram Kadar as he entered the compound. His black robes and keffiyeh billowed in the slight breeze. He looked very much as if he might fly. His black eyes shone as he fixed them on her face, and he smiled. His teeth were white and perfect. He was a handsome man, and he knew it well.

Victoria lowered her eyes and touched her forehead in salaam. "Ram Kadar." She said his name but did not return his smile. She did not like the way he looked at her. She would not encourage him with even a hint of anything beyond simple courtesy.

"It is good to see you here. You have come to petition Allah?"

"I have come here . . . to think," she answered truthfully.

"I have come to petition." Kadar moved uncomfortably near to her. "I intend to take a wife soon."

She did not look up at him. She felt his gaze sweep over her and instantly became self-conscious in her blue cotton British dress and high-heeled shoes. "Congratulations," she muttered.

He laughed when she did not look at him. He raised his hand as if to touch her face. She flinched, and he laughed again. "Such beauty should be behind a veil. Reserved only for the pleasure of a husband, Victoria."

"A veil will not do when one is working at the Mandate offices." She turned and brushed past him.

"And such a body is made for bearing children," he called after her as she hurried out the gates and into the souks of the Old City.

———

Only four china dinner plates had survived the long journey from Austria to Palestine. Leah would have grieved if it had not been for the note she found tucked into the packing crate:

My Dearest Friend,

What a joy it is for me to think that when you find this little message you will be safe in your home in Zion! And yet there is grief also that I remain here in Vienna without your face to smile at me from across the stage! My prayers go with you as I remember the words of Isaiah 52:9—"Break forth into joy, sing together, ye waste places of Jerusalem: for the Lord hath comforted his people, he hath redeemed Jerusalem."

All my love,
Elisa

Inside the envelope, Elisa had placed a hundred Austrian shillings. Austrian bank notes were worthless now, of course, but the note and the cash reminded Leah once again how far God had brought them to come to this moment. Instead of tears shed over eight broken dinner plates, Leah was able to smile and thank God for the four that remained.

20

Jerusalem Welcome

". . . And Shoshanna thinks she must be . . . *expecting* . . . such a pale little thing." Ida Sachar filled the ears of her husband and sons before she filled their plates.

"That Shoshanna! Such a yenta! She would say that *Moshe* was expecting if it would draw a crowd. What does she know?" Hermann Sachar chided as he spooned out potatoes onto his plate.

"So what do you think, Eli? *You* have seen her! Last night at the concert. Did she look like she *was. . .*?" Ida pried.

Embarrassed, Eli shrugged. "She played like an angel, Mama. She wore a black dress, and I—"

"Aha! A *black dress*! Very *slimming*." Ida's eyes narrowed.

"They always wear black dresses when they play." Hermann shook his head and rolled his eyes. "These women . . . as if there was not enough to talk about!"

"Shoshanna said she looked like she stepped out of a shop window in Beirut, or maybe Berlin. Everything matched! They have money, or else why didn't they sublet the apartment? I ask you." Ida's face betrayed a knowledge of such things.

Hermann lowered his chin and peered at his wife over the tops of his glasses. "First you say she is pregnant. Then she is rich. You also say she is a shiksa who certainly must not keep a kosher kitchen." He clucked his tongue. "All *this* and you have never laid eyes on the woman!"

"What do men know? Oy! Why couldn't God give me at least one daughter to talk to over the dinner table?" Ida snapped. "Pass the potatoes, Hermann. You do not understand these things."

Hermann obeyed with a look of disgusted amusement. "Those children," he said under his breath.

"*What?*" Ida's eyes flashed. She was ready for what was known as a *discussion*. This was an unusually loud conversation, which increased in volume as it changed from topic to topic until no one knew where it had started.

Eli marked the opening topic in his mind. This time the *discussion* was beginning with Leah and Shimon Feldstein. "Tales of the Vienna Woods," so to speak. He and Moshe exchanged glances and ducked slightly as they proceeded with their meal.

"I said," Hermann repeated loudly, "THOSE CHILDREN!"

"What children?"

"Those . . . *what are their names?* . . . the new ones. The rich pregnant ones."

"He is not pregnant! *She* is!"

"You yentas! How do you know such things!"

"Because we are women!"

Hermann rolled his eyes heavenward. "Thank you, God, that you made me a man."

Ida pouted. Only one phase of the *discussion*. Hermann pretended that it was over. Moshe and Eli knew better.

"So what about them?" Ida asked quietly, leading Hermann along.

"About who?" Hermann looked around in mock bewilderment.

Ida roared, "THE FELDSTEINS! The children! Oy! As *you* call them!"

"Well then, Ida, I'll tell you what, since you are asking me . . . *a man* . . . for an opinion! There they are in that little place, probably because they have no place else to go. And every yenta in the Old City is gabbing about them! But do I see the meat and potatoes of the Sachar house being shared with these strangers? Nu! They have arrived here, and old Aunt Idela is dead."

"She is spinning in her grave at one look at those apikorosim in her flat!"

"She is too dead to spin . . . or care. But *you* are not!" His lip was very far out. He had the look of a man with a budding case of indigestion. He turned to Eli. "This Leah plays like an angel, eh? *So!* You be the angel these *yentas* will not be! Take the leftovers."

"What leftovers?" Ida protested.

"And tonight we can live without your mother's fine strudel!"

"*What?*" Hands crashed down on the table.

Hermann's chin came up in defiant response. "That is my final word, Ida," he proclaimed. "I am the papa and this is my final word. You will package the food nicely and send a kind note to these poor children. And I will be able to hold my head up in shul because"— Now his fist slammed on the table—"MY WIFE IS KIND TO THE POOR AND THE STRANGER!" His eyes protruded slightly. The lower lip extended with the chin. This meant the *discussion* was at an end.

It was, of course, the answer to Eli's most fervent prayer. His arms laden with food, he hurried through the dark streets of the Jewish Quarter. Shimon and Leah Feldstein's flat was in the poorest of the poor sections of the Quarter. Leah's matching dress and shoes notwithstanding, he sided with his father. They could not be very rich and wish to stay in such a place. He had been searching for some reason to visit them to mention Victoria's name. To thank them for the ticket and then to talk about Victoria. Surely they knew her well. Or at least well enough to notice what a wonderful person she was. Had she mentioned his name to them? he wondered. Were they also part of the little conspiracy?

Dodging a particularly deep puddle, Eli considered that coming from a place so decadent as Vienna, these liberated Europeans would not be at all dismayed by the fact he and Victoria were in love.

A dim orange glow shone in the window of the Feldstein flat. The window was quite dirty, Eli noticed. It probably had not been washed in years. The contrast between that straining little light and the spotlight at Allenby barracks was startling. Eli could not imagine the woman he had listened to last night would choose to live in such a gloomy place as this.

Leaning against the wall for balance, Eli climbed the steps to the flat. It had always been a marvel to him that old Idela had managed to climb these steep steps at eighty-something. Her legs must have simply gotten into the habit.

On the stoop he waited a moment, trying to juggle his burden. Through the thin wooden door, the sound of peaceful music emanated. *Music? Here?* He knocked with his foot. The door swung back, revealing the enormous form of Shimon Feldstein. He was smiling. Strangely peaceful as if the music were coming from inside him.

"Shalom," he said.

Eli remembered his voice. "I am . . . my mother is . . . Ida Sachar . . . and I . . . she sent me here with this, in case you have not eaten."

Shimon stepped aside. The light behind him fell on Leah as she sat on an upturned packing crate. Another packing crate served as a table, complete with candlesticks and real china plates and linen napkins. A third crate was laden with food in all sorts of containers. Small tin buckets held stew. There were bowls of boiled potatoes and a bit of lamb. A phonograph stood in the corner of the clutter, playing some wonderful music. An orchestra. Violins. It was . . . so very elegant!

"Another one!" Leah said in delight. "Come in. Won't you join us? Everyone else is gone, and we have plenty."

Dumfounded, Eli stepped past the big man. He thought about how amazed his mother would be when she found out that everyone had brought supper to the new arrivals! Could any disaster have been greater for Ida Sachar than to have been left out of doing good when everyone else did good? The thought of it made him shake his head as he placed the Sachar offering on the crate. A quick glance showed there was no fresh strudel among the plates. This would please his mother. *No one else brought strudel!*

"My mother sent me with some supper. And strudel. Have you had strudel yet?" Eli asked, just to make sure. His mother would ask him if he asked.

Shimon unwrapped the package and inhaled deeply. "Not since Vienna," he replied. "And that was too long ago to remember."

Eli hesitated in his real purpose as Leah and Shimon filled his ears with the kindness of the Jewish Quarter. Eli told them his name again and watched their faces to see if there might be a flicker of recognition. There was none. This was disappointing. Shimon pulled up a crate for him to sit on as he told how Hannah Cohen had showed them how to start the primus stove. Eli mentioned that Hannah was their landlady and that she knew everything. He did not say, however, that probably every woman who came through the door had come bearing gifts and left bearing tales. *China plates! A phonograph! Candlesticks on a packing crate! Oy! But is she expecting?*

That question played over and over again in Eli's unwilling mind. He forced himself not to look at Leah for fear his eyes would lock on her stomach as he spoke. The sheer romance of this strange little dinner party made him flush slightly and think about Victoria. What would it be to be someplace with her alone? *Candlelight. Music. Maybe his child within her?*

He should not have let his mind wander from the trivial to the magnificent. Suddenly he blurted out, "Victoria sent me a pass to your concert last night." Pain and longing were etched on his face. "I saw her. I could not speak with her in public, of course."

Shimon and Leah looked at him blankly for a moment until the full meaning of his confession sank in. Leah smiled gently, sympathetically. "Ah. You and Victoria. . . ?"

What relief it was to spill it out to these strangers. So maybe he was interrupting their romantic candlelight dinner with his tale of misery! Why should any couple be so lucky as to have candles to blow out and a bed to lie on together and no one to say they could not, when Eli and Victoria lived in such torment?

He did not tell them everything, of course. There were some things he did not admit, like how he ached at night when he thought of her.

And then he finished with a sigh. "She looked so happy last night beside you both. It is so hard. We live in two worlds. You cannot understand what it is like." He hung his head, feeling the first violent wave of embarrassment. Why had he told them this? "It must be the music," he finished lamely and stood up.

Their understanding eyes followed him. "I am going to have tea with her next Tuesday, Eli," Leah said gently. "I would be happy to give her a message if you like."

"Oy! You are the only one who can do it without risk." He tugged his beard in thought. "I will bring a letter on Sunday." He smiled at Shimon. "Would you like to join us for morning prayers at shul? The men are less nosy than the women, I promise."

The music had stopped by the time Eli left. He descended the stairs and looked back over his shoulder at the orange glow of the candle through the window. The music began again. It floated through the grimy glass into the cleanly washed night stars. And then, as Eli watched and envied, the light of the candles went out.

———

Tonight an American double feature was playing at the London Palace Theater. *Charlie Chan in Paris* and *Song of the Thin Man.*

Charles and Louis had not stopped bouncing since Elisa had announced that she and Anna held four precious tickets for this evening's program.

Murphy read the advertisement over the dinner table.

"The world's greatest detective, Charlie Chan, spots forgery in gay Paree!" He lowered the newspaper and screwed his face up in an imitation of the Chinese sleuth. "Ah-so. What you think of that, Charles? You named Charlie too!"

Charles laughed and clapped his hands, ducking down in embarrassment at being named after a Chinese detective. "I . . . talk . . . be'er," he giggled.

"Better, better, *better,*" Louis corrected, sounding each letter T distinctly.

Murphy continued his imitation. He peered at Charles through squinting eyes. "Charlie Chan not say *the* or *a* when he talk. Not good for boy-detective learn English from Charlie Chan."

Charles frowned and tried again. "Bet-ter. I talk bet-ter!"

Elisa nodded approval and stacked the dishes. "He figures out the mystery quicker too. Charlie Kronenberger, master private-eye." She winked. "Go wash up. Comb your hair. Freddie will be here in five minutes with Mama and Papa."

As they ran happily up the stairs, Murphy took her hand. "You're more than I bargained for," he whispered. "Married a few months, and already you're a terrific mother of five-year-old boys."

"I should have listened when they told me you work fast," she teased. Then, changing the subject. "You're sure you and Papa won't come along?"

Murphy shook his head. Tonight he and Theo Lindheim would listen to Hitler's speech from Saarbrücken. Murphy had a reporter on hand in Germany to cover it live, but he wanted to hear for himself what pretense the Führer might have for serving up another portion of Europe on the Nazi platter. He did not trouble Elisa with the details.

"You and Anna have a good time. Theo and I will stay here and bemoan the condition of the world." He smiled at her, but she saw the reality behind his words. A moment of worry flashed across her face. She did not want to know!

Dressed in matching tweed jackets and knickers, the boys clattered down the stairs. Caps in place, they seemed the very picture of English schoolboys. Charles carried a magnifying glass in his hip pocket to aid in his search for clues. He examined Louis's hand under the glass as Elisa retrieved her coat and Freddie honked the horn outside in Red Lion Square.

They flung the door back to reveal Theo with his hand raised to knock. With steel-gray hair and craggy features, Theo appeared to have completely regained his health, but his eyes still betrayed sorrow at all he had seen over the last few years. Even a smile of greeting did not hide Theo's private anguish from his daughter.

"Two old bachelors . . ." he tried to joke as Charles and Louis led Elisa down to the waiting automobile and the enormous chauffeur.

She waved without smiling as Freddie opened the door and she slid into the backseat. Without being told, she knew the news Theo and Murphy heard tonight could not be good. Like the two small boys, she would stare at the screen and try to figure out "whodunit" in tonight's murder mystery.

Meanwhile, Murphy and Theo fiddled with the radio dial. There was no mystery left for them as they once again listened to the shrieking voice of Germany's undisputed leader.

Murphy stared at the radio perched on top of his huge desk. Behind them, a fire crackled on the hearth. Theo sat with his head back, eyes fixed on the low rafters, mouth pressed into a tight line.

Radio Cairo broadcast Hitler's Saarbrücken speech in its entirety. Still in his British uniform, Samuel Orde joined a small group of dedicated Zionists on the campus of Hebrew University where the speech was to be analyzed and discussed.

The room held a group of two dozen young men and women as well as a handful of professors and the Jewish Agency leader, David Ben-Gurion.

The British government's present policy of yielding to violence and pressure did not bode well for the Jews of Palestine—nor for the Jews of Europe who clambered at the gates of every embassy to escape the shadow of Hitler's Reich. Tonight, David Ben-Gurion was more grim than usual. The time of Hitler's speech in Saarbrücken had been announced by the Arab Council in the Middle East. That proclamation alone seemed ominous for the Jewish Yishuv.

Samuel Orde had known Ben-Gurion for ten years. When suspicious glances were cast at the captain's uniform, Ben-Gurion made it clear that Orde was present as his guest, his friend, and his advisor. *How would the English react to Hitler's newest attack on the Jewish settlement?*

There was no confusion in Orde's mind as to his government's response to Hitler's speech.

Orde stared at the radio at the front of the classroom. David Ben-Gurion sat with his hands clasped, eyes focused on the light fixture.

Hitler began his attack on the Jewish settlement in Palestine by first attacking democracy. *"The statesmen who are opposed to us say they wish for peace ... and yet they govern in countries which make it possible that these men may be removed from office. What if, in England, instead of Chamberlain, Mr. Duff Cooper or Mr. Eden or Mr. Churchill should suddenly come to power?"*

There was an ominous pause. Had the Nazi audience not heard that all three of these English statesmen had been booed from the chambers of Parliament for their strong stand against appeasement? Was it not clear that their public political careers had never been more bleak? It made no difference to Hitler or his audience. Hitler continued his attack on a personal level.

"We know quite well that the aim of one of these men would be to start another world war. He makes no secret of the fact. And we know further that now, as in the past, there lurks the menacing figure of that Jewish-international foe. And we know further the evil power of the international press which lives on lies and slander..."

Ben-Gurion smiled bleakly. "Well, he has managed to condemn everyone in this room. The Jews ... strange how this lord of darkness ascribes us so much power when by the millions we are so powerless. Of course, I would hate it if a man like him had something good to say about me," Ben-Gurion added.

Hitler continued. *"These enemies oblige us to be watchful and to remember the protection of the Reich. I have, therefore, decided to continue construction of our fortifications in the West with increased energy..."*

Orde exhaled loudly. "So much for 'peace in our time.' "

Ben-Gurion's lined face seemed suddenly older. "We can only hope that Chamberlain is listening. Hearing. That the English will use this *peace* as a time to rearm."

The voice of Hitler drowned out his comment. *"We cannot tolerate any longer the tutelage of British governesses! Inquiries of British politicians concerning Germans within the Reich are out of place! We do not concern ourselves with similar matters in England! They should concern themselves with their own affairs—for instance, with affairs in Palestine!"*

At the mention of Palestine, Ben-Gurion leaned forward. For nearly twenty minutes, Hitler raved about the unrest in the British Mandate of Palestine. He recited the minute details of every violent act against the government there. The Arab attack and murder of Orde's young sentry on the Old City wall was somehow twisted until in Hitler's mouth the English had fired upon innocent civilians in Omar Square. Upon such distortion of events the Führer based his argument that England had enough trouble of its own without concerning itself with what happened to a handful of Jews and Catholic protesters within the Reich.

"And if the entire Arab world in all its vast domain cannot tolerate the presence of Jews in Palestine, how then are we to tolerate them within our limited borders?" These words were established with thunderous applause by the Nazi audience of Saarbrücken.

Murphy and Theo exchanged glances. There was never a mystery about whom Hitler would blame for the world's problems. Murphy scribbled notes on the Führer's phrases and word choices: *"cannot tolerate . . . vast Arab domain . . . limited German borders . . ."* All of this was uttered at a moment when twelve thousand Jews had been deported to Poland without a word of protest from the League of Nations. And as for limited borders, the echo of German jackboots on the streets of Czechoslovakia had not yet died away.

"He's still raving about this living space for Germans," Murphy said under his breath.

"Such talk can mean only one thing." Theo did not finish the thought as Hitler's voice broke through the acclaim from his audience.

"If the English themselves cannot control the immigration of Jews to Palestine, if they turn them back and imprison them, then how can they condemn those of us who cry, 'Germany for Germans'?"

Here the speech was interrupted by an unending chant: *"Germany for Germans! Deutschland über Alles!"*

Murphy did not doubt that in Palestine the same chant was being repeated by the Arab Council with a slight variation: *"Palestine for Arabs! Jihad! Holy war! Jews to the sea!"*

The image made him shudder. Suddenly it seemed as though the fate of the coffin ships like the *Darien* was the only alternative left for the Jews of Europe. The dark waters of the ocean would not refuse them. The yawning chasms of the deep would offer them their only peace.

Hitler let the German voices of his audience carry the rest of his message to the world.

The cheering had not stopped before the telephone rang. The gruff voice of Winston Churchill was on the other end of the line.

"We should all be quite flattered that Herr Hitler has singled us out as personal enemies," Murphy quipped. "Winston Churchill. The press. And the heritage of my father-in-law."

Churchill also sounded amused. "Interesting minds these Nazis have. Hitler asks, 'Is this the trust and friendship of our Munich Pact? If we are friends and you trust us, why must England rearm? Let me have the arms and you show the trust.' "

Murphy laughed in spite of the dark truth in Churchill's humor. Theo simply frowned and stared at the radio as if it emitted a poison gas through the speaker. "Certainly interested in British troubles in Palestine tonight, wasn't he?"

Churchill's drawl became somber. "You have a good journalist in Jerusalem, I trust? There will be a story to cover soon enough, I'll wager."

"No one yet." At the statesman's warning, Murphy thought of Leah and Shimon and shuddered at the ominous words he was hearing tonight.

Churchill exhaled in amazement. "No reporter? Why? That is Hitler's second front against the Jews. And also against British foreign policy!"

Murphy tried to explain. "Just getting started . . . haven't had a chance to . . ." He mentally thumbed through a card file of reporters who had at one time covered Middle-East politics.

"There is no time to lose in this matter!" Churchill's voice carried the emphasis he might use on the floor of Parliament. "The British foreign secretary has sent his lackeys to Palestine to examine the question of Jewish homeland and immigration for the second time in sixteen months! That can mean only one thing—they mean to disavow our promise of a Jewish national home. The Woodhead Committee will most certainly reverse every other White Paper, and this will be done at the most crucial time in the history of the Jewish people!" He coughed. "And you do not have a reporter in Jerusalem to cover the outrage? Hitler's speech tonight must be reason enough for you to acquire one before the week is out!"

Murphy had only asked Winston Churchill to write a few articles, not to run the European operation for Trump Publications. He felt embarrassed, indignant—and properly chastised by the great man. "You would not be so insistent that I hire a man for a position in Jerusalem if you did not already have one in mind, Winston."

Churchill chuckled softly. He had been found out. Indeed, he did know of a man who would serve the purpose splendidly. The fellow was not a journalist by profession, but a staunch supporter of Zionism and the Jewish national home. Better than most men, he understood the cost of current British appeasement policies and had quite a grasp of the connection between Nazi Germany and the terrorist activities in Palestine.

"He is a brilliant fellow," Churchill said. "Reminds me of me forty years ago."

"And is he modest?" Murphy asked.

"To a fault."

"I am convinced."

"I thought you would be."

"Then how do I get hold of this boy wonder?"

"I have known his family for years. The lad is currently a captain with the British military in Jerusalem. He's had several articles published in the *Geographic*. Scholarly. Historical. I don't think it will raise any eyebrows if you contact him. But he may wish to write under a pseudonym." Churchill coughed slightly. "The name is Samuel Orde. I took the liberty of ringing the *Geographic* editorial offices for his address this afternoon."

21

Hopes and Dreams

The light from Murphy's study still burned, illuminating a square of sidewalk below the Red Lion House where Freddie parked the Duesenberg.

Both Charles and Louis had fallen asleep on the drive home from the theater. Freddie gathered them up in his massive arms to carry them up the stairs as Anna and Elisa climbed out of the backseat.

A tousled blond head resting on each shoulder, Freddie preceded the ladies with his bundles.

"Murphy can carry one, Freddie," Elisa called after him.

"Ah, Missus . . . they're both of 'em not so heavy as even one bundle of *The Times*." As if to make his point, he took the steps two at a time.

Anna laughed as he reached the landing, and then the laughter died on her lips. From the shadow beside the stairs, a man emerged. His face was half-concealed beneath the brim of a hat. He blocked the way of Anna and Elisa up the steps.

First startled, then alarmed, Freddie charged back down, still lugging the boys. *"Who d'ya think y'are, there?"*

The stranger's hat was doffed. A polite but strained voice said, "Mrs. Lindheim?"

Anna squeezed Elisa's hand as if to reassure her. "Mr. *Beckham*, is it not?" Anna replied coolly.

"Mother. . . ?" Elisa backed up a step.

" 'ey there!" Freddie bellowed as the boys raised their heads.

"It is all right." Anna held up a hand to quiet Freddie.

Beckham glanced at the big man with some amusement. He bowed slightly to Anna. "I am relieved you remember me."

"The British Museum," she said. "Hardly a day has passed that I have not thought of that encounter."

"Your husband is in the house?"

"You must know where he is." Anna was not unfriendly.

"Of course." Beckham seemed almost apologetic. "I have been *requested* to have a word with him. We realize the hour is late, but—" He glanced beyond Freddie toward the top of the stairs. "Perhaps we should talk inside?"

After a few minutes alone with Mr. Beckham behind the closed door of Murphy's study, Theo emerged. His face radiated peace and assurance as he embraced Anna.

"I will only be gone a short while," he whispered. "Something important has come up. Something I did not expect."

He could offer her no other explanation than that. And so, praying silently, Anna stood at the window beside her daughter and watched as Theo was led to a black government-issue sedan and driven away into the gray fog of London midnight.

———

Theo took his place at the long horseshoe-shaped table among thirty other men who had gathered at this emergency meeting called by the British foreign minister, Lord Halifax.

Some faces among the party Theo recognized. Lord Winterton, who had represented British interests at Evian. George Rublee, the American lawyer who had been in charge of the international refugee question since the Evian Conference. Chaim Weizmann, looking particularly aged and weary, waved and nodded tacitly at Theo. They were not seated near enough to one another to speak. Colonial Secretary Malcolm MacDonald glanced almost apologetically in Theo's direction. There was no mistaking the fact that Theo's plan of trade with Germany in exchange for Jewish lives and assets had gotten a favorable reply from the Nazis. If that was not the case, then why would such prominent men have bothered to come here to meet and confer in the middle of the night?

Portraits of long-dead English kings and lords gazed down regally from gilded frames on the red satin walls of the room. Illuminated by small lights, these painted onlookers had more color on their cheeks and more expression in their eyes than the living humans who met together amid the rustling of papers and clinking of water glasses.

Theo stared back into the smirking face of an amused King Charles II. Dressed in ermines and flowing wig, the king seemed warmer on his canvas than Theo felt in the drafty room. Ah, well, these kings had lived and committed their mistakes already. Now they were dust; it was someone else's turn to change the world or fail in the task. Tonight was a call to action, or a call to judgment.

Lord Winterton stood and banged down the gavel as a call to order. "HEAR YE, GENTLEMEN! PRAY SILENCE AS FOREIGN MINISTER LORD

HALIFAX ADDRESSES THE MEETING!"

There was a pattering of polite, if exhausted, applause from the gathering as Lord Halifax, pale and languid, stood to speak.

"Last week, we were so fortunate as to receive a suggestion for a possible solution to the economic woes brought upon the empire and the free world by the refugee question." He paused and inclined his head toward Theo. Others also looked at Theo curiously. Halifax continued. "The suggestion of a trade agreement with Germany, which would allow refugees to depart with a portion of their assets, was presented to German Foreign Minister von Ribbentrop." A long pause. "A representative of the Reich, von Ribbentrop rejected the offer outright."

A murmur of surprise filled the room. Theo looked unhappily at his clasped hands. Useless hands, tied, helpless to help others. How he had prayed for a different response from the Germans!

Halifax continued, raising his hand to silence the questions for a moment. "Three days later, however, our office received word that another high official in the Nazi government may well be interested in personally negotiating such an agreement in Berlin."

Theo exhaled loudly with relief as other members of the group first exclaimed their pleasure audibly and then applauded the news. Here at last was hope, some glimmer of light! There was a smile on every face around the table now.

Halifax nodded and raised both hands. He was the only man not smiling. Silence. "There are certain conditions for these discussions with the Germans, however." He waited as the word *conditions* cut through the exuberance of the group. Questions filled the minds of the men. And dread. There were always conditions when negotiating with Nazis. The terms were never favorable to anyone but the Nazis.

Halifax continued and turned his eyes toward Theo. The look was open and serious. These words were directed at him. "Those men with whom we have had contact have indicated that the plan must be drawn *in its entirety* for presentation at a meeting in Berlin *next week.*" He held up his hand again. This was not the only condition. "And . . . they request . . . no, *insist,* that Theo Lindheim, who is the originator of this plan, present it himself without members of the committee to accompany him to Berlin or to the meeting."

There was no response. Not a murmur of sound. Weizmann caught Theo's gaze and held it in strong sympathy and a hint of fear. *Theo to return to Berlin!* Were there any in the room tonight who did not understand the significance of that Nazi demand?

Theo looked up at the smirk of King Charles. *I am dust,* the portrait seemed to say, *and so too will you be, Theo Lindheim, if you return to Berlin.*

Halifax broke the thick silence. "Of course, it serves us no purpose to work to complete such a plan unless that condition is met. They have made that clear. And yet, we cannot expect one man to place himself in jeopardy when the entire scheme might be a ruse. As heads of various organizations with concern for the Jewish refugees and political refugees of the Reich, we thought that it was imperative that we keep this channel open with the Reich. They have given us a deadline of noon tomorrow to respond. We should have an alternate plan to present."

Blank stares were exchanged. What could be said at this late hour? Who had a better idea for some economic relief for the refugees and the governments expected to take them?

For an instant Theo wondered how the Nazis knew that he had proposed the original plan. How had his name been brought up in such a delicate matter? Perhaps that was a question he would ask later. For now, however, there was no denying that in an odd and frightening way, his prayer had been answered—not as he expected. Not as he would have wished or imagined.

For a moment he thought of Anna. Elisa and the boys. The baby. Those he loved with all his heart. There was no doubt that he would lay down his life for them, return to the hell of Dachau if it was for the sake of their lives. But that was not required of him. They were safe. That made this decision all the more difficult. A demand was being made on his life for the sake of strangers, people he knew only as thousands who shared a common heritage with him. He smiled slightly as he asked himself, *What would the Lord do?* In that instant, he knew what was required of him.

The expressions on the faces of the canvas kings remained unchanged as Theo stood slowly at his place. The eyes of the others around the table filled with respect, with fear. They doubted they would do the same in Theo's place.

And so the choice was made. Only hours remained between this moment of decision and the time when Theo would have to leave for Berlin. Hard work would fill the time.

———

In the dining room of the Hassan residence, in Old City Jerusalem, sat a dozen men whom Victoria did not recognize. Her stepmother poured strong coffee for them from the large brass samovar reserved only for guests.

As Victoria passed by the open archway, buzzing voices suddenly became silent. Her stepmother paused a moment in filling a cup. Victoria looked in at a still and sinister tableau, a council of darkness here within the walls of her own home.

Ibrahim, whose face betrayed a nervous guilt, hailed her with a smile. "It is only Victoria. Only my sister."

The urgent whispers of conversation did not resume. The eyes of these keffiyeh-clad men looked at her in her Western clothing as though she were a piece of meat in a marketplace.

She bowed in salaam. Something flickered in the eyes of several of these guests as they let their gazes sweep across her body and then return and linger on her throat. Instinctively she put a hand to her open collar. She backed up a step and resisted the urge to turn and run.

"Victoria works as a secretary for the British government," her step-mother volunteered.

A new interest sparked in the faces of the men.

Ram Kadar nodded his head and flashed a smile at her. "Such beauty should not be wasted on the Englishmen, Ibrahim."

Ibrahim glanced nervously at Victoria, then replied, "Perhaps if you will instruct her, Ram Kadar. She may be beautiful, but my sister is ignorant as women often are. The Englishmen, being also ignorant, do not seem to mind."

Victoria continued to smile throughout this unflattering flattery. She kept her eyes downcast and did not dare to meet the gaze of Kadar, who stared at her more intensely than the others.

"If my brothers and my mother will forgive me—" Victoria backed another step. She touched her hand to her forehead in salaam, and twelve male voices responded as she hurried up the stairs.

Victoria paused on the landing as the voices resumed. "It is only in these ways that the English will see our dissatisfaction." She recognized the voice of Kadar. "These politicians must return to England with their eyes smarting from the smoke of Palestine."

Late into the Jerusalem night, Victoria sat, unmoving, on the edge of her bed. A cold fear filled her. She had heard the whispers of her brothers before. She had not been surprised by the faces of Daud and Isaak and Ismael. But the words of Ibrahim somehow felt like a personal betrayal. *He was one of them! He was part of those who murdered the Englishmen and cheered the voice of the Arab Council in Cairo!* She had not known. She had not expected his complicity in the works of Darkness.

Victoria wished that her father would return from his buying trip in Iran. He would know what to do. He would talk sense to Ibrahim!

Never had Victoria felt so alone. Eli, though just a few blocks away, was another world from this world.

Not even Allah could help her now. It was Allah, was it not, who breathed the dark anger into the hearts of her brothers? It was for the sake of Allah that they gathered together and made their plans.

Victoria frowned. She must not speak the treason she felt in her heart against those plans. For Allah might whisper in the soul of Ibrahim Hassan: *"Your sister Victoria is a traitor to her people. Listen, Ibrahim! Victoria is no longer one of us."*

The entire Lubetkin household seemed preoccupied with tiny baby Yacov. Could it be that he was smiling already?

Frau Rosen declared that it was *not* a smile but a gas bubble in the infant's stomach! Aaron insisted that it was not gas but a genuine *smile*! Did Frau Rosen not see what innate intelligence the child had? Of course he could smile at such a tender age!

Such conversation made Etta smile. If there was one thing she could say about her beloved Aaron, it was that he believed that his children had been born with an understanding of the Law and the Prophets . . . they simply had to be taught to speak and read and write before they would *know* what they *knew*!

David was fascinated by his new brother; little Samuel was hurt because he was no longer the baby. For Rachel, the arrival of little bundle Yacov was the awakening of some hope within her that one day she, too, would present a son to her future husband.

She watched her mother nurse the child and suddenly was filled with a wonder at her own budding breasts. She had not thought of the changes in her body as anything but a bother until now. But there was something miraculous about the way this new and tiny life turned its face toward Mama. Something overwhelming about the look of joy and peace that filled Mama's eyes as she cradled the new Lubetkin.

As Samuel walked unhappily up to bed and David took one last big-brotherly look at the little one, Rachel stood in the doorway and absorbed the scene with a sense of awe. Perhaps someday she would sit where her mother sat and a man would look at her with the same love that Papa carried in his eyes.

"Good night, Mama," Rachel said, feeling as if she must turn her own eyes from such a private moment.

Mama looked up with a soft, dreamy smile. Had Rachel ever known her mother to wear such tender emotion so plainly on her face? "Good night *kinderlach*," she said. "Don't forget to say your prayers. Tomorrow is the Brith Milah of your brother. Rachel, wash your hair before bed, nu? David, take a bath."

These mundane instructions were issued in a tone laden with love. Tomorrow baby Yacov would be circumcised. Tomorrow another son would enter the Covenant! Such an event made the washing of hair practically a holy ritual—or at least that was the way Mama made it sound.

Rachel wondered if David noticed the magic that seemed to surround their mother and father. No. At the mention of *bath* David groaned and asked if Samuel must also bathe. Still smiling, Papa looked up and told him sweetly to mind his own business. Samuel's bath was not his affair.

Had Papa ever said such a thing in *that* tone of voice? This new baby Yacov must indeed be very special. Not even a scowl of authority accompanied Papa's words.

David shrugged and followed, grumbling, after Samuel. Rachel lingered a few seconds longer in the doorway, and when she left they did not notice her absence.

————

Like an old friend, the wishing star hung in the azure sky above Warsaw. From the window of her bedroom, Rachel watched it glisten blue and red in the reflection of the northern lights. It was a beautiful star. Her own star. Sometimes she thought it must be an angel God had placed in the sky to watch over her. Such thoughts made it impossible to be afraid of the dark.

Often she lay awake when the voices of her parents drifted up through the floor and she imagined what it would be like when she and Reuven were married. She would share her star with him. She would point to its place in the sky and tell Reuven, *I asked it to shine on you, too. I prayed that you would be handsome and smart and that someday you would make a good husband. And now I share my star with you....*

She had never met Reuven, although they had been pledged to each other many years before. He was three years older than Rachel, and Papa said that he was a kind young man and that he excelled in Torah and now at the Yeshiva.

When she asked if he was handsome as well, Papa had answered that he was handsome enough to make her forget such a question.

Rachel hoped that he was as handsome as her own father. She saw the way Mama looked at Papa. Handsome! Yes, and smart. From a good family descended from Baal Shem Tov! Someday Rachel wanted to look at her betrothed with the same light in her eyes that Mama had when she looked at Papa.

Rachel gazed very hard at her wishing star. "Do you hear me, little star? Someday when Reuven and I are married, I will thank you if he is all these things and handsome too."

She squeezed her eyes shut and said a prayer for Reuven. Then when she opened them the star seemed to be blinking a happy *yes* down to her. *Someday, someday, someday!*

In another year she would meet Reuven face-to-face. She would be almost fourteen and he would be seventeen—almost a grown man. She wondered if he would see how much she loved him even now. Would he imagine that she had sat at her window and dreamed what it would be like to have him beside her?

"Can you see my star, Reuven?" she whispered quietly. "Do you sit at the window of your room and wonder about me?"

She turned to see her silhouette reflected in the mirror. Long dark hair. Creamy skin. Tall and slender, she was halfway between a girl and a woman. "By next year when you meet him," Mama had promised, "he will not look upon a child."

Rachel was impatient for that time. The days moved so very slowly. Week by week new feelings awakened in her changing body. There was so much she did not understand. So many things she wanted to ask Mama. Instead, she whispered her secrets to the wishing star. She learned to cook. Learned to be the sort of woman she must be as the future wife of a future rabbi. These things she learned from Mama, as was proper.

From Papa, Rachel learned Torah. Mama had also been taught by her father. This was one of the things Papa loved about Mama. She was smart; she could talk with him. Other women cooked and cleaned and bore children, but Mama was a scholar, he said. No doubt young Reuven would appreciate such a gift in Rachel as well. This would also help her to understand the things going on inside the head of her future husband, Papa said. All the same, it would not be wise to talk about her lessons outside the family. And, he warned, she must never act as though she knew better than her learned husband! Knowledge was a dangerous thing in the hands of a woman who would use it to belittle her husband! The Eternal counted such misuse a grave sin! *Such a woman would be worse than a golem! A witless simpleton would be better than such a wife!*

Thus warned, Rachel applied herself to the study of the Torah with humility. *Thank you, O Eternal, that I who am only a woman . . . almost . . . may be privileged to study thy Holy Law. May I never use it against my future husband but for his pleasure only!*

Her prayer had become a promise to God, a vow that she would be the best wife young Reuven could have. He would never regret that his father and her father had struck a bargain and signed a contract of matrimony before she had learned to speak! Her entire life and education had been shaped for the purpose of fulfilling that agreement.

There was security in tradition, even for a little girl. A man was a man. Some were better than others, but all men knew their responsibilities before God. A woman was a woman. Some were more beautiful or clever than others, but it was possible for anyone to be a good wife and mother if she learned her duties.

All these things were ingrained into Rachel's life. Even now she knew what was expected of her. She did not fear failing in those duties. But suddenly, when she dreamed of Reuven and her future, there was a deeper longing within her. She could not put a name to it. Not yet. But it frightened her.

She sighed and whispered her prayer as she did every night,

Spirit and flesh are thine,
O heavenly Shepherd mine;
My Hopes, my thoughts, my fears, thou seest all;
Thou measurest my path, my steps dost know.
When thou upholdest, who can make me fall?

Rachel opened her mouth to continue her evening prayers, but tonight the wishing star seemed less remote than God. It winked and blinked at her, encouraging her to speak again.

"Little star, you are closer to heaven than I am. Please tell God that I want to be more to my husband than just a dutiful wife. Please tell Him that I wish . . . I pray . . . that one day my beloved will look at me the way Papa looks at Mama."

From the room below her, the strong, mellow voice of her father drifted up. Then Mama answered. Muffled voices. Loving words whispered with a sort of urgency. Rachel turned away from the window and tried to make out the words. Things spoken in the night between her parents were always like this. Just beyond her understanding. Perhaps they spoke another language? Was there some special secret language that only husband and wife could understand? Something that Rachel would learn someday when her own husband took her in his arms? *Someday . . . someday!*

Again she looked up at the wishing star and prayed, "Shine down on my own beloved rabbi so that one day he might teach me too."

The lonely whistle of a train sounded from the *Umschlagplatz*. Rachel turned her eyes in the direction of the sound. Muranow Square was dark and empty. Soft starlight glowed on the wet cobblestones. It was as if Rachel were the only person left in Warsaw. Then, across the Square a tiny flame flickered, illuminating a solitary man. One instant of light and then the shadowed figure was lost in the darkness again.

Rachel raised her eyes quickly to the wishing star. Suddenly it seemed cold and remote. An uneasiness stirred within her. A feeling of terrible foreboding that she did not understand.

22

Simple Gifts

The request to write for publication was not an unusual one for Samuel Orde. After all, he had published a number of historical monographs during his tour of duty in Palestine.

What was unusual was the subject matter editor John Murphy had outlined for him in the wire from London—the impact of current events upon members of the Woodhead Committee . . . probable outcome of their inquiry into the demands of the Arab Council . . . any daily events of significance in Palestine.

Orde read the telegram and then reread it a dozen times before he folded it carefully and put it into his pocket. He was certain of one thing; he would have to write under an assumed name if he accepted the assignment from Trump European News Service. His perspective would not be favorable to his own government in matters of their treatment of Jewish immigrants and his own belief that the hopes of a Jewish homeland were becoming more dim each day.

"Winston is behind this," he muttered to himself as Bowen, the duty officer, looked at him curiously.

"Pardon, sir?"

"Nothing. Thinking of an old friend in England." He pretended to be busy at his desk. In truth, he was already composing the lead paragraph to his first story.

It was all very confusing. First Rabbi Shlomo Lebowitz waited in line for three hours at the Office of Immigration in the British Mandate offices. When he reached the head of the line a very brusque and unpleasant Englishman behind the tall counter told him that he was in the wrong line.

"So this is the line I wait in to find out which line I should be waiting in?" Rabbi Lebowitz thanked him, then moved to the back of yet another line, even longer than the first.

In a muddled combination of broken English and Yiddish, he explained that his daughter Etta had been born in Jerusalem and she needed to come home again with her children from Warsaw. Several minutes of rapid-fire and unintelligible English had followed as a stack of forms had been carefully sorted out and passed across the counter to him.

Such a problem! He did not understand a word of it. Catching the Number Two bus to Zion Gate, he had shown the forms to two strangers, each of whom had given him different advice. Then a third fellow had joined in the discussion, and an argument had broken out. The old rabbi considered the observations of the sages about his people. *Three Jews together mean seven different opinions.* True? Of course true!

As the old rabbi walked quickly through narrow Zion Gate, it occurred to him that there were nearly three thousand Jews in his Quarter. This would truly be a confusion. Each one would have at least two different opinions about these papers, and there would be a very big argument about what was the proper way to fill out these things and get Etta and the family to Jerusalem from Warsaw. Such a thought made his head ache.

He tugged his beard and considered the havoc. The shouting. The red faces. He thought about how important it was that he not have to scratch out things on these forms so he would not have to wait in line again.

"So, Lord, I need the wisdom of Solomon, nu? Or . . . the wisdom of an Englishman." This made him smile. He looked to the left toward the Armenian Quarter, remembering the nice English Captain Orde who had brought in the hoity-toity Woodhead Commission to visit the school. Captain Orde spoke English. He spoke Yiddish. He spoke Arabic like a native shopkeeper in the souk. Here was a sensible fellow!

This line of reasoning led Rabbi Shlomo Lebowitz to the office of Captain Samuel Orde.

"Pardon me, Cap'n," said the duty officer. "I can't quite make it out, but I think this old Yid has some important documents for you."

Orde did not smile. He glared at his junior officer. "This is Rabbi Shlomo Lebowitz!" he snapped angrily. "A little respect, Bowen, or you'll find you're a private again!"

The tone made the young officer jump to attention. First he saluted Orde and then he saluted the old rabbi, who merely nodded and bowed slightly. *Yes, Captain Orde was the right man to see—a fellow without confusion on any matter!*

Orde addressed the rabbi with a sweep of his hand. "Sit, please,

Rabbi. How can I help you? Is anything wrong?"

"Wrong? Oy. No. Everything is *good* in Jerusalem, nu?" The rabbi raised his brows and tugged his beard. "The Arabs are *good and mad.* You English are *good and sick* of getting caught in the middle. And then there is me. I am *good and confused*! Things are *so good* in Jerusalem that everywhere I look there is a big shemozzl! True?"

Orde laughed in spite of the truth of the remark. "Of course true. And have you come here with a solution for us?"

The rabbi waved his hand as though he were brushing away a gnat. "The only one who can sort this mess out is *Messiah!*"

"My sentiments exactly."

"And I did not see *Him* walk in with the Woodhead Committee when they toured the Torah school, nu?"

Orde considered the old rabbi with curiosity. *Were they speaking of the same Messiah?* He agreed with an amused smile. "I was with them all day long in the holy places and I did not see the Messiah among them once."

"Ah." The old man stuck out his lower lip. "Just as I thought. Then they will not find the answer for Zion. That is certain, Captain. *So . . .* on to another problem. Smaller, maybe, but still I hope the Eternal has some interest."

Within fifteen minutes, the old rabbi had the matter of the immigration forms straight in his mind. This righteous Gentile would be most happy to help him fill out the papers. Indeed! All that would be needed after that was updated passport photos of Etta and Aaron and each of the children, as well as birth certificates. It might also be helpful to have proof that Aaron had lived and studied here in Jerusalem, that the couple had married there. Such papers would not be difficult to furnish and must certainly open the eyes of the English clerks inside the immigration office.

"I will write her a letter," said the rabbi.

Captain Orde considered that suggestion. "Too slow," he concluded, shaking his head. Was that worry in his eyes? Did he know something about this Woodhead Committee? Were they thinking about closing the quotas of immigrants? "Send her a telegram, Rabbi. As a matter of fact, write it out with the address, and I will do it for you. I also have a telegram to send today."

"Nu! Such a generous offer! I can pay, of course, but—"

"No. This one is a gift from a grateful captain to you. Your students were the best behaved in the Old City when I made the rounds with the commission. I had not a moment of worry in the Torah school. That was the only time I breathed all day long."

And so it was settled. *Such a gift!* The rabbi carefully penned his message. Not too many words, lest he cause the English captain unnecessary expense and thus take unfair advantage.

MAZEL TOV YACOV SEND PASSPORT PHOTOS BIRTH CERTIFICATES IMMEDIATELY JERUSALEM STOP GRANDFATHER

Afterward he wondered if he should have added the word LOVE before his signature. But he decided they knew he loved them. Otherwise, who would be *meshugge* enough to stand in line all day at the immigrations office?

————

It was Friday in Jerusalem, the Muslim holy day. The plaintive cry of the muezzin echoed from the tall minaret over the domed roofs and courtyards of Jerusalem.

Within the high, crenelated walls of the Old City, brown eyes turned with reverence toward the Dome of the Rock. Arab merchants shuttered their shops and joined the press of the crowds moving slowly toward the holy mountain.

Here Abraham had offered Isaac to God. Here Solomon had built his temple, and the glory of the Lord had filled it. Here Jesus had driven out money-changers from the courtyards and had proclaimed himself to be the Living Water that could quench the thirst of Jerusalem and all mankind. Here the battering rams and fires of Roman generals had left the Holy Mount desolate and without one stone upon another until the Muslims claimed it seven hundred years later. A varied history of bloodshed and brutality followed as the site passed from the hands of Muslim to Crusader and back again. Several hundred years of Muslim-Turkish rule had left Jerusalem a picture of squalor and disease. But even that did not change the fact that the site was holy to three faiths.

English soldiers stood as watchmen on the walls now. What did these Englishmen know? They were newcomers. They had arrived to liberate the city from the Turks and the Germans in 1917. It was the opinion of every sector of the Old City that the British were a silly bunch. They would soon be gone. They did not understand the tight-rope life here in Palestine. Their military governors were constantly tripping over the boundaries, sending thousands of years of tradition crashing to the stones. City water lines, electric lights, telephones had all come with the British Mandate. But none of it had yet reached through the gates of the Wall into the Old City.

Here, information was carried the old-fashioned way: from mouth to ear to mouth. Who needed telephones? Cooking was done on the little kerosene primus stoves. Lights were lit with matches. Matches were modern enough for the residents of the Old City. Water was stored in cisterns as God sent the rains to the city. It had always been that way, had it not?

Muslims worshiped on Friday. Jews on Saturday. Christians on Sunday. That way everyone got a day of rest of his very own.

On this day, as the Muslims spread their prayer rugs and listened to the resounding voice of their Grand Mufti, the Jewish women of the Old City pondered a modern problem in the local soup kitchen. This problem had been thrust upon them against their will. Crates of small colored boxes filled with powder had arrived in their kitchen from faraway America. The crates did not contain something useful like bullion. No. On the outside of the crates was the word: *JELL-O.* This was followed by *CHERRY* or *LIME*. The gift had come from a bigwig executive who worked for this company in America. He had visited the Tipat Chalev soup kitchen and gone away with his conscience stirred. *How could children live without Jell-O flavored gelatin?* He had sent enough to make certain that each child in the Old City Jewish Quarter would enjoy the benefits of the squiggly stuff and not grow up deprived.

Crates cluttered the dining room. Loose packets overflowed a table where the women kitchen volunteers pondered the generosity of the American.

"*Meshugge!* The man is totally *meshugge!* So why didn't he send shoes to the children?" asked Hannah Cohen as she stacked small packets of cherry gelatin in front of her.

"We can't cook shoes, Hannah." Rabbi Shlomo Lebowitz narrowed his eyes as he scanned the place. "If he worked for a shoe factory he would have sent shoes, nu? The man's whole life is Jell-O. True. Of course true! What else would he send?"

"Oy! But is this stuff *kosher*? I ask you," moaned Shoshanna Reingolt. "Can we *eat* it? I ask you."

Rabbi Lebowitz bit his lip and grimaced as he plunged a finger into an opened box and then into his mouth. "Sour! Oy!"

"You taste it without knowing if it's kosher?" exclaimed Hannah.

The rabbi licked his lips. "He seemed like a nice Jewish boy, this Mr. Lipwitz. A nice American-Jewish boy. Why would he send us something that wasn't kosher?" He grimaced again. "Even if it does taste terrible?"

Hannah and Shoshanna followed his lead. They dipped their fingers into the package of red powder and tasted. "PHUI! Gevalt! Oy! Oy! Oy! This nice Jewish boy thinks the children will eat this stuff?"

"He wasn't a boy exactly. Fifty is not a boy. He was old enough to know kosher, so I don't think we need to question the rabbi," said Hannah through gritted teeth.

Rabbi Lebowitz stared hard at the writing on the box. "We need someone who reads English. That is what we need. How are we supposed to figure out how to prepare this if we cannot read English? True? Of course true!"

The rabbi and the women were silent as they considered the problem. Tipat Chalev looked like a warehouse. The stuff might be kosher, but it tasted like poison. They could not read the instructions on the boxes. What had begun as an afternoon of excitement and joy with the twelve-donkey delivery of the crates had turned into sheer frustration.

"Well." The rabbi shook his head. "The modern world has invaded us. *Nu!*" This last syllable was uttered with a sigh of despair.

"Twelve donkeys' worth! Oy!" Hannah rested her chin on her hand.

"The children will expect to sample this great gift from the American bigwig." Shoshanna sized up the problem as she gestured toward the windows and two dozen faces gawking in.

"We need an Englishman." Rabbi Lebowitz thumped his hand on the table, sending a tower of Jell-O cartons toppling down. "An *Englishman* will know how to read the instructions, and I know one who will help."

"Yes. We need an Englishman!" agreed Hannah and Shoshanna in chorus.

Englishmen were as plentiful in Jerusalem these days as this unwanted Jell-O. The trick was to find one who could translate the directions from English to Yiddish. Or at least Arabic, which almost everyone spoke in the Old City. These English fellows seldom bothered to learn more than the rudiments of local dialect. They seemed to believe that English was the first language created by God and everyone else, therefore, should learn to speak it.

"Such a problem." The old man stood and slipped one packet of lime and one of cherry into his coat pocket.

"Going somewhere?" Hannah asked suspiciously. "Leaving this to me and Shoshanna, are you?"

He squared his shoulders. They ached from the burden of sixty-two years and this long day of work. "I am going to the post office." He produced a letter addressed to his daughter and the new baby in Warsaw. "If I miss the mail it will be Monday before I can get this off to Warsaw." He pursed his lips. "Besides, will we find an Englishman if we just sit here?"

"But what should we do with this stuff?" Shoshanna was not really asking. It was a statement of dismay.

"Send down to the Yeshiva school. Get some young men to move it," he answered as he shuffled toward the heavy wood door. "Tell Eli Sachar we need help moving boxes," he instructed. "He will pick the strongest students and send them to help. And I will bring back instructions for preparing this rat poison."

At that, Hannah put her hand to her throat. Perhaps it *was* rodent poison! Perhaps the nice American Jew had not meant for this powder to be eaten by humans at all. Ah, well. They would know soon enough. Either they would die, or Rabbi Lebowitz would come back with an Englishman!

To any righteous Jew it was a great honor to be chosen *sandek*, or godfather, at the circumcision of an infant. For Aaron and Etta Lubetkin, their choice of sandek for baby Yacov had become a matter of discussion among the community.

Dr. Eduard Letzno, the apostate Jew, the Zionist who no longer believed in the Eternal, took his place in the seat of the sandek as the circumcision ceremony began.

This apikoros wore a prayer shawl. On his head he wore a yarmulke just as any devout Jew must wear, but he had no beard. He fooled no one! His suit was cut like those of the people in Saturday Warsaw. He was no longer one of them. Why then, had Rabbi Lubetkin chosen such a man to be godfather for his son?

This was *such* a question! Oy! Frau Rosen led the yentas in the discussion. Would the Eternal bless this occasion? they asked. The kibitzers answered with a thousand clucks of their tongues and wags of their heads. "Oy! Oy! *Oy!* Such *gehokteh tsuris!*"

This phrase had been chosen as appropriate for the occasion of a circumcision; it meant "chopped-up troubles!" The yentas were careful not to let Rabbi Lubetkin and Etta hear their disapproval, however.

Frau Rosen hissed quietly like a steam radiator in the corner. "After all, nu? Nu! It is the privilege of the Papa and Mama to pick the *worst* sort of *trayfnyak* for the sandek if they wish!"

"Oy! They have done that!"

The yentas gathered around Frau Rosen as if to warm themselves by a stove.

"*God forbid* something should happen to Aaron and Etta! Oy! To think that the baby should be raised by such a *metsieh*!"

"He is no bargain! Oy gevalt!"

"Even if the man *is* as unkosher as ham, what business is it of ours? I ask you."

"Etta's father the rabbi would have something to say about this, I can tell you! You think a rabbi in Jerusalem would stand for such a thing? Oy! This Letzno fellow is practically one of the goyim himself!"

"True, true! But I know for a fact that Eduard Letzno comes from a good family. Even if he is a black sheep, he was *also* circumcised! You can't put *that* back!"

Hearts fluttering with the shock of it; tongues wagging with the sensation of it, the yentas of Warsaw lined up to witness the Brith of tiny Yacov Lubetkin.

A few feet away in the crowded room, Rachel eyed them angrily. She did not approve entirely of Dr. Letzno as choice of godfather for her brother, but the gossip of these women caused her cheeks to glow red with indignation. She, too, wished that he had a beard and dressed like a proper Jew, but Papa said that the heart of Eduard Letzno was sealed in the Covenant even though he lived like a goy! After all, had he not been the first doctor on the scene when the homeless Jews from Germany had been so much in need? His heart was Jewish, Papa said. So maybe he didn't need a beard.

Anyway, Rachel was certain that the baby would not mind *who* held him during the ceremony. Maybe Dr. Letzno could grow a beard before he saw Yacov next time. Then Yacov would not remember that it was the doctor who held him when Mohel used the circumcision knife! Rachel hated that part of the ceremony. Just the thought of her baby brother feeling pain made her head swim. And she was not the only one!

A chair was provided behind Mama . . . just in case. She had fainted when Samuel had been circumcised. This, too, had given the yentas something to talk about.

At last, all was accomplished for tiny Yacov Lubetkin as it had been for every Jewish male since the time of Abraham and Isaac. The baby slept peacefully in his cradle as the guests filed out with words of *Mazel Tov!* In the end it made no difference that Eduard Letzno was sandek. Everyone knew the apostate doctor was leaving for Palestine in three days anyway, so, the Eternal be praised, he would not be around to influence the life of the littlest Lubetkin! *Oy! Such a relief!*

Eduard and Aaron closed the study door and prepared to close a final chapter in their friendship together.

"There are several thousand new refugees in Palestine, and a shortage of doctors. But even if I was not needed there, I would not stay in Poland, Aaron. The very fact that your congregation is playing such a part in helping the refugees at—"

"Every Jewish welfare agency in Poland is helping," Aaron protested. "Why would I be singled out?"

"Because you are my friend." Eduard's dark eyes radiated concern.

"Do not flatter yourself, Eduard!" Aaron laughed. "You are not that important, nu? The Poles should suspect me because we grew up together and played stickball on the same team?"

Eduard shrugged. He was not laughing. "Men have been arrested for less."

"In Germany, perhaps."

"The voice of Hitler reaches even to Warsaw."

"And to Palestine. One place is as safe as another for us, Eduard. I am no Zionist. My congregation . . . my life . . . is here in Warsaw."

"Where the Catholic anti-Semites despise you."

"And in Palestine the Muslim Mufti makes speeches. Etta and I have decided . . ."

"Etta would like to go home to Jerusalem." Eduard crossed his arms as though this was his final argument.

"Etta is my wife." Aaron lowered his voice. "She will stay here with me and my children in Warsaw." He frowned. "Do not push me too far, Eduard."

The silence between the two men was uncomfortable. Eduard stared up at the leather-bound volumes of Aaron's library—all books of Hebrew literature and law. Aaron Lubetkin was an important scholar in the Jewish community in Warsaw. In Jerusalem, in the shadow of the Western Wall, there was a surplus of rabbinical scholars.

Eduard let his breath out slowly. "Yes. Well. I suppose I can practice medicine anywhere. But I see your point. A rabbi must have a congregation."

Aaron smiled. "My congregation is here in Warsaw. We are three million strong here in Poland. Only half a million in the Mandate. If you find a congregation for me in Jerusalem, then perhaps . . ."

23

Rendezvous

The vaulted stone roof of the Tipat Chalev soup kitchen was an acoustic masterpiece. The clatter of one tin plate on the floor would ring as if an entire shelf of plates had collapsed. The scraping of a spoon against a porridge bowl reverberated like the clanging mess kits of ten thousand half-starved soldiers.

People came to Tipat Chalev to eat, not talk. If they had to talk when the room was packed with hungry diners, they shouted. Or they went outside.

Such acoustics left room for only one speaker at a time to be heard and understood. When the kitchen volunteers were confronted with the sight of people coming through the door, they revved up their speaking volume to full blast.

Perhaps that is why Hannah Cohen now stood before half a dozen Yeshiva students and shouted orders at the top of her lungs. "Oy! Eli Sachar! Pick up your end of the crate higher! HIGHER! Now you! Ari! Lower your end! Careful as you back down the stairs! Oy! Do not drop this Jell-O stuff! Such a mess! Such a mess!"

Her voice ricocheted off the ceiling and slammed around the room, splitting the eardrums of Eli and his fellow students.

"EL-I-I-I! Not sooooo high! You'll scrape the doorframe! Nu! Josef just painted that doorframe!"

Eli tried to nod his apology around the heavy crate. He backed cautiously down the narrow basement stairs as the densely packed Jell-O crate threatened to break loose from Ari's grip and slam down.

"ELI-I-I! Do not let go! Oy! The crate will knock you down the stairs backward if you let go! *Careful* there! It will knock you over and you will break your neck and then what will I say to your mother, dear Ida, when you are dead from moving rat poison? *Careful*, Ari!"

If Eli had not been in such a tenuous position on the down side of a three-hundred-pound crate, he would have been irritated at Hannah Cohen. She was his landlady. She owned Cohen's Grocery and he could also hear her in the store when she transacted business. Nobody talked as loudly as Hannah Cohen. Mama had said they would get used to her long discussions about bananas and crackers or kosher sausage, but Eli had never quite gotten used to her piercing voice.

To have to listen to her today was almost unbearable! Today was the day when he would meet Victoria in Christ Church! And here he was, when he should have been dressing in his goyim clothes! How could this be? Why him, of all the Yeshiva students?

At the bottom of the stairs they manuvered around sacks of lentils, finally placing the crate according to Hannah Cohen's instructions. Eli mopped his brow. Ari mopped his brow and sighed. Hannah mopped her brow and sighed and thanked the Eternal no one was killed by this cursed stuff.

Panting with exhaustion after watching the dangerous descent, Hannah boomed down to Eli, "I asked for you *special*, Eli! Such a *strong* boy! Oy! If only I had been blessed with such a strong son to help me at the market, then maybe my back would not ache so bad, nu?" She touched her back and grimaced. Just watching the strong young men had made her ache! But it had not managed to lower the volume of her voice.

The knowledge that she had asked for him hit Eli with a hot rush of irritation. But he could not let on. Mama and Mrs. Cohen were friends, after all, and it would not do to have her saying to Mama, *Something is bothering Eli, nu? Tell me, Ida. You can tell me. I love him like a son . . .*

Eli gulped air and swallowed his first urge to shout back at her. "Always a pleasure to help you, Mrs. Cohen." He regretted saying that. What if she asked him to carry boxes of fruit for her sometime? Ah, well. Better to be polite than shake his fist in her face. "But now, I must leave. The others will manage without me. I have a . . . I was studying a passage of the Mishnah and suddenly . . . *such* a thought! It came to me as I was moving this crate! About the heaviness of a man's burdens. And so I must go write it down."

She clapped her hands once in awe. "Not only strong and handsome, but *smart*! So *proud* Ida must be!"

Ari was scowling at Eli as he ascended the steps to take leave of the work crew. Eli bowed slightly to Mrs. Cohen and then gave Ari the sort of look that said, *Too bad I thought of it first, eh?*

"*Such* a rabbi this one will make!" Hannah Cohen finally let her voice grow quiet in awe of the retreating Eli Sachar.

Out on the street and half a block away, Eli could hear her as she resumed her duties as supervisor. "PICK THAT END UP! LOWER!

WATCH OUT FOR THE DOORFRAME! NU! WATCH IT! OY! OYYYYYYY!"

The lobby of the King David Hotel seemed nearly deserted compared to the activity during Leah and Shimon's first day in Jerusalem.

"They've all gone to Galilee to guard the Woodhead Commission," volunteered the desk clerk as he took the receipt of Leah's cello. "They'll be back next week. Probably ready for an encore performance from you. Of course, a good concert will not make as much impression on them as an Arab attack, that is certain."

A portly English businessman overheard his words and volunteered, "That's the difference between the Arabs and the Jews, eh? The Royal Commission will be more impressed by explosions than good music. We'll be seeing the last of European Jews arriving here. I'm sure of that."

Perhaps the man was not aware that he was speaking to recent arrivals. Or perhaps he knew very well whom he was talking to. The thought that Jewish immigration might soon be halted altogether did not seem to be a concern. His expression did not alter when the desk clerk handed the instrument to Shimon.

For a moment Leah considered commenting on the tragedy the closing of Palestine would be to those who remained in Europe with no escape, but the words would be wasted on a man such as this.

At that moment, Victoria Hassan emerged from the administrative wing of the hotel. She glanced toward them. Leah was certain Victoria saw them standing at the counter, but the young woman averted her eyes and hurried on as if they were not there.

Shimon nudged Leah. He had seen her, too. He had noticed the way she hurried from the building. Leah sighed, feeling again that she had somehow insulted Victoria. She would be glad when Tuesday arrived so she could ask her.

Through the glass revolving door, Leah watched her. She was, indeed, beautiful. Sunlight gleamed in her long black hair. She wore a dark blue dress of simple cut adorned only by a silver chain necklace. High heels showed shapely legs. It was no wonder that Eli Sachar was interested in her. She did not seem to fit the Muslim world.

Leah resolved that she would tell Eli they had seen her leaving the hotel this afternoon. Any news of her at all might cheer him up.

Eli hurried toward the restrooms where Moshe had stowed a carefully wrapped set of khaki-colored clothes on top of a high water tank.

He slipped into an empty stall. A feeling of awe filled him! Mama would never suspect that he had gone to visit his Muslim sweetheart in a Christian church! All she would hear was how much he had helped

Hannah Cohen. How lucky she was to have such a son! How Hannah Cohen wished she had a crate hauler to call son!

He changed quickly, wrapped his Orthodox garb into the same paper and slipped it back on the tank. At this moment the first misgivings whispered in his ear. To walk from this place pretending to be anything other than a Jew was most certainly a sin. And to walk into a Christian church! Oy! The thought of it made him shudder.

He stared thoughtfully at the green moss on the walls of the lavatory. Outside he could hear merchants and peddlers hawking their wares. Would anyone notice that a Jew had entered the tiny cubicle, but a goy now emerged?

Eli drew a deep breath and winced from the rank odor in the air. Things would be better outside, he decided; he would think more clearly in the street. With that, he squared his shoulders and walked out into the teeming crowds in the souk.

Without the feather-like weight of his yarmulke on his head, Eli felt strangely undressed. In his khaki trousers and shirt, he blended easily with the English civil servants and off-duty soldiers strolling through Armenian Quarter. No one noticed him. No one at all. And yet he felt self-conscious. These English clothes were not for him. They felt sinful against his skin.

He walked quickly down St. James Road toward the Old City Wall. Just ahead was the Armenian Patriarchate Street, which ran parallel with the wall. The Byzantine tower of St. James Church was to the left. Christ Church was a short walk to the right, just past the barracks of the British soldiers and the headquarters of the Palestine police. In this ancient stone barracks known as Kishleh, every army since the time of Suleiman had housed its occupation forces. English soldiers with clean-shaven cheeks and short haircuts walked in and out of the building. They looked more at ease than Eli today, even though Jerusalem had always been his home.

He had been a toddler the same year that the English General Allenby had stood on a platform in front of Christ Church to accept the official surrender of the Turkish rulers—1917. What a year of hope that had been! Religious tolerance had been proclaimed right in this place as Eli's father had held him aloft in the cheering crowds. Christian, Jew, and Arab alike had formed committees to clean out the sewage from the moat that surrounded the Old City wall. Eli had grown up believing that one day there would be a Jewish homeland as the British promised. He had grown up with Ibrahim and Victoria and a dozen other Arab children who had mingled freely in their games. No one had been afraid then. Times were better than they had been with the brutal Turkish government. Until Haj Amin became Mufti, there had been peace. Eli never imagined that one day he would be sneaking out of the Jewish Quarter to meet Victoria in a place like this.

In all his years he had never set foot in a Christian church. That thought chafed his conscience just as the strange clothes seemed to chafe his skin. He prayed no one would recognize him: *"I saw a goy who looked just like you!"*

He told himself that he was here for Victoria. Here to finish their discussion. To be his wife she *must* convert! And for that one reason he had left his Orthodox clothing wrapped up and stowed on the water tank. On Yom Kippur, Eli would confess this sin to the Eternal and ask forgiveness. Somehow the end would justify his sacrifice of tradition for the sake of love. Would God see it his way? he wondered. Or was the Eternal looking on with disapproval already because Eli was even now breaking laws regarding the proper dress of a Jew? The thought made him shudder. It made no difference that he blended with the crowds. God was still watching. And Eli was about to enter Christ Church and sit quietly pretending to be one of *them* so he could be with *her*!

To his left, British guards stood in stone niches on either side of the iron gate of the citadel. Above them, soldiers patrolled the ramparts of the city wall. Eli stood for a moment pretending to study the young English protectors of Jerusalem. He considered the fact that it was still not too late to turn back. Still not too late to retrieve his clothing from the hiding place and return to Tipat Chalev to move what remained of the crates. He did not have to go through the great iron gate on his right and enter the courtyard of Christ Church.

He had not dared to look at the church. He had averted his eyes from the bell tower during the walk. *I do not have to enter,* he thought now as he pivoted to face the entrance. *Perhaps she will come here from the opposite direction and I will take her by the arm and we will find some other place—any place besides this place!*

Soldiers passed. An Armenian priest passed. Victoria did not come. He stared through the wrought iron into the courtyard of the church where an enormous oleander bloomed and plum trees dropped their leaves in memory of autumn in faraway England where their mother trees grew. Everything about this place was foreign. The English had built this stone church to lure Jews away from their faith, Eli had heard. He had grown up with the warning ringing in his ears that he must be polite to *them,* but he must not go into their building. Men entered as Jews and left as something else.

Minutes crawled by. Eli was angry at himself that he had thought this was such a good idea. He should have sent Moshe back with an alternate plan! But then, Moshe had also thought the strategy was sound.

A gardener worked beneath a plum tree. He raked and piled purple leaves onto the flagstones. Eli watched him, then turned and looked unhappily up the street toward Omar Square again. If she was coming that way, he would have seen her already. That meant she had either changed her mind, or she was already in *there.*

He drew a breath and stepped forward, laying a hand against the wrought-iron bars of the gate. *Still I have not entered. A silly thing to be this nervous. Moshe would not be nervous. Moshe sees them all the time.*

The wizened old gardener straightened his back for a moment, then leaned heavily on his rake. He was also dressed in rumpled khaki. He was an Englishman. Eli could tell easily by the white straw hat and the bright blue eyes that sparkled out from beneath folds of skin.

"Lovely day, isn't it?" the old man said to Eli after a moment.

Eli answered with a nod. He did not wish to give away his origins by speaking.

"Just raking up the last of the plums. The ones the birds got." He stooped and picked out a large half-eaten plum from among the leaves. "What a waste. Paid a boy to shoo them away, but more kept flying in. Finally, I gave the tree to the birds. There are no finer plums in Jerusalem. Don't mind sharing with the sparrows if they just wouldn't waste!" The old man stared at the plum, then glanced at Eli. He studied Eli with the same intensity with which he had looked at the plum. "Waiting for someone?"

Eli nodded again. He tried a slight smile for the sake of politeness.

"You won't find her out here." The gardener scratched his head. He tossed away the plum and scowled up at the ungrateful birds.

"Who?" Eli was startled by the old man's seeming knowledge of *her . . .* He took his hand off the iron gate as if it might burn him.

"Victoria. Are you not here for Victoria? She has been in the chapel." He looked at the sky as if it were a clock. "Half an hour. She was early. Come in! I did not notice you there, or I would have told you sooner. Come on. Through the gate and that way." He pointed his rake toward the entrance of the church, then returned to his work as Eli held his breath and plunged that first step into the courtyard of Christ Church.

The letter to Etta was duly deposited into the mail slot at the Mandate post office in Allenby Square. The old rabbi knew that it would take at least eight weeks to arrive in Warsaw. First it would travel by slow boat to England. Once there, it might float aimlessly from this capital to that. *Oy! The frustration!* But at least it was quicker now than it had been when he was a boy. Then it had taken maybe eight months for a letter to go from Jerusalem to Warsaw. And sometimes it did not arrive at all.

Ah, well. Rabbi Lebowitz himself was slowing down these days. The heat of the afternoon seemed to push him backward as he leaned into the incline up toward Jaffa Gate. He raised his eyes to heaven and smiled. The Jell-O in his pockets seemed to call, *Look up on the wall, old man! There are English soldiers there, nu?*

"Yes! Enough! I see them already!" The old rabbi passed through the teeming gate and turned right along the road of the Armenian patriarchate. The barracks of the Old City British soldiers was along this road, near to Christ Church. Plenty of Englishmen there might be willing to explain the mystery of the lime and the cherry powders.

He yawned wearily and studied the faces of the soldiers in search for *the one* who might meet his eyes and be of service to the cooks of Tipat Chalev.

Soldiers emerged from the stone barracks along the wall. Other soldiers stood in the niches on guard against wild Arab bands and old Jewish rabbis with bombs disguised as Jell-O packets. *Who to ask?* There was an abundance of Englishmen here, all moving this way or that without stopping.

Rabbi Lebowitz stopped in the center of the cobbled road. He frowned. He squinted. He shaded his eyes against the glare. There, in front of the gate of Christ Church, was a young Englishman dressed all in khaki who looked very much—no, *exactly* like young Eli Sachar!

But of course it could not *be* Eli Sachar. Eli was back at Tipat Chalev moving crates of this loathsome, troublesome stuff. The old man removed a box from his pocket and held it up to hail the young man at the gate.

Such similarity could not be ignored! God had sent this English look-alike especially to help, the old man was certain. He could say, *"You look just like a young fellow only a few blocks from here! Come see . . . and while you're at it, there is this stuff from America!"*

A crowd of Armenian school children passed between the old man and the miraculous twin. And at that moment, *OY!* the young man who looked like Eli Sachar but who could not *be* Eli Sachar stepped through the gate of Christ Church.

This was also proof that the young man could not be Eli. Every old one in the Jewish Quarter remembered the reason all the Sachars avoided passing within the shadow of Christ Church. Some, over the years, had even walked on the opposite side of the street from the building, while the more devout among them took a different route altogether.

But still, might this be some descendant of that early apostate Sachar who had walked into Christ Church a Jew and emerged as something else? Interesting. "Perhaps I should wait," the old man mumbled out loud. "There are reasons why these things happen."

Behind him the horn of a military truck blared loudly. He jumped and whirled as if he were a young man. Then he forgot all about the Sachar relative. He dropped the box of lime Jell-O as he leaped to the side.

The truck pulled up in front of the barracks and the British captain, Samuel Orde, climbed out.

The officer strode directly toward the old rabbi, his hand extended. "So sorry!" he apologized. "The driver was watching the children, and . . . are you all right?"

Rebbe Lebowitz smiled. Everyone in the Old City knew that Captain Samuel Orde was fluent in several languages. No doubt he was familiar with Jell-O.

"Just the fellow!" the rabbi cried happily. "Such meetings are not accidental, you know. You have nearly run me down just at a time when I need your help." He thrust the box into the captain's hand. "A gift from America. Crates and crates for Tipat Chalev. We do not know if we should eat it or clean the sinks with it!" The rabbi paused as Orde grinned broadly.

"It may be difficult without proper refrigeration, Rabbi."

"Proper . . . you *freeze* it?"

Orde laughed. He nudged his cap back on his head. "There might be something down at the quartermaster's warehouse. Perhaps we could make a trade. Tipat Chalev and the British Army, eh?"

The old rabbi nodded slowly. These Englishmen were really good fellows. It had been much better in Jerusalem since they had come. First the mail delivery had speeded up, and now this. Who cared so much if they sent their little fact-finding committees—as long as they only talked.

"Powdered milk? Maybe cocoa?" he grinned slyly.

"Into the truck with you." Captain Orde gave the order. "We'll see what we can do."

The Eternal be praised! All along the Merciful One had this in mind. Oy! Still sending manna in strange ways, nu? Giving this Englishman an afternoon of rest from guiding his silly politicians around Jerusalem. And all so you can bring powdered milk and cocoa to your children at Tipat Chalev! True? Of course true!

The rasping noise of the rake followed Eli beneath the high stone portals of a building that seemed to have been transported from the English countryside. He knew a little about Christ Church. His great-grandfather had fought against its erection as the first Protestant church inside the walls of Jerusalem. *We fear these English missionaries,* the old man had written in his journal in 1838. *They capture the minds of our youth and pull them from their roots. . . .* The old rabbi's battle against the *London Society for Promotion of Christianity Amongst the Jews* was still remembered. When the Protestants had opened a medical clinic, so had the Jewish Quarter. Other sects had become worried by the activities of these Protestants. A healthy competition sprang up because of it, and Jerusalem had become a better place. But in the end, a son of the old Rabbi Sachar had converted. He had walked through these portals a Jew and had emerged *something else.*

Eli looked up at the Gothic arches and wondered what thoughts must have gone through the mind of that young man to make him abandon his faith and his people? Since that day until this, no Sachar had ever set foot on the ground of Christ Church! Not until now! Eli wondered what the old rabbi would have said if he could have seen this moment.

He pushed the doors open and entered the auditorium. Spare and Gothic in construction, the place was one of the few buildings in Jerusalem with a wooden roof. *So English!* And yet in the center panel of the altar a Star of David and a crown were inlaid in the wood. There was no sign of the fearsome Christian cross in this building. Eli sighed with a release of tension. There were no graven images like the ones sold to pilgrims in the souks. No plaster saints. Only high stone walls and stained-glass windows and wooden chairs on the stone floor, and . . . *Victoria!*

She sat in a shadow at the very back of the church. She did not hear him come in, so he let the heavy door swing shut with a dull boom. She started, turned, and smiled with relief, motioning him to join her.

Every doubt, every feeling of foreboding melted away from him. He forgot about his clothing. He thought no more of his apostate great-uncle and the fury of the old Rabbi Sachar! He rushed down the side aisle. She stood and stretched out her arms to embrace him. And then, even here, Victoria kissed him, and Eli forgot entirely that they were beneath the wooden roof of the much-feared Christ Church! He could think of nothing but Victoria. Why had he ever worried? She loved him! That was all that mattered.

He stroked her soft hair and held her close. Delicate arms squeezed him as if she were afraid to let him go. He whispered her name. It was like a prayer.

"I thought you were not coming," she said at last. "I was so afraid you had changed your mind."

He pulled her deeper into the shadow of a pillar and kissed her again. "I have thought only of you." The words were almost entirely true. The doubts meant nothing now that they were together. It was always like that.

She took his hand and led him to the chairs. "We have to talk, darling. So much to talk about."

He did not want to talk, but he nodded and sat beside her. She leaned against his arm and he held her hand. He was grateful that they were alone in this place. Yes, there was much to talk about, but for a while, he simply wanted to sit here beside her and cherish her nearness.

24

The Barter

It seemed like a long time before Victoria raised her head and spoke. Her words were not about love, however. "Ibrahim is angry with me." Her dark eyes flashed resentment when she spoke the name of her brother. "He says he will not help us any longer."

"But *why?*" Such news startled Eli. All along he had interpreted lack of communication as a sign that Victoria had decided against his proposal. But it had meant something else.

"Because I would not promise him that I will not go . . . away with you."

"He knows how we feel," Eli protested.

"He hopes that you will join our people. He will not tolerate it if I should be the one to leave." She clutched his hand and stared bleakly up at the red glass of a window. "There is something terrible coming, Eli. My half brothers talk quietly among themselves. They become silent when I enter."

"Do they know? About us?"

Victoria shook her head. "Ibrahim will not tell them. I am certain of that. They would kill you, or have you killed. He does not like it that you have not joined our people, but he would never go so far." She bit her lip. "No. It is something else. Something . . . terrible," she finished lamely, letting her hands fall to her lap.

"Then we must settle this, Victoria." He was resolute. He took both of her hands in his. "I will speak with my parents and with the rabbis. We will settle the matter."

She shook her head. "I . . . I can't. Please, Eli. I just need a little time." She sighed and leaned against his arm again. "I am afraid."

Eli smiled in spite of her fears. He had won. She would be his wife. He would not tell her now that their marriage would mean he could not be a rabbi. He did not seem to hear anything else. "It will be all right now." He touched her cheek. "This is a good place to meet. We will come here every Friday, nu? Just like this. Time will pass quickly, you will see."

She nodded. "But still I am afraid when I am not with you." She pressed her face harder against his arm as if she might burrow into him and hide. "I see it in their faces. Little Daud. There is such hate in him now. He was such a good little brother. But now—and Isaak! He hates every Englishman and every Jew. He asks me always to tell him about things the British have me type each day. At night they go to meetings." She paused as if the faces of her brothers were before her. "I am afraid for them." She glanced up at Eli. "They are my brothers, and I am afraid for them! They argue with Father about the Mufti. At the table they shout about the British and the Zionists. And my stepmother is one of them. I hear her after my brothers storm from the house."

Somehow Eli could not find it in himself to share her grief about the Hassan brothers. He could think only of the fact that, like Ruth of old, Victoria would leave her people to be with him. His God would be her God. His people, her people. Was there anything else in the world that mattered?

He gazed at the altar of Christ Church as she spoke softly of her brothers. Her voice was a distant sorrow that receded behind his joy. He smiled at the Star of David. Strange to see that symbol in a Christian church. He had not expected it. It seemed as if it had been placed there just for him, a good omen that this was the ideal place for them to meet. Victoria's voice seemed far away.

"... and Daud's face was bloody. But not his own blood..."

"Don't worry. We will come here often. Maybe more than just Friday. No one will know. Everything will work out, you'll see."

"They would not tell Father where they had been. And then we heard about the British sergeant killed in Ramle..."

"When the time is right we will marry and leave this place ..."

"It is so hard to think that my own brothers..."

"Perhaps we will make a life in America."

"They think they are right. They serve Haj Amin, Shetan himself, and yet they think they are right."

Their thoughts poured out like water, but the streams flowed in opposite directions. And so they passed the hour in conversation even though they were not speaking to each other.

"If only there was a way, Victoria," Eli sighed and traced the Hebrew writing on the altar cloth with his eyes. *Incline your ear, and come unto me: hear, and your soul shall live; and I will make an everlasting covenant with you....*

She raised her head as though she heard a distant voice. "Perhaps we do not have to wait so long." She squeezed his hand and new hope filled her face. She looked up at the lofty ceiling. "May Allah help us," she breathed.

"I will think what we must do, Victoria. I will send word to you with Leah Feldstein on Tuesday. Maybe by then I will have an answer." He touched her face and looked deeply into her eyes. "Until then I make a covenant with you. My heart is knit to yours." He gestured toward the altar. "Here, in this place that is neither yours nor mine, there are no rules or laws that would forbid our love. For this moment and forever, I am not a Jew and you are not a Muslim."

"You are not a Jew and I am not a Muslim," Victoria repeated.

Eli smiled wistfully. "I had an uncle who entered this place one time and left it another sort of man. I feel . . . I do not know *what* I feel being here with you on this neutral ground. But I will pray and think."

"I cannot think any longer, Eli." Victoria leaned her head against his shoulder. "You must think for us both, or I will break. I only know I love you, and that I am afraid."

Eli nodded. In his heart he whispered, *I will incline my ear to you, O God!*

Samuel Orde had never seen so much Jell-O—crates and crates of the stuff and anxious, unhappy Jewish faces looking hopefully at him.

"You think he will take it?"

"For milk and cocoa? You think they would exchange such shlock merchandise?"

These words were whispered in Yiddish as Samuel Orde strolled among the boxes labeled cherry and lime. He personally did not care for lime, but soldiers took what they were served and so the Old City troops would eat the stuff and like it. He would arrange the matter with the company cook and quartermaster. Here also was a chance to rid the warehouse of a ton of rock-hard English walnuts that the cooks had been cursing since their arrival a fortnight before!

"The merchandise appears to be in order." Orde peered thoughtfully at a crate in the basement. The whispers at the top of the stairs grew silent with hopeful anticipation.

Can the Englishman be such a fool?

The old rabbi rocked coyly back and forth on his heels in an effort not to appear too eager. "Powdered milk *and* cocoa?"

"Yes, yes."

"And also!" The rabbi held his finger aloft. "Sugar? Flour, perhaps?"

Orde considered the request a moment. The cooks would not stand for sugar and flour to be traded. "No." He scratched his chin. "But perhaps we might throw in a few bags of good English walnuts. All the way from England. Very fine nuts they are, too."

Eyes lit up. Women restrained from allowing excited exclamations to escape their mouths. *Such a delicacy! Walnuts for the making of baklava and a thousand wondrous things! Could this Englishman mean such a thing?*

Rabbi Lebowitz tugged his beard as he pretended to consider. "How many bags of walnuts, Captain Orde?"

Orde mentally calculated. Of course they could have them all. They could use them as weapons against Arabs if nothing else. Perhaps shoot a few pigeons with slingshots. "I believe there are two or three dozen gunny sacks still in the warehouse."

"Not wormy, are they?" The old rabbi scowled cautiously.

"On my word!" Orde declared.

Another moment of hesitation, then Rabbi Lebowitz extended his hand. "A bargain, then! Five hundred pounds of milk. Twenty-five pounds of cocoa. And, God be praised . . . walnuts!"

———

Eli returned to the Jewish Quarter with his khaki clothes wadded up beneath his arm. He was smiling, relieved that there was no question of Victoria's feeling for him. *Time.* That was all she needed. Her request did not frighten him.

Two young Torah schoolboys charged past him on the street as if they were being pursued. Soon it would be Shabbat. Everyone in the Quarter seemed to be rushing around to get ready for the holy day of rest!

Eli let his breath out slowly. On this Shabbat he would truly be at rest. He strolled easily through the lanes of his neighborhood. Once again his eyes were able to focus on the faces of the people, on the cluttered shops and the round-bellied merchants who hailed him as he passed. Victoria would marry him. She would convert, and though they might have to leave Jerusalem, his heart would not have to leave his people!

"Eli!" A familiar voice called his name. "Eli! Come quickly!" The rusty voice of Rabbi Lebowitz shouted all the way from the steps of Tipat Chalev. "It will be Shabbat soon and we need to move these bags of walnuts!"

Eli did not mind this interruption. He quickened his pace as the cry of distress demanded, but he felt no resentment as the rabbi waved him up the steps and into the dining room where heaps of gunny sacks were stacked almost to the vaulted ceiling.

Six other rabbinical students had likewise been hauled into the task of shifting a ton of walnuts to the basement. Eli did not ask where they had come from. Nothing surprised him anymore, except the fact that his own black mood had evaporated.

He tossed the small bundle of clothes onto the table as Rabbi Lebowitz began shouting instructions.

"Eli! You and Yossi take that stack there, and . . ." For a moment the voice of the rabbi faltered. He looked at the clothes and then at Eli. Confusion crossed his face. He blinked at Eli, swallowed hard, and then began again. "Yes. I was saying . . . that stack there. If we hurry we will beat Queen Shabbat before she arrives, nu, Eli?"

————

If ever Eli had been foolish, this quiet Shabbat evening was the night. The candles were lit. The prayers were recited. The meal was served. All should have been at peace in the Sachar home.

Instead, Ida Sachar sobbed uncontrollably over her plate. "Oy! *Gottenyu!* My own son! The pride of my life, and now he tells us he is in love with a Muslim girl! Hermann! Hermann!"

"Be still, Ida!" Hermann snapped. But she would not be silenced.

Moshe looked at his distraught parents. He shook his head and threw his napkin on the table as he stood. "So he loves her! So my brother is in love with a woman who is not born on this side of the Street of the Chain! *So what?*" he yelled.

Hermann's face was purple with rage. "You be quiet also, Moshe! This does not concern you!"

Moshe defied his father. "Eli is my brother! It concerns me!"

Ida wailed and muttered, "Not one apostate son, but two! Oy! Where have I failed? What will the neighbors say?"

"Who cares what they say?" Moshe stood up, knocking his chair over.

"Go to your room!" Hermann pointed toward the stairs. "And if you do not show us respect, leave the house!"

Eli did not look up as Moshe shouted, "I'll do better than that! I will leave Jerusalem! And Palestine! This godforsaken heap of stone! I'm going to England to study as soon as my fellowship comes through, and Eli and his wife may come with me!" He stormed from the table.

"Two sons! Oy! Has a mother ever been so cursed?" Ida moaned and blew her nose.

"I love her," Eli said hoarsely. Why had he chosen tonight to tell them? Why had he not presented the marriage as accomplished? Ah, well, it would have been the same now or later.

"But she is not a Jew!" Ida wailed. "There are so many lovely girls in our Quarter! My grandchildren! What will the community say? And I was so *proud.*"

"Maybe too proud, Mama," Eli faltered.

Hermann slammed his fist on the table. "Leave us, Ida!" he bellowed.

"You will take his part!" she cried. "Listen to yourself! You will not be strong in this! That is why it has happened! You let the traditions of the family fall apart! You let Moshe go to Hebrew University instead of Yeshiva! *Now look!*"

Hermann glared at his weeping wife. "Leave us." His command was quiet, menacing.

"You will be sorry!" she shouted, running from the table and slamming every door in the house as she exited. "This is your fault! *Your* fault!" Her sobs echoed back down the hall from the bedroom.

For a full five minutes, Eli and his grim father sat in silence as they listened to the rise and fall of her grief.

At last Eli spoke. "You would think I died."

Hermann sighed. All the anger had dissipated into weariness. He spoke softly now, Ida's sobs a backdrop of grief to his words. "Do you know what your marriage to her would mean for you? For all of us? All your education, the sacrifice we have made for your schooling. It would not matter, Eli, if she converted. You would not even be fit to lead a congregation of lepers if your wife was an Arab." He paused, then laid down his napkin and rose slowly. "Think about it. You know what it will mean. You do not need the hysteria of your mother or the anger of your father to instruct you. You already know."

Eli nodded his head with a single jerk. He left his father standing in the dining room and retreated to the room he shared with Moshe.

It was semidark in the room, but Moshe sat in an overstuffed chair and pretended to study. He glanced up to see Eli stretch himself on his bed and turn his face to the wall. Moshe knew Eli wept only by the sound of an occasional sniff.

It seemed as if hours passed before Moshe spoke. "What will you do?"

Eli turned and wiped his eyes with the back of his hand. He sat up and wrapped his arms around his knees as he stared at the khaki shirt draped over the footboard of his bed. "Can I tear out the beard of my father? As long as I am here I must not see her again."

"But why?" Moshe tossed his book on the floor with an angry crash. "Can she not become a Jew?"

"She will never fit in. To marry her means that I turn my back on my faith and my family. You"—He searched Moshe's face—"could no longer call me your brother."

"Medieval nonsense!" scoffed Moshe.

"I would be dead to you. Dead."

"Turn your back on your faith? What are you talking about? So you will not be a rabbi! What has that got to do with anything?"

"You do not understand!" Eli looked away. "There is more to this than you know! More than I can tell you!"

"But you love her!" Moshe laughed in disbelief.

"Yes!" Eli cried. "So much that today I thought—" He did not finish. He did not tell Moshe that he had declared in Christ Church that for her sake he was no longer a Jew. "We shall not speak of it again, Moshe! I have much to think about. *What is right?* I do not know myself any longer! Too many voices!" Tears came to him again. "The world has gone mad, and we are in the center of its destruction!" He raised a hand to stop any further words from his brother. "No, Moshe! We shall not speak of it again!"

After a time the muffled sobs of Ida Sachar died away. Moshe's breath came in the deep, even rhythm of sleep. The moon rose over Jerusalem, outlining the city in crisp shadow. Only then did Eli get up. He stood at the window for a long time and looked toward the corner where Victoria would walk on her way to work. Then he looked toward the bell tower of Christ Church. He would not speak the deepest secrets of his heart to his family any longer. It would serve no purpose. For the sake of leaving his parents with at least one son in Moshe, Eli would not involve his brother. Moshe must not be implicated in his plan.

There in the moonlight, Eli steeled himself for what he must do. He would be alone in his decision. It must be so.

25

Wedding Day

Already the wagons of Warsaw's peddlers rumbled through the streets. The clop of horses' hooves against the cobblestones mingled with the voices of hawking merchants and bargaining housewives.

"Who could sleep with such a racket?" Etta Lubetkin asked as she braided her thick dark hair in the early morning light.

In the mirror she could see Aaron as he quietly recited the morning prayers. He held a finger to his lips, warning her to be silent until he uttered the final Omaine!

She simply redirected her chatter to the air. "Why should I be quiet when every peddler in Warsaw is screaming in the streets?" She studied her own reflection in the mirror. She was thirty-eight. Yes, it was time for those tiny lines around her clear blue eyes. Her skin was still as fair and fresh as it had been when she was a young girl in Jerusalem. Even after giving Aaron four children, her figure still delighted him. No doubt there would be other children if the Eternal, blessed be He, was willing. Aaron was certainly willing enough. He did not seem to notice those tiny lines around her eyes.

She glanced at his reflection in the mirror. He was praying toward Jerusalem, looking very handsome beneath his prayer shawl. He was concentrating very hard. Trying not to look at his wife sitting there in her white cotton shift as she plaited her hair. She was, he often said, his greatest distraction from things of the Almighty. Still beautiful at thirty-eight. Still as much on his mind as she had been when he had been a Yeshiva student in Jerusalem. He had married her before finishing his studies simply because without her he had been unable to think of anything but her.

And after the wedding? Aaron found that Etta offered him even more distraction and delight. At the advice of her revered father, the Rabbi

Lebowitz, he had begun to thank God for Etta every time she popped into his thoughts.

This morning as the sunlight streamed through the beveled-glass window to fall in little rainbows on her skin, Aaron closed his eyes tightly as he finished his prayers. ". . . And thank you, O Eternal, for the blessing of my wife. Omaine!"

At that, he turned and placed his strong hands on her shoulders and stooped to kiss her neck. His beard brushed her soft skin. She reached up and patted his head affectionately.

"You will be late to shul if you do not hurry," she warned as he kissed her again.

"Why are you not like other wives?" He did not move away. "Why are you not fat and shrill and harsh with me so that I can better study the Torah and discuss the words of the great rabbis without wishing I were here with you making more little Lubetkins?"

Etta laughed. "If you want me fat and shrill, just give me more little Lubetkins too soon, and I will grant your wish. Now really! You will be late to shul. They cannot start without you."

"Let them wait," he whispered. "You have rainbows on your skin."

"And what will you tell them when you are late?"

"That I was looking at rainbows."

"But the sky is clear."

"Then I will weep and say it rains." He kissed her once more as he had not dared to kiss her since the baby was born. "I have missed you," he whispered. "I will not be able to pray any prayer today except the prayer your father taught me: 'Thank you, O Eternal, for my Etta!' I will say it over and over and everyone will think I am meshugge!"

"You must go. You will be late." She said the words but did not push him away.

"Send David to tell them I am sick," he pleaded.

"A lie? You would put a lie on the lips of your son?"

Aaron smiled at his beautiful wife and pulled her toward the unmade bed. "Not a lie. Have you not read Song of Songs? 'I am sick with love. Thou art all fair, my love; there is no spot in thee.'" A lingering kiss melted her resistance. "'The roof of thy mouth is like the best wine for my beloved, that goeth down sweetly, causing the lips of those that are asleep to speak.'"

Etta drew a deep breath and made one last protest. "The children. Breakfast."

"You have nursed baby Yacov. Frau Rosen will feed Samuel, David, and Rachel." He smiled down into her eyes. "You can tell Frau Rosen that I will allow no one to nurse me but you."

Etta closed her eyes and savored the adoration of her husband. It had been a long time. She felt it, too. "I will send David to the shul with the message, and then I expect you to pray twice as hard tomorrow!"

He nodded obediently and released her. She threw on a robe, and fumbling with the sash, she stepped out of the room to call down the hall with the message for young David. She instructed the housekeeper about breakfast and gave strict orders that poor Rabbi Lubetkin must not be disturbed because he was sick and would not be nursed by anyone but his wife!

Frau Rosen, the plump, dour housekeeper, glared up from the foot of the stairs. As Etta finished her directives she thought she caught a hint of a smile on the old woman's face. Had she guessed the nature of Aaron's illness? Would she gossip at the bakery?

Etta raised her chin regally and retreated to the sanctuary of the bed chamber. She hoped that the Eternal would not see His way clear to send along another little Lubetkin today. Everyone in the neighborhood would count backward and remember that they had sent David to the shul with the message that Aaron was ill on that very day!

By dinnertime Aaron had quite recovered from his brief illness. He took his place at the head of the table and smiled benevolently at the subjects of his small domain.

Rachel, at thirteen, was the budding image of her mother at that age. Her wide blue eyes still carried the innocence and wonder she had as a tiny baby in her pram. Still she talked to the big, raw-boned cart horses of the Warsaw peddlers. Stroking the animals on the nose, she carried on conversations as her mother argued about prices of cabbages and chickens with the merchants. Rachel's raven-black hair curled gently around her oval face. She was a young beauty. Everyone said so. She was Aaron's firstborn and his pride and joy. Although others might disapprove, he had seen to it that the child was properly educated. She could quote the Torah as well as any boy her own age.

David, who was nine, had also inherited the cobalt blue eyes of his mother. Long lashes accented the clarity of those eyes and made him seem as though he was thinking very adult thoughts. The truth was that this serious boy was usually considering dropping a toad down the back of his sister. Aaron liked the boy. After a particularly diabolical prank and the punishment that must surely follow, Aaron was known to retreat to his own room and howl at the hilarity of David's latest. Of course, he never let David know his true response.

Little Samuel, too, had inherited Etta's eyes, but his features were much more like his father's. For this reason, perhaps, Aaron favored the boy somewhat. He was not pushed quite so hard in his studies as Rachel and David had been at his age. He was not so meticulous about his belongings or his room. Mrs. Rosen still made his bed. The other children resented this fact and called him *Prince Samuel*.

And little Yacov—at four weeks he was still an unknown commodity. His eyes were also blue, but the women of the neighborhood believed they could still turn brown in time. He was a quiet baby. Stuffed full of his mother's ample supply of milk, he would sleep the whole night through. Aaron described him as well mannered when he spoke of him to the men of the shul.

"What?" came the incredulous reply. "Well mannered at his age! Oy! Either you are slipping him a little schnapps at night or we have the makings of another Baal Shem Tov in our midst, nu?"

So. Perhaps this youngest Lubetkin would grow up to be another *Master of the Good Name!* Baal Shem Lubetkin? The thought pleased Aaron, even though the words were spoken in jest.

Aaron had no doubt that each of his four offspring would somehow grow up to honor God. They were good children. The Eternal, blessed be He, had showered blessings upon Aaron and Etta. The joy they found in each other had been enlarged through these four little lives. Aaron prayed over the meal and remembered to thank God for each of the children as well. He broke the bread and blessed it tonight with such a feeling of contentment that he was certain the Eternal could not be displeased that he had stayed home today.

From the opposite end of the table, Etta, also looking pleasantly relaxed, smiled and winked at him. "Is it not wonderful to see your papa so fit and rested after just one day, children?" A knowing look passed between husband and wife.

"I will still want to go to bed early tonight I think," he said, feeling genuinely tired.

Young Samuel studied his father with serious eyes. "Today at the bakery I heard Frau Rosen tell Frau Wolff and Frau Heber that what Papa has men *never* get over!"

At this news, Etta choked on her water while Aaron sputtered an incoherent reply and mentally took note that Etta must rebuke their housekeeper for saying such things . . . even if they were true.

"Frau Rosen!" Aaron bellowed loudly toward the kitchen. "Frau *Rosen!*" His voice betrayed his anger and the housekeeper emerged red-faced from the swinging door. She had heard Samuel's revelation. She looked daggers at the little boy and bowed slightly.

"I . . . would . . . like . . . more . . . chicken," Aaron said through slightly clenched teeth. This was enough to send the woman scurrying back to the kitchen while Etta shook her head and shrugged as if to ask: "So you thought she wouldn't figure it out? A woman like Frau Rosen? Such a yenta!"

"Eh?" Rabbi Lebowitz cupped a hand around his ear as the clatter of spoons against bowls nearly drowned out their voices. "You say Eli Sachar sent you to me?" He considered the young Austrian couple who stood before him amid the clamor of mealtime at Tipat Chalev.

Shimon nodded broadly, as if even a nod might not be understood through such a noise. "We were married in a civil ceremony in Austria."

"Hardly a wedding!" Leah shouted.

The rabbi nodded in agreement. What was a wedding without a canopy to stand under? What was memorable about having some magistrate pronounce that the honeymoon was now acceptable in the eyes of the state? "Poor children," he shook his head in sympathy. "So. You should have a proper Jewish ceremony, nu? A canopy in Nissan Bek Synagogue! A minyon to witness such a holy moment before man and the Eternal, may His name be blessed!"

Shimon looked pleased. "Then you will do this for us, Rabbi Lebowitz?"

"Such a pleasure for me, children. True? Of course true!"

A small boy squawked and his brother shouted for silence, which drowned out the rest of the rabbi's words. Had he given the time for the ceremony?

"When?" Shimon mouthed as the argument at the table grew louder.

"We will need a little time!" The old rabbi thumped one child on his head, which silenced the entire table. "After the kettles are washed, nu? Eight o'clock tonight."

———

The wonderful wail of the clarinet filled the air of Old City Jerusalem far into the night. There was dancing. There were cakes and cookies. There was even a little wine raised in toast to Mr. and Mrs. Shimon Feldstein in honor of their marriage tonight.

It was true that most of the women in the Old City were more than a bit irritated at Rabbi Lebowitz, however. "How can we provide a proper celebration on such short notice?"

"Oy! So you couldn't give the poor girl a little time to prepare for her wedding? It had to be at eight o'clock tonight after the pots are washed?"

"Only a man would do such a thing!"

When all was said and done, however, perhaps it did not make such a difference. The canopy was lifted up. The ring was given. The seven benedictions were recited. The bride was beautiful. The groom was pleased. And everyone in the Quarter came to celebrate the occasion!

"Mazel Tov!"

"Oy! And such a wedding, nu? Enough to bring tears from a stone! True?"

"Such a dress she is wearing, Golda!"

"The finest lace from Vienna, I hear. She shipped it to Jerusalem from Austria before the beast marched in! She wanted a proper wedding here in Jerusalem!"

"The girl has a head on her shoulders, I'm telling you."

"And such a heart! Look at the way she looks at him across the room, nu?"

"If only I could look at Yosef with such a look!"

"And she saved the real wedding dress until she could stand right here in Jerusalem before a rabbi!"

"She is a real *person*, this Leah Feldstein! I'm telling you! She is a *person*!"

"A credit to our community."

This was the conclusion of every woman among the congregation of Nissan Bek—a unanimous decision in favor of the sweet-faced Austrian refugee who had only a short time before been under suspicion. But even now, eyes narrowed and *The Question* was whispered behind raised hands: *"But do you think she is expecting?"*

———

Still in his wedding coat, Shimon remained two steps below Leah as she unlocked the door to the apartment.

The white lace of her wedding dress showed from beneath her warm coat. *How beautiful she looks tonight,* Shimon thought as he watched her. "Come here and kiss me, Mrs. Feldstein," he said gently, feeling the glow of a dozen toasts mixed with the nearness of Leah.

"Mrs. Feldstein. At last I am a kosher bride." She obeyed, caressing his face with her hands as she pressed her mouth against his.

The warmth of her kiss made him totter on the step. He said her name and pulled her against him.

"How was that?" she asked.

"More. We will discuss it later."

"Perhaps we should finish inside?" she giggled. "But how will you carry me across the threshold with your arm in a cast?"

At that challenge, he simply slung her over his shoulder and carried her laughing into the room. "How is that?"

"Not as romantic as I had imagined. Put me down!"

With a slight heave, he tossed her onto the bed. It was not the narrow cot they had shared, but a real bed—walnut headboard, mattress big enough for two, real sheets and quilts and down pillows.

Shimon towered over her as she blinked up at him in amazement.

"How's that?" he asked.

"But how? *Where*?"

"It cost us two place settings from the silver. One wedding present in exchange for another. I thought under the circumstances we were more in need of a decent bed." He lay down beside her. She raised up on one elbow and studied the rugged face of this quiet, gentle man.

"But where did you find such an elegant bed?"

"You do not recognize it? I bought it from the head housekeeper at the King David Hotel." He grinned sheepishly. "He threw in the bedding and the pillows for two serving spoons."

"I will not ask anything else." Leah covered her eyes with her hand and moaned.

Shimon laughed at her reaction to the black-market bed. It was best not to ask too many questions, she was right about that. "Anything for my Leah." He kissed her again and then, with his lips still against hers, he began to unbutton her coat.

"Now I have a surprise for you," she whispered. Her eyes were shining in the lamplight.

"I thought you might . . ."

"It is not what you think, my darling." Her smile broadened. "You must be the first to know. You are going to be a father, I think. I am practically certain."

He drew back, removing his fingers from her coat. The desire in his eyes softened to something else. Bewilderment? Tenderness? Fear, perhaps? His eyes skimmed over her body to her stomach. He blinked at her in wonder. "A baby?"

She guided his hand to touch her abdomen through the coat and the lace wedding dress. Nothing seemed different, and yet . . . "Part of you. And me. Us, together. Tiny now, just beginning, but I have such hope, Shimon!"

Tears streamed down the big man's cheeks. He embraced her gently, as if he were afraid of breaking something. He saw the face of Klaus Holbein in his mind as the tiny infant Israel had been dedicated on board the sunny decks of the *Darien*. The vision made him fearful. How he longed that their own child could be born in a world of peace.

Leah felt the dampness of his face against her neck. She stroked his hair and held him close to her. "You will be a wonderful papa, you know. I married you because of the way the street urchins gathered around you at the train station in Paris two years ago. That was when I thought, *Such a papa that one would make!*"

They lay together in silence for a long time. He managed to whisper, "How long have you known?"

"I have thought so since last month."

"But you did not tell me?"

"I wanted to be sure you did not feel trapped into marrying me," she teased. Then she kissed his forehead and his cheek and his mouth again. "And so, wake up from dreaming, Shimon. This is our honeymoon."

The joyous music of the wedding had faded. Nissan Bek Synagogue was dark and silent except for the sputtering oil lamps that flickered on either side of the ark.

Eli sat alone on the long wooden bench where he had first read Torah on the day of his Bar Mitzvah. How the eyes of his parents had shone with pride on that day! And a fire had been kindled in him at that very hour; a desire to serve the Lord here in this place, within the very shadow of the wall where Solomon's Temple had once stood.

Ah, the dreams of a boy. He had imagined the bright Shekinah glory of God as it had filled the holy mountain in answer to the prayer of Solomon. Eli had raised his hands and felt it himself, as if the light had touched him and the words of Solomon had only just echoed from the stones of the holy place to ring in his ears! Eli shouted the words of Solomon:

" . . . THAT THINE EYES MAY BE OPEN ON THIS PLACE DAY AND NIGHT, UPON THE PLACE THOU HAST SAID THOU WOULD PUT THY NAME: HEAR THE PRAYER WHICH THY SERVANT PRAYS TOWARDS THIS PLACE!"

The shout echoed in the dome of the great auditorium. It seemed to mock him. In this place so near to where Solomon stood, could God not hear him now? Would He not listen to the anguish of Eli's heart?

"Do you hear me, God?"

Silence. Eli stood slowly and covered himself with the bright silk tallith he had received on the day of his Bar Mitzvah. He had always imagined that one day it would also be the wedding canopy he stood beneath with his bride. But it would not be so. No rabbi would marry him and Victoria.

Eli stepped forward to face the ark. Shadows and light danced eerily against the walls. He bowed and placed his lips against the Hebrew letters embroidered on the garment as if it was not night—the darkest night of his life.

Tears stung his eyes. He quietly tried to recite the *Amidah*:

"Look . . . upon me . . . in my suffering. Fight . . . my struggles. Redeem me speedily, for thy Name's sake. . . ."

He lowered his head and wept in grief. He had failed. For the love of a woman he had failed his God and his people. He knew. He would not serve God in this place. Not here in the shadow of Solomon's wall. He did not know the One whom he longed to serve. He wanted to know God, but God was far away tonight. Victoria was real to him. He loved her.

Forgive my sin against you, I pray, if you can hear me! Forgive me. I cannot be a rabbi. I cannot serve you in this place . . . Eli cried out in a physical anguish at this grief. He dropped to his knees before the flickering lamps and his sorrow were lost in the shadows of the cupola.

26

The Inferno

"It is time," Hitler said to Himmler over lunch, "for another demonstration." He toyed with his plate of steamed vegetables as he considered the upcoming anniversary of the Nazi party's attempted coup of the German government in 1923. That event, celebrated each November, had ended with several of the old-guard Nazis dead, and Hitler himself in jail. He had written *Mein Kampf* while in prison, and so counted the time of his isolation as a great advantage for the principles of the Aryan race. This year, he decided that the occasion needed an extra touch of violence, something to show the world how far the German people had progressed beneath his guidance. For weeks he had pondered the problem. He had set his Gestapo chief to work on a solution.

"Only a small spark will turn a forest into an inferno, mein Führer," Himmler said obligingly.

"And who will strike the match?"

"There is a Jewish boy in Paris. Herschel Grynspan. You remember the name?"

"Ah yes," Hitler chuckled. "The one Hans Schumann used when he killed the French agent. What was the name? Le Morthomme, was it not? The Dead Man. Yes. I recall the incident quite well. The Jew Grynspan was given a gun that he did not know how to fire. He was put on the trail of Thomas von Kleistmann. Hans followed after him with a weapon he then used to shoot the Frenchman."

"Quite efficient. Grynspan himself believed that he had murdered the old man. Hans was able to simply walk away while the boy ran like an assassin and the French agent quietly bled to death." Himmler dabbed the corners of his mouth, then took another bite of cabbage as the Führer chewed on the smoothness of that Gestapo action.

"And where is the Jew now?"

"In hiding. The French officials as well as the British investigated the case. Witnesses reported that the old bookseller seemed to see someone else in the crowd. That there may have been a second shot a fraction after the first was fired. All is speculation, of course, and they are quite unsure who killed Le Morthomme." Himmler folded his napkin and sat back, satisfied. "Hans has remained close to the boy. Hans moves easily among the Jewish population of Paris. He reports now that young Grynspan is more than half mad. Hans has fed him daily on reports of actions against Jews until the mind of Herschel Grynspan is consumed with hatred. His parents were among those deported to Poland."

"Good." The Führer was satisfied. "Then we will arrange a little something to spur him on, Heinrich." Hitler's brow furrowed in thought.

Himmler nodded once. "We should not let this drag on much longer, however. Hans reports that young Grynspan talks of suicide daily now. Hans is afraid he will find him dangling from a rafter before we can find further use for him."

"That would be a pity. To lose such a carefully nurtured assassin at the moment before he can be put to use. Well then, issue the orders."

"Who will be the martyr to our great cause, mein Führer?"

Hitler closed his eyes in deep consideration of who might be the target of the Jewish bullet. "What was Commander Vargen's conclusion about Ernst vom Rath?"

"He is still under suspicion. He was closest to Thomas von Kleistmann among the embassy staff."

Hitler cleared his throat. A decision was imminent. "Vom Rath comes from a good German family?"

"Impeccable."

"His father is of the aristocracy?"

Himmler was always amazed by the details the Führer was able to remember. "Of the purest Aryan bloodlines."

Hitler smiled. "And yet his son may be a traitor." He shrugged. "We should make young vom Rath a national hero before he disgraces his family and betrays his Fatherland, Himmler. I think Ernst vom Rath will serve us better dead than he has served us alive."

————

Hans had been late in coming with food for Herschel this afternoon. There was a dance tonight, so Hans had left the attic after only a few minutes.

Herschel was alone with the radio. Rain thumped hard on the roof as the roar of cheering Nazis filled the room. Hitler had spoken, and once again the people of the Reich raised their voices in support of all he said. Had any of those among the audience been there when

Herschel's family had been driven across the German border into Poland? Had any one of them laid the lash on the back of Herschel's father or pushed his mother into the mud?

Such images first made him angry; then they filled him with despair. What could he do about any of it? Who was he? *Just another Jew.* In Germany, if he opened his mouth to speak out, the Hitler Youth would throw him to the ground and stuff his mouth with human excrement. Herschel had seen it with his own eyes, watched his friend and neighbor choke and vomit as the strutting members of the Hitler Youth had laughed and beaten him.

One Jew's protest meant nothing, Herschel knew. He could call a newspaper and say, "My family was deported by the Germans! They have nothing left! Everything was taken!" But if Herschel said these things, the newsmen would ask him who he was and where he was and where he was from, and then he, too, would be deported from France.

Martial music blared over the radio. The voice of German Propaganda Minister Goebbels announced that the speech of the German leader would be reprinted in its entirety in tomorrow's paper. Hitler had a voice; the whole world listened and trembled. He commanded persecution of the innocent, and the world fell silent for fear of answering that all-powerful voice!

Herschel stood wearily, bumping his head on the light bulb that hung from the ceiling. He lifted the mattress of his cot and stared at the rope supports across the frame. He looked from the ropes to the rafters. It would be so easy . . . so easy to end his life tonight. He had no wish to go on living in such a world. If he killed himself, perhaps his voice, his final statement, might be heard as well.

He knelt beside the bed and began to unknot the rope, loosening it from the frame. Threading it through the wood and then through the cross-weave of ropes, he discovered that there was plenty for a hanging. Herschel looked into the shadows of the rafters. He pitied Hans. It would be a terrible thing for Hans to find him strung up beside the light bulb. Herschel wondered if he should turn out the light before he put his neck through the loop. Or would it be more frightening for Hans to reach for the light and find Herschel instead?

He sat on an upturned wooden box and began to write notes of farewell. One to Hans. One to his uncle. One to his parents. And the last one to the silent world. Yes. At least death would give him one moment to be heard!

He heard the tramp of Hans' feet on the steps below. Quickly he hid the finished letters beneath clean paper. He could not let his friend know his intent. Hans would try to talk him out of it.

"Hey, Herschel!" Hans cried, poking his head through the trapdoor. "I brought you some . . ." His voice trailed off and his smile faded. He looked at the loose rope lying over the wooden bedframe. He looked then at Herschel and held up a piece of chocolate cake. "I brought you this," he remarked flatly. "And I see you have been busy." He entered the attic and towered over Herschel.

"I . . . the rope support broke. I was just—"

"You were just lying." Hans set the cake down. "Going to leave me, eh? Leave me to find you and then to explain what you were doing here? How I hid you?" Hans was angry.

"What is the use?" Herschel hung his head in his hands. "How else can I make a statement?"

"You are a coward!" Hans spat. "Who do you think will care if you die? There have been hundreds of suicides in Vienna. Thousands of Jews. And who cares, eh? You are going to be just another Jew, buried in a pauper's grave." Hans picked up the blank sheets of paper as if he knew there were notes written beneath them.

Herschel looked away dully as Hans read the first one. "Thank you for all you have done! Ha!" Hans scoffed. "You think anyone will care? Why not end your life doing something worthwhile, Herschel? Have you forgotten what you said? To kill a Nazi! Now *there* is a goal! And not just anyone—someone the Nazis care about! Kill one of their own, Herschel, and then they will listen to you! Have you forgotten?"

Hans Schumann's eyes blazed as he spoke, and Herschel hung his head in shame. Perhaps Hans was right. Suicide was stupid, futile, and selfish.

"You took my gun away. You sold it to feed me. Or so you said. How can I kill a Nazi? I have to untie my own bed to get enough rope to hang myself! You think I have not thought of how good revenge would feel?"

"If you kill yourself, Hitler will rejoice that another Jew is out of the way. So make them grieve in Berlin. Steal the laughter from their lips as they steal ours. Steal a Nazi life as they take thousands of Jewish lives. Make them grieve, Herschel, and they will hear you!"

"How?"

"I will help you if you mean it."

Herschel leaned forward, begging for that help. *"Yes! Tell me how!"*

Ernst vom Rath could not close his eyes without seeing Thomas's broken body before him. The sound of an automobile backfire outside the Paris Embassy made him jump, spilling coffee at the breakfast table.

Other members of the embassy staff eyed him with curiosity, perhaps suspicion. Obviously, whatever Ernst had witnessed in Berlin had left him shaken and nervous. Had he been involved with the escape of Thomas von Kleistmann, after all? Every glance seemed to ask that question. Was Ernst a part of some anti-Nazi undercurrent, in spite of his denials?

Ernst found himself raising his hand in the *Heil Hitler* salute with an added gusto these days. At times when his own voice echoed in the vast marble halls, he felt that perhaps he was overdoing his pretended loyalty. But the pretense was inspired by fear, by the vivid and horrible tableau of Thomas pleading for death on the floor of the Gestapo building.

This afternoon a new Abwehr officer was introduced to the staff as the replacement for von Kleistmann. This fellow was of powerful build with stronger Aryan characteristics than his unfortunate predecessor. Fritz Konkel was younger than Thomas had been. Only twenty, he had distinguished himself as a group leader in the early days of the Hitler Youth. He had learned to march and drill with a burnished shovel over his shoulder. Blond, tanned, muscled, young Konkel had once been chosen by the Führer himself from a line of other young recruits. "Here is the ideal of the Aryan race," the Führer had remarked. "It is specimens like this that we should send abroad as representatives of our race!"

Rumor held that Hitler himself had chosen this officer for duty in the Paris Embassy. He had overridden the selection of Abwehr Chief Admiral Canaris with a strong warning: "You chose the traitor Thomas von Kleistmann for the Paris Embassy, did you not? This time I shall trust no one but myself for such an appointment."

As the new man was introduced to each member of the staff, Ernst found himself perspiring. The radiators hissed behind him. As he shook the hand of the Nazi officer, Ernst mopped his brow and blamed the flush of his face on the heating system.

Konkel flashed an arrogant smile. "You do not know heat, Herr Secretary vom Rath, until you have stood in formation for hours in the sun and then looked into the eyes of our Führer."

If Thomas had been alive to hear such a comment, no doubt he and Ernst would have secretly ridiculed the young officer's devotion to sweat and duty and *der Führer*. But Thomas was not alive. Ernst was alone among the embassy staff in his loathing of such foolishness.

He managed a smile. "No doubt if the Führer were here at the Paris Embassy, we would not need radiators to make us sweat," he mumbled. A foolish thing to say. "His . . . personal warmth . . . would be sufficient, ja, Officer Konkel?" This was a nice recovery. Ernst had managed to put the ball back into Konkel's court.

"That is true," Konkel replied in the only way he could. This handsome Aryan god was strong and devoted, but not clever. His dullness, at least, was a consolation for Ernst.

Konkel proceeded down the line of introductions and then turned as the ambassador clapped him on the back and announced, "Officer

Konkel has been personally selected to manage the continuing investigation of the traitor von Kleistmann and his activities here in Paris. I
have been instructed by the Führer himself that every staff member is
to show Officer Konkel the utmost cooperation in his duties. Some
things are known, of course, from the confession given by von Kleistmann before his execution."

Ernst blinked. All other words faded from his hearing. *What confession? Had Thomas made some confession? Whose names were mentioned in some moment of weakness when the torture became unbearable?* Ernst pulled himself back to the droning voice of the
ambassador.

"Of course, the unquestioned loyalty of each remaining member of
this staff has been checked and rechecked. That is not at issue here.
What is requested is even the smallest item of information that might
have been overlooked. A name or place Thomas von Kleistmann might
have mentioned in passing."

At this, the pretty French maid from the German-speaking province
of Alsace raised her hand timidly. Thomas had spent time with this
witless woman. He had wooed her, and some whispered that she had
unlocked his door on the evening of his escape.

Officer Konkel eyed her with the same sort of interest that Thomas
had shown. He smiled. Raised an eyebrow. He strolled easily toward
her.

"What is it, Fräulein?"

She blushed, enjoying the gaze of this handsome replacement.
"Bitte, Officer Konkel . . . Thomas . . . er . . . Officer von Kleistmann
once wrote a letter to a woman in London. He burned it. I saw its
remains in the ashtray in his room."

Konkel clasped his hands behind his back. He rocked on his toes
and eyed the woman with a different sort of interest. "You perform your
duties quite thoroughly, Fräulein." He smiled. "I shall remember not
to leave correspondence where you might come across it."

A twittering of nervous laughter filtered through the group. Everyone
knew she and Thomas had occasionally been lovers. The motivation
of her jealous curiosity was evident to everyone but Konkel. "I thought
you should know," she stammered, flushing with embarrassment. "I
thought—"

"Why did you not mention this sooner?"

"I only just thought of it this morning. Preparing your room. It was
his room, and I . . . only just remembered it."

"A woman in London?" Konkel frowned thoughtfully over the top
of her maid's cap. "The name was Elisa?"

She nodded excitedly. "Yes. Yes. That was it!"

"Ah," Konkel nodded and grinned. This was not news. This was
nothing *they* did not know. "Yes. Thank you, Fräulein. We are aware

of this . . . relationship. Quite aware." He swept his hand over the group. "But these details are the sort we are looking for. Things that will help us piece together the puzzle and trace the line to its conclusion. Yes. It is confirmation. And if any of you has such a small incident that you think might assist, the Reich will be grateful, of course."

Ernst's mind went wild with thoughts of all the small hints he might have left inadvertently. Would some insignificant word or glance between him and Thomas be remembered and traced? Had Thomas told Elisa about his comrade in the Paris Embassy? If she were captured and tortured, certainly she would not have the strength to remain silent as Thomas had . . . as *they* said he had!

Ernst felt ill. He wondered if anyone noticed the way the blood seemed to drain from his face. Was he under suspicion, in spite of assurances by the Berlin Gestapo? In spite of the fact that he had taken the gun from the hand of Vargen and . . .

The ambassador was speaking again, smiling pleasantly, patting the new officer on his back. "We are quite sure that all this unpleasantness will soon be behind us. Forgotten and done with. Then we may all settle in again to our duties for the Fatherland here in France."

———————

Haggard. That was the word Leah would use for Eli Sachar as he took a seat on a packing crate and stared mournfully into his chipped china coffee cup.

"I do not mean to intrude," he said, mindful that arriving at dawn on the doorstep of a just-married couple was an intrusion. "But I have not slept all night."

Shimon sat shirtless across from him and pulled on his socks. "Neither did we," he mumbled in German with a quick look at Leah. She was dressed, but she stood making an irritated face behind Eli's back.

She shrugged. This was not *really* their honeymoon, after all. And the man looked as if he were near death. So she had offered him a cup of coffee on the condition that he would go get the water and give them five minutes to pull on something. Here sat Eli, not wanting to intrude, but . . .

"Your wedding," Eli said through a rusty sounding voice, "was so beautiful. I saw you together last night, and I knew that . . . I cannot . . . that no rabbi will . . . that Victoria and I . . ." He dissolved into tears.

It was embarrassing for Shimon to watch him weep. Leah was instantly ashamed that she had resented his being here when he was in such pain.

Shimon grimaced and glanced nervously at Leah. So? Would she help, already? Say something? Shimon was a touch hung over, and this was too much at 6:15 in the morning.

He whacked Eli on his arm. "Pull yourself together, man! Are you drunk? Finish your sentence!" he said gruffly.

Leah started to protest Shimon's roughness, but then she saw that Eli responded instantly with renewed composure.

"Yes. Yes. You are right. I am acting like a . . . you see . . . I told my parents about *us*. Me and Victoria. Of course I will never be a rabbi if I marry her, even if she converts, because it is forbidden for a kohen to marry a proselyte. You see?"

Shimon nodded, a broad *aha* nod. "I had forgotten that one. Yes. Well." Maybe the man had reason to weep. Shimon became more gentle. "So. Have you decided not to marry her, then?"

"What?" Eli sounded irritated. *"No!"* He looked insulted. "It is just that I think . . . we should not wait. There is no rabbi in the entire Old City who would marry us regardless of whether I leave the Yeshiva. And the women were talking . . . there are rumors that you are . . . maybe *friends* with the English priest at Christ Church? He brought you here, nu?"

Leah ran a brush through her hair and walked toward him. "Eli," she said gently, "Reverend Robbins will not perform the ceremony for you and Victoria unless both of you are Christians. At least I think that is the way it works." She bit her lip. "This is very serious business. More than marriage. More than leaving Yeshiva. More than disregarding the wishes of your family." She reached out to touch his hand briefly. "You cannot deny your faith!"

His chin went up defiantly. "But *you* did! I heard what you said about Jesus, the Christ of the goyim, on the night of your concert!" His tone was angry, accusing.

Leah sat down beside Shimon and fixed her clear brown eyes on Eli. "You did not hear me if you think that we have in any way denied our faith as Jews or our heritage."

Shimon interjected, "Hear me now, Eli. Leah and I believe that Jesus is the Messiah of Israel, the Holy One we watch for and pray will come to redeem His people Israel! First He came to redeem us individually, as the prophet Isaiah wrote in the fifty-third chapter. He died for our sins. The Lamb of sacrifice given by God for our sakes. But He will come again as King to redeem the nation Israel. It is written, and we are seeing the beginning of the fulfillment."

Eli frowned. A thousand arguments filled his mind. "Christians have slaughtered Jews in the name of Jesus for centuries!" His voice was bitter with the truth of this.

"Those who have done these things have never known *Him*," Shimon answered quietly. "Many who call themselves by Christ's name worship a false Christ created by Evil to serve Evil. The real Jesus said that this would happen."

As Leah prayed for the right words to speak, a thought came to her clearly. "Eli, suppose I say I am a disciple of Eli Sachar, and I take a gun and go into the marketplace and find a baby who is in the arms of its Muslim mother. Then I point the gun at the child and say, 'You are a Muslim. Eli Sachar is a Jew. In the name of Eli Sachar I am going to kill you!' And then I murder that child in your name."

"Never!" cried Eli.

Leah and Shimon exchanged looks. "Well, then? How must the Lord feel when the name of the Holy One of Israel is used so wickedly?"

"But . . . is this a *different Jesus* that you speak of?" Eli blinked at them as if they spoke a foreign language. "Different from the One whose name the goyim invoked as they slaughtered us over the centuries? As they murder us now in Germany?"

"Our Lord Jesus is as different from that false Christ as the bright sun is different from blackest night!"

"Tell me plainly *what* Jesus you mean? How can you say that name beside the word Messiah?" Eli looked startled at these words. He ran his hands through his hair and Leah noticed he was not wearing his yarmulke. She took his cold cup of coffee from the crate and warmed it with a drop from the coffeepot. She gently urged the cup back into his hands and he took a cautious sip.

Shimon began again carefully to explain what he knew as truth. "To cut off the real, historical Jesus from the name *Messiah, Holy One of Israel, Redeemer, and Lord* . . . this is the greatest blasphemy. Many Gentiles who call themselves Christians commit this blasphemy every day. I have felt their hatred." Shimon turned slightly to reveal the scars on his back and shoulder. "I have felt their lash and heard their curses. Seen them destroy others in the name of their false Christ." A strange smile played on Shimon's lips. "They called me Christ-killer even while they were killing innocent children! And inside my heart I heard the voice of the Lord whisper, *'It is they who killed me!'*"

He paused and looked deeply into Eli's eyes. "If there is any victory that causes Evil to rejoice, it is to hide our Messiah from us by distortion, brutality, and false doctrine."

Eli's face filled with a hunger to understand. Could it be that Jesus approved of the mercy and truth spoken of in the Torah? Then this was a very different Jesus indeed than the one he imagined!

Shimon reached around him to retrieve his Bible. "Through evil men, Satan himself has twisted the Holy Word of God until Jesus is made to appear to be everything we fear. To keep a son of the Covenant from recognizing the Messiah is a great victory for Satan against God, you see. Jesus was a Jew, descended from King David just as our prophets foretold. Put away the Gentile church and Gentile religion and persecution. Empty your mind of their lies and darkness. You must meet Jesus first through the Prophets, Eli, and then look at His life! Come to Him as a *Jew*, for the sake of your eternal soul! Face-to-face you must look at the real Jesus, and then you must choose to deny Him or believe Him."

27

Apostasy

His arms piled high with volumes of rabbinical commentary on the book of Isaiah, Eli cautiously climbed the stairs of the Sachar apartment. He kicked the door in an awkward knock. His mother threw open the door and her face displayed a range of emotion beginning with sullenness, changing rapidly to surprise, and finally relief as she called out, *"He is home! Eli is home! God be thanked! And his arms are full of books!"*

Eli entered the front room as Hermann looked around the corner from the kitchen. "What's all this?" he asked gruffly, but the relief was also evident in his eyes.

"Books from the Yeshiva library," Eli said as though nothing else needed discussion. True to his vow, he would not mention Victoria's name again to his parents. "I have met an apostate and a liar here in the Quarter, and I will prove his argument false through the words of the ancients."

Ida began to weep and mutter her thankfulness to the heavens. "You see! You see what a rabbi he will be! He is done with this foolishness! Oy! It is all over, Hermann: our son is back home."

"So leave him alone, already!" Hermann Sachar ducked back into the kitchen with a gesture that seemed to say, *I knew Eli was no fool.* He was certain the boy would see reason.

Eli did not tell them that this had nothing to do with what he had decided about Victoria. They would know soon enough. Why make things harder? He was angry at what Shimon and Leah had told him. Their gross misinterpretation of the Holy Scripture angered him and challenged his years of education. He had pulled every book and commentary on Isaiah off the shelves of the Yeshiva. In this matter of Jesus, he would not take the word of a Jew from Vienna. A musician from Austria—what could he know?

Throughout the afternoon, Eli studied the sources he spread across the floor of his bedroom. His mother brought him a food tray and left it beside his bed without a word. She did not wish to disturb the study of her son the rabbi. And he did not notice when she entered and when she left as he turned page after page of two dozen volumes.

Moshe finally broke the silence in a tone that was filled with derision, "Well, as they say in the world of the goyim, the prodigal has come home, eh?"

Eli looked up at Moshe. He had not understood the jibe. "What? Ah, Moshe. Shalom."

The food tray was untouched. Moshe picked up half a sandwich. "Do you mind?"

"No. I was just studying." Eli wiped his eyes. How different the world looked to him.

"So, you have made your choice." Moshe flopped down on his bed and bit into the sandwich. "Books over true love, nu?"

Eli looked down at the yellowed pages of a commentary and then back into the smirking face of his brother. "Sometimes, Moshe, there is more passion and love in the pages of a book." He frowned. "And all the answers are there. Truth."

"Well, forgive me. I am from the real world, you know, where love and truth are very rare these days." He seemed almost angry. "Where Arabs blow up Englishmen and Englishmen blow apart their promises of a Jewish homeland. And where Jews, even a Jew I thought more sensible than the rest, are afraid to love Arabs for fear of what might be said."

Eli looked back at the book. "Be quiet, Moshe," he said wearily. "You do not know."

"I know enough," Moshe said through his sandwich. "I am going to England. You be a rabbi. Victoria will marry some Bedouin camel driver, and the world will be a better place for it!"

"Be quiet," Eli said again more wearily. He had not even thought of all that for hours.

"So where is all the passion and love for you, Eli? My big brother. How will you embrace a book at night and call it by her name? What has made you so happy tonight?" Moshe snatched the reference volume from in front of Eli. He held it up to the light and began to read. "*Targum Jonathan on Isaiah Fifty-three*! Ho! Eli, what love! What truth and light!" He threw the book back on the bed in disgust. "May you be eternally happy with your books, Eli." He reached up and snapped off the light as if to make one final gesture of his contempt.

Eli was too exhausted to argue or explain. Indeed, this reference and several others he had found did change everything for him. He sat in the dark on his cluttered bed for a long time as Moshe kicked off his shoes and lay down to sleep without another word.

Eli did not resent his brother's derision. He expected nothing less. Moshe could not understand. Perhaps Eli would have a chance to explain to him later. Yes. When it was all over Eli would sit him down and explain. Tonight Eli had found truth. And everything was different, even his love for Victoria.

Etta held tightly to baby Yacov as they hurried through the crowded streets of Catholic Warsaw.

"Walk faster, children!" she called over her shoulder to Rachel, Samuel, and David. "We will miss our appointment."

Today's appointment was with a photographer who promised quick passport photos at a reasonable price. It was worth venturing beyond the borders of Jewish Warsaw for such a bargain, Etta reasoned. Besides, this way Aaron would not know she was sending birth certificates and photos to her father in Jerusalem in the hope that her own passport might be renewed in the British Mandate and new British passports acquired for her children.

Aaron would not have consented. So Etta had taken this matter into her own hands . . . just in case.

"How much farther, Mama?" complained Samuel.

"Hush," Rachel demanded in a frightened voice. Two young men leaning against a storefront eyed the little entourage with cruel amusement. They stepped away from the wall and followed after.

"Look! The Christ-killers have come out of their caves today!"

"Ignore them, children," Etta commanded in Yiddish as her back stiffened with fear. She held the baby closer and reached around to pull the other three children in front of her.

"Listen to this, Wochek! The Jewish bitch barks to her litter in Yiddish so we cannot understand!" taunted one of the men.

"She looks very rich, Wolfgang," the second muttered in German. "How do you think she gets her money? You think she sells herself to Poles, eh?"

Etta felt herself color with shame at the man's remark. Her heart began to pound with fear. They could hurt her. Hurt her children and no one would stop them. Such things had been done before. Why had she left the ghetto? For a few pennies! To keep the passport photos a secret from Aaron! *God forgive me! Help me!*

"Maybe she will give us a free sample, Wochek. You think so?"

"Or maybe she will pay *us*!" The voice was exultant at the idea.

Other Poles on the sidewalk turned to look and smile with amusement. A few encouraged the young men.

Etta could see that Rachel had grown pale with fear. The faces of the boys displayed a confused sort of anger.

A still-burning cigarette butt was tossed at Etta's face. She ducked and shielded the baby. Rachel turned, her bright blue eyes wide with terror. Walking just behind their two tormenters was the man she had seen in Muranow Square—the watcher! He, too, was smiling. His eyes narrowed with cold hatred.

"Ah, leave them alone!" shouted a thick-framed grandmother walking the other way.

That was all the support they received from the onlookers. Etta walked faster until she was almost running, pushing the children along in front. The long strides of the young men did not seem to be affected by her fearful pace. Still they jeered and mocked Etta. A hand reached out to snag the hem of her dress and pull it up.

Etta cried out and whirled around. The baby began to wail.

"Leave us alone!" Etta demanded.

In response, the men laughed louder and groped for her skirt again.

"Someone help my mother!" Rachel shouted. *"Please!"*

"Just a little taste, eh? I have never had kosher meat!" The amusement turned into a leer. This was no longer a game.

Tears stung Etta's eyes. She tried to speak, but fear choked her as a crowd of men now encircled her on the sidewalk, cutting her off from Rachel and David and Samuel as they screamed for her. Yacov still cried his innocent protest.

The two men walked nearer. Their intent was evident in their eyes. Two other young men stepped between them. "When you are finished with her, I want a turn . . ."

"Don't . . . please!" Etta begged. "Don't hurt my little one!"

The watcher spoke. "Smash the little pig on the sidewalk! The Germans sent us twelve thousand Jews! What do we need with another one?"

The crowd of men grew silent—the silence of anticipation. Who would reach out first? From the outer ring of the growing circle, Etta could hear the weeping voices of her children calling for her. She shielded Yacov, covering his head with her hands. They would not tear him from her; she would die first! Silently she breathed the prayer of the dying. Small bits of the holy words came to her mind as she fought against the panic. *O Israel . . . the Lord . . . our God is. . . . Where is the Lord?*

The young men reached out as if they possessed one mind. They took her by each arm. She struggled and screamed and fought for her baby.

Two more strong men grasped her ankles and lifted her kicking from the ground. They held her high above their heads like a sacrifice. The crowd cheered her anguish as she shouted to her children, *"Run! Run!"*

She arched her back as she fought against the iron grip of her attackers. In her wild struggle she could see that traffic still moved in the street as people gawked from the opposite sidewalk.

The tiny infant in her arms bleated as she squeezed him too tightly in her fight to hold him. The crowd of Poles roared at the sight of the Jewish woman's struggle. Legs kicking. Pretty head thrown back in a scream. And then, the roar began to fade. Still she fought! She shouted out against her attackers as they held her high above their heads. But something changed. First to the right, and then to the left, the circle of men broke and moved back. The laughter died, leaving only those who grasped her. Once again it was their strength against hers. Her voice against theirs. Once again she could make out the sobs of Rachel, Samuel, and David. And then one authoritative male voice cut through the last remnants of her torture.

"Put the woman down! I said . . . on pain of excommunication . . . put the woman down!"

The laughter stilled as she was lowered, weeping, to the sidewalk. A tiny Catholic priest, no more than five feet tall, glared threateningly up at the men who had started it all. At the break in the crowd, the children ran to embrace their unsteady mother. The voice of the baby was hoarse now from his shrieks through the ordeal. Etta could not stop crying. The tears flowed silently down her flushed cheeks.

"We were just having fun with this Jewess, Father," protested the first young man as the onlookers disappeared.

The priest slapped the man hard across the face. He reached up and clutched the collar of the second strong young brute, shaking him as if he were a small child.

"You are animals!" hissed the priest, who seemed very small next to the men. *"You call yourselves Catholics!"* He raised his voice to include the spectators who remained sheepishly looking on from the fringes. Even those few backed away, stepping on toes, bumping into the crowd gathered behind them. *"Call on the mercy of Almighty God, for He is your judge in this!"* His eyes burned with rage. He slapped the face of the second man with the back of his hand, then shoved him away. *"I know you both,"* the priest whispered threateningly.

"Oh, Mama!" Rachel cried, holding Etta around her waist. "I want to go home!"

Etta could only nod. They had spent such a long time getting dressed up for the pictures. Now, Etta's hair hung down and Rachel's bows were untied. The boys' coats and ties were askew.

The fierceness of the priest changed to calm and gentle concern as he turned his attention to Etta and the children. "Are you all right, daughter?"

Etta shook her head. *No, she was not all right.* But she was alive. The baby was alive.

"Do I need to take you to a hospital, daughter?" the priest asked.

Etta closed her eyes, trying to control the weeping. She could not speak. Rachel replied for her. "Our doctor," Rachel said boldly. She was angry—anger felt better than fear. "Herr Doktor Letzno is our doctor. He lives on Dzika Street. Yes. You may take my mother there."

The priest eyed the young woman with a hint of respect. She had taken charge. This was good. She was a younger version of her mother. Very beautiful, and very lucky that the men had not tried to rape her as well.

"My car is there." He pointed to a small black sedan at the curb. There was never a question that they might refuse to ride in an automobile owned by the Catholic church. Rachel shuddered as she stepped in after Etta. They could not go home like this. Dr. Letzno would be their refuge for a while.

Two plainclothes members of the Warsaw police sat smug and patronizing in the wing-backed chairs of Eduard Letzno's office. Etta faced them. She looked very alone and small on the wide leather sofa. Eduard sat at his desk. He stared at his hands in anguish. He was sorry now that he had called the police. Was he still so naive as to think that there was a shred of justice remaining in Poland for a Jew, whether a man or a woman?

"*You* say," began the thick, red-faced officer as he scanned his notes, "that you were going to a photographer?"

Etta bit her lip and twisted the handkerchief into knots. "Yes. As I told you. We had an appointment." Words came with difficulty.

"And why did you venture out of your own community for a photograph, eh? There are competent Jewish photographers."

Etta glanced at Eduard. Should she tell them that she wanted passport photos? Eduard did not help her in this matter. He simply stared darkly at his clasped hands. "I . . . heard this fellow Wolenski was very good and not expensive."

The officer flipped a page over the back of his clipboard. "Wolenski is known to us police." He paused. His eyes became hard. "He publishes . . . certain kinds of photographs. Black market. Obscene photographs."

Etta drew back as if she had been slapped. "But no! Passport photos—he advertises quick work."

The officer smiled. *So the Jewess wanted passport photos.* "We will check with Wolenski." His words were clipped, officious. "And so, *you* say you were simply walking along and—"

"But I told you." Etta's face flushed with shame. "They began to make . . . remarks. And then . . . advances."

The chin of the officer went up as if to dispute her. "The young men in question reported the incident to us differently."

Eduard looked up, startled by these words. "They came to you?" Eduard asked.

"Immediately," the officer replied. "The . . . incident . . . frightened them. They say this woman is the one who began it."

"*What?*" Etta gasped. Again her eyes filled with tears.

"You are surprised?" The narrow grin of the officer was like the leer she had seen on the faces of the attackers.

"But I . . . why would *I?*" she stammered.

"They were under the impression that you are . . . a prostitute." The grin remained unchanged.

"But . . ." Etta could not speak. She looked at Eduard. His dark expression became instantly angry.

"Frau Lubetkin is the wife of a rabbi," he said evenly.

"What has that to do with the charge, Doktor Letzno?" the officer shrugged.

"It was just as I have told you!" Etta cried.

"We have witnesses who say differently. The two men whom you first solicited on the street. And then there are many others who will testify . . ."

"But the priest! He stopped them! He will tell you!" Etta clenched her fists in anger and humiliation.

"The priest stopped the little prank. He brought you here. He says he did not realize that you are a prostitute, or he might have let the men teach you a lesson." He cocked an eyebrow. "So much for the priest."

"Eduard!" Etta wept openly as she looked to him for some help against this insanity. How could they say such things? How could they look at her and think such things?

"Frau Lubetkin is a devoted mother and—" Eduard's voice threatened to lose control.

"Many prostitutes are good mothers," smiled the officer. "Soliciting in Warsaw is against the law. We could put you in prison. There are fifty men who will testify in court as to what you are and what you were doing."

"But *they attacked me!* They threatened the life of my baby!"

"All a part of the sport. Jewish prostitutes should service their own kind. There are hotels near Muranow Square, are there not?"

The doctor rose from behind his desk. He moved to stand between the gendarme and Etta who now sobbed uncontrollably. The officer smiled up at him. Eduard did not strike the man, although it was an effort to restrain himself.

Eduard's words came in a hoarse croak. "You have made your point," he managed to whisper. "No need to insult Frau Lubetkin or her family further."

"Insult?" The officer glanced innocently at his taciturn partner. Both men were amused with their game of baiting. "I am simply warning this woman that if she ever solicits in the Catholic section of the city again, I shall personally arrest her. We can see to it she is in prison for three years at the least." He leaned around Eduard and fixed his steely gaze on Etta. "Do you understand, madame? Your children will be quite changed when you get out of jail. Much older. The littlest bastard will not remember you."

"Enough!" Eduard shouted. He did not touch the vile man in front of him, lest he also be thrown into prison.

"Remember you are leaving Poland, Dr. Letzno," menaced the second officer. "Unless you violate the law. Or perhaps strike a Warsaw gendarme. You know how difficult it is to leave the country or obtain a passport if you have a police record." At this, the man looked expectantly at Etta. Had she heard his threat? *No passport with a police record. No escape to Palestine, even for the wife of a rabbi.* "You do understand, do you not?"

Eduard stepped back. He closed his eyes for a moment and sighed. Yes, he understood. Etta was too broken to comprehend this evil game, but Eduard understood perfectly what they were after.

He cleared his throat and looked over their heads, through the window where a few snowflakes drifted down. These men had not spoken with the attackers. Nor had they contacted the priest. The photographer was just a photographer. "How much do you want?" Eduard asked.

The officers exchanged glances as if such a thought had never entered their minds. "There are fines, of course. Public disturbances. Soliciting openly . . ."

"There will be no more need of fabricated charges. We all know you can say what you like. You can find witnesses who are not witnesses and they will say what you tell them. I am a realist. Frau Lubetkin is innocent . . . the kind of innocence men like you will not understand. And so, it is time to speak openly. What is your price for leaving her alone?"

28

The Last Waltz

The soft light above the piano shone on Anna's hair. From across the room, Theo closed his eyes for a moment to etch this image of her in his mind like a treasured photograph. She played the gentle music of Brahms' Waltz in A flat. She swayed with the music and smiled as though she were dancing. The melody filled the tiny flat with the same elegance and warmth that had once been theirs in Berlin.

Theo knew that the surroundings did not matter. Even playing on a battered old upright piano had not dimmed the brightness of Anna's soul. This melody Theo would take with him; this vision he would cherish.

Outside, a strong wind chilled the city of London, breaking water pipes and sending everyone scrambling for the warmth of a fire. Theo would take his fire with him. Kindled and fueled by moments like these, memories of Anna had kept him warm. When every other image had hardened and died around him, he had stretched out his hands to the face of Anna. Dreams of her had kept him alive. Certainty of her prayers and faithfulness had commanded him to live when it would have been easier to die. And so, once again, he would carry Anna with him in his heart. He would think of her in London, here at the piano; moving to the music of a Brahms waltz.

As if she heard his thoughts, her hands paused in the middle of the melody. Did she feel his eyes loving her? She did not turn around. The wall clock ticked on with the rhythm like a metronome.

"Theo," she asked quietly, "who have they asked to present the plan in Berlin? You did not say."

He did not answer, but continued to gaze at the golden light of her hair. Her shoulders sagged a moment as she realized who.

"How long will you be gone?" she asked. Her words seemed

choked. She would not beg him to stay—would not put her love for him before what she knew *must be.*

He put his strong hands on her shoulders and stooped to kiss her hair. "A short time, they tell me. A few days." His voice sounded light and reassuring in spite of what they both knew. "I will be given a British diplomatic passport. You must not worry."

She nodded and rested her fingers on the ivory keys. What was there to say now? "The Lord will . . . be with you." She began to play again.

Theo sat beside her on the bench. "I have always loved this waltz," he remarked, comforted somehow by her understanding, "loved the way you played it."

She smiled when he looked at her, but he could see that tears streaked her face. "We have never danced to it," she managed to whisper.

"Because we hear it only when you play it." He took her hand and stopped the music. Then he lifted her to her feet and pulled her close to him, his cheek against her soft, damp cheek.

She raised her face to his and looked into his eyes—eyes bright with emotion, shining with love forged in the furnace of trials and crafted into an intricate beauty. "Dance with me tonight, Theo," she whispered. "Can you hear it? Can you hear the music? Dance with me, my darling . . ."

———

Eduard stood framed in the tall window. Beyond him, snowflakes whitewashed Warsaw until it looked clean and beautiful in its baroque splendor. But Eduard and Etta knew what lay beneath that glistening image.

"It is my fault," Eduard said softly. His breath fogged the window-pane. He could not look at Etta. She simply stared at his back in the weary realization of how desperate the situation for Jews in Poland had suddenly become.

"No, Eduard. Silly of me. I wanted only to keep it from Aaron, not let him know about the photos." She brushed her hair from her eyes. "You know how it is in the old neighborhood. Everyone would know . . . *passport photos for the rabbi's family.* And then the questions."

Eduard gazed at the curtain of snow that seemed to do battle with the black smoke of the chimneys. "I should not have called the police." His voice was filled with self-recrimination. "I had not guessed how corrupt they have become. Three years ago this could not have happened in Warsaw; before President Pilsudski died, this would not have been tolerated!"

He turned to search her face imploringly. "Justice has died in the hearts of men. You *must not stay here,* Etta! If such changes have come to the Poles since the death of one man, what will come to pass in Warsaw in another three years? There is no hand to stop it. With the exception of one little priest today, the Catholic church would turn its mighty eyes away from what happened to you."

He shook his head and rubbed a hand over his strained face. "I will call a photographer to come here immediately to take pictures of you and the children. We cannot delay in this matter." His eyes scanned the books of his library as if he was searching for something. "You are right. The people of your congregation must not know your intent."

Again he fixed his gaze on Etta. "Can you keep all this from Aaron? He must not know until the passports are an accomplished fact. Then you will present them to him and tell him what happened to you today."

Etta nodded a difficult assent. "But the children—" she began doubtfully.

"I will speak to them," Eduard promised grimly. "They will not talk about this after I explain." He sank down in a wing chair and stretched his long legs out across the floral carpeting. "Aaron has foolish hope for the Jews of Poland. And for the Poles." His brow furrowed. "Last week I stitched up the head of an eight-year-old Jewish child who was beaten with a metal crucifix because he did not bow his knee to the cross when a funeral procession passed. Every day there are more incidents. Since the German deportation, the violence has become more extreme." He did not add the thought that Etta and the children had been lucky today. "Now these men have your name. They know you want passports and exit visas from Poland. They may be back."

Etta visibly paled. "But why?"

"More money. Blackmail."

"But you paid them . . . so much, Eduard. And all the money I have saved is the gold coins I hoped to send to Papa in Jerusalem. In case he should need them for bribes."

"I will take that to him." He moved to his desk chair and wrote out a bank draft on his Warsaw account. "I have left this account open so they will not suspect I am not returning. You must use the money, Etta."

"But Eduard," she protested, "you have paid them so much already. How can I repay you?"

Eduard seemed not to hear her. He blotted the ink and tore the check from the book. Then he wrote another and yet another, leaving the dates blank. The checks lay on his desk. "Do not use them too close together. Cash them over the next few weeks or months. This will close the account. Hopefully we will have your travel documents in order by then. I will pray that you cash the last check on the day you leave Warsaw forever, Etta—you and the children, and even stubborn Aaron. Perhaps by then he will see that leaving is the only rational course of action."

It was Sunday. Eli walked alone through the crowded streets of the Armenian Quarter toward Christ Church. A stream of Englishmen and their elegant ladies were exiting through the wide iron gates where the Reverend Robbins stood shaking hands, smiling pleasantly in his clerical robes. *He is not the gardener, after all,* thought Eli as he watched the pleasant-faced old man.

But Eli was not disguised today either. He was dressed not in his brother's clothes but in the distinctive garb of the Orthodox.

He wore his black coat, the one he saved for holy days and weddings. The hem of his coat showed the fringes of the garment the Torah commanded the Chosen to wear as a sign of identity. On his head was a black, fur-trimmed shtreimel, no different than a hat one might see on a Jew in Warsaw. In spite of Eli's sandy-colored hair, light brown beard, and pleasant blue eyes, there was no mistaking today that a Jew was walking against the crowd leaving Christ Church, in through the iron gates. He waited beyond the Sunday-morning English chatter, until at last, Reverend Robbins raised his head and smiled in kind curiosity in Eli's direction.

Eli stepped forward and extended his hand—a brief and formal handshake. "I have come to discuss an urgent personal matter with you," he said stiffly.

The pastor looked over his shoulder for any stragglers who might overhear such a request. There were none. The congregation had gone to the luncheon buffet at the King David Hotel.

"You are Victoria's . . . friend."

"You have a keen memory."

"She has spoken of you often."

"She has never spoken to me of you," Eli replied, though not unkindly. The news had simply surprised him.

"I knew her mother well before she passed on. A gracious Christian woman. Things might have been very different for Victoria had her mother lived."

Eli was indeed surprised that Reverend Robbins seemed to know so much about Victoria's life. "Yes. Different." There was an awkward pause. What to say?

"Will you join me in my study? Perhaps it would be more suitable for our talk."

Eli followed him through the courtyard to the side of the building. An unmarked wooden door led down a flight of steps to a stone basement beneath the sanctuary. Neither man spoke another word until they were both seated inside a small book-lined room with a high transom window. The pastor clasped his hands on his desk. Eli did not remove his hat in spite of the hat rack by the door. For a moment he faced the pastor without speaking. The old man's eyes seemed to say that he knew already what Eli wanted to say.

"You see," Eli said. "I am a Jew." An obvious statement, but Eli wanted to let this man know that he intended to remain a Jew in spite of what he was about to request.

"And Victoria is Arab. Muslim. A problem for you both."

"You know her well, you say, and I believe you or she would not have wanted to meet me here. She must trust you. And so . . . I trust you."

A nod of thanks. A wave of the fingers urging Eli to speak on.

"So, Reverend Robbins." Eli found this more difficult. "I have returned to Christ Church to ask . . . to request your help. You seem to know . . . everything. And so you must know we cannot be married in the Jewish Quarter. Not right now."

"Things are very difficult."

"But we must marry. Things are growing more difficult every day. I am certain that she needs to live beneath my protection."

"And whose protection are you under, Eli?"

"God's protection."

The answer was without hesitation. The firmness of it surprised the old man. "You are not a Christian," he said, as if that was his interpretation of Eli's response.

"And you are not a Jew. But you believe in the Jewish Messiah, as I do. This makes it acceptable to me that you could perform the ceremony for Victoria and me."

The old man's eyebrows arched with astonishment at the reply. "I am not a rabbi—"

"She needs the legal protection of marriage to me. You are authorized to perform the ceremony. Later we will wed in the Old City beneath a canopy after she has taken the appropriate instruction and—"

"She is not a Christian."

"You will tell her about the Messiah. About God's sacrifice of His only Son just as our Father Abraham offered Isaac. And she will believe you."

"But . . . how can you know such a thing?"

"Because it is the truth. And Victoria will know that if you explain it correctly. I have searched the ancient references, and it is clear they knew that Isaiah fifty-three spoke of Messiah. *Targum Jonathan on Isaiah Fifty-three*. You know that reference?"

"Why, no . . ."

"Rabbi Jonathan Ben-Uzziel was a disciple of the great Hillel. Surely you know his work?"

"Why, no . . ."

"I will lend you the document, and you will show her and explain to her what it means." Eli felt some irritation at the Protestant clergyman's lack of scholarship in the matter of the Messiah of Israel whom he served.

"Why don't you tell her yourself?"

"I want her to know Him because He is Truth, not because she loves me and I tell her. Women will say and do many things for the sake of love. I will teach her other things after we are married."

"You are a confident young man." The pastor leaned forward as if to study Eli in amazement. "And learned."

"Yes," Eli said sadly. "I would have made a good rabbi. But men will give up many things for love, nu?"

"Well, I . . . I do not see how I can refuse if Victoria is also . . ."

"Just teach her, and there is no doubt. So. I can offer you some little payment. We cannot delay in our marriage. I request that you keep this matter altogether a secret. Her brothers will kill her if they find out."

"And you as well."

"Maybe even you, Reverend Robbins." A slight smile. "But we are all under God's protection. I will find her a place in the Christian Quarter where she will stay until we find a way to leave Palestine and the Middle East. My brother is going to school in England. Perhaps you will write us a letter of recommendation."

"I would not have thought it," said the pastor dryly.

"What is that?"

"When I first saw you I thought you were a fearful fellow without much . . . what is the word . . . *moxie*."

"Never mind first impressions. I thought you were the gardener."

The last rays of sunlight shone dully on the tarnished green copper dome of l'Opéra. On the crown of the cupola, the statue of Apollo played his lyre as he watched the silent intrigues of Paris below.

Horns blaring, taxis rattled past the ornate facade of the building.

"Academie Nationale de Musique," Ernst vom Rath's mother read from the window of their taxi. Her round, pleasant face beamed at the sight of the eight rows of double columns, gilded arches, and colonnades of l'Opéra. "The French are *so* . . ." She did not finish her sentence but shifted her attention to her son, who looked away from the building to the rows of restaurants and shops on the other side of the broad avenue. "Ernst—" She patted his hand. "You seem so . . . sullen."

He managed a smile in spite of the resentment he felt at this unannounced visit from his mother and sister. "I wish you had let me know, that is all."

"You sounded so homesick. Lonely." His mother sounded hurt. "We thought you would be glad to see us."

"Glad, yes. But, I have no arrangements for you. I . . . I might have gotten tickets for the opera, at least." He did not let them know that to be near this building felt something like standing at the gates of hell itself. It was every reminder of all the things he wanted to forget.

His mother laughed with relief. "Is that all? Well, we have taken care of that already! There will be tickets for the three of us waiting at the hotel concierge's desk. We saw to it in Berlin."

Ernst felt the blood drain from his face. He tried to look pleased. "Ah. Nice. Very . . ."

His mother looked alarmed. She pressed her hand to his forehead. "Ernst. You are not well? Is that it?"

"Tired, Mother. The embassy, you know. So much happening. I am just tired and I have had so much on my mind."

"We have come to help you take your mind off all that. When we saw the postcard, I said to your father, *He needs a visit to cheer him up, Ernst does!* And we bought the tickets that same afternoon!" She sighed with contentment. "And we needed a break as well from all the dreary *heiling* of Berlin."

"Mother!" he chided. "You must not—"

"Oh well, not around the embassy, at least, but that is why you are so gloomy. That is why we all are so gloomy. Hermann Göring and his four-year economic plan! Ha! We are ordered to save empty toothpaste tubes for collection. Did you know? They are melting down toothpaste tubes to make their fighter planes! The old elegance of our Germany is gone, I'm afraid, Ernst. But now we are here and we can forget all that for a while, ja? No doubt at the opera tonight we will run into all our old friends who had the good sense to leave until *he* is finished with his schemes."

Ernst looked forward at the cab driver who just happened at that moment to glance into the rearview mirror. Their eyes caught for an instant, and Ernst was filled with the unreasoning fear that somehow every word his mother had said would get back to Wilhelmstrasse in Berlin. Back to men like Göring and Hitler and . . . Vargen.

Ernst took his mother's gloved hand. She saw the fear in his eyes and immediately felt it, too. "Ernst, what is it?" she asked quietly.

He lowered his voice to a whisper. "*Not even here.* Not even *here* must you say such things, Mother. They are watching . . . everyone."

"I did not mean . . . I would not injure your career or—"

"I am not speaking of my job at the embassy. Mother, you still do not know what they are, what those men are capable of!"

Frau vom Rath studied the face of her son for a moment. She brushed back a lock of his hair and then turned to look at the opera building as they rounded a corner. Best to talk of light things. Things that did not matter. "Yes. l'Opéra. Red silk walls, I remember. We are in the third tier. A box, Ernst. We will be able to see everyone and everyone will see us."

29

No Place to Go

This morning Hans Schumann brought Herschel a stack of outdated copies of the Yiddish daily paper, *Pariser Haint*.

"I thought you would like to read up on all the news," Hans said cheerfully. "These were free, anyway, because they are from last week. The story is so much more complete than just a little word of news on the radio. Of course you want to hear everything about what your family has been through."

At this, Herschel managed a feeble nod. He did not know if he did indeed want the details of his family's torment filled in. He was helpless here in Paris, so impotent against the forces that gripped them. He stared at the stack of newspapers and stood up angrily. "I do not want to read about it."

Hans looked surprised, hurt by the rejection of his helpfulness. "Well, then. As you wish."

"I want to go out," Herschel croaked in a hoarse, desperate voice. "I do not care any longer if they catch me! Let them deport me too!"

"Herschel!" Hans admonished, taking him firmly by the arm. "Have you forgotten? You have things to do! Things to make *them* listen to you! To all of us!"

"I want out!" Herschel tore himself from Schumann's grip, pushed past him, and clattered down the steep stairs to a narrow landing. Hans called after him. Someone opened a door in the hallway of the rooming house and then closed it again quickly at the sound of Hans shouting down from the attic.

"Come back! You have no place to go! Come back here!"

Herschel put his hands over his ears as he charged down two more flights of steps to where the light of day shone through the glass pane of a door.

Herschel had no coat. He slammed the door and ran out into the brisk November wind, but did not feel the cold. He ran along the boulevard, lifting his face to the light. He thought of the streets of German cities. The automobile horns sounded the same. He imagined what he would have done if the Nazis had come for him, if they came for him now in Paris. He would run. They would scream their obscenities at him and shoot their guns, but he would outrun them all and hide. *Yes!* He *must* hide!

He slowed his pace. Hans had not caught up with him. The cold sidewalk was crowded with people who did not see him, did not know why he was running.

He stopped and looked toward the green dome of the great Paris opera house. He remembered music playing in his father's shop and he thought of Elisa Lindheim and her violin. Probably dead, like everyone else in Vienna. Or dying. Or wishing to die.

He turned in the center of the sidewalk like a lost child. Before him was the display window of a gunsmith's shop. Herschel walked forward and leaned his forehead against the glass pane. A display of weapons was laid out on red fabric—large barrel revolvers and smaller caliber pistols. Different sizes of bullets down to the short stubby cartridges.

Herschel remembered Thomas von Kleistmann. He thought of the death of the old bookseller. He remembered his own wild firing, and then . . . Herschel frowned. A second gunshot had followed his. Why had he not remembered until now? That other gunshot had crumpled the old man. Then Herschel had run wildly through the bookstalls to escape. He had run and run until he had slammed into Hans and been taken to the attic to hide. And that filthy Nazi von Kleistmann still lived, still strutted in the German Embassy and raised his hand to *Heil Hitler* and rejoiced at the news of twelve thousand deported to Poland!

Herschel stared at the weapons. He shivered, suddenly aware of the cold. He wanted to go somewhere—maybe to dance with pretty girls at the community center as he had done before. Life had not been so bad. But it was cold now, and he did not have a coat. He walked back along the path to the rooming house where Hans had helped him hide from the immigration people and anyone else who might want to catch him.

Hans was waiting for him in the attic. He was reading the old copies of the newspaper and shaking his head when Herschel returned.

Snow dusted the slate roofs of Warsaw. Wrapped in heavy wool coats and leggings, the Lubetkin family trudged toward the *Umschlagplatz*, where the great locomotives hissed and shuddered beneath the roofs of the train sheds.

Etta held the baby close against her. The boys' cheeks were red with cold. From behind her muffler, Rachel's breath rose in a steamy vapor as she followed her papa to where Dr. Eduard Letzno waited beside his trunks on the platform.

Aaron raised a mittened hand in greeting. Rachel watched her father's sad eyes as he beheld his friend for possibly the last time.

The two men embraced, clapping each other on the back in a manly, tearless sort of grief.

Goodbye! Was there ever a more difficult word to say? Here in the Warsaw *Umschlagplatz,* where thousands of goodbyes were uttered and millions more were yet to be said, Rachel pitied her father this loss of a true friend. She saw pain in his eyes as Eduard Letzno climbed the steps into his compartment.

"Jerusalem!" Aaron whispered the name like a Shabbat blessing, and Etta thrust a paper-wrapped package into Eduard's hands as the train whistle shrieked and baby Yacov awakened with a startled wail.

"For my father, Eduard!" Etta called through a cupped hand over the din. "Embrace him for us when you see him!"

Eduard held up the package, smiled and nodded in reply. Yes, he would personally deliver the package to Grandfather. He would embrace the old man for them. *"Jerusalem!"* he mouthed.

And then as the train chugged and lurched ahead slightly, Eduard Letzno looked over the heads of those who loved him in Warsaw. Those sad, gentle eyes held a moment of recognition, an instant of fear at what he saw.

The train pulled away. He looked at Aaron and then out beyond them. He called something to Aaron, but his words were lost beneath the whistle. He pointed. Aaron looked back, but he saw nothing but masses of people waving and calling out their own sad farewells.

Eduard shouted again! Aaron raised a hand in helplessness. He had not heard. He did not understand.

A moment later, the train clacked out of sight, and the crowds of the *Umschlagplatz* diminished to be replaced by others.

———

"Two out of three is not *so* bad," Rabbi Lebowitz said, defending himself against the scowls of the old women in Tipat Chalev soup kitchen.

"What are we to do with them! Oy *gevalt!*" Hannah Cohen pointed an accusing finger to the tables where two dozen Torah schoolboys labored without success over walnuts that were harder than Jerusalem stones!

Hammers raised and crashed down, sending still-intact nuts spinning off dangerously across the room. The wood of tables dented with the blows. When one lucky blow fell hard enough to crack the shell, then the meat of the nut was also smashed into a mere worthless mess.

"Bags of them!" moaned Shoshanna. "Bags and bags and *bags*!"

"Nothing but *shlock* merchandise!" another woman muttered from inside the kitchen.

"We might have gotten sugar if we had held out," Hannah Cohen said woefully.

This last accusation cut too deeply for the rabbi. As head of the Center for Charitable Distribution of Food, he had done his best. How could he know these English walnuts were of better use as weapons!

A hammer smashed down! A nut squirted out from beneath the steel and hurled toward the disapproving cooks! They squealed and scattered and the nut struck the rabbi on his cheek.

"The final blow," he muttered as the hammer-wielding worker cried out in shame.

"I did not mean to do it, Rabbi Lebowitz! It . . . it was an accident!"

Now all hammers fell silent. Eyes turned in fearful astonishment at the sight of the great Rebbe holding his bruised cheek. The offending walnut ricocheted and tumbled down the basement stairs.

Rebbe Lebowitz opened his mouth. *Calmly. Gently.* These walnuts were fashioned and tempered like steel, but the old rabbi would not curse them. Not out loud, anyway.

"Put away your hammers, my little stonecutters. If the Eternal, blessed be His name forever, wishes for these nuts to nourish us here at Tipat Chalev, then *He* will have to send us an instrument to crack them for us. True? Of course, true!"

He turned to Hannah and Shoshanna and said regally, "Still we have milk and cocoa. Two out of three is not such a bad bargain!"

"And this . . ." Shimon said with a flourish, "will be my finest performance of *The Nutcracker Suite*!"

Before the delighted eyes of a dozen children, Shimon placed a row of walnuts on the wooden table of the mess hall then raised his cast-encased arm and smashed it down on them.

No one spoke as he smiled slyly and raised his arm to reveal that the nuts had been split perfectly! Shells lay in pieces, while the meat remained intact!

"A-h-h-h-h!" the children proclaimed in chorus. Then, "I told you he could do it!"

"You did not!"

"Yes, I did! Now will you believe me?"

While they argued over his miraculous performance, Shimon handed out the nuts to his audience and emptied his pocket of yet another twelve English walnuts. He lined them up perfectly on the table of Tipat Chalev as the shelled nuts were crammed into watering mouths and eyes turned to watch the plaster cast rise and fall with the precision only a percussionist from Vienna could master.

The crack of nuts brought resounding applause from the Old City children. More *o-h-h-h's*, and a few *oy's* of amazement echoed from the vaulted ceiling, bringing Leah and the cooks of Tipat Chalev from the kitchen.

"You should see what he can do!" a ten-year-old boy proclaimed to Hannah Cohen.

Proudly, Shimon handed out the shelled nuts to the children. He glanced at Leah and winked. Rabbi Lebowitz appeared behind the women and peered over their shoulders as Shimon laid out another row along the crack in the table.

Again the large plaster cast raised up. Two little girls held hands over their ears in anticipation of the loud smash that followed.

Miraculous! Amazing! Cleanly shelled nuts on the table! This giant man from Austria had come to the Old City soup kitchen just in time to relieve the disgrace of the old rabbi's British Army walnuts!

The old man raised his eyes to the heavens and thanked the Eternal! He nudged the disapproving Hannah on his right and the scowling Shoshanna on his left.

The two women exchanged astonished glances. "This fellow is better than a hammer!" cried Hannah.

Rebbe Lebowitz stuck out his lower lip in proud victory. "Did I not tell you?" he chided the women. "The Eternal has provided His own device for shelling these stones! Ha!" He raised his gnarled hands up in gratitude.

"More! More! More!" the children begged.

Shimon shrugged apologetically. "All gone, I'm afraid!"

Rabbi Lebowitz pushed his way through the kitchen crew. "Nu! We have plenty more where those come from, Shimon Feldstein! You are sent from God! It is an angel who brought you here!"

At that, the old rabbi rushed forward and took Shimon by the plaster cast. He led the towering giant toward the steps of the basement. Throwing back the wooden door, he snatched up a lantern and stepped onto the narrow landing. Shimon followed, ducking his head beneath the low doorframe.

"There! You see!" crowed the rabbi, gesturing toward dozens of gunny sacks marked: H.M. WALNUTS. JERUSALEM. Now the rabbi said very loudly, "These I traded with the British Army quartermaster for some boxes of useless American powder called Jell-O." He smiled and patted Shimon's cast. "You may henceforth consider yourself employed, Shimon. From kettle drum to soup kettle, nu? Official Tipat Chalev nutcracker."

The rattling furnace inside the offices of the British Mandate had not managed to keep up with the fierceness of the renewed cold today.

Strands of damp mist-covered hair clung to Victoria's neck as she paid her fare and boarded the bus in front of the King David Hotel. Every window of the bus was shut tight, and yet the freezing air of the afternoon seeped into the compartment as the bus lurched forward along King George Avenue toward Jaffa Road.

"Tomorrow will be colder yet," an old woman moaned knowingly. "You would think I would be used to it after seventy-nine years." Her mouth split in a toothless grin as Victoria swung into the empty seat beside her.

"I will never be used to it." Victoria blew steamy breath and brushed drops of mist from her forehead. "And tomorrow the Englishmen insist that all the women in the secretarial pool wear their best English suits . . . short Western skirts!"

The old woman tapped her temple. "They shall kill our women, these English and their short skirts."

"Tomorrow there are important gentlemen coming from London to tour the offices," Victoria offered. "And so we must dress up like proper English secretaries in London. Even though it will be so cold."

Now a young Arab merchant leaned forward. He spoke to the old woman, lest he offend the young woman by speaking directly to her. "Tomorrow will be hot enough. Those Englishmen are in for a big surprise I hear, and if I were an Arab secretary I might find a reason to stay home tomorrow."

Victoria turned around and frowned at the young man. Such staring was not proper, but she could not help it. Was there to be yet another demonstration? Another show of Arab hostility against the English and the Jews?

She glared at him as if it were somehow his doing. He spread his hands in innocence and then looked quickly out the window to where the great citadel and the wall of Jerusalem loomed ahead. He had possibly said too much. And yet, did everyone not expect what was to come?

The brakes of the aged bus squealed in protest at Jaffa Gate. It was still several blocks through the Old City to her home. How very different life was here in the Old City than it was where she worked for the British government. In her office it was impolite not to look straight into the eyes of the Englishmen. *How very different!* She sighed and grimaced and turned her eyes downward in modesty as she passed through the gate and into Omar Square.

To her right she could plainly see the spire of Christ Church where she would once again meet with Eli. She stopped for just a moment and let herself imagine him walking up the Armenian Patriarchate Road to meet her. *He will smile. He will touch my face. He will say how desperate the hours have been without me . . . And I will say . . .*

At that moment, her reverie was interrupted by the voice of her youngest brother as he called her name across the Square. Her smile faded. Weariness filled her eyes as she spotted not just Ismael but Daud and Isaak with him. These three were half brothers to her and Ibrahim, and the sight of them was never a cause for rejoicing in Victoria.

Short and dark like their mother, they lacked the fine-chiseled features of Ibrahim. Spoiled by their father and mother alike, they did not work in the family oriental rug business, but spent their time in the souks and coffeehouses where they had caught the spirit of rebellion that grew in such places.

"Salaam, Isaak," she said flatly as he took her by the arm.

"You are late," Ismael said. "We came looking for you."

"Worried," agreed Daud, who was the least intelligent and least offensive of the three.

"You need not have worried. The bus is usually late." She shrugged off the hand of Isaak and began walking home as if they had not come for her.

Now began the probing questions. "The English politicians are coming to the King David Hotel again tomorrow." This was a statement of fact.

"What time are they to arrive?"

Victoria laughed. "How should I know who is coming? Or when they will arrive?"

"Everyone in Jerusalem knows they are coming back from Galilee tomorrow."

She looked hard at Daud. He was the only one she could intimidate with a look. "Well, *I* do not know of it!" she snapped.

Daud looked confused. Could they have the date wrong? His questioning look was nudged away by Isaak.

"You must sleep all day at your job for the English, Victoria. You never know anything."

She did not reply, but pushed her way through the crowds of late shoppers in the souks. *I know enough to have you arrested if you were not the sons of my father,* she thought angrily.

"You can tell us," Daud tried again clumsily. "We are your brothers, after all."

Victoria turned on him. The look on her face made him put up his arms in case she would strike him. "Ibrahim is my brother!" she hissed. "That is all I can be certain of since I see no resemblance to my father in any of you."

Isaak took her roughly be the arm. "*You* . . ." he threatened.

She let her voice drop as shoppers in the souk stopped their bargaining to stare at the confrontation. "Take your hand from me . . .

unless you wish to deal with my brother."

Grudgingly, Isaak released his grip. She glowered at him another moment, then spun around to walk the remaining distance through the vaulted souks to her home, alone.

When she entered the house, Victoria did not answer the shrill voice of her stepmother.

Another cry, *"Change your clothes and come fix dinner for your brothers! I have a headache tonight!"*

Now Victoria called back over her shoulder, "I have a headache also! They will have to fix their own meal!" At that, she slammed the door of her bedroom and then stood panting in the center of the room. She expected her stepmother to pound at the door and then beat her, but the only sound she heard was the ticking of the clock on the night table behind her and then the slamming of the front door as the three brothers arrived home.

Theo refused to allow Elisa to accompany him to Heathrow airport with Anna. "You know how I feel about goodbyes," he remarked lightly. "Take care of my grandbaby, now promise me."

Elisa nodded. Her father's eyes were radiant and happier than she had seen in some time. He told her he was going away on business. The nature of the business was not discussed, but Elisa knew her father well enough that his business had something to do with the refugee question. She did not ask. His unspoken calling gave her peace. Not everyone in the world was silent, after all. While great governments made proclamations and held meetings about the refugees, Elisa knew Theo was *doing something*!

So it was that Theo kissed her goodbye on the sidewalk in front of the Red Lion house. He hugged Charles and Louis and told them that he had left a birthday gift for them with Anna in case he could not get back to London in time. At these quiet words, Elisa thought she saw an instant of pain on her mother's face. Perhaps not.

Anna kissed her and promised to be back in time for a nice lunch at Claridge's Hotel with Sir Thomas Beecham and Frieda Hillman.

"Bring the notes about the next Charity Concert," Anna reminded her. "We are going to stage it right in the Claridge's ballroom, Theo," she said proudly. "The management is donating the place for the night."

Theo shook his head in amazement. "From Claridge's to a soup kitchen in Prague and a refugee camp in Poland! Only you, Anna!"

The banter seemed almost too superficial. They had talked about this, after all, this morning over breakfast. For a moment Elisa wondered if the record was playing over again to avoid other things being said. *But what things?*

Freddie Frutschy glanced at his watch and then at the threatening sky. "If we don't hurry, sir, you'll not be going anywheres from the looks of the weather." He opened the car door and stepped back as Theo cast one last look at Elisa. Again she thought she saw *something* in his eyes. Sorrow, hope, love seemed thinly veiled beneath light chatter about an already much discussed event.

Could she ask him in these final moments if there was something more he was not saying? How long would this goodbye be? Suddenly Elisa felt like a small child being left behind on her first day of school. Freddie started the car. Theo raised his hand to her behind the glass of the window.

She stepped forward and put her hand against his through the glass. "I love you, Father!" she called.

He mouthed the words back, *God bless you!* And then Freddie pulled away from the curb.

―――

Ibrahim knocked softly on Victoria's bedroom door. She did not answer and so he knocked again and turned the latch, nudging the door open slightly.

He had expected to find her in the room, but instead she sat on the balcony where the last rays of sunlight had made the western sky a tapestry of bright colors like the fabrics in the souk.

At the sound of the groaning hinges, Victoria turned her head and looked at him. Her dark eyes smoldered with anger. She tossed her hair in a defiant gesture and put her finger to her lips to silence him as she stood, reentered her room and closed the door to the balcony behind her.

"Have you come to warn me?" she asked coldly.

Ibrahim simply blinked at her in amazement. Indeed, he had come to warn her about the demonstrations tomorrow, but how did she know? "Where did you hear?" he asked.

"On the bus."

"The bus!" he exclaimed. That meant that everyone in Jerusalem was aware.

"And"—she gestured back toward the balcony—"our brothers are talking. There. Down in the courtyard where every little bird may carry its voice to the ears of the English."

"The English will know soon enough."

"If they know my brothers are involved, then they will dismiss me from my job at the Mandate administration. They will think I am a spy." Her eyes filled with tears as she sank onto the bed.

Ibrahim did not move to comfort her. "This is men's business," he said more harshly than he intended. "I came to warn you not to go to work tomorrow, that is all. What difference does it make if you work for *them* or not?"

"It makes a difference to me!" she cried. "That is the only place I am treated like a human being with a mind except for . . ."

"Except for Eli?" Ibrahim finished. She was pouting as women sometimes did. He would not yield to her display of foolishness. "I will not bring him to you until he is *one of us.*"

She looked away, defiant in her anger. "And do you think he will ever be one of us if you and our half brothers are part of . . . whatever is going to happen tomorrow?"

"We wish only for a free Arab State."

"Then go to Jordan! Or Syria! What does it matter? The English are *good* to us! Jews and Arabs! I *work* at the Mandate administration! I *cannot* hear this!" She covered her ears.

Ibrahim did not reply. He waited. She lowered her hands, and then he spoke gently. "There will be no violence."

"So you say each time! Do you think I am blind? Or only stupid?"

"Only a demonstration of Muslim displeasure for the English Woodhead Commission. They will see—"

"That we are barbarians."

"Not barbarians! . . . Conquerors! As the Prophet has written, as Allah has whispered, *Jerusalem will belong to the faithful! To those who bow down . . .*"

"I have heard the sermons of Haj Amin," she said scornfully. "He promises Paradise for those who die fighting *Jihad! Holy War!*" She moved to the window and looked toward the Dome of the Rock just beyond the housetops of the Old City. "What use is Jerusalem to us if we are dust? Can Allah mean that we are to kill those who have always lived beside us? Can you fight also against Eli because he is a Jew?"

"If Eli is not with us, then I will fight him." There was a coldness in Ibrahim's eyes which made Victoria shudder inside.

"But, he is like a brother to you."

"He loves you. That will make him see reason." It was as if Ibrahim was not listening.

"Then you are also one of them," Victoria whispered. "You believe the words Haj Amin speaks to the people."

"He speaks the words of Mohammed. The words of Allah. He will be king over Jerusalem, and those who follow him will be exalted."

"Haj Amin is an assassin!" Victoria drew back. She looked at the hands of her brother. Could those hands do the bidding of a leader like Haj Amin?

"It is the will of Allah—" he began.

"That you murder the innocent tomorrow?"

"There will be no murders tomorrow."

"But you will make certain no more Jews come to Palestine."

Ibrahim shrugged. "A few more tires will be burned in the streets." He attempted to lighten the darkness of her imagination. "A demonstration that will hang in the noses of these Englishmen. Burn their eyes a bit. Black clouds of burning rubber. No violence, Victoria." He took a step nearer. "I came only to warn you that you must not go to work tomorrow."

"Then I will lose my job."

"So be it," he said coolly. "Arab women do not need to work for the English unless they serve their brothers in some way."

Now Victoria turned on him. There was no doubt what he was asking of her. *"Get out,* Ibrahim! *You* . . . I thought you were not like our half brothers! I did not think that you . . ." She stammered in her rage against him. "I will leave this house before I consent! Spies are still hanged in Palestine! It makes no difference if they are women! Get out!" She cried too loudly now and the voice of her stepmother called gruffly up the stairs.

"What is wrong with the princess now?"

Ibrahim bowed slightly. "Salaam, Victoria." He backed up a step into the corridor and closed the door, blocking her black look. Then, with a smile, he inserted the key to her room into the lock and turned it as she gave a desperate cry against her imprisonment.

From the tall minaret beside the silver dome of the el-Aqsa Mosque, the cry of the muezzin went out over the dusk of Jerusalem.

Pacing in her small, Spartan bedroom, Victoria did not stop to kneel, or bow to pray as her brothers did downstairs. Could she pray to such a God? Allah? Through His prophet He demanded death and domination over all who did not believe the words: *There is no God but Allah, and Mohammed is His prophet!*

Throughout the city, men with faces bowed low uttered these words. These were the same men who, like the half brothers of Victoria, planned riots and rebellion and plotted for the murders of those who did not follow Haj Amin!

Victoria *would not bow* to this Allah! She raised her chin in defiance as she faced east toward the Dome of the Rock. Fading sunlight shone dully on the tarnished dome as her faith died.

"I will not pray to you," she whispered. *"You,* who have made my life a prison! *Never again will I bow to you!"*

And so she stood throughout the moments when all the Muslim faithful touched their foreheads to the ground. All that she had been—everything she had been taught as a child—evaporated like an unheard prayer. Emptiness and anger replaced the words " . . . and Mohammed is His prophet!"

Victoria lay on her bed and watched as the final rays of sunlight faded into the darkness of a moonless night. She wanted to weep, but did not allow herself even that small luxury. One sigh, one tear, and her stepbrothers and their mother would gloat and laugh among themselves at the misery of the one they mocked as *the princess*.

Hours crept by. The bells of Christ Church tolled ten o'clock; then the key rattled, and her door swung back. Daud held a tray of food. Behind him, shadowed in the backlighted corridor, stood his mother.

The woman's bitter voice preceded her into the room. "Is *the princess* sleeping?" Then she commanded, "Set the tray down, Daud, and leave us." She snapped on the light, and Victoria sat up, blinking against the glare.

"I am not hungry." Victoria did not look at the tray of food. She was, indeed, very hungry, but she would not show even that to this woman.

"We did not want you telling your father that we locked you up and did not feed you." The woman narrowed her eyes. There was no hint of kindness. This gesture of food was only to protect herself against the anger of her husband.

"If my father were here—" Victoria began.

"He is not here. And so you answer to me." She held up the key and smiled an unfeeling smile.

"When my father returns—" Victoria spoke carefully. She must not give in to the tears of anger that pushed at her throat. "When he returns from Teheran, then you will answer to him for this."

The smile broadened. "It was your own brother Ibrahim who locked the door and brought me the key, remember? For your own protection, my dear girl."

"You harbor rebellion in my father's house! You encourage your sons and my own brother against the wishes of—"

The woman took a threatening step toward Victoria. "It is you who rebel against my authority!"

"You are not my mother!" Tears brimmed in Victoria's eyes against her will.

This pleased the woman who stood over her. "Your tears do not move me as they do your father. The matter is settled. You will remain here. We will give you no chance to warn these Englishmen you are so fond of."

"*Warn* them?" So this was the reason for her confinement. There was no thought of safety for her, after all. "You think they will not notice when I do not come to work? You think they will not ask me *why* and how I knew? You warn them by keeping me prisoner here."

The reasoning of this penetrated the mind of the woman. She eyed Victoria for moment longer and then challenged her. "If you tell them of the meeting here today, they will arrest your father."

Victoria did not argue that, even though Amal Hassan hated the politics of his wife and sons. "Just let me go." Victoria was once again in control.

The woman considered the request. "It means a lot to you, this job with the English?"

Victoria chose her words carefully. With this woman, to show too much pleasure for anything meant that the object of her pleasure would be somehow denied her. It had always been so since the day the woman had married Victoria's father. She had possessed a kind of cruel beauty then, but the years had twisted the beauty into ugliness, and the cruelty had only become more harsh.

"My job with the English is just a job. They pay better than anywhere else in Jerusalem, that is all."

The woman understood money. "Greedy little princess. Never enough for you, eh?" Her eyes narrowed as she thought what to do. "You will stay here," she said at last. "I will send word you are ill. And when your father returns, we will speak of finding you a husband. That will quiet your rebellion!"

"Please—" Victoria begged.

The begging pleased the woman, as had Victoria's tears. "When your father returns we shall discuss . . . your future." She stepped out before Victoria could reply. The key turned in the lock, and Victoria finally let herself weep.

———

Jerusalem was still asleep. The sun had not yet risen when the rattle of her doorknob awakened Victoria.

Ibrahim's voice called gently to her. "My sister, are you awake?"

Victoria sat up in drowsy confusion and pulled the blanket around her shoulders. Why had Ibrahim awakened her before dawn?

"Ibrahim?" she questioned, forgetting last night's fears as he unlocked the door. "What. . . ?"

She turned the knob and her brother stood before her, holding a tray with fresh fruit and a small bowl of boiled eggs. He brushed past her and placed the tray on her chest of drawers. He was not smiling.

"We have some bad news," he said quietly.

Victoria felt herself groping for the bed. "Is it Father?" she managed to ask.

Ibrahim smiled slightly. "A messenger came from Hebron last night while you were sleeping. The sister of our mother has died."

She put a hand to her head in relief. "Aunt Antoine?" she asked feebly.

Ibrahim nodded. "We are the only children of this branch of the family. Get dressed. We must mourn for her in Hebron today."

Victoria blinked in understanding. Her relief that it was not her father far outweighed any sorrow she might have had for the loss of her mother's sister.

She looked at the breakfast tray and suddenly felt ashamed for her thoughts against Ibrahim last night. Only her dear brother would have thought to bring breakfast to soften the blow of bad news. In the next instant she remembered Leah. *The King David Hotel. Tea at four o'clock.* "My job—" she said, unable to find a way to explain that she had an appointment with a Jewish woman this afternoon.

"I have taken care of all of that." Ibrahim's voice was matter-of-fact. "I sent a messenger to the home of Tasha with word that there is a death in the family."

Well, then, that was taken care of. Victoria could only hope that Leah would think to ask the right department supervisor when Victoria missed their appointment.

A strange light filled Ibrahim's eyes, as if he knew some wonderful joke and yet would not tell her. Yes, there was amusement on his face. "What is it?" she asked. "Why do you smile at such a moment?"

He shrugged. "I suppose I am grateful it is not Father," Ibrahim replied curtly as he left the room, shutting the door behind him.

———

The morning sun shone through the windshield of Ibrahim's borrowed car as he left Jerusalem. After five minutes passed, Victoria knew that they were not going to Hebron.

"Hebron is south." She shielded her eyes from the bright glare of dawn.

"Yes," Ibrahim replied. "We are taking a different route."

"You are lying, Ibrahim!" Victoria shouted as they topped the rise. The narrow road led east to Jericho and then on down in a twisting, rutted track to where Allenby Bridge crossed the Jordan River into the country of Trans-Jordan.

"Yes," Ibrahim smiled again. "I am lying, my sister."

She looked at his face, illuminated by the fiery light of the desert sun. "But *why?*" she cried. Her hands trembled. "Why are you taking me away from Jerusalem?"

He pulled down the visor and glanced mockingly at her. "For your own protection, Victoria."

"My protection! From what? From whom? Is it Eli? Ibrahim, are you taking me from Eli?" Tears of frustration came against her will.

Ibrahim glanced at her, a glint of power in his eyes. He was enjoying his sister's tears. She struck his arm with her fist, and he responded with a slap across her mouth. She jerked back against the car door and remained there huddled and sobbing as blood from her lip trickled down the glass windowpane. The mountains of Moab stretched out in desolate monotony before them. An hour passed, and still Victoria wept.

At last Ibrahim answered her. "There are certain . . . *demonstrations* planned for this afternoon. These will occur near the King David Hotel. By tonight it will be done, and we will come home."

"Why?" she wailed miserably. "Oh, Ibrahim. Not *you*! Have you forgotten Eli?"

"If your heart was right you would turn the heart of Eli like a river into our camp! And you would help us fight the English!"

"I will do neither!" she warned, staying well beyond his reach. "Am I the only child of our father?"

Again Ibrahim raised his hand as if to strike her, but he thought better of it. It would not do to have her return to work tomorrow with a bruised face. It would not be wise to give anyone opportunity to ask questions of her. Perhaps she would answer their questions; then he and his half brothers would all be hanged at the end of British ropes.

"There are only a handful of us in Palestine," he said. "And yet we send the English foxes running for their dens when the sun goes down! We control the roads. The night is ours. Think what we might do with more men and decent weapons." He was talking for his own pleasure now. Victoria stared out toward Trans-Jordan where mountains melted into heaps of sand. A thousand questions filled her mind. She pictured the faces of her friends and co-workers. If Ibrahim had been frightened enough to carry her away, then what was planned? An assassination? A riot in the commercial district?

"You have done enough already," she muttered.

"We are only beginning, my sister." He licked his lips and squinted through the dust-covered windshield. "Tomorrow you will be grateful that I took you away today. You will thank me that you are alive."

30

Storming the Gates of Hell

Berlin appeared far below as the plane suddenly descended through the gray vapor of clouds. Theo watched out the window with a mix of nostalgia and apprehension. This was a homecoming, to be sure, but not the kind he had dreamed of.

There were no sailboats on the lakes. The Spree River was a colorless line winding through the city. Trees in the parks and woodlands were without leaves. The central city itself seemed torn and ravaged. Heaps of masonry were everywhere mingled with earthmovers and scaffolding that climbed the facades of buildings like barren vines. Tiny automobiles crept like bugs along the roads. The face of Theo's beloved Berlin was being changed, rebuilt to match the monumental ideals of the superrace of Aryans.

Theo smiled as the plane passed over a building that seemed like an old friend. The structure of Lindheim's department store remained the same. Now it bore the name *GERMANIA* in bold neon letters across the top floor of the building. Giant swastika flags draped every side from ledge to sidewalk. But still, the cornices and arches of the windows were unaltered. The broad doorways that opened to the sidewalks of four different avenues were unchanged. Lindheim's department store still roosted firmly on an entire city block of Berlin. *What they called it did not matter.* Theo still knew the place better than anyone ever could. From the soil beneath the basement to the steel girders and stone facades, Theo had hovered over every aspect of its creation until it had become the finest store in all Germany—one of the finest in all Europe. Today there was no other friendly face below to greet him, only the weathered stones that had once contained Theo's dreams.

He looked beyond, toward Wilhelmstrasse. The house he and Anna had built there was gone. The stones of some new Nazi public ministry were rising up to take its place.

Theo looked back at the old Lindheim store. He would have liked to have one more look around inside, but such a thing would not be possible.

He sighed as the plane dipped lower toward the large square of turf marking Tempelhof Airfield. Not so long ago, he had left that same field with shafts of lightning splitting the air around his tiny biplane. He had almost made it across the border. Almost. The wind had broken a wing strut, and he had managed to land in a cow pasture—in the field of a Bavarian Nazi party member.

Theo flipped open his passport folder. *British diplomatic pass. His face. Citizenship listed as Great Britain.* But one thing Göring had insisted on when he demanded that Theo Lindheim return to the soil of the Reich was the change of name—from Theo to *Jacob Stern,* the name given him when he was interned at Dachau.

Jacob Stern—the sole survivor of the Dachau *Herrgottseck!* Like the gray stones of Lindheim's department store, Theo had been renamed by his Nazi persecutors, but they had never managed to change anything else about him. The stuff that made Theo who he was remained the same.

He wondered if Hermann Göring would see *that* in his face when they met again after so many long and bitter years. He was almost certain that the false name on the British passport would become an excuse for the Nazis to arrest him once again. He prayed that he would at least be given the chance to present the economic plan of the governments he represented. That much alone would make this journey—and what would follow—worth the suffering.

He pressed his lips together tightly as he studied the rooftops of the great German capital. How many thousands of people huddled fearfully beneath those roofs and prayed that someone would help them escape? Theo carried them all inside his heart. He was one of them. He, too, had loved this land that was now determined to destroy him.

Like those who opposed the Führer's evil, the Spirit of the true and loving God had been driven underground. No longer did His love pervade the churches or His beauty fill the woods and rivers of Berlin. The god Wotan lived here now. The Chancellery building on Wilhelmstrasse rose as a new temple to an evil god.

The sound of traffic in Allenby Square echoed inside the large post office. With the clamor of busy Jerusalem in her ears, Leah copied the new post office box number onto the return address of her first letter to Elisa.

She held the envelope for a moment and imagined her friend holding it in faraway England. Flimsy paper and ink was a tenuous link at best, but Leah found some pleasure in the thought that Elisa's fingers would touch the envelope and cherish the words written inside.

London. A world away. What news would Elisa hear about the Arab demonstrations? She would be concerned until the letter arrived. She would look out on her London street and wait for the mailman just as Leah had seen her do when she had hoped for a letter from Thomas von Kleistmann. How far they had come since those days!

A blue-uniformed mail clerk hurried by. "Bitte," Leah asked, then, remembering these were Englishmen, she started again. "Excuse me, please. How long will it take for my letter to reach London?"

The face puckered in thought. The aging civil servant scratched his head. "Several weeks, at least, miss. Depending on what boat it gets on. Military mail goes some faster than the private stuff."

"Ah." A twinge of disappointment rose up in Leah. Several weeks. By then her news would be old and stale. What news would there be between then and now? Would the distinguished gentlemen of the Woodhead Commission have submitted their recommendations by then? Would the matter of Jewish immigration to Palestine have been settled forever by then?

Leah laid her cheek against Elisa's name for a moment. Then, as an Arab man deposited a stack of envelopes into the mail slot, Leah also slipped her hopes and fears down the brass chute.

It would be weeks, or perhaps months, before Elisa's reply came back to Jerusalem. Leah pocketed the shiny new mailbox key. The key would be her link to London, and yet, it would be a long time before she could hope to find anything in their box.

There were other matters to tend to before she met Victoria for tea at the King David Hotel. Across from the broad steps of the post office in Allenby Square stood the imposing edifice of Barclay's Bank. Only one hundred fifty-three dollars remained of the cash Murphy had slipped into Shimon's pocket. It seemed like a small sum to deposit in such a large bank, but the thought of a bank account somehow settled Leah. A post office box. A bank account. They were no longer strangers in Jerusalem, but residents with proof that this place was indeed home! Leah filled out the appropriate forms and passed their American dollars under the iron grid of the teller's window.

At home in Vienna she had known the bank tellers by name. They had known her and smiled in greeting when she walked into the bank on the Ringstrasse. It would be the same here, she decided. *"Guten Tag* . . . hello," she said to the dark-skinned Arab bank teller. He did not smile or even acknowledge her greeting.

"You would like to keep some out?" he asked in a brusque businesslike manner.

This was a small defeat. Perhaps the divisions of the Old City reached into the bank as well, she reasoned. She signed the form and withheld four pounds from the amount. This would buy tea for Victoria and groceries for a few days, perhaps.

The bank was not far from the commercial district of New City Jerusalem and the King David Hotel. An Egged bus sputtered by, but Leah determined she would walk everywhere in Jerusalem. There was no reason to waste money on bus fare when she had two good legs that had carried her over the Alps from Austria!

Walking briskly along the sidewalk, she peered into the shopwindows and mentally made notes about the location of this business or that. In this section of Jerusalem, Leah could almost imagine that she was in Europe again. Window displays showed off the same Paris fashions Leah had seen in the more modest shops in France. A sign in a tailor shop advertised the latest in men's suits, cut after the style of the finest tailors in London and Rome.

Shop signs in English, German, and French gave Leah a sense that she was not so very far from her European roots, after all.

She stopped a moment at the frantic intersection and looked back toward Jaffa Gate and the Old City walls. Behind those stones it seemed that time had not moved. The passions and conflicts of Mount Zion were ageless and unchanging. She hummed a few notes of the melody from Bloch's Solomon's Symphony. Melancholy and poignant, it seemed to fit the timeless tragedy of Jerusalem.

Around her, the horns of automobiles blared. The whistles of traffic policemen directed the discordant symphony. But behind the wall, only the music of Solomon seemed appropriate.

The road sloped away to the weathered headstones of a cemetery. The tower of the YMCA building rose to the south, and Leah could easily make out the fortress-like stones of the King David Hotel across from it. A bus chugged up the slope toward her, then halted at a bus stop where half a dozen people stood.

Leah did not see the two cars until a battered sedan roared around the front of the bus, blocking its way. The bus driver laid on his horn as the doors of the car flew open and two frightened-looking Arab youths leaped out and ran directly toward her before jumping into a second car. A moment later it tore past Leah and sped away.

Instinctively, Leah froze as the bus driver crammed his vehicle into reverse and stepped on the gas. The mouths of the waiting passengers opened to scream, and at that moment Leah threw herself to the sidewalk. There was time for nothing else. She did not hear the blast as the white heat passed above her. Suddenly the screams dissolved into silence and bright light. Around her, chunks of debris clattered to earth and she tucked her head even tighter beneath her arms.

The air was silent, filled with the stench of burning rubber and seared flesh. She felt no pain. No fear. A strange, detached calm surrounded her, although she knew that death was everywhere. For an instant she wondered if perhaps she, too, had died, and then she raised her head to the devastation that surrounded her. Where six people had stood, there was a black hole in the sidewalk. Nothing was left of the Arab car. The front of the bus was shattered, the driver vanished. Chunks of metal smoked in the torn asphalt.

Leah tried to cry out, but her own voice was lost in the silence of the destruction. Suddenly people were running everywhere. Two British soldiers spotted Leah where she lay. She raised her hand and called out to them. She could not hear her own voice or their response. Their mouths opened in a soundless shout as they ran to her side.

Only then did the pain scream in her ears, as if the hot metal shards had pierced her head. She wept! She called the name of Shimon! What was wrong with her voice that she made no sound? And then she knew . . . *she could not hear.*

At the sound of the blast, Captain Samuel Orde ran with a hundred others out the entrance of the King David Hotel. A cloud of blue smoke billowed up from what remained of the bombed car. The scent of cordite was heavy in the air. Such a scent meant only one thing to a soldier: death had come again to Julian's Way.

Stunned, the onlookers gasped and then cried out the names of co-workers who had just left the building for the bus. In a matter of seconds, the horror before them sank in, and Orde found himself jogging purposefully across the driveway of the hotel, cutting through blackened hedges and dodging smoking hunks of steel that littered the street and sidewalk like a battlefield.

Cars were already backed up on Julian's Way. Some were disabled by flattened tires and shattered windshields. A green taxi sat sideways in the road. A steering wheel and part of a dashboard lay on the hood. Miraculously, the stunned driver seemed to be moving—and there were other signs of life amid the debris and crumpled bodies, as well.

Orde stepped over the body of a woman. Too late for her. He covered his mouth and nose against the sickening smell that mingled in the smoke. A group of soldiers reached the bus, demolished from the front axle forward. Moans came from inside the wreckage. *Survivors!*

He looked to the right toward another body—a woman on the sidewalk. "Dear merciful God!" he cried, not knowing where to begin. And then the woman moved; she raised her head slightly, then let it fall back against her arm. In that instant Orde recognized her. *The musician! Leah Feldstein!* She was so close to the center of the blast; so near to the black crater! *How had she survived?*

She sat up as Orde ran toward her. Her face contorted with pain and she covered her ears with her hands as she called out.

"Shimon! Help me, Shimon!" And then, "Why? *Oh Jesu! Jesu! Warum?*"

Another officer joined Orde's dash to her. "It is Leah Feldstein!" he exclaimed. As they stepped over the fragments of what had been a living human a few moments before, the officer cursed the Arabs and shook his fist heavenward as if his curse of the Arabs became a curse against God as well.

Leah stretched her hand out toward Orde. *"Bitte!"* her words were all in German. *"Bitte! Hilf mir! Mein Gott!"* Her hands returned to clutch the sides of her head in agony.

"Mrs. Feldstein," Orde said as he knelt beside her and embraced her. "It is over. You are safe." His eyes focused on a victim just beyond her. "By the mercy of God, you are safe."

She sobbed uncontrollably. The wail of sirens pierced the sounds of muffled sobs. The curses. The prayers. The awakening shrieks of agony that came with consciousness. Leah Feldstein heard none of this. She leaned against Orde's chest and wept quietly until an ambulance came to take her away.

News of the bomb blast on Julian's Way swept through the city within minutes. Shop grates clattered down and shutters slammed shut before the first ambulances reached the scene. Eyes turned toward the distant echo of sirens and bullhorns. Fear touched Arab, Jew, and Christian alike. From house to house, a census was taken: *Who is not here? Who might have been on Julian's Way near the King David Hotel?*

In the Jewish Quarter, the name *Leah Feldstein* was passed from person to person. *"She had gone to tea at the King David Hotel, so her husband says. Poor thing. He is sick with fear. Look at him . . ."*

Shimon sat beneath the cupola of Hurva Synagogue. His borrowed prayer shawl had slipped off one shoulder and his yarmulke was askew on his head. The men of the congregation sat with him in silent vigil. Eli had forbidden him to leave the Jewish Quarter. Things would be dangerous for a while. Who could say what would happen now?

Shimon turned his eyes upward to the mural of Moses casting down the tablets of stone upon the sinning Hebrews. If it had not been for Moses' prayer to God, all the Hebrews would have perished in that terrible moment of wrath. Shimon ran a hand over his eyes. *Remember your covenant, O Lord,* he prayed silently. *And remember Leah for my sake. . . .*

Hours passed. As others drifted off for dinner, Shimon and Eli sat in silent vigil. Eli's agony was as intense as Shimon's. He could think of nothing but Victoria. And how could he know if she was safe or dead?

Near dusk, urgent whispers sounded behind them in the foyer. *English voices!*

"Shimon Feldstein . . . told he was here . . ."

Cold fear swept throughout Shimon's body. His breath came too quickly as he stood and tried to reply. "I . . . am . . . Shimon . . ."

The face of an English officer turned toward him. The eyes were kind and weary and full of sadness. "Mr. Feldstein," the officer began, "I am Samuel Orde, captain of the Highland Light Infantry here in the Old City. I—"

"Is she dead?" Shimon blurted out. He did not care who this fellow was. He wanted to know. That was all.

"No. She is . . . she sustained only slight injury. She is . . ."

Shimon's shoulders sagged with relief and he slumped back down onto the seat. "Thank you, eternal and merciful—" He jerked his head up. "Where is she?"

"Hadassah Hospital. She is asking for you. I have a car—"

Shimon was out of his seat and by the side of Captain Orde before the officer finished the offer of a ride. He took a step and then turned to look back at Eli. The young man had not moved. His shoulders were still hunched forward in grief and worry. *Victoria!* Eli could not even say her name out loud.

———

Theo had not forgotten the sense of heaviness that clung to the city of Berlin, but he had not felt it until he stepped, once again, onto the soil of Tempelhof Airfield.

The night he had attempted escape from this place, even the storm had not seemed as dark as the evil presence he had fled from. Still the Darkness remained—almost a tangible, physical oppression that caused Theo to falter in his steps and pray silently that the Spirit of the living God would surround him. He looked up at the flat gray skies above the city with the feeling that even now an ancient and unseen war was taking place. The battlefields were the hearts of all who remained in this desolate land.

Long ago Hitler had struck at the Christian pastors. Most of the shepherds of Germany were dead or imprisoned, and so the flock was scattered, devoured by fear and beaten by the staff that was crowned with the crooked Nazi cross.

Strangely, Theo felt no bitterness as he made his way toward the doors where Gestapo agents stood in trench coats to scrutinize each passenger. Perhaps these creatures of darkness had once been men, but they were men no longer. Like Faust, they had sold their souls for a price. Now they walked the thin wire of brutality and hatred above the hell that waited eagerly for their fall.

The end would come for them. Theo had seen that truth during his days of suffering in Dachau. But the end was not yet. The battle for these tortured souls had been won by Nazi darkness and now hell yawned open and cried out to be fed with innocent sacrifices.

For this reason, Theo had returned to Berlin. Agreeing to this mission represented his individual attempt to storm the gates of hell. If even one innocent life could be saved by this journey, then heaven would rejoice. The Darkness would flee before the light of even one remaining candle of the Covenant!

The mist clung to Theo's face like tears—the tears of a holy and loving God for those in Germany who had sold themselves to an ancient idolatry. Hitler was right in what he claimed. The ancient Nordic gods lived on. They demanded Aryan worship. They craved human sacrifice.

Theo looked toward the edge of the airfield. Rows of bright new bombers and fighter planes were on display there. Like hounds of sport in a kennel, they waited for the command to kill. Theo knew the command would come. There would be no peace. The German god of creation was also the god of destruction. What Hitler could not have he would destroy.

Theo whispered the name of Jesus, loving Savior and Messiah. The true Jesus bore no resemblance to the brutal masters who had driven the Spirit of God from the German churches. *"I believe in the Lord, the true God of Israel,"* Theo whispered as if the words protected him from the heaviness around him. *"And I know the end of the Book! The Lord will reign in Jerusalem and every knee shall bow. It is written!"* His words were not audible to any of those around him, and yet, Theo felt that the words of his heart were heard. The candle was small, but the light was alive! The Darkness fled back from him.

He presented his British diplomatic passport to the tall, thin Gestapo agent at the gate. The officer scanned it. He looked at the document and then down at his list. "Yes. Herr Stern." He raised an eyebrow and appraised Theo coldly. "We heard you were coming to Berlin. British Ambassador Henderson is waiting for you in the next room. You may pass through inspection. Your luggage will be sent separately to the British Embassy."

"Danke." Theo tipped his hat. His leg ached from the weather, and he limped more slowly than usual toward the door.

Behind him he heard the Gestapo agent remark loudly to a clerk sitting to his left, "You know which Jews are kikes? Every Jew, once he has left the room." The joke was punctuated with a roar of laughter that followed Theo out of the customs area to where Nevile Henderson waited impatiently for him.

31

Even in Sorrow, We Will Believe

Etta did not see them come. Aaron had gone to the shul and she was upstairs bathing Yacov when she heard them knocking on the door. Moments later, Frau Rosen appeared in the doorway, out of breath, eyes wide.

"It is two men from the Warsaw police, Rebbitsin Lubetkin! They say they must see you. Not Rabbi Lubetkin, but *you!* A personal matter, they say!"

Etta felt ill, but she managed a feeble smile all the same. "Probably nothing. I mislaid my handbag the other day and reported it."

A bad lie. Frau Rosen's eyes narrowed. No one had asked her about a handbag. Why had she not heard of it if this happened? "I let them into the study," she said. Caution had replaced alarm. Curiosity pulled her mind toward a thousand different possibilities, and she knew a missing handbag was not one of them.

Etta maintained her composure. "Thank you. Finish washing the baby and dress him. I will be back in a moment." She turned the little one over to the housekeeper and swept past her as if this were nothing unusual at all.

Now that Eduard was gone from Warsaw, Etta was alone in her conspiracy to keep Aaron from hearing about her ordeal. She would not tell him until the Mandate passports arrived from Palestine. But what if these men wanted something more from her than Eduard had given them?

Her heart pounded hard as she slid back the doors to the study. The two men were pretending to look at the books on the shelves. They could not have understood any of what they saw. The thick, red-faced officer was flipping through a book of Hebrew poetry from back to front as if it were written in Polish.

Etta eyed them for a moment. Fools and buffoons. Brutal and unscrupulous. And now they held something of their own making over her head. Fear left her suddenly at the sight of such ignorant lumps thumbing through books they did not understand. Indignation took the place of fear. It gave her courage to confront them.

"What do you want?" she asked, with surprising harshness.

They turned, and coolly appraised her. "So," said the red-faced man in a thick peasant speech. "Herr Doktor Letzno has gone off to Palestine."

"Yes. You seem to know everything. And what you do not know you make up. In this instance, you are correct. He is gone. What has that to do with me? Why are you interrupting my work?" This tone was startling. The blue eyes of Etta Lubetkin flashed her outrage.

"Well, my pretty Frau Lubetkin." The red-faced man smiled. His teeth were decayed, his face lumpy, and his nose discolored from too much cheap brandy. Etta smelled the brandy on his breath.

"How dare you address me in such a manner?" she snapped.

"Why don't you have us arrested?" laughed the man. His partner sneered and nodded at the jest.

"You are in my home. If you have something to say, say it and leave." Etta crossed her arms defiantly.

"Well then, to the point, Ivan." The red-faced man deferred to his partner, who stepped forward.

"Frau Lubetkin," the second man said patronizingly, "we were talking about the matter of fines, just now. We let you off too easily, you see. Such an error could cost us our positions."

"Yes, blackmail could get you fired!" Etta snapped. She felt strong in her defiance of them. She had recovered from her ordeal now. She could handle them. "Shall I call your captain and report what you have done?"

The red-faced man chuckled and rubbed his bulbous nose. "It was the captain who informed us of the error. Not enough money, you see. Not enough to keep you out of jail for prostitution. You did not pay a big enough fine, Frau Lubetkin. And so we are here to arrest you."

Etta's self-composure faltered only an instant. She swallowed hard and raised her head in such an aristocratic gesture that the grins of these bullies faltered a bit. "You are swine," she said in Yiddish.

They exchanged looks. Angry. Instantly threatening. "We know what you said, you Jewish whore, and now you will pay us or we will take you to jail. There is a cell for women like you. The men of the police force visit it often."

Etta could not find her voice at this threat. For a full minute she stood in the center of Aaron's study. She glared at them, and they seemed frozen by her look. She thought through all of it. All the implications of what they said. Probably they could do what they wanted with her. Put her in a place like that. Keep the key in their own pockets, and . . . The thought sickened her. She must tell Aaron. There was no other way. But until she could tell him she must pay them.

Eduard's checks! She looked through the door to where her handbag sat on the sideboard beside the silver tea service.

"A nice place you have here," said the red-faced policeman. "You Jews are wealthy people. You live better than honest, hard-working Poles, don't you?"

Without a word she turned her back and went to her handbag. She pulled out the first of Eduard's checks and held it in her hands. The movement of a rustling petticoat sounded on the stair above her. Frau Rosen glared down at her—questioning, angry, revolted by whatever was happening with the mistress of the house.

"Frau Rosen!" snapped Etta. "You will see to baby Yacov now, please."

Frau Rosen nodded reluctantly and turned from her eavesdropping.

Etta did not go back into the study. She waited in the foyer and held the check for the blackmailers to see. They came out and she preceded them to the front door. Opening it to a cold blast of air, she stepped out and they followed. Then she stepped back in and handed them the check. "There will be no more," she warned.

They looked at the amount on the check and seemed pleased.

She glared at them for an instant. "You may drink that up as well, but there will be no more for you. Do not come back into my neighborhood or on my street or to my home. There will be nothing more for you here."

With that, she closed the door, shutting them out. She slid the bolt and then peeked out around the lace curtain of the foyer window and watched as they clapped each other on the back and tramped through the snow across the Square.

The bomb blast had killed indiscriminately. Four Arabs were dead. Five Jews. The numbers of wounded were equally divided as the ambulances screamed up Mount Scopus to Hadassah Hospital. Twelve seriously wounded. Eight of those critical. Thirty-two came into the wards listed as stable. Leah Feldstein, with ruptured eardrums and a miscarriage in process, was one of those in the last group.

Eduard Letzno had not anticipated this horror as he had toured Hadassah Hospital on his first day in Jerusalem. When word came of what had happened and the ambulances had begun to arrive, the resident physicians had looked upon Eduard's presence there as providential.

While teams had worked together on the critical patients, Eduard and three medical students had labored to assist those with superficial wounds, cleaning, stitching, and bandaging those who were in no real danger.

In the case of Leah Feldstein, there had been little to do. She had told Eduard she thought she was pregnant. Her bleeding was certainly not heavy enough to threaten her life, but miscarriage was inevitable. An IV was administered. She was put to bed. Eduard was more concerned with the possibility of loss of hearing in her right ear, which was damaged more severely than her left.

He explained all this to her grieved husband as they stood together outside the crowded ward.

"She is . . . she has lost the baby?" asked Shimon.

"She is a lucky woman that she sustained no other injuries—or worse," Eduard tried to comfort him with the realization that she might have been in the morgue right now instead of in the hospital ward. This thought only struck the big man with a more terrible kind of grief— what might have been, what almost was!

"But she is *all right*?" he clutched Eduard's arm in a vise-like grip.

"I see no reason why she will not have other children. The pregnancy was in the very early stages. She tells me she had not even consulted a doctor yet. We will keep her here for observation, of course." Eduard could not escape the intense and searching gaze of Shimon.

"But her hearing . . ." Shimon rubbed his eyes. "She is a concert musician, you see. A violin-cellist." His voice broke. "Herr Doktor! This is all my Leah knows to do. Music is her life, you see, and—"

This news alarmed Eduard more than the young woman's spontaneous abortion. She would probably conceive again, but he could not be optimistic that there was not at least some damage to her hearing. And there was nothing at all that could be done if that was the case. "We will monitor her progress, of course," he replied almost curtly. It was a habit he had formed to shield himself from the emotions of his patients. "In the meantime, Herr Feldstein, there are many dead and seriously wounded here today. Count yourself and your wife lucky in this case that she is alive."

Mercifully, a nurse called Eduard's name and he was spared further discussion. "You may see her." He managed a near smile as he brushed past the big man to confer with the mother of a young man who had lost his right arm in the blast.

———

Shimon was shaking as he entered the large ward. Twenty beds filled the room, some surrounded by white curtains. The air smelled of antiseptic and floor wax. The soft murmur of voices filled his ears. He stood unmoving as he scanned the rows for Leah. He wished he did not feel so weak, so frightened and sick. She was the one who was hurt, not he. Why did his knees feel as though they would buckle if he took even one step?

A nurse emerged from behind a curtain. "You are looking for someone?" she asked.

"Leah Feldstein."

"On the end. By the window." The face was kind and sympathetic. Shimon heard a baby cry and only then did he realize he was in an obstetrics ward. He put a hand to his head. The sound made him feel faint. It seemed too cruel to put her here where she would hear the babies.

He walked unsteadily to the end of the ward and peeked cautiously in through the slit curtain. *Yes. Leah.* She looked . . . awful. *Glass bottle. Needle in her arm. Pale and tiny. Her head bandaged. Ears covered with gauze. She will not hear the babies after all.* The realization made tears come to his eyes. His throat burned with the agony of emotion he felt he must master.

White iron rails guarded her bed, as if she were a small child and might fall out. He stepped into the cubicle. The curtain clung to him as he sidled up toward the head of the bed. He did not want to wake her. *Why did we not stay in England? Or America? Lord, did you bring us here for this?*

He stood beside her for a quarter of an hour and mourned. For their lost life in Vienna. For their lost child. For lost innocence. Once he had believed that the world was mostly good—people mostly good-hearted; nations just; governments trying their best. But standing by Leah, he remembered again the child Ada-Marie. The faces on the *Darien*. Evil was somehow personal and real. It had chosen to destroy the People of the Book because to do so would be to make the Covenant of that Book a lie and God a liar!

Shimon clenched his fist and raised it slightly in anger at this personal Evil that had killed their child and the children of the *Darien* and now nearly Leah. *"No matter what you do,"* he whispered hoarsely, *"we will not curse God! Give up! You cannot defeat Him! Kill us and we will be with Him! Drive us into the sea and He is there! You will not have your way with Shimon and Leah Feldstein or our children! Even in sorrow we will believe in the promise of our Holy Messiah!"*

Such words were nothing Shimon had learned in synagogue as a boy. They were not a prayer, certainly, but instantly he felt a heaviness lift from him. He inhaled deeply as if he had just run and won a terrible race against his own despair. Only now did he feel that somehow he would have the strength to encourage and comfort Leah. He squared his shoulders and prayed for help. He touched her arm, and her brown eyes opened in confusion. First relief, then deep sorrow filled her face at the sight of Shimon.

It was her turn to cry. Silent tears dripped from the corners of her eyes. "I am so sorry," she whispered, reaching up to him. "No baby, my darling . . . so sorry . . ."

He knelt beside the bed and touched her face, careful of the bandages. "We will have others, the doctor says."

"I cannot hear you," she replied, fumbling beneath the blanket to pull out a clipboard with paper and a pencil attached to a string. "I cannot hear anything." She closed her eyes with a sob and covered her mouth. Then she looked at him. "I am so sorry," she choked.

He was shaking his head, speaking words that she could not hear. *I love you. Everything will be fine. Do not be afraid. We will have a family. You will hear your own music again. You are alive, my dearest, and nothing else seems important right now.*

"I cannot hear you, Shimon." She managed a pitiful smile through the tears. "You have to write it down." And then as he nodded and began to write, she talked and told him what happened. "So fast . . . so fast . . . I saw them. Arabs. They left the car and trapped the bus, and then I fell down. Maybe someone pushed me down. A light flashed; I couldn't hear, but there were people hurt everywhere. The English soldier came and shielded my eyes. I did not get to Victoria. Eli's note is still in my pocket. I . . . started bleeding in the ambulance and I knew . . . the baby was . . . going away . . . I'm sorry."

Shimon finished his scrawled note. He had written down all the things he had said to her and then added: *This is the eighth blessing of the Amidah—the Shemoneh Esrei. I prayed it every week in synagogue and never believed it before now. But now I am praying this for you, Leah.* He finished the note in Hebrew:

Heal us, O Lord, and we shall be healed,
Save us and we shall be saved,
For you are our glory.
Send complete healing for our every illness. . . .

And then he wrote in German: *For Leah's ears, for her womb, and for her heart, we ask healing and we will give you thanks.* Then again in Hebrew:

For you, divine King, are the faithful, merciful Physician.
Blessed are you, Lord, who heals the sick of His people Israel!

In German he wrote: *I do not know any other prayers for such a moment, but now I pray it in my heart and not just on my lips. The Lord will hear and answer. Be comforted, my love!*

Leah read the prayer out loud and in those ancient words of the *Shemoneh Esrei,* she found the comfort her heart longed for.

"I will keep it here beside me in bed. Will you bring my Bible?" Shimon nodded in reply.

"And will you also bring me good stationery? Elisa will hear about this in the newspapers. I must write her and tell her."

He nodded again, then gave her a warm, relieved embrace. He pressed her strong, calloused fingertips to his lips. Leah's soul was music. He heard it even now in the antiseptic clatter of Hadassah Hospital, amid the sweet cries of babies which were not their own.

———

Samuel Orde had returned to the hospital with Shimon Feldstein. His purpose for doing so was more than an act of mercy, however.

He waited in a small anteroom set aside for medical consultation. It was urgent that he speak with Dr. Letzno about the woman's condition. There were a number of questions she could possibly answer. The sooner Orde was able to speak with her, the better.

Impatient and haggard-looking, Dr. Letzno pulled open the door and confronted the British captain. "There are injured people here, Captain Orde," he said sharply. "Make this quick."

"Leah Feldstein . . ."

"What about her?"

"She was closest to the blast. She is the one survivor who was close enough to see the terrorists."

"A fact I am certain she would like to forget."

"I need to speak with her about it. If she can identify the men—"

"The woman has undergone a miscarriage, an emotional loss as well as physical. Tonight she is not a witness but my patient, Captain Orde."

"I do not mean to appear calloused," Orde began.

"Then save your questions at least until tomorrow!" Dr. Letzno snapped.

"If I do that the perpetrators may get away."

"It seems that they have already done so."

"We have roadblocks on every road leaving Jerusalem. But roadblocks will do us no good if we do not have a physical description of the terrorists who have done this." Orde was firm. "If we catch them, perhaps it will prevent others from being hurt in the future."

The doctor seemed to hear him. He sighed and mopped his brow. There was so much grief here today. So many hurt. They must stop such a thing from happening again, catch the animals who had done this thing! He nodded. "She is sedated. I cannot guarantee anything. Come on, then." He opened the door and expected Orde to follow him to the ward.

The halls were quieter now. Some still sat on the long benches at the end of the corridor, waiting for word, but most of the relatives had gone home. Orde had not realized that it was nearly midnight until he glanced at the clock above the nurses' station.

The doctor walked quickly toward the ward where Leah rested. The long room was dark except for the dim lights on the call buttons beside each bed.

The countenance of the doctor changed as he stood silently over the sleeping form of Leah. His face became tender and in the shadowy light, Orde saw a transformation from brusque impatience to compassion. The doctor did not shake her to awaken her, but simply took her hand in his and waited for two minutes before he rubbed it gently.

Leah inhaled deeply and turned her head toward him. She opened her eyes to blink up in bewilderment at Dr. Letzno. Only then did he turn on the light above her bed. He wrote out the purpose of Captain Orde's visit.

"Yes," Leah said sleepily. "I saw them. Am I the only one who saw them?"

Orde nodded and took the note pad. Could she describe what she saw? The faces of the men?

"It all happened so fast," she closed her eyes.

The doctor continued to hold her hand. "She may be too exhausted," he said to the captain. "I cannot allow you to push her."

Leah opened her eyes again. They were clearer. More aware. And they were filled with the memory of what she had seen. "I saw them both quite clearly," she said in a strong and certain voice. "Both of them. Young Arab men. And a third man who drove the getaway car."

Orde smiled with relief. Would she know them if she saw them again? He scrawled the words in large block letters.

"I could *never* forget their faces," she replied. "You must catch them. Such men . . . anyone who would do such a thing . . ." She paused as if to regain composure, and then as Orde took down every word, she described the details of what she had seen. Everything was clear before her. "They were hardly men. Very young. Not twenty years old. The driver of the second car was older. He wore a red fez hat, and when he shouted, I saw he had a gold tooth in front . . ."

An hour later, Orde hurried to the telephone to contact the officers on duty at headquarters. Leah Feldstein's mind had taken a perfect photograph of Evil. Faces were etched indelibly into her mind.

He read the descriptions to be transmitted to the soldiers manning the roadblocks. Fifty-one Arabs had been detained for questioning. A strict curfew was in force. And now there was a witness who even remembered the color of the cuffed trousers of both the younger terrorists.

This news turned the dismal gloom of military headquarters to hope. *The cellist Leah Feldstein saw everything! We'll catch the blighters, then, won't we?*

32

Dark Counsels

The sounds of night surrounded the Dead Sea where Ibrahim had parked the car to wait. A warm breeze swept across the waters from Trans-Jordan, and in Victoria's dream she heard the shouts of millions on that wind: *"There is no God but Allah, and Mohammed is His prophet! Drive them into the sea! Jews to the sea! Eli! Eli, be one of us ... one of ..."*

The million raging voices blended into Victoria's voice, and she thought she called the name of Eli out loud as she slept. A sudden fear took hold of her. She must not speak his name. Not in her sleep.

"Victoria." She heard Eli's voice. *"Victoria!* Wake up, Victoria!" It was not Eli but Ibrahim who called her. "Get out of the backseat. *He* is coming!"

Victoria opened her eyes and fought to remember where she was. *The Dead Sea. With Ibrahim. Waiting for someone.*

In the distance she could hear the soft sputtering of a motorboat engine on the water. Ibrahim flicked the headlights once. Twice. A third time. The steady thrumming of the engine replied in a slight change of course, and now it cut an unswerving path toward the automobile.

Victoria sat up quietly and brushed her hair back as she studied the intense profile of her brother. Even in the darkness his eyes seemed filled with a strange light. Excitement, as if he were watching two mongrel dogs fighting to the death in the street while the men shouted wagers around him. Victoria had seen that look before on the face of Ibrahim. It had frightened her then, and it frightened her now.

The motor thumped louder, and again Ibrahim flicked the lights. A fraction of a second was enough to illuminate a small, dilapidated boat carrying three men with their faces turned toward the shoreline of Palestine. Two were Arabs, dressed as the Bedouins who camped around Amman. The third man was of fairer skin. His bald head had no covering. Victoria knew by this that the man was European. His mouth was a cruel hard line, lips pressed together in disgust.

The bald man's face seemed to burn into Victoria's mind. That second of light filled her with foreboding. "Praise be to Allah," Ibrahim whispered. "He has come at last!"

So the man with the cruel mouth was the one they had been waiting for. Victoria shuddered as the motor of the boat coughed and died. There were words murmured at the shoreline. The guttural accent of German was plainly distinguishable. She stared forward, trying to find some movement in the darkness outside the car.

Footsteps approached. The man was invisible in the blackness. And then hands touched the half-open glass of the window. Victoria drew back from the thick pale fingers that almost touched her face. And then the voice spoke. "I am Commander Vargen, here at the command of the Führer of the Third Reich. *Heil Hitler!*" Without further speech the door opened and the man with the cruel mouth slid in beside Ibrahim.

Freddie lifted Charles and Louis up on his shoulders as they waited in the wings of the theater for Elisa. Her box was stuffed with mimeographed sheets containing notes on the score and changes of rehearsal schedules. She tugged on the stack of papers, then groaned as they tumbled out onto the floor. Frieda Hillman looked on, amused.

Freddie placed his young charges down on the stage and stooped to help her retrieve her papers.

"Well, Missus . . ." he said, holding up an envelope and squinting as if to look through the paper. "What's this now?" Frieda leaned over for a quick glance, then returned to adding still more papers to other boxes.

Elisa took it from him, frowning as she recognized the neat German script of the handwriting, then the postmark. Paris.

Her hands began to tremble as she passed it back to Freddie. "You open it," she said hoarsely.

He nodded and stood slowly to his full towering height as he slit open the envelope with a penknife. His face was a scowl of disapproval as he silently scanned the letter. He shook his head and then shook it again as if he could not comprehend the meaning of the message.

"What is it, Freddie?" Elisa managed to ask.

He did not answer for a long time. He opened his mouth, then closed it again as he considered what to say.

"Do you know anyone named von Kleistmann, Missus?" He put a big paw beneath her arm and guided her to a bench as the boys played on a backstage platform.

"Thomas," she replied dully.

"That's the same. Now sit down, Missus. Sit before you read, will you now?"

———

Rachel did not mean to listen. The door of her parents' room was slightly ajar. Mama sat on the yellow coverlet while Papa paced at the foot of the bed. Papa's eyes were full of pain and worry as Mama pleaded with him in a voice so desperate that Rachel scarcely recognized it.

"I sent the documents to Father in Jerusalem. Eduard will make certain he receives them."

"But Etta! *Why?*"

"I am a daughter of Jerusalem! My birth certificate, my old passport can be renewed. For the sake of the children, Aaron! We *must* be prepared!"

"You are a citizen of Poland now, Etta! We will have to take our place at the end of the quota line like everyone else!"

"Father will do what he can for us in Jerusalem! He is a rabbi! They will listen to him! At least we can send the children—"

"You have been listening too much to Eduard!" Papa took off his coat and threw it onto the bed.

"You said they were following Eduard. But *look!*" Mama jumped to her feet. She went to the window but did not pull back the curtain. Fear crossed her face. "You know we are also being watched, Aaron. Ever since you came back from the refugee camp, you have been followed! I cannot go to market without some horrible man trailing along behind! I am a woman, but still I have eyes to see what is happening! You bury your head in the sand, Aaron, and *you may well bury us, too!*"

Rachel had never heard them argue. The sound of it, the sight of their faces, made her stomach churn.

Papa's face was red. "Read the newspapers, Etta! Do you think we will be safer in Palestine than we are here? *In Warsaw* there are no riots! We have not had a pogrom in months! Jerusalem has violence every day! I cannot leave the congregation! I *will* not! The police may follow us all day long, but there will never be a crime for which they can arrest us! I am a rabbi! A humanitarian, not a politician . . ." His own words made him falter. He fell silent suddenly and rubbed a hand across his face as Mama glared at him unhappily.

And then Papa looked toward the door. He saw Rachel. He saw by her wide, terrified eyes that she had heard everything. His anger exploded.

"What are you doing there?" He stalked to the door. *"Why are you sneaking around the halls!"*

"Oh, *Papa!*" Rachel cried as if his anger was a physical blow. "I did not mean to—"

"*Go to your room!*" He slammed the door in her face and she ran weeping up the narrow stairs to her bedroom.

The volume of the argument dropped low. It hissed up through the floor like escaping steam. It did not stop for hours until, at last, Rachel fell into an exhausted and restless sleep.

———

Three other wire services already placed the name of Leah Feldstein at the top of the list of wounded in the Jerusalem bombing. Murphy read Samuel Orde's dispatch aloud as it clacked the full story over the TENS office wire.

RENOWNED CELLIST LEAH FELDSTEIN SUFFERED MINOR INJURIES
STOP THE INVOLVEMENT OF FOREIGN INSTIGATORS SUSPECTED
BY BRITISH OFFICIALS STOP

This was an element no other reporters had even mentioned. Murphy inwardly cheered Orde's thoroughness as the story added a dozen minor details that transformed a flat tale of violence into a three-dimensional portrait.

COMMENTS OF THE ROYAL COMMISSION OF INQUIRY HEADED BY
SIR JOHN WOODHEAD IN JERUSALEM HAVE EXPRESSED CONCERN
FOR SAFETY OF ALL RESIDENTS OF PALESTINE MANDATE STOP
SUCH EVENTS HAVE GIVEN RISE TO QUESTION OF HOW AN INDE-
PENDENT JEWISH STATE WOULD SURVIVE SUCH ONSLAUGHTS ON
ITS OWN WITHOUT PROTECTION OF BRITISH MILITARY FORCES
STOP

Murphy frowned at this paragraph. "In other words," he said dryly, "Ol' Woodhead thinks maybe a Jewish homeland is not such a grand idea after all—eh, Orde?"

The dispatch continued:

BRITISH MILITARY SOURCES IN JERUSALEM HAVE DRAWN PARAL-
LELS BETWEEN ACTIVITY OF FOREIGN MERCENARIES IN SPANISH
CIVIL WAR AND RECENT EVENTS IN PALESTINE STOP NEARLY
TWENTY THOUSAND BRITISH TROOPS NOW OCCUPY MANDATE
TERRITORY IN ATTEMPT TO KEEP PEACE STOP

Murphy had been in Spain. He had seen the planes of the German Luftwaffe over Madrid and Barcelona. He had watched the weak Fascist armies of Franco become strong and brutal with Nazi men and equipment. The same thing was happening in Palestine. This time it was twenty thousand British soldiers who would be tied up away from whatever might happen in Europe. And Murphy was certain that Hitler's "last territorial demands in Europe" were really not the last. How convenient to intimidate England into remaining tied up in Palestine while at the same time closing off further hope of a Jewish homeland!

"Hitler really is a genius," Murphy remarked to Harvey Terrill. "Diabolical. Evil. And brilliant."

"You want to edit Orde's piece or shall I?" Harvey scanned the page.

Murphy shook his head. "Print it word-for-word the way he wrote it. We can hope there will be a few out there who can read between the lines, Harvey." Murphy pocketed a copy of the story. "Anyway, I'm going home. Leah Feldstein is okay. That is the only news my wife will care about. I need to tell her before somebody else calls her with only half a story and word that Leah was hurt."

Harvey saluted. He knew Murphy had been working for fourteen hours straight today. "You want me to call if there's anything else, Boss?"

Murphy nodded wearily. He needed a shave and a shower and a good night's sleep, but there was enough implied in Samuel Orde's story to keep him wide awake. The gates of hell were slowly swinging open in Palestine. Churchill had called the Mandate Hitler's second front against British foreign policy. After today, Murphy believed that Palestine might well be the first front against England and certainly against the Jewish people.

"I'm going to sleep light tonight, Harvey. Keep me posted on this one." He frowned and stared out the dark window where the bright headlights of a bus swept over Fleet Street like searchlights. "Something's coming," he muttered.

All the lights of the Red Lion house were blazing when Murphy arrived home. Freddie Frutschy greeted him at the top of the stairs. The big man's expression was an unhappy scowl as he wrapped his enormous hand around Murphy's.

"She's heard the news, huh?" Murphy asked quietly.

For a moment Freddie looked perplexed. "Yessir. And an unhappy way to hear such a thing, too. I stayed right here with her an' the boys 'til you come home."

She was not in the front room. Murphy stepped past Freddie. The radio in his study played Benny Goodman live from the Algonquin Hotel in New York. Murphy remembered how much Leah liked Benny Goodman.

Elisa appeared in the doorway. Murphy could tell she had been crying. "Oh, Murphy!" she said softly.

Murphy put his arms around Elisa and she began to weep softly. "Don't worry," he said. "She's okay. I got the story from Jerusalem, and she's . . ."

Elisa stiffened. "Jerusalem? What—"

"Leah," he answered. "You heard about the bombing. But Leah is—"

"Leah? Bombing?" A look of such anguish filled her eyes that Murphy knew she had not heard.

"You *don't* know!" He turned to look at Freddie who stood at the door wringing his cap. "What's happened?"

"A letter for the Missus. From Paris again." He frowned. "Some bad news. I thought it best I stay close until you arrived."

Elisa was still digesting the fact that Murphy had mentioned Leah's name in connection with a bombing. It was almost too much. She sat down and tugged the rumpled letter from her pocket. "Leah," she whispered.

"She's all right, I tell you!" Murphy sat down beside her. He raised a hand in farewell to Freddie "Thanks, pal." A nod of acknowledgment and the big man left them alone.

"Was she hurt, Murphy? Was Leah—" Elisa asked.

"Only minor injuries." Murphy opened the letter. He scanned the words. Each phrase was like a shock of cold water:

> Thomas von Kleistmann died the silent death of a hero. Gestapo in Paris mentioned the name of Elisa Murphy in connection with the activities of von Kleistmann opposing the Nazis. Take every precaution for your safety and for the sake of those who remain in Germany whose names you know. Their lives depend on silence. Please destroy this communication. God bless you. God restore our nation. *Heil Deutschland!*

Murphy lowered the letter and took Elisa's hand. "I'm so sorry, Elisa."

Elisa could not speak. Tears brimmed in her eyes, and she pressed her lips together and shook her head as if to resist any more crying tonight. She leaned against Murphy, letting him cradle her in his arms. She was glad she had not heard the news about Leah in Jerusalem from anyone but him. She could trust him that her friend was all right. Somehow that also comforted her in the grief she felt for Thomas tonight. It had drawn her away from the knowledge that he was dead. *Leah is alive!*

Murphy did not speak for a long time; he simply held her. "The postmark is Paris?" he finally asked.

Elisa nodded, then sat up to search her pockets for the envelope. "I . . . must have thrown it away. Or . . . I don't know. But it was Paris."

Murphy moved to open his rolltop desk to retrieve the first postcard. He had tucked it beneath the edge of his desk blotter. It was not there. "Did you see a postcard here?" he asked in a puzzled voice.

She joined him to search for the postcard. "No. I never . . . what is it about?"

Murphy looked at her thoughtfully, then explained.

They looked in every drawer and cubbyhole in the massive desk. The postcard was not there.

Murphy tried to think. He might have gathered it up accidentally with something else. Taken it to the office. Maybe it did not matter. He took the letter from his pocket and knelt before the blazing hearth. He touched a corner of the paper to the flame and held it there until it flared up, then yellowed and blackened. *The silent death of a hero.*

Carved out from the labyrinth of stone corridors and secret tunnels that honeycombed the mount beneath the Dome of the Rock, a small square room lay hidden deep below the surface. In the room, a square table, bathed by a single shaft of light, held a black leather letter case.

Three sets of hands ringed the fringe of light around the table, the faces shrouded in shadow. It seemed as if the light had come into the room only for the sake of the letter case; as if this leather folder were on display, and the men had come to worship it.

"Open it," instructed the voice of Doktor Hockman to Haj Amin. "You will find it as I promised."

Delicate hands and embroidered tapestry sleeves reached for the letter case, hesitated, and then opened it. "I was expecting . . . hoping for Officer Georg Wand. He trained my men." Haj Amin Husseini was not pleased by the arrival of Commander Vargen.

Vargen spoke up, not to defend himself, but to explain. "Wand is dead. In service to the Fatherland. But you may read for yourself my rank and experience."

The swastika and the eagle were emblazoned on the letterhead of the paper. The greeting was a personal one from Adolf Hitler to the Mufti. In the shadow, a hint of a smile tugged at Haj Amin's narrow lips. "Ah," he said at last. "You fought with the Turks against the English in the war."

"He aided in the disposal of the Armenians at that time, Your Excellency," Doktor Hockman spoke up quickly. "He did not fight against the Arab armies."

"It would not matter if he had," said Haj Amin lightly. "I fought with the British against the Germans and the Turks, but you see now how time has changed all that. The English are our enemies, and you are now here in Palestine—perhaps hoping to claim the territory once again for Germany?"

"Our goal is the same as your own," Vargen said coolly. He would not be baited. "We wish to see the end of British power here and the end of the Jewish problem. For that reason the Führer sent me as his personal representative."

"And what do you think of our efforts? We have claimed the roads and fields for our own after dark. The streets of Jerusalem are under my control. One word, and—" Haj Amin was pleased with himself.

"A good beginning. Small and unprofessional, but a beginning nonetheless."

Haj Amin ignored the jibe and scanned the papers without emotion. Lists of the names—Jews—Englishmen—Christian Arabs . . . targeted for assassination. Riots planned for Safed. Haifa. Jaffa. Galilee. And Jerusalem, of course. Routes for the rioting mobs to follow. Shops to be destroyed. Everything was clearly laid out with German precision.

Haj Amin read and read again. He laid the sheaf of papers back in the light. "All this planned for the same day, the same hour. It is not possible."

Hockman cleared his throat as if the word *impossible* was blasphemous. "Commands are not given that are impossible to follow."

"I do not have men enough or army enough for such widespread actions," Haj Amin protested.

Vargen smiled. This little Muslim knew much but he had much to learn. "Your *people* will be your army! Call on them! In every city and town they will come."

Haj Amin shook his head slowly. "Not even the voice of the prophet could arouse them to *this* in one moment! They will not be moved . . . not *this far!*"

"You must provide the reason." Vargen's voice was patronizing.

"I have called for a holy war. Some fight for the sake of Allah because I demand it, but most—"

Vargen leaned forward until the light illuminated his face. He was the teacher, Haj Amin the pupil. "Not alone for the sake of a *god*! Only fools will fight and die for the sake of a god alone. In the Reich . . ." He paused for effect. "Our Führer has learned that the love of a god and love of a country will not turn the hearts of men to his will." He crossed his arms and sat back again. "Ah, but when the enemy *defiles a woman*! Perhaps not even a woman of your house, not wife or mother, but a woman of your own race—you see? In days of old a virgin was presented as a sacrifice to the gods. There are lessons in legend, Haj Amin. Find me a woman to sacrifice to the gods, and the people will be yours!"

Haj Amin sat back in confusion. "But . . . we worship Allah. The law forbids such—"

"You worship your own ambition," Vargen hissed, "the god of yourself! The god of the adoration of your Muslim followers!"

"I will not be insulted by this . . . madman!" Haj Amin stood.

Hockman raised a hand to calm him. "Please, Your Excellency. Herr Vargen speaks . . . in a figurative sense! He is a poet who teaches you the way to achieve your goals!"

Haj Amin did not sit. "Speak on then, poet," he warned. "But remember I have only to raise my hand and *you* are the sacrifice!"

Vargen laughed. He was unafraid of the threat. "Find me a woman, Haj Amin, and I will find a Jew who will violate her. This small act will give you an army which will roar over the English and the Jews of Palestine with a storm of revenge!"

There was a long silence in the square stone room. Haj Amin sat down slowly in his chair. His hands flitted into the light and picked up the papers. *"A simple matter of rape?"* There was amusement in his voice.

"The rape of a Muslim woman *by a Jew,*" Vargen grinned. "Even a prostitute will suffice. It is the subject matter that will create the explosion—a proven method in the Reich."

Haj Amin rarely laughed. Outside in the dark corridor, his bodyguards exchanged wondering glances when the laughter of their leader reached their ears.

"There is time to consider the characters in our play." Haj Amin wiped away tears of mirth. "Hitler is right! Was there ever a match struck that could cause a greater fire? *A rape!* Indeed, this poet understands men's passions!"

There were other matters of business to discuss, but Haj Amin was still chuckling to himself as he made his way through the passageways to his private residence just beyond the courtyard of the Dome of the Rock.

33

A Chink in the Wall

A thick fog blanketed Berlin. The British Embassy was dank and musty-smelling as the moisture seemed to permeate the walls.

Ambassador Henderson sat at the breakfast table in a heavy wool tweed jacket. He cracked his soft-boiled egg with a nervous tapping of his spoon as he discussed the bombing in Jerusalem with Theo.

"My dear Mr. Stern . . . Mr. Lindheim," he said in an amazed tone, "you cannot expect the British government to turn over any portion of Palestine to the Jews after something like this! Good heavens! Why would a Jew wish to live there? They cannot protect themselves, certainly."

"Where else are the refugees supposed to go?"

"Go? I ask you why that matter has fallen squarely on the shoulders of Great Britain? Why are we supposed to decide such a thing?"

"Because Great Britain occupies Palestine. And the various commissions have whittled down the land area that was promised as a Jewish national home. Acre by acre, the area for Jewish settlement and purchase of land grows smaller."

The spoon smashed irritably down on the eggshell. "But *why,* in heaven's name, do the Jews wish to settle there?"

"Chaim Weizmann has said that there are two places in the world for the Jewish people: the countries where they are not wanted, and the countries where they cannot enter. Where are they to go, then?"

"Well, if I were a Jew, I would not choose Palestine!"

A sad smile. "I would not choose Palestine either if there were any place else to go."

"Ah, well," Henderson smiled patronizingly as he lifted the dripping spoon to his lips. "Maybe your little talk with Hermann Göring will change all that, eh? This little trade arrangement should open the doors to a few more places. *The United States?* Certainly with all their self-righteous prattle about our management of Palestine, they will open their own doors for immigrants if your plan is successful, eh? That is why you have come." He raised his coffee cup as if to toast Theo's mission. "And so, here is to your success, Mr. Lindheim. May you get the monkey of immigration off the back of Great Britain." He slurped as he drank.

Theo found it a waste of time and energy to argue with a man as shortsighted as Henderson. Instead, he ate his breakfast and listened politely as Henderson gabbed on about what a nice fellow Hermann Göring really was, what a splendid sportsman and hunter, what a droll and witty fellow, always ready with a joke.

Theo did not respond with the information that he knew Göring well. He knew enough to be certain that Göring's idea of what embodied a good hunt would no doubt be found in their meeting at Karinhall.

For two hours after breakfast, the staff artist of the Palestine British military intelligence sat beside Leah's bed and sketched portraits according to her direction. Orde looked on silently over Harry Smith's shoulder as eyes were widened and eyebrows altered to meet in a solid line. Lips too full were erased and made thinner.

"Yes. Yes. That is more like it," Leah whispered in amazement as the picture in her mind became a tangible reflection of the men she had seen on Julian's Way. The images were not exact likenesses, but they were close, she said. And the face of the burly, unshaven driver with his gold tooth was very close indeed.

When she was satisfied with Smith's efforts, she looked eagerly at Orde. "Find these fellows in Jerusalem, and you will have the murderers."

Orde thanked her with a nod, and suddenly her strength left her. She lay back wearily on her pillow and closed her eyes. She had been working very hard, and she was tired. She did not say goodbye.

The two soldiers left her sleeping as they hurried off to headquarters to reproduce the faces Leah had given them. They would appear on a thousand posters to be posted throughout the city.

Lucky, Tasha and Mr. Parks had called Victoria when she returned to work in the transportation department. She was lucky she had not been there. It was terrible. The explosion was horrible. And that nice cellist who had played so beautifully and liked Victoria enough to give her tickets to the Woodhead concert was also among the injured. She was in Hadassah Hospital, they said. And Victoria was very lucky she had not been there!

There was nothing else talked about all day. Hardly any work was done. Victoria tried not to listen, tried to forget that her own brother had known enough about what happened that he had not let her come to work!

By the time the Mandate offices had closed, Victoria was ill from all she had heard and all she knew but did not say. The guilt of her brothers had somehow blackened her own heart. Because of her, Leah Feldstein was in a hospital! Because Victoria did not run to the Palestine police with the word that *something* was planned, people had died.

At least that is the way it felt. *Was there anything I could have done?* she asked herself a thousand times. The answer came in the memory of a locked door. A lie with which Ibrahim had carried her away from Jerusalem. No. There had been no chance. But what about now? Should she go to someone? Tell them that Ibrahim had been worried about her because he knew about the terrible *something* that had happened?

She scanned the lobby, crowded now with uniformed British soldiers. Every bag and parcel was searched as residents entered the hotel through the revolving doors. Should she tell someone now? Tell them that Ibrahim *knew*? But others had known something was coming. The man on the bus had been talking about it. A demonstration, everyone had thought. What could Victoria say to these English soldiers? *Arrest my brothers. Imprison them. Maybe they know who bombed the bus on Julian's Way!*

Victoria did not know what to say. Ibrahim had denied that he knew any details. He swore to her that he had heard the rumors and was frightened for her well-being. But what of the man they had picked up on the shores of the Dead Sea? Victoria was certain that Ibrahim was not innocent, but she did not dare accuse him since she could not be sure of the scope of his involvement and guilt.

Such thoughts made her exhausted, yet, she must do one thing before she went home to bed. She caught the bus to Hadassah Hospital. Leah Feldstein was injured, and Victoria knew she would not sleep unless she saw her. After all, Leah had been coming to meet her, coming for tea at the hotel! Victoria felt responsible for Leah's condition, too, and so she hurried through the glass doors of Hadassah and asked for Leah's ward number. The Jewish staff looked at her oddly, but Victoria didn't care. She had to see Leah—no matter what.

––––––––––

It was almost noon. Dr. Eduard Letzno had not slept in thirty-one hours. Sunlight had not touched him since he had entered Hadassah twenty-six hours before. It seemed much longer ago than yesterday since he had come here. He had seen lifetimes end. He had heard the stories of the wounded, watched the tears of families fall, given hope, and taken hope away. Before he had even had a chance to see the stones of Jerusalem, he had become as much a part of the city's history of grief and travail as the stones themselves.

His smock flecked with blood of Jerusalem's wounded, Eduard caught a glimpse of his own reflection in a window. Beyond this ghost-like apparition of his face was the Dome of the Rock. The city wall encircled the holy mountain, embracing houses and shrines together. Christian. Muslim. Jew. All gathered into one unyielding ring of stone. Ironically, Eduard saw the great sight for the first time with his own face superimposed upon it. He had helped to save an Arab boy while he had been helpless to do anything for a Christian child the same age. A Jewish merchant had died in his arms. Yes. Eduard was part of the stones and flesh of Jerusalem, a fragment of living history after one day in Palestine. *I was there. I tended the wounded and dying.*

He ran a hand over the sandpaper skin of his unshaven cheek. In the reflection of the window he did not look like a physician, but a butcher.

A strong hand clapped him on the back as he stared at the glass and then beyond at his new city. "Go on, man! Go get some rest," said the guttural voice of Dr. Johann Kleinmann. Dr. Kleinmann had once been the head of a great German hospital. Once . . . a long time ago. Much longer ago than the lifetime that was Eduard's yesterday.

"So, Herr Doktor," Eduard managed a smile. "I am finished then?"

"It was good you were here. Good for us. Maybe not so good for you on your first day here, eh?"

Eduard did not share what he was thinking, did not tell the doctor that since yesterday Eduard considered himself a native of the city. "I made one more round. There are several among the wounded who can go home. I have taken the liberty of signing their papers for discharge. They will need follow-up care, of course."

"Fine. Yes. So, now you go home, too. Sleep. Eat something. I will tell Nurse Cominski to make the outpatient appointments beginning tomorrow at eight o' clock for you." Another thump on the back. "I would hate to lose you to exhaustion before you have even started officially."

"Yes, I need to unpack." Eduard looked again toward the Old City. "There is an old man I must see. Father of a friend in Warsaw."

"Fine. Fine. But pay your calls after you sleep a few hours or you will be of no use to us here in Hadassah Hospital—unless you plan to donate your body to science. I had a few hours sleep last night, and now so must you. An order from the chief of staff, eh?" A finger tapped against Eduard's chest to make the point, and then Dr. Kleinmann hurried down the corridor as his name was called over the P.A. system.

Eduard's dull fingers fumbled with the ties of his smock as he made his way down the steps to the physician's locker room. He showered at the hospital and then put on his same clothes. He smelled mildly of his own sweat tinged with antiseptic as he made his way outside to the bus stop. He carried Etta's precious package beneath his arm. He had intended to visit her father in the Old City immediately following the orientation tour of Hadassah. His orientation had simply taken a bit longer than he expected. He would sleep later.

The fresh air smelled good. He filled his lungs with it as the bus rattled toward Jaffa Gate. The slanting rays of the sun trapped light and shadow on the wrinkled complexion of the wall and suddenly it did indeed seem ancient. On the ramparts, British soldiers patrolled, while pigeons waddled along the crevices without concern for whose stones these really were.

The printed words on the yellow note paper were comforting to Leah, better than a wish for speedy recovery or the heaping basket of fruit on the bed table beside her:

> Do not worry for anything. We are feeding that husband of yours at Tipat Chalev along with the other children, so rest and be well. . . .

This was written in the firm hand of Hannah Cohen as she and Shoshanna Reingolt and Ida Sachar gathered around Leah's bed. The fruit was presented with strict instructions that Leah must eat so many of this and so much of that each day lest her bowels become sluggish while she was in the hospital. After all, sluggish bowels had killed many more Jews than Arab bombs could ever kill, nu?

Leah happily informed them that she had been released by Dr. Letzno to return home to her own bed tomorrow. This information resulted in a long discussion between the ladies about who would prepare and bring the meals in what shift. Leah could make out something about menus and what sort of herbal teas were best in cases of miscarriage. And then the animated conversation came to a sudden halt.

The eyes of Ida Sachar narrowed as she watched Victoria enter the ward. Leah observed the interaction of characters like someone watching the drama of a silent movie. Victoria seemed quite nervous as she entered the ward. At the sight of Eli's glaring mother, she paled visibly and paused, as if considering which way she might escape.

Perhaps Leah should have let her go, but she called out Victoria's name impulsively. The three visitors looked from Victoria down at Leah as if she were a traitor.

"Victoria is my interpreter," Leah said cheerfully. "And my first friend in Jerusalem." She motioned for Victoria to come forward.

The ladies seemed stunned. It was obvious that they knew this was *the girl* who had nearly lured Eli from the fold. They did not approve. Not at all. Indeed, the Hassan family was well respected in the Old City, but the unwritten law had been violated, and Victoria had crossed the boundary. It had to be *her* fault. Everyone knew what a good boy Eli was, nu?

Leah put out her hand to Victoria. She welcomed her warmly as a blizzard of cold disapproval filled the little space.

"Well then," said Hannah crisply, "she does not need *us* here."

Smiling through tight lips, the three women made their farewells to Leah. They nodded acknowledgment to Victoria and then walked stiffly from the ward.

Victoria looked ill. She looked as if she might need to lie down. Leah patted the bed. "Sit, before you fall."

Victoria nodded and obeyed. *"Eli's mother."* Her lips formed the words. Leah did not need to hear in order to understand. *"She hates me."*

Leah gazed at the beautiful young woman in sympathy. Then she pulled a note from under her pillow. "I was praying that you would come, Victoria." Leah handed her Eli's note. "I was bringing this to you at the hotel when *this* . . . happened."

Victoria began to weep silently. She held the note with trembling hands and shook her head from side to side. "I am so sorry," she said again and again. "There was nothing I could do."

Leah could not hear her, but she patted Victoria's arm and tried to comfort her. Leah could not know that Victoria wept not because Eli's mother was so hostile, but because Leah was hurt and somehow Victoria felt responsible.

———

"Rebbe Lebowitz?" the red-bearded Yeshivah student eyed the rumpled European suit of Eduard Letzno. "Why do you want to know?"

Eduard held up the brown paper package as if it was proof. It, too, was rumpled from its long journey in train compartments and ships and finally an airplane. "I have brought a gift for him from his daughter Etta in Warsaw," Eduard said.

At the mention of Etta the young man's face brightened. He grinned broadly, showing widely spaced teeth like missing keys of a piano. "Nu! Why did you not say so? The Rabbi Lebowitz has gone to the Western Wall to pray! This is his custom each day at this time," he said as though he was letting Eduard in on a family secret. "And he prays for his daughter and son-in-law and the grandchildren there . . ."

Eduard's head was pounding with exhaustion and dizziness. He felt as if he had drunk a gallon of wine. He swayed slightly.

"The wall? You mean the Wailing Wall?"

"The very same." The pale blue eyes wandered up to Eduard's hatless head. Surely Eduard was no Jew. "Would you like to wait for him?"

Eduard shook his head in a firm *no*. To sit would mean not getting up until he slept. "Which way?" he asked, looking up at the weathered stone blocks and cracking plaster of Nissan Bek Synagogue. There were no English soldiers, even though the Dome of the Rock was plainly visible just beyond the thick fortress walls of the synagogue.

Only pigeons strutted above the arched windows. The cold winter sky was a clean, blue contrast to the dusty earth and the jumble of buildings of Jerusalem. Today there was no black smoke. No burning tires or explosions; as yet, the streets and alleyways of the Old City were almost deserted.

The memory of yesterday was still a fresh wound. There were funerals to be held outside the walls of the city. Again, Jerusalem mourned her dead.

Eduard looked up at the clean patchwork of the sky as he trudged up the slope of a narrow street. Framed by the grimy facades of the houses and shops, the sky seemed like a clear river to Eduard's weary mind. In spite of what he had witnessed yesterday, he had no doubts that Etta and Aaron must come home to Jerusalem.

Dr. Letzno's conviction brought tears to the eyes of Rabbi Shlomo Lebowitz when Eduard stood at his side along the deserted stones of the Western Wall. The gnarled hands of the old man reached out to take the package from Eduard. His frail arms embraced it as if it were a child. He thanked Eduard and then turned back to face the stones, which seemed almost the same color and complexion as he was. In a sing-song voice he began to pray, holding up the package before the hovering angels and the Shekinah glory that seeped down through the crevices of God's throne room. A slight wind stirred. The fringes of the old man's shawl twirled and the fabric tugged against him. Ah, the wings of the angels fluttered. The photographs and birth certificates had finally arrived! Was this not some chink in the wall of British bureaucracy? And from this chink, might a door be carved for Etta and Aaron and the little ones to enter?

To this end Rebbe Lebowitz prayed as Eduard looked on patiently. Eduard knew the prayers, but he did not say them. He shut them from his mind as the superstition of an old man. It was this sort of superstition, he believed, that would be the death warrant of the Jews of Poland. Eduard did not believe any longer that there was a God who heard their prayers. Not even here at the chink in heaven's floor. He had no hope in miracles or prayers any longer. Without any emotion, he watched the old man sway and hum his requests.

At last the rabbi turned and embraced Eduard with a kiss on his cheek. "I have been praying you would come with an answer just today. I have been asking the Almighty if perhaps I should leave them alone in Warsaw, already. If they are not maybe better off there after such terrible things happen right here in Jerusalem, nu?" The old man sighed and took Eduard's arm as if they were old friends. "But now at the hour of my darkest doubts and fears God has sent you to me, Doktor Eduard Letzno. And so, you must come home with me. Share a meal. You have come a long way to answer the prayer of an old man. And now I will not rest until Etta and my dear ones are here in Jerusalem with me."

34

Twilight of the Gods

Eli had arranged it all: a wedding at Christ Church! A furnished room in the Mahaneh Yehuda district of the New City where she could hide until Eli managed to find a job in Tel Aviv. And money enough for her to buy a pretty dress to be married in!

The note was like a reprieve from the doubt that had imprisoned her these last terrible weeks. Now the plots of her brothers would mean nothing to her! She and Eli could move far away from Jerusalem!

Her hands trembled with joy as she wrote her thanks to Leah and the request that Leah and Shimon might come to a very small wedding at Christ Church next week. A happy nod, a quick kiss, and Victoria hurried out to catch the bus home.

Suddenly the whole world looked different. Sunlight pierced through the circle of clouds, illuminating the Old City in light as Victoria's bus moved down the slope of Mount Scopus and then on to Damascus Gate.

Sheep bleated in their pens outside the gate. Heavily laden donkeys moved among the press of shoppers. Women with baskets on their heads and thin veils covering their faces walked with effortless grace in spite of their burdens. Crates of fruits and vegetables were stacked beside open sacks of lentils and coarsely ground flour. Victoria saw it all today as if she were seeing it for the first time. And yet she knew this would be among the last times she walked these crowded, cobbled lanes. She felt no remorse or regret, but amazement that at last she was leaving. Eli was taking her away, and there was no one in the entire Old City whom she could tell about it!

The tall minarets pointed skyward like lances among the shops and houses. The voices of the muezzins filled the air of the marketplace, silencing all conversation except the braying of the animals. Rugs were placed on the hard ground and the faithful all knelt and bowed. Here and there English soldiers and a few brave or foolish tourists in the Arab Quarter looked on as the population sank to its knees. Victoria hesitated a moment. Not to bow would make her more foolish than the tourists who had come here in their ignorance of danger. Victoria was well aware of the eyes that watched every corner of the Arab Quarter from the Damascus Gate. She also bowed and knelt toward Mecca as she hid her intentions from those who might question the look of happiness on her face.

She called on the name of Eli as if he were her god now. When she finished and raised herself once again, she looked up into the face of Ram Kadar. His black robes and keffiyeh seemed especially black today. There was no speck of dust on him. Except for his thick mustache, he was clean-shaven and scented as if he had anointed himself for an occasion. His white, perfect teeth smiled at her. She averted her eyes from his tanned face.

"Salaam, Victoria," he bowed graciously. "Have you heard the news? Your face has such joy. I have been watching. I followed you from Damascus Gate." So many words from Ram Kadar seemed strange.

"Salaam," she answered, still not looking directly at his face or daring to smile. "I am just home from work, and . . . what news?"

"Your father is home! I have spoken to him already." He lowered his voice slightly. The clamor of the Quarter resumed around them.

"My father?"

"Home from Iran. And he will have a surprise for you!" He seemed giddy. His nearness made her own joy dissipate. The note from Eli felt warm and dangerous in her pocket.

"Then I must go," she said, turning away from him.

"I will walk with you." It was not a question or request. He stepped a pace ahead of her as if to clear her path. His head was high and proud. His eyes swept the stalls within the twilight of the covered bazaars as if he, too, were seeing them for the first time.

He knew the way to the Hassan home. Through the streets of the tinsmiths. Past the shoemaker's shops. Along the street where prayer rugs were heaped up on display. The finest rugs were sold by Victoria's father.

Ahead of them she could see that the new Persian carpets were stacked just inside the shop. Yes, her father was home. That knowledge brought her no pleasure. The presence of Ram Kadar and his self-assurance as he walked with her gave her a sense of foreboding.

Within the shop, Victoria's father stood talking to Ibrahim. He still wore his business suit, English-made pin-striped, and on his head he wore a red fez. He was clean-shaven and unrumpled in spite of his journey, but when he looked up to see his daughter in the doorway, he seemed weary and sad.

Victoria pushed past Kadar. "Father!" She ran to him and embraced him. She clung to him longer than she might have if Kadar had not been there.

"Victoria, my daughter. You have missed me, eh? Allah be praised, I have come home to find you all in health in spite of the many reports about Palestine."

"She was praying just inside the gate when I saw her," Kadar said. "I wanted to walk with her here. An unveiled woman alone in the Quarter? Well, soon we will remedy that Western rebellion."

Victoria turned to face Kadar. What did he have to say about her lack of a veil? And why had he been so presumptuous as to walk with her to her own home? "I thank you, Kadar. And now I wish to spend time with my father."

"Victoria!" Her father sounded shocked. "You forget your manners! Fix us tea."

Victoria blinked up at her father in surprise. She looked at Ibrahim, who had not said anything at all to her. He would not look at her. His hands brushed over a deep red carpet and he pretended to study the threads and pattern of it.

"But, Father," she began.

He smiled at her strangely. "Do you not know, Daughter?" he asked.

"Know what, Father?"

He laughed nervously and looked from Ibrahim to Kadar, then back to Victoria. "Allah has willed that you are to be married."

Her breath came hard. *Could they know about Eli?* "What . . ."

"You have not spoken of this with Ibrahim? Just an hour ago we settled the contract. You and Ram Kadar are to be wed."

Her eyes widened. She felt the blood drain from her face. What could she say? To be ungrateful or rude would result in a beating, a locked room. And yet tears of outrage came to her eyes in spite of her battle for self-control. "My father . . ." she began.

"Ram Kadar is a man of substance. He will treat you well." Her father looked aloof, beyond discussion. Ibrahim glanced at her with an uneasy guilt. Could her brother see on her face the accusation of betrayal?

Victoria wanted to shout her refusal; she wanted to beat her fists against her father and brother, to run from the arrogant self-assurance of Ram Kadar. Somehow she managed to master herself. To do otherwise would have been foolish.

"I had not imagined such . . . an honor, my father. Forgive me if I seem . . . ungrateful." She dared to meet the steady gaze of Ram Kadar. "I simply had not expected Allah to answer my petition in such a way."

Her answer pleased Kadar. It also pleased her father, who sighed with relief. Only Ibrahim dared to look at his sister with open suspicion. Only he knew better.

Her father clapped his hands together happily. "Then we shall set the date."

"As soon as possible," Kadar replied with a gracious bow. "Soon there will be pressing business that I will be required to attend to."

"Please—" Victoria calmed the sense of panic that threatened to break through her voice. "A woman needs time for such important arrangements as this. I must prepare myself."

Ibrahim's eyes seemed openly hostile. He shook his head; he knew she would not consent or submit willingly, and yet, Victoria was smiling pleasantly. Her hands trembled. Her eyes were pained behind the soft words and nod of compliance.

"Ram Kadar is an important man," Ibrahim blurted out. "He is a member of the council, and Victoria must fit his schedule, not expect him to fit into matters that are so trivial. The wedding should be soon. This week."

"No!" Victoria turned on him with a fierceness that startled her father and Kadar. "It is none of his business, Father. Tell Ibrahim it is none of his affair! I need time, I tell you! I must not be rushed!"

"Well . . ." Amal Hassan straightened his fez and shrugged in apology for his daughter's outburst. "In this matter it is the bridegroom who suffers as the days pass on, and so—"

Kadar seemed amused. He liked her spirit. He would tame it soon enough, as a man tames a headstrong horse. "I have waited this long. I can wait two weeks more for her."

Victoria swallowed hard. She felt her cheeks flush with the thoughts of her deception. In two weeks she would be the wife of Eli Sachar, and all this would mean nothing. A bad dream to be forgotten.

"You are gracious," she said softly, letting her eyes linger on the face of Kadar.

He took her hand and bowed to kiss it. "My darling," he replied. *"Habibi . . ."*

It was difficult to keep her composure. Difficult not to jerk her hand away. Somehow she managed to maintain her smile.

"And now, my father," she bowed. "It has been a long day. A difficult day at the offices. There were many innocent injured and so the workload is greater for those of us lucky ones." She let the venom she felt toward Ibrahim pierce him with a hard look.

Ibrahim smiled. Yes. This was better. More what he expected from Victoria. A look of hatred and rage. Much better than this simpering acceptance of a marriage she certainly did not want. He touched his hand to his forehead in a nearly imperceptible salute. Enemy to enemy. Betrayer to the betrayed. Ibrahim preferred this to Victoria's charade.

"Perhaps Ibrahim will prepare your tea, Father. I am unwell from the difficulty of the day." She smiled up at Kadar. "Forgive me."

Kadar offered a deep bow. She stiffly embraced her father before she walked silently back to the stairs that led into the house. She passed her stepmother in the hallway.

"Well, if it isn't our princess! Soon to be a wife! Soon to be gone from this house, Allah be praised."

Victoria did not reply. She went straight to her room and lay down on her bed while the bitterness of her anger washed over her. She stared up at the ceiling and considered Ibrahim's betrayal of her and Eli. If she had a gun, she would kill him. Or a knife—

But Victoria had no weapon tonight except her ability to pretend that a marriage to Ram Kadar was just what she wanted. She would play the game. She would disguise the truth that the thought of such a marriage revolted her. And she would think what she must do.

After dinner Ibrahim entered the room of his sister. He did not turn on the light.

"What do you want?" she asked angrily.

"I want to let you know that I am no fool."

"It will take more than words to prove that to me now, Ibrahim," she hissed.

"What I have done is for your own good."

"And for the good of the Arab rebellion, I suppose."

"You will come around."

"You *are* a fool."

"I am watching you. Know that. Every move, I am watching."

"Then watch me tomorrow, my dear brother. Watch me buy a pistol and load it and shoot you."

"Then you will hang."

"Not if I say you tried to molest me."

"You would not do such a—"

"If ever you come to my room again, I will inform Ram Kadar, and then I will not have to kill you myself."

Ibrahim was silent. Ram Kadar was a loaded gun, and Victoria could indeed point that weapon at Ibrahim's head. He bowed in salaam and backed from the room. He would not bother her here again.

The moment Etta had been dreading arrived. The strain showed on her face as she watched Aaron lead the two Polish policemen into his study. He slid the door shut, letting his eyes look up quickly to where she stood trembling on the landing. He frowned, nodded to her in a gesture of reassurance. But she was not reassured. Aaron did not know why they had come. She had never told him what had happened. What would he say when those men laid out their wicked slander before him?

In a few minutes, she knew. From behind the door, Aaron's voice roared against their impudence and crookedness.

"Get out!" he shouted. "Leave my home and do not bother to come back! I shall report your blackmail to the proper authorities and then we shall see how long you carry a badge in Warsaw!"

Another voice shouted back. "You will be sorry. We have the justice of Poland on our side. She has a police record, you know! And so will you if you are not careful!"

The second thug joined in. "You know what your chances will be to emigrate if you have a police record!"

The door crashed back with a startling noise. Aaron's face was tight and flushed with fury. He stepped out of the study. "Get out!" he said again. "I am a citizen of Poland, as free as any man. I will not leave my country, nor will I live beneath the threat of stray dogs like you!" He clenched and unclenched his fists. The men wanted him to strike out, but he did not.

"Filthy Jew," muttered the red-faced men.

"I would stay off the streets if I were you," said the second.

Aaron flung open the front door. Snow flurries blew in as the policemen stepped out. The house seemed very cold. Aaron looked up at Etta as he slammed the door shut. He said nothing as he stalked back to his study and closed the door behind him.

———

The postcard from Paris, addressed to Elisa Murphy in London, lay on the desk of the Gestapo Chief Heinrich Himmler. Beside that was an envelope with the same address—the same distinct handwriting, the same postmark from a Paris post office not far from l'Opéra.

Himmler flipped open the thick file of correspondence from the German Embassy in Paris. There were handwritten requests for additional stationery, rubber stamps, and office supplies. The Gestapo chief sorted out the nondescript memos according to handwriting. Those written by Ernst vom Rath were placed neatly beside the Paris postcard and the plain white envelope addressed to Elisa Murphy. Himmler replaced the rest of the material and deposited the file in the re-file basket.

Himmler did not need a handwriting expert to see that the script on the embassy memos matched the writing on the letters to Elisa Murphy exactly. For Himmler, this was a relief. Of course, Ernst vom Rath had been suspected of disloyalty to the Nazi party. These communications to Elisa Murphy were simple proof of the man's guilt. Himmler only wished he had been able to acquire a copy of the letter that vom Rath had sent to the woman. Its contents might have shed some light on the extent of vom Rath's disloyalty.

He dialed the Führer's private line as he tapped his pen beside the name of Elisa Murphy. A male voice answered. Himmler stated his name, and after a moment the voice of Adolf Hitler came on the line.

"Good news, mein Führer," Himmler said cheerfully. "We have made a definite connection between vom Rath and the traitor Thomas von Kleistmann! Yes. Now it is certain that our sacrifice for the celebration of the November Putsch is not innocent. We are simply executing a traitor against the Reich."

Hitler seemed pleased by this information. He liked things well planned out. Even now he was discussing the routes and targets of the rioters for the demonstration against the Jews. Trucks would be on hand to transport the demonstrators out of their own neighborhoods and cities so that there would be no personal feelings involved when they attacked various Jewish homes and establishments. Of course, all this must seem very natural and spontaneous, the response of German outrage against a Jew murdering a member of the German Embassy. It was good to know clearly that vom Rath would die a martyr for their own cause. He was a minor actor in the play against Hitler, anyway. As for Elisa Murphy, she was more useful alive now than dead.

Himmler was amused by the enthusiasm in his leader's voice. Hitler was directing the entire November celebration as if it were a Wagnerian Opera. He had already made notes on Ernst vom Rath's funeral service. All this would fall on the anniversary of the Beer Hall Putsch, Hitler's attempted coup in November of 1923. Germany needed martyrs.

Himmler wrote a few notes on the back of Ernst vom Rath's envelope; then he gathered it all up together and placed it in a new file that he labeled *Götterdämmerung—twilight of the gods!*

35

Best-Laid Plans

A single thought obsessed Herschel Grynspan now: to take vengeance on the Nazis for the persecution of his family.

He pored over the accounts of the situation in Poland until the lines published in the *Parisian Daily* were memorized like the script of a play in which he must act.

> *... Critical situation of Polish Jews deported from Germany. Overnight, more than twelve thousand persons have been rendered stateless. Rounded up and deported to Zbonsyn, the no-man's-land between Germany and Poland, their living conditions remain inhuman and depressing. Twelve hundred of them have fallen ill and several hundred are still without shelter. As there is a risk of epidemic, Red Cross doctors, with the help of private doctors, have distributed typhus vaccinations and ten thousand aspirin tablets. A number of instances of insanity and suicide have been recorded.*

These vivid images were reenacted in his mind with the face of his mother and father and sister placed alongside words like *epidemic, typhus, suicide, insanity ... aspirin.*

He was fed and sheltered, yet even here thoughts of his own suicide plagued him. Would not death be easier than living like a hunted animal?

Had it not been for the urges of Hans to give his life a purpose in revenge against the Germans, Herschel would have used the rope from his bed to end the torment.

The obsession of his hatred kept him alive through these days and nights. Tonight, Hans gave him a date to look forward to. A day when his desire for vengeance would be accomplished.

Hans passed him a cigarette; his eyes seemed animated as he explained his plans.

"These filthy Nazis." Hans swaggered as he paced in the tiny cubicle. "They have their big celebration coming up. The one where they celebrate the failed coup in the Munich beer hall. You remember?"

Herschel did indeed remember. Every year in mid-November the strutting Brownshirts and their S.S. companions roamed drunkenly through the streets of every German city looking for Jews to bash. Herschel nodded. The thought of it made him angry with new intensity. "Yes. It is the same each year."

Hans lifted his head like a hunter sniffing the wind. "They celebrate the deaths of their comrades. They glorify the fact that Adolf Hitler was tossed into prison. They make speeches and spew their venom. And they will surely find more Jews to beat up this year, too."

"If I could." Herschel's eyes smoldered with hatred as he conjured up the images. "If only . . . I would shoot them all down! Every one of them! A machine gun in their stinking beer hall, and they would be sorry! All of them!"

"Ah, but you are in Paris," Hans said. "They are back in Germany. We must think what you can do here to disrupt their little celebration, eh?" He patted Herschel on the back. "We must give them a new martyr. And where will you find him in Paris, eh?"

Herschel's eyes glazed as he thought of it. He had made deliveries to the embassy before. It was a simple matter. "The German Embassy!" he whispered, as if the idea was his own, as if the idea had not come straight from the dark minds of those he most wanted to hurt. Suddenly, the idea spawned in Darkness became Herschel's own plan. "I know of someone in the embassy in Paris. If I could find him—"

Hans frowned and shook his head. "It does not matter who dies as long as it is a German, eh, Herschel? Providence will direct you to the one you are to teach a lesson! We Jews are not dogs—we are humans! They will hear that in their Nazi meetings. Let their speeches be tainted with sadness as they lose one of their own kind! Have we not lost hundreds?" Hans picked up the newspaper to make his point. "And now, how many more are dead? Even today? Maybe your own family, Herschel. Who can say?"

Herschel clutched his sleeve. "You must help me!" His voice shrilled with desperation. "It is the only thing to do—the only thing I *can* do. There is no other way!"

Hans sighed with relief. No more needed to be said. The frail young Jew had finally reached an end. Herschel Grynspan would follow every instruction, say every word that was put into his mouth. On November 7, he would walk into the German Embassy of Paris with one goal in mind.

———

Victoria's eyes flashed a warning to Ibrahim as she left the house for work. *Do not follow me or bother me,* the look seemed to say. He simply stared at her in a silent, sullen reply.

It was cold this morning. Water had frozen on the stones of the streets, making them slick. Fires burned in smudge pots throughout the Old City, and Arab merchants stretched out their hands to the warmth as they spoke about the curfew and discussed the faces on the posters that had appeared magically on the walls of houses and shops last night. These English were offering a large reward for the capture of the terrorists. A thousand pounds for each of the men who had bombed the bus on Julian's Way. Such a reward made every man search the face of his neighbor to see if perhaps a murderer was lurking there.

Victoria passed through the pedestrian entrance to Jaffa Gate before she noticed the faces on the posters. She looked away and then looked again harder. She frowned and stepped back, trying to deny the similarity she saw there to Daud and Isaak in the sketches. The chin of this one was too round, the lips of the other too thin, the cheekbones not defined enough. And yet, there was enough there to make her breath come faster with apprehension.

She boarded the bus and paid her fare mechanically. *It could not be, and yet . . .* The posters were also taped up inside the bus. Passengers squinted into the penciled eyes of the sketches. Did everyone see someone they knew in those faces?

Victoria forced her eyes away from the posters. She looked out on the busy intersection of Allenby Square—the post office and Barclay's Bank, taxis and civil servants hurrying through the cold wind that swept over the city.

The bus turned onto Julian's Way. A section of the road was under repair. Scorch marks were evident on the cracked sidewalk near the bus stop. The broken-off trunk of a sapling was being trimmed back. On the pocked wall of a building, the wind blew a poster up and then back down, showing small glimpses of the faces. Chin. Eyes. Mouth. Nose.

Victoria stepped from the bus and stood transfixed before the flapping paper. *Isaak's nose and mouth. The eyes of Daud!* She felt sick. She wished she could sit down someplace.

She put a hand to her forehead, aware that her brothers stared back at her, daring her to speak—accusing her of betrayal just as she now accused them of murder.

She turned back toward the bus and impulsively raised her hand to stop the driver from closing the doors. She hurried back on and paid her return fare again. She did not need to look at the posters again; she was certain now.

Staring at her hands, she tried to think where she should go, whom she should talk to. At Jaffa Gate she looked up on the ramparts of the citadel of David, where British soldiers stood bundled up against the cold wind. Their eyes scanned the buses. Of course, they would look at every bus today. It could happen again, couldn't it?

Victoria tucked her scarf tightly around her neck as she walked quickly back through the gate and into Omar Square. She glanced over her right shoulder toward the bell tower of Christ Church. In that moment she knew what she must do.

———

The voice of Reverend Robbins was gentle and reassuring as he introduced Victoria to the British captain. "You have done the right thing in coming here, Victoria," he said. "And now if you will tell Captain Orde everything, just as you told it to me."

Holding a cup of tea in her hands for warmth, Victoria found that she still trembled as she repeated the story of the midnight trip to the Dead Sea, the German man who had ridden back to Jerusalem with her and Ibrahim . . . and then the posters. Victoria could not bring herself to say that she was certain. Somehow the fact that Isaak and Daud were the sons of her father made it impossible for her to accuse them openly.

"I am afraid they have gotten themselves into something," she said haltingly. "I do not know what it is. But . . . I am afraid for them. Things are so uncertain these days, and young men so full of passions. I . . . cannot tell you more than this."

Samuel Orde sat on the edge of the pastor's desk as he considered the words of the young woman across from him. She was brave to say anything at all. It would be difficult enough to speak up if one suspected a stranger in the street. But to have to talk about her own family! The strain showed on her face, and Orde pitied her.

"Miss Hassan, I would like you to return to your home." His words were also gentle.

She looked up sharply. "I am leaving there soon."

Reverend Robbins nodded. This was the only mention of the upcoming marriage.

"If possible, I would like to ask that you return to the house just for a while. Keep your ears and eyes open for us."

She bit her lip and searched the face of Reverend Robbins for some hint as to what she should do. He answered for her. "Victoria is to be married here on Friday."

Orde rubbed a hand over his cheek and frowned. "Would you be willing to help us until then?"

"I did not intend to become a spy in the house of my father." She paused, then added, "And you must understand, my father is not part of this. He is a good man. He would not . . ." Her voice faltered. She realized that there were many questions in the eyes of Captain Orde.

Had he somehow seen that there was more that Victoria was not willing to say?

"No need to report anything to us but something unusual, Miss Hassan—for instance, if that German fellow should come around again. You understand? If there is some involvement on the part of your brothers with the perpetrators of the rebellion, the best thing for everyone in Palestine is to put the rebels where they belong." He smiled reassuringly.

Victoria was not reassured. Her head moved in acknowledgment. "I have a job at the Mandate offices. I am missing work even now."

"I can square it with the office. I will tell them you have a special assignment with me. You will still have your job when you return."

"All right, then . . ." She looked fearfully at the captain. "I do not want my brothers harmed because of . . . because I have come here. Please?"

Reverend Robbins cleared his throat at the sight of tears in her eyes. "The captain is a fair man, Victoria. You have done . . . are doing the only thing you could do." With that, he stood and saw the captain out. When he returned, Victoria sat staring thoughtfully at his desk.

"I had hoped that this would be the week of my freedom," she said. "That I could leave the Dome of the Rock and have no shadow or guilt follow me away."

Reverend Robbins placed a hand on her shoulder before he sat down again. "I think your hope has been realized, Victoria," he said, opening his Bible. "God is clearly showing you the darkness you leave behind." He patted the open book. "I have seen the hunger in your eyes for the Light. The same Light your mother knew, God rest her soul. I should have told you sooner," he murmured, as if talking to himself. "But I was afraid for you. I saw no way for you to escape as long as you lived in that house. But it is time now. Time for us to speak honestly, dear girl. This is the week of your freedom. Yes. I am certain of that."

A handful of posters had been torn from the walls in the souks. They lay face up on the table between Leo Vargen, Hockman, Ram Kadar, and the Hassan brothers. In a corner of the room to the right of Vargen, Ibrahim's father sat with his head bowed. He wept silently as his wife stood over him.

Vargen's voice was cold and unfeeling as he directed his question to Ibrahim. "Where did your sister go after she left Christ Church?"

"She is coming home. I left her in the souks. She was walking slowly. Shopping. Looking at things as if she were a tourist." He shrugged. "I do not know."

"You think she has recognized the faces of her brothers?" Hockman looked first at the poster and then at the hunched figures of Isaak and Daud.

"My sons," Amal Hassan said quietly. "*Why?* Why *my* sons?"

Vargen ignored the man. Such sentimental nonsense did not address the issue of Victoria Hassan. Why had she gone to the King David and then returned immediately to the Old City? And why had she gone to Christ Church?

"You assumed she would be of service to us, Ibrahim." Vargen raised an accusing eyebrow. "Now you believe she could be our undoing?"

"All I know is that she was behaving strangely this morning. I followed her, as I have told you. She was behaving strangely."

Vargen stuck out his lower lip and sat back, crossing his arms in thought. He turned to Hassan's wife. "Go upstairs and take her clothing." He snapped his fingers and the woman hurried away, leaving her broken husband to shake his head in grief and amazement at what had come upon his house.

Vargen directed his attention to Ibrahim. "When she comes home, see to it she is locked in her room."

Kadar straightened. "I do not believe ill of her." He scowled at Ibrahim. "No harm must come to her. There is an explanation to this."

"Until we have the explanation," Vargen said quietly, "your beloved will have to remain under our watchful eye. Anything less would be foolish." He raised his head angrily, "Just as you have all been foolish and careless in your handling of the situation here in Jerusalem." His eyes narrowed. "Before we have even started, the British could stop us. All it would take is one word from a silly young woman, and all our plans could come crashing down." He looked at the weeping father. "And what about him?"

All three brothers leaned forward fearfully. "He will not say anything!" declared Daud.

"Is that true, Mr. Hassan?" Vargen asked with amusement in his tone. "Your sons will hang, you know, if word of this gets out. You understand?"

The elder Hassan nodded silently. He understood only too well.

Victoria hoped that at this odd hour of her mid-morning return, no one would be home. She had not taken two steps into the foyer before she realized what a mistake she had made to return here at all.

Ibrahim, Isaak and Daud stared openly at her. Her stricken father did not look up. The German and another man were smiling curiously at her as if they knew something about her that she did not know yet. Ram Kadar stood. His face looked pained.

"Salaam," she managed to stutter.

There was no reply. Ibrahim answered after a long silence. "Salaam, my sister. Why are you at home at such an hour?"

"I did not feel well," she answered. "I came home for a few minutes only. To take some aspirin. I am going back to work." She pretended not to notice the face of her father.

The German smiled more openly now. "You are a clever girl," he said in a low, menacing voice, "but you will not be returning to your job at the Mandate office this morning."

She tried to act indignant. "Who are you to say?"

"You will escort her up to her room, Ibrahim," Vargen instructed. "Go along, Kadar. Teach your bride-to-be obedience."

"Father!" Victoria cried as Ibrahim took her by one arm and Kadar by the other. "Father!" But her father did not lift his eyes to her.

She did not fight them, realizing that they would hurt her and she would still be locked in her room. They did not speak to her. Passing her stepmother in the hallway, Victoria caught a glimpse of her dresses and clothes for work on the floor of Ibrahim's bedroom. "What are you doing with my clothes?" she protested.

Kadar grasped her arm more tightly, a signal for her to be silent. "You will wear the traditional clothes of a Muslim now," he said. "There is no reason to wait."

They let go of her arms in front of her bedroom. Ibrahim turned the latch and stepped aside for her to enter. The closet door was open, the rack empty. Drawers were empty and lay piled on the floor. On the bed was a stack of folded robes and veils.

Ibrahim gave her a slight push forward as he stepped out and closed the door, locking it behind her.

———

It was barely light in the tiny apartment of Leah and Shimon. Leah rolled over and wrinkled her nose. Something smelled strong and unpleasant. She resisted opening her eyes.

Leah heard music far away, as if in a dream. She sensed the light of morning filtering through her eyelids. Was she dreaming? Opening her eyes, she looked around their tiny apartment. Shimon was cleaning the dingy glass of the windows. The pungent smell of ammonia filled the room and made her eyes water, awakening her against her will.

Still the music played. Beethoven. Sonata for Piano and Violin. *A dream?*

The lid of the phonograph was propped open. Leah could see the tone arm bobbing across the record. It was a recording she had packed with special care. The violinist was Elisa on a recording made years ago in Salzburg.

Leah sat up. She put her hand to her head. One of the bandages had come undone during the night. "Shimon?" she laughed.

He turned and bit his lip as he looked for the note pad and pen they had used to communicate for the last few days. He held up a finger for her to be patient. There it was, beside the phonograph. He held it up. A message was already written: *Would you like coffee or tea?*

"Tea this morning, please. And after Elisa is finished playing I would like to hear a little Benny Goodman, if you don't mind."

Victoria was dressed in the traditional robes of her Muslim sisters. A veil covered her face. She studied her reflection in the half-light of morning. She looked the part of a Muslim woman, but she knew her heart had forsaken that life and begun a new one. She was a prisoner, and yet, this morning she finally felt free.

It was a twenty-foot drop from the rail of Victoria's balcony to the flagstones of the garden below.

Sheets and blankets were knotted together, then tied to the railing and threaded down to the ground. She stuffed a pillowcase with clothing and tossed it onto the stones where it landed with a dull thud.

For a moment Victoria peered over the edge of her prison. A cold wave of fear gripped her. The rope passed just outside the window of the room where Daud and Isaak slept. Had they heard her? Were they waiting below to catch and beat her? She prayed for help.

Somewhere in the city a rooster crowed. Soon the merchants and peddlers would awaken. Jerusalem was stirring. If she intended to escape this house, it must be now!

She held her breath and swung herself over the railing. For an instant she clung tightly to the makeshift rope, unable to move.

The bells of Christ Church chimed six as the sun began to push up over the horizon.

"Help me, please," Victoria whispered. She did not address her prayer to anyone in particular. Allah, the god of her fathers, she now hated. Eli's God she did not know. Once more she looked over the railing. Once more she heard the chiming of the bells from Christ Church. *Go,* they seemed to urge. *Go now!* Taking a deep breath, she slipped down and down, finally collapsing onto the stones at the bottom.

A light flicked on behind the curtains of her brothers' room. Stifling the urge to cry out, she gathered up the pillowcase and fled toward the high wooden gate of the courtyard.

They will hear you! Her heart thumped a desperate warning. She forced her trembling hands to pull back the bolt carefully and quietly. The hinges groaned as she slipped through the narrow opening and eased the gate back in place.

First Victoria looked up the street and then down again. She couldn't decide which way she should run now that she was free. She had not really believed she would get this far.

She could not go to work today. Perhaps her brothers would look for her at the King David Hotel. Perhaps they would come into the offices and pull her out from behind her desk while the shocked Englishmen looked on.

Eli! Did she dare run to his home for shelter and safety? It could not be! The fury of Haj Amin and her brothers would turn there, and the day would become a day of massacre in the Old City.

Again she raised her eyes to the crowded skyline of the Old City. The purple sky lightened and a beam of light crashed against the bell tower of Christ Church. *Come!* the bells seemed to say. *Come in.*

That was it! She could hide in the garden of Christ Church. She could crouch behind the shrubs in the courtyard until Eli came for her! And then. . . ?

Victoria could not think that far ahead. Over the wall she heard the voice of Daud shout the alarm: *"Victoria is gone!"*

She began to run wildly through the deserted streets. Her robes clung to her legs, holding her back as if she fled in a nightmare.

Her breath pushed and pulled against the veil that hid her face. Just ahead she could see the crowded souk where farmers stacked their produce for a day of selling. There were no Muslim merchants in the souk today. The stalls were ominously empty. There were no Muslim women shopping early beneath the vaulted roofs. Only Christians. Armenians. Jews.

Victoria was frightened. She did not stop to listen to whispered words of warning that passed from one merchant to another.

"Something happening today . . ."

"I will not stay open long this morning!"

Victoria emerged on the other side of the souk into the Christian Quarter. She looked back over her shoulder to see if she had been followed. *They will come! They will come looking for me! Any minute they will be here!*

She began to run again, bursting through a group of startled Copt priests, past the entrance to the Church of the Holy Sepulcher, and finally into Omar Square where Christian Arabs already thronged on their way in and out of Jaffa Gate.

She dashed across the Square, bumping into two British soldiers.

They shouted something to her, then laughed. She did not hear their words. And then, when she was certain she could run no longer, *Christ Church!*

36

Saturday People

Herschel had never seen so much money. Almost a thousand francs were laid out on the rough wool blanket on his bed. Hans smiled benignly as Herschel lifted the bills up and let them flutter down like leaves.

"But how?" Herschel asked in amazement.

Hans shrugged evasively. "Let us say a collection. From friends."

Herschel ran his hands over the money. He could scarcely believe it. This was much more than he expected or needed. "All of this . . . so much!"

"You will need a new suit of clothes. You cannot check into the hotel in the rags you are wearing. You will need a large trench coat, something with deep pockets for the gun. And the gun. Of course, you will need to buy a suitable weapon. The rest is for your escape."

Herschel managed a smile. "Escape . . ." He repeated the impossible word. Then he frowned. "I have decided that I must see my uncle and aunt again. And my friend Nathan, before—"

Suddenly Hans looked angry. "You will jeopardize everything if you go back there! I forbid it!"

Herschel blinked stupidly at him. "Forbid? But I . . . I want to see my family at least before—"

Hans raised his eyebrow and studied Herschel for a moment. "Who found you this room, eh? Who has been your friend? You are worried to show your face, and who takes care of you? I do!"

"I wish only to know if they have any word about my parents."

"Why? So you can back out now? After I have brought you all this? Made it possible for you to be a hero and avenge your family and your people?"

Herschel was silent for a moment. It began to rain again. It had not stopped raining for two weeks. He looked at the money and thought about the new coat he would buy. The business suit. The gun. "You have been my friend," he said with a note of shame at his obstinacy. "I will not fail in this." Thus he dropped the issue of visiting his uncle and his friend Nathan. But he had made up his mind. There was a good chance he would not see them again. A very good chance that he would not walk out of the German Embassy alive. There were things he wanted to say. He would go to them after Hans left Paris for good tomorrow.

"I am grateful you see reason," Hans looked relieved, although Herschel had not told him his intentions. "I am leaving tomorrow. I will read the papers and wait for word. When you escape, you will know where I will be."

"Marseilles."

"And then Portugal. Lisbon." He tapped his forehead. "You memorized the address?"

Herschel nodded again and began to gather up his fortune, stuffing the bills into the pockets of his ragged sweater.

———

No footprints marred the virgin white snow of Muranow Square this morning. Beautiful and glistening, the pristine blanket looked soft enough to sleep on.

Beyond the borders of the Warsaw ghetto, the goyim children would be building snowmen and pitching snowballs at one another.

But today was a special day in Muranow Square. Parents helped little boys and girls to dress in the clothes they had laid out yesterday for Bar Mitzvah service at the synagogue. Here in Muranow Square there would be no snowball fights, no noisy shouts or soggy mittens.

Rachel did not envy the raucous freedom of Catholic Warsaw. She loved the peace of their way of life.

Papa, looking more worn than peaceful, descended the stairs.

"Baby Yacov has a sniffle, children," he said, avoiding Rachel's eyes. "Your mother will not be going to services this morning. Rachel, the boys will stand in the upper gallery with you, nu?"

Rachel felt ashamed. She could not forget the anger of her father's voice toward her. She had not meant to listen in. She was wrong to have done so. She must ask God to forgive her this morning. She must pray that Papa would also forgive her.

He opened the door to a cold blast of wind; then, as the boys walked ahead, Papa touched Rachel on the arm and lifted her chin until his warm, brown eyes held her sorrowing gaze.

"Forgive me for shouting, little one," he said gently. "To speak harshly is more a sin than drawing blood. This morning I asked God to forgive me, and now I ask you."

"Oh, Papa!" she cried, wrapping her arms around him. "Oh, Papa! I am so very sorry!"

He laughed, and everything was all right again. Mama called that they should go out or stay in, but at least shut the door! The voice sounded bossy and confident. Mama was all right again. Rachel followed Papa quickly out the door.

From every house, black-coated figures emerged. Cheeks were bright with cold. Little trails of footprints crisscrossed Muranow Square. All feet pointed toward the steps of the great domed synagogue at the end of Przebieg Street. Mamas and papas. Old men and women hobbling on canes. Strapping young men in proud new beards and broad fur-trimmed hats.

Peace filled Papa's face as Rachel looked up at him. *Black hat and coat. Black beard and dark eyes. Breath a vapor that kept time with each crunching step. All this framed by the white backdrop of the snow.*

Yes. Everything felt normal again. Rachel would not worry. Perhaps everything Papa had said was right. After all, she did not see any sign of the watcher this morning in Muranow. Had he given up? Decided that the Jewish rabbi was not worth watching, after all?

And then, as the peace seemed to descend over them, something in her father's face changed. There were murmurs now instead of greetings. Children looked up sharply at their parents as big hands clamped tensely around little fingers. The rhythm of her father's breath quickened and his eyes flicked nervously toward the end of Pokorna Street, and then he swung around to look over his shoulder at the far end of Muranowska Street.

Instinctively Rachel followed his gaze. Samuel and David also mimicked the searching glances of their father and the other adults walking toward the synagogue.

"What do we do?" shouted a short, round man. "Rabbi Lubetkin?" he called to Papa.

"Ignore them." Papa's voice was calm, almost patronizing.

In that same instant, Rachel saw them at the ends of the streets. There was a wall of them: Poles, Saturday people. They glared down toward Muranow Square. They did not speak among themselves. There were some men on horseback. *Policemen?*

"Papa!" David cried in alarm.

"Ignore them," Papa said in that same, too-calm voice. "Keep walking, children. Into the synagogue. Do not look back. Do not act as though you are frightened."

Rachel was frightened. She had heard of pogroms. Such demonstrations were common in the outlying provinces—Jews attacked and beaten by the Saturday people.

Rachel felt her heart beat faster as they neared the steps of the synagogue. The great carved doors loomed up like a fortress. They swung open, and families hurried up the steps.

"Slowly," Papa warned again. "We do not see them."

Rachel wanted to run. The silence of the Saturday people was ominous. There were hundreds of them. Why did they stay just beyond the ghetto border? Were they content to send their hatred through the morning air on looks alone? Would they attack?

One step at a time, Papa nudged the children ahead of him. The color was gone from his face. There were others walking behind them. The doors of the synagogue would not be closed and bolted until every Jew on the street was safely in.

"Women and children upstairs to the gallery," Papa instructed. Still rational, he helped the more frightened of his congregation to remain calm.

"Oh, Rabbi! Is it a pogrom? Are they coming? Are the goyim coming here too?"

Papa raised his hands to quiet the murmur that bordered on panic. "We will have our Shabbat service," he said. "Morris? Is everyone in?" A long last look out at the Square. A nod. "Then close the doors. Slide the bolt. Lock up tight."

———

Eli stood with his cheek against the stones of the Western Wall as the sun rose. Lists of the dead and wounded had been posted. The name of Victoria had not been among them. For this, Eli gave thanks.

The faces of the young Arab men on the posters above the lists troubled him. He could not be certain, but two of the terrorists bore a marked resemblance to the two youngest brothers of Victoria and Ibrahim. *Her brothers?* What, then, was Eli to do if this was so? Surely someone else in the Old City would identify them! Someone would report this to the British authorities and they would be arrested if the sketches on the posters *were* Isaak and Daud! Such a thing was not Eli's responsibility, after all. There would be many in the Arab Quarter who would recognize the likeness.

Almost as soon as that hope entered his mind, another thought chased it out. What Muslim would dare to report that the faces on the posters seemed like those of the Hassan brothers? Even for money, it would take a brave man to speak up.

How could Eli report them and still look Victoria in the eye? They were her brothers, after all! And yet, if they did this thing, many innocent people had died at their hands. The unborn child of Leah and Shimon was among the lost.

This morning Eli had watched from a distance as Shimon helped Leah up the steps of their flat. The women of the Quarter had whispered among themselves, *She was expecting, poor thing* . . . Eli had not gone to visit. How could he face the couple with the images on the posters burning in his mind? *Shalom. I hope you recover. Oh, by the way, I think I know who bombed Julian's Way, but I am not talking . . .*

Was it enough for Eli to pray that someone else in the Old City would recognize them and be courageous enough to speak up?

Eli stood before the wall and prayed that very thing. But when he had finished, he realized that a prayer for justice was not enough. If other men went to the authorities, Eli would be one more confirmation of their report. If no one else went, then Eli alone would do what he knew was right. He would pray now that Victoria would understand and not hate him for it.

Victoria was gone. She had vanished into the crooked streets of the Old City like a vapor. Ibrahim released the knot of her makeshift rope and let it fall to the cobblestones of the courtyard below. His brothers stood behind him, angry. They spoke of finding her, of taking her far away so that she could not betray them. But where to find her?

It was time, Ibrahim reasoned, to tell them.

"She will be with the Jew, Eli Sachar," he said in a low, menacing voice.

Silence fell over the three brothers as they considered Ibrahim's words and wondered how he could know such a thing.

"Eli? The Jew friend whom you have put above your own brothers?" asked Isaak.

"How do you know such a thing?" Ismael demanded, putting a rough hand on Ibrahim's shoulder and spinning him around.

"Eli?" Daud asked stupidly. "Eli Sachar? The Jew?" He could not understand.

Ibrahim licked his lips. His mouth felt dry, and he tasted the iron taste of fear. "Victoria loves him."

"But he is a Jew!" Daud declared.

Ismael shoved Daud. "Shut up!" he hissed. Then he stepped close to Ibrahim. "She loves this Jew, Eli Sachar? Tell us how you know this."

"I have known for a long time. I did not discourage it, thinking he would join us."

Ismael's face contorted with rage. He spit into Ibrahim's face. "You are the flesh of swine. You have given our sister to a Jew?"

Ibrahim wiped the spittle from his cheek. He clenched his fists and considered using the dagger beneath his shirt, but he restrained himself. "If we find Eli Sachar we will find Victoria," he said. "That we must do first. For the sake of Daud and Isaak, we must find her and bring her back." He glared into the smoldering eyes of Ismael. "Later, I will settle with you. When we have her back, then I will fight you."

Ismael nodded brusquely. He turned to Isaak and Daud. "You two go to the caverns beneath the Dome of the Rock. Find Vargen. You must hide there in case she has already betrayed you. Ibrahim and I will find her and bring her back. No word of this must be told to Ram Kadar or Vargen. Do you understand? We will need this marriage as an alliance." He grabbed Daud's shirt. "Before Allah and the prophet, you must swear that you will say nothing to them! Swear it!"

Trembling, Daud raised his hand. Then Ismael repeated the demand to Isaak, who also agreed.

"Get out of here, then," Ismael demanded. "Ibrahim and I will find the Jew and Victoria."

———————

The frost of winter mingled with the breath of worshipers to fog the windowpanes of the Warsaw synagogue. Rachel watched through the lattice of the women's gallery as the men of the congregation, heads covered by the wool of prayer shawls, faced toward Jerusalem. The words inscribed above the ark proclaimed an awesome warning: KNOW BEFORE WHOM YOU STAND.

Although women were not required to pray the *Shemoneh Esrei*, Rachel let her lips move silently with the lips of her father as he recited the eighteen blessings. She had done so all her young life until the prayer was carved in her heart as clearly as in the heart of any man.

Blessed art thou, Lord our God and God of our fathers,
God of Abraham, God of Isaac, and God of Jacob. . . .

Like a flock of birds across the sky, other names filled the silent prayer of Rachel. *God of my grandfather who worships you in Jerusalem, God of my own father, Aaron Lubetkin. . . .* She changed the words each time and so never tired of finding new ways of tracing her family lineage to the God of her fathers. She did not trust her own heart to reach out to this great and awesome God, but she had family connections, after all. So maybe God would listen—even though she was just a woman and perhaps not even that, yet. Perhaps the great, mighty, and awesome God would turn His attention for an instant to the women's gallery and hear this woman-child as she whispered her blessings and requests:

. . . Master of all,
Who remembers the gracious deeds of our forefathers,
And who will bring a Redeemer with love to their
*   children for His Name's sake.*
King, Helper, Savior and Protector.

With this last word *Protector,* Rachel squeezed her eyes shut tight and grasped the lattice tightly as she prayed. *Protect us please. My papa . . . I heard him and Mama talking. I am afraid. I am afraid for all of us. I am just a girl and you are the Awesome God, but I am here praying like the men. I hope you do not mind. Papa says Dr. Letzno has been followed, and now for a week I have seen a man outside in the street watching our house, too . . .*

Rachel opened her eyes with a start. She had fallen far behind on the recitation of the blessings. Papa had already repeated the sixth blessing of forgiveness:

Forgive us, our Father, for we have sinned. . . .

She tried to bring her lips back in time with the voice of Papa:

Blessed art thou, Lord, Gracious One who forgives abundantly.

She stared hard at the smoke rising from the silver lamps that hung above the heads of the men in the auditorium. Did God hear their prayers, or were these words just like the faint traces of smoke? There was no room to doubt. *No room!* The look on Papa's face told her that a terrible Evil stood even now at the gates of the Warsaw ghetto! Darkness had cast its long shadow over the house on Muranow Square. It touched the rabbi who prayed with his people in the voice Rachel loved like no other.

"OPEN UP! CHRIST-KILLERS . . ."

Sound the great shofar to proclaim our freedom . . . !

Voices and shouts rose up outside the synagogue, the pounding of fists against the doors resounded in the hall. But Rabbi Lubetkin did not raise his voice to compete with the sound.

Lift up a banner for the ingathering of our exiles. . . .

The booming sounded more urgently on the doors. The heads of worshipers jerked slightly upward. Eyes widened with fear. *They have come! The Poles have come to the ghetto! The Saturday people have come! They are here! Pogrom! Pogrom!*

"OPEN UP, JEWS, IN THE NAME OF THE POLISH JURISDICTION OF WARSAW!"

"WE DEMAND THAT YOU OPEN THE DOORS!"

"JEWS! . . . JEWISH BOLSHEVIK SWINE!"

Cries rang out in the women's gallery. Mothers pulled their children close as the locked doors strained against the force of a bench used as a battering ram.

Rachel clung to the lattice. Her brothers, mute with fear, hung on to her arms in desperation. She did not look at the straining doors; she could not focus her eyes on the confusion of the men below as they turned to one another and shouted words no one could understand. She looked only at Papa. He stood with his feet together. Still he faced Jerusalem. Still his lips moved unfailingly in the *Shemoneh Esrei*:

Rule over us, thou alone, O Lord
With kindness and mercy,
And vindicate . . .

No one else was praying. No one except Rachel and Papa. Her own voice was drowned out by the shrieks of terror that filled the synagogue, but she prayed aloud—she prayed with Papa!

And let all wickedness instantly perish.
May all thy enemies be quickly cut off . . .

Boom! The hinges of the doors splintered! Boom! The frame crashed crazily inward. The voices of hatred swept in on the winter wind. Talliths were blown off and heads bowed against the force of this cold breath!

Others surged around Papa as he stood unmoving in the presence of the King. Children wailed as the roar of the Poles crashed over the congregation like a breaking wave.

"POLAND FOR POLISH! JEWISH SCUM GET OUT! BACK TO RUSSIA, FILTHY COMMUNIST SWINE!"

Rachel cried out as clubs fell on the heads of the men. Talliths became red with blood. She shouted as two Poles spotted her father and charged toward him, their clubs raised high.

Establish peace, well-being, blessing, grace, loving kindness, and mercy upon us and upon all Israel, thy people!

"GET THE CHRIST-KILLING PIG! KILL HIM! KILL HIM!"

Rachel tried to scream, but the scream caught in her throat as the men raced over the wounded Jews toward Papa. Her breath came in short jerks. "Papa . . . Papa . . ." she managed to whisper. Then, "God. God . . . oh . . . oh, *God!*"

But God did not seem to be listening that day in the synagogue of Muranow. Blackjacks landed on the rabbi's shoulders and back. Red blood soaked through the white of his tallith even before he crumpled to the floor.

Rachel clung to her terrified brothers, their faces buried in her skirts. They did not see their father fall. From this high view, perhaps Rachel was the only one who saw as the rabbi was dragged out the side door into the bloodstained snow of Muranow Square.

As she watched, the prayer on her lips became a scream that went on and on far into the night.

It would not be said by future historians, Herschel reasoned, that the avenger of the deported Jews of Poland had died in rags. After all, Herschel's father had been one of the finest tailors in Germany. Should his son now put him to shame?

Herschel chose a fine dark blue wool suit from the rack, a coordinating necktie, shirt, new socks, and shiny black shoes. He tried on a dozen overcoats, finally deciding on a camel-colored trench coat of the cut worn by the American actors in the detective movies he had seen in Paris. He paid cash and tossed his tattered old clothing into a trash can in the alley behind the shop as he left through the back door.

The cold winter air of Paris felt good on his face. He felt renewed, alive again, like a man with an important mission to fulfill. In his seventeen years he had never had such a sense of control and power as he felt at this moment walking through the St. Martin district of Paris toward the home of his uncle. He carried a secret with him! Hans was long gone, and now the plan, the idea, the courage were all his own. No one else would take credit when it was accomplished! He would go down in the history of his people as a man like David, facing the Nazi Goliath—or perhaps Bar Kokhba, fighting against the tyrants of Rome. He might fall, as Bar Kokhba did, but at least he would not be forgotten as those nameless thousands who now languished in the deportation camp.

Herschel stopped for a haircut and a shave, although he scarcely had a beard. He tipped the barber, who stared at his young customer with the curiosity of the old toward a young man of means.

The money in Herschel's pocket gave him a sense of freedom and power. The immigration authorities of Paris would not think to chase down a fellow dressed this well and carrying so much cash. Herschel stopped at a haberdashery and bought a fedora, which he pulled down slightly over one eye. His reflection in the mirror pleased him.

Only one item remained for him to purchase: the gun. Once again he found himself looking over the weapons in the window of the gunsmith's shop. He could afford to pick carefully. He could purchase the best. But he would buy the weapon later, after he visited his uncle one last time.

37

Snowflakes on the Wire

Eli buttoned his overcoat around him as he hurried down the Street of the Chain toward the citadel at Jaffa Gate. Every few yards the posters glared accusingly at him. The shoppers had returned to the market-place. They haggled over prices as if nothing had happened. Did any-one but Eli notice the eyes that stared out beneath the bold letters: WANTED IN CONNECTION WITH THE JULIAN'S WAY BOMBING!

Heaps of baskets against a wall half concealed the faces on the posters. The eyes of young Daud looked out at Eli. *Victoria's brother!*

Eli's heart beat faster as he stepped around a group of four Arab men who stood in the center of the street as they glanced furtively at the sketches and then spoke among themselves in low, urgent tones. They knew—maybe everyone in the Arab Quarter knew. But they would not speak up.

Eli looked straight ahead, for fear his eyes lingering on the sketches would betray that he also knew. Past heaps of citrus fruit, sacks of beans and lentils, he hurried. From the corners of his eyes he saw the white posters—like opaque windows from which those familiar, threat-ening faces stared. He turned to glance back as conversations behind him fell silent and the scuffling of feet clattered over the cobblestones.

A dozen Muslim boys were jogging through the bazaar, tearing away the posters. No one tried to stop them. No one dared protest. The faces of the guilty were crumpled up, tossed into the air by one boy and batted playfully by the next and then the next until the paper ball fell into a puddle.

Eli stepped aside as they shoved past him and nearly knocked a Greek Orthodox priest to the ground. They made it seem like a rough game, the sport of adolescents jostling through the streets. But every-one knew. Everyone understood that the game was a warning concealed beneath the raucous laughter of defiant youth.

Eli wiped his brow as the boys continued up the steps, leaving a trail of crumpled paper behind them. He was grateful that he would not have to look at the glaring white faces of Daud and Isaak any longer.

He emerged into Omar Square. Even beneath the watchful eyes of British sentries on the wall, the posters had been torn away. Only those on the wall itself remained.

In spite of the cold, Eli was sweating. He looked up at the soldiers on the ramparts. Their presence did not reassure him. He ducked his head slightly and cut across the Square to the entrance of the citadel where two sentries stood in niches on either side of an arched doorway.

"I wish to see—" he stammered, then began again. "Captain Orde, please."

Eyes narrowed with suspicion. "Your business?"

There were hundreds of pedestrians in the street. Eli could not speak his purpose. "I am from the Jewish soup kitchen, Tipat Chalev. You know it?"

"Yes."

"Good. Well, we are having some trouble, you see, with the English walnuts we were traded. I will need a word with Captain Orde since we feel we have been cheated."

Indignation was a certain way to get in to speak to the British officer in charge. This worked well. The eyes of the soldier widened. *The Jews of the Old City feel they have been cheated by the British government in an issue of food?*

Within minutes Eli stood before Captain Samuel Orde.

———

Shimon heated water on the primus stove and helped Leah bathe in a tin washtub as the music of Benny Goodman played on the hand-crank phonograph. In her head Leah could hear an irritating ringing over everything. "Like a trumpet hitting high A," she explained to Shimon. "But I can hear you beneath it. You don't need to shout, my darling."

Shimon felt like shouting for the joy of having Leah home. She was thin and shaky, but she insisted on dressing this morning, and sat curled up on the bed as she drank her tea while Shimon finished the windows.

He waved broadly at two British soldiers whom Captain Orde had stationed as sentries on the roof across the street. Their constant gazes in this direction had made him get up before dawn to clean the windows and take them a pot of steaming coffee. He had not meant to awaken Leah with ammonia, even though she accused him of waving the bottle beneath her nose like smelling salts. Later, she insisted, he would have to go into the New City to telegraph Elisa in London that

Leah was at home and well. She must not worry.

He was just finishing the last panes of the front windows when he caught sight of Reverend Robbins walking quickly up the street. The minister also spotted the soldiers on the rooftop. He looked from their perch toward the apartment and his expression displayed a grim approval at their presence.

"The Reverend from Christ Church is coming to pay a call," Shimon said over his shoulder.

"You think he will come inside this time?" Leah asked, remembering his hesitance to enter the apartment the first day.

Shimon shrugged. Reverend Robbins was climbing their stairs and seemed quite anxious to reach the top. Shimon gathered up Leah's nightgown and shoved it under a pillow as the minister banged urgently on the door. "This is the way Christians knock when they visit someone they think is deaf?" Shimon asked wryly, amused but surprised by the demand of the gentle pastor's fist on the door.

"Coming!" Leah replied. She got up and opened it herself as Shimon stood smiling proudly behind her.

Reverend Robbins did not smile back. He seemed not to notice at all that it was Leah who had answered—Leah who addressed him; Leah without the bandages on her head.

"Shalom," he said, having somehow forgotten entirely that she had been injured in any way. "May I come in?" He glanced nervously over his shoulder, then slipped in before they could reply. "I am glad to see you have sentries here." Then, "Oh. You are up?"

Leah nodded, baffled by his agitation. "Is something wrong?" she asked.

"Please sit," Shimon offered. "We have coffee. You would like coffee?" The lightheartedness of the moment before had vanished with the anxiety the minister brought into the room with him.

"Something has happened," he began without introduction. "Victoria came to me this morning at Christ Church. We need your help."

"And so, you see," the pastor finished, "her brothers took all her clothes. Every modern dress that she owns. They locked her in her room without explanation."

"I will pack some of my things for her," Leah said in quiet consternation.

"She would like to see you, if you are able," the minister said to Leah. "And," he looked at Shimon, "I need your help locating Eli. I cannot go ask for him without arousing curiosity in the Quarter—probably even hostility. There is no time to wait in this situation. If Victoria is married to Eli, her family will have no legal recourse in the matter of forcing her to marry anyone according to Muslim law. I am prepared to perform the ceremony immediately."

Shimon nodded. It must be accomplished for her safety. At least then Eli would have the legal right to ask protection from the British for his wife. Except for the signatures, Reverend Robbins had already completed the legal forms. It was a simple matter of finding Eli and bringing him to Christ Church today.

Eli left the citadel as Captain Orde called the British military headquarters with the news that a possible identification had been made of the two primary terrorists in the bombing. The apprehension of the Hassan brothers would have to be carried out in an orderly fashion during what looked like a routine patrol.

Orde believed that the brothers were still at their Old City residence. He requested that additional troops be sent to the citadel in case there was a violent response by the Muslim population to their arrest. To Eli's satisfaction, Orde mentioned that several members of the household were innocent, and special care must be taken that they were not hurt in the operation. Orde did not tell Eli that Victoria had come to see him. The less the young man knew, the safer the two of them would be.

For a moment, as Eli emerged from the citadel, he was tempted to walk back along the Old City wall to Christ Church. He stood in the crowded street of the Armenian Quarter and gazed solemnly up at the bell tower. Then he looked to his left toward Jaffa Gate. Victoria would be getting off the bus there, he reasoned. He would intercept her at the pedestrian entrance and guide her quickly back to Christ Church, away from whatever terrible things were happening within the Arab Quarter and her own home.

He began to walk slowly toward Jaffa Gate and Omar Square, trying to think how he could explain to her that she must not go home, that her two youngest brothers were about to be arrested for the bombings. He could only pray that she would forgive him, that she would not blame him. Perhaps in time she would thank him.

Rabbi Lebowitz's kitten perched on his shoulder and leaned against his head as he stood in the doorway of Tipat Chalev to answer Shimon, who towered above him.

"Eli Sachar? I have not seen him all morning? He was not in class. Is he ill, perhaps? Did you try his house?"

"His mother says he left before dawn this morning. She thought he was on his way to morning prayers." The usually pleasant face of the big man was lined with concern, even urgency.

The rabbi scratched the kitten beneath her chin as he considered where Shimon might look. "Perhaps he has gone to the Western Wall. I am just going there myself to pray. We can walk together, nu?"

A light of impatience flashed across Shimon's face. He considered the request for a moment. "I will run ahead and look in the souks for him. If you see him later at the Wailing Wall, please tell him that it is most urgent that I see him. I will meet him at my apartment. Will you tell him that if you see him?"

The rabbi's face clouded. He nodded and put the cat on the floor. "Some time ago, I saw him enter Christ Church. His mother says he has become involved with a girl from the Muslim Quarter. Is that what this matter is about?" There was no unkindness in his voice, only concern.

Shimon took his hand. "I cannot say. Truly, I cannot."

Rebbe Lebowitz nodded in understanding. "If you see Eli before I do, tell him I pray for him today at the Western Wall. Tell him no matter what happens, my door is open to him. So. I hope you find him, whatever this is about."

———

Muslim houses faced the Wailing Wall, so it was not unusual that Ibrahim and Ismael strolled along the street where old and young Jews gathered in the cold to pray.

Ibrahim scanned the black coats and hats. He paused to look at the swaying forms beneath their silk or woolen prayer shawls. He watched. He waited until a slight movement displayed beard, hair color, or profile which was not that of Eli.

The Wailing Wall stretched on; Ismael was impatient and angry. The hilt of his dagger was hidden beneath his jacket, but he kept his hand on it as he walked.

"He is not here." Ismael said gruffly. "I say we go into their Quarter and demand she be returned."

"Shut up," Ibrahim commanded. "That is not the way we will get her back. You think Eli will hand her over and let us leave the Jewish Quarter as if nothing is unusual?"

The sing-song chants of a hundred Jewish prayers rose up. Eli's voice was not among them.

Ibrahim turned to walk back the other way. He stopped a young Jewish boy and asked about Eli Sachar. "We are trying to deliver an important package to him," Ibrahim said. It did not matter that the lie made no sense. The boy believed it.

"I think he went that way," the boy pointed toward the street that led to the souks.

Ibrahim thanked him, and then very calmly and deliberately left by the same way.

———

Shimon ran ahead of the old rabbi to scan the worshipers along the Western Wall. He asked a young Orthodox man if he had seen Eli Sachar.

"Very early," said the fellow. "He was just leaving when I arrived."

"Did he say where he was going?"

"He did not say. But he left in that direction. Toward the souks. Not unusual. Maybe to go to market for his mother." He tugged his earlobe in thought. "He seemed preoccupied, I will say that." Then he smiled. "Like you!"

Shimon did not comment. He thanked him as he left, feeling foolish. Certainly the Protestant pastor of Christ Church could not have aroused any more curiosity than Shimon was managing to do right now.

Shimon walked quickly along the street of the Western Wall to where a narrow alleyway climbed up toward the Street of the Chain and the bazaars of the Old City.

———

Victoria's eyes were shining happily into the mirror of the choir robing room at Christ Church. Leah's beautiful burgundy dress and matching pumps fit Victoria perfectly. The rich color made her smooth olive skin glow with the excitement she felt.

She turned and embraced Leah, who seemed pale and wan compared to Victoria. "Oh, Leah!" she cried. "It is perfect! And today is perfect!"

Leah stepped back to look at her with a pleasantly critical eye. She tugged at the collar, making it straight. And then with a broad smile she agreed with Victoria, "Perfect. Now all we need is the groom and the best man, yes?"

Victoria nodded nervously as she glanced up at the clock. It seemed that they had been waiting hours. Surely her brothers would have turned the city upside down looking for her. Would they think to come here as well? Would they take her away before Shimon came with Eli? The strain of these fears showed momentarily on her face.

"I have no regrets," she whispered, as if to herself, "except that we did not do this sooner." Then she looked deeply into Leah's eyes. "I have always loved him. Since we were children, you see. He was always so big and strong, yet gentle. Not like the other boys. And yet I did not think it could ever be."

She sighed and looked toward the ceiling. "But now our hearts meet here in truth before the one true God. And suddenly the things that kept us apart and fearful for so long do not matter anymore."

She closed her eyes as if to drink in the truth of what she had just said. "I am not afraid, Leah. God is not a terrible God of vengeance and hatred to me anymore. I have found His nature in Jesus." She turned to rummage in the pillowcase and pulled out a small Bible bound in mother-of-pearl. She held it gently in her hands for a moment and then held it out for Leah to see. "You see? The prettiest one!"

Leah frowned in thought. It was identical to the Bible she had given to the little beggar in the souk on their first day in Old City Jerusalem. "Yes. It is . . . did you . . ." She hesitated to ask.

Victoria nodded her head happily. "I went back to find him after I left you. I paid him twice what you paid for it." She held it to her heart. "And it is the greatest bargain, the *greatest treasure* of my life. I was ready, you see, before anyone told me! I was ready to meet the living Jesus! It was so easy for me to believe, Leah," Victoria said. "I am going to find that little boy after all this is over, and I am going to return this to him and teach him to read."

Radiant. That was the word for Victoria today. Leah was certain that Eli would be pleased with the beauty of his bride.

———

Etta watched it all from the upstairs window. The shouts and obscenities echoed throughout the Square like a howling, evil wind. She saw the upraised fists, watched the heavy brass crucifix high atop a staff as it waved over the mob, encouraging them forward to the steps of the synagogue.

The shouts of *Christ-killers!* became a chant that fell in rhythm with the crashing of an upraised bench against the doors of the synagogue.

She dashed down the stairs to pile chairs in front of the door. But the mob never came to her house. They vandalized the great Warsaw synagogue, but when they finished, they drifted off, laughing into the snow-covered side streets of the Square.

Silence overtook the Square. Snow began to fall again as men and women staggered out to help the injured in the street. The cold nearness of death stood beside her. She did not weep as she watched; it was all too much like a nightmare, unreal in its madness. Her children. Her husband. What had become of them? Fear for their safety drove everything else from her mind.

Baby Yacov slept peacefully in his cradle throughout the pogrom. She did not pick him up for fear even a small cry from his innocent lips would call the darkness of Evil here to devour him.

A group of women and children emerged from the building. They were surrounded by men with bloody faces who formed a circle of protection for them as they moved down the steps and then across the Square. They were coming here; somehow Etta knew even before they had directed their staggering legs toward the house. She put on her coat and hat and pulled mittens over her trembling hands as she ran down the hallway to pull away the heap of chairs from the door.

In her mind she replayed the faces and forms of the desperate human circle moving toward the house. Her children. Frau Rosen among the women. But Aaron was not among them. She had not seen the face of Aaron in the dark ring that glided soundlessly across the stark white snow.

Chairs were scattered everywhere in the foyer. She pulled back the bolts and threw open the door; then she heard their weeping—not just the voices of women and children, but the men as well! Their sobs ascended on the vapor of their breath. They were not individuals now, but one single unit of moving anguish—black coats torn, bright red blood clinging to beards and soaking white collars. The scarves on the heads of the women were untied. Buttons dangled; shoelaces trailed in the snow. Hands grasped fabric and flesh around them. No one let go, and the expression on every face was the same. The horror in each pair of eyes was identical. No one was untouched. No one separate in their grief.

Etta spread her arms as she stood on the top step. As she cried out to them and urged them to hurry, she seemed to embrace them, to join the circle of anguish.

Rachel clung to her little brothers. "Mama!" she sobbed, and the boys joined her cry. "They took Papa! They took him away! Oh, *why,* Mama? They have taken Papa!"

Etta wiped her tears and wiped her mouth. Her legs would not carry her forward to them. They had to come to her. "My children!" she called them. "Rachel! Oh, my Rachel!"

Rachel broke off from the slowly circling group. Her arms out, fingers wide, she ran to Etta and embraced her. The boys followed, and a smaller circle was formed in the snow of Muranow Square.

"Where have they taken him?" Etta wept, as she called to the men. "Where did they take Aaron?"

"To the prison on Ginsea Street!" someone replied. "They called him a Communist! They beat him! They took him from the pulpit as he prayed! His blood marks the way!"

Across the Square, Etta could see other small circles moving in their own orbits toward other houses and side streets. No one was alone. Not one.

"Who else? Who else did they arrest?"

"Only the rabbi! Only Rebbe Lubetkin!"

———

Etta shook the housekeeper by her shoulders as she sobbed uncontrollably in the parlor. "Listen!" Etta demanded. "Enough of this!" A slap across Frau Rosen's cheek quieted her at last. "Listen to me! You must stay here. Lock the doors when I leave and do not open them until I return!"

"Yes . . . yes, Rebbitsin," the woman sniffed. "It was so terrible!"

Etta would hear no more. "Stop it! Think of the children! Feed them now. Take care of the baby. I will be back."

"But where are you going? Rebbitsin? You cannot go there!"

Etta's look was stern. She picked up her handbag and demanded that Frau Rosen obey her. There was some sanity in obedience, at least.

Without a backward glance, Etta left the warmth and safety of the house and trudged off alone across the empty Square.

The snow crunched beneath her boots while fine flakes swirled about her head, stinging her cheeks and clinging to her eyelashes. She had no more tears to shed. She would find Aaron. She had learned the game of the Warsaw police. She knew well why Aaron had been arrested. *No immigration papers if one has a police record. No country will admit a criminal ... not a prostitute or a Communist!*

Inside her handbag, Etta carried Eduard's bank checks. If they were lucky today, she would speak to the right officer, someone corrupt and filled with greed. And then perhaps Aaron could come home again.

The shops on both sides of the street were closed. An artificial twilight hung over the Jewish district of Warsaw today. There was no sign of human life here except for Etta, bent against the snow and wind.

Two blocks farther, she reached Ginsea Street where the great stone facade of the prison loomed over every other building. This was in Catholic Warsaw, and Etta could clearly see automobiles and red streetcars up ahead in the busy intersection. She had worn her camel-colored coat today, the one with the red fox collar. The Poles would not know she was Jewish by these clothes. She would be safe today. Until she opened her mouth in the police station, she would be safe!

Let them bring a crucifix before her—she would kneel and kiss it for the sake of Aaron. She would do what they asked. She would pay them. She would beg them!

She reached the corner of the street to Catholic Warsaw. They had flowed down this very street this morning—a vile flood of hatred. They had chanted the name of their Christ as they battered the doors of the synagogue. How Etta hated them! How she hated them all as they passed her now!

She looked up at the web of electric wires that crisscrossed above the street. Snow fell onto those wires and balanced there above the crushing chaos of the traffic below. Neat, perfect lines of snowflakes clung to the wires while other flakes were trampled and soiled by the feet and tires of Catholic Warsaw on this Sabbath day.

We are those snowflakes on the wire, Etta thought. *How narrow is our world, how precarious our balance!* And then she closed her eyes in a wordless prayer for help from the God who fashioned each snowflake. *Let not my feet slip from your way! Not for the sake of Aaron even. Let me kneel only to you, my living Lord!*

To the left was the prison where Aaron had been taken. To the right was the spire of a magnificent cathedral—the very one whose priest had come to her help in the street when the Poles had taken her. That priest—also a very fine snowflake who perched on the wire. Had he not risked his own safety to help Etta that day? And the Darkness had parted for him. At the sound of his voice the men had put her down and backed away.

Etta turned to the right. She walked through the thickening snow flurries toward the Catholic church. She smiled, confident that there was more inside that building than the cold metal image of a dead god. Inside the cathedral was a living man who somehow must have understood the compassion of the Eternal One and taken the Law into his heart! One righteous Gentile in all of Warsaw! Yes, Etta would ask for his help. Such a brave man would not refuse her.

She thanked the Eternal as she quickened her step, praying that the priest would be there. She did not even know his name, only that of his church. Somehow she knew that was enough.

38

Faith in the Shadow of Death

The Number Two bus from Mount Scopus and Hebrew University emptied its passengers outside the city walls near the pedestrian entrance of Jaffa Gate.

Eli was so busy looking for Victoria among the women passengers that he did not notice the glum face of his brother Moshe as he approached.

"Well, Eli," Moshe said, his voice still bitter, "you have come to wait for me?" He slung a bag of books over his shoulder and stopped before the niche where Eli waited.

"I was just—" Eli could not offer him an explanation. He did not want Moshe to know his plans until everything was settled. Over with. "I will walk with you a ways. You are going home?" He fell in stride with Moshe, entering Omar Square to continue along the Street of the Chain.

"Home. Yes." Moshe sounded regretful, almost apologetic. "For a few days, anyway." He did not look at Eli.

"What are you saying?"

"My fellowship has come through. I am going to England. Oxford. I begin this coming semester."

"I envy you," Eli said as they pressed on through the narrowing street into the clamor of the marketplace.

"You? Envy? You have all this. What more do you want? So certain of your life, Eli. Serve your God in the Old City of Jerusalem. Carry on. I do not know what I believe anymore." His words were not accusing, but still there was an unmistakable edge of bitterness.

"Mama will miss you," Eli said.

"She will have her son, the rabbi." Bitter amusement. Almost mocking.

Eli did not reply to that. He longed to tell Moshe the truth, but his brother would know soon enough. "We will all miss you, Moshe."

The clanging of hammer against metal in an iron foundry drowned out Moshe's response. Eli raised his head to look through the human current moving up the street ahead of them. He stopped, grasping Moshe's arm.

"What?" Moshe looked up to follow Eli's gaze. He frowned at the sight of Ibrahim Hassan and his brother Ismael pushing their way purposefully toward Eli. There was no mistaking that they wanted to speak with him. Their faces seemed hard and set with anger.

"Come on," Moshe said. "We'll go back."

The clank of the hammer beat out a rhythm above the murmur of the crowds. Eli shook his head. "I have to speak with him sometime," he replied, sensing there was no escape.

Angrily, Ibrahim shouted out Eli's name. His face was menacing. A few seconds and the two Arabs stood scowling before Eli and Moshe.

"Where is she?" shouted Ismael. He reached out to grasp Eli, but Ibrahim shoved his brother back.

"I will handle this!" Ibrahim roared, and the heads of strangers turned to look.

"Where is who?" Eli replied sharply.

"Victoria! What have you done with her?" panted Ismael, clenching and unclenching his fists.

"I do not know what you are talking about!" Eli shouted back over the roar of the foundry fire. The pounding of hammers behind them fell silent as the Arab ironmonger raised his head to see the confrontation between the Jews and his own countrymen.

"You son of a Jewish pig!" Ismael screamed. "Where is my sister Victoria?"

Again Ibrahim shoved Ismael away. "I said I will—"

Eli responded in equal anger. "I do not know where she is!" He feigned unconcern. "And why should I? I am a Jew! I will remain a Jew! She is Muslim! I have no interest in—"

"You lie!" Ismael slammed forward against Ibrahim, who held him back.

The crowd of onlookers grew. Arab faces glared with sullen hostility at Moshe and Eli. Dark eyes considered them from beneath checkered keffiyehs. Hands drifted to the hilts of hidden daggers. And the murmur of conversations and haggling began to grow silent.

"I am going for help," Moshe whispered hoarsely from behind Eli. Then he backed up one step and another, passing through the smoldering crowd until he emerged through the fringes to run wildly back toward the citadel to the British soldiers.

Eli felt the cold knot of fear in his stomach. A circle of Muslim faces ringed him as Christians and Jews alike scurried away from what looked like certain murder.

Long coats were pulled back at the waist and the hilts of daggers were in plain sight. Brown hands grasped the daggers, ready to unsheathe the weapons at the right moment. Behind him, Eli felt the heat of the iron foundry. The fires hissed and made a dull roaring sound.

Eli spread his empty hands. "I have not seen her for a long time, Ibrahim, *my friend!* Not since I was with you. You remember?"

The blame shifted to Ibrahim. Ismael spat on the ground. "I have heard of the foolishness of Ibrahim. But now I will settle with you, Jew."

Eli managed a weak smile. There were beads of perspiration on his brow. "Tell him there is nothing to settle, Ibrahim!" he laughed a short, nervous laugh. "I have not seen her since we were all together. I have no interest."

Ibrahim's face tightened with indignation. "No interest! You are a swine, indeed. To trifle so with us. To pretend."

"Ibrahim!" Eli put a hand on his arm. *"Brother!* We are beyond these things, you and I!"

Ibrahim now spat and tore Eli's hand away. His eyes were full of hate. He stepped forward. The ring of rough Arab men tightened. It was settled. There would be a killing today. Blood was hot. Hearts raced with the smell of imminent death.

Eli backed up into the shadows of the foundry. The smell of molten metal filled his nostrils. The blacksmith stepped aside as Ibrahim and Ismael unsheathed their knives.

"Where is she?" Ismael's voice was low. "What have you done with her, Jew?"

"Nothing." Eli stammered. "I . . . swear. I do not know where she is!" He looked to Ibrahim for help, for some sign of the friendship that once had seemed so strong. A cold smile was frozen on Ibrahim's face.

"He is mine," Ibrahim growled. The steel blade of Ibrahim's dagger glinted with the orange reflection of the fire.

"Ibrahim!" Eli shouted, backing up until he tripped over a large piece of metal and fell to the ground.

Instantly a resounding roar erupted from the spectators as Ibrahim leapt forward, falling upon Eli. With a cry, Eli grasped the wrist of Ibrahim, pushing back against the downward thrust of the knife that hung inches above his neck.

The shouts of encouragement for a quick death of the Jew merged into a roar, hovering over the struggle taking place on the floor of the foundry.

Eli's face was contorted with the effort. Ibrahim's sweat dripped onto his cheeks. Ibrahim smiled above him, confident of his strength.

Eli jerked his knee hard into Ibrahim's groin, sending him sprawling back with a look of startled pain. The roar grew louder. This was not a simple slaughter; the Jew could fight, after all! It was more sport for the spectators, even though the end would be the same for the Jew!

Eli lunged toward Ibrahim, knocking the raised dagger from his hand. He slammed his fist against Ibrahim's throat, and the Arab's face filled with pain. He struck at Eli, a hard blow of his forearm across the bridge of Eli's nose. Blood spurted out, spraying Ibrahim's clothes with red.

The cheers rose—the first blood was Jewish blood! Eli grasped Ibrahim's shirt and slammed him back against the stone floor. Blood. There was blood everywhere. Ibrahim broke Eli's grip as the fabric of his shirt tore apart, and both men rolled away from each other for a fraction of an instant. Eli clambered to his feet and lunged against Ibrahim, who had only managed to climb to one knee. They fell to the stones again, rolling over and over as they struck equal blows.

Ibrahim reached for the dagger that lay just beyond his grasp. Eli cried out as he slammed his fist against Ibrahim's jaw, knocking him back against the stone of the firepit. Ibrahim looked up to where hot pokers of iron protruded from the fire. He reached up, grasping a poker. In that same instant Eli screamed and threw himself down against Ibrahim, then clutched him by the hair and slammed the Arab's head hard against the stones of the firepit. Ibrahim's face convulsed in agony. His mouth opened to cry out. Once again Eli lifted his head and crashed it down on the stones. Ibrahim's eyes rolled back. He went limp, his chest rising and falling in convulsive breaths.

The cheering died. The rush of the fire was the only sound. Eli released Ibrahim and turned slowly, sliding off to sit against the firepit. He was heaving with exertion. Only a few seconds elapsed before he managed to focus his eyes on the grim hostile faces that glared down at him from the semicircle just beyond the foundry entrance.

Ismael stepped forward. He kicked at the foot of his unconscious brother. He held up his own dagger. His mouth curved in a smile of contempt as he considered the exhausted Jew on the floor before him.

"Now it is *my* turn," he said. A new cheer erupted as he crouched to spring with his knife upraised.

Instinctively, Eli reached up to the rough stones to pull himself upright. Instead, he grasped the end of a poker, pulling its glowing tip from the white-hot coals of the fire. It turned a fiery arc in his grasp, ending slightly upturned. The gleaming orange tip was driven into Ismael's belly as the Arab lunged forward to kill Eli. Ismael's scream drowned out the tumult of the cheering Arabs as the metal spike pierced him through. His eyes widened in anguished surprise; his fingers spread, dropping the dagger. Working open and shut, his mouth formed soundless screams.

As if caught in time, Ismael hung there, impaled above Eli who looked on with horror at what he had done.

"*No!*" Eli shouted. "No! *Victoria! Victoria!*"

In one final convulsion, Ismael grasped the steel of the poker and fell backward to the floor.

Eli scrambled to his feet. There was total silence now as the Muslim crowd looked at the quivering body at their feet. "*Allah!*" the whisper rippled through the crowd. And then a cry of new rage swelled up against the murdering Jew who trembled before them. "*Allah Akhbar! Kill the Jew! Kill him!*"

"I did not mean to!" Eli cried. "Oh, God! *God!*" He knelt beside the body of Victoria's brother and wept, not caring anymore that he was soon to die.

The toes of scuffed shoes moved slowly forward. There was no hurry. Who would strike the first blow? Knives were drawn. They would make this Jew pay for what he had done!

Suddenly, from the pack, another cry went up. Men were flung to each side with startled cries of indignation.

"ELI!" The bellowing voice of Shimon Feldstein cried as he smashed through the mob, using his cast as both shield and weapon. Men fell to the right and left. Others scrambled back from the formidable giant with the plaster arm.

Then the shrill whistle of a British soldier was heard. The crackle of gunfire passed over the heads of the mob. "IN THE NAME OF HIS MAJESTY, YOU ARE ORDERED TO DISPERSE!"

The order came late. Already the mob was running back through the labyrinth of the souk. Thirty Arabs scrambled over toppled baskets and upturned wares to dissolve into the shadows of the marketplace.

Shimon, his jaw set, blood dripping from his cast, stood towering in front of Eli, who still wept and cried out the name of Victoria.

Captain Samuel Orde rushed into the foundry. Moshe was at his side. The soldiers did not pursue the fleeing spectators of the fight. Two dozen soldiers stood ready before the door, their weapons loaded, their eyes scanning the rooftops.

Shimon stepped past the unconscious form of Ibrahim and the dead body of Ismael. He clutched Eli by his bloody shirt front, wrapping his thick arm around him in an embrace. "Come," he said, looking down at the dead man. "We must hurry."

———

Etta Lubetkin's eyes took in every fearsome detail of the great Gothic cathedral that towered over the cold street. A white vapor of snow concealed the uppermost sections of the spire, but the faces of demons and gargoyles leered down at her from pillars and buttresses.

Standing in the niches of the facade, stone images peered down at her with cold, unfeeling eyes. Were those stone hands raised in blessing or curse? Did they direct the myriad hideous demons carved into the vast structure of the church?

For a moment she considered abandoning her quest for the one righteous Gentile in Warsaw. *How could a man so kind and brave serve within the walls of a place so adorned with idolatry?*

She prayed again before she put her foot on the bottom step of the steep stairs, then looked up at the figure of the Gentile Christ on the cross. That symbol had led the mob that battered down the doors of the synagogue. She feared and loathed that symbol. And yet, beyond these fearsome portals was a man who had called on the name of God in his compassion for her.

She raised her hands to push through the massive bronze doors. Inside the cathedral was almost as cold as outside. Great arches reared up to join at a peak in the vault three stories above the ground. Rows of wooden folding chairs filled a vast auditorium of stone and beautiful stained-glass windows. The carved image of Mary sat above the altar, a crown was on her head. Rows and rows of red votive candles decorated the steps beneath that image. To either side of the main auditorium were small niches where saints gazed over their own candles.

Etta shuddered at the sight. She scanned the vast, echoing interior of the cathedral in search of the priest. Here and there men and women knelt in their own private petition to some saint or another. Etta did not see the priest among them. Had she made a mistake to come here? Surely to enter such a place was a violation of Torah.

She would walk no farther forward into the gaze of these stone images. Etta was certain now that she had made a mistake by coming here. She turned to go, lowering her eyes from the baleful glare of a being who scowled out at her from a cluster of carved leaves. She looked only at the floor as she silently repeated the Shema: *Hear, O Israel, the Lord our God, the Lord is One!*

Then she heard her name. "Frau Lubetkin?" The voice of the priest sounded startled, yet he seemed pleased to see her.

She gasped as she looked up to see him emerge from the shadows of an arched alcove just off the foyer. "I . . . I do not know what to call you," she said awkwardly.

He smiled gently. "I did not properly introduce myself that day. Father Kopecky. But . . . why are you *here*, dear lady?"

"Please . . . I should not have come. Forgive . . ." She turned to go.

"Frau Lubetkin!" he called and the kindness in his tone stopped her, just as he had stopped the evil men by his voice. "Please wait. Is there some way I may help you?"

She stood with her back to him. She could not move. Not a step. And then she began to weep. She turned to face him and in spite of the leering, laughing stone faces above her, she told him everything.

Inside the thick walls of the citadel, Orde led young Moshe Sachar to one side as the medic examined Eli in the infirmary.

"Go home now. Tell your family what has happened—that your brother is unhurt, but that for a while he will have to stay in hiding."

"He had no choice. He did not start it." Moshe felt compelled to defend his brother, although no defense was necessary. It was obvious what had happened.

"We understand that. But—" He paused and looked toward the door and the city that lay behind. "You know as well as I what may be made of this. It is best if we place him in protective custody for now."

Moshe nodded, still defensive. "They wanted to know where their sister was. But my brother, you see, is going to be a rabbi, and so he has decided he cannot marry her, and so he has not seen her. We were just walking along, you see, and they came up, and then . . ."

Orde nodded and guided the distraught young man to the door. "It's all right. We know. Tell your parents we understand self-defense around here."

Moshe looked pained as he left. It was such a nightmare. He left the citadel and ran through the Armenian Quarter toward home.

Shimon looked on from the doorway. His clothes were splattered with blood, but he was uninjured. He listened to the quiet reassurance of Samuel Orde to Eli's brother and he waited until the young man hurried away before he entered Orde's office.

Orde exhaled loudly as he faced Shimon. "Do you know where the girl is?" he asked wearily.

Shimon nodded. "I was looking for Eli when I came upon the fight. She ran away to take refuge in Christ Church this morning."

Orde nodded curtly. "I thought as much. Her half brothers are suspects in the Julian's Way bombing. They have vanished. The stepmother said the two other brothers had gone to find their sister who had run away." He spread his hands. "Does Eli know any of it?"

With a shake of his head Shimon replied, "They are to be married. She is waiting there now for me to bring him to her."

Orde pressed his lips together in thought. "Get him cleaned up," he said quietly. "There are clothes in my locker; we are about the same size." He frowned. "I'll just jog over to Christ Church and have a word with her. Explain what happened. Maybe it will be easier coming from me."

Dressed in the uniform of a British captain, Eli entered the office of Reverend Robbins where Victoria waited for him. The captain had already told her about the attack on Eli at the foundry. The death of Ismael was clearly self-defense. *Yes. Victoria understood all that. Yes. Eli must be told that she loves him. That she still wishes to marry him.*

Orde, Shimon, Leah, and Reverend Robbins waited outside in the hallway. Muffled sounds of grief penetrated the door. Eli wept. Victoria comforted him. Half an hour later, the two emerged from the room hand in hand. Their eyes were red from the tears they had shed together, but a look of radiant peace filled their faces.

"We wish to be married," Victoria said with her head held high. "Please. We do not wish to delay any longer."

The minister looked questioningly at Orde, who nodded. At this point the marriage seemed more important for keeping the peace in the Old City. If Victoria was Eli's wife, who could then say that the Hassan brothers had been defending her honor?

Reverend Robbins led the couple to the small chapel enclosed by stained-glass windows where Leah sat praying. Shimon and Samuel Orde held Eli's prayer shawl aloft as the wedding canopy. There, beneath the covering of God, Victoria and Eli became husband and wife.

There was a tinge of grief to this moment of fulfillment. Beyond the walls of Christ Church, the first howls of sorrow and rage rose up above the Muslim Quarter of the Old City as the body of Ismael Hassan was carried home. Bitter, silent, hungry for revenge, Ibrahim Hassan followed after.

39

Peace Within the Walls

It had been absurd, of course, to think that Haj Amin and Ram Kadar would not hear of Victoria's connection to the Jew, Eli Sachar.

Beneath the Dome of the Rock, Ibrahim sat with his two remaining brothers. Commander Vargen, Hockman, and the Mufti looked on as Ram Kadar stalked angrily from the meeting. He had been deceived by the Hassan brothers. He had been made to think that Victoria was unsullied and pure, fitting to be a wife. All along Ibrahim had known otherwise. Ram Kadar left the room rather than satisfy his impulse to kill the man.

Vargen eyed the grieving brothers with a mixture of disdain and amusement. "And you still believe she is with this Jew?"

Ibrahim nodded. "We have checked everywhere. I do not see how it could be otherwise."

Hockman sighed thoughtfully. "But the Jew is under the protection of the English. In hiding."

Haj Amin spoke up. Until this moment he had listened without comment. "Yes. The English have him. The Arab Higher Committee has already demanded justice for the murder of Ismael Hassan. The British refuse to divulge the Jew's location. They claim the incident was a matter of self-defense." The Mufti let his eyes linger on Ibrahim's bruised face. "Of course, this issue of self-defense makes no difference to the propaganda we are making of the incident to the Woodhead Committee. I plan to declare Ismael a hero and a martyr before the assembly." He nodded toward Ibrahim. "You may find some comfort that your fool of a brother will not have died in vain."

Vargen smiled broadly. "*Excellent!* And as for the girl, we may wish to whisper that she is believed to have been kidnapped and murdered by this Jewish swine, Sachar." He clapped his hands together with pleasure. "It is all working much better than we planned, Haj Amin." He indicated a stack of lists and plans for the upcoming actions throughout Palestine. "You should inform the Arab Higher Committee of our conviction that the girl has come to harm. They may make the public announcement. It should also be relayed to Radio Cairo as well as to our leaders in Damascus and Amman."

Ibrahim stared at him in amazement. "If she is with Eli, it is of her own choice!"

Hockman shrugged. "Does that matter? It serves the cause just as well either way. Remember, Sachar killed your brother and now perhaps he laughs at you as he lies in bed with your sister. No doubt she laughs as well."

These words caused Ibrahim to cry out in fury. He held his head in his hands. *I have been betrayed! Betrayed by a man I once called Friend! Betrayed by my own sister! They will pay for their betrayal!*

Haj Amin looked upon Ibrahim's anguish with some pity. He addressed the two younger brothers. "You are being taken north to Haifa to fight against the British there. As long as your sister is alive and in the hands of the English and the Jews, you are not safe in Jerusalem. And then there is the matter of the posters . . ."

"Inshallah," muttered Daud and Isaak with one voice. "If it is His will." They looked reproachfully at Ibrahim. He had brought this upon them. *Death and disgrace.* It was his fault for trusting the Jew. Now they would all pay for the folly of Ibrahim Hassan.

Haj Amin clapped his hands, summoning a bodyguard to the door. "You must call Ram Kadar back into our presence," he instructed. "He must be made to play the role of the anxious, grieving bridegroom left without his bride." Haj Amin inclined his head toward Vargen. "I am certain Kadar would kill the woman himself if he had a chance, but this will be better for the sake of appearances."

"You have learned much from the Führer," Vargen said. "Of such small incidents, whole governments and nations topple, and new kingdoms arise."

Haj Amin raised his hand languidly as he looked up toward the heavens, *"Inshallah,* Commander. May it be His will."

———

Herschel wished that he had listened to Hans and never returned to the home of his uncle. The meeting had not been the sentimental farewell of one man to another as Herschel had envisioned. It had ended in a terrible argument. Without any apparent regard for the fate of Herschel's parents, his uncle had stormed and raged and called him ungrateful. Herschel had run from the house, slamming the door behind him, closing that chapter of his life with irrevocable finality.

For a moment his old depression returned. He was alone. Utterly alone. Perhaps, he thought, he should return immediately to the shop of the gunsmith, buy a gun, and turn it on himself! Then no matter what happened, he would never again feel pain or fear or loneliness.

"Wait! Herschel! Stop, will you?"

Herschel stopped on the sidewalk but did not turn around. He looked down as the slap of his old friend's shoes sounded behind him. Nathan Kaufman, breathless and flushed, nudged him hard on the shoulder. He stood panting before Herschel, admiring the new clothes and the new Herschel.

"I will be late," Herschel told him brusquely.

Nathan looked very young compared to Herschel. "Late? Late for what? You stay away all this time, and the first thing you tell me is that you will be late! What is all this?" He tugged on the overcoat and grinned at the gleaming shoes. "You look like a rich man."

"I have a job. I cannot be late." Herschel began to walk and Nathan walked beside him.

"There is a dance tonight at the Aurora Sports Club. You want to come? Remember the carefree days, Herschel?"

"There have never been carefree days for me. At least your papers are in order. Mine have never been." He raised his head, resisting any memory of happiness. "No. I have business. I cannot meet you."

"You look different," Nathan said, and the tone of respect in his young voice once again instilled a sense of mission in Herschel.

"We all have to grow up." Herschel sighed and looked away, a dramatic and mysterious gesture that made Nathan frown and nod as if he understood.

"Well, yes. But at least come to the dance, will you?"

Herschel's feeling of importance was evident in his voice. "I have things to do."

Nathan did not argue further. "Then will you meet me later? At the restaurant *Tout Va Bien*? You know it. On boulevard de Strasbourg."

"Yes," Herschel agreed, although he knew he would not go there. It would save any further questions from Nathan, who seemed very much a child now.

"Good! Nine o'clock. All right?"

Herschel shook Nathan's hand in farewell and boarded the Metro, getting off at Strasbourg-St-Denis as Hans had instructed him. He quickly ran up the steep steps and looked to his right. There was the Scala Cinema where he and Nathan had watched dozens of subtitled movies in the carefree days. The sight of the marquee made him shake his head in wonder. Could such entertainment still go on when the world was such a terrible place?

To the left was the sign for the Hotel de Suez. Strange that Hans had recommended that he stay in a hotel patronized by Arabs from the French colonies of North Africa. This had always been a place Herschel and his friends had avoided. They had often stepped from the Scala Cinema and seen men in strange red fez hats enter the lobby of that mysterious place. Ah, well. It was close to the Metro station.

He shoved his hands into his pockets and walked resolutely toward the hotel. The gold lettering on the door was flaking, the tiles of the foyer marked with muddy footprints. A handful of guests sat reading their papers in the flowing Arabic script. The ancient clerk behind the counter did indeed wear a red fez, although no one else did. The hooked nose of the proprietor almost bent over his upper lip when he smiled at Herschel.

"How may I help you, monsieur?"

"A room." Herschel's voice quavered and he began again, consciously trying to strengthen and deepen his voice.

"A room, please."

"You are not French?" asked the old man, turning the register for Herschel to sign.

"No. German." Herschel remembered Hans's instructions. When the green registration card for foreigners was presented for Herschel to sign, he was to explain that he was a salesman from Hamburg and his luggage was still at the station. "I will complete the formalities when I collect my luggage."

The old man bowed slightly in acceptance as Herschel counted out payment in advance for the room. Three francs. The old Arab, still smiling, placed the key in his hand and directed him toward the wrought-iron cage that served as the elevator.

"A pleasant stay . . ." He looked at the signature on the register and repeated the name Herschel had given. "Herr Heinrich Halter."

Herschel smiled, trying to shrug off the feeling that the old man somehow doubted that he was a salesman from Hamburg. It did not seem to matter much anyway. It had been easy. Hans had told him there would be no problem.

The message from the proprietor of Hotel de Suez was short and to the point. At the Berlin headquarters, Gestapo Chief Himmler sighed with relief as he read it. With a cheerful nod he picked up the telephone and dialed the private quarters of the Führer in the Chancellery.

"We have just received an update from Paris. Yes. The guest has arrived at Hotel de Suez on time. He has said and done everything exactly as he was instructed. Like a trained dog, this little Jew. He mimics every word, just as he was told."

This information and the anticipation of the drama to be played out in Paris and in Germany strengthened the outline of the Führer's speech for the coming celebration. It was now very clear that a hand stronger than that of a mere mortal was guiding this war against the Jews. An earlier dispatch from Vargen in Jerusalem indicated that events were happening all on their own, quite without a need for premeditation. The English Woodhead Committee trembled in their hotel rooms at the sound of a balloon bursting. Small incidents were gathering into an avalanche that would soon sweep the enemy from the face of the earth. "First in Jerusalem," Hitler quoted, "and then to the ends of the earth. . . ."

———————

A murmuring darkness slid over the walled enclave of Jerusalem. Samuel Orde had been waiting for the darkness before he dared to move the newly married fugitives.

With his beard shaved, dressed in the uniform of a British officer, Eli was not recognizable. Victoria was also dressed in the uniform of a British soldier. Her long black hair was tucked up under a pith helmet, and she carried a rifle slung over her shoulder as she climbed into one of the armored cars in front of the Old City barracks.

They all felt the eyes of the Mufti's watchers following the progress of the vehicles. There were six armored cars in the line of a convoy. Outside Jaffa Gate, they split off two-by-two, each pair taking different routes to various destinations in the New City.

Eli held Victoria's hand as their armored car swept down and then through the residential district of Rehavia, past the Montefiore windmill and then around the city walls toward the Mount of Olives and the Garden of Gethsemane. Eli had explained that he had rented a small room for him and Victoria, but Orde protested. There was no place in all of Palestine safe enough—except one place that Orde knew.

Through the slit windows in the vehicle, Eli could see that place nestled on the slope of Olivet at the edge of Gethsemane. The seven golden onion-shaped turrets of the Church of St. Mary Magdalene glowed in the moonlight like a gingerbread castle in some Russian fairy tale. Each dome was topped by the cross of the Russian Orthodox church. Surrounded by aged pines, the compound was populated by White Russian nuns and a handful of followers of the Russian czar who had managed to escape the massacres of the Bolshevik Revolution.

Here, on the hallowed slopes of Olivet, this small core of Russian faithful had found refuge and a sanctuary while men like Joseph Stalin murdered their Christian counterparts by the millions in Russia. Still living within the green iron gates of the compound was a Russian general who had led the Imperial Cossack Guard of Czar Nicholas into exile after the Russian royal family had been murdered.

Samuel Orde explained these things to the couple as he drove. He knew these people, knew the Mother Superior well. They were people who understood as well as any sect in Jerusalem what it meant to be hunted. Eli and Victoria certainly qualified for such a classification. The old nuns would take them in, give them a place to sleep and provide them with the privacy they needed. More important than that, there was no possibility that the men of Haj Amin would think of searching for them beneath those seven golden domes. Never would they imagine that Eli Sachar, the Jewish rabbinical student, would take his Muslim bride to a Russian convent!

Orde was quite pleased with himself for the idea. Besides, there was no more beautiful place in all of Jerusalem. Tonight they would close their eyes and smell the scent of the pine trees. Perhaps somehow, near the place where Jesus prayed, Eli and Victoria would find one night of peace within the safety of these walls.

The British armored car followed the stair-stepped stone fence that surrounded the Russian convent. A narrow lane crept up the slope of Olivet at the back of the compound. Lights were still shining warmly in the windows of the residence buildings. They were waiting for the arrival of their guests, Orde explained. Mother Superior had been notified early that afternoon and had prepared a place for Eli and Victoria that same hour.

Gravel crunched beneath the tires of the vehicle. The lane was so narrow that there were only inches on either side of the steel plate.

Orde stopped in front of a green wrought-iron gate. He turned off the lights and let the engine idle. Moments passed before the gate swung inward. Only then could he drive forward so the doors of the armored car could be opened.

"Here she is," Orde said as he peered out the slit at a tiny figure dressed completely in white from head to foot. "Mother Superior." A lined, pleasantly smiling face welcomed them as they stepped from the protection of Great Britain directly onto the soil of the Russian convent.

The old woman touched Victoria on the arm. "Welcome," she said in a voice much younger than the lined face. In the lantern light, the slightly hooded eyes of the old nun twinkled kindly. "Welcome. Welcome, Captain Orde."

No one spoke as she locked the gate and led them along a narrow, well-worn path. The two-story buildings of the compound nestled in the lower corner of the property, surrounded by pines and cyprus trees that whispered and swayed above their heads. She did not seem to need the lantern for herself. Her feet knew the path well. She held it out for the others who stumbled along the shadowed ruts and bumps of the uneven path.

She did not stop at the main building, but continued down a short flight of steps to a flagged courtyard, then across to a small structure that she called the *guest house.* Beneath its simple archway she recited the names of the Russian aristocracy who had stayed here at one time or another during their long exile. "Not a palace," she said with a warm look meant for Victoria, "but comfortable."

And so it was. She opened the door to a sitting room illuminated by soft candlelight. A Victorian setee was placed in front of a fireplace where broken boughs and hissing pine cones burned, infusing the room with warmth and fragrance. Photographs of emperors and patriarchs and Russian aristocrats occupied the spaces on one entire wall. The names of these fell from her lips like the names of old friends. Looking down from among them was a large photograph of the Grand Duchess Elizabeth Feodrovna, who carried out the plans for the building of the church before she was killed by the Bolsheviks. She was buried in a chapel on the grounds, explained the old nun.

When she had made the introductions, she looked at Victoria's clothing with pity. Men's trousers and shirt. Heavy coat and boots. Not the sort of wardrobe for a woman's wedding night. "There are night clothes on the bed for you, dear," she whispered conspiratorially. "And some for your husband as well."

"We could not bring their belongings out of the Old City," Orde explained. "I will bring the things Leah packed for you when I come back tomorrow to pick up Eli."

Victoria gripped Eli's hand. "Pick him up? But why?"

"Statements. Depositions about the struggle. Your brothers. There are still questions that must be answered for the official record. We can't take the risk of bringing officers and equipment out here during the daylight hours. It will be simpler—and safer—for Eli to come into the city."

Eli squeezed her hand. "It will be all right. A formality only, and I will be back here."

The Mother Superior raised a crooked hand. "Tonight is not a night to think of business, children." She opened the enameled green door that led to the bedroom. Thick down quilts were turned back. A bowl of fruit and cheese with a small bottle of wine sat on a sideboard lit with candles, along with a plate of bread. Victoria looked at the plain whitewashed walls, thankful that there were no photographs gazing mournfully down at her. Above the bed hung a Russian Orthodox cross that seemed to glow in the flickering candlelight. "And so, children, the good captain and I bid you good night. God's blessing."

Orde smiled self-consciously as he shook Eli's hand and muttered, "Good luck, mazel tov, and shalom." He tipped his hat to Victoria and then followed the frail old nun out of the house, closing the door behind.

Eli stood with his hand resting on the footboard of the intricately carved olive-wood bed. Still in the pith helmet, Victoria lingered at the side of the bed.

The crackle of the fire in the sitting room was the only sound inside the house. Outside, pine branches tapped against the roof and high windowpanes. Candlelight made shadows dance on the clean stone walls of the bedroom.

Victoria bit her lip and looked away self-consciously toward the open door of the sitting room. It seemed hard to believe that at last they were alone.

She lowered her eyes, feeling suddenly shy at the warmth of Eli's gaze upon her. She reached out and felt the fabric of the long white cotton nightgown the old nun had laid out for her on the coverlet. It was beautiful—trimmed in soft eyelet lace, with tiny buttons all the way down the front, and full, loose sleeves.

Then she touched the buttons of the borrowed khakis she wore and looked up at Eli, who smiled at her. She laughed and pulled off the pith helmet, letting her long black tresses tumble down over her shoulders.

She smiled as his eyes filled with emotion—bright, loving. All the months of longing, and now they were here.

"Funny," Eli said in a hoarse whisper. "Every night I fell asleep dreaming of you. Of this moment. Now I am afraid to reach out. Afraid to hold you. Afraid this is only a dream." He did not move toward her and so she walked slowly around the bed to where he stood. She took his hands in hers and lifted them to her lips in a kiss.

"I am not a dream, Eli. But if I were, I would wish that you would never awaken." She held his hand to her heart and then raised her face to his as he bent to kiss her. "No dream, my love," she whispered. "Touch me . . . touch me."

40

Hell Has Nothing Better Left to Do

Field Marshal Hermann Göring sent his private car to fetch Theo from the British Embassy. Long, sleek, and glistening black, even the raindrops stood at attention on the highly waxed finish. Two stiff swastika flags flanked the front bumpers. The chauffeur wore the black uniform of the S.S. He saluted with a *Heil Hitler* as he held the door open for Theo.

For just a moment, Theo hesitated before the curving driveway of the British Embassy. He turned to look at the softly glowing lights of the old mansion. It was not too late to turn around. Not too late to go back inside and send word he could not meet with Göring. Perhaps he could even catch the morning plane back to London. To Anna. Elisa. His children and grandchildren yet to be. Everything within him yearned to live only for those who were his own family. But what of other families? How many prayed tonight within this very city? How many prayed for help? For a way out? For a voice that might speak for them since their own voices had been so ruthlessly silenced?

Theo tossed a quick salute at the British union jack that hung limp in the evening mist. He looked at the plush red-velvet interior of Göring's car, and then he took one last deep breath of air before he plunged in. As he exhaled, he whispered a secret farewell. *Jacob Stern.* There must be a reason Göring had insisted his passport be issued in the name of the Dachau prisoner. Was Theo to become that prisoner again? Or worse?

He caught himself, restraining his mind from thinking about the possibilities as the limousine slowly drove past the floodlighted Reich Chancellery building on Wilhelmstrasse. He found his eyes looking toward a balcony that opened off the Führer's private quarters. The balcony was a new addition—designed so the Nazi god could review his marching troops and adoring masses.

Theo shuddered. The heaviness of Hitler's living nearness was oppressive. The evil on this street was a thick black curtain that made Theo long for one more clean, untainted breath of air. He whispered a prayer against the Darkness, but here, where the backlighted windows gleamed as if illuminated by a lampless power, Theo's prayers were whispered with difficulty. A great weight pressed against his chest. He could not take his eyes from the dwelling place of the one who had made life more terrifying than death for so many. *What words are being whispered behind those curtains? What plans are being made? What demons hiss their commands against the People of the Book? Against true Christians who protest? This is not the evil of a mere man,* Theo reasoned. He tore his eyes away from the crooked cross of the swastika flag that hung everywhere. *The broken cross. Symbol of ancient evil. Everywhere!*

The car continued down Wilhelmstrasse and then turned at Leipziger Strasse where the building that had been Lindheim's loomed up. Had the route been chosen on purpose? Had Göring laughed and instructed the S.S. driver to take Theo past the grand old building for one last look?

The windows held displays that were only half as full as they had been in the old days. Theo could see that the German economy and Göring's four-year economic plan was in trouble.

Theo was glad they had driven this way. Seeing the barrenness in the windows of Lindheim's department store gave him courage and a sense of hope. Perhaps Göring might be serious about a trade agreement. Foreign money for Jewish lives.

He caught the glance of the driver in the rearview mirror. Was the man in the S.S. uniform studying Theo so that he could report reactions later?

"The displays at this store are quite bare," Theo said, hoping that his words would indeed be repeated to Göring. "I am surprised to see such a grand old place stripped down. It must be difficult for the German women after so many years of good shopping here."

The eyes in the rearview mirror hardened. The amusement and curiosity sharpened to resentment, as if to say, *How dare anyone criticize—even if it is true!*

Eventually the cluster of city lights dwindled to a sprinkling of lamps scattered across the farmland beyond Berlin. Theo had been told that he was to be in Göring's home, that it had been his wish and he intended to discuss the ransom of human life over a quiet dinner at Karinhall. Theo had not questioned the reason for that request until the broad gates of the estate were swung open. As the car rolled up the drive, Theo could see that the front of the house was illuminated not by electricity, but by an enormous bonfire on the lawn.

A ring of S.S. and Brownshirts stood solemnly around the leaping flames. Their colorless faces turned to watch as the limousine pulled to a stop in front of the large house that Göring had named after his late wife. Lights glowed in every room. On the upper story, a shadow moved in front of a tall arched window. The shadow looked out as if to measure the effect on Theo as he emerged into the cold night air. Then the shadow moved away.

Theo looked toward the members of Hitler's private legion. They still watched him with cold and lifeless eyes. Theo did not move from beside the automobile. He watched for a moment until the front doors of Karinhall swung open, bathing the porch in light.

"Herr Stern?" asked a deep and resonant voice. "Herr Jacob Stern?"

"Just admiring the beauty of the bonfire."

He glanced over his shoulder at a tall S.S. officer who wore the insignia of a colonel. The man was unsmiling. "The Field Marshal is keeping a vigil in memory of the slain who died in the November Putsch."

Theo nodded. He remembered all that. He turned away from the flames, from this mystical appeal to the spirits of the dead Nazis.

The heat of the flames seemed to cling to his back even as he walked into the mansion. The light of the fire still burned as an after-image in his vision when the hulk of Field Marshal Hermann Göring appeared in the foyer to welcome him.

From his passport folder, Herschel pulled a black-and-white snap-shot of himself. He held it up to the dim light of the lamp on the bed table.

Herschel. Smiling and happy as he stands beside the banks of the Seine River in Paris, he mused. *The river is still there. Unchanged. But where has that boy gone? Was I ever there at all? I cannot remember what it was like to smile.*

Nathan had taken the picture—so long ago, it seemed. Herschel studied the features of his image and wondered if that was really himself. Perhaps that hour of happiness was just a dream.

But he had awakened. He looked at his watch. Nathan would be waiting for him at the restaurant. Waiting for the Herschel who no longer existed except in this photograph.

Herschel turned the photograph over and then neatly wrote his farewell on the back:

My dear Parents,

   I could not do otherwise. May God forgive me. My heart bleeds at the news of 12,000 Jews suffering. I must protest in such a way that the world will hear me. I must do it. Forgive me.

                                                              Herschel

He propped up the photo, face out, smiling at him from the bed table. This picture of happier days was all he had left—a sort of miniature memorial of what life might have been for him, for thousands of others who never dreamed it would all come to this.

Herschel fell asleep with the light still burning. He slept with the fitful howling of twelve thousand desperate voices ringing in his mind. The faces of his mother, father, and sister rose up in tortured images, interposed with smiling black-and-white photographs of the better days. The stark contrast of what had been somehow made what was now seem all the more evil. *The world will hear me. I must do it. Forgive me. Herschel.*

The majority of the staff members had left Paris to attend the coming celebrations of the November Putsch. Ernst vom Rath was left as the senior staff member in charge of the German Embassy in Paris.

The days had been long and uneventful. Tonight when the gates closed and the Nazi flag was lowered, Ernst changed into his dark brown suit and traveled on the Metro to the Strasbourg-St-Denis station. There was an American musical film playing at the Scala Cinema. The marquee was emblazoned with the title:

MARIE ANTOINETTE
starring
TYRONE POWER - NORMA SHEARER

The film was the talk of Paris because of its atrocious portrayal of the life of the French queen who had been beheaded just a few miles from the theater where the film now played. In France, the film had become a poorly dubbed comedy and the audiences had left the packed theater every night with their sides aching from the American interpretation of the mindless queen.

Ernst needed a laugh. His life in Paris had taken on the same depressing monotone quality it had in Berlin. Of course, in Paris he was not required to strut and heil and applaud the Nazi superstition as long as he was not in the embassy.

A fine mist cooled his face as he walked to the end of the line that snaked down the sidewalk and ended just at the door of Hotel de Suez.

Ernst was sorry that he had come alone. Of course, lately he had gone most places alone. Tonight in the midst of the Paris theater-goers, however, his loneliness seemed a heavy burden.

Couples were everywhere. Pretty girls held tightly to their escorts. They kissed beneath a forest of umbrellas and laughed about things they had been told about the movie.

"Ah, yes! And in the news film there is a section showing Charles Lindbergh as he accepts the Nazi service cross from Hitler. Imagine!

Who would think he would do such a thing? Remember how we cheered him when he landed? It is a betrayal—a betrayal of France!"

So even here in the line of a movie theater, Ernst could not escape the rotten propaganda of his nation's Führer. A young woman looked at him strangely from beneath her umbrella. Could she see that he was German? Perhaps the cut of his clothes, his unsmiling face . . . She whispered to her companion in a barely audible voice, "Be quiet. He is one of them. A filthy *bosche!* Do not speak about the Germans."

Ernst looked away as if he had not heard. For several couples in front of him there was silence along the line. He looked up at the marquee and then down at his shoes as if he were considering something. Then, without a word, he left the queue and walked quickly back to the Metro station to take the next train back to the embassy.

———

Once again Etta rode in the black automobile of the Warsaw priest, Father Kopecky. She looked out the window at the brutal streets of the city and yet she felt safe within this tiny ark.

Father Kopecky was indeed a man of great authority. His indignation rattled the iron cages of the Warsaw jailers, causing them to turn around and point fingers of accusation at everyone besides themselves.

"I will send the car to fetch you at your home at nine o'clock tomorrow morning," said the little priest. "Then the director of the police will be back in Warsaw. He is not a parishioner of mine, but his mother is faithful. The fellow will listen to me." He smiled slightly. "Or I will have a word with his mother. A formidable woman."

Etta managed a smile at his words. She was tired. So weary. Had there ever been such a day of fear and trial? She closed her eyes for a moment and prayed that Aaron was unhurt. She prayed that a deep and peaceful sleep might come upon him so he would not know he was in a jail cell. As for herself, to think of sleep, in spite of her exhaustion, made her feel guilty. How could she sleep with Aaron in prison?

As if he heard her thoughts, Father Kopecky said, "You must let your heart have peace now, Sister Lubetkin. The prophets of old suffered much more than this, and yet the Lord was with them."

She nodded and averted her eyes from the cross he wore around his neck. It surprised her that he spoke of suffering prophets. Those could not be the same as the prophets of Jewish Warsaw.

"Besides," he continued, "I am your witness, am I not? I only wish you would have come to me sooner and we might have ended this blackmail business before it got started." He considered her silence and then began again more cheerfully. "Ah, well, it will be finished tomorrow. This is Warsaw, not Berlin. You will see. In Poland we have our fanatics, but the law is still the law. Go home now to your children and rest. Tomorrow night your husband will be at your side. I promise."

————

For the thousandth time, Ernst considered vanishing from his Paris post. If he left, he decided, he would do it with more success than Thomas von Kleistmann had done. He would have a plan. Passports made up under several different names. A destination far away from the probing eyes of Gestapo agents and S.S. goons like Officer Konkel.

Only one thing stopped him from leaving, from vanishing into the woodwork: his family. Still in Berlin, they might fall under the punishment of Hitler's law that if any one member of a family transgresses, all are held accountable. His aging father was already known for his disapproval of the Nazi party and the crushing of the Reichstag parliament. His father had warned him during Ernst's last terrible visit to Berlin that he must tell no one about the death of Thomas; that he must not speak out again, or he might find himself also crucified in some dark Gestapo torture cell.

Tonight, the face of Ernst's father swam before him as he lay down on his bed. The old Prussian aristocrat would be hunted down and arrested in place of Ernst. If the Gestapo could not catch Ernst, they would take his father and mother hostage, and . . .

What was the use? Ernst was trapped. He turned over and stared at the wall. He should be grateful, he reasoned, that he was serving in Paris instead of Berlin. The only thing that could be better is if he could go to America. *If only he could somehow go to America and bring his family there!*

He fell asleep with that prayer on his lips, and dreamed sweet dreams of freedom.

————

Over an elegant supper of veal and asparagus, Hermann Göring chatted with Theo as if they had never met before, as if the name Jacob Stern was really Theo's name. Surrounded by half a dozen ministers from within the Nazi Economic Ministry, polite conversation drifted toward the possibility of expanded trade for Germany and the lifting of the international Jewish boycott against German goods.

In all of this, no mention was made of the exchange of Jewish assets for increased trade. Nothing seemed to connect the two intertwined subjects. It was as if Göring was saving the real purpose of this meeting for after dinner, after his flunkies and assistants were sent their way and Göring and Theo were alone.

The large grandfather clock in the study struck ten o'clock. Theo half smiled. He recognized the chimes of that old clock, just as he had recognized paintings taken from the walls of his house.

At last only Theo remained. He was a captive. He had come in

Göring's car and so must leave the same way, if he were to leave at all.

That thought crossed his mind as he followed Göring into an enormous library. One entire wall contained the collection of rare books that had once been Theo's prize possession. How insignificant such possessions seemed to him now!

Göring turned to face him. Smiling, he addressed Theo by his real name for the first time.

"A brandy, Theo?" he asked, pouring two snifters with amber liquid before Theo answered. "You always did appreciate fine things." He extended the glass to Theo, who took it with a nod and then looked at the wall of books.

"Yes. In some things our tastes are the same, I see."

Göring swirled his brandy, then sipped it. "In aircraft. In books." He smiled again, without any pretense or sign of embarrassment. "In paintings. And . . . in women."

Theo met his gaze. There was bitter amusement in Göring's eyes. Old friend turned enemy. "You have done well, Hermann," Theo replied, feeling pity for the man he had once known.

"And how is Anna?"

"Better than you would imagine, I am sure."

"Did she know you would be meeting with me?"

"She knew I would have discussions with Field Marshal Hermann Göring. Second in command only to the Führer himself."

Hermann lowered his bulk onto the sofa as he spread a hand for Theo to sit opposite him. Theo continued to stand for a moment. He turned to look out the window to where the bonfire blazed with renewed vigor and the sentinels of the morbid vigil began to sing the Horst Wessel song.

Göring broke the silence in the room as the distant voices served as backdrop. "You never were a very good Jew, Theo," Göring said. "When first I heard you were one of them, I defended you. Said it couldn't be, that such a patriot of the Fatherland was one of them."

Theo tore his gaze from the flames as he turned to face Göring. "Strange. I was also surprised when I heard you were a part of this. . . ." He lifted his hand toward the bonfire. "You have come a long way with your Führer. A long way from yourself."

Göring laughed. "You just did not know me, Theo. I was always this."

"No, Hermann. Brash and foolish perhaps. The perfect candidate for a hero in Germany. But you were not *this*. To be what you are now takes years of slow hardening of the heart."

Resentment twitched on Göring's face. "Sometimes one must be hard for the sake of one's race and nation. For the cause of victory, Theo, we Aryans make ourselves hard. We must root out and destroy,

you see—kill even the roots of those who do not belong among us."
His eyes narrowed. His face hardened beneath his jowls. "You were
never one of us."

"I am grateful for that, since I have learned from you what such
belonging means."

"We are the power of Germany now, and you see what we accomplish," Göring countered.

"The death of freedom."

"Freedom is not dead in the Reich."

"Only those who desire freedom."

"Freedom is redefined by the standards of race and purity of blood.
If we do not rule over you, then surely you will rule over us."

"You have forgotten that God rules over all."

"Which God? The Jewish God? The Christian God?"

"They are one and the same."

"We have chosen another god who will rule over millions across
the world. Those who follow your weak and worthless God of love will
die, Theo, because they have no strength to fight."

Theo did not answer him. He looked first at the fire outside on the
lawn; then he looked up at the shelves of gleaming leather-bound
books on the wall just behind them. Göring had taken them from Theo's
shelves and replaced them in exactly the same order. He ran his finger
along a row of books until he gently touched the small blue and gold
volumes containing the complete works of the poet Lord Byron. There
were seventeen volumes in the set.

"You are familiar with these books?" Theo asked.

Göring nodded, pleased at his own memory. "The definitive edition.
Published in 1833, I believe. Quite valuable."

"But have you read them?" Theo chose one book, took it down,
and opened it.

"No. But I am familiar enough with the value of such editions that
I did not allow them to be burned."

"The value is not in the binding, Hermann, but in the words within."

"A fundamental difference between you and me. We see value in
different ways."

Theo thumbed through the pages. "Yes. And that tragic reality separates us."

"Tragic to whom?" Hermann scoffed. "Not tragic to the Aryan race.
Only tragic for those over whom we rule and those over whom we will
rule around the world very soon."

"And after your rule ends? What then, Hermann?"

"The Third Reich will reign for one thousand years."

"So I heard. But you will not. And so, what then?"

"Others of our race—" Göring was flushed at the mention of his
own end. "They will remember what we have done here."

"Yes. I do not doubt. I pray they will remember." Theo lowered his gaze to the pages of the book. "It is a pity you have not read—"

"To what purpose?"

"A vision of judgment. It is written here. The words of a man long dead still speak in these pages." Theo's gaze silenced Göring. "Here Lucifer had much to say to God about the souls of kings who stand in judgment." He began to read:

> On the throne
> He reigned o'er millions to serve me alone. . . .
>   . . . they are grown so bad
> That hell has nothing better left to do
>   Than leave them to themselves: so much more mad
> And evil by their own internal curse,
>   Heaven cannot make them better, nor I worse.

Theo raised his eyes. Göring's face was set with defiance. "What has *that* to do with me?" he demanded.

"Surely you must listen, Hermann, before it is too late for you!" Theo sat down across from him. "You say the whole world must serve you, bow to you, slave for the sake of your Aryan god and ideals."

"Yes! That is how it will be!"

"You reign over millions."

"Yes!"

"But you serve only the Prince of Darkness and Death!"

Göring paled a moment. Had he heard the whisper of some warning in his own soul? He did not answer. Thoughts—and even a shadow of fear—crossed his face. And then . . . the hardness descended like a curtain of steel. He snatched the book from Theo's hands and stared at its pages, then stood and stalked to the window, throwing it open to the chill of the night. He shouted to the men who ringed the fire.

"Come in!" he called. Then he shut the window and turned, smiling, to Theo. "I have brought you here to kill you," he said in a cheerful voice. "And I find that you have strengthened me. Deepened my convictions as to certain *values* . . ." He strode to the fireplace, and in a gesture of contempt, tore the pages from the book and tossed both book and pages into the flames. The fire roared hungrily, devouring the pages and then the book cover as Theo watched.

A dozen S.S. troops crowded into the room. They looked at Theo with the same hunger as flames for fragile paper.

"Tonight we are going to offer a sacrifice to our gods." Göring swept a hand over the wall of books. "You are right, Theo. Our ideas of value differ. I should be more careful what I consider worthwhile." He turned his gaze on the eager young Titans. "Burn these books. All of them. Not one page of this filth shall remain in the Reich."

Theo stood. He stepped back and watched grimly as the men

shouted and threw the precious volumes down in irreverent heaps on the floor and then carried them out by the armload to the funeral pyre.

Göring clasped Theo by the arm and led him to the window to watch as sparks of truth rose up to appease the god of Nazi ignorance.

"That is you, burning out there, Theo Lindheim. All your thoughts. Everything you are. See how the flames of our fury consume you. And you are dying there. Page by page, word by word, letter by letter, you blacken and shrivel and perish! I don't have to kill your miserable Jew body—I have a much better plan! You can take word of your death back to England. Tell them that you have witnessed the death of your God and yourself tonight."

"Someday you will stand before Him in judgment, and then you will know that every word you tried to destroy and every innocent life you took is eternal," Theo replied. "You are the one who burns out there—your last chance to cling to Truth."

Göring's face registered disdain. "What is Truth?" he asked. "Truth is what we make it to be." He smiled cruelly. "Tomorrow you will see the truth of our Reich, and you will believe in the power."

41

Plotting the Course of Destiny

The embers of a thousand books sparked in the cold night air and reflected on the shining finish of the black Nazi limousine as it pulled slowly from the driveway. From the window of the automobile, Theo could see Hermann Göring presiding over the conflagration of books. He gloated in his window. Somehow he still believed that by destroying the pages, he had destroyed the Truth that accused him and would, one day, condemn him.

Göring had never seriously intended to consider the exchange of lives for trade agreements. Theo had been brought here for a far more sinister purpose. He would be Göring's personal mouthpiece to carry back to Britain the message of death.

Theo looked out the back window. It was a miracle that the automobile was indeed speeding back to the British Embassy with him alive inside it. He could still see the orange glow from distant Karinhall. A sense of foreboding filled him as he wondered what answer had been planned for the world and the Jews of Germany tomorrow. God was still alive, but Reason was indeed dead. Hitler, Göring, and the rest ruled over millions, but they ruled to serve only the Prince of Darkness.

Victoria awoke in the half-light of predawn. Eli was already dressed. She watched him from the bed as he stoked the fire with a fresh supply of pine boughs.

"Eli?" she called sleepily to him.

He replaced the poker and stood slowly. His face was filled with regret that he had to leave her, on this, their first morning together. He returned to the bedroom and stroked her hair as he sat on the edge of the bed.

"Why are you up?" she asked, taking his hand and laying it against her cheek. "Come back to bed."

"I can't. It is almost light."

"It's the middle of the night. Come back to bed." She smiled a dreamy smile and pulled him down against her on the bed. She wound her silky arms around his neck and kissed him until he kissed her back with an unresisting hunger.

"It is almost light," he mumbled.

"It is just the moonlight. Come back." She fumbled with the buttons of his shirt.

"Captain Orde said . . . he said . . . I should meet him at the gate before the sun comes up."

She kissed him harder. "It is the moonlight, Eli."

It was hopeless. At her urging, he was helpless to leave her. "All right. I'll stay. Even if they see me leave. Even if the Mufti himself should spot me from the city wall. If you say it isn't dawn but the moonlight, I will stay with you. What is anything compared to this?"

Suddenly, she released him. She sat up, leaving him panting, his shirt half-buttoned. "No!" she exclaimed, wide awake. "You cannot leave the convent in the daylight! The whole area will be filled with Arabs by morning! You must go now, Eli!"

He protested. He kissed her neck and resisted leaving. "It is the moonlight."

"It is the dawn! Almost morning! You must go now by the cover of dark!"

"But, Victoria," he whispered, in pain.

She leaped out of the bed and quickly buttoned her gown as she searched for his jacket. "You must hurry." She held it for him to put on. "If the Arabs see you, then they will know where we are. We will have to find some other place, and—oh, hurry, Eli, before the sun comes up!"

"I will be back tonight," he sighed with resignation. Pulling her against him, he muttered, "May we have an eternity of nights and mornings and days together."

"I will be waiting here for you."

"Dressed like this, I hope." He stroked her cheek and smiled down into her eyes.

"Waiting for you."

––––––––

Still out of breath, the Arab messenger was shown directly into the bedchamber of Haj Amin Husseini. He wiped sweat and mist from his brow as he bowed low before the Mufti.

"What word?"

"As you predicted," the messenger said. "I watched the British captain bring Eli Sachar into the British headquarters. Sachar wears an English uniform. He has shaved."

"And the woman?"

"I did not see her. She was not with them, but I followed Captain Orde. He picked up Eli Sachar from the grounds of the Russian convent."

"You are certain of this?" The Mufti's eyes animated in thought.

"No. I mean, I did not see Sachar at the convent, but the armored car pulled up to the gate in the back. It stopped a moment. The gate swung back and then the armored car drove away. It did not stop again until it reached British headquarters, and then Sachar got out."

This news pleased the Mufti. "She is there, then," he said under his breath. "At the Russian convent in Gethsemane." He was smiling, a rare smile. This all seemed so easy. "We shall have to think of a way to draw her out." He tugged his earlobe.

"The walls are ten feet high. She will not come out from their safety," protested the messenger.

"We will send her news." The Mufti clapped his hands, summoning the muscular bodyguard into his room. "Go awaken Commander Vargen," he ordered. "We must discuss the nature of our announcement about the trial of Eli Sachar."

The messenger frowned. Trial? The Jew was obviously under British protection. "A trial?" muttered the man.

"People will believe anything they hear on the wireless, will they not? The wording must be perfect. She will come. You will see. Victoria Hassan will come to this very door and plead for the life of Eli Sachar."

"But that would be suicide."

"A small matter when love is involved."

———

As if anticipating a coming conflagration, citizens of the Old City Jewish Quarter had begun building barricades across every street into their Quarter.

Eduard Letzno had volunteered to set up an infirmary in the Jewish Old City; he arrived just after dawn with a carload of medical supplies.

Rabbi Lebowitz helped him set up in a back room at the Hurva Synagogue; then both the young doctor and the old rabbi had joined the crews filling sandbags and filling canisters with water.

There would be a Muslim funeral in the Old City today, and the rage would no doubt flood the narrow banks to sweep away any within its path.

On this day, Rabbi Lebowitz would not travel to the Western Wall to pray. He would not mail his letter to Etta and Aaron in Warsaw. He would not pass beyond the boundaries of the Quarter. There was no question of that.

Within the great synagogue, he led prayers for Eli Sachar. Everyone knew the truth of what had transpired in the foundry. But truth had little meaning when weighed against blind fury and a rampaging mob.

There was no radio here to spread the word of Muslim outrage. No radio was needed. Not one shop opened. The bells of the Christian Quarter tolled the hours over empty streets. The British soldiers were doubled in force along the wall. Everyone knew what was coming. It was only a matter of when the violence would erupt.

For a moment Herschel could not remember the name he had signed on the hotel register.

"Monsieur?" asked the man on the other end of the telephone line.

"Ah. Yes. This is . . . Heinrich Halter. Room 22. Please send up strong coffee and croissants."

As he took the room service tray and paid the porter for breakfast, it seemed strange to Herschel that he felt so calm this morning. And hungry as well.

If he had any remaining doubts, they had dissipated last night. Herschel had not eaten anything since noon yesterday; he devoured his breakfast hungrily. His depression was gone. A resolute excitement replaced it. Today was the day! The Nazi monster Adolf Hitler would hear Herschel's message. He would raise his head and know that at least one Jew was not a lamb to be led quietly to the slaughter!

Dressed in his new suit, Herschel took one last triumphant look at himself in the mirror. His one regret was that Hitler himself was too far away to be his target. His one fear was that he would not be allowed into the German Embassy, and that all of this would come to nothing.

He placed his fedora on his head and pulled the brim low. Then, carefully filling the pockets of his overcoat with his identification in case he was shot dead, Herschel left the Hotel de Suez and walked briskly toward the gunsmith's shop called *The Sharp Blade.*

He lingered outside for a few moments trying to decide which weapon in the display window would be best for his purposes.

The smiling face of the proprietor appeared at the other side of the window, welcoming the young customer into the shop.

So many guns. Herschel had not imagined that there could be so many weapons to choose from.

The owner of The Sharp Blade, a man named Carp, showed him nearly every revolver available in the store. Herschel's head was spinning. He did not know what would best kill a man. Should he choose an automatic or a small caliber pistol?

He picked up one and then another, measuring the weight of each weapon in his hand. He could not decide. An hour passed and still Carp labored over his one lone customer.

At last, the small, balding shopkeeper asked in exasperation, "You are so young. Why do you need a gun?"

How could Herschel explain? The reply Hans had given him to such a question entered his mind. "I am a foreigner. I have to carry large amounts of money for my father."

Carp nodded his head with relief. He would help the boy decide. "Something to frighten away thieves, eh, young man?"

"If they should attack I would wish to do more than frighten them."

"Ah, well, any one of these will wound and kill. You need something easy to handle."

"Yes."

"Easily concealed and quick and simple to use!"

"Exactly," Herschel nodded seriously as he imagined attempting to conceal one of the larger weapons in his pocket. They were so heavy, certainly someone at the German Embassy would spot the bulge.

Carp held up his trigger finger in pleasure. "Then I have just the thing for you. A small barrel, 6.35 caliber pistol." He held up the small gun. It looked like a toy compared to many of the others.

"But will it do the job?"

Carp laughed at the question. "Would you not run if someone pointed this at you and began to pull the trigger?"

Herschel smiled also. He nodded. Yes. This would be perfect.

———

The pistol had cost Herschel two hundred forty-five francs, including ammunition. He had plenty to pay for it. He inwardly thanked Hans for providing the money that made all this possible.

He smiled as he left the shop. Monsieur Carp had showed him how to load the weapon and how to fire it. Herschel strode quickly to the Tout Va Bien restaurant and went directly into the restroom. With steady hands, he loaded his gun with five bullets and then held it for a moment of thought. Soon these bullets would enter the body of a Nazi. Herschel nodded his head. *Yes!* All his own pain would be transferred to the enemy through these five tiny bits of lead!

He slipped the weapon into the left inside pocket of his coat before he left the restaurant and descended into the Metro. At Strasbourg-St-Denis station, he caught the subway train for the German Embassy.

———

Ambassador Nevile Henderson was visibly agitated when he returned from an early morning telephone call. He sat across the breakfast table from Theo Lindheim on the morning after Theo's trip to Karinhall.

"My God, man! What did you say to Field Marshal Göring? He's normally such a jolly fellow. I've never heard him so distraught before."

Theo did not reply. Instead, he stared out the window of the ambassador's residence into a murky-gray Berlin morning. *How appropriate,* he thought. *The world is dividing itself between light and dark, and only the British are still attempting to see shades of gray.*

"How could you antagonize the Nazis so?" Henderson continued.

Without answering the question Theo replied, "Exactly how did Göring express his displeasure?"

"He's ordered, no, *demanded* that you be expelled from Germany at once. Twenty-four hours, he said. If you're not off Reich soil in twenty-four hours, he's going to have you arrested!"

Ernst looked up from where he sat at his desk in the embassy to find an immaculately uniformed Konkel staring at him from the doorway. The Abwehr officer had an odd smile on his face. *Definitely an unpleasant smile,* Ernst thought.

Ernst decided that a touch of bravado was required to overcome the quaver he felt in the pit of his stomach.

"Getting a late start for the celebration, aren't you? The ambassador and the others have left without you."

"I have been detained briefly by important business for the Reich," replied the officer haughtily, "but now I find that all matters are in order and proceeding as they should, so I am free to leave. I shall certainly arrive in time for the solemn remembrance ceremony."

"Well, then," shrugged Ernst with as much nonchalance as he could manage, "Heil Hitler! Naturally, I will be here giving my full attention to the words of the Führer's speech as it is broadcast to the world."

That same curious mirthless smile evoked a small shudder in Ernst's frame, despite every effort he could manage to repress it.

"Before I can depart," added Konkel, "I must give you instructions about a matter of importance to Reich security."

"Certainly, Officer Konkel."

"We have had reports to the effect that there is a violent uprising being planned by gangsters of international Jews. We even have reason to believe that such violence may be directed against Reich property here in France. I have certain contacts who have pledged to bring me advance word of any such activity, and I do not intend to miss receiving the information because of my absence."

He fixed a piercing stare on Ernst. "Naturally, it falls on your shoulders, vom Rath, to accept such an important message. You must not, under any circumstances, be absent from your post. Is this obligation completely clear?"

"Quite understood. I'll do my utmost to aid military intelligence in this delicate and important matter. How will I know this individual when he arrives?"

"I have instructed both the housekeeper and the porter to be expecting someone who will indicate that they have an important message to deliver to the person in charge, whereupon the fellow will be shown immediately to you."

Ernst was puzzled by the apparent change in Konkel's high regard of him. *Perhaps it's a trap to see what I'll do,* he thought. "And what do I do with the message when I receive it?"

"Have no fear," said the Abwehr officer bluntly, "you'll receive explicit instructions that will leave no doubt about what to do." He gave a Nazi salute of textbook precision and spun on his heel to leave.

Ernst called after him, "Be thinking of me working away here all alone."

Through the same strange smile Konkel agreed, "I can promise you, we will all be thinking of you." Then he was gone.

42

The Hour of Agony

Beyond the walls of the Russian convent, all Jerusalem simmered. Emotions, like white hot coals, waited for even a slight breeze to whip them into a frenzy.

Proclamations were made from the Dome of the Rock, and Ismael Hassan became a holy martyr to the cause of the Jihad against the Jews. From Damascus and Amman and Cairo, radio broadcasts declared that the murderer Eli Sachar must be turned over to the Arab Council for justice! The return of the kidnapped Muslim bride of Ram Kadar was demanded. Speculation was made as to whether Victoria still lived or if the murderer had killed her as well after he had violated her.

In reply, the BBC of Palestine announced that Eli Sachar was in custody and being detained for questioning. So, a war of accusation and defense was being made over the airwaves of the Middle East. Vengeance was demanded with a new fervor. The dreaded winds of rumor and lies began to whip against the coals of hatred.

Behind the walls of the convent, Victoria heard none of this. Dressed in the borrowed habit of a novice nun, she walked freely about the compound. She felt no apprehension; there had been no reason for fear. After all, Eli had been taken to the British military headquarters for routine questioning. A deposition. A simple statement of fact about the attack. He would be back as soon as the sun went down again. Victoria longed for that moment.

She sat down on the low stone wall surrounding the flagstone courtyard. The sun had broken through the heavy piles of clouds in the east over the mountains of Moab. Shafts of light beamed down on the bulbed domes of the Russian church, as if that place alone was in heaven's spotlight.

Victoria watched the shifting light and shadow for a few moments and then opened her precious mother-of-pearl Bible. The wind rustled over the onion-skin pages until they flipped open to the story of Christ's agony in Gethsemane. She began to read:

My soul is exceeding sorrowful unto death: tarry ye here, and watch.

She raised her eyes to ponder the ancient olive trees whose roots, it was said, dated back before the prayer was uttered.

Abba, Father, all things are possible unto thee; take away this cup from me: nevertheless not what I will, but what thou wilt.

Within the peaceful enclave of this convent, the suffering of Christ in the garden seemed tangible and immediate. Somehow she felt that if she climbed the tiny footpath up the slope tonight, she would find Him there. Perhaps tonight, when Eli came back, they would steal away together to Gethsemane and talk to Jesus about suffering.

She turned her face toward the gentle slope of Olivet as it rose behind the church. In these whispered memories of Christ's suffering, Victoria found a measure of peace.

————

Herschel had changed trains at the Paris Metro station rue Madeleine, and arrived at the Solferino station near the German Embassy a few minutes past ten o'clock.

He stood across the street from the embassy, staring up at its grim walls and the blood-red flag waving lazily from the flagpole above the entryway in the middle of the block.

Herschel nervously fingered the pistol in his coat pocket and thought about the five little messages it contained. He raised his right foot, preparing to step down from the curb and cross the street, when an oncoming truck made him draw back. It passed without stopping, but Herschel did not immediately move again.

What am I standing here for? he pondered. *Why don't I just go in and get it over with? This all seems too easy; it can't possibly be this simple to kill someone. Maybe I should go around the block to see where the guards are located.* Then a terrible thought struck him. *What if this isn't the right entrance and I can't get in?*

At that moment a voice behind him startled Herschel. "Pardon, monsieur, may I be of assistance?" It was a short, trim man in the dark blue uniform of a Paris gendarme.

"Yes. I mean no—that is, no, I'm all right, thank you," blundered Herschel. He kept himself from running away only with the greatest difficulty, reminding himself that he was dressed as a prosperous businessman.

The policeman was apparently taken in by the disguise, for he continued in a helpful tone, "Ah, you are German, are you not?" He followed Herschel's nervous gaze across the street to the embassy. "Can I be of some help?"

Herschel grasped at the first reply that came to mind. "Is this the main entrance to the embassy? I didn't realize that it was so large and I am supposed to meet someone . . . to . . . to discuss business. I am a businessman from Hamburg, you see," he concluded lamely.

"But of course," the gendarme replied. "You have arrived correctly at the main entrance, just there beneath the flag."

Herschel still hesitated, still held back from crossing the street.

"Was there something else, monsieur?"

I've got to go in now, thought Herschel. *He's expecting me to cross the boulevard and enter the building. I've got to go in now.* "No, nothing, thank you, officer. I was just admiring the building and the way the flag moves in the breeze."

With that, Herschel finally stepped off the curb and crossed the street to ascend the steps into the German Embassy.

These Germans! thought the policeman fiercely. *What ugliness they must have in their souls!* He continued on down the block, swinging his nightstick jauntily as he went.

———

The horrifying news about Eli blared over the radio of the Russian convent and sent the Mother Superior out searching for Victoria. How would she tell her? How could the old woman break such news to one so young and hopeful as Victoria? The Mother Superior found her sitting quietly in the courtyard.

Victoria walked beside the frail old Mother Superior across the grounds of the Russian convent. Here, on the fringes of the garden where Jesus had suffered and prayed alone in agony, Victoria felt a peace she had never known. The old nun pointed toward the gnarled trunks of the ancient olive trees where He had prayed and then been betrayed.

"They say the Romans cut down the trees when they destroyed Jerusalem. Ah, but the roots of olive trees live on, you see. Buried in the soil, hidden, they live on and then send forth shoots and live again. Yes. Those are the very trees. Their roots go deep into the centuries when He was here."

She looked up at the onion domes of the Russian church. "The trees are a better reminder of His agony than all these buildings." She paused and toyed with a small silver cross that hung around her neck. "I knew the Grand Duchess who built this church. She was killed with the rest of the Czar's family when the Bolsheviks took over. Her body came to rest here, as she wished." The old woman held up the silver cross. "This was hers. It is passed on from each of our Mothers Superior to the next." She smiled at the memory. "Now I wear it."

"Such sorrow you speak of," Victoria said. "And yet I feel such peace here, as if even now the Lord prays there in the garden."

The old woman turned her eyes upon the young woman. "Then you have found the secret of Jerusalem. City of sorrow. City of hope. We are not bound by time in this place." She lifted her head as the wind brushed over them. "Time, after all, is not a thing you can touch. This moment as we speak—where is it?" She spread her hands as though letting a bird fly free. "It is gone. And so, we can look forward to eternity from here. We can see what Jerusalem will be, what is promised and sure. We can choose not to think about the dark side of faith, but know that Christ has called us to be friends. And the Russian word for friend is *drougoi*."

"*Drougoi,*" Victoria repeated.

"The word gives a sense of being reflected in somebody, like a mirror. A friend, you see, is in a way *another of yourself*. Of all creatures on earth, we are made in God's image and are given His freedom."

"It seems no one is free in Jerusalem," Victoria said quietly.

"Men are even given the freedom to hate, instead of love. To destroy, instead of create." She frowned and looked deeply into Victoria's eyes. "And for those who love, freedom can mean suffering. As Jesus suffered there." She raised a hand, as gnarled as the olive branches, to point to Gethsemane. "It was because He loved us that He suffered. Suffered for our wrong choices and the freedom we abuse. And if you suffer, my child, you will learn! You will reflect Him even more. *Drougoi.* That is how the great saints and martyrs came to be like Him."

"I am a coward," Victoria said softly. "I do not want to suffer. I want only to stay in a place like this. Very close to heaven. And I want to love my husband and live in happiness."

The old woman patted her hand. She sat in silence and looked to the ancient trees where Christ prayed. She needed help to say what she needed to say! How could she tell Victoria the news that blared over the radio every half hour?

"Sometimes the best dreams vanish," the old woman frowned. "I remember when I was sixteen, living in Moscow. The Bolsheviks murdered the husband of the Grand Duchess."

"The woman buried here?"

"Yes. He was the Czar's uncle, and they murdered him to make a point. No other reason than that. I remember kneeling beside her. Beautiful woman. All in black. And their sons . . ." In a gesture of despair, she raised her hands. "They suffered. All of them. But . . . you must remember, even suffering is not permanent. Time will pass and so will the moment of your greatest agony . . . My dear . . ." She faltered.

"What is it?" Victoria drew back, suddenly aware that all this had not been idle talk. Mother Superior had been trying to tell her something. "Tell me. *What?* Is it Eli?"

The old woman nodded. "I heard it on the radio. I did not wish you to hear it alone."

"Please?" Victoria begged. Tears filled her eyes.

"They say on Radio Cairo, he has been handed over to the Arab Council for trial. They accuse him not only of the murder of your brother but also the rape and possible murder of a woman they claim is the wife of a Muslim named Ram Kadar. Could they mean you?"

And so it was said. Peace vanished, cut down to the roots like the olive trees. Victoria's dreams and hopes were tossed as kindling onto the fire of the Mufti's ambitions. She turned her eyes from Gethsemane toward Jerusalem where Jesus had been tried, condemned, and crucified even in innocence. So, it was to be done again in Jerusalem. Once again an innocent man was to stand in the house of the Mufti on the spot where the Sanhedrin had judged Jesus. The hour of agony had come.

———

Herschel stepped through the heavy doors to the lobby of the German Embassy. He found himself facing a reception desk topped with a telephone and an ornate fountain pen in a marble holder. A tiny replica of the Nazi flag waving outside stood on one corner of the desk, while the wall behind it was occupied with an enormous and fierce-looking bronze eagle clutching a swastika. The room was completely empty of people, however.

Now what do I do? thought Herschel. "Hello?" he called, hesitantly in French, and then somewhat louder in German. "Hello. Is anyone here?"

Down the corridor to his right, a door opened and an elderly man shuffled into view. Herschel grasped the butt of the pistol in his pocket, then relaxed as he noted the man's age.

The man moved with his head looking down at the floor. He was buttoning the fly of his trousers as he scuffed toward the lobby. When he finally caught sight of Herschel, he straightened his back as best he was able and attempted to look dignified. "Your pardon, monsieur. I did not hear you come in. May I help you?"

"Is there no one here except you?" inquired Herschel in an anguish of frustration.

"No one, monsieur. They've all gone to some sort of celebration or something."

Herschel could no longer keep the desperation from his voice. "But I must see someone in charge!"

This phrase seemed to penetrate the old porter's brain. "Someone in charge . . . of course, of course, how stupid of me! Third Secretary vom Rath is here. He is in charge."

Herschel actually breathed a sigh of relief, until a moment later when he realized what the presence of "someone in charge" meant. "Can you take me to him? I have an important message to give directly to the person in charge."

"Certainly, I'll show you right in," offered the porter, turning to shuffle toward the stairs at the left of the lobby.

No! Herschel's mind screamed, *he can't go with me!*

"That's quite all right," said Herschel, attempting to sound calm. "If you'll just point me in the right direction, I'm sure I can save you the bother."

"How very kind of you," agreed the old man. "Secretary vom Rath's office is just up the stairs at the top. You can't miss it; all the other offices will be closed."

Herschel thanked the man, who turned away without further comment and seated himself at the reception desk.

Herschel took the stair steps two at a time. Inside his coat pocket he kept his hand pressed tightly on the pistol to keep it from bouncing against his leg. He wished he had a hand that he could keep pressed against his pounding heart as well.

All at once he arrived at the head of the stairs and an open doorway. Herschel marveled that his body seemed to be moving so rapidly, when his mind seemed to be dragging along so slowly. Abruptly he found himself facing another desk, this one with a thin, aristocratic-looking man seated at it, reading a newspaper and smoking a cigarette.

"Yes, can I help you?" asked Ernst vom Rath.

Herschel made no reply. His body, which a moment earlier had been all in rushing motion, seemed rooted to the floor. His tongue stuck to the roof of his mouth. He could not even will himself to speak, much less draw the gun from his pocket.

"Did you have a message to deliver?" prompted Ernst. "Something to do with Jews?"

As if Ernst were reading the script for his own destruction, the words *message* and *Jews* exploded in Herschel's brain, freeing his mouth to work, his body to move. *My father,* he thought wildly, *at last I can strike a blow for you . . . for you!*

Drawing the pistol from the pocket of his overcoat, he pointed it at vom Rath even as the secretary was rising from his chair to gesture to his visitor to seat himself.

"You filthy Nazi!" shouted Herschel, pulling the trigger, "Here, in the name of twelve thousand persecuted Jews, is your message!"

"Here . . . is . . . your . . . message!" he repeated, punctuating each word he screamed with another shot from the gun.

Vom Rath collapsed backward into his desk chair as if suddenly overcome with extreme weariness. His mouth opened and shut, but succeeded in producing only one syllable over and over. "Why? Why? Why? . . ."

The old porter reached the top of the stairs and stood panting for breath. He had come up as fast as he was able after the shots were fired, but he had heard no other sounds since. He peered cautiously around the doorframe into Ernst's office. Herschel Grynspan still stood in the middle of the room, the empty gun hanging from his hand as if it were a useless appendage.

Herschel made no movement, except to sway slightly. He seemed to be looking at vom Rath, who was slumped to the floor, his white shirt a soggy mass of crimson. The porter turned and stumbled down the stairs as he ran to telephone the police.

The old nun embraced Victoria as she left her at the door of the guest house. Victoria entered the sitting room alone. More alone than she had ever been.

She closed the door behind her and stood in the center of the room. The fire had died out. The charred end of a pine bough lay on the cold hearth. Victoria thought of Eli as he had stoked the fire just this morning. Where had that moment gone? It had vanished even as they lived it. All that was left now was the eternity Mother Superior had spoken of. Victoria must cling to that faith, that whisper of truth, or she would go mad.

Eli had been betrayed, handed over to the Mufti and the Arab Council for judgment. The cup of sorrow had not passed; she must drink it, here in Gethsemane.

Victoria's eyes lingered on the white cotton nightgown lying on the neatly made bed. "Eli," she whispered, wishing she could call their moment back.

She opened the top drawer of a writing desk to find clean white paper and a pen. Carefully, she wrote her farewell and thanks to Mother Superior. She did not want to tell the old woman what she had in mind. She folded the sheet and slipped it into an envelope which she propped on the mantel. Beside that, she left her Bible and a second note: *For Leah Feldstein.*

She looked out the window. A gentle fog was drifting over the Mount of Olives and Gethsemane as if to shield the world from the sorrow that was there.

The courtyard was deserted. Victoria looked back one more time at the little house where she had known one night of happiness. Then she slipped out the door and made her way through the clinging mist toward the gate at the rear of the compound that led upward to Gethsemane.

Still in the habit of a novice, she might have been just another member of the small Russian community going to pray. Ghost-like, she glided out of the safety of the convent grounds and disappeared among the gnarled trees of Olivet.

————

Adolf Hitler was holding court in the formal reception room of the Rathaus building in Munich. He was wearing a simple brown uniform with a single lapel ribbon and a swastika armband, to show his solidarity with the crowd of eager national socialists. He was greeting delegations from all corners of the Reich as each German state sent representatives to the memorial service of the Beer Hall Putsch.

The bespectacled head of the Gestapo, Heinrich Himmler, stood unobtrusively in a corner of the room watching the proceedings. An aide in the uniform of the S.S. entered the hall and scanned the crowd briefly before locating Himmler. The aide strode quickly to Himmler's side and bent to whisper in his ear. Himmler nodded twice, grimaced once, and dismissed the aide with a jerk of his head that was as close to anger as the calculating Chief of Internal Security ever betrayed.

Catching Hitler's eye, Himmler received a look that indicated the Führer had also seen the aide's arrival. A moment later, the two withdrew to a private office.

"Well," demanded Hitler at once. "The sacrifice—has it taken place as planned?"

"Yes, mein Führer," Himmler began. "Only—"

"Only what?" growled Hitler ominously, his petulant anger bubbling just beneath the surface.

"Vom Rath is not dead. The Jew Grynspan shot him—excuse me, mein Führer, shot *at* him—five times, but only two bullets struck him. One of the wounds is only minor, having lodged in his shoulder."

"And the other?"

"Much more serious. The last bullet penetrated both stomach and spleen, as well as grazing a lung. It is considered very unlikely that he will survive the combination of injuries."

Hitler lapsed into thought, gazing off into a silent contemplation that Himmler did not even dream of interrupting.

A few moments passed, then Hitler spoke. "Certainly he will not survive beyond two days. I sense this. I have a vision of him lying in his coffin surrounded by wreaths of flowers and grieving comrades-in-arms." The Führer paused to favor Himmler with his most direct and intense gaze. "However, it would be inconvenient if our martyr of the Fatherland lived. We will dispatch my personal physician to attend to him immediately. Is my intention clear?"

"Completely, mein Führer." Giving a precise salute, Himmler exited to see that Hitler's directive was put into immediate execution.

43

Last Chances

Etta kissed each of the children goodbye and left them with the reassurance that Papa would be home today. The good priest, Father Kopecky, had promised as much, and they must pray and believe.

The expression on Frau Rosen's face was doubtful, almost accusing. After all, had it not been some folly of Etta's that had brought this disaster down on the household and the community? There was much that needed explanation.

Father Kopecky did not get out to knock on the door. He simply waited as the engine idled and exhaust fumes rose up through the snowflakes.

Etta, feeling lighthearted and confident in the veracity and respect her witness commanded, felt better than she had since the incident in Catholic Warsaw had happened. The priest was correct: she and Eduard should have called on him when the threat of blackmail was first made!

She threw open the door and climbed into the car. She greeted him with a cheerful smile, but this morning the priest seemed subdued. The radio was on. News from Paris. The priest was shaking his head in distress as he turned up the volume to drown out her optimism.

The director of police eyed Etta with some doubt. How could he not believe her story with Father Kopecky sitting here to back her up?

He turned his gaze on the priest as if Etta were not there. "You have heard the news from Paris?" the director asked, rubbing a hand across his paunch as if he had indigestion.

"Yes," the priest nodded, not certain what that had to do with two corrupt policemen and the arrest of a rabbi in Warsaw.

"This is all tied up with those Jewish deportations, you know," explained the director.

Etta jumped in. "My husband headed a relief committee for the Jewish deportees."

The director eyed her coolly. "The arrest of your husband has nothing to do with the unfortunate incident you had in the street. I can promise you, if you had come to this office when you were first approached by the corrupt officers, I would have personally dealt with them." He seemed to say this for the benefit of the priest. "And they will be dealt with now." A quick frown of sincerity.

Father Kopecky nodded as if he knew it all along. "Your mother is such a pious woman. I knew her son would also be fair. The Rabbi Lubetkin will be released then?"

"I have nothing to say about that," said the director. Yet another finger was being pointed. "You will have to speak with the head of internal affairs. That matter is in the government's jurisdiction, I'm afraid."

"What?" The priest leaned forward.

"As I told you, Father, this has to do with the deportees. There are other leaders of the Polish Jews who are being detained for questioning."

Etta was stunned. "But why? What have they to do with government affairs?"

The director sighed wearily. He did not know everything, but he offered them the explanation he had gotten. "Apparently the Jews have begun their conspiracy of assassination. We were warned . . . the government was warned by the intelligence service of another country that the next few days might be days of violence of the Jews against other races." He nodded at the bewilderment in Etta's eyes. "Your husband has been known to have strong connections with a leader of a Zionist group here in Warsaw. You have connections yourself."

"Dr. Letzno?"

"Yes. That is his name. He is suspected to have contacts with the Communists in Russia. Of course, the Communists would like to take over Prague. The Jews will help them."

"Propaganda from Hitler!" Etta proclaimed. "Nonsense!"

"All the same, you see what happened in Paris this morning. And in Palestine. The Jews have begun to assassinate public officials." The director was adamant in his belief that the shooting of Ernst vom Rath was somehow connected to events in Poland.

"My husband is a humanitarian, not a politician. He certainly has nothing to do with any violence against public officials."

"He has had some contact with the parents of the young killer. Grynspan. Herschel Grynspan is the boy's name."

Father Kopecky leaned forward. "But the shooting only happened this morning! If Rabbi Lubetkin was somehow related to such a thing, why was he detained yesterday? *Before* the shooting?"

The director shrugged. "Not my department. How do I know how they know these things? We have just been advised to keep an eye on the leaders of the Warsaw Jewish community because there is a widespread Jewish plot underway." He shrugged. "Your husband has been implicated."

"Aaron would never harm anyone," Etta protested. "You cannot hold him."

"I do not hold him!" exclaimed the director. "You are talking to the wrong fellow!"

The junior officer at the British headquarters brought in yet another communication from the Arab Higher Committee and the Arab Council.

Orde and Eli sat with the secretary taking his dictation. They sipped steaming cups of coffee as the story of the fight in the souk unfolded.

"I was trying to pull myself up when he lunged," Eli said wearily as if reliving the moment was too much for him. "The metal rod was above me. I grabbed it and it whipped forward. He fell on it. It was an accident."

Orde leafed through the stack of typed Arab demands. "They have a different story, and—" Orde frowned and pulled out a contract, written in Arabic and signed by Victoria's father and Ram Kadar, with Ibrahim as a witness. "Marriage contract," Orde said. "Reads more like a business transaction for cattle." He passed it to Eli, who read it and shook his head. "Well, at least I've got her free of all that."

Orde was still frowning. He scratched his cheek in thought as he pulled out a second document sealed with the official seal of the Arab Higher Committee. "A marriage certificate," Orde said. "They are claiming that her marriage to this fellow already took place."

Eli did not need to wonder why the document had been forged. It was part of the propaganda that was only beginning. Already he had heard the claims that he had kidnapped the sister of Ismael Hassan and that the kidnapping had then led to murder. "If such tricks were not so deadly, they would be laughable."

Orde sighed and sipped his coffee. "Deadly. Yes. I'm afraid we will have to move you out of Palestine as soon as possible. I spoke with the high commissioner. No one in the government is fooled by this."

Once again the junior officer poked his head into the room. He had an astonished look on his face. "Captain Orde! Wait until you hear this one!" He motioned for Orde and Eli to follow to the radio room.

The frantic voice of Radio Cairo crackled over the air waves:

"The body of Victoria Hassan has been found in an alley in the Old City. The murderer Jew, Eli Sachar, is being handed over to the Arab

*Higher Committee for trial ... Ram Kadar, husband of the murdered
woman, vows that he will personally take revenge for the killing and
rape of his wife."*

Orde looked first at the junior officer and then at the radio operator.
"Propaganda."

"That's not all," the radioman turned up the volume.

*"In Paris, this morning, a young Polish Jew has shot a high ranking
member of the staff of the German Embassy. Hitler has proclaimed that
the incidents in Palestine and now in Paris are part of a world-wide
conspiracy of the Jewish Bolsheviks, and that responsible governments
must unite to stop such ..."*

At this point the reception whined and howled, obscuring the words
that followed.

Victoria made her way through the stones of the cemetery on the
slope of the Mount of Olives. On the crest of the hill she looked back
toward the masses of people who already crowded into the Old City
through St. Stephen's Gate. There were fewer mourners moving through
the south entrance of the Dung Gate. There, the sheep destined for
slaughter milled in the stock pens. A few donkeys were corralled as
their masters were searched by English soldiers before they passed
into the Old City on their way to the funeral.

Englishmen would not dare to search a woman in a nun's habit,
she reasoned. She set off cross-country toward the Dung Gate on the
south side of the Dome of the Rock.

It was an hour before she reached the entrance to the Old City. The
questioning stares of the young soldiers greeted her.

"Today is not a good day to enter the Old City, Sister," one said,
tipping his cap in respect.

"I have need to go to the Church of the Holy Sepulcher today," she
said piously. "I have a vow to fulfill."

The soldiers exchanged worried glances. A few more Bedouin shepherds fell in line behind her, waiting to be searched. "No one is being
searched at St. Stephen's Gate," an old Bedouin whispered behind
Victoria. "There are too many people there. Too many. But they have
nothing to hide from the English, anyway. It is a small inconvenience."

"Sister, today is not a good day to enter the City. There is a funeral
for a Muslim brother and sister today. Didn't you see the crowds? From
all over Palestine. The Mufti has made a regular event out of it."

"It surely will not be started before I can walk to the Church of the
Holy Sepulcher. That is, unless you detain me here longer."

One of the soldiers rubbed his cheek. He would warn her one last
time. "Well, you ought to stay there until this thing blows over. Maybe
all night, if you have to."

"If there is trouble I will not leave."

He waved her through. "There will be trouble, all right! Be careful, Sister."

Victoria inclined her head slowly and crossed herself as she had seen the sisters do. She hurried past the shuttered butcher shops and picked her way around the animal droppings for which the Dung Gate was named. Except for mourners heading toward the entrance to the Haram and the Dome of the Rock, the streets were empty. There was no sign of Christian or Jew here today.

She stepped into a public restroom and removed the wimple from her head. Then she loosened the scarf that tied back her hair and draped it loosely over her head like a veil. She could only hope that the Muslim crowds would not notice that the clothes she wore were those of a Russian convent novice.

Victoria stepped outside into a crowd of mourners who spoke angrily among themselves about the words of the Koran in regard to vengeance in such a case. "This Jew should die a slow death. He should be made to suffer as the families of those he murdered will suffer!"

Victoria walked with her eyes downward until they passed through the Armenian Quarter to the Wailing Wall. There was not one Jewish rabbi there today.

"They are afraid," said one old man in a fez. "And rightly so! We will cause them to suffer as well. The Koran demands it. A tooth for a tooth!" Victoria noticed he had no teeth, but he pulled out a dagger from his belt all the same. "How can this Sachar fellow pay all the penalty himself? No matter how he suffers, it will never be enough. I say all the Jews should suffer!"

"Brother and sister both killed by the same hand! She was raped and beaten, they say! We will make certain the Jew violates no one else."

For a moment, Victoria considered revealing herself to them, but then she thought better of it. When the crowds fell silent to listen to the Mufti, then she would speak. She would pull off the scarf and run to her father. She would reveal to all of them the truth that Eli had not done what he was accused of.

"They will bring in the coffins side by side," a tattooed old woman whispered to Victoria.

"Brother and sister," added another old woman. "Jerusalem has never seen such a thing as this!"

Victoria looked away. She could not answer. Would even her revelation stop what was to come? These people had no concern for her brother Ismael. They did not know the family or Victoria. She walked among the people who had come to mourn and bury her, and they did not know who she was!

It was unsettling. The side street into the Street of the Chain was packed. The crowd from her street backed up as entry to the Haram slowed to a crawl.

Victoria looked up at the spikes of the minarets. The Mufti's men stood there, rifles slung over their shoulders, looking down on the crowds. Their gazes seemed without emotion, like a cat eyeing a wounded bird and waiting . . .

———

"But she is gone, I tell you!" The voice of Mother Superior shouted to Eli over the telephone, causing the other nuns in the office to stare at her. Had they ever seen Mother Superior so upset?

The hands of the old woman trembled as she held the note Victoria had written. *Thank you for your kindness. I will remember. . . . Must return to my home and family to prove I am well . . . for the sake of my husband.*

She read the words to Eli who had also heard the Arab broadcast and had telephoned so that Victoria would not worry. But the call had come too late.

"I do not know when. I stopped back by the guest cottage only a few minutes ago and found this note of farewell and a Bible left beside it for her friend Leah. But she was gone, and no one at all saw her leave."

———

From the upper-story windows of the Tankiziyya, the Mufti could look straight down on the crowds who moved along the Wailing Wall as they jostled toward the entrance to the Haram. The Haram itself, courtyard of the Dome of the Rock, was filling up fast. Estimates were made of twenty thousand and then thirty and now forty thousand with thousands more filling up the roads on their way to the shrine.

All this, and it was still two hours before the appointed time of the funeral. It was more than he had hoped. Allah had given bountifully to the ranks of the army of the Jihad! Today the name of Allah would be *He Who Destroys!* In every city and village in Palestine the muhqtars were ready to release their wrath at the same moment the spring uncoiled here in Jerusalem!

Haj Amin turned to Vargen and Hockman in his pleasure. "It will take only a word," he said. "They have come here for this! This show of death is what they have been waiting for to enliven their spirits! Today will be a day they speak of for generations to come."

"The second coffin adds a little something, I think," Hockman said as he looked out a side window into the courtyard where the two coffins lay side by side. "The rape and murder of a woman. It is the stuff great explosions are made of. You have done well."

"She was a prostitute," Haj Amin explained. "My men disfigured her face enough so that even those who know Victoria Hassan would not be sure who it was."

"The crowds do not care, anyway. They have come for a show. A dead woman is good enough, lying at the side of the brother who tried to save her. Now, that is splendid!"

Word had already come of the bungled attempt on the life of a German official in Paris by a young Jew. The timing was impeccable, even if the Jew's aim had not been. Vargen had no doubt that the Führer would make good use of the incident regardless. The planned violence in the Reich would erupt at the same time as the demonstrations here in Palestine. Such events would leave the world, especially Great Britain, reeling.

"Tomorrow the Woodhead Committee makes their announcement about the immigration question," Haj Amin muttered with pleasure. "We will make certain they are aided in their decision."

———

Etta stood trembling in the anteroom of the office of the Minister of Internal Affairs. Beside her stood the little priest, Father Kopecky. "Courage, my child, courage," he whispered.

The door into the minister's private office opened and the secretary emerged. "You may go in now, Father." The tall, thin-faced woman, with her hair pulled back severely from her face, addressed herself to the priest as if Etta were not even present.

They walked into the office together, and stood before the desk of Poland's Minister of Internal Affairs. The man gave them no word of acknowledgment, nor any offer for them to be seated. He continued to scan the contents of a file folder that lay spread out in front of him.

At last Father Kopecky broke the silence by asking, "In the light of the evidence you undoubtedly have read, Minister, surely it's clear that Mrs. Lubetkin's husband should be freed."

The minister finally looked up from the papers to scrutinize Etta and Father Kopecky from under heavy eyelids and bushy eyebrows. "I'm surprised at you, Father, getting yourself mixed up in such an affair. Do your superiors know of your involvement?" Before Father Kopecky could reply the minister continued, "Aren't you aware of what is happening in Germany? At this moment, the Germans are taking steps to eliminate the problem of the Jewish Bolshevik conspirators in their midst. We here in Poland will do even better than that. We will not let the problem grow to the size that it has in Germany. We will take steps right now to insure that we do not have any difficulty controlling our Jews."

Father Kopecky was almost speechless with disbelief, and into the silence that followed the minister's remarks, Etta blurted out, "But I can pay—I can pay for my husband's release!"

Father Kopecky looked at her with horror, and Etta stopped abruptly, but the minister only shook his head slowly and gave a single snort of disgust. "You Jews!" he said. "You think your money will save you— well, no longer. We are rounding up all Bolshevik agitators, and we'll round up many more before we're through. You'd do well to keep that in mind, Father."

"Is that all?" gasped Etta. "Is there no appeal?"

"In due time, your husband's case will be considered," concluded the minister. "And now, I have more important business . . ." With a negligent wave of his hand he indicated that they should leave.

44

At the Hour of Our Death

The Bible on the mantel convinced Eli of Victoria's real reason for leaving. She was going to the Muslim Quarter, yes, but she was not going home. As he replaced the receiver, he stared out the window to the panorama of Jerusalem beyond. The Muslim crowds, they said, were beginning to gather in the courtyard of the Dome of the Rock for the funeral of Ismael Hassan. That was where Victoria was going. She would show herself there to convince the people of the lies of Haj Amin Husseini.

In such a place, at such a time, there would be no one to help her. Even the British soldiers along the wall took their posts behind the stones and peered out at the multitudes with a sensible fear.

It was easy for Eli to walk past the sentries of British military headquarters and out of the building. Dressed in the uniform of Captain Orde, the men saluted as he passed on his way to the motor pool.

"Captain Orde asked me to bring the car around," he explained nonchalantly to the same sergeant who had parked the vehicle for them this morning. A salute and an obedient nod was followed by a set of keys placed in the palm of Eli's hand.

Within two minutes from the time he left the building, he was driving alone toward the Old City walls.

From the Hill of Evil Counsel, Eli could plainly see the onion domes of the Russian church and the Dome of the Rock across the steep Valley of Kidron.

Fog moved like currents of water around the low spots on the road ahead. It snagged on headstones protruding from the hillside beneath the Muslim holy place.

From every side road, Eli could see shadowy forms of the Muslims who were coming to mourn and to express their outrage today. They poured onto the main road in front of the car. Keffiyeh-swathed heads turned to stare with resentment at the British armored car that forced them to move to one side as it crept past. He drove by the convent and cast one searching gaze over the pine-studded grounds. *She was gone! Gone!*

Eli found himself searching every woman's face. He slowed the speed of the vehicle until it moved no faster than a walk as he looked for Victoria among the crowds. When he was certain she was not among one group, he sped ahead to the next. It occurred to him he did not even know what she was wearing. He had left her this morning in the white cotton shift. Would she have put on the uniform of a British soldier again? He scanned the mob for a helmet, but then realized that no sane Englishman would dare to come among this group.

Thousands jostled before St. Stephen's Gate. Like grains of sand through a funnel, they poured into the Old City and onto the Via Dolorosa as they inched toward the Dome of the Rock.

Still a hundred yards from the Old City gate, the crowd no longer moved to one side for the armored car. Like the fog, they surged around him, bringing him to a dead stop. He inched forward, reluctant to park and climb out to make his way on foot.

"Victoria," he muttered as he tried to search the sea of intense faces which swept by. "I am here, Victoria. Come on. Please! Please, pass by me!"

But she did not pass. He waited and watched for ten minutes as the mourners walked around him and then closed off the road. *Would she be wearing a veil?* He narrowed his search to a study of eyes. She was not there. She could have walked from the convent to the gate in half the time that had passed since he left the British headquarters.

He blasted the horn. Faces turned angrily to stare at the steel-plated vehicle. He inched ahead and blasted the horn again until the growing resentment on Arab faces caused him to simply pull to the side of the road and wait for a few more precious minutes.

He whispered the words of the Shema as he switched off the motor and set the brake. Pocketing the keys, he opened the door and stepped out into the human current. He looked back at the hundreds of faces moving toward him up the slope. He could not see them all, but he knew she had already entered the Old City. She was inside the gate of St. Stephen. Perhaps even in the courtyard of the Dome of the Rock.

His mouth was dry with fear. He stepped into the mass of surly Arabs who surrounded him with hostile glares and unspoken curses. He tried to push ahead, tried to break through the slow deliberate pace. The ring of resentment tightened around him, holding him back.

Moving with tiny, shuffling steps, he reached the high arched portal of St. Stephen's Gate where the closeness shoved him against those he walked with. The Arab stares became more obvious. The questions were asked among themselves. *"What does this son of an English pig have to do with us?"*

"Must they come here to threaten us even as we weep?"

"What is he doing?"

"Why is he here?"

"A spy!"

"Then a poor spy. Why is he dressed like that?"

Eli pretended not to understand them. He lowered his head and pulled the brim of his cap down over his eyes. Only at this moment did he realize that he was now among the mourners of the man he had killed. He had concentrated so intensely on finding Victoria that only at this instant did he remember why the thousands packed the narrow entrance.

Just as many thousands surged forward from the opposite direction of Via Dolorosa. Eli tried to think where Victoria would go. To her home? Had she meant that? Was she returning to her home?

That could not be. She was an outcast. Ibrahim would not kill her, but the others would not hesitate. The thought made him shudder. A sense of hopelessness descended on him. *To find her in this. To hope to take her safely away!* But what other hope was there for them? Better to die here searching for her than to live with the knowledge that she had simply vanished into the maw of the schemes of Haj Amin Husseini.

He turned to enter the Haram with the rest. A gruff Arab voice challenged him. "Hey, English! What do you think you are doing?"

"I have come—to pay respects."

"No son of the prophet needs your respect. You intrude! You are not welcome here!" growled another emotion-laden voice.

Eli replied carefully. "I knew him well. Did you know him?"

"No," he answered. "But the family is known."

Eli's voice now cracked with emotion. He did not stop or look as if he might turn back. "I knew him well. Like a brother. I have more right to weep than any."

Yet another voice demanded, "And did you know the sister also? Victoria? The wife of Ram Kadar?"

Eli frowned. Fear stirred in the pit of his belly. "Not so well."

"They are bringing her coffin now," the voice called back from the portals of the Dome of the Rock. "I can see it. Ya Allah! There they bring two coffins into the gates!"

Eli gasped for air at those words, even though he knew it could not be. She had left the convent only two hours ago. She could not be dead. Another trick! It was another trick!

All around him wails rose up—cries to Allah, cries for mercy, cries for vengeance! Through the gates, Eli caught a glimpse of two coffins bobbing over a sea of heads already packed into the courtyard. The screams and wails increased in volume as the wooden coffins glided inward toward the sanctuary. *"Brother and sister! Brother and sister!"* cried a toothless old man who clutched Eli's sleeve and sobbed hysterically. *"Ya Allah! Two of them murdered! Two in the same family!"*

Eli felt sick. Waves of nausea swept over him. He tore himself free of the old man's grip and leaned against the stones of the portals as one continuous wail rose up. *It could not be! She had left the convent only two hours before! Oh, God! Could it be? Could it?*

The caskets were closed. It was another deception, an added fuel to the fire of passion. Two from the same family, they said, and yet the second casket could not contain Victoria! Or could it?

Eli raised his eyes. Three rough-looking Arabs strode confidently along the ramparts of the wall that encompassed the courtyard. They openly carried their rifles. There could not be a Muslim burial without the firing of rifles. Eli looked across the vast field of shrieking mourners. There were men with rifles at every station along the stone enclosure. These men displayed no emotion in the midst of the hysteria. They had not come to watch the mourners. They had come for other reasons—for what was to follow the funeral.

"Two coffins!" shrieked a woman. "Ya Allah! Oh, God!"

Eli pulled himself straight. He began to move forward with the rest. Victoria was not dead! His heart gave him courage. He would get close enough to see. Somehow. She was alive! Somewhere in this mob of teeming thousands, she too was making her way forward to declare the deception, to stop what was to come upon Jerusalem! How many would die today? How many would fall if it happened as the Mufti planned it?

Eli had never before set foot on the grounds where Solomon's Temple once stood. Where Jesus preached and prayed. Where the Romans had made the glory of the Holy of Holies desolate.

It was still a place of desolation. Darkness had come to hover where the Shekinah glory had descended. Death was near in the chanting hysteria of the waiting masses who crammed together until moving became almost impossible and breathing itself, difficult.

"ALLAH! YA ALLAH!" shrieked a hysterical woman who tore her clothes and beat her face at the sight of the coffins.

Madness!

Eli pushed forward as yet another woman convulsed and frothed at the mouth as she stood wedged upright among the others.

The entire courtyard was a powder keg, and Eli was a lighted match slipping cautiously by. The wind of insanity was already rising into a confused roar.

He tried not to think of his own death. If Victoria were here, if she were alive, he must find her and take her to safety. And if she was indeed within the plain wooden coffin that sailed above him like a ship, then he would die with her! He would die gladly and count his own death among the millions of Jews who were slain upon these same stones.

He shouted against the gale, yet no one heard his voice. No one but God. Eli wept as well, sensing not only the tragedy of what was happening to him and Victoria, but a greater, heart-rending tragedy that had begun with the corruption of this once-holy place.

He felt desperately alone. Mourning for Victoria. Mourning for Jerusalem. Mourning for his people who longed for the Return. Mourning for the Messiah who had wept for what He knew would come upon the Holy City.

"For the Temple that lies desolate," he cried, *"We sit in solitude and mourn!"*

He wedged his body between two men and inched forward toward the platforms where the coffins were being lowered.

"For the walls that are overthrown,
"I walk in solitude and mourn!
"For our glory that is departed,
"For our wise men who have perished!
"For the priests who have stumbled!
"For our kings who have despised Him,
"We sit in solitude and mourn!"

Eli shouted at the top of his lungs this ancient lament for the fallen Temple. Yet no one could comprehend what he said. They seemed not to notice his uniform. Certainly, no one guessed that a Jew walked among them. Or that it was the very Jew accused and already judged by the Arab Council. *"Look down on me, O Lord!"* he cried. *"May I see her face before I see your face! O Lord, save her! Help me find her!"*

As Eli slowly pushed forward from the north toward the coffins and the raised platform, Victoria moved with difficulty toward the same goal from the south. It did not matter, she realized, what she was wearing. Each individual within the shrieking and wailing crowd had some private vision of death that preoccupied them. Men and women seemed to see only the coffins—and only themselves.

They scratched their own faces with fingernails or bits of stone until frenzied eyes peered out from bloody cheeks.

Victoria did not mourn, not even for her brother whom she knew lay in one of the wooden boxes. Her only thoughts were of Eli—of stopping the madness around her.

She found strength in this. Her father would surely sit on the dais beside the coffins. Did he know she still lived, Victoria wondered? Or did he believe the lie?

He would know soon enough. He would stand beside her and proclaim an end to this deception!

This thought, *this goal,* strengthened her to push forward. Foot by foot she gained ground. She turned sideways to squeeze between bodies. She stopped and stood on tiptoe to peer over the bobbing heads to where four men removed the lids of the caskets and propped them up for all to see the dead bodies within.

A new howl arose, loud enough to be heard throughout the British Mandate. Victoria paused in her struggle to look at the ashen-faced body of her half brother. Only now did the reality of his death settle on her. The finality of his end. Such a wasted, evil life. There was no more hope for him and that indeed caused her to grieve.

The face of the dead woman beside him was covered by a thin veil—thin enough so that those around the platform could see the mutilated features. Victoria cried out at the sight. This was meant to be her! The body was the same size and build. But even her dear father would not know by the face that it was not Victoria. *Poor woman! Who was she? What animals they are to do this to her!*

Some among the masses fainted, only to be held upright by the sheer press of those surrounding them. The howling was deafening, the hellish misery of those who were dead inside even while they still breathed.

Victoria pressed on with renewed determination as she looked up to see her father emerge from the doors of the Dome of the Rock and slowly climb the steps of the platform to take his place behind what he thought were two of his children. *Such grief on his face! Had there ever been such sadness in the eyes of any man?*

Ibrahim followed. Their stepmother came after that, veiled in mourning robes. She leaned heavily against a woman who walked beside her.

Impossible as it seemed, the noise of the tumult increased in volume. Death had given the Muslims of Palestine one voice.

Surrounded by his bodyguards, that voice emerged in the form of the Grand Mufti, Haj Amin Husseini. Victoria pushed harder to move forward.

The Mufti did not try to discourage the madness raging before him. His blue eyes measured the success of weeks of planning. If every man of Britain's twenty thousand troops in Palestine were to come against this crowd, the British would fall. A hundred thousand packed the courtyard of the Haram. Thousands more pressed upon the gates to be let in. Soon, the voice of Haj Amin would release them.

The woman! Eli had to see! Had to get closer! Someone flailed out wildly and struck him in the face as he groaned and pressed closer to the platform.

Haj Amin stood still and silent above his faithful followers and those who had been suddenly recruited into his fold by the call of death.

None of that mattered to Eli any longer. If they had sacrificed his beloved to their strange and terrible God, then Eli wished to die as well.

It took all his strength to crowd forward. A few inches at a time, he gained his way to a mere twenty yards from the platform where Ibrahim sat between his parents. Eli had not stopped looking for Victoria—a living Victoria among the multitude.

He stared at the figure of the dead woman. There was little that was visible, except for her hands. They were not the hands of Victoria! No. The sacrifice was not her!

He turned around once again, hoping to glimpse her face. *She is here;* he knew it now! *But where?*

He turned toward the platform again to stare at the face of Ibrahim. *Once friend.* Had he allowed this terrible deception, knowing that Eli would come, that Victoria would also fall into the trap?

Haj Amin raised his hands, and a massive shudder convulsed the crowd. Silence slid like molten lava from the front of the platform to the far reaches of the courtyard.

Ibrahim stood. He stooped and plucked a flower from a basket and walked forward to place it in the hands of the dead woman. Then he turned as the ripples of howling began to subside in anticipation of the Mufti's words.

In that instant, Ibrahim's eyes caught Eli's. He looked away and then back again. His eyes locked with Eli's, and he *knew!*

With a shout of recognition he pointed and shouted Eli's name. He ran to a row of bodyguards who all sparked to life. Eli managed to turn. He tried to work his way back. *Back where?* Without knowing it, the crowd of people around him pressed tighter, pinning him where he stood.

More urgent words to the Mufti, who then stepped forward to the microphone. The silence was not complete yet. He could wait. The rabbit was caught in the snare. Kicking and struggling to get loose, it was, nonetheless, trapped.

Eli cried out. His voice carried, and faces turned to stare at him. Men looked up at the gesturing Ibrahim and then down at the man in the English uniform who struggled and shouted as he attempted to get away.

"Allah is good to us, my children," intoned the Mufti. "Allah Ahkbar!

God is great, and here is proof for us today! Allah the Avenger has sent to us the murderer of these two faithful . . ."

From her position to the right of the platform, Victoria's eyes followed the Mufti's gesture.

Eli! Arms pinned. Hat off. Hair falling over his pale forehead as he struggled.

"No!" she shouted at the top of her voice. *"I am Victoria Hassan! I am not dead! It is a mistake! That is not Victoria Hassan in the coffin!"*

Some turned to stare at her. Was she insane? Ah, well, there were many here today who were insane.

"You have come to mock us!" the Mufti roared, and there was total silence except for the echo of his voice against the stones. *"Allah is just! Eli Sachar, you are delivered into our hands for justice as the prophet commands!"*

Victoria continued to shout and push against those around her. *"Eli!"* she screamed in horror.

He heard her voice. Called out her name. *"Victoria! Victoria!"* His eyes searched wildly for her. Hands reached out for him. Yes! This was the one the Mufti was addressing! This is he! The one in the English uniform!

"Eli!" she screamed. The loudspeaker of Haj Amin drowned her out. Ibrahim saw her. His eyes darted nervously. He rose again and whispered to the Mufti. There was no time for the cat to play with the wounded bird. They must strike now or perhaps be discovered in their deception.

"There is the man who killed them!" Ibrahim screamed and pointed to Eli. His face was contorted by hatred, as if he believed the lie.

The crowd went wild! Those surrounding Eli tore at him from every side! They lifted him high above their heads, as they had the coffins, for all to see. *"ALLAH AKHBAR!"*

"Victoria!" Eli cried as he saw her only yards away. His fingers spread wide as he reached for her! She strained to touch him! The gulf was too great. His eyes embraced her one last time.

"No!" She pounded on those between them as she struggled to reach him. *"You cannot do this! Cannot! He is innocent! Innocent! I am Victoria Hassan! He has murdered no one!"*

Those around her did not notice the fury of her fists. They did not hear her above the tumult. Even if they did hear, they did not care.

Daggers were unsheathed by the thousand and raised skyward to receive the Jew as he was passed above them. Leaving a wake of blood, Eli was swept away from her over the heads of the mob, carried on a current of rage.

45

What Is a Lifetime?

Murphy stepped off the red London omnibus at three minutes after six in the morning. The Fleet Street office of TENS had been running wide open since yesterday when the news of the Paris assassination attempt and word of the Palestine riots had both clacked over the wires within minutes of each other. Murphy had gone home for three hours of restless sleep while Anna and Elisa had sat up and listened to the news on the BBC.

Elisa still did not know that her father was in Berlin, but mention of Herschel Grynspan as the would-be assassin was enough to keep her wide awake. Murphy had left her with the promise that he would call the moment he heard anything new.

He had not counted on the fact that every few minutes word of fresh violence would be clacking over the wires into *Trump European News Service.*

Two dozen of the best American journalists in Europe sat at their desks, with their eyes riveted to typewriters. Murphy took a deep breath before he pushed through the swinging door and into the thick of it.

No one seemed to notice that the boss had arrived. The unrelenting tap of fingers on keys and the blue haze of tobacco smoke filled the newsroom, reminding Murphy that this office was a reflection of the battles taking place right now in Palestine and in the hospital room of Ernst vom Rath in Paris. Both events, though seemingly distant and unrelated to each other, could affect the fate of millions of Jews trapped within the Nazi regime. Murphy knew *that* well enough. The truth of it made him shudder and pray that Ernst vom Rath was still hanging on to life.

Harvey Terrill, night desk editor, had never left the office. The weary, frantic little man raised his bald head and scowled in Murphy's direction. Three cold cups of coffee stood amid the devastation of his desk.

"Hi-ya, Boss," he said glumly.

"Bad night, huh?" Murphy swung past him and motioned with his briefcase for Harvey to follow into the glass-enclosed office.

Harvey gathered up a stack of transmissions and hurried after Murphy. He kicked the door shut with his foot and sat down, looking like a man suffering from shell shock. Then he laid the sheaf of transmissions on Murphy's desk.

"The German diplomat has been promoted by Hitler."

"Vom Rath?"

"Right. Now he's the head of the German Embassy in Paris. Nice job if the guy lives."

"And?"

"He might make it. Hitler has sent his personal doctor to take care of him. We can hope."

"And Palestine?"

"Twenty new incidents since last night." Harvey rubbed his bald head forlornly. "Mostly in and around Jerusalem for the worst of them. One major attack in northern Palestine near Mount Carmel. Twenty-four hundred troops of the Royal Scots Grays Horse Regiment arrived in Haifa yesterday from India and spent their first night in the Holy Land fighting Muslims."

Harvey passed the next few minutes ticking off the incidents one by one, counting on his fingers twice through.

"Any word from Captain Orde?" Murphy asked quietly, with a sense of foreboding.

Harvey passed the short dispatch across the desk to Murphy. "Just this."

Murphy scanned the page:

ARAB REBELLION BELIEVED BY BRITISH INTELLIGENCE SOURCES TO BE FINANCED AND LED BY FOREIGN AGENTS STOP MANY INNOCENT KILLED ON ALL SIDES STOP NO PEACE IN OUR TIME IN PALESTINE STOP

Murphy pondered the brief message, putting it all together. "Foreign agents. No peace in our time." He shook his head and looked up at Harvey. "We don't have to think very hard to figure out who the foreign agents are, do we?"

"We can't print it, Boss, until we have proof. They gotta catch a Nazi in Jerusalem before we print it. Otherwise they'll say we're just a bunch of paranoid journalists."

"Like Churchill?"

"Exactly."

Murphy scowled at the message. He read it again, then picked up a wire describing the struggle of Ernst vom Rath to live. Another told of the anguish of the Jewish adolescent who pulled the trigger. Still another related violence against Jews in Poland. Beyond the glass window of his office, the machine-gun rattle of the typewriters waged a war of words. "Seems as if only the innocent get hurt, doesn't it, Harvey?" He narrowed his eyes and looked out on the rain-slick London streets as he remembered German bombers over Madrid. "We're not paranoid. England is already at war with the German Reich in Palestine, but Chamberlain is too dumb to know it." He handed Orde's dispatch back to Harvey.

"What do I do with it?"

"Give it a banner headline, Harvey. NAZI AGENTS INSTIGATE RIOTS IN PALESTINE. Got it?"

"But, Boss—"

"And get me a line through to the British colonial secretary. I want a box right below that with a story about the Woodhead Commission's decision on Jewish immigration."

"But they haven't decided yet."

"They decided before they ever set foot in Palestine!" Murphy snapped. "Now *do* it."

———

Hitler was conferring with Dr. Joseph Goebbels, Reichsminister of Propaganda, just before his limousine was scheduled to take him to address the horde of Brownshirts gathered to hear his memorial address.

Heinrich Himmler entered the room, an unmistakable look of satisfaction beaming from his round face.

"Mein Führer, I have the latest dispatches, which I thought you should hear before attending the ceremony."

"I have been expecting you," remarked Hitler. "Stay, Goebbels, you should hear this also."

"The BBC has just announced the findings of the Woodhead Commission's review of British plans for a Jewish state in Palestine."

"And?" encouraged Hitler.

"They have concluded that to go forward with such a plan would unnecessarily antagonize the Arab population. It is the commission's strong recommendation that the partition plan be scrapped."

The Führer's eyes began to glow with anticipation.

"Furthermore, reports have arrived of new violent outbreaks in Palestine that are taking place even as we speak. It seems there is a massive Arab uprising in response to some Jewish atrocity."

The light in Hitler's eyes intensified.

"Finally, it is my painful duty to inform you that Secretary vom Rath has tragically succumbed to the wounds inflicted by the Jew assassin Grynspan."

Hitler could not repress the urge to give a little jig-step of delight. He beamed at the two men with him in the room.

Rumors of vom Rath's death were already circulating in the packed hall. A growing rumble was heard as Brownshirts exclaimed in louder and louder tones: "What are we waiting for? The Jew dogs must be taught a lesson they'll never forget!"

The official announcement that vom Rath had, in fact, died came just before the Führer strode onto the platform to speak. A tense silence fell over the crowd in anticipation of the Führer's words.

Hitler approached the microphone. The Brownshirts leaned forward almost as one in anticipation. They waited, but still Hitler did not speak.

Some in the crowd could not stand the tension any longer and began to murmur again: "Kill the Jews . . . break their heads . . . all Jews are guilty . . . kill the Jews."

The Führer, obviously in the grip of the strongest emotion at the death of the fine young Aryan, vom Rath, indicated with a shake of his head that his grief was too powerful; he could not speak.

The Brownshirts could no longer restrain themselves. They surged from their places and out into the streets of Munich, shouting: "Smash the Jews! For one dead German ten thousand Jews should die . . . no, a hundred thousand . . . no, millions . . . smash them all!"

The Führer stood on the platform, his head bowed in silent, personal suffering. In a soft aside, spoken just for the ears of Reichsminister Goebbels, Hitler remarked, "The S.A. must have their fling."

A sharp and urgent rapping on Theo's door pulled him from sleep.

"Mr. Lindheim!" It was the voice of Ambassador Henderson. "Wake up, my good man! For heaven's sake!"

As Theo moved to open the door, he could hear the rumble of a fleet of trucks outside the embassy gates. *Could it be*, Theo wondered, *that Göring has gone back on his promise to allow me twenty-four hours to leave Berlin?*

The face of Henderson was gaunt and pale in the corridor. He pushed past Theo, closing the door behind him as he took Theo's arm and guided him to the window overlooking Wilhelmstrasse.

"What is it?" Theo asked, startled by Henderson's intensity.

Henderson pulled back the curtain and gestured for Theo to look.

Most of the windows at the Adlon Hotel across the street were dark. The street itself was deserted except for a line of trucks which passed in slow procession around the corner from the Interior Ministry to Wilhelmstrasse.

"That German chap has died in Paris," Henderson explained, his voice hoarse from agitation. "Those trucks are coming from Gestapo headquarters."

Theo could see the open-backed trucks were loaded with men. "Then there will be reprisals,"—he quietly finished Henderson's thought—"Demonstrations." He frowned. Would one of those trucks stop outside the British Embassy? Had Göring arranged for his arrest tonight?

"Quite." Henderson nodded curtly. "It has already begun in Munich. There is not much time, I'm afraid. Please gather your things as quickly as you can. I have arranged for you to leave early. There is a British transport plane fueled and ready at Templehof. The car is waiting for you in the drive."

"Five minutes," Theo agreed, and Henderson left him. Then, as if to signal that even five minutes might be too long, an eerie orange glow lit up the night sky somewhere beyond the Adlon Hotel.

Theo buttoned his shirt as he took one last look out the window. *Berlin was burning!* Herman Göring's bonfire of books had been only a small demonstration of the conflagration that the Nazis planned for the Jews of Germany. *Kristalnacht*, the Night of Broken Glass, *had begun*. Perhaps this night too was meant to be just a small taste of what Hitler planned for the People of the Covenant.

Theo would carry the warning back to England. He could only hope that someone would listen, that something might be done before it was too late.

A fine mist drifted over the Mount of Olives. Two white-robed figures walked slowly among the ancient trees of Gethsemane. One, an old woman, clung to a small silver cross that hung around her neck. The other, young and beautiful, carried the sorrow of the ages in her eyes as she looked out over the Jewish cemetery below.

The old woman reached up and plucked a gray-green leaf from the branch of a gnarled tree. She held it out to the young woman and pointed to a single raindrop on the leaf.

"Drougoi," said the old woman. "The Lord is also weeping for you today."

The young woman held the captured teardrop gently in her hands as she watched the body of Eli Sachar being lowered into a grave surrounded by a cluster of black umbrellas. A ring of British soldiers led by Captain Orde stood guard around the perimeter of the mourners, lest an Arab sniper fire on them as they grieved. Leah and Shimon stood to one side.

"The captain has spread the story that you took your own life rather than endure a forced marriage. For your safety it is best that no one knows the truth. Not Eli's loved ones. Even your own." The old woman looked back toward the mourners.

"I have no loved ones," Victoria said quietly. "Captain Orde is right about Eli's family. Let them believe what they need to believe. They must not carry the burden that he loved me. That he would not have been a rabbi after all . . ." Her voice faltered. "They must have their own illusions. It makes no difference."

"What will you do now?" asked the old woman. The distant sounds of sobbing drifted up to them. Ida Sachar called the name of her son again and again. His brother Moshe stood apart, unshielded by an umbrella. His hair dripped water onto his grim, hard face. No one looked up toward the two women on the knoll of the hill.

The young woman did not answer for a long time. She looked again at the teardrop on the olive leaf, proof that the Lord suffered with her. "Yes, in the Old City they say that I am dead," whispered the young woman. "And so I am, in a way." She smiled sadly toward the grave. "It is just as well."

The old rabbi intoned a prayer in Hebrew and then tossed a handful of dirt into the grave. The sobbing grew louder. Moshe's face broke with emotion. Angrily, he brushed away his tears.

The young woman did not weep as she watched. "They suffer," she said, "but they do not know that time is nothing, do they, Mother?"

The old woman shook her head in pity for the mourners. "It is a blink of an eye since Jesus wept here. It will be that long until He returns to this very place, Victoria."

"Yes. I believe that. And so . . . I would like to wait here for that moment. To be near to Eli while I wait. To grow more in the likeness of my Friend."

The old woman touched the silver cross and closed her eyes in a moment of thought. "You may be waiting a lifetime."

"What is that?" Victoria raised her hands as if releasing a bird. "It will be gone. Is that not the secret of Jerusalem? All the lifetimes. All the grief. It will end, and I will stand before my Lord with Eli again at my side. Please, do not send me away. I want to serve here until then."

The old woman nodded her assent. "His will be done," she said softly. And the two women walked back home along the path where Jesus walked.

If you would like to contact the authors,
you may write to them at the following address:

Bodie and Brock Thoene
P.O. Box 542
Glenbrook, NV 89413

Danzig
Passage

Danzig
Passage

Bodie Thoene

Research and Development By
Brock Thoene

BETHANY HOUSE PUBLISHERS
MINNEAPOLIS, MINNESOTA 55438

Cover illustration by Dan Thornberg,
Bethany House Publishers staff artist.

Published by Bethany House Publishers
A Ministry of Bethany Fellowship, Inc.
6820 Auto Club Road, Minneapolis, Minnesota 55438

Printed in the United States of America

Library of Congress Cataloging-in-Publication Data

Thoene, Bodie, 1951–
    Danzig passage / Bodie Thoene.
       p. cm. — (The Zion covenant) ; 5)

    1. Holocaust, Jewish (1939–1945)—Fiction.
2. World War, 1939–1945—Fiction.
I. Title. II. Series: Thoene, Bodie, 1951–   Zion covenant ; bk. 5.
PS3570.H46D27   1991
813'.54—dc20   90-12354
ISBN 1-55661-081-5   CIP

This book is dedicated to you, dear friend and reader. We have come far together, haven't we? You have read enough to know our hearts by now and so *we really are* friends! Your letters have cheered us and encouraged us. Your prayers for this ministry have called a mighty strength to help us and guide us as we work. Your prayers and encouragement are as much a part of the work as the writing of it. Philippians 1:2–6 and 1:8-11 best says how we feel about you!

Baruch Hashem!
Brock and Bodie Thoene
May 1991
"In my Father's House."

The Authors

BODIE THOENE (Tay-nee) began her writing career as a teen journalist for her local newspaper. Eventually her byline appeared in prestigious periodicals such as *U.S. News and World Report*, *The American West*, and *The Saturday Evening Post*. After leaving an established career as a writer and researcher for John Wayne, she began work on her first historical fiction series, The Zion Chronicles. From the beginning her husband, BROCK, has been deeply involved in the development of each book. His degrees in history and education have added a vital dimension to the accuracy, authenticity, and plot structure of the Zion books. The Thoenes' unusual but very effective writing collaboration has also produced two non-fiction books, *Writer to Writer* and *Protecting Your Income and Your Family's Future*, as well as a new frontier fiction series, The Saga of the Sierras. Along with their prolific writing schedule, Brock and Bodie make a home for their teenagers in the California Sierras.

Books by Brock and Bodie Thoene

The Zion Covenant

Vienna Prelude
Prague Counterpoint
Munich Signature
Jerusalem Interlude
Danzig Passage
Warsaw Requiem

The Zion Chronicles

The Gates of Zion
A Daughter of Zion
The Return to Zion
A Light in Zion
The Key to Zion

The Shiloh Legacy

In My Father's House
A Thousand Shall Fall
Say to This Mountain

Saga of the Sierras

The Man From Shadow Ridge
Riders of the Silver Rim
Gold Rush Prodigal
Sequoia Scout
Cannons of the Comstock
The Year of the Grizzly
Shooting Star

Non-Fiction

Protecting Your Income and Your Family's Future
Writer to Writer

Contents

Prologue

WEST BERLIN—AT THE WALL
November 9, 1989

Ten thousand candles flickered in feeble contrast to the floodlights that drenched the concrete wall with light. Television cameras panned, capturing a sea of hopeful faces. News anchors made their reports, while chanting throngs provided a united chorus in the background.

"TOR AUF! TOR AUF! Open the gate! Open the gate!" The shout resounded from the East and was echoed in the West. The words were no longer a plea but a demand. *"TOR AUF!"*

The whole world watched this uprising of the human spirit. Men and women who had never known life without the Wall stood transfixed before their television sets to stare in wonder as the earth seemed to shift. Here was a miracle. Unthinkable, but real.

"TOR AUF!"

"For twenty-eight years this Wall has stood as the symbol of division for the world," a commentator said above the din. "A twenty-eight-mile-long scar through the heart of a once-proud capital city . . ."

The camera view was crowded with bright, exuberant faces. Bottles of champagne popped open and bubbled in joyful celebration as thousands roared and rushed toward the barrier.

Young. So young, these faces. They had lived always in the gray shadow of this Wall. It had ordered their existence; it had dictated the boundaries of freedom. It had held them captive by its very existence.

Now, denim-clad men and women climbed onto it; trumpets rang out; hammers and chisels clanged down to break off chunks of concrete as horns honked and people danced along the Wall.

"Berlin is Berlin again!"

The camera caught an occasional glimpse of gray hair or a lined face streaked with tears. But few remained who remembered Berlin when it had been Berlin. Before Hitler. Before the war. Before the Communists.

Berlin had been beautiful, yes; and it had been proud. It had become too proud and that pride had sown the seeds of violence and destruction. Few among the crowd this night could remember clearly when the Wall had first begun to appear. It was not a mere twenty-eight years before. The scar upon the heart of Germany was much older than that . . .

Elisa Lindheim Murphy wiped tears from her cheeks. She held tightly to the gloved hand of her husband as the crowd surged forward toward the Wall. At seventy-five, she was not a young woman anymore, but tonight she felt twenty again!

Fifty-one years exactly had passed since her father, Theo Lindheim, had witnessed the violence of Kristal Nacht in Berlin. Elisa wondered if these young people remembered that tonight was the fifty-first anniversary of that shame and sorrow, when the wound which had formed this concrete scar had been gouged deep and bloody across the heart of the nation.

She and Murphy had been young in those days, young like the people who danced and embraced on top of the Wall.

"They are kids," Murphy laughed.

"So were we." Elisa squeezed his hand.

"I didn't think we would live to see this." He raised his hand and whooped with the others. They moved slowly amid the crush.

"Hey, old grandfather!" shouted a young bearded man to Murphy. "What do you think? Berlin is Berlin again!"

Murphy nodded and raised his eyes toward Brandenburg Gate. Tears of joy brimmed over. "What does he know about Berlin?" Murphy said to Elisa. His thoughts were on the eastern side of the Wall, where the heart of Berlin had beat, where he had seen Elisa for the first time from a window at the Adlon Hotel.

"Perhaps it is good they can't remember, Murphy." Elisa forgave this youthful ignorance easily. "Let them be. It is better they can't imagine the waste of it, the heartache of what might have been."

The passage of time had not managed to extinguish the brightness of Elisa's blue eyes. Her shoulders were as straight as the day she had given her first concert at the Prussian State Theater. She knew what had been. She had been born there, had grown up and fallen in love and had her heart broken there. Her dreams had been shattered like the glass of Jewish shops along Unter den Linden. She and her family had been hunted, fled, and then returned to help those who remained. The full circle of love and tragedy had been enacted behind that Wall. She could tell these young people a thing or two about Berlin!

Fifty-one years ago tonight Berlin had heard different shouts. Stones and hammers had smashed businesses and lives; prisoner lorries had rumbled through these streets, beneath the pillars of the Brandenburg Gate. Seventy thousand had been arrested and imprisoned on that night.

Lindheim's Department Store had been burned because it had once been owned by a Jew. Its smoke had mingled with that of the synagogues of the city and with the smoke of those who perished. New Church had opened its doors for refuge, and in so doing, had sealed its fate.

Theo Lindheim had seen it all from the window of the British Embassy in Berlin. He had heard the cry of the Jews who begged for refuge.

"Tor auf! Tor auf! Open the gate!"

On that terrible night the gate remained closed, and Theo had seen the vision of what was to come.

Elisa fingered the yellow slip of stationery in her coat pocket. It bore the logo of the British Embassy, and beneath Theo's message was his signature and the date: *November 9, 1938.*

Suddenly, as they neared the gate, Murphy asked her, "Do you have it?"

She nodded, took the paper from her pocket, and held it up. "All these years I kept it," she said, "only half-believing that this moment would come. Papa is here tonight, coming home with me at last."

"TOR AUF! OPEN THE GATE!"

Guards yielded at the stroke of midnight, and the crowds surged together in one vast embrace. At last the scar which Hitler had carved upon the heart of Germany was being erased!

Murphy pulled Elisa closer to him as they walked forward toward the East. Fifty-one years of marriage. Children, grandchildren, and soon a great-grandchild. Fifty-one years of joy and sorrow; the fullness of life and death. But this was the first time Elisa could look up at him and say, *"I'm going home."*

The Opera. The University. New Church. Lindheim's Department Store—all were altered or gone forever. But tonight the Wall was coming down. Perhaps heaven offered another chance to the descendants of those who had destroyed the nation with hatred.

Elisa walked on with the knowledge that she and Murphy might not live to see what Germany made of that second chance. She prayed for the people of East and West together; prayed that true light would shine here, lest a more terrible darkness rush in!

"Tor auf," she prayed quietly for those around her. "Open the gate."

1

Martyr

November 9, 1938

The face of Big Ben's clock glowed like a full moon behind a veil of London fog. The chimes of the great bell tower rang out eight o'clock and were answered by the lonely bellow of a fog horn.

Below the crinoline spires of Parliament, the black waters of the Thames slid toward the sea. It was Thursday night, and most of the theaters and concert halls in London were dark and empty. The panic that had swept through the city with rumors of impending war had been replaced with tranquility. Nearly everyone believed Prime Minister Chamberlain. Peace was at hand. The Sudetenland of Czechoslovakia had purchased "peace in our time." The citizens of London had put away their gas masks and filled in the trenches that had crisscrossed Hyde Park. Flags and bunting were hung from public buildings and streetlamps in anticipation of the celebrations planned for the twentieth anniversary of the Armistice. It had been twe 'y years since the end of the war to end all wars. This year England had plenty to celebrate. The lions of war had been tossed a small bone and placated at last!

Tonight, London was safe. Safe beneath her fog.

The black bowl of the sky above Galilee was dusted with ten thousand bright stars. An arch of gold and silver glittered in the Milky Way, the constellations almost lost against such a backdrop.

Sharon Zalmon knew the constellations by name. She had learned them all in an astronomy class at the University in Warsaw two years before. The sky above Poland was not quite like the sky above Galilee, however. The lights of the city of Warsaw obscured the glory which the shepherd David had written about in the days when Israel had been a great nation.

Tonight, on duty in the tiny Jewish settlement of Hanita, Sharon only glanced at the stars. There was no time for contemplating their glory, no time for writing new psalms. On this night there was no nation of Israel. There was only the memory of what had been, the hope of what could be once again. On this night, as in the times of David, enemies hid in the dark ravines of Galilee. They crept toward the outpost where Sharon stood guard with an old shotgun. Their single purpose was to destroy the memory of what Israel had been and to make certain that the nation would never exist again on the soil of Zion. *Kill the people of the Covenant! Kill the dream! Destroy forever the promise God made to the shepherd King, and to his people!*

At the cry of *Jihad,* Holy War, enemies came from Jordan and Syria and Egypt and Iraq. They banded together, united by hatred, beneath the banner of the Prophet Mohammed and Allah. Their shouts in the city of Jerusalem grew silent; now they moved through the darkness of Galilee beneath the peaceful stars. They slipped toward the tiny mound of sandbags where Sharon Zalmon kept watch, planning to inflict the dreamless peace of death upon her and all the Jews of Hanita.

It was early yet. Sharon looked out over the black rolling hills beyond the perimeter of the settlement. Shifting the aged shotgun in her hands, she rested the heavy barrel on top of the sandbags.

Three minutes before, Lazlo had left her here and went to patrol the barbed barricade between this position and the next. The Arab gangs had cut through the wire before and had killed settlers. For this reason, the settlement posted stationary guards like Sharon and moving patrols like Lazlo, who would make his rounds and return in a few minutes.

Something terrible was coming to the Jews of the Yishuv; after the Jerusalem riots, everyone believed it, even the British High Command. They had sent Captain Samuel Orde to help the Jews of Hanita. Sharon had heard of this Englishman who was known as *Hayedid, The Friend.* Scheduled to arrive tonight, he would no doubt be out here to make the rounds of the patrol. This thought made the night seem not quite so dark, the unseen enemy not so terrifying. *Hayedid, The Friend,* would help them.

Sharon looked up briefly at the constellation of Orion as it moved toward her from the horizon. She could just make out the stars where the ancients said his sword hung from his belt. *The stars remain unchanged since that time. Our dreams remain the same,* she thought.

In that moment, she heard the sound of a stone as it slithered down an embankment twenty paces from the barricade beyond her post!

The sound jerked her back to the present earth; back to this small patch of ground that the dreamers had purchased and cultivated and made to blossom from desolation. They must now defend it as well. They must not look up at the stars and dream, or all their dreams would be destroyed!

"Who is it?" she demanded. Her heart pounded as she tried to fix the exact location of the falling stone. Was it there, behind the outline of a boulder? Or to the left, where the ground dropped steeply away? Or maybe it was behind her. Perhaps it was only the footstep of Lazlo as he made his rounds.

She lifted the heavy barrel of the shotgun and pointed it out toward the boulder. If someone were there, he would not escape the blast of a shotgun. Lazlo had showed her. She did not have to take careful aim. The small pellets of this old British hunting gun would down a Holy Struggler like a pheasant rising from a bush. Still, the sound of movement left Sharon frightened. What might be beyond the reach of the shotgun's range? Her mouth went dry; she licked her lips and listened. What had she heard?

"Is someone out there?" she asked again. Her voice sounded small and vulnerable in the night. She wished Lazlo would hurry. She thought of calling an alarm, but what if it was nothing?

The silhouette of the land stretched out like an unmoving sea beneath the rolling star scape. Surely, Sharon thought, she would see movement if the stone had shifted outside the barbed wire fence!

Why did Lazlo not return? Was it not time for him to call out the password and leap into the circle of sandbags?

At that instant, another stone clattered down a few feet from her. She opened her mouth to call out the alarm just as a hand clamped down hard over her mouth.

Sharon Zalmon had no chance to scream.

Searing hot pain filled her, followed by terror and then a rush of warmth as she was pushed down onto the dirt floor of the outpost. She blinked twice in amazement at the brightness of the stars above Galilee and the realization that she was seeing them for the last time. Then the dreams died. Just that quickly, it was finished. The darkness of the land overwhelmed the brightness of the skies above Galilee, and the peace of death came once again for a child of the Covenant.

The German Führer promised weapons for the revolt of the Mufti's army against the Jews and the British. He made good on that promise.

On a dark field in Jordan, Haj Amin Husseini walked through the stacks of heavy crates containing rifles and ammunition from Germany. He felt the satisfaction of a man with great power behind him.

As Grand Mufti of Jerusalem, Haj Amin had also kept a promise to Hitler. He had issued the call for a Jihad, a Holy War against the Jews and English infidels. Riots even now rolled across Palestine. These thousands of weapons would assure victory and an Islamic kingdom for Haj Amin.

For a time, to be sure, Haj Amin was forced to flee from the English law, which even now pursued him for inciting the riots in Jerusalem. But Haj Amin had no doubts about the ultimate outcome. He had Adolf Hitler behind him—an ally almost as powerful as the Prophet Mohammed and the Koran! Both Hitler and the Prophet proclaimed the destruction of the Jews. The Islamic religion provided passion to the people, while Hitler supplied crates of weapons and Nazi commandos to help accomplish that goal.

The three motors of the silver German airplane sputtered to life. Haj Amin extended his hand to each of his faithful commanders and the fair-skinned Germans among them. They would carry on while he was in exile. He had communications in place which assured that orders from Berlin and Baghdad would be followed with the same devotion as if he remained in Jerusalem.

"Allah is great." Ram Kadar bowed low before Haj Amin. "It will be a short time before you will return to us as king in Jerusalem."

These words made Haj Amin smile. "It has been two thousand years since any king has ruled over Jerusalem alone. I have seen the Prophet in a dream, Kadar; the promise is given to *me*! Soon, indeed, I will sit on the throne, and you will sit at my right hand."

Others kissed his hand as he passed through the ranks. All vowed to finish what they had begun. There would be no more Zionist settlers. A new Arab Kingdom would take the orchards and the fields the Jews had cultivated and distribute the bounty among the True Believers. Thus it was written, and thus it would be accomplished.

The final words of the Mufti were almost drowned by the hum of the engines. As he boarded the plane to flee from British justice, the Jihad Moquades repeated his words over and over to one another.

"This is only the beginning! The Prophet has promised us victory in the Mother of All Battles against Jews and infidels! Only the start! The world and Paradise belong to those who believe this!"

The plane had barely lifted off the crudely constructed airfield before the Holy Strugglers cheered and cracked open the crates of new rifles and bullets—enough to kill every Englishman and Jew three times over. The Mother of All Battles against the Jews had begun, even as it began throughout the Reich of the great German Führer, Adolf Hitler.

It was early evening in Berlin. The headquarters of the Gestapo on Albrechtstrasse was lit up; each department prepared for the monumental task ahead tonight.

Teletypes clacked an urgent directive to every police headquarters across the Reich. What had begun in Munich and spread to Berlin must now be enacted in every city, large or small, with even one Jew as a resident.

It was a night unlike any other in the history of Germany—perhaps in the history of the world.

Lists of Jewish names and businesses, compiled over long and arduous months of work, were reproduced and transmitted to the appropriate authorities. Within an hour, the roads of Hitler's Third Reich were packed with truckloads of eager storm troopers dressed in civilian clothing and studying long lists of Jews in the neighboring towns where they were assigned to duty. No man was allowed to participate in the demonstration in his own neighborhood, lest he come across a Jewish neighbor and take pity. Instead, the targeted victims would all be strangers to the troops. Thus the Jews became impersonal, generic vermin of the sort the Führer raved about in his speeches. *Every Jew an enemy, man, woman, child—no better than bacilli whose purpose is to infect the pure Aryan race!*

Destinations were predetermined. Targets had been marked long before Herschel Grynspan had ever contemplated the assassination of Ernst vom Rath in Paris. The orders came directly from the top, inviolate and explicit in their instruction.

TO ALL STATE POLICE HEADQUARTERS AND BRANCH OFFICES: ALL SECRET SERVICE COMMANDS IN THE MAIN AND SUBDIVISIONS . . . URGENT! IMMEDIATE DELIVERY!

SUBJECT: MEASURES TO BE TAKEN AGAINST JEWS TONIGHT.
  AS A RESULT OF THE DEATH OF EMBASSY SECRETARY ERNST VOM RATH IN PARIS, ANTI-JEWISH DEMONSTRATIONS ARE TO BE EXPECTED THROUGHOUT THE REICH TONIGHT. THE FOLLOWING INSTRUCTIONS WILL BE OBSERVED:
1. DEMONSTRATIONS AGAINST THE JEWS AND THEIR SYNAGOGUES WILL TAKE PLACE SHORTLY. MEASURES WILL BE TAKEN TO PROTECT GERMAN LIVES AND PROPERTY (E.G., SYNAGOGUES MAY BE SET ON FIRE AS LONG AS THERE IS NO DANGER OF SPREADING FLAMES TO NEIGHBORING BUILDINGS).
  A. JEWISH SHOPS AND HOMES MAY BE DESTROYED BUT NOT LOOTED.
  B. THE OFFICERS ASSIGNED THIS DUTY WILL PROCEED TO ARREST AS MANY JEWS IN ALL DISTRICTS AS THE AVAILABLE JAIL SPACE WILL HOLD. PRIMARILY WELL-TO-DO JEWS WILL BE CHOSEN.

The German attention to detail had been honed to its sharpest cutting edge for just such a night. Those who had conceived the idea and brought the plan to reality smiled pleasantly at one another as they raised their wine glasses in congratulations.

Tonight was a night unlike any other in the history of Germany, after all. What nation had ever brought such discipline and organization to the goals of violence, destruction, and chaos?

A thick file, filled with memos, letters, and photographs of the traitors, lay open on the coffee table in front of Adolf Hitler. Others in the room, sitting across from the Führer, cocked their heads in an attempt to read the upside-down writing beneath the Gestapo insignia.

Hitler relaxed in his favorite overstuffed chair. He held up the photograph showing Thomas von Kleistmann crucified on a cross of ordinary planks taken from the scaffolding of a construction site on Albrechtstrasse. He leaned forward briefly and picked out the picture of Ernst vom Rath, dead on a hospital bed in Paris.

"Traitors, both of them," he commented.

In the background, a recording replayed the voices of Ernst vom Rath's father and another man who sounded near to tears.

"Herr vom Rath, every Jew in Germany deplores the murder of your dear son. . . ."

The Führer raised a finger to stop the recording. "And who is this again?"

"A neighbor of the vom Rath family. A Jew. He is the cantor of the neighborhood synagogue. Come to beg for pardon, I suppose."

"Play it over again," Hitler ordered calmly.

"Herr vom Rath, every Jew in Germany deplores the murder of your dear son by one of our own."

"It was not a Jew who killed Ernst." The elder vom Rath's voice cracked with grief. *"Ernst was no Nazi, and it was the Nazis who have had him assassinated. I know who killed him. It was Hitler and his vipers."*

Hitler's expression remained placid, unchanged, as he listened. Those in the room with him looked at their leader with alarm, expecting rage at such words from the mouth of Ernst vom Rath's father.

The recording continued uninterrupted. *"But, my friend,"* said the Jewish cantor, *"it was not the Nazis but a foolish young Jewish boy. We grieve with you—"*

"No, Reverend," protested vom Rath. *"I know what you think, but the Nazis are behind it. Ernst was too outspoken. Last time I saw him he seemed troubled . . . as though he knew."*

Once again Hitler raised his finger as though the recording bored him. It was stopped, and he shuffled through the thick folder again, laying photographs of the two dead men side by side.

"Both traitors," he muttered. "One is now ashes, sitting in an urn on his mother's mantel. The other—" He held up the photograph of Ernst. "We must spare no expense for the funeral."

Himmler dared to speak. "How should we silence his father? The old fool is telling Jews that we have killed his son."

Hitler smiled. "Then he is not such a fool."

A chittering of agreeable laughter followed, and the Führer held up notes posted in Paris and addressed to Elisa Murphy in London. Both were quite clearly the handwriting of Ernst vom Rath. These were proof that the German diplomat was a traitor to the Reich and that he deserved what he got. He would now be made into a martyr for the Reich to serve the convenience of the Nazi party. What did vom Rath care? He was stone dead, anyway.

The Führer considered the photograph of Ernst's father—white-haired, dignified, aristocratic. It would not be good to kill the old man or arrest him for treason after making his murdered son a hero.

Hitler snapped his fingers impatiently. "This old man has Jews as friends, does he?"

"Yes. Quite a number."

"And he blames the death of his son on us, does he?"

"Entirely. We have showed him the picture of Herschel Grynspan, but still he believes we are behind it."

The Führer raised his chin in thought. "Then we shall pay off the old man with a position, some post where he might faithfully serve the Nazi party. Perhaps he should be made head of Jewish affairs in some city. We will send him quotas for the arrests of so many Jews a week." He raised his hands as though this was merely a thought for consideration. "That should eliminate his Jewish friends."

Now the laughter was uproarious. Every man in the room agreed that no one could neutralize opposition with the finesse of Adolf Hitler.

"And what about the woman in London vom Rath sent the messages to?" Himmler asked, tapping the address on the postcard.

"You are having her watched?" Hitler questioned Himmler carefully.

"We have an agent on duty now."

"Good." That seemed to satisfy Hitler. He snapped his fingers a few more times and then pushed the photographs across the table to Himmler. "I want this picture of Thomas von Kleistmann copied and circulated around the military. Send it to Admiral Canaris in the Abwehr. It will not hurt for these reluctant patriots to see what happens to a proven traitor. Crucifixion will have some effect. Not every traitor can be as lucky as Ernst vom Rath, eh? To die at the hand of a Jew and be made into an eternal martyr. No. It is good if they see the boards and the nails and the blood. It will make them think about it before they fall into something they may regret."

Hitler stretched and stood, moving slowly toward the curtained window. "The British Embassy in Berlin will hand over Theo Lindheim. And as for his family in London, we should plan something very discreet for them. Nothing flashy. We do not want to give the other side a host of their own martyrs to draw strength from, ja, Himmler?"

At that, he pulled back the heavy drapery and looked out over the city. Vengeance for the death of martyr Ernst vom Rath had just begun.

2

The Mouth of Hell Has Opened

From his window at the British Embassy, Theo Lindheim could see them clearly—two Gestapo officers waiting outside the gates as the staff car from the German Foreign Ministry entered. The bright lights from the Brandenburg Gate lit the sidewalk where they stood watching truckloads of storm troopers drive past slowly. To the east a new and terrible light illuminated the underbelly of the clouds. Berlin's finest synagogue was on fire.

Mr. Kirkpatrick, first secretary of the embassy, entered quietly and stood at Theo's elbow for a moment to gaze out at the scene. Kirkpatrick had served for six years in Berlin. He knew everybody and everything, and up until this night he had been able to maintain his puckish Irish humor in even the most grim situations. But tonight an edge of fear crept into his voice as he took Theo by the elbow and urged him back from the window.

"One of our guards spotted three men on the roof of the Adlon Hotel," he warned, drawing the curtain. "All it would take is one bullet through the glass, and the Nazis could claim another assassination by the Jews, eh?"

Theo nodded. He sat down slowly on the bed. "I would not be mourned in Germany."

Kirkpatrick glanced at his watch. "We cannot transport you as planned, but the American ambassador should be here shortly." He frowned. "The Nazis have sent a minor official from the foreign office to discuss your extradition and arrest. They claim you came here as the hub of some great Jewish plot to assassinate German leaders around the world. They have presented our ambassador with a sheaf of documents on your criminal activities." He peeked out the curtain as the lights of another vehicle turned onto the Embassy Drive. "Your case should take most of the night to discuss. By then you should be well on your way." He looked again, then smiled. "The American ambassador. At the gate."

Theo resisted the urge to look out the window. Kirkpatrick hurried from the room, leaving Theo alone to contemplate his fate. He was safe, for the moment, inside the British Embassy. The Nazis would not take him from here by force. There were other channels, legal methods of getting what they wanted. Clearly, Theo Lindheim was about to become another political issue for the Nazi Propaganda Ministry to use against England. Theo found himself rethinking the British policy of appeasing the Nazis. Since Prime Minister Chamberlain had barely noticed when Germany swallowed Austria whole, and then had presented Hitler with a massive piece of Czechoslovakia on demand, certainly Theo Lindheim was not in safe hands at this moment. What was one man, after all? And no doubt the Gestapo had compiled a convincing case with forged documents and half-truths. *You can see, the father of Herschel Grynspan once worked for Theo Lindheim. The connection is quite clear. . . .*

Like a mouse drawn to a trap, Theo could see the iron rod poised above his head, ready to break his neck. At this moment the British ambassador, known for his weakness and vacillation in the face of arrogant Nazi demands, discussed his case with the German Foreign Ministry representatives. The man had never held out against the Germans on even one small point—except in his argument with Göring about the proper way to hunt a stag, perhaps. Theo was grateful that the American ambassador had called to request a meeting with Henderson tonight.

Theo switched on a light and took paper and pen from the writing table. He closed his eyes and drew a deep breath as he tried to picture Anna and Elisa in London. Tonight was the benefit concert for refugees in Prague. It would just be finished. They would not have gotten word yet about the riots here in Berlin. He would write Anna and tell her that he was not afraid. Death had been very near to him before, and he was no longer frightened of it. If he did not make it home to her, Theo wanted to tell her, including details of his meeting with Hermann Göring. How he pitied the fat German Field Marshal and all of Hitler's minions!

Even as they raged against the innocent in the streets of Germany; even as they bartered for the life of Theo downstairs, they had brought themselves into a judgment far greater than they could ever imagine.

Kirkpatrick had said it would take the entire night for the ambassador to consider his case. By then, Theo supposedly would be out of Germany. But if not, Theo wanted Anna to know that, although he trembled at the evil these men brought upon others, he no longer feared what they would do to him.

"A perfect peace has filled my heart," he wrote in that terrible hour. "The mouth of hell has opened wide here, yet I believe in the coming justice of the Holy One. Even now I feel His perfect love, and all fear is cast away from my heart, cast into the fires and burned away. . . ."

Lights shone brightly from the windows of the house in Red Lion Square. Automobiles crawled slowly around the corner and crowded against the curb outside the residence of John and Elisa Murphy. Taxi drivers who had picked up their passengers after the Refugee Relief Concert at Royal Albert Hall now grumbled about fares being the same in fair weather and foul. Unless the fog lifted, they warned, it might be difficult to find a cab later.

The night air was filled with the sound of rattling motors, laughter, and the music of a jazz band Murphy had hired to entertain the orchestra members after the concert. The music was more of a beacon than the lights of the house.

Little Charles Kronenberger rubbed a peephole through the steamy window to peer down at arriving guests. The orchestra members, toting instruments of all sizes, were easy to spot. Men in overcoats and women in furs and high heels called to one another as they blended with arrivals from the Press Corps and members of England's clergy and a handful of politicians crowding up the stairs.

Charles called to Louis, who was looking for his missing right shoe beneath the bed.

"They all came!" he cried.

With a gesture of triumph, Louis held up his wayward shoe and ran to join his brother at the window. His eyes widened at the sight of so many people carrying small paper-wrapped packages. Admission to tonight's party was a new article of clothing or a pound note to be tied on the limb of the money tree. Charles and Louis were the gift-takers and the tree-tenders tonight.

"See, Charles," Louis chided as he tied his shoelaces. "I told you they would come. Even the journalists have come. They don't work all the time."

Charles nodded. Louis had been right after all. This afternoon when Murphy had told Elisa and Anna about the German fellow who had died in Paris, both women had grown very pale and sad. Anna had looked away through the window as if she could see something very terrible there. Charles had seen such an expression on the face of his mother in Hamburg when his father had been arrested. Hopeless. Despairing. It made him worry again. It made him wish that Theo was not away someplace in Europe. It made him wonder if they would cancel the concert and the party to follow. He had taken Anna's hand and followed her gaze over the rooftops of the London twilight.

Louis nudged him hard on the arm, bringing him back to this happy moment. "You were wrong," Louis pronounced with finality.

Charles laughed out loud. How wonderful it was to be wrong about such a thing! In spite of bad news from far away, tonight would be a happy night after all!

He looked in the mirror at the thin pink scar that traced his upper lip into his left nostril. He smiled at himself, pleased that he and Louis looked so very much alike. He still pronounced his words with difficulty, but he was learning to speak like other children. Seeing the six-year-old's toothless grin, Anna had winked at him and told him how handsome he was, and that he must be her escort since Theo was away on business and would miss the party. And when, for a moment, the sadness in her eyes had made him long for his own mother and father, Elisa had taken him on her lap and reminded him that his parents were both in heaven and could see him and Louis very clearly from there. "They will be watching, Charles," she whispered. "And they will be very proud that you are helping other people tonight. They will want you to be happy, ja?"

Now, as the music of the jazz trio vibrated up through the floor, the two boys ran for the door and clattered down the narrow stairway to the light and noise of the great room.

———

Captain Samuel Orde looked rumpled and exhausted as he followed Zach Zabinski toward the small white building that served as the Hanita infirmary.

Moshe Sachar followed six paces behind the Englishman. His face reflected the exhaustion of renewed grief as he looked at the lights of the building and realized what lay within it.

Orde jerked a thumb back toward Moshe. "There is a rumor that there is also a price on Moshe's head. The Mufti himself has demanded that the second Sachar brother be executed for his role in the killing of Ismael Hassan. Totally fabricated nonsense, of course, but then, we have seen what the Muslim fanatics can do. Putting a price on the head of Moshe Sachar simply keeps the fires burning a little longer."

Zach turned toward Moshe. "You may not be any safer here than in Jerusalem." He motioned toward the infirmary to make his point. "But you are welcome, of course."

Moshe nodded in reply as Orde answered for him. "He will undergo the same training as your men." He reached the door of the infirmary; the sound of sobbing filtered out. "We will begin training tonight." Zach opened his mouth to protest that training on such a tragic night was out of the question. Orde had already thrust open the door and entered the room, now a temporary morgue and place of mourning.

One bloody sheet covered two bodies lying side by side on the concrete floor. A dozen members of the settlement sat on cots or stood against the wall to weep or stare in silence at their fallen comrades.

Two women huddled together on the end of a cot. They wept loudly and did not look up as Orde entered with the others.

Zach's face instantly reflected his own pain as he looked down at the bodies. Bare feet protruded from the sheet, making it simple to identify which was the body of a woman and which a man.

Orde eyed the scene coolly, with the demeanor of a man who had seen such things many times before. He gestured toward the weeping women. "Get them out of here," he instructed.

The two clung more tightly to each other as if to protest that they had the right to be here.

"This is Sharon Zalmon's sister," Zach started to explain.

"Then all the more reason for her to leave," Orde said. He glanced around the room to where a young man leaned in a corner beside a tray of surgical instruments. He stared silently, but his face was a mirror of intense suffering. "What about him?" Orde asked. "Husband?"

"Fiance," Zach replied.

"All right," Orde said with authority. "Any of you who are family or close friends will have to leave now."

Hostile eyes regarded him. "We are all either one or the other," said a man who stood at the heads of the bodies. "There is no one in the entire settlement who is not a friend. And we are all like family."

Orde modified his command and searched each face for tears. He pointed to those who had been weeping or were now still sobbing. "Out, please. This is a battle, and we have work to do."

As if to back him up, Zach gently spoke to each one by name and requested that they leave the building. One by one, they shuffled out past Orde, whom they regarded as an intruder to their grief. Seven men, including Moshe and Zach, remained.

Orde slammed the door and then lifted the sheet from the faces of the fallen.

Zach's voice faltered as he named them. "Sharon . . . Zalmon. She is . . . was . . . twenty-one. From Poland."

Orde did not seem to notice that the ashen face below him was delicate and pretty. Blue eyes stared blankly up at the captain as he knelt to examine the wound. Flecks of blood were on her face, her short brown hair matted. A strangely peaceful smile rested on the still-pink lips. Five minutes of silence passed as Orde lifted the chin slightly and learned everything he needed to know.

Then he turned his attention to the man. "Lazlo LaPierre," Zach muttered the name, but none of that mattered to Orde. The method of killing was identical. This was the only detail of significance.

"Quite professional," he remarked as he tossed the sheet back over the two. "You say there was no sound?" He searched the faces of the men in the room for the one who had found them.

A small man with ruddy cheeks and a shock of black curly hair nodded once. "I was at the next post. I heard nothing. When Lazlo did not come on schedule, I sounded the alarm. Then some shots were fired."

"From our own men," Zach added. "Suddenly everyone seemed to hear things everywhere outside the perimeter." He gestured toward the bodies. "We found them. And the cut wire. It looks as if the alarm was given just at the moment Sharon fell. She was still . . . well, moving slightly when we found her."

Orde stared hard at the blood-soaked sheet. "And so the attackers fled." Pushing his cap back on his head, he considered what it all meant. "And you did not send a patrol out after them?"

Zach seemed startled by the question from an Englishman. After all, Captain Orde knew that the Jews within the British Mandate were not supposed to have weapons to fight with, let alone the means to pursue the enemy. "No. We brought our friends here. There are double guards at the perimeters now."

Orde seemed not to hear what Zach told him. He clasped his hands behind his back and paced up and down beside the bodies. "They were killed by the same fellow. I am certain of that. A professional. Not the sort of messy wound I've seen from the Muslim assassins. Not the same at all." He paused and raised a finger. "I would say we have an excellent chance of catching them."

"Catching?" Zach blinked at him in amazement. "But we are . . . self-defense. Defense of this place is all we are permitted by law—"

"Nonsense." Orde gestured first at the bodies and then at Zach. The men in the crowded room suddenly seemed awake. Moshe Sachar stepped back and ran his fingers through his hair. He had dreamed of such a thing after his brother had been murdered. But he was not a real part of Hanita. He had never held a gun, and yet he wanted to go along. "I would like to help," Moshe said.

"Of course," Orde said with a smile. "You know the area. You've been on a number of archeological digs in Galilee. That is why I brought you."

"But I thought we would have some training." Zach looked concerned. He knew what lay in wait beyond Hanita at night. If a Jew left the settlement after dark, he did not come back.

"Right," Orde said briskly. "Training. We begin tonight."

———

The red silk-covered walls of Cafe Sacher glowed with soft candlelight. New patrons who had swept into Vienna from Germany on the first wave of the Anschluss crowded the tables. Most of the familiar faces of the old patrons had vanished from the opulent restaurant overnight as Austrians of power and influence had been arrested or forced into exile. Instead of the black dinner jackets and silk top hats of the after-concert crowd, the patrons wore uniforms adorned with medals of the Reich. Nonmilitary guests sported swastika lapel buttons and clicked their heels, giving the *Heil* in greeting.

The faces in Cafe Sacher had changed indeed, and few remained to notice or mourn the change. Here and there a few foreign newsmen managed to procure a table on slow nights, but they were last to be served, often spoken to with a distinctly cold, unwelcoming tone by the help. Things were not the same at all.

But Cafe Sacher still had music, candlelight, and bright conversation. Still the very best food in the Greater Reich. Nazi soldiers and officers alike considered Vienna a most desirable city for duty.

Many times wives and children remained behind in Germany, while mistresses conveniently transferred to clerical positions in Vienna. This was particularly true among members of the elite S.S. Corps, who were expected to provide the Reich and the Führer with the bounty of their own Aryan offspring. Often promotion and rank depended on the ability of a man to reproduce sons for the Fatherland. With such high expectations, therefore, S.S. Commander and Gestapo Chief Heinrich Himmler made it possible for a man to have a wife pregnant at home as well as a mistress within easy access of his duty assignments.

For this reason Lucy Strasburg had been transferred from Munich to Vienna and was waiting anxiously at Cafe Sacher tonight.

S.S. Major Wolfgang von Fritschauer was already two hours late for their scheduled rendezvous. He had warned her impatiently that he might be late this evening, that something important was brewing. He had been angry with her tears and her telephone calls, but he agreed to meet her anyway. Lucy found this comforting. Wolf was an important and busy man, yet he would come to meet her, to hear her news. Although he had never said the words, she was certain of his love for her. He was two hours late, yes, but he was coming. His secretary had phoned in the reservation for their usual table and had warned the Sacher headwaiter that Fräulein Strasburg might be waiting a while and must be treated with all courtesy.

Such a command from Wolfgang von Fritschauer was always taken seriously. Every few minutes an attentive waiter passed by and asked after her needs, warmed her coffee, and then went on as if it was not unusual for a beautiful young woman to be sitting alone in one of the finest cafes in Vienna. In the kitchen, of course, waiters exchanged looks and shook their heads in obvious disdain of Lucy and her arrogant S.S. officer. They had all seen her waiting for him dozens of times. He was a refined aristocrat. She was beautiful, yes, but definitely a country bumpkin from Bavaria. She did not even know which fork to use or what wine to drink with which course. No one doubted why the swaggering Nazi officer kept company with her. Only Lucy Strasburg seemed unaware.

Whispers filled the kitchen: *"Himmel! So this is the future of the Aryan race? Put two beautiful blond bodies together—one without a brain and the other without a soul! The Führer will have very pretty little idiots to run his Thousand-Year Reich!"*

"Do they all have to bring their harlots here? Why not meet them at a cafe in the Seventh District where the red lights are always burning?"

"S.S. Major von Fritschauer does not meet her in a place like Sacher's for her sake. He comes here because it is he who likes it, and she is too dumb to know his motives are not the purest adoration!"

The whispers of truth may have been quiet, but the laughter that followed was uproarious.

Tonight the waiters tossed a coin and vied for the pleasure of waiting on the mistress of Officer von Fritschauer. She was beautiful, after all, a delight to look at. Her dresses, selected by the major, were chosen to show off her perfect proportions; the waiters had overheard this bit of gossip from conversations that von Fritschauer had at dinners with fellow officers. He discussed her in the same way the aristocracy might discuss the attributes of a fine brood mare. He was envied by his comrades, who often expressed the hope that when he was finished with her they might have a turn with her. To this request, von Fritschauer always chuckled with contentment and wagged a forbidding finger. For pure pleasure, there was nothing to compare with his "little cow" in Vienna. They would have to find their own concubines, he said.

Lucy was not only beautiful, she was also overly cordial to the waiters at Cafe Sacher. She called them by their first names and asked about families. She encouraged them to call her Fräulein Lucy until the major had overheard the offense and had demanded that the waiter be fired on the spot. She had intervened on the fellow's behalf, but he simply disappeared one night after work. It was rumored that the major had accused him of being a Jew and of making improper advances to Fräulein Strasburg. From that moment on, the staff of Hotel Sacher treated Fräulein Strasburg as if she were a duchess. They overlooked her Bavarian peasant familiarity and answered her in single syllables.

"How are your children, Fritz?"

"Fine, Fräulein Strasburg."

"Are you staying in Vienna for the holidays, Johann?"

"No, Fräulein Strasburg."

Over the weeks she had grown accustomed to the aloofness of the attendants. Still, she smiled and asked the questions as though she were talking to an old friend in her village market. *Beautiful. Friendly. Ignorant.* This was the final assessment of Lucy Strasburg by the all-

seeing staff of Hotel Sacher. Tonight they might have added *hopeful*
and *anxious* to their list.

The diners scarcely noticed when the string quartet finished playing
and left their chairs for a few minutes' break. But Lucy noticed. This
was the second break the musicians had taken since she arrived. Two
and a half hours had passed, and Wolf had not come or even called.

She glanced at her watch, a fine Swiss watch Wolf had given to her
for her birthday. He told her that when she looked at it she should
remember who she belonged to. It seemed that she spent a lot of time
looking at the watch, waiting for Wolf. The doubts flooded over her in
a wash of panic. Suppose he did not show up tonight? He had been
very busy the last two weeks. He had not come to her apartment, and
tonight he said he only had time for a quick meal. Suppose he had
another girl? Suppose he would not be pleased with her news?

The thought made her tremble. Nervously she wound the watch and
stared bleakly toward the door of the restaurant. She was not hungry.
Apprehension had driven away her appetite. She glanced down at the
watch again and tried to remember who she belonged to—*S.S. Major
Wolfgang von Fritschauer, declared by the Führer himself to be a perfect
example of German manhood. Devotion to the Fatherland kept him
from her, not another woman!*

These thoughts suppressed her anxiety once again. The little Austrian waiter Johann paused and bowed at her elbow. *Would she like
more coffee, perhaps?*

Lucy smiled nervously and nodded. She made yet another attempt
at conversation. "The weather is getting very cold, isn't it, Johann?"

"Quite, Fräulein," Johann agreed without looking at her face. He
started to go.

"Does it snow much this time of year in Vienna?" she asked, an
edge of desperation in her voice. Could he hear it? Could he hear she
simply wanted to talk to someone? Anyone?

"Sometimes, Fräulein," he answered. Then he bowed slightly and
smiled that properly distant smile as he gazed at her hands. "Will that
be all, Fräulein?"

She wanted to ask him to sit down, to talk a bit with her. But that
was impossible, of course. Wolf had told her she must not speak to
other men—waiters and grocers and such. They might get the wrong
idea about her. And if they had the wrong idea about her, it was a
reflection on his manhood. Wolf had been very angry with her when
he explained these things. She was careful now about being too
friendly.

"Thank you, Johann." She dismissed him and lifted her cup to her
lips. The coffee was strong and very good, but Lucy only sipped it.
Perhaps it was the coffee that made her hands shake. She should not
drink so much coffee; it would not do for Wolf to see her hands tremble.

Such a sign of weakness made him angry and sullen. He had been angry with her for crying, and this evening she would tell him how sorry she was, and that she would not cry again.

The string quartet returned and flipped through the music on their stands. They began to play a song that Lucy knew Wolf liked. She did not know the composer, but he did. This music always made him smile, and she wished he was here to hear it right now.

She looked toward the arched entrance of the restaurant, and at that moment Wolf strode in. His overcoat was unbuttoned, and drops of rain quivered on the visor of his peaked cap. He looked very handsome in his uniform, as always, but something smoldering in his eyes frightened her. His strong jaw was set, giving his face a hardness she had seen before. His ice-blue eyes seemed to look right through her relieved face as he spotted her and made his way through the tables to the corner where she waited.

She remained seated, although she wanted to jump to her feet and kiss his hand in gratitude that he had come. He loved her after all! It did not matter that his face was grim and irritated. He would look at her and want her again; she knew it!

She did not speak. He did not like it when she spoke first to him in public. Often he had things on his mind and did not want to be interrupted in his thoughts. She could tell by the look on his face that this was one of those nights.

He removed his gloves and tossed them on the table. Then he took off his coat and gave it to the waiting attendant. He doffed his hat, smoothed back his thick, close-cropped blond hair, and sat down. He did not acknowledge that she was there. Maybe he was waiting to see if she remembered the rule about not disturbing his thoughts. He lit a thin cheroot and inhaled deeply before he crossed his legs and sat back to appraise her. His eyes appraised her royal blue knit dress and swept over on her softly curled golden hair, pausing at her throat, finally lingering on her breasts. Then he smiled slightly and spoke.

"Well, Lucy, I have neglected you."

Tears of relief welled up in her eyes, but she controlled herself as he required. "I have missed you, Wolf," she said softly. "I was hoping that tonight we could—"

He interrupted her with a wave of his hand. "Have you ordered?" he asked.

"No. I was waiting. Waiting for—"

The edge of hardness returned to his face. "You should not have waited. I told you I might be late. There are important things happening tonight in the Reich. I had a sandwich at headquarters."

She flushed. He was unhappy with her. "I thought—"

"It is best if you do not think," he said, flicking the ash of his cheroot.

She did not reply. Emotion was too close to the surface again. She should not have presumed. Wolf always told her not to presume anything.

He continued as though speaking to a junior officer. "You said you had news for me?"

This was not the way she had imagined telling him. She bit her lip and looked at the flame of the candle for an instant. The music he liked was playing. Did he notice it?

"Well? Really, Lucy. I am busy. You cannot imagine how difficult it was to get away. Tonight of all nights, you have to talk to me or die!"

Her hands began trembling again. She put them on her lap so he would not see. She wished she could tell him how much she loved him, how much his harshness hurt her, especially now. She had hoped that she might give him the news while she was in his arms.

He sighed impatiently and looked over his shoulder at the exit as though he would stand up and leave.

"Wolf," she said in a cracking voice. "I have good news. Well, I hope you will think so."

"I could use good news."

"I am . . . we are . . . going to have a baby, Wolf." She smiled hopefully. Had he not told her that more than anything he wanted to give her a child? His child? Had he not spoken of fulfilling her highest purpose as a woman?

Wolf smiled at her, then let out a short laugh of satisfaction. He reached across the table and pulled her hand into his own strong grip, then touched her cheek with as much tenderness as he ever displayed. "A child?"

She laughed too, but not too loud. The tension melted. "Yes! You are pleased, Wolf? I can tell you are pleased."

"Pleased! It will mean a promotion. I told you. A raise in my salary. I was afraid something was wrong with you, but you really are my good little cow, aren't you?"

Lucy did not hear his words, only the tone of his voice. Wolf was happy with her. He was happy with the thought that she would bear him a child. She had nothing at all to worry about. They would be married in a civil ceremony at the Rathaus, and no one would even think twice about the fact that she was pregnant beforehand. Such things were common in the Reich these days. Her parents would not know until the matter was all settled. And then they would be glad that their daughter had married an aristocrat and an officer. The reason would not bother them once she and Wolf were married. And if her family insisted, she would ask Wolf if they might also find a priest to marry them a second time!

She began to babble all these things as she held his hand. *The*

wedding. Her family. A priest. Marriage, so that the child would have a
father and mother and a name . . .

"I would like my parents to meet you, Wolf," she said. And then
she looked into his face. None of her emotion reflected in his eyes,
only a sort of cold derision for her.

She drew back, horrified. She had been talking too much, making
plans. He did not like that in her. "Oh, Wolf. I did not mean to—"

He shook his head and pulled his hand away. "You have thought
all this out, have you, Lucy?"

"I thought . . . I mean—"

"What have I told you about thinking too much, Lucy? It is for me
to think, ja?"

"Of course, Wolf. I did not mean . . ."

He was cool and businesslike again. "So I will tell you what we
will do. Just outside Vienna the S.S. has a very nice place for young
women like you, and S.S. officers like me who make little babies for
the Führer. It is called a *Lebensborn*. A very nice place where you will
have all your needs met. You will be pampered and well fed and you
will have the baby. An S.S. baby. S.S. babies are considered worthy of
such special treatment. As are mothers of S.S. babies."

"You will be with me, Wolf?"

"Fathers are forbidden to visit. Such visits often cause difficulties."

"But if we are married—"

"We did not speak of marriage."

"But the baby—"

He snapped his chin up in an impatient gesture to silence her. "We
did not speak of marriage," he said firmly.

"But—"

"I told you. No commitments, eh?"

"But the child must have a . . . father. A name."

He smiled patronizingly. "Of course. I am the father. He will have
my name."

She frowned. "Then we will . . . marry?"

He looked at her with incredulous amusement. "Lucy, little cow."
He tapped her on the forehead with his finger. "I *am* married. I have
a wife in Prussia. And three children. All girls. We will hope this one
is a son."

She blinked at him in horror. *Married!* How could it be? All this
time, and he had not told her! All this time, and he had led her to
believe . . .

"So," he continued matter-of-factly, "you will have a lovely pam-
pered stay at the Lebensborn. It is a resort, really."

She could barely speak. "Our . . . baby."

"And when you deliver the child, I will adopt him if it is a boy. He will be raised in Prussia with my other children. A very nice home, I assure you."

"But, Wolf—" Tears came in spite of her vow. "I thought . . . I *hoped* you loved me." She bit her lip and stared hard at his hands. Such beautiful hands. She loved his hands because they were the most gentle part of him. Would those hands now take her baby away and never touch her again?

His tone became conciliatory and patronizing. "You will be cared for afterward as well, of course. And if the child is as fine as I expect, then we will continue our relationship. Really, Lucy. I should think you would be relieved. You receive all of the pleasure and benefits of being an S.S. mother and none of the responsibility for raising a child."

She did not reply. She thought of all the things he had said to her over the last few months. Everything made sense now. All of it was suddenly terribly clear to her. Words about the nobility of motherhood for the sake of the Reich. His praise of beauty and perfection. None of that had meant that he loved her! He intended to give her baby to his wife, and all the things she had dreamed of would belong to another woman. How would her family react to such news—her father, and the priest at home?

"We will raise him in the State Church," he added. "It does not bother me that you are Catholic. The child will never know the difference."

Wolf checked his watch. "I cannot stay any longer." He held himself aloof, as though they were speaking of business. He tossed some money on the table for her. "Have something nourishing to eat," he instructed. "And take a cab home, will you? Tonight I do not want you out walking. There are important demonstrations planned for tonight. You are carrying a baby for our Führer, and so you must be especially careful."

He stood and then bent to kiss her cheek. "Heil Hitler," he said in farewell, and then he left her sitting alone and stunned at Cafe Sacher.

3

Inferno

Neither the acrid smell of smoke nor the crash of breaking glass could drag the sixteen-year-old boy into reluctant consciousness.

"Peter!" The voice of his mother came as a hoarse whisper. "Wake up! Peter!" She shook him gently in spite of the terrified urgency of her tone. "Wake up! Get up! *Quickly!*"

Peter Wallich opened his eyes to see his mother's shadow against the wall, backlit by an eerie orange light.

Was he still dreaming? His gangly body remained tangled in the blankets, binding him like the ropes of his dream. He blinked and then closed his eyes, certain he was dreaming.

He had been fighting *them* again, even in his sleep. His arms and legs had lashed out against the skull-faced phantoms dressed in the black uniforms of the Hitler Youth Brigade. They had tied him up and beaten him as they shrieked through wide, grinning mouths, *"You cannot hurt us, Jew-pig! We are dead already! Already dead!"*

"Peter!" The voice of his mother penetrated the dark image once again. "Wake up!" The hand on his shoulder was less gentle, the voice impatient. *Frightened!*

He opened his eyes to the strange light, fully awake at last. He smelled the smoke. The exploding of glass and the harsh voices in the street below pierced his confusion with a terrible clarity. *"Judenschweine! Verrecken! Die, Jew-pigs!"*

Peter sat bolt upright. He kicked himself free from the blankets as he grabbed his knickers and pulled them on in one quick movement. Then, his nightshirt half tucked into the waistband, he stood transfixed beside his mother. His eyes stared at the yellow fire that seemed to dance and sway in midair beyond the lacy web of curtains.

Vienna was burning!

He looked at his mother. She stared in unblinking horror toward the window. Her long red hair, always neatly pinned up, tumbled down around the shoulders of her dressing gown. At 5 foot 8 inches, Karin Wallich was as tall as her son, but tonight she seemed very small next to him.

A woman's scream echoed up from the street. Peter's mother winced and clutched his arm. More crashing glass. Now she looked back through the darkened doorway of the bedroom as if she expected the shouts of Nazi voices and the pounding of fists against the front door at any moment. Her wide brown eyes brimmed with tears. In spite of the terrifying sounds emanating up from the streets of Vienna, Peter could only think how weary his mother looked. Weary and very, very sad.

She took his hand. "Come to the window, Peter," she whispered softly, as if she had wakened him to watch the first snow fall.

He obeyed without speaking. The floor felt cold beneath his bare feet. He reached to pull back the curtain. She stopped his hand with her arm and warned him with a look. Then she parted the lace a mere inch to reveal a slice of the inferno that raged beyond the thin pane of glass. Putting his eye to the slit, Peter gasped.

"The synagogue!"

Ashes swirled up. Tongues of fire leaped from the broken windows of the synagogue at the end of the block. The great cupola of the building resisted the ring of flames that danced around it. For a brief instant Peter hoped the city fire department might come and save the shell of the imposing edifice. Then, his mother directed his eyes to the west and then to the east. The horizons of Vienna glowed with a false and horrible dawn.

"There," she said. "Do you see? Not just our synagogue, but all over Vienna . . ." Her voice faltered. She stepped back and sat down heavily on the edge of the bed as Peter continued to watch the fire. So beautiful. So terrible. The burning of the Torah scrolls. The defying of God himself, it seemed.

As Peter watched, orange sparks showered the cupola, glowing bright as stars. Then the orange pinpoints deepened in color and spread in broad, hot patches on the surface of the roof. Suddenly a blade of flame pierced through the dome. Then another stretched upward. Within moments the roof collapsed with a tremendous roar and the fire blazed skyward through the skeletal frame of the building.

Hearing someone in the room whispering, *"Why? Why?"* Peter realized with a start that it was his own voice. He turned briefly away from the scene to look questioningly at his mother. Light and shadow played on her pale face. Gold reflected in her hair until it seemed to him that she was also being consumed with flame. He looked down at his own hand. *Yes. The inferno touched him as well.*

And then he saw *them* moving slowly up the narrow street from the synagogue—a dozen of them in the back of an open truck. They were not phantoms, these arrogant Nazi gangsters; they were the stuff this nightmare was made of.

Wildly, they gestured and shouted as the truck approached a Jewish shop. By law, each Jewish business was required to identify itself by displaying the name of the owner painted in large white letters across the window. Not even the most illiterate Nazi could miss such a sign. And so, as they rounded the corner to turn on the street they saw the name *J. SINGER* stenciled across the window of the lingerie shop.

The truck squealed to a halt. A clamor of shouts echoed up, ricocheting off the facades of the surrounding buildings. Men tumbled out of the truck, directing curses and obscenities toward the Jewess who owned the once-fashionable shop. Peter thought he saw a movement of the curtain in the window above the store.

"Frau Singer," Peter said softly. The gracious old lady was a legend in the neighborhood, a legend of kindness. A widow for twenty-eight years, Frau Singer had supported herself with the lingerie business. When times had become desperate in Vienna, she had held classes in corset making for the young women who hoped somehow to leave Austria. *Surely such a trade will be useful in the world beyond the Reich,* she reasoned. But as for herself, she chose to remain in Vienna. *Bad times cannot last forever. I will wait it out. Even Aryan women are in need of excellent corsets. Good times will return for my little shop. . . .*

But good times had not returned. Stones heaved through the window, destroying even the smallest of Frau Singer's hopes.

At the mention of the old woman's name, Peter's mother joined him at the window. She held her hand over her mouth as she watched a large stone being handed down from the truck and passed from man to man like a bucket brigade. Then the last fellow hoisted the stone to his shoulder and hefted it through the air into the shop window.

The name of *J. Singer* shattered into a million shards of jagged glass. More obscenities rang out as yet another huge stone was hurled to smash what remained of the shop name. A ragged guillotine of glass hung above the display. Glass fragments slithered down to cover the sidewalk with shimmering crystal.

Peter glanced back along the route the men had taken to come this far. In their wake it looked as if the dome of the sky had shattered and fallen to earth. The street, the sidewalk, caught the reflection of the raging fire until even the ground seemed to be burning.

"What did we . . . do . . . to them?" Peter's mother croaked.

Peter did not reply. The Nazi answer to that question was a Jewish boy named Grynspan who had mortally wounded a German in Paris. That answer was enough to unleash a wave of fury that swept across all of Hitler's Reich.

From the other direction a second group of storm troopers moved inexorably toward the first group. Behind them lay the rubble of their hatred. Everywhere along the route, Peter saw men pounding against doors with axe handles and crowbars. Although the lights inside Jewish apartments remained off, the Nazis knew the location of each Jewish residence as well as they seemed to know the stores and businesses.

From the high angle of the third-story window, the scene took on a surrealistic appearance, as if Peter and his mother had awakened to a vision of judgment and hell. Peter shuddered and looked back through the doorway toward the front door. It was locked and bolted. But Peter knew, as did his mother, locks and bolts meant nothing at all tonight. Nothing if you were Jewish.

Now the terror began in earnest. More screams. Shouts and demands reverberated through the street.

"Filthy Jew pig!" A middle-aged man in his night clothes was pushed onto a pile of broken glass. "We Germans have had enough of your treachery!" The toe of a jackboot swung up to catch the man in his face, throwing him back against the wall.

Three doors down and across the street, the plate glass of a window burst outward. A human body flew screaming through daggers of glass and then fell in a bloody heap on the sidewalk.

Others, pulled from bed, were herded into the street and beaten. More storm troopers came. A fire truck moved slowly past; the fire brigade made no move to put out the fire that consumed the synagogue. Firemen sat languidly on the fenders of their truck and watched to make certain the fire did not spread to Aryan buildings. German-owned shops must be protected, after all.

A distant explosion rattled the windowpanes. Peter's eyes widened with horror. Flames and smoke billowed over the rooftops. "It is the Hietzinger Synagogue! They have blown up the Hietzinger!"

His mother crowded next to him, as if she could not believe it. Her head moved slowly from side to side in disbelief. The most beautiful synagogue in all of Vienna! A series of explosions followed in quick succession, as each of twenty-one synagogues were demolished in turn.

The Aryan citizens gaped from their windows, some smug and satisfied, others grim. Still others seemed numbed by what they saw.

It all made perfect sense. The destruction and violence was so organized, so methodical; it had to have been planned long before. Peter stared at the fragments of lettering that identified the corset shop as a Jewish enterprise. The edict ordering labeling of Jewish-owned shops had been carried out just the week before. *LETTERS TO BE STENCILED IN BOTH HEBREW AND GERMAN MUST BE CLEARLY VISIBLE FROM THE STREET.* Frau Singer had smiled and shrugged as the sign painter carefully painted the Hebrew letters she ordered. *NO NAZIS NEED APPLY,* the sign read in Yiddish.

"Those hoodlums will not know the difference," she had chuckled when it was finished.

Such small displays of defiance and humor had lifted the spirits of the Jewish community in Vienna. Frau Singer's business had improved the past week.

But tonight the civilian Nazis of Vienna came like vultures after the front line of destroyers were finished.

A portly couple from two doors down appeared outside the shattered window of Frau Singer's shop. Good people. Moral, upright citizens. They reached in through the shattered glass to pull out lingerie from the debris. Underwear. Nightgowns. Stockings. These things they stuffed inside their coats until they looked fatter than ever.

Peter's mother gasped indignantly and rapped sharply on the window to admonish them.

They looked up furtively, wondering who had seen them looting. Everyone had seen them—everyone who was not being beaten and dragged away. And others were coming to join the plunder.

"What am I doing?" Peter's mother cried as she stepped back from the window and pulled Peter away as well. "Those thieves! What is to stop them from coming up here next? Stay away from the window! They might see us and come up here!"

She put her hand to her forehead in a gesture Peter had seen made by the heroine of a movie before she swooned. He guided his mother to the edge of the bed.

"We are safe here, Mother." He tried to reassure her even though he was uncertain as well. "They would not dare to break into this apartment. Herr Ruger is not Jewish. Why would they think to come here?"

She nodded, glanced at the front door again and then back toward the eerie light. "Do not go near the window," she managed to whisper. "They must not see us here. Herr Ruger would also be punished."

Herr Ruger was away on a business trip. He had left the key with Peter along with strict instructions on the care and feeding of his two cats, Mozart and Gert. Tonight, when news of the death of Ernst vom Rath had been broadcast on the radio, Peter had insisted that they all come here to sleep, just in case there might be a demonstration. Another mass arrest, perhaps, like the one in which Peter's father had been taken.

Herr Ruger's cat Mozart rubbed against Peter's leg and then jumped onto the windowsill to stare out peacefully upon the carnage below.

Peter moved to the window again and peered around the golden tabby toward their own neighborhood. No smoke; nothing happening there—*yet*!

"I should have known," Mother moaned. "Why didn't we bring the Fischers here with us?"

"The storm troopers are not there yet, Mother," Peter reported. "I can sneak out the back, through the alley. I know a short cut. The Nazis are staying on the main streets. I'll bring the Fischers back."

She shook her head in stern disagreement even though she knew he was not asking permission. Since her husband's arrest two months before, Peter was the man of the house. He was telling her what he was going to do. "Peter, do not go!" she cried as he pulled on his socks and shoes.

Reaching for his coat and cap, he said confidently, "I know this neighborhood better than anyone. I tell you, they won't even see me, these Nazis!"

He was not afraid. A strange sense of adventure filled him, first with excitement and then with guilt. *Such a terrible night*, he thought. How could he feel anything but anger and sadness? He was grateful, at least, that he was unafraid.

Peter took one last look at his mother on the edge of the bed. She would be safe here. He did not doubt that.

"Just keep away from the window," he warned. "And if Marlene wakes up, don't let her know what's going on out there." He gestured toward the second bedroom where his nine-year-old sister and baby brother were sleeping. Marlene should stay asleep; otherwise she would be gawking out the window before they knew it!

"Be careful," his mother managed to say. She turned away from him, biting back the emotion. But he had already seen in her eyes that she felt everything he did not yet feel. Fury. Grief. Fear.

He buttoned his coat and slipped out the door quietly. Hanging back in the dark hallway for a moment, he listened as the bolt slid into place on the other side of the door. Satisfied, he ran quickly down the stairs, then through the long, narrow corridor that led to the back door of the building. He reached for the knob, then froze as a gruff voice penetrated the door from the outside.

"Stand here. If there are any Jews hiding in the building, they will try to sneak out the back way. Heil..."

Peter stared at the knob for a moment. He had almost touched it, almost betrayed himself. What could he do now? They were guarding his escape route, looking for Jews in the shadows! He had better re-think his plans.

Turning on his heel, he walked back toward the front of the building. It was more sensible to hide in plain sight. Smarter to walk through the demolished street just like the other Germans who now roamed to watch the assault against the Jews. No one would question that. If challenged, he would pick up a stone and prove that he was not a Jew. That would work. Tonight, no one would dare deny a good little Nazi boy the right of tossing a stone through a plate glass window.

He drew a deep breath and stepped out into the smoke-filled street. The mob had grown. The violence became more fierce. Men and teen-age boys held clubs aloft. Some carried cans of kerosene. All of them, though dressed in civilian clothes, wore the jackboots of their storm trooper uniforms. Screams and explosions and breaking glass filled the air of Vienna with a long, continuous roll of destruction.

————

Called to Berlin to report on Secret Police progress in Vienna, Otto Wattenbarger was on hand when the first directive was sent out from headquarters. Seldom had anyone seen this sullen Austrian smile, but tonight he smiled.

"There," he said. "This will solve a lot of problems in Vienna."

"In all the Reich," agreed Heinrich Himmler, rolling his stamp of office across an official document. "This is long overdue."

"The directive comes from the Führer, then?" Otto clasped his hands behind him and watched as the second wave of trucks rolled ominously up Albrechtstrasse.

"We have all had a hand in it," Himmler replied icily. He disliked not getting credit for the coming raids. After all, no matter who conceived the action, it was ultimately Himmler's elite corps who would begin it and carry it through to its violent end. "It is this sort of thing that demonstrates the strength of our race, don't you think?"

Otto's mouth twitched as he agreed with the head of the S.S. and the Gestapo. He must show no sign of wavering or disapproval for what was to happen tonight. "Ja. The Führer seals us to him with blood. It is true."

Himmler seemed to approve of the answer. He silently considered the red-bearded Austrian before him. Questions about his loyalty had arisen over the last several months. After tonight, Himmler could reply easily one way or the other to the superiors in Vienna who had suspected the true fidelity of this sullen and solitary man.

The eyes of Heinrich Himmler narrowed as he considered the case that had been presented to him. "You are suspected, Officer Wattenbarger."

The unsmiling face looked amused at the news. "Everyone is suspected, Reichsführer Himmler. I myself trust no one."

"A wise policy. But what do you trust in?"

"My own loyalty to a just cause. Our party. Our people. Our Führer."

Himmler raised his chin slightly. This was a stock answer. Memorized and repeated by rote by those who even now awaited execution. "Which cause? Which people?" Himmler queried. "I myself requested to review the case. It would be a pity to mistakenly lose even one loyal officer who is Austrian by birth— or so you seemed to be."

"I am what I have always been."

"We have had to replace many native Austrians with those more agreeable to our methods. And our goals." He clasped his hands on the desk and tapped his thumbs together thoughtfully. "Tonight our goals and methods are made public for all to see. No hypocrisy in the Reich. Not like Western nations. We do not want our Jews, and so we get rid of them. Those countries condemn us, and yet they do not want to take them. We are partners with the West in this enterprise. Only we are not hypocrites about the matter."

Otto inclined his head slightly as if this discussion of well-established doctrine was not really necessary. "All of this is true."

"I knew you would agree." Himmler paused. The reflection of Otto's face glinted in his glasses. "But the question has been raised whether you are hypocritical also. Do you agree with the Reich policies to save your own skin? Or . . . perhaps the skin of others who do not agree with us?"

From the beginning, Otto had felt eyes watching him. His private thoughts and motives were concealed beneath a veneer of coldness and cruelty. He did not blink or turn away from torture, even the torture of those whose hearts had been knit to his by the shared goal of the end of Hitler. He had pulled the trigger and blown the heads off his own compatriots when they could not stand Gestapo torture any longer and so became a threat to the resistance. He no longer considered his actions murder, but rather, an act of mercy and self-preservation. In this way, he had been able to remain in a position to help men of great stature escape to freedom. He had made decisions about life and death: which man must be sacrificed so another might be saved. Otto felt his own soul condemned to a hell in which his fellow Austrians hated him, even as he did what he must for Austria. He had come too far to lose it all now.

It was important that no fear show on his face. He knew what the message of fear told these men. Fear was weakness. Fear was guilt of some violation of their twisted code. "Someone is wasting your time, Reichsführer Himmler," Otto replied coolly. "If I were the investigating officer, I would address a case like this by looking first at those who accuse me of disloyalty. What is their motive? Jealousy because I do a job without flinching? Or perhaps, it is they who are disloyal. Eliminating me would make their job easier." He raised his eyebrows with a sigh of resignation. "Me? Like I said, I suspect everyone. Everyone but myself."

"An interesting defense."

"A better defense is the performance of my duty. Which"—he raised his hands and then let them fall to his sides in a gesture of frustration—"I am kept from tonight."

Himmler scratched his chin as he scanned the papers in front of him. He did not respond for a time; at last he jerked his head up as if satisfied. "Our Reich gives splendid opportunity for young men," he remarked as though Otto had applied for a job in a bank. "Forgive me. I, too, trust no one. I question and reevaluate everyone. It is the job. We have considered you for promotion, you see, and so had to make certain that you are not involved with . . . hypocrisy." The corner of Himmler's mouth turned up in a tight-lipped smile. "You are promoted." He scribbled his signature on a slip of paper that had been prepared ahead of time. Laying it aside, Himmler then handed the photograph of Thomas von Kleistmann to Otto, who looked at it without emotion.

"A messy job." Otto managed to tinge the words with a hint of amusement.

"It is impossible to recognize the man, of course, but he was linked to traitorous operations in Vienna."

"He failed miserably at his task, then." The humor in his voice satisfied Himmler.

"The Führer has asked that the photograph be circulated in Intelligence departments as an example of what happens to a hypocrite."

"A unique sort of death. Will the Führer have him bronzed and hang him in St. Stephan's?"

Himmler laughed, a short burst of laughter. He would have to remember to tell the Führer about the comment. "Well, I am certain you can carry out this order then." He handed the signed slip of paper to Otto, who read it as though it was a grocery list.

Here was the final test of his hardness and loyalty. It was everything he had dreaded over the last two months. Quietly, Otto had been searching for some way to save the life of Michael Wallich, a well-respected attorney in the government of the Austrian Republic before the Anschluss. Otto had supplied information about the well-being of Wallich and encouraged that negotiations be stepped up for a ransom. Now Otto was commanded to execute Michael Wallich upon returning to Vienna next week.

Otto's hand did not tremble as he read the order for Michael Wallich's execution. In a gesture of unconcern, he folded the slip in half and slid it into his pocket. "Is that all?"

The murder of this good and innocent man had been first on Himmler's mind. Now there were other matters to address. "Next week we begin meetings in Vienna to establish the final borders of Czechoslovakia. The Hungarians, who did not cook this stew, want to eat at our table. It is important that you organize unrest among the Hungarians in Vienna. We will need some demonstrations." He waved his hand as the sound of an explosion rattled the windows of the office. "But, never mind. We will discuss details later. There is enough going on tonight."

4

Auf Wiedersehen

Once the place had been called Sisters of Mercy Hospital for the Infirmed. But sisters no longer glided through the antiseptic halls; mercy had long since vanished. Only wards of patients, now called inmates, remained. Soon, even they would be gone. In the interests of the State, they would be eliminated to make room for yet another fine hospital for citizens of the Reich.

The smell of antiseptic did not completely mask the strong smell of urine in the boys' ward for the hopelessly defective. Twenty beds lined each side of the room. In those beds lay boys from ten years old to fourteen, many of whom had come here as tiny children to be cared for by the sisters. Cerebral palsy robbed some bright children of their ability to speak or care for themselves. Polio or accidents had paralyzed others, but left their minds quick and active. Others, like Alfie Halder, were judged to be mentally incompetent.

Alfie lay awake on his bed. A strange bright light came through the barred window and flickered on the empty beds. Some of the boys had gone away today and were not coming back: the boys who could not walk or speak. The orderlies had taken them out one at a time this afternoon and this evening. Werner, Alfie's friend, had cried tonight. Werner was ten. He had contracted polio last year; Alfie, fourteen and very big for his age, carried him places. Alfie liked it when Werner talked about the American president who had polio and yet was still president. Werner wanted desperately to go to America and told Alfie all about it. *"The Promised Land,"* Werner called it.

But tonight the orderlies had come to take Werner away, and Werner had cried and looked at Alfie with sad eyes.

"Where are you taking him?" Alfie asked the orderlies.

"To the Promised Land," the ugly-mouthed orderly said, and then he had opened his big lips and laughed as Werner cried and cried. Werner did not seem happy about going away, even though he had always wanted to go to America.

Others had gone, too—Michael and Heinrich and Fredrich. But they did not know they were leaving, and so they did not cry like Werner.

Alfie thought about Werner's dream of America and felt sure his friends would be happy there. But Alfie felt lonely tonight without them. The orange light from outside the window made moving shadows on their made-up beds. Something inside Alfie felt bad, and he did not like it. He felt like he used to when they first made him come here. He missed Werner already, just like he missed Mama.

Now that Werner had left, who would call Alfie by his real name? The orderlies called him *Dummkopf*. They did not know his real name. Only Werner knew that Mama used to call him Alfie before she died and they put her in the stone shed at the New Church graveyard. After that, Pastor had come to visit sometimes. He knew Alfie's name and promised that soon he would be out of this place. Then there were no more visitors for anybody. *Verboten*, Werner had told him. Now, nobody was left to call him Alfie.

He sat up and hugged his knees and closed his eyes to say his prayers. *"Ich bin klein . . . I am small, my heart is pure, nobody lives in it but Jesus alone."*

The door banged open, and a light caught him sitting up. It was forbidden to sit up after the lights were out.

"What are you doing, Dummkopf?" shouted Ugly-mouth.

Alfie lay down and did not answer. Sometimes they beat him, but maybe tonight they had other things to do.

"Leave the poor idiot alone," said Skinny-man as they wheeled the gurney in and to the side of Dieter's bed. Dieter had been hurt in a car accident. He could not speak. They lifted him onto the gurney.

"Let the Dummkopf sit up if he wants. Poor monster. By tomorrow he'll be dead, and where's the harm?"

Dead. Alfie knew the word well.

He lay very still, wishing they had not noticed him. He felt the nearness of the empty beds. Soon his bed also would be empty. He remembered Mama, beautiful in her best dress as she lay unmoving in the coffin. He wanted her to open her eyes and speak to him, but they closed the lid, and that was death. When someone was dead it did not matter if they closed the lid and never opened it again.

"Hey, Dummkopf!" said Ugly-mouth as they wheeled Dieter past. "Sit up and say Auf Wiedersehen!"

Alfie did not sit up. He held his breath until they closed the door behind them. Then he let his breath out in a slow groan. He bit his lip and dug his fingers into his palms. *All his friends!* He got up and tiptoed quickly to the window. Through the bars he could see a great fire in

Berlin. The clouds were lit up. Smoke poured out of a building. This also meant death.

He wished he had asked Werner what to do. He did not want anyone closing the lid on him. He turned to look at the ward. Half the beds were empty. Only Wilhelm and Daniel were next before his bed. *What would Werner do?*

Alfie closed his eyes tight, hoping the answer would come. Then he saw it. He knew what Werner would do. Werner had told him about the pillows and sneaking out the window.

Alfie took Werner's pillow and stuffed it under the sheets of his bed. He stepped back and looked. Yes. It looked as though someone were sleeping in Alfie's bed. The orderlies would think he was still there.

Out the window would be harder. There was a storage room two doors down the hall that had a window with no bars. But the window was very high. Above the shelves. Alfie could climb up, maybe even crawl out, but it was a long way to jump.

The Promised Land. Death!

Alfie looked back at those who remained sleeping in the ward. He could not take them with him. He looked at the barred window and the fire beyond. With a shudder, he went to the door and opened it a crack. The hall was empty. Lights reflected in the green tile floor. He could see the door to the storeroom.

"Hurry, Alfie," he said aloud to himself. "They will come!"

He nodded in agreement and slipped out, running to the store room and jumping into it. He closed the door behind him and looked to where the same orange light shone close to the high ceiling. He grasped the shelves and climbed up easily, just as he had climbed the trees at home.

A flimsy chain lock held the transom window. Alfie broke it easily and pulled down the frame. A blast of cold air hit his face as he lay along the top shelf. He laughed. The air smelled clean, not like the ward. It smelled like the Promised Land!

He did not care that it was a long way down to the ground or that it was cold and he was still in his pajamas. Alfie looked toward the row of trees that bordered the high wall of the hospital. He could climb those, too!

With that, he swung his legs around and eased himself through the window. He hung there for a moment, then smiled and let himself drop.

The ground of the flower bed was soft and muddy. He was not even hurt. For an instant he stared up at the brick wall to the little window. Then he let his gaze drift to the window of his ward. "Auf Wiedersehen," he said, then ran toward the linden trees and the wall.

He did not feel frightened, yet the hands of Berlin's Pastor Karl Ibsen trembled as he fumbled to insert the long key into the lock of the churchyard gate.

"Hurry, Karl," his wife Helen urged as she looked over her shoulder. "Tor auf! Open the Gate!" Fear filled her voice, a fear echoed in the hearts of the dozen Jewish members of the congregation who had come to Berlin's New Church for sanctuary.

Karl fixed his eyes on the leaping flames of the great synagogue that burned only a block away. By the light of the fire, he found the keyhole. The latch clicked, and the gate swung back on its hinges, moaning in chorus with the groaning timbers of the synagogue.

The inferno illuminated marble headstones in an unearthly dance of shadow and light. Karl stepped aside as the trembling members of his flock filed hurriedly into the cemetery. Their huddled forms reflected the shimmering colors of the fires. Faces grim with terror looked up to watch the Star of David twist in the blaze that consumed the cupola. Molten metal shrieked and folded inward, collapsing to the cheers of a thousand Germans who watched in the street beyond.

"The church key, Papa." Lori, Karl's sixteen-year-old daughter, tugged the iron key loop from his hand and rushed ahead to open the rear door of the church building. Karl slammed the gate and bolted it securely from the inside. For an instant Karl stood transfixed as Nazi cheers rose in volume and the fires soared to singe the belly of a cloud of billowing smoke.

A small hand tapped urgently on his arm. "Papa, *please!*" Karl looked down to see the pleading eyes of ten-year-old James. His blond hair fell over his forehead and moved slightly in the unnatural wind that swirled from the fire. The air filled with a terrible roar as the entire dome collapsed. More cheers. The triumphant cry of Aryan voices almost drowned out the rumble of destruction.

"Papa!" James pulled his father's arm hard, straining to move toward the safety of the open church door where Lori waited for them. She raised her hand to beckon as a shower of ash rained down, momentarily obscuring the light.

Karl let himself be pulled along by James. He covered his nose and mouth and squinted against the sting of the smoke. His lungs ached. His mind reeled with the unreality of what was taking place tonight in Berlin.

James and Lori were coughing hard as the four tumbled into the church and slammed the door, bolting it securely. For an instant total darkness overwhelmed them. He heard the sound of a woman weeping softly, the hacking cough of a man, the sniffle of a child—hollow echoes in the vast, empty building.

The light of the fires penetrated the thick smoke and filtered through the high arched stained-glass windows of the church. Karl wiped his eyes with the back of his hand. Through the soft hues of red and blue glass, he could see the group sitting in the front pews. Men and women clung to one another, their heads raised as they listened to the last triumphant cheers of the mobs.

Still holding tightly to James's hand, Karl walked toward them. Their world burned tonight, these Jews of his own congregation. These people of the Covenant, believers in Messiah, had become the hated victims of Hitler's storm troopers. On such heads fell all the blame of one foolish boy's actions in Paris. And Pastor Karl Ibsen felt powerless to help them in the face of such vengeance.

He looked toward the plain wooden cross suspended above the altar of the church he had pastored for ten years. He had watched as other Protestant pastors had been arrested, led away, and replaced by state-appointed clergymen. He had privately anguished while he publicly distanced himself from the politics that ravaged the church in Germany. He had been successful in walking the tightrope. He had managed to shield the Jews of New Church. But tonight, the tightrope had been cut. A yawning abyss opened beneath him. For the sake of his eternal soul, he must plunge over the edge.

"What should we do?" croaked the voice of Henry Reingolt as he put his arm gently around the shoulders of his wife. Their three-year-old son lay sleeping in his mother's arms, oblivious to the terror of the night.

Karl sat down slowly. James sat beside him, while Lori stood gazing solemnly at the rose window that seemed alive with light and movement.

"What shall we do, Pastor?" Reingolt asked again. Did Pastor Karl have no answer for them? He had not failed them before now. When the racial laws had begun to destroy their lives, Pastor Karl had found ways to help. The church had eased some of the pain for them. But what was to happen now? They had not thought it could come to this.

"All of you stay here," Karl answered in a low voice.

"Will they kill us?" asked Reingolt's wife in a terrified voice.

"For tonight you will stay here," Karl said. "This will pass. They cannot keep on with it forever. Tomorrow we will decide what we must do. Perhaps we can find a temporary place for the children with the Protestant charity in Prague, just until things return to sanity. But you are all safe here tonight." More cheers from the mob penetrated the windows and shook confidence in his statement. No one spoke until the cheering died away. "You will stay here," Karl said firmly. "I will be back by morning."

"Back?" Helen sat forward and took her husband's hand as if to prevent him from leaving. He caught her gaze and held it in his steady brown eyes until her fear and resistance melted into understanding. Of course he could not stay here in safety when others of the congregation remained in grave danger. He must go to them, help them—if he could.

James clung to his father's arm. "Let me go with you, Papa," the child pleaded.

"You must help your mother, James," Karl said gently.

Only Lori was silent. She stood with her head raised slightly as she listened to the sounds of vengeance outside in the streets. Karl had not noticed how his daughter had grown into a young woman. Tonight he looked at her as if he had not seen her at all since she was a little girl. Her thick blond hair, braided, framed an oval face much like her mother's. Such a night, such a crisis, demanded that children suddenly become adults. Perhaps that had happened to Lori. With a glance she understood instantly why he must go. She nodded almost imperceptibly, as if to give him her blessing. Her blue eyes mirrored concern.

"The Kalners, Father," she said. "I telephoned. There was no answer. Please see if they are all right."

Karl stood. Suddenly he understood his daughter's unwavering agreement with his decision to go out into the midst of the riots. *The Kalner family—Richard and Leona Kalner, members of the church, are Jewish by birth. Their son Mark, like James, is ten years old. Jacob, three days younger than Lori, is handsome, athletic. Is he also interested in Lori's safety?* Karl wondered.

Helen reached up and took her husband's hand. She whispered the names of other members of the congregation who had not made it to the church. "We will pray, Karl," Helen said.

He nodded, brushed her cheek with his lips, then hurried out the side door of the church into the unnatural night.

Leona Kalner had long since removed the family name from the tiny window above the mail slot. These days it was better not to display a Jewish name in any neighborhood of Berlin.

There had been other apartments before this one when Leona had been careless; she had placed their name above the mail slot. As flies swarmed toward death, members of the neighborhood Hitler Youth converged to beat her sons as they walked home from school.

Perhaps tonight she imagined some safety in anonymity. But there was none. The Gestapo kept a complete file on the Kalner family, as it did on every Jew in the Reich. The fact that they were members of New Church made no difference. Days before, the yellow card bearing the name *KALNER, RICHARD: JUDEN* had been plucked easily from a file containing 500,000 records of potential enemies of the State.

Being a convicted criminal as well as a Jew, Doktor Richard Kalner's name and most recent address appeared on the list. The vacant window above the mail slot made no difference at all.

From the first broadcast of Ernst vom Rath's death, Richard had resigned himself to what the long night must bring. Had Hitler not spoken of reprisals that would take place against every Jew in the Reich in such an event? "The entire Jewish race will be held responsible for the rash act of even one Jew," Hitler's voice had growled for all the world to hear. No nation had challenged such a policy. Therefore no one could be surprised at the ferocity of Nazi vengeance for the murder of one of their own by a young Jew in Paris.

The apartment was lit by the fires that raged through all Berlin. Jacob was banished to the attic to hide with ten-year-old Mark. The two boys had protested, saying that they should stay downstairs and fight the Nazis, to defend their few remaining possessions.

"You are the only possessions we have that matter," Richard Kalner had explained. "Do not be so brave, Jacob, or they will succeed in destroying everything."

Leona, who maintained faith in the nameless mail slot, held out hope. "Maybe they will not come here. It is just a precaution. Do as your father says."

Fully clothed, dressed for the cold November night, Jacob and Mark crouched in the narrow crawlspace that led to the roof. If the Gestapo came, they were instructed to flee to New Church for refuge.

A small skylight above them provided ventilation for the attic and access to the steep roof. The dirty panes of glass reflected the blaze of Berlin's great synagogue, illuminating the boys' hiding place.

For hours they had listened in silence as the orgy of violence rolled over the city. A dozen times the phone rang. Richard did not answer, fearing the Gestapo might be checking.

Mark studied the shadowed features of his brother. In the strange light, Jacob looked much older than sixteen. His nose, broken in a fight with a gang of Hitler Youth, gave his face the look of a prize fighter. This distinction, along with his athletic build and large, thick hands, had earned him the nickname *Max,* after the German boxer Max Schmeling. Even after Schmeling had been soundly beaten by the American Negro, Joe Louis, Jacob still enjoyed being called Max. He bore the title proudly, as if it signified knighthood.

Mark deferred to his brother's wishes. "Max," the younger boy whispered at last, "you think the Gestapo has forgotten?"

As if the mention of the Gestapo might draw them to the Kalner residence, Jacob silenced Mark with a frown and a finger to his lips. It did not matter that Father and Mother were just below them; Jacob was in charge.

"But they have passed us by," Mark began again. He was tired of this cramped position. His back hurt, and he wanted to go to bed.

Jacob nudged him hard. "Shut up, I said." Then with a jerk of his head he indicated the soot-covered skylight that led to the steep shale roof. His gesture seemed to say that the Nazi storm troopers and the

Gestapo were everywhere tonight, maybe even prowling over the rooftops, perhaps hiding outside the skylight, where they could listen for the whispers of concealed Jews.

The younger brother's jaw jutted slightly forward in resentment. His eyes stung from the smoke that drifted into the attic. Mark wanted to believe that the Nazis were not coming tonight. Maybe they had forgotten to add the Kalner family to their list of Jews. But Jacob did not believe in miracles. The long night was far from over.

Mark closed his eyes and leaned against a rafter. He listened to the voices of his father and mother below. He could not understand what they were saying, but the fear in their voices was unmistakable. Outside, a truck rumbled past the building. Far away men were shouting. *Why do Nazis always shout?* Mark wondered. *Everyone can hear them easily enough without the shouting.*

For a time, Mark listened to the rustle of an unseen mouse in the corner of the attic. They had disturbed its sleep, invaded its home— just like the Nazis.

Opening one eye, he could see that Jacob also leaned against a rafter. His eyes were closed. Not even fear had kept him awake. Mark followed his brother's example and finally let himself drift into an uneasy sleep.

5

Retribution

From his position at the punch bowl, Murphy conceded that Elisa had been right all along about the perfect acoustics of the main room in the Red Lion House. Of course, tonight's musicians were a world away from the classical long-hair types she originally had in mind to play for the party. Famous and much-loved by the radio fans in the States, the trio had begun to make a mark in Europe.

In front of the bay windows of the crowded room, *D' Fat Lady Jazz Trio* belted out the raucous melody of a Fats Waller song. A massive, large-mouthed black woman in a shiny red dress rocked and swayed and tapped her feet until the oak plank floors vibrated. Her eyes widened coyly as she sang, *"Yo' feet's too big!"*

Charles sat cross-legged on the floor, just an arm's length from the tapping red patent leather shoes. Half a dozen other children who had come with their parents squealed with delight as the ebony songstress reached down to pluck off the tiny shoes of an eight-year-old girl. The woman held them up with the musical explanation, "Oh, ba-by! Yo' feet's too big!"

Party hats askew, faces red with laughter, the children howled and held up their feet, waving them in the air. The laughter of Charles, clear and bell-like, made Murphy laugh, too. He had never seen the child so joyful and without care, never seen his bright blue eyes so free of pain.

Murphy was glad they had gone on as if nothing had happened in Paris. International crises seemed a small matter compared to the happy face of Charles. Elisa and Anna had both squared their shoulders and shaken off the news. Elisa had not mentioned it again. Whatever foreboding she felt was well concealed.

Elisa, radiant, wore a royal blue satin evening dress with a trim waist that had made her grimace when he helped her with the buttons. "There's not room enough in here for two," she had smiled over her shoulder as Murphy kissed her back and slipped his arms around her. In another week or so Elisa would have to hang up this particular dress until after the baby was born. For the moment, however, she was still a knockout—smooth cream poured into a slender blue mold.

Murphy eyed her approvingly as she chatted with several members of the press corps. He was glad she was his wife; otherwise just seeing her would be an agony of longing.

He caught her eye and touched his hand to an imaginary hat in salute. She raised her glass slightly in acknowledgment of his admiring glance. He pointed up toward the bedroom with his thumb and raised his eyebrows questioningly. She rolled her eyes in disapproval and turned to chat with the round-faced Betty-Boop wife of Harvey Terrill. *Ah well,* Murphy thought, *I'll try again later. After all, Elisa can't unbutton the dress without my help.*

He grinned and handed a cup of punch to the vicar of the little stone church across the square.

"Lovely party." Vicar Hight raised the cup as if to smell the punch. "Interesting music." He blinked toward the gyrating trio who pounded out a rhythm the likes of which had never been heard before in Red Lion Square. "Wherever did you find such an unusual group?"

The fame of *D' Fat Lady* in America had obviously not reached the ears of the astonished vicar yet. In Paris, crowds stood in line for hours to hear the group. But this was London, after all.

Murphy was glad they had included the neighborhood cleric on the guest list; otherwise the noise might have been a subject for his next sermon. He seemed quite taken with the energetic performance of *D' Fat Lady*.

"They were playing at a little club in Soho. Trying to earn enough money to get back to New York on a cattle boat," Murphy joked.

The vicar's eyebrows raised a row of furrows on his high forehead. "Most unusual! Most, *most,* unusual!" He sipped his punch and nodded his long, thin head in time to the music.

"Glad you approve." Murphy refilled the clergyman's cup and looked around the room at the faces of the guests. Nothing like a pastor or two to add respectability to a get-together.

Elisa's orchestra friends listened with a sort of stunned astonishment. The music seemed totally improvised and, after all, members of the London Philharmonic did not often visit the kind of places *D' Fat Lady Trio* performed. This was a novel experience. Perhaps some quietly wondered how a fellow like John Murphy had ended up with a musician like Elisa, and how such a mismatched union could last. But for the most part, cellists and horn players and violinists thumped him on the back and told him what a *smashing* couple they made, and that they were certain to liven things up in London.

Murphy's friends put a different emphasis on the situation. *"How'd he ever end up with such a classy dame? You think she's got sisters?"*

Elisa had no sisters, but her mother still turned heads. Anna moved among the guests, speaking first in English and then in German, French, Czech, or Polish. Whatever nationality was represented here tonight, Anna always had a warm comment on the tip of her tongue. The only people she could not understand were the members of the jazz trio. This brand of English, she confessed to Murphy, was quite beyond her reach. Even the language of their keyboard was totally unfamiliar to her.

Anna stood to one side of the piano and shook her head in awe. Charles and Louis sat beside Philbert Washington, the piano player, watching his ebony fingers fly over the ivory keys while he tap-danced at the same time.

"I will ask Nana to teach me to play piano like this," Louis said gravely in German. "This kind of piano I like."

At that, Anna rolled her eyes in mock dismay and retreated to the kitchen to check on the supply of hors d'oeuvres.

Charles, on the other hand, was fascinated by Hiram Jupiter, the trumpet player. He held the shiny silver instrument to his lips and bent back and back until the trumpet pointed up at the ceiling. Notes wailed out like a human voice, surpassed in volume only by the voice of the Fat Lady herself.

It was only a matter of time before the less stodgy of the orchestra members had American jazz pounding in their blood. One by one, instruments were unsheathed—trumpets, trombones, clarinets. And *D' Fat Lady Trio* grew in numbers as well as in volume.

In the center of all of it was Dr. Patrick Grogan, Charles's American speech therapist. To the amazement of everyone, the normally serious scholar borrowed a fiddle and joined in with what he termed "Irish-American jazz." Red hair flying and face flushed, he danced a jig and whooped as loud as anyone! Charles decided that he would never be intimidated by Doc Grogan again after such a lively show. Strange how this music cracked the reserve of the most sedate personalities!

The evening was a wonder, a miracle. The London *Times* society correspondent promised a stunning write-up. "Who would have imagined that a benefit for refugees could turn out to be the party of the season?" he babbled ecstatically. "Surely you could not have found this group penniless in a club in Soho? A cattle boat to New York, you say? Good heavens!"

Murphy then confessed that the group was second only to Glenn Miller in U.S. popularity. The correspondent seemed unclear about the identity of Glenn Miller, so Murphy let the Soho story stand.

When the Fat Lady finished her song, the applause was deafening.

Charles and Louis cheered the stiffly bowing orchestra members who now flanked the trio. Rowdy pressmen and the less expressive guests joined together in a shout of approval and a cry for more. The trio had grown to a band of twenty-two.

The Fat Lady leaned down and cupped her big pink palms around the chins of Charles and Louis. "Oh, babies, so you likes D' Fat Lady's singin'!?"

The twins nodded vigorously, their bright eyes filled with the wonder of warm chocolate skin and hair black and curly like a lamb and lips that split the happy face in a dazzling smile.

"Would you babies like fo' Fat Lady t' sing somepin' jes' fo' you?"

Murphy thought the blond heads might bob off the shoulders of Charles and Louis as the boys nodded enthusiastically.

The Fat Lady had so many teeth! She laughed and showed them all. She dedicated the next song to *Charlie* and *Louie,* who both blushed with pride at the attention. Although the vast majority of those at the party were still unclear as to who D' Fat Lady was and where the group had come from, Charles and Louis had become fans listening to the radio in New York. Finally meeting D' Fat Lady in person was more than either had expected, it seemed.

"Well now, babies, then D' Fat Lady gonna sing you what my Mama use t' sing me 'fore I went t' bed." She winked at Elisa, who nodded with approval. It was nine o'clock—bedtime. Perhaps this moment had been prearranged between the two women.

The Fat Lady stood up straight and tall in her glittery red dress. She filled her lungs and opened her mouth to sing.

*"Hush! lit-tle baaaaby! Don' you cry! . . .
Mama's gon' sing you a lul-la-bye!"*

The first bar was sung without accompaniment—very slowly, almost like a love song, Murphy thought. But it did not take *D' Fat Lady* long to get wound up. The trumpeter joined in, and then the piano as the lullaby turned into a full-fledged attack of Cotton-Club jazz. Heads bobbed. Sweat flew. Feet tapped.

She pulled Charles and Louis up and began to dance with them while the trumpet player wailed.

Never had there been a moment to equal this one in the boys' lives. To dance! They had never danced. To laugh! They had never been anywhere where the very air seemed filled to bursting with laughter! They danced and mimicked the movements of the tap-dancing piano man. And when the trumpet wailed its last, *D' Fat Lady* took their hands in hers and made them bow with her and bow again while everyone applauded wildly.

———

"But I want to go!" insisted Artur Bader, the fiance of Sharon Zalmon. "I will kill them with my bare hands!" His face was contorted with rage. Tears streamed from his eyes as he spoke.

"You will get us all killed." Orde roughly brushed away the man's tears. "Go and sit Shivah. Cry for her for seven days. Cry until you have no more tears, because if you wish to beat the Arab gangs, you must not cry again." He turned slowly, looking over the group of determined faces who stared back at him. In the end he chose six who showed no sign that they had mourned. "Those who come with me tonight— or any night—must not sniffle or cough or slip on a stone."

"I will avenge her!" cried Artur. Others joined in angry agreement. "They will find the bodies of their women and children when they return from here!"

Without thinking, Orde slapped the man across the face. The room grew suddenly silent as though he had slapped them all. He stared back at each one with a withering look. His eyes demanded that they listen and learn from him.

At last he spoke. "We are not making war on the Arab nation, but on Arab gangs. Toward the ordinary Arabs, we will refrain from cruelty and brutality. A coarse and savage man motivated by revenge makes a bad soldier. And after you are through with your grief—" He looked at Artur Bader. "Then you will behave with respect toward Arab wives and children and innocent individuals." He smiled a slow, knowing smile. "But you will not let a single culprit escape." He addressed the others. "Do not imitate the British Tommy. Learn his calmness and his discipline, but not his stupidity, brutality, and vengefulness."

This was lesson one, words spoken to the grieving men of Hanita over the still-warm bodies of their loved ones. To Moshe, this Captain Samuel Orde seemed a strange man, yet a man to be admired as well. Weariness seemed to vanish when he spoke. The meaning of *Haganah,* or *self-defense,* took on a thousand nuances.

The others, the ones with runny noses or coughs or tears in their eyes, simply listened to the instructions Orde issued to the six who would leave the compound tonight. They would bring back a few checked keffiyehs, the Englishman promised. Tonight they would see what could be done with the help of Almighty God!

Then the English Zionist insisted they stop and pray, the strangest instruction of all. Orde would not take them unless they knew how to pray, and pray silently.

As Orde made his entreaty to the Almighty for the safety and success of tonight's mission, he kept his eyes open and watched the men, noting those who did not bow their heads. From this group, two more men were eliminated from the patrol. They, like the men with sniffles, were placed on the sideline. The mission was too dangerous for athe- ists, Orde insisted, and this eliminated Moshe from the group.

He was about to argue when a knock sounded at the door of the infirmary. Zach opened it, revealing a middle-aged Arab in traditional dress flanked by two other members of the settlement. Bowing in salaam, he looked first at Zach and then at the bloody sheet. His eyes were wide as he explained the purpose for his visit.

"My friends," he said in a voice thick with sympathy, "our village heard that you were raided tonight. That some had been killed. May Allah the great and merciful have compassion on you, our neighbors."

"And have you come to tell your neighbors this only?" Orde interrupted, looking sternly at the man.

"No. We heard that an English officer came through the gates and now will go after the criminals who have done this thing." He waved a hand toward the bodies. "Our village knows where these wicked members of the Mufti's gang are hiding tonight, and I will lead you there."

"For a price?" Orde asked, staring hard at the man's head covering.

"For friendship." The Arab spread his arms wide and smiled broadly. His glance involuntarily flicked to the bloody sheet, then back again to Orde.

Orde did not return the smile. His eyes were hard and cold, dissolving the overly eager smile of the Arab. A muscle in the man's cheek twitched as he struggled to maintain the illusion of grinning friendship. Orde stepped closer and, pushing the Arab with one finger, backed him out the door.

"How do you know these details?" Orde queried, and the dozen members of the settlement followed Orde and the Arab out into the darkness.

"We have spies who have seen them. A shepherd. The vile enemies of peace are hiding in a wadi not far from our village."

Again, Orde pushed the man back until they stood in a circle of light that came from the window of the little morgue. "How many raiders?" Orde asked in a flat tone.

The Arab shrugged. He was nervous; he did not like the finger of the Englishman pointing at him. "Fifty, maybe."

Orde reached up and took the edge of the man's head covering between his fingers. Then as beads of visible sweat formed on the Arab's brow, Orde poked two fingers through a tear in the fabric. "How many men came through the barbed wire, friend?"

At this question the Arab grew dark and sullen. His mouth turned down and his eyes were black with hatred of this Englishman. "How could I know that?"

"Because you were there." Orde jerked the keffiyeh from the Arab's head and tossed it to Zach. "Take this to the cut in the wire. You will find the patch missing from this keffiyeh is still there."

Zach stared at the hole in the fabric and then, as an angry realization filled his face, he tossed it to a young man who ran into the darkness toward the fence.

"No. Me? I was not there!" protested the Arab, backing out of the light.

Orde jerked him back. "You are a liar." He smiled coldly. "And a murderer of women."

"No!" Sweat poured from the accused. "Not me, Englishman! I did not . . . not my dagger!"

"Were they killed with a dagger, then?" Orde pretended surprise. "How would you know that? Did you see the wounds?"

The Arab laughed nervously. He looked from one angry face to the other. Friends. Neighbors. They had lived side by side a long time. "I did nothing wrong!" he protested. "Let me go. I see I am not welcome here among you anymore!" Once again he tried to back out of the light. This time hands from the circle pushed him inward.

"You are the spy," Orde said coolly, certain of the truth. "You have not come here to help, but to lead us into a trap."

"No! It is not so! I am a friend! They know me!"

"They do not know you well enough." Orde raised his head to the sound of footsteps running toward the group. The circle parted and the young man with the keffiyeh came into the light. He held up the head covering in one hand and then presented a small square of cloth to Orde.

"It is not mine!" cried the Arab. "I borrowed—"

Orde held up the torn keffiyeh and fit the fragment of fabric into the hole for all to see. The match was perfect. An angry murmur circled the group. The Arab trembled as he stared at the evidence of his treachery.

"You led them here to the weakest position in the line. You brought them to kill the woman."

"Not my dagger!" the Arab screamed.

"You knew she was on duty tonight, didn't you?"

"I know nothing!" he begged.

Orde slapped him hard on the cheek, sending him whirling to the ground. He lay there for a moment on his belly as Orde stood over him; then, in a voice dark with rage, the man muttered, "Allah Ahkbar. You are all dead men." In one swift movement he rolled over and pulled the trigger of a revolver pointed at Orde. The shot missed the side of Orde's head by an inch, and he slammed his foot down on the wrist of the terrorist. In that same moment he drew his own gun and fired once, killing the man instantly.

The circle leaned back in shocked disbelief. As the report of the second gun shot echoed in the distant wadis, they looked at the Arab, at one another, and then at the Englishman in astonishment.

Orde did not speak for a moment. He did not lift his foot from the wrist of the dead man. Great sadness filled his face as he leaned down to pry the revolver from the fingers of the assassin. He held the weapon up for all to see, and his eyes met those of Artur Bader.

"Tonight we prayed that we might bring to justice the enemies who murdered our brother and our sister." The Jews were no longer surprised that the Englishman identified himself with their besieged community. In that moment he had become brother to Sharon and Lazlo. The grief of the family was his own. "We did not have to go out to find the enemy. He came here to us. And this is what will come of all who seek to destroy the chosen people of the Lord God of Israel!"

He stepped away from the dead man and presented the weapon to Artur. "Believe it. This is your first lesson tonight. They are many and well armed. They would murder our women and drive us into the sea. They would trap us and lead us to destruction. But the Lord has not forgotten His covenant. He will bring all deception into the light. Learn this tonight, and remember it in the long struggle for survival that is ahead." He searched each face and won each heart to loyalty to his leadership. "We will do what is in our power, and the Lord will do the rest."

———

Members of the press corps seemed drawn to Elisa, while Murphy was equally plagued by musicians from the Philharmonic.

As D' Fat Lady began to belt out another tune, a dozen latecomers pushed into the packed room. Murphy was uncertain who they were. He certainly did not know any of them, and they did not look like classical musicians.

Three British members of the woodwind section had cornered Murphy and were simultaneously expressing their support for the appeasement policies of Prime Minister Chamberlain.

"Saved us from another war, he did."

"A brave man to stand up to Hitler."

"I know what war is about. Toured the front in France during the Great War. Clarinet in one hand and gas mask in the other."

Murphy simply listened with steely silence. These were colleagues of Elisa's, after all. There was no use arguing with such ignorance. They would find out soon enough what Chamberlain had traded for the illusion of "peace in our time." For the moment, at least, Murphy would let them believe that things would go on as they always had. He might have said much after a day like today. Reports poured in that new waves of violence were heating up to a rolling boil, but he had not shared the news with Elisa. This was a joyful night after all, and he would not let one shadow cross the light in her eyes.

For this reason he interrupted the clarinet player and stepped away when Harvey Terrill appeared in the room. Harvey had been left at the offices of Trump European News to man the clacking wire machines during the party.

Harvey's face showed lines of concern. His thinning hair was disheveled, and he looked as if he had fallen asleep in his suit. But then, he always appeared as if he had been on a bender, even though he never touched a drop of liquor.

He stood swaying beneath the arched doorway into the room and looked past the smiling faces. He seemed not to notice the song of *D' Fat Lady*. He was looking for Murphy. Something was up.

Murphy inched through the crowd. Reaching through a dancing couple and avoiding the intoxicated embrace of Doc, the speech therapist who was slurring his words, he tapped Harvey Terrill on the arm. Harvey's face filled with relief, then worry.

"Something's up, Boss," he said over the din.

Murphy motioned toward the door of his study. He had kept the door locked in anticipation of the overflow crowd tonight. With Harvey at his heels he unlocked the door and slipped in, warding off a drunken journalist from the INS who assumed the door led to the men's room.

Harvey fought past the man and slammed the door. Murphy locked it behind them as the shunned newsman continued to knock and demand to be let in, too.

The music, laughter, and the pounding fist on the door followed them into the study, but at least they were protected from the eyes of rival newsmen. Harvey had managed to slip in unseen by his wife, who attended the gathering without him.

"Some party," Harvey said glumly, then went to business.

"Let me have it."

"Nazis are rioting in Germany. Timmons wired in from Berlin. But it's not just Berlin. Everywhere, from Austria to the Sudetenland, the Gestapo has rounded up thousands of Jews. They're arresting thousands, he said." Harvey shrugged. "He was calling from a public phone booth near the Friedrichstrasse train depot. I could hear them shouting in the background. They got Timmons. The phone went dead."

Murphy crossed his arms and sat back against his rolltop desk. He would put in a call to the German Embassy. He had connections there. But first, there was something else Harvey wanted to tell him. "Is there more?" Murphy leveled his gaze at the little man.

Harvey worked his mouth nervously. "And there was this guy—" He started his sentence in mid-thought, as if someone suddenly turned up the volume on a recording. "He came into the office tonight and brought this." He produced a crumpled envelope. "Said it was something . . . about your father-in-law. Theo Lindheim." Sweating, Harvey thrust the envelope into Murphy's hand. "So here it is."

The envelope, addressed to Murphy, bore lettering in German script. Murphy did not open it, but instead thanked Harvey, who seemed frightened. "A German?" Murphy probed.

Harvey nodded.

"Tall and dark-haired?" Murphy considered his source at the German Embassy.

"No. Short. Thinning gray hair. About fifty. Overweight, with thick spectacles."

It did not sound like anyone Murphy knew. "No name?"

"The guy came in the back way. Through the alley door. Wouldn't come clear inside. He just said you gotta have this tonight." Harvey glanced toward the fireplace and then toward the window as if he sensed some danger. "He seemed so secretive. Scared, even. I didn't know. I locked up and came right down here."

Murphy nodded and bit his lip. He was anxious to read the letter, but not with Harvey looking on. "Go on back to the office now, Harv. I'll make a couple of phone calls, tell the German Embassy that a TENS Berlin reporter has apparently been illegally arrested. Where was he?"

"Friedrichstrasse Bahnof."

"They won't hold him. Don't worry. I'll wrap things up here and grab a couple of copy writers. With everything breaking this fast, it sounds like we'll have the wires jammed with stories before long."

Harvey edged toward the door. "There was stuff coming in from Vienna when I left."

"Grab a sandwich on your way out." Murphy pocketed the letter as if it were of little interest. In fact, it burned in his hand. The messenger must have been terrified to pass the letter along through the hands of an ordinary reporter like Harvey. Most likely he had been tailed by Gestapo in London.

Murphy put an arm around Harvey's shoulders. "Just don't mention this to anybody, will you, Harvey? Especially not Elisa."

Harvey placed his hand over his heart in solemn oath.

The intoxicated guest still banged on the study door. "Take this guy out with you," Murphy instructed Harvey. Then, as he opened the door his eyes caught Anna holding a tray of hors d'oeuvres and smiling. Instantly, her smile faded. *Something to do with Theo* the look said as she stared at Murphy framed in the doorway.

Murphy looked away and closed the door against her knowing glance.

Beyond the heavy door, the Fat Lady crooned, *"I'd rather be bluuuue!"*

Murphy tore open the letter and began to read. The message was written in all capital letters in English:

THEO LINDHEIM TARGETED FOR ARREST BY GESTAPO IN BERLIN. YOU ARE ALL WATCHED VERY CLOSELY. BE WARNED. IT IS NOT FINISHED YET.

No other word; no signature. Murphy felt the blood drain from his face as he read and reread the message. *Theo in Berlin? He had told Murphy and Elisa that he was going on a business trip to Switzerland. Geneva. He would not go to Berlin! Somebody was way off on their information—unless . . .*

He jammed the letter into his pocket and burst out of the study to see Elisa. *Just to see her!* His heart was pounding as the implications of the warning raced through his mind. Suddenly the illusion of personal peace vanished for him. The towering form of Freddie Frutschy stood smiling over the assembly like an enormous bear in the corner. Then Freddie noticed the look on Murphy's face. He moved toward him. With a jerk of his head Murphy indicated that the big man should keep a close watch on Elisa. There were so many people here tonight, people Murphy did not know.

Anna worked her way toward him through the crowd. Her smile blinked on and off as she politely acknowledged those she passed. Her eyes betrayed her concern. Murphy could not shut her out again.

"What is it?" she asked quietly, imploring him to speak the truth.

"Anna . . ." He drew a deep breath and then stepped back into the study, pulling her after him and locking the door. "Where is Theo?" he asked bluntly.

Anna looked at the floor and then up into Murphy's eyes. "How much do you know?" she asked.

"Anna, is Theo in Geneva?"

She hesitated, then shook her head slowly. So, the warning was true. They had sent Theo to Berlin to present the economic trade plan in hopes of securing the release of Jewish assets in Germany.

He answered his own question. "So. They asked him to go."

"How do you know this?" Anna pleaded. Tears brimmed in her eyes. "Has something happened to him? What news have you heard?"

"There are riots in Germany. Retaliation against the murder of vom Rath. We expected as much."

"But what of Theo? How could you know about this? I only knew because I guessed. We decided Elisa must not know. He left under a false name and a British diplomatic passport. Top secret, they said. How can you know this?"

Murphy did not take the note from his pocket. His fingers closed around it as he considered what he should say. "Somebody recognized him in Berlin," he replied, trying to sound calm, although his insides were churning. "You know, we newsmen always hear rumors. I wanted to check this one out with the boss."

Anna sat down heavily in the chair before the fire. She looked terribly weary, much older than she had looked a few minutes ago. "And what rumor have you heard? You must tell me. Is my Theo dead, John?"

He laughed—a short, incredulous burst. "Anna! I told you all I know. Someone recognized him in Berlin. I heard about it."

"And there are riots in Berlin. Against the Jewish people. Ah. Göring never intended to negotiate with Theo for the release of even one, did he?" She looked up, suddenly angry. "I am going home with our sons. My little sister is in Berlin with her family. I sent her our phone number with Theo. Perhaps there will be a phone call." She stood. "I must go home." She trembled as Murphy took her by the shoulders.

"I did not mean to worry you." He was mentally kicking himself for the tactless way he had handled the matter.

Anna patted his cheek affectionately. "Say nothing to Elisa," she said. "I am . . . I have learned that Theo and my sister are in God's hands. I know it here." She tapped her temple. "It has not yet sunk in here, however." She pointed to her heart.

She drew herself erect, and with a smile on her face she made her way through the crowd to hug Elisa goodnight. Murphy watched her with admiration and then instructed Freddie to escort her safely home.

Murphy tried to smile as Elisa slipped her hand in his. "You sure do know how to pick a band, Mr. Murphy!" She tucked her arm through his and leaned her head against his shoulder.

"You didn't realize I knew so much about music." He attempted to sound light, relaxed. It worked; she did not seem to notice that he was searching every face, looking for some unseen threat.

"Even Horace Bently, the publicity man at the Opera House, is impressed. He says that the Fat Lady could have been the finest contralto in the world with such a voice!"

"She would have added an interesting aspect to Wagner's operas. Dress her up in a Viking helmet and . . ." He was babbling, noticing all the faces he did not recognize.

"Well the success of the party is due to you. Charles and Louis are going to remember this night forever. Tap dancing with D' Fat Lady—much more exciting than an evening of Bach!"

Murphy wanted the party to end. He looked at his watch. *Nine-thirty!* This could go on indefinitely. Who were all these people, anyway?

The piano player began a slow jazz piece. Sandwiches and hors d'oeuvres disappeared at an astonishing rate. The offices of American News Agencies on Fleet Street were abandoned for the most part. This party could, indeed, last until morning.

But it did not. Murphy glanced up as someone began shouting from the arched doorway. The music died down.

"They've done it! The Nazis have. . . ."

The voice rose and fell, struggling to be heard against the din.

"All hell is breaking loose! I just got it over the wire! Where is Ted

Richter? Richter? INS! Come on! I tell you, the Nazis are tearing up the place over there!"

Murphy never got a clear view of the face of the man who was calling for Richter. Drunk and sober, the members of the press suddenly stampeded for the exit, pocketing sandwiches, grabbing coats in a mad scramble. Within moments, the room had emptied by half.

Murphy watched the mass exodus with a sense of relief. He did not move from Elisa's side. He would not.

"Well, now we know who all the guests were," Elisa said. "Your friends, darling."

"My competition," he said.

"You're not going to the office?"

"I sent Harvey back. The staff will manage without me."

"What is it?" Her brow puckered with concern.

"Riots in Germany. Nazi retribution."

"Jews?" she asked.

He nodded a reply. He would not give her more details. She had been through enough. Unless she asked, he would not tell her. And even then, he would not tell her everything he knew.

6

A Tour of Hell

Peter Wallich found himself among a crowd of thousands in Vienna. He did not recognize the faces of those who ran past him. He looked back toward Herr Ruger's apartment, where his mother waited.

The smoke stung his eyes. A shout sounded from above, and he turned his face upward as two Nazis gleefully tossed a small dog out of a fourth-story window. The creature landed with a yelp and managed to drag itself a few feet before it collapsed. Furniture rained down from the apartments above the shops on the north side of the street. Clothing floated like tormented spirits in the turbulent air.

Peter forced himself to keep walking. He tried not to look up as a crowd gathered on the sidewalk below an apartment.

"Throw him down!" jeered the mob. *"We'll catch him!"*

There was nothing left to throw out of the window except an old Jew and his wife. Screams and pleas for mercy blended with Nazi curses and laughter.

"Tell us where it is, old man!" shouted two big S.A. men as they dangled the old man over the pavement by his bare feet, four floors above the sidewalk.

"There is nothing more! Nothing I tell you!"

"Tell us where you've hidden your gold, or—"

Peter looked up for a fraction of an instant. His breathing grew shallow with fear as he recognized the old watchmaker's wife tearing at the men who held her husband.

Peter looked away. He jogged toward the corner; a few more steps and he was safely out of sight. But he heard the final agonizing cry as the man hurtled to his death.

After a moment of total silence, a mighty cheer rose up. Peter felt suddenly ill. Leaning against a lamppost, he fought for breath as the crowd surged around him. His sense of adventure vanished as the scream echoed in his mind. *Now* he was afraid! Fear made him want to run. And if he ran, they would recognize him for what he was and chase him down as certainly as hounds chase a rabbit.

He had forgotten his purpose. For a moment he could not think why he had come out or where he was going. He looked up at the flames of Turnergasse Synagogue. Another explosion sounded, far away. Peter shook himself free from the terror that rooted him to the sidewalk. He pushed himself away from the streetlamp and staggered numbly toward his own neighborhood. Remembering the Fischer family, he quickened his pace and moved in and out of the throngs who had come out for the show. The street widened and the crowd thinned. Peter hoped they had not reached his apartment building. Perhaps there was still time to lead the Fischers back to the safety of Herr Ruger's apartment.

He jammed his hands down into his pockets and leaned forward as he walked, as if struggling to move against a great wind. He no longer looked to the right or left. Shop windows were broken everywhere. Men and women, even small children, reached through the showcase windows to gather what they could.

On the corner, two policemen watched the looting. They talked with each other as if nothing unusual was happening. Peter pressed past them. They did not challenge him.

He felt the crunch of glass beneath his feet as he turned onto his own street. He stopped and gasped. The scene was the same. The destruction was complete.

A large open truck was parked outside his apartment building. Uniformed Nazi troopers and Gestapo men in trenchcoats supervised the loading of Jewish prisoners into the back.

Peter stepped back into a shadow to watch. He looked up at the window of the Fischers' apartment. The window was open; lace curtains wafted out.

He followed the facade of the building to the window of his own apartment. The light was on; shadows of men moved inside, searching, tearing the place apart.

Peter clenched his fists. His nails dug into his palms as he battled the urge to run screaming at the Nazis who now shoved Herr Fischer out the door of the building. The man was hatless. His overcoat was open, revealing his nightshirt tucked into his trousers.

The butt of a rifle urged him, stumbling, toward the back of the truck. In the dim light, Peter could see blood on his face. His nightshirt was splattered with blood. He wore a bewildered, frightened expression. His captors looked confident and righteous, amused by their own cruelty.

Peter was too late. With horror, he recognized the faces of a dozen

boys his own age peering out from the back of the truck. Adam Sie-
benson was only fourteen, and yet, there he was, jammed against the
wooden slats of the vehicle.

Peter could do nothing. Blood drumming in his ears, he turned
away to walk back toward Herr Ruger's apartment. He tucked his head
down in the collar of his coat, fearing that he might be recognized as
a Jew by someone in the district. It would only take one hostile neighbor, and Peter would find himself in the back of a prison truck headed
for a concentration camp!

He stared at his shoes and the shards of glass beneath his feet. He
no longer raised his eyes to gape when men shouted and women cried
out. In the center of the street a pile of furniture, doused with kerosene
and set ablaze, illuminated the area like daylight. The carnage and
looting proceeded with ease by the light.

Peter fearfully tugged the brim of his cap down low over his eyes.
He grimaced as the fumes of kerosene and smoke stung his throat.
Such bitter smells did not seem to bother the rioters. They laughed and
jeered at their victims as if the air were untainted. Only Jews seemed
to cough. Only the tormented seemed to wipe their eyes and cover
their noses against the smoke of Vienna. Trying not to cough, Peter
plunged on through the crowds. He did not think of the Fischers any
longer, only of himself. Of Herr Ruger's apartment. He wished his
mother had not awakened him tonight. His nightmares had been much
less frightening than reality.

He glanced ahead toward Frau Singer's shop window, nearly picked
clean. The mob moved away from him, farther up the block where new
targets were being hit.

Only half a block to safety! Peter looked up toward the window of
Ruger's apartment. Still dark; a good sign. They had not come there.
The hounds had not sniffed them out!

Against his own will, Peter quickened his pace to a jog. The glass
cracked beneath his feet. People darted in and out of the demolished
shops at the far end of the block. For them, the night was a celebration.

The flames of the Turnergasse flared and then dimmed, leaving the
after-image of terror etched on Peter's mind. He lunged toward the door
and tumbled, panting, into the dark foyer of the apartment building.
Kicking the door shut, he groped toward the stairway and clambered
up on his hands and knees. Too weak from fear to stand, he clutched
at the banister and pulled himself up step by step. The howling of the
mob penetrated the heart of the building. Visions of darkness pursued
him and seemed to pull him back.

Until now, Peter had not noticed that his face was wet with tears.
Had he wept openly in the street? The thought brought a new wave of
fear over him. They beat anyone who wept, Peter knew. And then they
arrested them.

He wiped his cheeks with the back of his hand. On the landing, he pulled himself upright and managed to climb the remaining stairs. Leaning heavily against the doorjamb of the apartment, he knocked softly, fearful that a neighbor might hear and peer out at him.

"Who is there?" His mother's voice trembled.

"Mother?"

The door swung wide, and he fell into her arms. She closed the door and locked it, then guided him to the sofa.

"You are safe! Safe!"

"They took Herr Fischer, Mother! And some of the boys in my class! I am too late! Too late!" He was filled with remorse. Why had he not brought someone else along to Herr Ruger's apartment tonight? Why had he not known what would happen?

His mother cradled him but said nothing. She stroked his back and stared through the window at the dying glow of the Turnergasse Synagogue.

The murky waters of the Danube slid silently beneath Stephanie Bridge. The fires around the city reflected orange against the moving blackness of the river.

Lucy Strasburg leaned heavily against the stone railing of the bridge and stared into the current. Beyond her, on either side of the banks, Vienna was rocked by violence and torment. She did not think of those she saw being beaten in the streets on her long walk here. It simply seemed a suitable backdrop to the chaos of her own life.

On the Stubenring she watched an old Jew leap to his death as storm troopers broke into his apartment. Vienna was filled with the presence of death tonight.

This was the important demonstration Wolf had told her about, the Reich business that had made him late to see her! This was a reflection of the glory of the Reich he served! For the fulfillment of fire and destruction Lucy carried the child of Wolfgang von Fritschauer.

She disobeyed him. She had not eaten as he instructed her, and yet now she vomited into the Danube. She had not taken a cab to her apartment, but had wandered aimlessly through the streets for hours, hoping that somehow a stray bullet might find her, or a trooper might mistake her for a Jewess and kill her.

Foolish hope. She was so Aryan that the club-wielding Nazi patriots nodded their heads in respect as they passed her. One policeman asked her why she was out tonight. *Was it to see the Jews get what they had coming?* he asked.

And so Lucy had come here, where others had come to end their lives. She longed for the cold water to silence her problems. She watched it move away and imagined it carrying her into a long, un-troubled sleep.

Her eyes were dry. She was past crying. She had been a fool. She had thought that Wolf loved her as she loved him. *Married!* She had interpreted everything he said through her own twisted idea of imag-ined love. She had left the church, her home, her job in Munich for the sake of being near him when he asked.

Dying would be easy compared to facing her family with the truth. It was bad enough that she was forced to admit the truth to herself.

She looked across the rooftops toward the Seventh District where the men of Vienna took their pleasures at the brothels and cabarets of the city. She had scorned the women who lived and worked in such places. But was she any different? Lucy let her eyes move from one fire to another on the horizon where synagogues and Jewish businesses were being destroyed by a man-made hell. She was consumed by a hell of her own making. The smoke made her eyes burn as she looked back at the water and wondered . . .

As a child she had heard that there was another hell which burned beyond this world. What if the waters of the Danube did not carry her to a peaceful sleep but into that raging inferno beyond life?

Lucy feared the possibility, and fear alone kept her from throwing herself over the rail and into the water. She feared God and feared hell and feared her own terrible sin. She might escape Wolf and this un-wanted baby, but what if the frescos of Judgment Day in the church were true? Even the Danube could not let her escape all that! Perhaps death was only a door to something worse than this.

An open truck rumbled across the bridge. Haunted-looking men peered out at her from between the slats. Where were they being taken? What sort of hell awaited them at the end of the Nazi road?

Lucy looked down at her own hands. Her nails were perfectly man-icured, painted red, as Wolf liked them. The watch on her wrist re-minded her that even her soul now belonged to him. She had sold herself, and there was no way to buy back what she had lost.

"I am a whore," she said aloud. "I belong to S.S. Major Wolfgang von Fritschauer, and I am his whore."

Lucy did not need to jump off Stephanie Bridge to die that night. The hopelessness of this terrible truth killed something in her heart as certainly as the dark currents of the Danube could have stolen her breath forever.

Lucy stepped away from the cold stone and wiped mist and ashes from her cheek. Hell had come to earth tonight. Lucy could not think about any torment more terrible than her own.

She walked slowly back toward Franz Josef's Kai, where elegant hotels and shops lay untouched by the violence of the demonstrations. People milled around everywhere, enjoying the spectacle. She moved

among them, not noticing or caring that tonight was a night unlike any
other in the history of the world.

———————

Something terrible had happened downstairs. Charles could tell
because the music stopped and people were shouting. The party was
over.

Louis rubbed the sleep from his eyes and joined Charles at the
window. Members of the press corps and their ladies piled into a long
line of taxis, and still there were not enough taxis for everyone.

*"Ten bucks! Come on, Phipps! I'll pay the fare and give you ten bucks!
Lemme sit on your lap!"*

It was strange to see grown men fighting over how many bodies
could be crammed into one vehicle. Charles would have laughed at
them except he knew down deep that something bad had happened.

"What do you think?" Louis frowned, pressing his forehead against
the cool pane.

Charles shrugged. He did not know. Maybe they should call Elisa.
There were still some guests at the party. The members of the orchestra
were not pushing and shoving on the curb. Either they had gone out
the back way or whatever was happening did not affect them. He could
hear the low murmur of voices through the floor. The voices did not
sound happy anymore. Nobody was laughing.

He looked at his pajamas and bare feet. Maybe they should both
get dressed. He was scared. Maybe the Nazis had come into London
the way Hitler had come into Vienna without anybody knowing it. The
newsmen had run around and looked unhappy on that day, too.

"Some-thing . . . bad," Charles stammered. His mouth did not want
to talk. "Hitler, maybe."

Louis' eyes got big. He nodded, remembering the way the grown-
ups had acted in Vienna. He looked out the window and then hugged
Charles. He was crying now, and he needed Charles to comfort him
again. It was always that way when things were bad. Charles was
stronger than Louis.

Horns hooted angrily outside. And then, as Charles held his trembling brother, the voice of D' Fat Lady began to sing again. There was
no trumpet or piano behind her. The song was slow and sad. Her voice,
deep and rich, pierced the walls until it sounded as if she were right
there in the room with them. Charles had never heard her sing so
beautifully, not in all the times he heard her on the radio.

Go down, Moses . . .
Waaaaay down, way down in Egypt La-and!
Tell ol' Pha-raoh! Tell 'im!
Let. My. People. Go!

She sang songs like this for a long time. Instruments from the orchestra joined in. Charles sat still with his eyes shining in the dark as he listened. He could hear the sweet cry of Elisa's violin playing. He knew the voice of her instrument as easily as he would recognize the voice of his mother. Tonight it was sad, crying music like Charles had never heard before. Louis fell asleep with his head still cradled in Charles's arms. Charles stroked his brother's hair the way Mama used to do, and eventually he fell asleep as well.

———

"Tor auf! Tor auf! Bitte! Please! Open the gate!" Desperate voices of hundreds filled the air outside the British Embassy. Theo wondered if his friends were among those begging to enter. He frowned and thought of Anna's only sister. Little Helen. She and her family were not Jewish, but here in Berlin, they might be brought under suspicion because of their relationship to Theo.

Embassy Secretary Kirkpatrick was no longer filled with the assurance that Theo would be out of the Reich by morning. He glanced nervously at Theo's packed luggage as he explained the negotiations taking place downstairs in the office of the ambassador.

"The Nazis have stated that since you are an escaped criminal of the Reich, you will be arrested the moment you leave the compound. Of course you are safe as long as you remain here within the walls of the embassy." He cleared his throat nervously, as if he did not believe what he had just said. "They have told the ambassador that the Führer would much rather this matter be settled through proper political channels, that in light of what happened in Paris, it would be a gesture of goodwill by His Majesty's government if—"

"If I were handed over immediately," Theo finished.

Kirkpatrick nodded once, then looked toward the shuttered widow. "There are hundreds of Jews outside the gate, begging to get in, begging for refuge. It is the same at the American Embassy." He gestured toward Theo's valise. "You must leave your luggage. Come with me. Hurry."

Theo picked up two sealed envelopes. The first contained his letter to Anna. "A letter to my wife—" He held it out to Kirkpatrick. "She is in London. The other is to my sister-in-law. She lives here. Please see that they get delivered, will you?"

Kirkpatrick took the notes and pocketed them with a preoccupied nod of agreement. "Please, Mr. Lindheim. We must hurry."

Newly waxed hardwood floors squeaked beneath their shoes as Theo followed Kirkpatrick down the broad hallway of the old mansion to the back servants' stairs. Theo could not help but wonder if the Nazi downstairs could hear them, if even now his eyes turned upward with the knowledge that his prey was attempting to leave by the back door.

"Tor auf! Tor auf!" The pleading penetrated even here.

Kirkpatrick glanced over his shoulder at Theo and held a finger to his lips as if he, too, felt the eyes of the hunter.

The corridor was dimly lit by electric lights that had been converted from gas lamps at the turn of the century. The electric wires ran exposed along the baseboard of the wall, evidence that embassy renovation had been halted since the discovery of listening devices installed by German electricians in remodeled rooms downstairs. Were others planted elsewhere in the embassy? Neither Theo nor Kirkpatrick spoke. Theo did not ask where he was being led, nor did Kirkpatrick offer explanation.

Somewhere in the building a telephone rang insistently. Theo counted ten rings before it fell silent.

Kirkpatrick led the way down a steep, narrow stairway. The scent of freshly baking bread drifted up, a strange contrast to the distinct odor of smoke that blanketed Berlin. Kirkpatrick did not switch on the lights. With a touch on Theo's arm, he guided him across a tiled floor.

In the kitchen, a tall, cadaverous man in a chauffeur's uniform waited silently beside a much shorter, stocky man dressed in a business suit and a raincoat. Both looked up when Theo and Kirkpatrick entered the room.

Wordlessly, the short man shook Theo's hand; then Kirkpatrick offered a silent farewell. Theo's eyes had adjusted to the darkness, and he followed the short man toward the servants' entrance to the embassy.

The chauffeur preceded Theo out and opened the door of a black limousine that bore the insignia of the American ambassador. With a nod of his head he motioned for Theo to get in, and be quick about it.

Sliding into the backseat of the car, Theo looked up to see that Kirkpatrick had already closed the embassy door. In a moment the chauffeur started the engine and pulled slowly around to the front entrance of the building. Theo did not look out the curtained windows of the vehicle, but he could clearly hear the cries of Berlin's Jews who had gathered outside the embassy gates to beg for asylum. *"Tor auf!"* Then other cries arose—shouts of the men who had pursued them there.

"It will only be a moment, sir." The chauffeur turned his long face to look at Theo. He heard the people too, and his eyes reflected anger and frustration that there was nothing to be done. "We'll have you out of here in no time." Perhaps there was some comfort in the fact that Theo, at least, could be helped. The chauffeur sprang from the car and circled around. A moment later he opened the door and stepped aside as the short man in the raincoat slipped in beside Theo. The door shut quickly behind him.

Once again the short man shook Theo's hand. "Ambassador Hopewell," the man smiled. "We'll give you a lift to the airfield." His hand-shake was as warm as his eyes. "They're quite intimidated by us Americans, these Nazis are." He seemed pleased. "I'll be flying with you to London tonight."

Theo barely managed to repress a shudder. He felt the nearness of those who would not be leaving Berlin by their own free will tonight.

"Tor auf!"

If he looked out the window, would he see the faces of friends and family pleading to go with him? Such a thought robbed him of any relief he might have felt.

The climb over the wall was easy. Alfie wondered why he had not done it before. Perhaps it was because Mama had always told him to be a good boy; and good boys, she said, obeyed.

Alfie jogged along the wooded lane that wound through the park outside the hospital compound. It was dark, but he could see the bright light of Berlin and the big fire. Home was there somewhere.

The cold stung his bare feet. Sometimes he stumbled and almost fell, but he did not slow down as he ran. Mama had said that he was a good runner. A deer in the forest. A fine strong boy. Here he was not a Dummkopf.

The air cleared his lungs and he was not afraid anymore. The city was ahead. He would go home and get some clothes, and—

Suddenly it came to him that he could not go home. Mama would not be there. She was at New Church. Dead. Alfie stopped running now. He braced himself against a tree and struggled against the confusion that filled his head. "Dummkopf!" he said aloud. What had he been thinking of? He had been so happy that he had forgotten Mama was gone.

But there was still Pastor Ibsen! Pastor would be at New Church. He would be glad that Alfie had come back!

The other children at New Church would be glad to see him, too. Lori had always been nice to him. She did not let other children make fun of him. And Jamie had been his partner in hide-and-seek. Together they had found a dozen places to hide that no one knew about. And Pastor's wife, Frau Helen, had loved Mama. He could still remember the comfort of her hug when Mama had died.

Such thoughts led to a decision as easy as climbing the tree. Alfie would go home to New Church! They would be glad to see him come home.

The American ambassador seemed in no hurry to leave Berlin. "Turn here!" he ordered the chauffeur, who turned toward the brightest glow on the Berlin horizon. Then he looked sternly at Theo. "The President will ask me what I have seen. I intend to have something to tell him."

And so, like tourists cruising through hell, they viewed the carnage. Theo followed the example of the American and rolled his window down slightly so that he might hear as well as see what was happening.

The largest fire in the city consumed the wealthy Fasanenstrasse Synagogue near the zoo railway station. Clouds of dense smoke rolled up from the three domes of the stone building. The interior of the synagogue was a white-hot furnace; tiles of the roof glowed from the heat that devoured the rafters. Theo did not doubt that passengers arriving by train from the West could clearly see the conflagration. He watched without comment. After all, what could he say at such a sight? Did it matter that he held memories of this place and this city in better times?

The embassy vehicle inched along, hindered by the thousands who gathered in central Berlin. Dozens of men and women rushed into a smashed toy shop in the arcade on Friedrichstrasse to scoop up merchandise.

"Come on! Free Christmas presents!" they shouted.

Theo knew the owner of the elegant little shop. Anna had purchased Elisa's dolls there. Theo wiped a hand over his eyes. *Am I dreaming?* he thought. *Can this be happening?*

Gangs of youths followed the looters, smashing plate glass windows, glass display cases and counters, partitions, and even leftover toys.

The American car watched the destruction from a discreet distance with the engine still running. Five other shops in the arcade were plundered within minutes of the first.

A short distance away, on the corner of Jaegerstrasse, a second-story pawn shop became the focus of violence. Nazi youth with lead pipes broke the windows and threw fur coats down on the heads of the waiting crowds. Around the corner a tailor's shop was looted. In the doorway the tailor's dummy, with a hat on its head, was hung from the neck. *GRYNSPAN THE TAILOR!* read a sign pinned to the chest.

In front of one magic shop, children lined up holding broomsticks with string and safety pins tied onto the ends. A policeman laughed as they fished through the broken window for boxes of tricks.

While older boys and young men threw typewriters and furniture out onto the street, another gang wheeled a piano out of a music store and began to play the latest Berlin tunes for the onlookers.

The ambassador sighed heavily, glanced at his watch, and tapped the chauffeur on his shoulder. "I have seen enough," he said. The limousine slid by a shoe store where dozens of laughing men and women sat on the curb and tried on stolen shoes.

These were the scavengers, Theo noted. They came in after the Rollkommandos, the wrecking crews who proceeded from shop to shop under the command of a leader. This was not the spontaneous outbreak the Nazi propaganda machine had been speaking of. From start to finish, it seemed highly organized and well thought out.

"He owns the young people," Theo whispered, heartsick as he gazed at the evil light in their young faces. How thankful he was that his own sons had been forbidden to belong to the Hitler Youth because of their heritage! How grateful he was that they would soon be leaving for American schools, thanks to the help of Mr. Trump! Once, Theo had imagined Wilhelm and Dieter as part of Berlin. He had thought they might become businessmen, or maybe belong to the German Reichstag. But now, on this night, he saw the destruction that Hitler had brought to the souls of Germany's young people, and he rejoiced that his sons were not considered worthy to be part of German culture.

Everywhere they passed beatings and arrests; every streetlamp provided a spotlight for a tiny human drama. The audience cheered as Jewish men were kicked and stripped and beaten.

The ambassador hastily scribbled notes, writing down the names of ransacked shops he knew to be owned by Americans. Some official protest could be made based on the destruction of American-owned enterprises—three small businesses among hundreds now in ruins.

Ambassador Hopewell rolled up his window as a shout of *"Hang the Jew in his shop window"* was called by a jeering young man in a storm trooper uniform.

"And now we take our leave, eh, Mr. Lindheim?"

Theo nodded curtly. He also raised his window but could not take his eyes from the spectacle.

"You lived here your entire life?" the ambassador asked, many questions summarized in the one. *Has it always been this way with the German people? How did you survive their hatred?*

"Nearly all my life," Theo said in barely audible voice. "And life was nearly always good here."

The eyes of the ambassador narrowed with doubt. "But how—" He swept his hand toward the flames of a newly lit bonfire of furniture and clothing on the sidewalk. A Jewish couple in their nightclothes wept and begged for mercy in this tableau of horror beyond the window of the limousine. Theo wanted to jump from the car, to drag the couple into the vehicle and speed away. He could do nothing. Nothing but watch and wonder how . . .

Finally the vehicle turned onto a dark street, an obviously Aryan street. There was no destruction here, only silence and unlit windows.

Finally Theo found an answer for the American. "It is happening because we thought it never could happen here." He looked away at the slumbering houses. "We were naive. We were asleep. The Christian

Church was also asleep, Mr. Hopewell. And now we have lost our children and our nation to the darkness of that terrible sleep."

Theo did not look back toward the glowing skyline during the short trip to Tempelhof. The ambassador did not ask him any other questions, but did provide him with an answer as they turned through the gate of Tempelhof Airfield.

"They will not question you," Hopewell said. "We are blackmailing the Nazi thug who will examine your papers." He shrugged. "Sometimes we have to play the game by their rules."

7

The Death of All Hope

Pastor Karl looked in the rearview mirror of his automobile. New Church shone bright in the reflected light of the dying synagogue. He turned onto Friedrichstrasse and glimpsed the torch-bearing gangs in the shopping district eight blocks ahead.

For the first time he regretted his decision to drive the old Damlier-Benz to the Kalner apartment. Even from this distance he could see the shimmer of broken glass on the cobbled street. Crowds of spectators ringed the storm troopers as they hefted stones through plate glass windows and doused heaping piles of furniture and merchandise with kerosene. Suddenly bonfires blazed on the boulevards of Berlin's finest shopping district. Ten thousand voices raised in triumphant cheers against the Jews.

Karl slowed and pulled to the curbside. He gripped the steering wheel in astonished horror at the sight unfolding before him.

A fire truck lumbered indolently around the corner of Wilhelmstrasse. It blocked the intersection, helping to hold back the human tide from the government section of the city.

Hundreds of people swarmed the truck, climbing onto the idle equipment to sit beside firemen and watch the planned conflagration.

A group of two dozen rowdies emerged from a side street half a block from Karl's car. They seemed intoxicated with the pleasure of their task; their young faces filled with a wild excitement as they called out to yet another group on the opposite side of the wide street.

"Are we too late here?"

"Never too late until every Jew is dead!" came the reply. "Heil Hitler!"

"The next block over!" shouted another young man.

Karl tugged the brim of his hat low over his forehead and walked

toward them. They looked no older than Lori, no older than Jacob
Kalner, whom they would kill with little provocation tonight. The
thought made Karl shudder. He wondered if he was too late. *The next
street over. The street where the Kalner family lived. The pogrom was
just beginning there.*

Karl felt the gaze of a thousand spectators looking down from the
apartments above him. Some members of his congregation had lived
on this street, including two families who left the church when Karl
had refused to allow Lori and James to join the Hitler Youth. When he
did not expel the non-Aryan members of the congregation from the
church, still another spate of defections had occurred.

Karl looked up at the darkened windows of one such home and
saw the fires reflected in the glass. He wondered if that man and
woman, who had denounced his pro-Jewish policies so loudly, now
looked out and recognized him. Perhaps they stood just beyond his
view and made cynical bets about his purpose for going out on such
a night as this.

"There is Pastor Jew-lover. Probably going to the Kalners' . . ."

Karl quickened his pace. He stepped off the sidewalk to pass
around the gang of laughing young men. The cans of kerosene they
carried were all the same: government issued. These young storm
troopers, dressed in civilian clothes, still sported their military boots.

They stood languidly on the street corners, exchanging stories
about the old Jewish cloth merchant they had beaten, the daughter
they had raped after locking her mother in the closet.

"Teach those pigs a lesson . . ."

A wave of fury washed over Karl. He wanted to shake them, to shout
at them. Nazi law made it illegal for Aryans to have physical relations
with Jews, but the rape of a Jewish woman was permitted, condoned,
even admired.

Karl felt his face flush with shame and anger. He ducked his head
and walked even faster, turning down the side street where the Kalner
family lived.

He moved into the shadow of a shop entrance and looked up for
the white Hebrew lettering required by all Jewish shops. He had managed to duck into the doorway of an Aryan shop. Breathing a sigh of
relief, he took a moment to think, to look up at the window shades of
Dr. Richard Kalner's apartment. No movement. No light. The place
looked vacant from the street. Karl wondered if they were there. Had
they sat in the dark and let the telephone ring in their fear that the
Gestapo would be calling to check on Richard's whereabouts? Karl
frowned at the thought. He wished they had foreseen this, they had
devised some sort of telephone signal in the event of just such a night.
But then, who could have imagined this?

The shrieks of Jewish victims echoed up the dark street. There was not much time. Karl stepped from the shadows and half jogged across the street to the three-story apartment building. He looked to the right and the left. The Nazis, preoccupied with the beating and arresting of a father and son, did not look up. Haberdashers. Karl knew them. He had purchased his hat at their store. He touched his fingers to the hat brim in a gesture of futility and frustration. Another ten minutes and the Nazis would be here, breaking down this front door, beating Richard and Jacob, doing whatever they pleased to Leona Kalner.

Karl charged through the foyer. He considered the elevator, but did not want to wait. Taking the stairs two at a time, he reached the third-floor apartment in a matter of seconds. He stood panting for a moment, then knocked softly. He waited. There was no light under the door. Two newspapers lay outside on the threshold. Perhaps the Kalners really had left town.

"Richard," he whispered hoarsely. "Richard. Leona. It is Pastor Karl. Are you there?"

Ten seconds passed. There was no response. He raised his hand to knock again. Then the door opened, and the dark silhouette of Richard Kalner appeared, half concealed by the door. His long arm reached out and grasped Karl by the lapel of his heavy coat, pulling him in and quickly shutting the door behind him.

"Pastor Karl!" Leona was weeping softly.

"What are you doing here?" Richard sounded angry.

Karl rubbed a hand over his face. Relief and fear flooded him. He had hoped there would be nothing more to do than return to the church and report that they had slipped away.

"Get your things. No—" he stammered. "No. Best you don't bring anything more than a toothbrush. Thank God you are all right. They're coming. We have a few minutes at most. Come on!"

"We decided not to go to the church," Leona said in the dark. She did not get up from the couch.

"You are in enough trouble already." Richard's voice sounded near to tears. He had not let go of Karl's coat. "Now get out of here, Karl!"

"Not without you. No time to discuss it. Where are the boys?"

"We aren't going," Richard said firmly. "Get out of here. If they are coming and they find you here—" He did not finish the thought.

"A dozen are already at the church. I cannot be in any more trouble than I am already—unless I let you face this alone. Then I will have the Lord to answer to."

"He is more merciful than the Nazis," Richard said. "Now go back."

"You have five minutes," Karl insisted, breaking free of Richard's grip. "Get the boys. I am not going back without you."

They stood in the dark surrounded by silence, except for the approaching sounds of breaking glass and screams and shouts of exultation.

Leona stood. "Richard?" she pleaded.

"I am not like the others at the church," Richard said. "I am a political. Once a member of the Reichstag. Already I have been arrested. This time they will not let me off so easy, Karl. You do not want me at the church."

Karl turned to Leona. She seemed fragile in the half light. "Get the boys, Leona," Karl ordered. "There is no more time for discussion."

She obeyed him, as if she had been waiting and praying for someone to come for them.

Richard also sounded relieved. "Take them, then," he said. "But I must stay here. I am a danger to whoever helps me." He shrugged. "I had already instructed Jacob and Mark to go to you if the Gestapo came."

"I can hide you, Richard." Karl ran a list of places through his mind as Leona called to her sleeping sons in the attic. "For Leona's sake, Richard. For my sake. We need to try until we can find some way to get you out of this."

The violence in the street grew more insistent; there could be no question that the men were coming here. Yes. Dr. Richard Kalner was on their list.

Sleepy voices echoed from the attic crawl space. "What?"

"What is it, Mama?"

"Is it over?"

"Come down," Leona instructed calmly. "We are going to New Church. Pastor Karl has come for us."

"Papa too?" Marcus asked.

"Papa too," said Leona.

Richard moaned softly at that, then nodded his head. "All right." He ran his hand through his hair and gathered up their coats. "Dear God . . . Karl."

At that moment there came the explosion of shattering glass directly below. Then a stone smashed through the window. Leona gave a little cry.

"No! Oh, no!" And then, "Jacob! Mark! The Gestapo!"

Karl grabbed Richard's hand and checked the bolt on the door.

Wordlessly the two men moved into the bedroom to stand beside Leona. She wept and trembled silently. Richard put his arms around her. She buried her face against him as shouts and obscenities followed still more stones through the window.

"We know you are in there! Hey, Jew-pig! Richard Kalner! We know you are there!"

The thump of jackboots sounded against the stairs. They were taking the steps two at a time, just as Karl had. An instant later, their fists and crowbars hammered against the thin wood of the apartment door.

———

Shouts and curses resounded from below. Jacob slammed his hand against the latch and thrust back the skylight. A shower of ash and soot descended through the opening as he hefted Mark up and then pulled himself out onto the slick slate roof.

Carefully he lowered the window back into place, shutting off the sound of blows and the cries of his mother. Mark was crying. Tears streaked the dust on his face. Again and again he called first for his mother and then his father as Jacob dragged him away along the ridge-line of the steep roof.

In the streets the voices of a thousand tormentors and victims covered the boy's cries. His small agony was lost beneath the howling of the night. Jacob did not try to quiet his little brother. He simply held tightly to his arm and propelled him away. From one building to the next, jumping over narrow gaps, sliding down one roof and creeping up another. Always he moved toward the dark streets, the quiet streets, where *they* had not yet come.

In the distance he could see the illuminated stone figures atop the Brandenburg Gate. A block from there he could make out the storm troopers beating people outside the gates of the British Embassy. Tiny human figures in the streets below cringed beneath the blows and fell onto the glass-strewn sidewalks.

"Why don't they fight back?" Jacob cried in rage and frustration. He dragged Mark into the shadow of a chimney. Holding tightly to his brother, Jacob leaned against the warm brick and tried to think what they must do next. He peered cautiously around the corner of their hiding place. No one had followed them. For the moment they were safe, but how would they get down? Which would be the safest route to New Church? Throughout the city he could see the orange glow of fires. Yet some streets were still dark, sleeping on as if nothing were happening, as if hell itself had not come to earth.

Smoke lay thick across the rooftops. Jacob's eyes burned and watered.

"They were hurting Mama, Max!" Mark sobbed. "They hurt her! I want to go back! I want to . . ." His breath came in short spasms of anguish as he replayed the scene.

"I have to think!" Jacob shouted, feeling the crushing weight of responsibility and fear. He had not imagined that it would come to this. Now he was truly in charge. His brother's safety depended on him. He stared, transfixed, at the leaping flames of the dying synagogue. He had never been in the building before, and yet those flames singed his heart. He clenched his fists, again wishing that he could stand and fight them. But he could not. He must run and hide for Mark's sake, for the sake of the promise he had made to Papa.

"What will we do?" Mark cried. "Oh, Max! What will we do?"

In reply Jacob removed his belt and made a loop that he fastened around Mark's wrist. He then tied the other end around his own wrist, cuffing them to each other.

He put his big hand on Mark's shoulder. "First you must stop crying," he said firmly. "We must go down to the street."

"No!" Mark shook his head in terror.

"Listen to me!" Jacob cuffed him impatiently. "We *must* go down. If we stay here they will see us and know that we are Jews. They will shoot at us."

"In the streets they will catch us! Please, Max!" Mark crouched lower against the bricks as if he wanted to disappear into the chimney.

"We are going down. Going to New Church. If you cry, they will see your tears and they will know. You must not cry, Mark! Do you hear me?"

This did not stop the flow of tears. "But they have got Mama and Papa, and they will come for us at New Church, too!"

"Then we will fight them at New Church! But we must go down. We *must* get to the street and walk through them. You cannot cry! They will beat you if they see you are frightened. They will know what we are!" He removed his handkerchief and gruffly wiped the tears and soot from the cheeks of his brother. "We cannot be babies," Jacob warned. "Tonight we must be brave!" He said the words convincingly, although he did not feel very brave. Mark wiped his nose on his sleeve. He tried to smile, but his eyes betrayed his misery. He nodded. He would not cry in front of the Nazis. *He must not!*

Jacob patted him gently and pointed toward the dormer window leading to the attic of the Thieste office building. Perhaps the window was unlocked. They could get off the roof and sneak down the stairs.

The drone of an airplane engine passed overhead as the boys crept along the ridge of the roof. Jacob looked up, resenting and envying the freedom of flight. For an instant he wondered what it would be like to launch himself and Mark from the steep roof, to fly free for a few seconds and then be free forever! The thought made him pause and peer out over the edge.

"What is it?" Mark cried in alarm, as if he could see the terrible thought pass through Jacob's mind.

Jacob looked up at the blinking lights of the plane that passed far above the smoke and the terror of German revenge. He watched the plane as it circled and passed over the city once again. Then Jacob shook himself free of the force that urged him to fly away forever.

Without answering Mark, he crept forward again, straddling the roof, bracing himself on the slick shingles lest he slip and take his brother over the edge with him.

———

Great plumes of illuminated smoke rose in the night sky over the city of Berlin. The British transport plane circled back over the city for one last, astonished look after takeoff.

Theo Lindheim rubbed a hand across the stubble of his unshaven face as his gazed wearily down on the city that had once been his home, the nation he had loved.

In some quarters shone the even lines of streetlamps; the calm of a city asleep. But in other neighborhoods, different, brighter lights glowed. A group of small sparks rushed together in the center of one street before dispersing again. On another corner the sparks merged to transform a building, a shop, a synagogue, into a brilliant orange and yellow flower that grew upward into the night sky.

The facades of Protestant churches and Catholic cathedrals were illuminated by the raging infernos that consumed the great synagogues of Berlin.

Theo pressed his forehead against the glass of the windowpane and watched the blossoming fires. There were far too many to count. The meaning of Hermann Göring's warning became clear.

"That is you, burning out there, Theo Lindheim. All your thoughts. Everything you are. See how the flames of our fury consume you. And you are dying there. . . ."

Surely this night was the death of all hope that reason might prevail in Germany. The words shrieked by Hitler now took human form: *"Juden! Verrecken! Jews perish!"*

Theo Lindheim was the messenger Göring had chosen to tell the Jews of the world: *"You blacken and shrivel and perish! Take word of your death back to England! Tell them you have witnessed the death of your God and yourself tonight!"*

Was he to carry the message that there was no hope, no justice? Was he to cry to an unhearing world, to live his last days in the knowledge that the nations had turned silently away while millions died?

The sorrow of such a task was almost more than Theo could bear. A physical pain clutched his heart, and silently he cried out to God for some other answer.

Berlin dropped to the horizon behind the retreating airplane. Other glowing cities appeared out of the darkness. Another and another and still more.

What do you see, Theo?

Theo turned to answer, startled to find that the others on the plane were sleeping soundly.

What do you see? The voice was clear, nearly audible above the drone of the engines. Theo knew the voice well; he had heard it speak before in other dark hours.

Theo studied the chaos below and answered in a whisper, "Destruction, fire, division—the death of justice and mercy."

They have turned from my truth and from my people. All the things they do to others will come upon them and their children. The voice was not angry, but filled with sadness and certainty of what was to come to the people of Germany.

Grief struck deep in Theo's heart. Germany had, after all, been his home. "But not forever, Lord," he pleaded.

Tell me the date, Theo, the voice spoke gently.

For a moment Theo could not remember times or dates, as though years meant nothing and time did not exist. Was he sleeping like the others on the plane? Was this a dream?

"November," he replied haltingly. "November 9, 1938."

Remember the date. From this night there will be fifty years of judgment; then they will remember this night and all their sins. For one year they will pray and repent, and after that will come a day of jubilee when I will break down the walls. Many will call upon my name, and I will answer . . . I will forgive.

Theo leaned his cheek against the cool windowpane and looked down over Germany. The entire horizon seemed to be in flames, hours before the light of dawn.

Fifty years? For Theo that meant an entire lifetime. He would not live to see the fulfillment of that hope. And how many others would vanish between this terrible night and the promised night in a far-distant future?

"But what should we do now?" Theo asked imploringly.

No answer came; only the monotonous drone of the engines as the plane slid toward the borders of the Third Reich.

8

No Quiet Place

Armed only with a child's crayon and a piece of paper, Captain Samuel Orde made his frontal attack on the terrorists hiding in the Arab villages beyond Hanita.

PLEASE IDENTIFY ATTACHED CORPSE KILLED DURING TERRORIST
ACTIVITIES AGAINST HANITA.
SIGNED, SAMUEL ORDE, CAPTAIN
BRITISH COMMAND, HANITA

He pinned the note onto the coat of the dead man and glared at the men who gathered around him.

"This"—he pointed to the body—"is the reason I will not take atheists along on any sortie against the enemy. Look at him!" He seemed angry. "This could be you. His body is dust. His immortal soul now regrets the wickedness of his life!" He glared at Moshe and then at each observer in turn. "Think about it."

The men of Hanita exchanged astonished looks. Samuel Orde preached with the zeal of a prophet in the wilderness. Some were angered by his boldness, but most were simply surprised.

Orde opened the trunk of his staff car and spread out a canvas tarp. With a jerk of his thumb, he instructed the four men chosen for tonight's action to load the body into the car. He bowed his head and prayed for the family of the fallen enemy and for the safety of the coming mission, but not for the dead Arab. It was too late to pray for him.

With a resounding Amen, echoed by a handful of the uneasy men, Orde issued a Webley revolver to each of the four troopers. This astounded those who watched and envied the lucky few who were privileged to carry such a weapon. Orde presented one bullet per gun to his troops and ordered them into the car. Without explanation, he sped off down the road toward the village.

Moshe watched and waited at the gate with the others as the red taillights grew small and then disappeared behind a cloud of dust.

No one spoke. They stood with arms crossed over their chests and stared off into the darkness, listening and hoping, and considering the eccentric English soldier who thumped his Bible with one hand and his enemies with the other. Definitely odd.

Fifteen minutes passed. Zach looked at his watch. "They should be near the village now," he said.

"The question is not where, but why . . ." another remarked.

"Four bullets," added another puzzled voice.

Moshe started to remark that it was not so very far from this place that Gideon had routed the enemy using only clay pots and trumpets, but at that moment, a distant shot rang out. Then another and another echoed from the hills and wadis until it sounded like a hundred guns firing at once.

The men of Hanita stepped forward in alarm. The last echoes died away, and still these men stood transfixed and frightened by what they heard.

"They must have been ambushed," said Artur glumly, and his eyes filled again with tears.

"Fifty Arab Moquades." Zach frowned and shook his head sadly. "I knew the Englishman was a fool. Now he has gotten more of us killed."

Moshe did not speak. He was glad he had not mentioned Gideon in the face of such a massacre by Arab gangs along the road.

"Should we go after them?" Artur held up his gun.

"Do you want to die as well?" Zach demanded.

Artur did not answer; Moshe thought that perhaps this fellow did indeed want to die.

"What else can we do?" Artur said. "We asked for help from the English and they send us this reject from a Gentile Yeshiva school!" He was raging now, pacing back and forth in front of the gate. "Shall we call the British Army and tell them that their preacher has just been killed by fifty Arab raiders? Tell us what to do?"

"He's right," agreed two grim-faced settlers who still had blood on their shirts from carrying Sharon and Lazlo in from the fields. "What did those British think they were doing? They send us a crazy fanatic! He preaches the Bible to the People of the Book, and then he gets more of us killed!"

An angry murmur filled the night air. "What did they expect one lousy man to do? What use is one English soldier to us anyway?"

They debated further about whether to call in the British to retrieve the bodies from the road. It would have to be done in daylight. That much was agreed to.

Then, a small double light swept up over a distant hill and then down again. Was that an English vehicle? A truck? Had the British soldiers come upon the ambush?

Moshe stepped out of the crowd and walked toward the end of the dirt road which led from Hanita to the highway. Again the lights rose up and then disappeared behind a hill.

Zach stood at his elbow. "What do you think?"

Moshe managed a smile. "Captain Orde's staff car," he said in a low voice.

"You are certain?"

"The right headlight is off a bit. He bumped it going around a narrow corner in Jerusalem. It is Orde, all right."

The others rushed forward with a cheer as the vehicle turned onto the lane. Hands reached out to thump the battered vehicle as it passed through them and then entered the compound.

Orde set the brake, turned off the engine and then stepped out of the car to face the same thumping as his battered car.

"You're back!"

"Of course," he frowned. "What did you think?"

"You made it!"

"Were there many of them?"

Orde shrugged off the queries and scratched his head languidly. "You'll have a briefing in the morning," he said gruffly. "But for now, I am in need of sleep. My quarters?"

Enthusiasm waned as Orde stalked off to a tent set up especially for him. The others, including Orde's four troopers, retired to the camp kitchen where a briefing took place in spite of the commander's absence.

Over cups of coffee, they considered the events of the evening and this strange English soldier.

"What happened?" Zach demanded that Larry Havas, an American from Cleveland, give the details of the sortie.

"Like I said, he dumped the body at the entrance to the village. Arranged it like he was laying a stiff out in a coffin. Hands folded over the note. Pointed the index finger at the writing. It looked like the guy was pointing at the note, you know? They won't miss it."

"And then?"

Larry shrugged. "Then he said, 'Gideon routed the Philistines not far from here. Great acoustics.' And then he sort of spread us out along the road. One on each hill. He fired first. We fired at five-second intervals." He grinned sheepishly. "Guess we woke up the neighbors."

Moshe considered Zach Zabinski for a moment. With his receding hairline and countenance of a scholar, thin and fine-boned, Zach did not have the look of a man in charge of a settlement of three hundred. His sunburned face displayed the sensitivity of one better suited to working in a library than plowing the hard fields of Palestine. Moshe guessed that such a face seldom smiled; but tonight, Zach smiled slowly and raised his eyebrows in appreciation.

"We asked ourselves what one man can do," Zach said with a shake of his head. "They will think we have an army here. And the Muslims are not so eager to go to Paradise . . . or Hell . . . quickly. Our Englishman has bought himself some time, I would say."

"Do you trust him?" asked Dori Samuels.

Zach nodded. "When he looks us in the eye and talks about Zionism and God, I believe him. When he walks away or drives down the road I wonder about his motives. We asked for a troop of British men to defend us. We got one man. Maybe he is as good as a troop. We will see."

Larry Havas laughed again. "All the way out there the guy quoted to us from Isaiah—he's more Zionist than Ben-Gurion!"

"But effective," Moshe interjected, conscious that he was an outsider, but more aware of Samuel Orde's methods than the others were. "I saw him in action against the Mufti in Jerusalem. He is all he seems to be, and more. I am sure of his sincerity." Moshe's eyelid's sagged, heavy from the long trip and the unending tension since their arrival here.

"Some say he is responsible for the death of your brother," Zach said, testing Moshe's defense of the Englishman.

"My brother was responsible for his own death," Moshe said flatly. "Captain Orde brought me here for protection, and I will not be so foolish as my brother was to leave him."

"You believe in him, trust him, this Christian fanatic?" Larry sipped his coffee and waited for Moshe's careful reply.

"Entirely."

Zach nodded with resignation. "When you have been plowing all day and repelling snipers and infiltrators all night, and when you have gone out to relieve a sentry post only to find the girl who guarded it dead and mutilated, you are not particularly glad to see strangers. Particularly not British officers, I admit it. I was . . . maybe still am . . . suspicious."

Larry added, "He has the smell of a soldier about him. Maybe he can help. But what we need from the English are real guns with more than one bullet, and the legal right to use them when we are attacked. Tonight he has made the death of an Arab terrorist legal because he signed his name to it. But if I had killed him—or you, or any of us— we would be arrested by the same people Captain Orde works for."

"I will wait and see," Zach sighed. "What else can we do but wait and see?"

———

As she wandered through Vienna, a flash of emotion ripped through

Lucy's dull senses. She had wanted to belong to him forever; every waking moment had been spent imagining life as the wife of Wolfgang von Fritschauer—little Lucy Strasburg, from a village in Bavaria, wife of a wealthy Prussian aristocrat! But she meant no more to him than the cattle on his estate. She must not let herself love him, even if she longed for him to hold her again.

Her thoughts returned to Wolf. *Remember who you belong to.* He would not ever let her forget that she belonged to him; body and soul, Lucy was at the mercy of Wolf. He would never let her leave him willingly. If she tried, he would simply have her taken to the Lebensborn where she would be locked away until the baby was born. *His baby, not mine. The child I carry for him and for the Reich. Pure Aryan sons for the future of the Thousand-Year Reich.*

Shouts and cries of anguish drifted on wisps of smoke, but Lucy did not hear them. The cries of her own heart were too loud to hear anything else.

She had no place to run, no safe haven where she might hide, no refuge where Wolfgang von Fritschauer would not find her. *"Remember who you belong to!"*

Lucy regretted that she had told Wolf the news. Maybe there was still time. Perhaps she could tell him that she had been mistaken; that she was not pregnant. For the first time she considered the possibility of having an abortion. Such a thing would have been simple for her a few years ago. And if she were Jewish, the government would not only encourage it, but pay for the procedure and sterilize her without charge. But she was Aryan, her family pedigree had been researched before Wolf had even dared to take her into his bed. For an Aryan woman, abortion was forbidden by law and punishable by prison, even death. Beyond that was the higher law of the faith—the killing of the unborn was counted as murder by the church. Lucy feared that law and judgment as much as she feared the Nazi racial edicts.

Killing the baby was not an option for her. Lying about the pregnancy to Wolf would be foolish. He wanted everything verified by an S.S. doctor; to attempt to deceive him would mean that she would be locked inside the S.S. maternity home immediately. And after the child was born, who could say what would happen to Lucy?

She frowned and stepped back to make room for a gang of young Nazis who pushed a dozen Jews down the sidewalk.

"What are you looking at?" a young Austrian shrieked and pounded a prisoner across his shoulders. *"Pig! It is verboten to look at an Aryan woman!"*

"I only . . . she is out alone . . . and I . . . this night . . ." The prisoner attempted to explain but was silenced by kicks and blows to the stomach.

Lucy looked up sharply, realizing that she was the reason the man was being beaten. He fell to the ground and lay in his own blood.

In this way the Nazis of Vienna honored her, the perfect Aryan woman. Fair-haired, blue-eyed, striking in beauty, she inspired men to violence and hatred . . . *for a look*!

The terrible irony of it made her suddenly feel ill again. She averted her eyes in shame and hurried on, looking for a quiet place to rest. In all of Vienna, it seemed, there was no quiet place left for anyone.

The beams and timbers of the Red Lion House creaked and groaned in the darkness as if the noise of tonight's party had made the walls ache. Elisa lay awake in the darkness, staring at the ceiling and wondering if she should wake Murphy.

The dream had come to her again tonight. Fresh and terrifying in its detail, she had seen the trains filled with children as they headed into the blackness of the East. On the battered cattle cars, uniformed skeletons had stood guard and laughed when the little ones stretched their arms through the slats and begged for water. Elisa, with one tin cup, had tried to reach them all. She had run beside the train and cried out for help as the water splashed out and fell to the blood-red ground. Only then, when the last drop had spilled, did she wake up.

The grandfather clock in the foyer chimed two o'clock. Elisa reached out and touched Murphy's back, finding comfort in his nearness and warmth. This nightmare had not returned since they moved into the peaceful old house. She had begun to think of herself as free from all that, free from the sense of helplessness she had felt over the suffering of so many. After all, here in London they were doing what they could to ease the suffering. Concerts and benefits, and parties like tonight's had netted several thousand dollars in aid for the homeless refugees who still flocked to Prague. Schools had formed in southern France for refugee children. Things were being done which did not require Elisa to risk her own safety or that of the baby she carried.

But in the small quiet hours of this morning, none of it seemed sufficient. She sat up and cradled her head in her hands as images of Berlin and Vienna paraded before her. Timmons had wired that the synagogues were being burned, shops and homes destroyed, men arrested. Berlin. Vienna. Cities she had once called home. The children of her dreams came from those cities.

Elisa heard a stirring in the front room—the sound of feet against the oak plank floor, then padding across the thick Persian carpet in the center of the room. A small knock sounded on the door. Without waiting for reply, Charles nudged it open and stood silhouetted in the doorframe.

" 'Lisa?" he said in a small voice. He was too tired to care how well he formed the words. "I dreamed."

"A bad dream?" She put out her arms to him, drawing him to the bedside and under the covers.

"Uh-huh. Real bad. Lots and lots of men chasing. 'Lisa, can I stay?"

His little toes were ice cold against her legs. She cuddled him close, holding his feet in her hands. "Yes, you can stay. Don't be afraid," she whispered in German. "You are safe."

"No," he replied in English, "not me and Louis. The men was chasing other kids. I saw them."

So, they had the same dream—similar, anyway. The realization was sobering. "Were you in the dream?" she asked.

"Ja. I told them kids to come here. To Red Lion, and we will take care of them."

She smiled in the dark at his answer. At least he felt unthreatened here. "That was a good thing to tell them."

"But, 'Lisa, they couldn't hear me. I was talking in English, and they was German-talking kids, and they can't hear me." He sounded so sad that Elisa wondered if he was still half-dreaming.

"Go back to sleep, Charles," she urged gently.

"But I couldn't talk German. Because, you know, my mouth was all—"

"You are safe now, Charles."

"But *they* are not!"

"Then I will tell them myself to come," she whispered, feeling his little body relax. "I will tell them in German so they will hear me . . . *Kommen sie hier, bitte. Kommen sie, Kinder . . . ist das gut, Charles?*"

Charles sighed with renewed contentment. "*Sehr gut,* 'Lisa."

Soon his breathing regulated, growing deep and even with sleep. Elisa lay her cheek against the softness of his hair and closed her eyes to pray that he would never again be touched by the darkness which raged through the streets of Germany even now.

There are so many like him, Lord. So many little ones. If there is more that I can do, show me. Show us. Help us.

Jacob and Mark straddled the ridge of the steep roof. A strong breeze whipped them with ash, still warm from the Berlin fires. Fragments of voices blew past them; the curses of Nazis and the cries of their victims blended into an unintelligible chorus.

Jacob halted when the dormer window was ten feet directly below them. A metal rain gutter sloped down the slippery shale roof to provide a handhold.

"Listen," Jacob said as he examined the rusty bolts that held the pipe in place. "We will keep the pipe between us. We must slide down feet first on our bellies to the roof of the dormer."

Mark swallowed hard and then obeyed, positioning himself with his feet dangling over the steep angle of the roof.

Jacob held up his hand, displaying the belt that linked them. "Don't be afraid. If you slip I have you."

This was true. Jacob could hold him, Mark knew, but could the pipe support their weight? And what if Jacob slipped? Mark could not hold him. "But what will I do if you slip?"

Jacob laughed as if such a thought was impossible. "Then we will both slide off the roof. Just be sure to aim for the head of a Nazi, ja?"

Mark managed a weak smile. Jacob lay down on his stomach and grasped the rain pipe. Carefully, he eased himself off the ridge. Mark followed, clinging desperately to the groaning metal of their lifeline.

The leather soles of their shoes slipped against the shingles as they scrambled for footing, as if a strong hand grabbed their ankles, trying to pull them over the edge to fall three stories to the sidewalk.

"Hold tight!" Jacob urged as they inched lower, hand over hand.

The edge of the roof seemed all too near; the fall to the cobblestones seemed too possible. Metal cut into Mark's fingers. The shingles tore at his knees and stomach. He kept his eyes riveted to Jacob's grim face. Their breath rose in a steamy vapor to mingle with the smoke.

"Just a few more feet," Jacob whispered tensely.

Mark looked over his shoulder at the roof of the dormer. Only four feet to its safety. Beyond that was empty space; below he could see men sloshing kerosene into a shop while a crowd looked on.

Mark's hands ached from the cold metal. He could not find bracing for his feet. Only hands and arms kept them from sliding off into the abyss.

Jacob did not seem frightened. He slid down another few inches and then waited until Mark followed. "Just a little farther . . ." The words were accompanied by the groaning of breaking metal as the pipe pulled free from its rusted anchors.

"Max!" Mark gasped as his section of the rain pipe bowed and broke free beneath him. He clung tighter to the useless metal as he began to skitter down, past Jacob, who struggled to grasp a fragment of still-connected pipe.

"Hold on!" Jacob cried hoarsely as the length of the leather belt snapped taut. Mark dangled crazily at the end, just out of reach of the dormer. Jacob strained to hold him up with one arm while his other hand grasped at the end of the rain pipe.

"Let go of the pipe!" he ordered, his face full of pain and fear as he struggled above Mark. If he could swing his brother to the right, the boy could touch the dormer roof with his feet, slide onto the perch and . . .

Mark released the metal, which clanged and sparked as it rolled and launched from the roof, tumbling down and down. He reached up and grasped the tether with both hands. He kept his eyes on Jacob's face and on the big hand that clung tightly to his end of the belt while his other hand gripped one remaining anchor in the roof.

"I'm going to swing you over." Jacob's words were halting, pained with the exertion. "Get your feet on the roof."

Mark kicked his legs, swimming toward the little island of safety. The toe of his shoe brushed it; then he swung away again, causing Jacob to cry out as if his strength threatened to give out.

"Again!" Jacob urged. "Come on!"

One more swing of his arm to the left and Mark found himself with his feet straddling the peak of the dormer. Still he dangled like a fish on a line below Jacob, but there was at least hope beneath him now.

"I can feel it!" Mark said. His hand was numb from the tight loop around his wrist. "How do I get down?"

"Untie the belt. Drop down."

Untie the belt? Their one link? Mark balked. Although Jacob was in a worse position than he was now, Mark was too frightened to think of letting go. "Max!"

"Untie the belt or you will *kill us both*!" Jacob whispered back angrily. "*I can't ... hold ... on!*" Blood oozed from his fingers where the metal bracket cut into them.

Mark gasped and reached up to fumble with the loop of leather around his wrist. His full weight pulled it tight. The fingers of his free hand could not pry the leather loose. He moaned with fear as he looked up at the exhausted face of his brother. Blood dripped from Jacob's hand onto Mark's cheek.

"Come on!" Jacob cried through gritted teeth.

"I'm trying!" Mark stood on his tiptoes on the dormer, trying to relieve the pressure and ease the weight. His arm felt as if it would break loose from its socket. His fingers dug at the leather, found the barest fraction of give, then, finally, pulled it loose.

Suddenly free, he fell down hard against the dormer. His feet slipped to the right, and he dangled by one arm just like his brother above him.

Mark's throat constricted with fear, but he didn't dare shout. With a loud thump, Jacob slid down and hit the dormer, then without hesitation scrambled to pull Mark up beside him. They were safe!

They sat panting atop the little roof. Burning cinders blew past them, and one landed on Jacob's coat sleeve. He did not have the strength to brush it off. Mark slapped it for him and then hung his head and closed his eyes, refusing to look out over the edge where they had nearly fallen.

Five minutes passed, then ten. Wrapping his bloody hand in a handkerchief, Jacob spoke at last. "We will break the window and swing in over the top." His eyes were calm, his voice even.

"Break the window?"

Jacob mocked him. "Yes. Break the window. You think anyone will wonder about one more broken window tonight? Look out there—" He swept his injured hand toward the panorama of the city: bonfires in the streets, broken glass shimmering on the boulevards like sunlight on the water.

Without further explanation, Jacob scooted forward until his legs dangled in front of the window. With a hard kick backward, he shattered the panes with the heel of his shoe. Then he looked back at Mark with a smile of smug satisfaction, "Well, then. It seems we have smashed the window of an Aryan-owned business." He raised a finger. "That makes the score Jews, *one*; Nazis, *ten thousand*." He grasped the edge of the roof and slid down through the window. "Follow me," he called. "Mind the glass." Jacob reached a hand up to help his brother, who was still almost too frightened to move. "Hurry up!" he coaxed impatiently from inside. "Or I'm leaving without you!"

Mark began to cry again as he lowered himself off the little roof. Jacob clasped him hard by the legs and hefted him into the dark storage attic of the Thieste building. Then both boys collapsed onto the floor.

9

To Pray and to Fight

The city of Berlin was not like Alfie remembered it. Everywhere there were people. Hitler-men were smashing shop windows and hitting other men. Women reached through the broken windows and took things out! There was shouting and screaming and Alfie could not think where he was.

His flimsy pajamas were soaked with sweat and covered with mud. He stopped on a street corner. He could not walk any farther because of the glass that sparkled on the sidewalks.

A group of laughing women walked toward him. Their shopping bags were full of clothes and they talked about what they had gotten like Mama used to chatter about sales and bargains at the stores.

"Look!" shouted a fat lady who pointed at Alfie. "I'll bet he's a Jew!"

"Hey you! Are you a Jew?"

Alfie frowned and stared back at their faces. They had the same mean look as Ugly-mouth when he called Alfie Dummkopf.

"Are you a Jew, boy?" called another woman. "Or only sleep walking?"

Alfie was much taller than all of them. They made a circle around him and sneered up at him. He thought about breaking through them and running, but there was the glass . . .

"Answer me!" said the fat woman. "Are you a Jew? Should we call the police to arrest you?"

"I am going to church. But the glass . . ." he said slowly. "I have no shoes."

Peals of laughter rose up. "Well, there's a shoe store with free shoes right across the street. The Jews are having a sale! A giveaway!"

Alfie could see the broken window of the shoe store. Men were sitting on the curb trying on shoes. Maybe if he was careful he could walk around the glass and get a pair of shoes.

"I am not a Jew," Alfie said earnestly. "But I need shoes. Danke." He was polite even though they were not polite. He pushed through them and jumped from one tiny glass-free cobblestone to the next, reaching the curb where the men sat passing shoes from one to another.

"I need shoes, too," Alfie said. "I don't have money."

"These are free, boy!" A jolly man in leather pants reached up and pulled him down to the curb. "A gift from the Jews to the German people."

"That is nice of them," Alfie said. Smoke was stinging his eyes. Someone passed him a nice pair of shoes that were only a little too big, then gray woolen socks. He put them on. The shoes did not have laces, but it did not matter. With the socks they fit just fine.

"Where are the Jews?" Alfie smiled broadly as he stood. He wanted to thank them for the gift. The shoes made him feel as if he could run fast. It had been a long time since he had new shoes.

In answer to his question the men at the curb roared with laughter. *"Where are the Jews, he says?"* They did not answer Alfie and he was ashamed that he asked. They all knew the answers. Why was he so dumb?

Shirts and trousers and coats came flying out of the broken windows along the broad Avenue. Other people were out in their pajamas, too. A big crowd of men and women wandered about with the cuffs of pajamas and nightgowns showing out the bottom of their coats. Some people dressed in the street—right on the sidewalk they pulled trousers over their nightclothes and then walked on and put on another layer.

Alfie found trousers, too big at the waist. He picked up a heavy coat, too short in the sleeves. "Where are the Jews?" he asked. "Why are those men hurting those people there?"

No one took the questions of this big teenage boy seriously. Everyone knew where the Jews were, after all! Alfie was the only one in Germany who wanted to thank them for the clothes.

———

Explosions continued at regular intervals throughout the long night. Even as the gray Vienna dawn seeped in around the window shade, two more charges roared in quick succession to demolish the last of Vienna's synagogues.

Peter had fallen asleep with his head on his mother's lap. He opened his eyes only when his baby brother cried and Marlene wandered out in her nightgown. She rubbed her eyes and then stood blinking at Peter and her mother, who were fully dressed.

"What is going on?" She made a face at the smell of smoke. The steady drone of a truck passed on the street below. Three rapid pops of rifle fire sounded from somewhere in the distance. "Mama?" Marlene asked again. "Why are you dressed?"

Peter sat up and eyed the rumpled form of his sister with sibling contempt. "Leave it to Marlene. The Nazis are blowing apart our world and she can only ask why we are dressed."

Marlene's expression changed from sleepy confusion to fear. "Mama? What does he mean?" She stared at the window, afraid to look beyond the back-lit shade.

Karin Wallich chose her words carefully. "A pogrom, Marlene. But we are safe here. They will not think to look for us here." She glanced at the clock. Not yet six o'clock. The riots had been in progress only a few hours, yet it seemed like days since she had awakened Peter. "Go back to bed, Marlene," she instructed as if the event was not at all unusual.

Marlene walked numbly toward the window shade. Peter sprang up and blocked her. She tried to go around him, suddenly desperate to see what was outside. Peter grabbed her by the arms and she cried out, although he had not hurt her.

"I want to see!" Her screeching whine set Peter's teeth on edge.

"Marlene!" Karin was up, wide awake and filled with fresh fear as she pushed her daughter away. "You must not . . . *must not* . . . go near the window until they are finished!"

"They can smell a little Jewish girl," Peter snarled. "You want these Aryans to catch a whiff of you and—"

Karin turned on him now, angered by the cruelty in his voice. She raised her chin, ordering him with a look to be silent. Marlene whimpered, rubbing her arm where Peter had grabbed her.

"He hurt me," she sniffed. "I only wanted to—"

"You can let her go out there as far as I'm concerned!" Peter scowled at her. Marlene could not take anything. Mother shielded her, protected her, pampered her, even though their peaceful world was irrevocably shattered.

Peter sat down heavily on the sofa and stared at the photograph of Adolf Hitler that hung on the wall above the radio. Herr Ruger had apologized for the picture, explaining that it was only for show in case the Gestapo should ever come with their list of questions. For this same reason, Herr Ruger wore the Nazi armband and said *Heil Hitler* as naturally as he had once said *Grüss Gott*. After Peter's father had been taken, Herr Ruger had given Peter an armband as well in case he had to travel outside his own neighborhood. He was a strange man, this Otto Ruger.

Karin Wallich was still uncertain of Herr Ruger. He seemed to move altogether too naturally among those who now set explosive charges around the support pillars of the synagogues and doused the floors with kerosene and laughed as they lit their pipes and tossed their matches into the buildings. She did not trust his paternal interest in Peter; she deplored the swastika armband slipped into her son's pocket. And yet, last night, she had no choice but to obey the instructions he had left with Peter.

"If there is even a whiff of trouble in the air, you must bring your mother and sister to my apartment. It is the season for violence again. The season of martyrs."

Herr Ruger had proved to be right. His *knowing* disturbed Karin Wallich most. She had expressed her doubts to Peter, but they had come to Ruger's apartment anyway.

"There now, Marlene," Karin soothed her daughter. "You are just tired. The noise awakened you. Go back to sleep and when you wake, we can go home again."

Peter leaned back against the sofa and closed his eyes as his mother led Marlene back into the bedroom. How he longed for sleep—sleep without dreams, without warnings that played in his own mind. He really despised his little sister, yet she was now his responsibility. Father had told him it might come to this—Peter in charge of protecting Mother, Marlene, and baby. Such responsibility had come too soon. Eight months ago, before the Nazis marched into Austria, Peter would have welcomed being a man. Now, with the arrest of his father, Peter wished only for his lost childhood to return. But the scene beyond the window shade convinced him—that dream was gone forever.

———

Of course Wolfgang von Fritschauer had an extra key to Lucy's apartment. He had found the apartment for her, after all, and in the beginning he had spent as much time here as he had in his own quarters. But Lucy had not expected to see him this morning. Not after the things he had said to her last night. Somehow she had not expected to see him ever again—except perhaps to place her baby in his arms and watch him walk away.

He stood over her bed, swaying slightly as if he had been drinking. His hat and overcoat were already off when Lucy realized that she was not dreaming.

"Wolf?" she asked sleepily.

He did not reply, but sat down on the edge of the bed. His uniform was impeccable, but there were flecks of blood on his face. *Is it his own blood?* she wondered briefly.

He began to unbutton his tunic as if he had the right. He motioned for her to move over. "I have been working all night near here. Too tired to go home." He did not ask permission, simply pulled off his boots and lay down beside her. She did not protest when he reached out for her. After all, what did it matter now? What was done was impossible to undo. Was that hell beyond the Danube any fiercer because he had come to her as he always did, and she did not send him away?

Only the hell of this moment mattered to her now. Somehow the nearness of Wolf made her existence seem less terrible. She was grateful that he wanted her, even if he did not love her. Now she would not wonder or hope. *No expectations,* he said. *No commitments.*

Within her remained only despair and physical hunger for him. With her hopes and dreams for the future reduced to ashes, no illusions were left. And so she yielded to his desire just like any other woman who worked the back streets of the Seventh District.

Later, Lucy felt awake for the first time since she had met the handsome S.S. officer over a year ago in Munich. She lay beside him, studying his features as he slept. Always she had interpreted his cold expression as the smile of an aristocrat, the look of a man who was better than other men. And also better than her. Now she watched his thin lips and pictured the smile again. *Cruel and distant. Charming only when he had something to gain.* She had feared the aloofness of his smile. She had melted in its charm. But now that she knew the truth of it, she would never again cringe beneath it or be wooed by it.

Yes, Wolf was the picture of Aryan physical perfection. But then, so was she, wasn't she? Wasn't that why he had chosen her? In this way they were equals. The realization gave her confidence; she would not be afraid of his disapproval any longer.

For the first time she wondered what his wife looked like. Maybe she would ask him, wonder out loud to him about the woman who would take her baby from her.

Lucy's heart felt cold and distant as she looked at the sleeping form of the man she had loved so deeply. She did not hate him; she simply viewed him as he must view her. He was someone she would use, as she had been used. She would make her smile into a reflection of his smile. And her hands would no longer tremble in his presence.

At all costs, she knew she must not go to the S.S. maternity home. She must somehow remain free in Vienna until she could win her freedom in another place.

The gate of Lebensborn was locked on both sides—on the inside to keep lovers out, and on the outside to keep the women in.

She studied Wolf's profile in the semidarkness. This man demanded instant gratification of his desires. She must make him see that the lock on Lebensborn would deny him access to that satisfaction. She must sell herself to buy precious time.

Early morning found the violence in Berlin undiminished. Thousands of shops to be wrecked, after all. What was sleep compared to the thrill of destroying in one night what it had taken generations to build in Germany?

Jacob and Mark woke to the sound of a fire truck clanging wildly past the Thieste building. Fire had spread from a Jewish-owned shop to an Aryan building, and several trucks rushed to the scene.

"Where are we?" Mark raised his head to blink in confusion at the strange surroundings. File cabinets, stacks of boxes, and unused office furniture were piled everywhere. Mark and Jacob had fallen asleep near a large wooden desk with chairs stacked on it. There was no light except for the ever-present illumination of the fires.

"The Thieste building." Jacob sat up slowly and crawled over to peer out the window they had come through hours before.

"Ah." Mark remembered; the memory brought a renewed stab of worry for their parents. "Can we go back home?" he asked miserably.

Jacob did not reply. He simply stared down at the wreckage beneath them. The street had not yet been touched when the boys had slid in to the attic. Now, it was smashed as if a bomb had exploded. People walked through it, picking over the merchandise that had been thrown into the street. On the corner, men with guns surrounded a group of two hundred Jewish men. A truck was waiting to carry them away. *Away to where?*

Jacob scanned the tiny figures for some sign of his father and Pastor Karl. Were they down there? And what had happened to Mother?

"We're going to New Church. Father told us to go there; if Mother is free, she will look for us at New Church."

The thought of seeing his mother filled Mark with a new energy. He jumped to his feet and picked his way through the cluttered attic to the stairs. He reached for the light switch, but Jacob stopped him.

"The building may have a watchman," Jacob warned.

"He will be out stealing with the rest of them," Mark said, but they made their way through the office building without light all the same.

In the lobby, a single lamp burned at the vacant desk of the night watchman. Jacob nudged Mark hard, and they ducked behind the banister at the foot of the stairs.

He jerked his thumb toward the glass doors leading from the building. Outside, the watchman leaned against a pillar and smoked a pipe as he placidly watched the looting of a shoe store across the street.

"How will we get out?" Mark asked.

In reply, Jacob took his hand and simply walked across the lobby and through the doors. The watchman did not see where they had come from, but he turned and raised his pipe in acknowledgment. His eyes swept over the two boys in amusement.

"Guten Morgen," he greeted them. "It looks as though you two have been in the thick of the fray." His glance lingered on the blood-soaked handkerchief wrapped around Jacob's hand.

Jacob nodded curtly and raised the hand with an air of nonchalance. "Plenty of glass broken last night. I got careless." He kept walking, pulling wide-eyed Mark after him.

"A battle scar," laughed the old watchman. "You can tell your grandchildren you got it the night we taught the Jews in Germany a lesson, eh?"

Jacob managed a laugh and stepped off the curb to hurry away through the ruins toward New Church. This time Mark did not cry. Terror and exhaustion had left him numb, and he followed Jacob like a sleepwalker.

The entire city crawled with looters. No one attempted to stop the thieves. In the frantic scramble of Aryan citizens to snatch useful items from the bonfires, no one paid any attention to two soot-covered boys walking briskly toward New Church.

Jacob prayed that they would not come face-to-face with anyone who knew them, who knew they were Jewish. In the past two years hardly a day had passed without some arrogant Hitler Youth gang confronting Jacob. Lately they had been careful not to challenge him without several members on hand to help out. He had beaten every boy his age in an eight-block radius. Tonight, those familiar faces were nowhere to be seen. Jacob guessed, correctly, that they were busy in another neighborhood of Berlin.

The people they passed on Friedrichstrasse were strangers to them. Jacob looked at the eager faces of these noble members of the superrace. Many of them, with their dark eyes and hair, fit the Nazi caricature of a Jew much better than either Mark or Jacob. Both boys were fair-skinned and fair-haired. Mark had curly hair, which was a sign of Jewish origin according to the propaganda, but other than that, their faces were just faces. Jacob unconsciously touched his crooked nose, the nose of a street brawler. Together with his fierce green eyes, it marked him as a young man to be careful of.

This dirt-caked, angry face cut a swath through the Aryan populace this morning. The defiance in his eyes made even grown men step around him. If anyone had looked down into the younger boy's eyes, they would have seen a different story. Confusion, shock, fear for his parents filled his face, marking him as a victim. But Jacob met every glance with an angry glare. Such a look could only exist in the eyes of a leader of the Hitler Youth. And so, no one stopped them. No one asked why they were roaming the streets of Berlin at four in the morning. Their purpose was clear enough.

————————

"Be there!" Jacob slammed his fist on the locked door of New Church. *"Be there!"* he growled again impatiently.

From the other side of the door he could just hear Lori Ibsen's muffled voice. "Who is there?"

"It's me, Jacob Kalner. Me and Mark. Let us in!" He looked back nervously, hoping that no one had seen them scale the stone fence of the churchyard.

He leaned heavily against the door, as if he could melt through the thick wood. Lori fumbled with the latch until it clicked open and the two boys fell into the church. Instantly a crowd gathered around them, firing questions from every side.

"Where is Papa?"

"Pastor Karl?"

"Why did Richard and Leona not come with you?"

"Are they following after?"

Mark began to weep again. He shook with sobs, unable to speak, but giving the terrible answer by his tears.

Frau Helen enfolded the little boy in her arms and gazed steadily into the sooty face of Jacob. "Where is my husband? Where is Pastor Karl? Did he make it to your flat?"

Jacob nodded. Overcome with exhaustion, he groped for a place to sit down. "He came," Jacob said dully. "He was going to bring us all back here."

"Then the Gestapo . . ." Mark sniffed and buried his face against Frau Helen's sleeve. "They banged on the door and broke it. They hurt Mama. I heard them."

"There was no chance for them to get away," Jacob explained. "They arrested Mama and Papa and Pastor Karl. Mark and I went out through the skylight. Over the rooftops."

Lori stepped forward. Even in the dim light of the church Jacob could see an angry glint in her eyes. Her fists were clenched as if she wanted to hit someone. This was one of the things Jacob admired about Lori Ibsen. If she had been born a boy, no doubt they would have fought with each other. Or perhaps they would have fought side by side against the Hitler Youth. This morning Lori looked strong in spite of her slender figure. "Where have they taken them?" she demanded. "We will go after them. Tell the Gestapo they have made a mistake. Your parents are Christians. My father is a pastor. They have made a mistake."

From a dark pew, a woman snorted in ridicule at the words. "The Nazis do not make mistakes. It does not matter, Lori, who is a Christian. What matters is who is not a Nazi."

Frau Helen stared up at the rose window above the altar as though there might be an answer written there for her. "What to do, Lord?" she whispered.

Jacob said sternly, "You cannot go out there, Frau Helen. You must not think of it."

"But if I can find where they have taken them—"

Mark clung tighter to her. Jacob shook his head in disagreement. "We have seen what they are doing. Sooner or later the Nazis will grow tired, but right now they are still wrecking everything in sight, arresting everyone who questions them—not only Jews, do you understand? We should stay here. If they release my mother, she will come here and tell us. If Pastor Karl is set free, he will come home. We should stay here."

Jacob had not mentioned the possibility of his father being released. That would not happen—not without payment of a big fine, like the last time. But the Kalner family had no money left to pay the Nazi jailers; Richard Kalner might never be released. For Mark's sake Jacob did not say these things, but all night long the terrible reality of the situation had played over and over in his mind.

Frau Helen let her breath out slowly. She put her hand on Lori's arm, then touched her face. Lori's cheeks were wet with tears of frustration.

"Jacob is right, Lori," she said softly. "Your father will come here. We must be here to meet him when he comes."

––––––––––

Two cots stood in the newest tent at Hanita—one for Captain Orde, the other for Moshe Sachar. Moshe crept quietly to his cot. He was certain that the English captain heard him and was aware of his presence. Nothing, it seemed, slipped past Orde. And yet Orde pretended not to hear Moshe until he slipped beneath his blankets.

Then, as Moshe stared up at the black canvas, Orde spoke. "Well?"

Moshe frowned. "Well what?"

"What did they think of tonight's mission?"

"They are somewhat impressed. Somewhat suspicious. They definitely think you are a real . . . what is the American word?"

"Nut."

"That's it. A religious fanatic."

Orde laughed for the first time in days. "Good. Let them be a bit intimidated."

Moshe snorted his disapproval. "And what is all this about not taking an atheist out on patrol? You cannot treat these men like students in Shabbat school! You sound more . . . fanatic than my brother. And that says a lot."

"I feel strongly about it."

"Ridiculous."

"I would hate for my Jewish brothers to be killed and end up in the same unpleasant fix as the Muslims we must fight. I pity even the

Holy Strugglers of the Mufti. They will wake up dead, and then it will be too late for them."

"You should have been a preacher, not a soldier," Moshe scoffed. "Such nonsense will not go down well with the Jews of Hanita. Or anywhere else in the settlements. If you pity that dead assassin who killed the girl tonight, keep such misplaced pity to yourself!"

"If men's hearts were turned toward God, there would be no need for soldiers. Then I *would* be a preacher. As it is, the world is a rotten place. And I am speeding men to hell against my will."

Moshe let out an angry laugh. He did not like this conversation. It was too much like the talks he had once had with Eli. Love or duty. How to reconcile the two? "Then why are you here?"

"Because forces exist that will push you Jews into the sea. A darkness much bigger than the Arab Mufti or even Hitler would destroy every last living son of the Covenant."

"That is our problem, Christian!" Moshe propped himself up on his elbows. He was genuinely angry now—maybe not at Orde, but at the governments who looked away while the darkness pressed nearer to the Jewish people.

"No. It is my problem. Because I am a Christian and a Zionist who believes you will have your nation. God has promised it, and that is why Satan fights so hard against it. And so I must fight against those who seek to discredit God's promises."

This perspective made very good sense from Orde's point of view, but still it left Moshe feeling frustrated and bitter. After all, had Eli not believed in the same promises and died at the hands of an Arab mob, anyway? Where was the justice? Where was this great God of Israel? Moshe thought all these things but did not say them.

"Don't push us. Don't push these men. If they are killed and go to hell fighting Arab gangs, that is not your business. This world is hell enough for us. We have no homeland. No peace. No safety. What could be worse? Leave your God out of it, I say! Teach us to fight, and we will make our own heaven here in our homeland!"

Orde did not reply for a long time. Moshe wondered if he had drifted off to sleep in the middle of the conversation. Then he said, "Without the Lord, Moshe, all the training I give you will not make a difference. With God you will defeat them with clay pots and trumpets; the sea will open before you, and you will walk on dry land."

"Then we won't need you." Moshe lay down hard on his pillow.

"Yes. You will need me. Until you believe what I tell you is true, you do need me to teach you to pray and to fight."

10

A Day of Mourning

Ambassador Hopewell slept soundly in his seat as the plane passed over the border of the Reich into Holland.

Theo glanced at him as the drone of the engines changed to a different tone during the descent. *From G to C,* Theo thought as he recalled the way Anna interpreted all engine noise into a musical scale. The thought made him smile for the first time in days. He checked his watch and wondered if Anna had heard of the riots in Germany. If word of the pogrom reached England before he did, Anna would be frantic with worry.

The landing on the grass airfield was rough and bumpy. Hopewell still did not awaken. Nor did he stir when Theo got off the plane and limped toward the small terminal.

"Only thirty minutes," the pilot called after him.

Theo waved acknowledgment, then hurried to make the telephone connection with London. Twenty minutes passed before the operator came on the line to announce that the call to London was through. Anna's voice followed, surprisingly clear, clear enough for Theo to know that she had heard what was happening in Germany.

"Oh! Theo, darling! Where are you? Berlin?" She sounded frightened. "Are you all right? Are you with Helen and Karl?"

Theo dreaded telling her that he had not dared to even go see her sister and brother-in-law. A visit from him might have put them in jeopardy. "I am coming home," he replied, trying very hard to sound light. "Just refueling in Holland. We'll be in London by morning." He paused, uncertain if she was still on the line.

He did not need to tell her about Helen. "You could not see my sister," she said, disappointed but understanding.

"It would not have been safe for them to have me as a visitor, Anna.

But I left your letter with the British Embassy. They are clear about the situation and will see she gets it."

"Did you see what they are doing in Berlin? Is it true?"

"I saw enough, Anna. It's true—whatever you have heard in England, and more besides." His voice sounded hollow and very tired.

"They have gone mad!" she cried. "Oh, Theo! Thank God you are safe! But the others . . . our friends. My family! What will come to them?"

The pilot rapped loudly on the glass of the phone booth. "She's all fueled, Mr. Lindheim. Two minutes." He held up two fingers and then hurried back to the aircraft.

Theo cradled the telephone, suddenly desperate to talk to her, to comfort her and be comforted. Only Anna would know what he was feeling tonight. Only she could soothe away his sense of hopeless frustration and personal failure. "So much to tell you, Anna. Meet me at the airfield in London. Call Murphy and Elisa. We can breakfast together."

At those words the tension left her voice. Theo was all right. He was coming home. *Breakfast together!* Never had such an ordinary thing sounded so wonderful.

———

The buzz of the telephone awakened Charles from his restless sleep. He snuggled closer to Elisa and lay very still to listen to Murphy's raspy whisper.

"From Amsterdam? Amsterdam? How did he sound? Good. Yes. Of course. I'll run by the office and then we can go together. Right. Thanks for calling."

Murphy replaced the receiver, picked up the alarm clock and peered at it for a moment before Elisa spoke.

"That was Mother?" she asked, her voice foggy.

"Uh-huh. Go back to sleep."

"It's about Papa, isn't it?"

"Yes. He's on his way back to England."

"From where?" she asked, sounding very awake.

There was a long pause as Murphy considered how much to tell her. What would it hurt for her to know about Theo's trip now that he was safe? "He has been in Berlin. Negotiating for economic relief for the refugees."

Elisa raised up on her elbow and considered the news for a moment. Then she lay back down and stared up at the dark ceiling. "I thought so. I could see it on Mother's face. You really don't need to keep everything from me, you know. I am not that fragile."

"I didn't know about it either, not until last night." His voice cracked. "A note was brought to the office. Harvey Terrill brought it along with the news of the riots."

"A note?" She put an arm protectively over Charles, who still pretended to be sleeping.

"From a German. His description didn't sound familiar, but I don't doubt his message."

"Which is?"

"We're being watched. I've asked Freddie if he can move into the studio downstairs just to keep an eye on you when I'm gone. And . . . I want you to carry the gun." He cleared his throat nervously as though he expected her to argue.

"Okay. If you think it is necessary, Murphy."

"You know how to use it?"

She gave a short, sarcastic laugh. "Well, I can load it and pull the trigger. At least I could make a little noise with it if I had to."

Murphy sat up and swung his legs over the side of the bed. "Elisa . . . those other notes . . . the ones from Paris?"

She listened in silence, considering the unsigned message from Paris that had told her about the death of Thomas von Kleistmann. "What about them?"

"Have you put them . . . *away* somewhere?"

"No. I thought you had them."

"Yes. On my desk. They're gone now. Do you think the boys could have maybe . . . I don't know. Maybe they took a scrap of paper to write on or draw on?"

Charles's eyes opened wide as he heard Murphy's question. He had never taken anything from Murphy's big desk. Louis would not take anything either. They remembered their father's desk in Hamburg. It was fun to play under, but *verboten* to touch anything on it or in it!

"No!" Charles sat up beside Elisa and shook his head in horror at the thought that Murphy could imagine the brothers would take even a scrap of paper without permission. "Me an' Lou . . . we don' take nothing!"

Charles's response broke up the discussion. Murphy switched on the lamp and blinked at the rumpled little boy in their bed. "What are you doing here?" he asked gruffly.

"He had a dream," Elisa explained. "I thought he was sleeping."

"Go get into your own bed, Charles," Murphy ordered, an unusually harsh command. He was angry that Charles had heard about the gun and about tonight's communication from the German and the missing notes. Murphy looked sternly at Elisa as Charles slipped from the covers and padded quickly out of their room. The boy closed the door behind him as Murphy demanded. Still, Murphy's unhappy voice drifted after him.

"Why didn't you tell me the kid was . . ."

Charles did not sleep the rest of the night, but lay awake considering what it all meant.

The first soft light penetrated the stained-glass windows of New Church. A patchwork of colors and images spread over the sleeping fugitives like a quilt. Unbroken windows meant safety, Lori thought as she looked out over the pews where men and women lay stretched out, head to head, foot to foot.

From the choir loft beside the huge pipe organ, Lori could see them all. Her mother slept with James at the opposite end of the front pew. Jacob Kalner and Mark had climbed into the choir loft to tell Lori everything they had seen out there, but now they, too, had dropped off into the deep dreamless sleep of exhaustion. Only Lori remained awake to watch, to stand vigil and pray until her father came. She did not doubt that he would come. In her mind she could imagine an angel loosening his chains and setting him free just like the story in the book of Acts. She did not want to be like the doubters who questioned such a miracle. When he came home, she would run to the door and throw it open and tell him she had believed all along.

But she had not expected the Gestapo to come to New Church. No one who had taken asylum there expected the crash of fists and gun butts against the door.

From her perch, Lori could see the faces of the fugitives as they raised up in sleepy confusion. Fear flooded their eyes as realization struck them. The same fear rooted Lori to her seat.

Jacob Kalner was on his feet in a moment. At first Lori thought he would leap over the rail and fight the intruders, but instead he grabbed Mark by the arm and took Lori by her hand. Dragging them up the steps toward the pipe organ, he warned them to be quiet. No one must know where they hid!

The outer doors splintered and split open. Clear light washed in, dulling the colors of the windows with harsh reality. It did not matter if the windows were broken or intact. No one was safe, not even here in New Church.

Inside, the giant organ bellows smelled of dust and moldy leather. Lori, Mark, and Jacob crouched close together inside its dark interior.

They could hear everything clearly as the threats of the Gestapo officer ricocheted off the vaulted ceiling of the church and permeated every corner with arrogance and anger. *Why have you sheltered enemies of the Reich? Why have you not allowed your children to join the Hitler Jugend? Are you also an enemy of the Reich, Frau Ibsen?*

Each answer Helen Ibsen attempted to make was cut short by the stamp of a boot against the stone floor and a tirade about ungrateful citizens who wanted all the benefits of the Fascist government but were unwilling to make the necessary sacrifices.

The sacrifices, Lori thought grimly, *are human.*

The officer turned his attention from cursing of Jewish members of New Church to the little blond Aryan son of Pastor Ibsen. "Now, here is a handsome child." Lori was sickened by the sound of a smile in the evil man's voice. "What is your name?"

"James." The reply was sullen.

"Do not talk to him, Jamie," Lori whispered. Jacob nudged her to silence.

"James. Ja. A good name. From the Holy Bible." There was the popping sound of a riding crop slapping against a boot top. Hitler also carried a whip, and such props had become the fashion of the Nazi party members. "So, James. You are blond. Obviously Aryan. And yet your mother and father keep you here in this dark place, away from others who are your equal in race. You cannot go camping or hiking with boys your own age, ja?" James was expected to reply, but he did not. Inwardly, Lori cheered her little brother. The officer continued. "Instead you are forced to stay here in the company of Jews and enemies of the Fatherland. How do you feel about that, James, being here with these *Untermenschen*? Look at them! Can you not see a difference in the way they look and carry themselves? Look at the big nose of that woman. And her eyes set close to each other. You see she is a Jew. Very different from you. How do you feel about being made to stay in the same room with these pigs?"

"Papa says the Lord was a Jew. I guess I like it fine."

The officer snorted in derision. The crop slapped harder against his boot. He was growing impatient with the game. He turned on Frau Helen. "I see how you teach him! How you fill his mind with nonsense!" He snapped his finger and suddenly the church was filled with the boy's screams as James was grabbed up and carried out. Helen Ibsen cried after her son, but was held back. No one else spoke.

"We will see to it that James is properly educated, Frau Ibsen. You may weep if you will, but I tell you this. Your son will forget about you soon enough. In one month color will return to his cheeks and he will become strong and disciplined and will not think about you except to marvel at your backwardness." His boot heels clicked against the slate floor as he circled the group of new captives. "You have another child, Frau Ibsen. You have also refused to allow her into the party organizations. It may go easier for you and your husband at the trial if you will voluntarily tell us where she is."

Helen spoke through clenched teeth. Her words were full of pain. "She is with friends. You cannot . . . take our children from us."

"But they are of minor age. With their parents in prison they naturally become wards of the state. Now, *where is your daughter?*"

"You think we would ever allow her—"

"You have no choice!" A clap of the hands and the shouted order followed. "Search the place! Find the girl!"

Lori trembled all over. Her teeth chattered with fear and grief. Jacob put a hand on her shoulder to steady her as jackboots slapped against the floor of New Church. Lori held tightly to Mark's hand as footsteps clambered up the stairs to the organ loft. Would they think to look in the bellows? This had always been a wonderful place to hide in a game of hide-and-seek. She prayed that some soldier would not know of a similar hiding place and look here.

Lori could feel Mark's heart pounding wildly as the soldier entered the loft. The man's breath was clearly audible as he stooped to search under the seats and around the pipe organ. Only the thin leather of the bellows separated them from capture. She bit her finger to stop the chattering of her teeth.

"Any luck, Dietz?" a voice called up the stairs.

The reply of the hunter was like a shout in her ear. "Just a minute, Paul. There was something . . . I thought I heard . . ."

Lori held her breath and prayed that the man would not hear her heart pounding in unison with Mark's. And then, for a wild moment, she considered turning herself in, walking out of the bellows and going to prison with Mama. The Nazis would send her to prison if she refused to join their organization. And then she would be with her mother. What other future did she have?

Jacob's fingers tightened on her shoulder, holding her back. With a shake of her head she realized that if she gave herself up, it would also mean the end for Mark and Jacob. She closed her eyes and leaned back against him. His heart beat in a calm rhythm, as if he were not afraid. Somehow it soothed Lori.

The soldier cleared his throat and spit on the floor before he turned to call down. "Nothing up here but dust and hymn books."

Lori let her breath out slowly, quietly, as the soldier retreated down the steps.

Moments later, other men shouted the results of their search. *"No one else in the building!"* They had searched from bell tower to basement and found nothing.

"Come on, then." The Gestapo leader did not sound disappointed. After all, he had made quite a catch. "Put a chain and padlock on the church doors, Sergeant. If anyone is in here, they will starve soon enough."

Within moments, the shuffling of feet and the crash of doors marked the exit of prisoners and their guards. But even after the building grew silent and empty, the three remained in the hiding place to listen and wait in case someone remained behind.

Someone had thrown them into the street, and Alfie picked them up—rings with diamonds and rubies in them and two jeweled necklaces. In the deep pockets of Alfie's new coat the jewelry jingled softly. One for Frau Helen Ibsen and one for Lori. Papa had always brought him a present when he came home from a long trip; it seemed like a good idea to bring something home to Lori and Frau Helen. He had picked up a toy truck for Jamie, but a Hitler-man had knocked him down and kicked him hard and taken it from him. That explained why so many people were getting beat up. They had things other people wanted. Like the truck.

At dawn Alfie finally spotted the steeple of New Church. Across from it lay the smoking ruins of the church where the Jews went on Saturday. It was all burned to pieces. Four blocks away, Alfie stopped and stared at the terrible sight. *"Where are the Jews?"* he muttered aloud again. He looked at his shoes and his trousers and coat. His fingers closed around the jewels in his pockets, and suddenly he knew where the Jews were and why everyone had laughed when he said he wanted to thank them.

The face of Ugly-mouth flashed in his mind, and he remembered the empty beds in the ward and why he had run away! In the streets he had heard people cry like Werner. He had seen them loaded into big trucks. *"Where are they going?"* he had asked.

"East."

"To a better place."

"The Promised Land."

Now Alfie realized that they were going to the same place Werner was going. The lid of the box was closing. Probably all the beds in the ward were empty this morning, empty like the smashed shops. Alfie shuddered. His clothes were stolen. Everything was stolen from the Jews! Alfie would tell Pastor Ibsen that he had taken the things and they needed to be given back!

He frowned and stared hard at the smoldering ruins of the synagogue. "But who is left to give the things back to?"

Alfie stepped off the curb and walked slowly toward New Church. He felt ashamed that he had been so dumb, ashamed that he had stood and watched while men like Ugly-mouth beat up people and hauled them away. He had felt only confusion when he had seen it. Only confusion. But now he was ashamed that he did not know when everyone else did. He would not have stolen the shoes or the trousers or the coat. He would have walked barefoot all the way here to New Church and let the good pastor find him old shoes and clothes to wear. Frau Helen and Lori would not want his presents because they were stolen. Mama had told him about stealing, and he had never once taken anything that was not his. Now, one night out of the hospital, he had suddenly become a thief!

Three police cars drove slowly past him toward New Church. A cold lump of fear made him forget that he was hungry. Had the police come to arrest him? To take him back and close the lid on him, too?

Alfie's eyes widened as the police cars slid to a stop in front of New Church. He halted in his tracks and stared as men piled out and ran to each door and began to shout and pound! Had they heard that Alfie was coming to New Church? *"No,"* he said dully. He watched as the doors collapsed inward and men charged in. *"Pastor did not take anything. It was me!"*

Alfie did not walk forward to confess his guilt. He simply stood weeping on the corner and watching as familiar families were dragged out and loaded into the cars and vans. "Frau Helen!" he cried weakly. And then, he saw the blond hair of little Jamie! Poor Jamie! His eyes were scared, like Werner's eyes when they took him away.

"I'm sorry," he cried softly. "I'm sorry!" Alfie sank down on the curb to wait, certain that they would come for him as well.

———

Sleep was a muddle of dreams for Moshe and he lay restless in the tent at Hanita. Through a mist he saw the face of his brother Eli, pale and lifeless on the stone of the Temple Mount. He heard the screams of the rioters in Jerusalem as Haj Amin Husseini stirred them with the passion of his own hatred against the English and the Jews. Far away his mother and father looked on and wept over the body of Eli. Then his mother raised her eyes toward heaven and cried out that Moshe, as well, had been killed.

Through the jumble of bloody images, Moshe knew he was in a tent; knew he was only dreaming. Yet he could not remember where he was or why he had come here. *The archaeological dig at Gilboa? The secret training camp for student members of the Haganah?* Then the image of Captain Orde came to him.

"We'll have to hide you out for a bit, Moshe, until we can get you to England. The Mufti, it seems, thinks you had something to do with the death of Victoria and Ismael Hassan. There is a price on your head. The Hassan family is keen on wiping out both brothers of the Sachar family."

Straight from Eli's muddy grave Moshe had left Jerusalem. He and Orde had driven to Hanita, only to find still more bodies beneath blood-soaked sheets.

The memory awakened Moshe with a start. He was tangled in the blanket of his cot. Light filtered through the tan canvas of the tent, creating a dusky gloom inside. He could hear the crunch of footsteps on the gravel, the sound of shovels slapping against the ground as two fresh graves were prepared for the fallen of Hanita settlement.

He turned his head toward Captain Orde's bed. The blankets were smoothed and made up in military fashion. Orde had managed to straighten up his side of the tent and slip out without awakening Moshe.

Moshe sat up, feeling chagrined. Not even the sound of breathing escaped the attention of Samuel Orde. Moshe had slept through a complete tent cleaning, and the captain was gone. Well, there was the difference of a true soldier and a fellow like Moshe who would rather have been out on a solitary dig or sitting in a classroom at Hebrew University.

The tent flap opened, revealing the librarian face of Zach Zabinski.

"Shalom," he said, taking in the tousled appearance of the newest fugitive. "Where is Captain Orde?"

Moshe rubbed a hand across his face in confusion. "I barely know where I am myself. Orde? I don't know. He isn't here."

That was obvious. Zach frowned and stared at the empty cot and the perfectly arranged belongings of the Englishman.

"Well, did he say where he was going?" Zach demanded.

Moshe shrugged. "I didn't hear him say anything except his prayers just before I fell asleep."

"Get up!" Zach snapped. "He's gone, then. Just gone."

"Gone?"

"Nowhere in the compound. Not in the settlement, and no one saw him leave."

Entirely awake at such news, Moshe swung himself off the cot and pulled the cold trousers over his bare legs.

"Is his auto still here?"

"Yes." Zach was angry with Moshe. "You said you trusted him. We asked you to keep an eye on him—"

"My eyes were closed," Moshe said defensively. He did not admit that his mind had been hearing other voices and seeing dark images while he slept.

"Well, he is not here. And for a man to leave the settlement alone . . . especially today. The whole world has gone crazy, Moshe. Word just came in over the BBC that the Nazis have decimated the Jewish communities in Germany. At the same time, we were being hit last night—twenty-seven attacks throughout the Yishuv. The Jihad Moquades of the Mufti have been slitting Jewish throats in Palestine from north to south. That crazy Englishman is going to get himself killed if he is out of the settlement, and the British High Command will blame us for it!"

Moshe finished dressing, but did not make up his cot. Pulling on his heavy blue cable-knit sweater, he followed Zach out into the misty morning air.

Larry Havas, an empty revolver tucked in his belt, strode purposefully toward the two from the mess hall.

"Where is he?" he demanded of Moshe.

The conversation in the tent was replayed, ranging from concern to blame. Why had Moshe trusted Orde, and why had Moshe not kept an eye on him? Reports came from other men and women as every foot of the settlement was searched again. Orde was not in the latrines. Not in the kitchen. Not at any sentry post. Not in the machine sheds or the barns. No one had seen him leave. He was definitely on foot, and probably well into enemy territory.

Larry Havas, who was American in every sense of the word, peered off over the rolling hillsides scarred by ravines and stubborn brush. "Crazy Englishman," he said. "Hanita is like a little wagon train circled against the Indians—only the Moquades are a lot meaner than any Indians I ever heard about. He's had it out there." Larry grimaced and patted the revolver in his belt. "I sure hope he didn't take all the ammunition out with him."

The settlers had other things to tend to in Hanita. The graves were dug; the dead awaited burial. While the sentries kept watch, Moshe again found himself among mourners, and again he let himself weep for his brother Eli and for all who had fallen here and in the Reich throughout the night. The fate of the fanatic British captain seemed a small thing compared to the news of what had happened in Germany and the reality of two dead people lowered into the damp clay of the settlement. If Orde had gotten himself killed by being foolish that was his own fault. Sharon Zalmon's only fault was that of being Jewish. It was enough to earn her and a thousand others their own plot of ground this morning.

11

No Right to Hope

It was a morning unlike any other in the history of Germany. A gray pall of smoke hovered over every city in the Reich. When the last synagogue had been incinerated and the last shard of glass had fallen to the street, the people came out to tour the devastated Jewish districts to see for themselves just what had happened. By the thousands and tens of thousands, Germans wandered speechless through the wreckage. And by their coming, they removed forever the excuse that they did not know what was being done to their Jewish neighbors.

On that cold day in November, no one in Germany could say, *"I did not know. I did not see...."*

Blackened fragments of Jewish lives filtered down in a gritty film that clung to the majestic new buildings erected in Berlin and Nuremberg and Hamburg. Ash coated the Nazi monuments and statues, a black and white relief like a photographic negative. But there were no actual negatives. Men and women alike were arrested for taking pictures; the Ministry of Propaganda did not fancy the idea of photos of destroyed Jewish shops and synagogues shouting accusations from the front pages of foreign newspapers. Even one photograph was worth a thousand self-righteous news stories. Without pictures, however, the destruction remained a private matter. As the Führer said, no other nation had offered to help Germany solve her Jewish problem; what right did any nation have, therefore, to interfere in a purely German solution?

Everyone understood that there were bound to be a few sanctimonious proclamations in the Western press, but all that would soon be forgotten. Other news would occupy the world tomorrow.

But on this morning, good German housewives brought their children to see what had been done to the Jewish vermin. Some regret arose among the stunned, silent crowds. In the ashes of one bonfire lay the remains of a perfectly good chair. Might that chair not have been used by an Aryan family? A half-charred bolt of cloth lay amid the rubble in a street, cloth that might have been made into pretty dresses for Aryan children. Such excess shocked the frugal Germans; such waste. Everything that had been destroyed would have belonged to the great Aryan race in time. Why had it not simply been confiscated and given to the German population?

This whispered question lay on many complaining lips this morning, but few other questions were voiced. Of all those tens of thousands of good German people touring the wreckage, few dared utter a single moral objection to the violence. A few fools interfered with the beating or arrest of a Jew; their interference, in turn, led to their own arrests. It seemed much wiser, then, to limit one's disapproval to the smashing of good, usable material goods. Never mind the smashing of lives. Never mind that 70,000 men were being loaded into cattle cars and shipped to any one of a hundred concentration camps. Never mind that women were left without sons and husbands, children without fathers. The Nazi Reich was evenhanded in its justice, after all. Soon all Jewish families would be in the same place.

On November 10, the Berlin headquarters of the Secret State Police sent out a wire at the instruction of Gestapo Chief Himmler.

TO ALL STATE HEADQUARTERS AND BRANCH OFFICES:
BUCHENWALD CONCENTRATION CAMP IS FILLED TO CAPACITY WITH CURRENT DELIVERIES. THEREFORE, FURTHER TRANSFERS TO BUCHENWALD ARE TO BE CANCELED, WITH THE EXCEPTION OF TRANSPORTS ALREADY UNDER WAY. TO PREVENT ERRORS, THIS H.Q. WILL BE INFORMED WELL IN ADVANCE OF TRANSFERS TO THE DACHAU AND SACHSENHAUSEN CAMPS.

Pastor Karl Ibsen stood in line with three thousand other newly arrested prisoners outside the warmth of the railway terminal, Bahnhof Friedrichstrasse. Damp mist from the Spree River clung to his face and hair and soaked through his coat. Like the others, he had not slept in over twenty-four hours. The stubble of a reddish-gold beard frosted his face; his eyes stung with the stench of Berlin's burned-out buildings.

On the platform, two dozen S.S. strutted above the prisoners. At the opposite side of the miserable group, soldiers patrolled with dogs. Prisoners were not allowed to sit down or speak or relieve themselves. Respected men who had once taught at German universities or practiced medicine or led a congregation in worship were forced to defecate or urinate in their clothing. They had learned in the early hours of their captivity not to question, not to ask for favors from their guards.

THE ZION COVENANT

• 118 •

Karl spotted Nathan Thalmann, a faithful member of his congregation. Their eyes met. In a look, Karl hoped to give Nathan encouragement and hope. Nathan simply shook his head and looked away. *What was the use?* A Christian of Jewish heritage, Nathan had been singled out when he went to the aid of an old shopkeeper who was being beaten to death. His concern, like that of Karl, had brought him here to the gates of hell.

An S.S. officer, resplendent in his tall boots and black uniform, walked out onto the platform. He spoke briefly to one of the guards who nodded, saluted, and then fired his machine gun into the air with a burst that sent the prisoners to the pavement in their fear.

Screams pierced the morning, then silence followed by the laughter of the guards and the officer.

The officer stepped forward and looked over the faces of his prisoners. He was still smirking.

"Well, Jews!" he boomed, and his voice carried well in the still, cold air. "How do you like the sound of guns, eh? The last sound Embassy Secretary vom Rath heard before a Jew shot him full of holes. How do you like the sound of death?" He raised his hand in signal, and half a dozen weapons sputtered an ominous warning.

Although the guns shot over them, prisoners ducked, shielding their heads, covering their ears. Once again there was total silence. No one dared breathe as the echo of machine-gun fire died away.

Karl looked across the street toward the Winter Garden Theater. Only three weeks before, he and Helen had gone there. They had eaten at the Aschinger Restaurant on the next block. Karl focused on those places, reminders of a saner world. How far away!—a gulf separated by guards and dogs and strutting Nazi officers.

The officer assessed the grim faces of the three thousand captives before him, reveling in their fear. "You do not enjoy our humor, I see." He shrugged. "Wait until you experience the jokes of the Concentration Camp Commandant, eh?" He seemed pleased with himself, keeping his men amused with his great wit. "Well, Jews, we have gotten the news that Buchenwald is filled. Sachsenhausen is also filled. There is still room enough in Dachau for most of you, however. How do you fancy a little train ride to Bavaria?" He raised his chin as if waiting for an answer. The breath of the silent captives rose into the air like steam from a stewpot, giving the illusion of heat. "What? Not anxious to see Bavaria? Ah, well, it is very cold. I hope you have all brought your warm ski clothes."

In fact, some men among the group were dressed only in nightshirts and stocking feet. Karl had given his sweater to one older fellow at the police station. Karl's overcoat was warm enough for now, but he regretted not having the foresight to put on woolen socks and heavy boots instead of street shoes. Perhaps Helen would be allowed to send him a package. She would think of such things without being told. She would feel the ache of the cold in his limbs as if it were her own.

The officer smiled as he spoke. Then his tone changed to a patronizing whine, as if reprimanding naughty children.

"What? You forgot your gloves and cap? You do not have shoes? Well, without your shoes you will no doubt lose your feet."

A cry rose up from a small group of women clustered beyond the outer perimeter of the guards. At his words, they covered their mouths in horror and wiped angry tears from their cheeks.

These were the wives—Aryan wives of arrested Jews, Karl guessed. He admired their courage to follow their husbands and face the ridicule of the Nazi guards. The women stood on tiptoe and strained to see their husbands as they peeled off their own coats and sweaters and held up bundles that were forbidden to be passed to the prisoners.

Karl searched the group of women for some sign of his wife, but Helen was not among them. No doubt she had heard of his arrest. Karl hoped that the Gestapo had released Leona Kalner, who would have carried the news to New Church. He thought of Jacob and Mark escaping over the rooftops. If they managed to make their way through the riots, surely they had alerted Helen to his fate.

He had not seen Richard Kalner after their arrest. The two men had been separated immediately. Karl had not been beaten badly, but Richard was almost unconscious when they threw him onto the truck.

Karl shuddered at the thought of what would happen to Richard Kalner. At that same instant, the press of prisoners surrounding him parted slightly. For just an instant, he caught sight of Richard's bloodied face. *Right eye swollen shut. Cheek blue. Lips cut and puffy. Brown hair caked with his own blood.*

Richard saw Karl, too. He raised his hand and let it drop. He did not look away even when the shrill wail of the train whistle announced the beginning of their journey. The two men moved toward each other in hopes that they might be loaded into the same freight car. Then they could talk. After the doors slid shut, they would be free to talk.

The airplane passed over the industrial center of London. Smoke from hundreds of factory chimneys mingled with fog to blacken endless blocks of identical houses with soot.

Theo watched as thousands of workmen made their way in the gray morning light toward the huge barn-like factories that cluttered the docks along the Thames River. With the eye of an experienced Luftwaffe pilot, he could easily see what perfect targets the English factories would make from the air. He scanned the riverbanks for possible anti-aircraft guns. Although Parliament had been discussing the need for defense from air attacks, nothing was being done. That fact, coupled with the brutality he had witnessed last night, frightened Theo. What would it take to awaken England? Life seemed to flow on peacefully, monotonously, as though nothing at all had happened in Germany.

He looked across the aisle at the sleeping American diplomat who had helped him pass so easily through German customs. Hopewell's mouth hung open, his head flung back. He had not uttered a word since five minutes after their takeoff from Tempelhof. Had he seen all the fires across the landscape of the Reich? Had he witnessed enough to sound the alarm for his own countrymen to hear? And, wrapped in their own apathetic dreams, would the Americans want to hear?

Theo frowned and looked down across the city of London. In Germany, they battled the Nazis, a tangible enemy. Here, the enemy was less obvious—the apathy of people who would simply rather not have their personal comfort disturbed. As the plane dipped lower toward the airfield, Theo prayed that the sleepwalking world might awaken before the darkness also crossed their threshold.

As if startled by an inward alarm clock, Hopewell sat up suddenly, yawned and wriggled a finger in his ear.

"Is it London yet?" he asked as the drone of the engines slowed and deepened.

Theo nodded and pointed down. "You've been sleeping since Berlin."

"The only way a diplomat can sleep at all." Hopewell smoothed his rumpled suit and straightened his bow tie. "*En route* somewhere. That's the best sleep I get these days. And I can tell you, after what I saw last night, it may be a while before any of us is able to sleep through an entire night." He checked his pocket watch and squinted in thought. "I called Joseph Kennedy last night before we left. You know Kennedy, American ambassador to England? Blasted pacifist thinks Hitler is a swell fellow, and we ought to mind our own business. That sort of rot. Anyway, we'll be having breakfast together this morning. I'd appreciate it if you could join us. Maybe open the eyes of the blind ambassador, if you know what I mean. We can go over the dispatches from our consulates in Germany as they come in this morning. Seems to me that might be of help to you as well, eh?"

———

Moshe felt out of place among the mourners of Hanita who gathered in the mess hall after the brief services. He left them there and retreated with his own grief to the privacy of his tent.

The strong smell of onion greeted him as he entered. Before his eyes adjusted to the gloom, he knew he was not alone. Samuel Orde lay on his cot. He took a bite of a raw onion as though it were an apple and then answered Moshe's astonished expression.

"If you are going to bunk in my tent, you cannot live like a pig."

The captain gestured toward Moshe's unmade bed. "I am not your mother or your maid to clean up after you. Keep it neat, or I will throw you out on your ear."

The words slapped Moshe in the face. He exploded with anger. "Where have you been? The whole camp was looking for you, and believe me, these people have more important matters to think about this morning than the whereabouts of some arrogant Englishman!" He tossed his coat onto the unmade cot. "And I will make up my cot when I'm ready! At least I do not stink like an Arab onion field!"

"Exactly." Orde took another bite. "That is because you have not walked through an Arab onion field recently." He held the onion up. His meaning was clear. Samuel Orde had been deep in hostile territory, and he had come back safely.

"So what? Am I supposed to be impressed? You made me look like a fool this morning. I stood up for you. No one trusts you, but I stood up for you."

"You are a fool. You all are. Fools and infants facing something you cannot possibly imagine or fight against because you haven't the slightest idea how to do it." He threw the onion at Moshe, who tried unsuccessfully to dodge it. "That is why I am here."

He stood and pushed past Moshe. Moshe followed angrily after him. In the daylight he could see that Orde was filthy and scratched. Even without the onion the Englishman smelled of sweat. Orde walked toward the mess hall. It did not matter to him if Moshe tagged along.

The murmur of conversation fell silent as he entered the building with Moshe at his heels. Eyes widened. The missing-and-presumed-dead Englishman was alive. How had he reentered the compound? Where had he been? Hostility showed on the faces of many who looked at him. After all, how could anyone slip out of Hanita and return alive on today of all days? *He must be a spy,* some thought. The accusation was not on their lips, but in their eyes.

"Where have you been?" Zach demanded. "We were looking."

"He has been to an Arab onion field," Moshe blurted out harshly. Orde's strong aroma confirmed his words.

Zach was not amused. "And what did you find there?"

Orde lifted his chin slightly, exuding the authority of his rank and addressing the men of Hanita as though they were his soldiers. "Come with me," he commanded, pointing to the same four men who had driven out to deposit the dead Arab on the threshold of his village. Then he also pointed at Moshe and Zach. "You come as well." He smiled coolly at Moshe. "And if you wake up in hell tomorrow, you have only yourself to blame."

"Where are we going?" Zach was defiant, suspicious.

Orde turned back the others who followed them curiously across the compound toward the gates. Only the six he had chosen were allowed to hear what he had to say next. He passed out bullets enough to fill each Webley revolver completely. Only then did he explain where he had been and where they were going.

"I tracked the trail of the men who raided you last night. I found where they keep their weapons stashed."

"So. This is news?" Larry said. "The Arabs have weapons, and we are left with guns for shooting clay pigeons and target practice."

Orde ignored the complaint. "You Jews of the settlements have been fighting a defensive war against the Muslims for too long. Such tactics will not save your lives or your settlements. You will never put down the enemy that way." He looked out beyond the barricades. "We will wage a new kind of war."

"We?" repeated Zach skeptically.

Orde turned on him fiercely. "Yes, WE! You must stop thinking of me as an Englishman and consider me as one of you—fighting the same fight as you, with the same idea in mind and the same goal! I am with you with every beat of my heart. So let's have no more of these suspicions." He shifted his gaze and abruptly took charge. "Henceforth, we will not wait for the men of the Mufti to come to us and murder us in the settlements. We shall go out and meet the enemy in the open, near his villages. We shall carry the battle to him."

The law of the British Mandate declared such actions by Jews were punishable by prison and death. Orde wore the uniform of the British government.

"But that is illegal," Larry Havas protested.

Orde waved his hand in dismissal of such puny matters. "Leave such little details to me. But first we will need weapons. The Holy Strugglers have kindly provided fine German-made rifles for us just a short hike from here. The seven of us will fetch them and carry them back to Hanita under cover of night."

———

By the time the plane had bumped down on English soil, the London presses were running hot with the news of *Kristal Nacht*, the Night of Broken Glass. From all indications, the violent night rolled over into a violent morning. The breaking of glass and lives continued after the breaking of a new day.

Murphy had been up since Anna had telephoned with news that Theo was *en route* across the Channel from Holland. He had not stopped to eat breakfast, instead going immediately to the TENS office for three hours of work. As he walked quickly beside Anna toward the tarmac, his stomach rumbled. It was only 7:00 A.M., but it felt like the middle of the day.

Word had somehow leaked that some American bigwig diplomat was flying in straight from Berlin. Dozens of reporters from various news agencies jostled for position at the gate. Anna held Murphy back from the hubbub. She did not want to have to fight her way to Theo.

The hum of conversation rose to a shout as the grim American ambassador emerged from the plane. The man looked surprisingly rested and unruffled after last night's ordeal. He fielded questions easily, replying that he had a report to make to President Roosevelt before he went into much detail, but that he had been witness to the blackest night in history since the Dark Ages. Pens flew at this reference to darkness and ignorance. Bulbs popped frantically, stinging Ambassador Hopewell's eyes, but missing the exhausted and disheveled figure of Theo Lindheim as he stepped from the plane and searched the crowd for Anna.

"Theo!" she cried, standing on her tiptoes and waving. "Theo! Over here!" For the first time, she let her heart admit that she had spent every moment of his absence wondering if she would ever see him again.

She wept happily as she pushed through the reporters and ran to Theo. It didn't matter that he was unshaven and rumpled; she wrapped her arms around him and said his name again and again as he stroked her hair. But when she looked up into his face she saw only sadness there. She had seen this look when he spoke softly about the men in the *Herrgottsecke*, the prayer corner, at Dachau, when he spoke about the Covenant—grief coupled with helplessness. She reached up and touched his cheek.

The reporters did not notice him. Murphy hung back for a few minutes while Anna and Theo had their silent reunion.

"One look at you and it all recedes," Theo said at last. "Like a bad dream, Anna."

She looked searchingly into his eyes. "But it is not a bad dream, is it, Theo? And it will not go away like we all hoped, will it?"

"We are past hoping now, Anna," he answered. "Unless we fight, we have no right to hope."

12

Through a Wall of Fire

Hours passed slowly inside the stuffy organ bellows. Lori slept standing, leaning against Jacob, who held her up. A wooden brace pressed painfully into his back. He imagined them all dying in here, being found by some organ repairman sent to find out why the bellows did not work.

"I have to use the toilet," Mark croaked. His voice shattered their miserable silence, and Lori woke up as Jacob knocked Mark on the side of the head. Mark began to cry. "I have to . . . I need to use the toilet," he wailed.

"Shut up!" Jacob hissed, kicking him in the leg.

"Leave him alone," Lori demanded, suddenly too uncomfortable to care anymore. All she wanted was to get out. Out of the dust and the darkness. To breathe real air again. "We can't stay in here forever. *Leave him alone!*"

Jacob groaned as his endurance faded. He was hungry. They had not eaten or had a drink since last night. He needed a toilet, too. Lori was right. They could not stay in here forever. *Die standing up in the bellows of a pipe organ? Even the Nazis could not think of a worse prison.*

"Come on, then," he said through parched lips.

The trio tumbled out of the bellows, each stumbling in a different direction, away from the enforced closeness.

A cloud of dust followed them. Cobwebs streamed from their hair and hands and clung to their clothing as though they had been entombed for a hundred years.

Like a bird trying to fly, Lori raised her grimy hands toward the high window where a shaft of light beamed down into the little room behind the organ.

Mark stumbled toward the door. A helmet of cobwebs coated his curly blond hair and hung from his chin. He pushed hard against the door, then kicked it when it did not yield. His face was desperate. Jacob grabbed him by his jacket and pulled him back. "You want them to hear us?"

Mark began crying again. "I don't care. I want to go to the toilet. I can't get out. It's locked."

Lori shook her head at the two warring brothers. With an air of aloofness, she reached over and grasped the handle of the door. "Pull," she said, opening the door. Mark broke free and charged out the door, clattering down the stairs as quietly as an army on the march.

Jacob stared angrily after him, then brushed the dust from his clothes and followed. Lori came last, closing the door behind her. She stood at the head of the stairs for a moment and listened to the hollow echo of their retreating footsteps. A knot of apprehension formed in her stomach. Her eyes brimmed with tears. She did not want to go down into the emptiness of the church. Mama was not there. James had been taken away. Papa was arrested. And Lori was alone. It did not matter that Mark and Jacob were downstairs; she was still alone.

A wave of dizziness hit her as the reality of it all sank in. She would walk down the steps into the auditorium where Papa preached and Mama played the piano and Jamie fidgeted in the pew with his friends . . . but they would not be there.

Lori sat down on the top step and stared at her shoes. It occurred to her that she had not had her shoes off since yesterday morning, just before breakfast, when they had all eaten together and talked about ordinary things. Papa had gone off to his study to work on his sermon. Mama and Lori had done the dishes. Jamie had prowled around outside through the fallen autumn leaves in search of a pocketknife he had lost. *Only yesterday?*

"Lori?" Jacob stood at the bottom of the stairs. His hand was on the banister as if he wanted to come up. His face reflected concern. "They have all gone." Then, "Are you all right?"

She bit her lip and shook her head slowly. "No . . . I . . . I am not all right."

He climbed the stairs and sat down below her. "We are safe here for now."

"I was hoping this was all a terrible dream. While we were inside the bellows, I could not quite believe they came and took Mama and Jamie and . . . the rest."

He reached up and patted her awkwardly on the arm, as though consoling a teammate after losing a game of soccer. "All night last night I kept thinking I would wake up. I wanted to wake up." He gestured toward the light. "And now it is morning."

"Oh, Jacob, what will we do?" She rested her head in her hands and closed her eyes against the light.

He exhaled loudly and cleared his throat, trying to force away the sadness in his own voice. "First, we should eat something. I'm hungry."

Lori looked up at him in disbelief. Everyone was taken away. Only the three of them were left in this place, and all Jacob Kalner could think about was his stomach. "Eat?"

"Breakfast."

"But where—"

"I sent Mark to look for the communion bread. Do they keep the wine in the same place?"

Alfie's stomach rumbled. It was long past time for lunch. He was hungry, and he thought about mealtimes in the ward. He remembered the way he had fed Werner with a spoon and Werner had told him funny stories between bites. Werner was gone now, and that fact made Alfie more sad than hungry. Maybe even if he had food he would not be able to eat it. He decided not to pay attention to the pain in his stomach. The hurting in his heart was much worse.

People still milled about everywhere in the streets of Berlin. Some came to look and not steal. Their faces were sad too, Alfie noticed. Some of them would look and shake their heads and then look away. Maybe some of those sad-eyed people had friends like Werner who had been taken away in the night.

Alfie walked slowly along with the crowds. Glass crunched beneath his shoes and he was worried that the glass might cut his new shoes. He followed a man in a business suit who wore a hat like Papa used to wear. The man said over and over, "My God, we are animals! *Animals!*"

A lady in a brown coat stood beside him. She shook her head and said, "Not even animals would do such a thing."

Alfie thought she was probably right. He liked animals. He had a dog once, and she was nicer to Alfie than anyone. Her name was Sally, and she thought Alfie was smart and wonderful. But that was a long time ago, before Mama died and they took him to the hospital.

If the lady in the brown coat had asked him, he would have told her that dogs were very much nicer than people. But she did not ask, and so Alfie followed the man and the lady for a long time through the wrecked parts of Berlin. After a while they came to an apartment building and went in through the front door, and Alfie was alone again.

He looked through the glass of the door and watched them get into a lift. He wished he could have told them about his dog and Mama and Werner.

The rumble of a car engine pulled him around. A green police car drove by him with men in a cage in the backseat. "They are Jews,"

Alfie said aloud. He said what he knew was true so he would not forget it. "Jews they are taking. And boys who cannot walk, like Werner. And boys who cannot talk, like Heinrich and Dieter. And boys who are dumbheads, like me. Just like Jews." He frowned. "And nice people like Frau Helen and Jamie. People who love Jesus. They are taking them with the Jews."

Pastor Ibsen had once promised that he would help Alfie get out of the ward. He had not been able to help. Alfie had been sad, but he did not blame the pastor. Now Alfie wondered who would help Pastor and Frau Ibsen? Where were the police taking Jamie and the others? It was a sad day in Berlin.

Alfie began to walk again, past houses and apartments he did not recognize. Alfie was not sure where he was. Mostly the street was quiet. *Everyone must be tired from smashing things all night,* he thought.

Alfie's stomach began to hurt too bad to ignore. Up ahead was a wide street. A traffic policeman was directing cars to turn because the street was blocked. The man wore a uniform and white gloves. His eyes looked stern and sad. He blew the whistle in his mouth and waved for some taxis and cars to stop and others to go. Alfie watched him for a while and then made his decision. Everyone was arrested. Everyone Alfie wanted to see was gone. It was best, he reasoned, if maybe he got arrested, too. What was the use of anything, after all, if there was no one to be with?

Alfie waited until the policeman signaled for people to walk across the street. He hurried to reach the policeman first.

"Bitte," Alfie said, showing manners as Mama said he must.

"Ja?" The policeman did not look as if he wanted to talk.

"I need to be arrested."

The policeman stared at him with the whistle hanging on his lip. "Arrested?"

Alfie nodded. "I stole these clothes last night."

The policeman blinked at him as if he did not hear. Horns began to honk. The policeman waved cars through while Alfie stood quietly beside him. Then the policeman whistled and more people crossed the street.

"Nobody will miss those clothes, boy," the policeman said. "Most of Germany would be in prison if it mattered."

"But everyone is arrested."

Crowds brushed past them as they talked.

"Are you a Jew, then? I've got nothing against Jews. I was standing on this corner before Hitler, and I have nothing to do with that. Go home, boy; go home to Mama until this thing passes. Don't speak to another police officer. That's my advice. Now get going!"

Alfie did not argue. It was not polite to argue with a police officer. He nodded his head with a jerk and hurried to the opposite sidewalk.

"Home to Mama," he repeated. The policeman did not understand anything at all. Alfie raised his eyes for some sign of the smoke from the Jewish synagogue beside New Church. A thin black smudge floated overhead and then to the east. Alfie followed it back a different way than he had come. Some streets were not damaged; in others, everything was ruined. In front of a smashed grocery store, broken tins of crackers were scattered everywhere. Alfie kicked a tin with his toe and a wrapped packet of crackers fell out. Alfie picked it up and put it in his pocket. He would eat it later, when he was home with Mama.

Wolf seemed lost in thought as he sipped his coffee at the breakfast table. This was the sort of mood that always before had commanded silence from Lucy. But she was no longer afraid of him, and so she spoke anyway.

"I did not take a cab home last night." She announced her disobedience confidently.

His blue eyes flashed anger. "I told you—"

"I wanted to see," she shrugged, "and so I walked. No one would hurt me, anyway." She reached up and pulled back the curtain, revealing the smoke that tarnished the sky above Vienna. "So you spent the night Jew bashing. Was it fun?"

He answered her with a black look. "A waste. Not that I care for the life of one Jew, but the destruction of property—"

"I saw for myself. Better to hand it over intact."

Wolf appraised her with surprise. He did not imagine that she had a brain in her head to form any opinions at all.

"Orders came from the top," he said with dissatisfaction.

She buttered her toast with real butter. "All this over one German diplomat?" she asked, enjoying the freedom to question him.

He answered truthfully, suddenly opening up in a way he never had before. "It was all arranged ahead of time. This was Hitler's answer to the Armistice Day celebrations of the democracies. France and Britain have their big parades to celebrate the defeat of Germany, and Germany smashes the Jews who, according to Hitler, caused us to lose the war. It is a game with him. A way to let the little men wield power against those who are more helpless than they." He stopped and eyed her quizzically. "Do you understand?"

She nodded and smiled. She understood perfectly about people wielding their power against the weak. She had not understood before last night, but now it was very clear. "And this place?" She swept a hand around the kitchen. "Where did it come from?"

She had never asked before. In all these months she had simply accepted the apartment and furnishings as though Wolf had handpicked it all just for her.

"Where do you think?"

"A Jew? Or a political prisoner?" Genuinely curious, she had spent hours considering the tasteful decorating of the flat. The delicate furnishings and petit point chair seats indicated a woman's touch.

"A Jewess. A musician, I hear. A friend of mine at the Gestapo knew it was vacant and managed to hold it. I owe him a favor now." He seemed amused that he was only now telling her this.

"What is his name?" she asked boldly.

He frowned. This frank questioning was unlike Lucy. She had always been so timid with him before. "What does it matter?"

"I would like to send him a note of appreciation, Wolf. Tell him what magnificent taste he has. And how we have enjoyed this place." She poured coffee into his cup. "It is always a good idea to cultivate the Gestapo, ja?"

He laughed in amazement at the new Lucy. "Pregnancy is good for you, my little cow. It sharpens your wits."

"Then maybe you should call me your little fox instead."

At this Wolf laughed again. "The English would call us a pair— Wolf and vixen, eh?"

"I like this place. I would like to stay here as long as possible, until I have to go to Lebensborn. I would rather be free to walk about Vienna and go to work. Peasant stock, you know, unlike your soft-handed aristocratic women. I enjoy work. I cannot imagine sitting around a resort with a clique of fat, gossiping mistresses doing needlepoint until the baby comes."

Wolf found himself enjoying this side of Lucy. He eyed her for a moment and then agreed to her request with a shrug. "If you prefer. But I insist you see the doctor there regularly. The Lebensborn obstetrician is the best, of course. The clinic was taken over from two Jewish doctors after the Anschluss. You may change your mind about staying there after you see it."

"It is not just Vienna I would miss, Wolf." She touched his hand and smiled the reflection of his most charming smile.

His gaze swept over her and then back to her face. "I stayed away too long," he said, his interest renewed. "I was bored. Now I see it was wrong of me."

Lucy, no longer the beggar she had been, intrigued Wolf. He had taught her the game, and she intended to play it without conscience.

"I'll stay here, then." She decided the matter without further discussion. "You have a key to this place. It would be quite unpleasant for you if I was locked away behind the gates of your little S.S. farm and you could not visit when you liked."

He considered that inconvenience for a moment and then agreed. "Then you should stay here as long as you like." He was not really thinking of her, but of his own appetites. Yesterday Lucy would have seen it differently, but overnight she had become a realist.

"It is cold," she said. "I will need another coat. Something to keep me warm this winter. Fox fur would be appropriate. After last night there should be some very nice ones without owners, I would think."

He shrugged in acquiescence. She was right. "For the baby," he said.

"No. For me. The fox will keep me warm, and I will keep the baby warm. But first you must bring the fox."

He frowned slightly. As if he had heard another whisper from her heart, he said, "Remember who you belong to."

"Why, to you, of course, my Wolf. You do not want me to look inferior to the women of other officers."

He grunted and continued to stare thoughtfully at her. "And remember who the child belongs to."

She did not lower her eyes from his, but looked at him with amusement, as though she could not understand what he was getting at. "The Führer?" she asked coyly.

He clouded at her joke. "It would not be wise for you to make plans—"

She looked at him with scorn. "You know me better than that, Wolf."

He shrugged again, content with her answer. She had silenced his doubts. A woman like Lucy could not see past the next hour, he reasoned, let alone leave him.

"Well, then. We will enjoy ourselves for now, my little fox."

————

Reichsmarschall Hermann Göring's angry face flushed with emotion beneath the rouge he had carelessly applied before this morning's meeting.

"I wish you had just killed Jews instead of destroying so many valuables!" he said bitterly to Reinhard Heydrich, who had come to the meeting as a representative of Gestapo Chief Himmler.

Heydrich raised his long narrow head defensively. "Plenty of Jews were killed. And there will be more!"

The stenographer took notes furiously, hardly glancing up at Heydrich. The large, beaked nose of the iron-willed Aryan was still raised proudly, his blond hair slicked back, every hair in place. The S.S. uniform remained impeccable in spite of a long night's work directing the attacks against Jews and the arrest of over 70,000 men. His thin lips turned slightly downward as Minister of Propaganda Goebbels spoke up in defense of the violence.

"The attack on Ernst vom Rath is perceived as an attack on the entire German nation. Therefore every Jew must pay."

Göring's eyes bulged. He slammed his fist on the table and shouted. "The synagogues demolished, yes! Jews arrested and held for fines, yes! But don't you see? If a Jewish shop is totally destroyed and its goods thrown out into the street and burned, it is not the Jews who suffer the damage; it is the German insurance companies! Furthermore, the goods that are being destroyed are consumer goods, belonging to the people! In the future when demonstrations against the Jews are held, they must be directed so they do not hurt *us, us, us!*" Göring emphasized each word by pounding his meaty fist on the conference table of the new German Air Ministry.

Silence descended as the dozen men before him sat in deep thought. Insurance companies. No one had thought of that as they destroyed millions of marks worth of plate glass.

Göring sat back and looked at his thumbs. The entire episode had not turned out as he had expected. Theo Lindheim had slipped away through the tumult of the riots without even being stopped or questioned. Someone would pay for that oversight. Apprehending Lindheim had been the responsibility of the Gestapo. Theo might have been worth millions to the Reich treasury in ransom. Now that opportunity had been lost, and Jewish goods, which should have simply been confiscated as the owners were hauled away, smoldered in the ashes.

He looked sharply at Heydrich and Goebbels, who seemed pleased with the excesses of Kristal Nacht. After all, it had given the Jews a certain vision of their future.

Hermann Göring rested his hands on his fat paunch and eyed the committee that the Führer had appointed to settle the Jewish problem once and for all. "It was insane to clear out a whole warehouse of Jewish goods and burn the lot. German insurance companies will have to pay, and all those goods were things I need desperately for the economic plan. Whole bales of clothing." Again he smashed his fist against the tabletop.

Goebbels, as thin and emaciated as Göring was fat, rubbed his hands together and grimaced slightly in thought. "Why not simply make a law?" Making laws always seemed to provide solutions to such matters as who would pay for what. "Why not simply exempt the insurance companies from having to pay?"

Göring considered the suggestion. A murmur of approval rippled around the table. "I am going to issue a decree," he said, his anger finally giving way to practicality and the power he had to remove all obstacles. "And I am going to expect the support of all government agents in channeling the claims so that the German insurance companies will not suffer."

From the far end of the table a small, timid-looking fellow raised his hand at that suggestion. He smiled nervously, his left eye twitching behind thick spectacles.

Göring waved a hand expansively at the little man. "For those of you who have not met him, this is the representative of the insurance industry, Herr Hildegard." He sniffed impatiently as Hildegard opened his briefcase and removed a file folder, laboriously laying it out before him.

"This is a delicate situation," Hildegard said sadly. "You see, many of the German companies have reinsured in foreign countries."

"Explain this, please," Göring said. "Most are soldiers and politicians. Explain the term *to reinsure.*"

The little man drew himself up, suddenly confident in his role as advisor to this august body of Nazi leaders. "Simply this: German companies did not wish to carry all the risk themselves. So part of the risk is also borne by foreign insurers in countries like France and Belgium and Switzerland, you see?"

Heads nodded in unison.

Hildegard continued his explanation. "We would like to make a point, Herr Field Marshall, that we must not be hindered in fulfilling the obligations the contracts call for. Even to Jews. We must make certain that there is no loss of confidence in the German insurance companies, or our foreign companies will pull out. It would be a black spot on the honor of German insurance companies."

A few moments passed in thought. Göring sucked his cheek and toyed with a pencil. "It would not blacken your honor if I issued a decree, a law sanctioned by the state, forbidding you to pay."

Heydrich leaned forward, a spark of amusement in his cold pale eyes. "Why not this? The insurance may be granted, but as soon as it is paid to the Jews, it will be confiscated. That way we will have saved face."

The spidery insurance executive clasped his hands together and nodded vigorously. "I am inclined to agree with General Heydrich."

At last Göring grinned, then laughed. "You'll have to pay, then. But since it is the Aryan people who really suffered the damage, there will be a lawful decree forbidding you to make payment to the Jews. After all, it is the Jews who incited the demonstration, is it not?" Göring pointed his meaty finger at the little man. "By my decree, you will not make payment to the Jews, but to the Ministry of Finance."

"Aha!" cried Hildegard with relief. The solution was so simple.

Göring continued with a sharp warning. "As Minister of Finance, I will tell you that what is done with the money is my business."

Others rushed to join in the economic reprisals against the Jewish victims of Kristal Nacht. Schmer, a junior member of the Finance Ministry, spoke up for the first time. "Your Excellency, I should like to make a proposal. I understand that this morning the Führer decreed also that a fine of one billion marks is to be levied against the Jews for provoking the German people into demonstrating against them. Perhaps with that fine, the insurance companies could be refunded?"

Göring balked at the very thought that any money extracted from the Jews might be given to any entity but the Reich Ministry of Finance, which he headed. "I would not dream of refunding the insurance companies," he blustered. He turned to Hildegard. "That money belongs to the state. You will fulfill your obligations, you may count on that!"

Göring looked pleased; suddenly all the destruction of property had turned to advantage for the Four-Year Economic Plan he had struggled with. Suddenly, through the insurance payoff and the fine of one billion marks against the Jews, the coffers of his Ministry of Finance were filled. No longer did he need consider economic plans like the one proposed by Theo Lindheim. No, the Reich was free to discard outright the scheme that would have allowed Jews to emigrate with a portion of their wealth in return for trade agreements between Germany and the Western nations.

Göring muttered under his breath, "If those bleeding hearts in England and America wish to have the Jews, they must take them as paupers." He raised his eyes to the group. "Not one penny will be taken out of the Reich. We have shown the Jews their way out, eh? They will leave this country through a wall of fire."

13

Night Squad

From across the street, Alfie watched as men worked to nail boards across the doors and low windows on New Church. Signs with the crooked cross on them were nailed up also. Alfie could not read very well, but Mama had taught him some words like STOP and GO and NO and DANGER and *VERBOTEN! Forbidden!* It was the biggest word Alfie knew, and he had been very proud when he learned it. It kept him from walking on the grass in the parks and going in the wrong door.

When the Hitler-men made laws about the Jews, another word went up with *VERBOTEN,* the word *JUDEN.* Signs everywhere said *Jews Forbidden!* Alfie had learned the word *JUDEN,* too, because Mama said that otherwise he might only see the word FORBIDDEN and think he could not enter into a place. He was not a Jew, and so he could go in even though the word FORBIDDEN was written on a sign.

The sky was getting darker, and Alfie looked at the Nazi signs all over New Church—the word VERBOTEN painted with a lot of other words. He waited as two men hammered up the last sign. On the top was the crooked cross, then letters and words:

CLOSED BY ORDER OF THE REICH GOVERNMENT FOR VIOLATION OF RACE LAW AND STATUTES CONCERNING ILLEGAL PROTEC-TION OF CRIMINAL *JEWS.* TRESPASSING *FORBIDDEN.*

Among all the letters, Alfie could make out those two words that Mama said he could ignore: *JEWS . . . FORBIDDEN.*

The sign was not for Alfie because he was not a Jew. The church was boarded up, but the cemetery where Mama lay in the stone shed was not closed. For the first time since last night, Alfie felt good again. He had crackers in his pocket, and over the fence he could see the top of the white stone building where all the Halder family was dead together under the same roof.

The men loaded their ladders and tools into the back of a truck and drove away. They did not see Alfie looking at the graveyard and the place where Mama lay. Other cars drove past, but they did not notice him as he walked across the street and into the little park beside New Church. He followed the wall along the side of the church. Stopping at the metal gate, he shook it hard, but it was locked. It did not matter; Alfie knew another way into the churchyard—a secret he and Jamie kept because of hide-and-seek. No one could find them when they played around the church because they were the only ones who knew.

At the rear of New Church stood the shed where the gardener kept his tools, built almost against the wall that enclosed the churchyard. Between the shed and the wall was a space where Jamie could scoot through easily. It was harder for Alfie because he was big, but just like old times, he dropped to his hands and knees and crawled into the space. A plank covered a hole that went right through the wall and into the cemetery. Grown-ups did not know about it because the slab of an old tombstone leaned back and covered the opening.

Alfie laughed when he crawled through into the churchyard. He felt the same kind of happy feeling that always came to him when he and Jamie ran to hide and nobody could ever find them! Alfie hadn't played with Jamie in a long time, and now Jamie was gone, but Alfie remembered how to do it and where to go.

Alfie knew where to hide. It was not really a game anymore, but he decided that maybe he did not want to be found or arrested after all. This felt good! He felt smart!

He picked his way carefully through the headstones and the other square stone sheds where families liked to be dead together. He had one more secret that he had shared with Jamie, a secret better than the hole in the wall behind the tombstone.

The place where Mama was buried stood just a little ways in back of the church. It was square like a big stone box. HALDER was carved in the stone above an iron gate that opened into a room where the Halders were stored in the walls behind stone partitions.

Alfie touched the gate and looked in. Mama had told him not to be afraid of this place. Six generations of Halders slept here, waiting until Jesus would come wake them up. She explained that generations were grandmothers and grandfathers who lived a long time before Alfie, and that one day they would be alive again and very pleased to meet Alfie. He looked forward to that and thought how fine it would be if Jesus came and everyone woke up while he was there.

"Hello, Mama," he whispered, leaning his head against the bars.

Mama's place was the very top space against the back wall, right above Papa's space. Her name was carved in the stone covering that hid the coffin: IRENE HALDER. Papa's name was also carved on the stone that covered his space: ALFRED HALDER.

But here was the secret Alfie shared with Jamie: Papa's space was empty. He had disappeared in a shipwreck, and so they could not put him in his place to wait for Jesus. Mama just had the name carved there so it would look as if Papa was there. A memorial, she told Alfie. A way to remember Papa.

Alfie clung to the bars and looked at their names. He was glad he had come back here. He cried a little bit, but not because he was sad. He cried because he was happy that someday for sure they would all wake up and they could hug and laugh and talk about good things.

It was almost dark when Alfie reached his hand up on the stone ledge above the gate. He knew just where the key was. It was long and heavy and rust red, just like the last time Alfie and Jamie had used it.

Alfie unlocked the gate. The hinges groaned inward, and he stepped into the echoing little room. Then he closed the gate behind him and locked it tight. Now Alfie was safe. He had come home to Mama, just like the policeman said, and he wouldn't tell anyone where he was. This was his place. There were lots of empty chambers where he could hide if someone came. And in the back, in an alcove, a square stone trapdoor opened to a chamber below. There were much older Halders down there, and it was damp and musty. Mama never went down there, but Jamie and Alfie had explored it all with a tickle of fear and excitement in their stomachs.

This chamber held the most wonderful secret of all. Alfie had brought food and candles and blankets and had hidden them all in an empty space so that they could keep warm and have lots to eat and could see in the dark while everyone else looked and looked for them in hide-and-seek. He had intended to surprise Jamie next time they played the game, but then Mama had died and the men had come . . .

Alfie suddenly grew very tired. He touched Mama's name and remembered to say his prayers as she taught him. And then, without bothering to eat his crackers, he climbed into Papa's empty place and went to sleep.

———

A tall neon sign announced the appearance of an old comedian at the Winter Garden Theater in Berlin. Otto parked the car across the street and sat for a while to study the smiling faces of uniformed officers of the Reich and their women. Furs and diamonds glittered in the harsh light. Complexions seemed lifeless in the unnatural glow.

This was the one theater in Berlin where people could still come with some measure of freedom. The resident comic had been arrested and released a dozen times for insulting the state and the party. He was always back to his old routine within a matter of days. Goebbels came here sometimes; Hermann Göring was a regular customer. They came because this was the only way they could face the truth and face themselves—through laughter. Strip away the joke, and the truth was a hideous monster. Laugh, and it was almost bearable, like releasing steam from a pressure cooker.

Otto had intended to go in tonight, but if he heard even one fragment of truth covered by a joke he knew he would go mad. He should mingle among these people, hear their music, know their faces. But he could not. Not now. Tomorrow he would return to Vienna and pass a cyanide tablet through the bars to Michael Wallich. Tomorrow he would be merciful and let the man die an easy death before he was forced to die a difficult one. Ease of death was the mercy of the Third Reich, the justification of murder. Like the truth, it was cloaked with laughter. Cyanide and gas, killing the helpless. Otto had heard the stories. Today they had shown him the photographs.

"God!" He gripped the steering wheel in anguish; he wanted to tear it apart with his bare hands. He had seen the neatly stacked bodies in a row and heard how painless it had been, how merciful.

Otto knew he was going back to whisper to Michael Wallich that he brought him a more merciful end than the death the Gestapo had planned for him! *No torture. Just a little pill, and Michael Wallich would be laid out for a photograph. Not so gruesome as the picture of Thomas von Kleistmann. Not crucifixion. Just this pill . . .*

Otto could not think clearly enough to walk inside the theater and grin among the other living dead men. They would turn their hollow eyes on him and know that he was a traitor to their conspiracy of death.

He had seen too much; he had walked among these specters and reported their intentions. And no one had believed his report. All this had been useless. Useless! In England they said they were listening, but their listening had not saved Thomas. Or Austria. Or Czechoslovakia. It would not save Michael Wallich from dying or save Otto from helping him into his grave!

The thin veneer of cold control finally cracked and fell away from Otto Wattenbarger. He had done what he needed to do, but today he had seen the photographs, and he could no longer pretend to smile or listen to the music.

He started the car and drove slowly past the neon sign. He would have to regain his sanity again somehow, or he could not return to Vienna. Whatever cause he lived for would be gone unless he could find his mind again tonight. If not, he would be better off to swallow the pill he carried in his pocket for Michael Wallich. Indeed, that seemed the most merciful solution right now for Otto.

But if he died an easy death, would they also crucify Michael?

Would Michael talk, and others die? From their tortured mouths would the rest also be condemned?

Perhaps another time Otto would listen to the music. But not tonight.

———————

Whole streets throughout Berlin seemed deserted, buildings shuttered and dark. As Otto drove from place to place, he measured the destruction and felt small and useless in the face of it.

"What can one man do?" he muttered aloud as he passed the boarded facade of New Church and the burned-out hulk of the great synagogue.

From there he drove into the wide parks that lined the rivers. A bed of dead leaves carpeted the ground beneath trees that seemed lifeless and barren. Like those trees, the freshness of illusion and hope had fallen from Otto. He knew too much to believe in the goodness of men's intentions. He had seen too much darkness to believe that God's light was not in danger of being snuffed out forever in the soul of mankind.

Many who believed in the goodness of humanity had already given in to evil. Beyond Germany, people spoke out against this barbarity but did not fight it with their hands as well as their mouths. They, too, had given up righteousness for the sake of ease. Their consciences were satisfied with moral outrage, but nothing further was accomplished.

"I too am evil, my Lord," Otto wept as he passed the high walls of a hospital where the state had murdered the weak and given beds to the strong. "I am dark!" he cried. "But I long to be light!"

The headlights of his car swept over the dull face of the river Spree. He had seen the sunlight sparkle on its water. He could remember when he had sparkled in his own goodness. Now even kindness in his life seemed tarnished. The sunlight on the water had only been superficial. Night had come to Germany and to the world and to Otto Wattenbarger.

And in seeing what Germany had become, he saw himself.

———————

Orde formed his small troop into a single file with about five yards between them. As he placed them in position he took a moment to look steadily into each man's eyes. Satisfied that he saw no lingering doubts, he laid a clenched fist on his mouth in a renewed demand for silence, then clapped each shoulder as he received a nod of agreement.

Moshe wondered how Orde had picked up the trail of the raiders. He himself could see no sign of their passing. But Orde walked unerringly across a rubble-strewn hillside, turned up another canyon and followed an ancient watercourse to where it opened out onto a broad plain. Still without making a sound, he pointed to the marks on the ground that plainly showed the assembly point of another group.

A few hundred feet along the trail it became obvious that their present path would carry them very close to two Arab villages lying on the sweep of the plain below them. Zabinski started to point this out but changed his mind at a sharp look from Orde, and merely waved his hand in the direction of the villages. Orde nodded curtly and indicated by a motion of his hand that they would avoid the trail.

Several hours later, Moshe recognized that this was no stroll on the countryside. They had tramped miles from the compound and its relative safety deep into Arab territory. If apprehended here, they would not live long enough to worry about being handed over to the British authorities. What remained of their corpses would be dumped in some ravine, and no one would ever know of their fate.

Passing the outskirts of a village, they heard approaching voices and jumped into a culvert at the edge of a field of onions. Only a thin screen of brush sheltered them. Arab farmers bantered back and forth, exchanging coarse jests.

Moshe drew the British-made pistol from his belt and started to raise his head from the dirt of the culvert. In the next instant a vise-like grip closed over his wrist, and Captain Orde's other hand firmly pushed Moshe's head down. With a start, Moshe realized that Orde was paying more attention to his patrol to see that they did not do anything foolish than he was to the passing Arabs.

Moving out when it was safe, they continued. It was dusk, and the glow of firelights in the Arab villages was beginning to show against the gathering shadows of the Galilean evening. Orde turned abruptly away from the plain and into the fringe of hills. At the base of a dusty cone-shaped mound, he held up his hand to call a halt, then waved toward a rocky outcropping about halfway up the slope. In the lee of a cliff, Moshe saw the outline of a crude structure, only barely distinguishable from the rock pile.

With a sweeping motion, Captain Orde indicated that his commandos were to spread out on the hillside, with himself near the center of the line. At another gesture they drew their pistols and then began moving forward cautiously. The little arc of men crept slowly up toward the shepherd's hut. Moshe listened keenly for any sounds from the shelter. His eyes darted back and forth to catch any hint of movement. There was no sign of human presence. Orde signaled the all clear and they approached the deserted structure. Through clenched teeth, Zach spoke for the first time. "This is what you brought us all this way for? To attack an empty shepherd's hovel?"

"Empty?"

Zach snorted once, then a look of comprehension crossed his face. He plunged inside, followed by Larry Havas. A moment later the two men dragged long, heavy crates out of the hut. Moshe stooped to enter and returned with leather bandoliers of cartridges swung over his shoulders. Emerging from the structure he heard a cracking sound as Zach pried open the lid of his crate.

An unmistakable note of shocked triumph echoed in Zach's voice. "Rifles! Real weapons! Still in oilcloth, and German, I think."

"Of course German," Orde replied softly, "what else? You can manage to carry six apiece, plus ammunition. Put the rest back inside and take cover."

Exultation filled every face, a heady excitement at the prospect of being able to defend the settlement with real weapons. Then the full import of Orde's words sank in.

"You mean we're not ready to leave now?" asked Larry nervously. "If we stay very long, we're gonna get caught. I mean, the Arabs won't leave stuff like this alone."

"Precisely."

"What do you mean, precisely?" demanded Zach.

"I mean," Orde said, "we're waiting for them to return."

The little band wasted no time in dividing up the weapons. They examined the barrels to see that the rifles were not plugged with grease. They distributed cartridges and loaded each rifle. Orde inspected each soldier and issued last-minute instructions. Then he glanced at his watch and gathered them in a tight circle like a coach on the sidelines with his soccer team.

"The horse is prepared for battle—" He thumped Larry Havas on the back. "But tonight you will see that victory is from the Lord." Without further introduction, he turned his attention to the Almighty. "We thank you, Lord, for the victory you have given us. We ask your mercy for the men who are about to die because of their own foolish actions against your people Israel. Amen."

The six troopers barely had time to bow their heads before the prayer was finished. Their nervous expressions reflected surprise. Orde held up a finger and in a sudden gentle voice said, "Remember, this is your land, promised to you by the Eternal. You must do your part, just as the Israelites did, and the Lord will be with you. Think of Gideon. Do not be afraid of them, although there will be many."

It was apparent that Orde himself was thinking of Gideon. He stationed his men in a ragged semicircle among the rocks that overlooked the trail and the hut. Once again he demanded silence. A distant night bird sounded a lonely call above Moshe.

In spite of Orde's encouragement, Moshe's unsettled conscience nagged him as the long minutes passed. From his perch above the trail, he had a clear view of the door to the hut. Anyone entering would be within his sights. He had practiced firing an old rifle in Haganah training, but for the first time he realized that the targets would be real and human. Minutes dragged into hours, and the night deepened.

Moshe told himself that the Arabs who came—if they came tonight—were coming in preparation for attacking another Jewish settlement. He thought of Eli. He remembered the body of the pretty young woman at Hanita. With these vivid memories he managed to strengthen his resolve. But waiting like this, with a weapon in his hands, still felt cold-blooded.

A half moon was pushing against the blackness of the eastern sky. The hills seemed to light up with its strange fire. Then suddenly the silence was broken.

Far down the narrow canyon the sound of happy voices drifted up through the stillness. Startled, the bird fluttered away from the nest above Moshe. The Jihad Moquades tramped up the trail noisily, without fear.

Whatever doubts Moshe had were quickly replaced by a sense of panic. This was not a mere handful of men approaching, but a large troop of fighters. A long line of lights moved and swayed upward. Moshe tried to count them, but when he reached seventy-five, his mind went blank. He looked up at the steep embankment above him. Would he be able to escape up it? Too steep, impassable. He envied the night bird and suddenly felt angry at the English captain for making them stay here and fight when they should have taken their weapons and made a dash back to Hanita!

Moshe blinked hard; at least three times more lights gathered now than when he had stopped counting. He could make out the features of the Holy Strugglers by the glow of ancient lanterns and modern flashlights. Moshe suddenly realized that Captain Orde was not surprised by the numbers of Arabs coming boldly to this place. He had expected it. Like Gideon, he had known his men would be vastly outnumbered.

Voices and laughter grew clearer. Unlike the farmers of this afternoon, these men did not jest among themselves; instead, their conversation was full of boasting about last night's attacks against a dozen settlements, how the Jews and the English were quaking with fear in their holes! Another added how easily the Jewish throats had bled, and how he regretted that these new weapons would replace the pleasure of the old ways of fighting.

It was the last thing he ever regretted. Two dozen Arabs moved into the clearing and toward the door of the hut. Orde shouted, "In the name of the British government—" The startled faces of the Jihad warriors raised to the rocks. Their hands reached for their weapons, and a shout of rage and alarm swept through the line.

Orde did not need to issue the command to fire. Each of the Hanita fighters picked out a lighted figure and claimed it as his own. Their fingers tightened automatically around the triggers, and the air thundered with what sounded like a thousand Englishmen tucked among the rocks. The blast of rifle volleys resounded amid screams filled with terror.

The Arabs attempted to fight back. Those in the clearing shot wildly up into the rocks as they fled back down the path. Lights and lanterns tumbled down the dusty slopes at the side of the trail.

Moshe kept his sights on the door of the hut as Orde had instructed. Two men charged for its shelter and tumbled back to the ground. A third dropped in midair and fell like a stone on his dying comrades. One Arab pushed forward, shouting for his men to have courage for the sake of the Mufti and Allah and the Prophet! His flashlight went spinning out of his shattered hand, and he fled away after his troops. Moshe continued to fire after them. Larry and Zach and the others continued to pump bullets into the blackness.

Three times Orde called for a cease-fire. One at a time his six soldiers heard him, and the night became silent once again.

Orde scrambled down from his position. "Now we need to hurry," he said as the breathless men gathered around him.

A dozen bodies littered the clearing. Orde removed a folded slip of paper from his jacket and pinned a note on the robe of one of the fallen enemy.

PLEASE IDENTIFY ATTACHED CORPSE. KILLED WHILE PROCURING SMUGGLED WEAPONS FOR USE AGAINST BRITISH FORCES. SIGNED, SAMUEL ORDE, CAPTAIN

"Will they come back?" Zach asked.

"Yes," Orde said calmly. "Gather what you can carry. Wait for me at the head of the trail."

Each man shouldered six rifles plus leather bandoliers of bullets. No one questioned Orde any longer. They had managed to face at least three hundred Arabs and lived to tell about it! For the moment they still lived, anyway!

Moshe trailed after the others as Samuel Orde dashed into the hut. The minute he remained inside seemed longer than the hours they had waited for the Moquades. At last he sauntered out easily, a grenade in his hand. He tossed it into the hut and made a run for a heap of boulders just as the whole structure lifted from the ground in one giant explosion.

The rumble of a rockslide was still audible fifteen minutes later as the seven men scrambled over an obscure goat path by the light of the moon. Carrying forty-two new rifles and four thousand rounds of ammunition for the protection of the Jewish settlements of Galilee, the new trainees of Orde's Special Night Squad melted undetected into the labyrinth of the rugged hills.

14

Nameless Prison

Hitler made a bad attempt at tossing the blame for Kristal Nacht to Winston Churchill and Anthony Eden in England. *"It is no accident,"* he proclaimed, *"that this vile little Jew in Paris holds the same views about our Reich as Winston Churchill and his Jew-loving cronies!"*

For seven days the world cried out in mourning and in outrage against the Nazis. Churchmen and diplomats and politicians had one voice: *"We must find a place of refuge for these poor, downtrodden people! Somewhere in the wide world we must find a haven for them!"*

Men and women fleeing Germany spent the nights in cold, wet irrigation ditches on the borders of France and Holland and what remained of Czechoslovakia. Turned away at the crossings, they returned by cattle truck to German concentration camps.

Those who managed to escape into other countries bordering Germany also went into camps for aliens with the promise that they would stay for two weeks, no longer, and then they would be returned.

In the United States, the cry for mercy rang out so loud that President Roosevelt appointed another commission to decide how the refugees might best be taken into the country. America seemed to be having a change of heart. Perhaps the torch of freedom might burn brightly again.

The wilderness of Alaska was chosen as a likely place for the settlement of unwanted Jews. A very good place. They could not possibly cause trouble there.

American church leaders sounded the warning that Christian concern must not be allowed to wither and die. America had traditionally been a land of refuge for those who were persecuted, and so a hand must be extended. Homes must be provided.

Inundated by telegrams, President Roosevelt announced that he had every intention of taking in as many refugees as possible.

Here was hope! In England, Elisa and Anna and Theo read Murphy's news wires with joy, praying that they would prove true.

Spurred on by this show of support, the British Prime Minister finally admitted publicly, *"It seems all the reports from Germany are indeed true!"* Although further settlement of Jews in Palestine was out of the question due to the daily violence, perhaps there was a colony somewhere in the British Empire that could allow the Jews to settle.

By the seventh day, however, Kristal Nacht had become old news. Leaders in England and the United States as well as France seemed irritated that the Jews had gotten in the way of Nazi clubs. The Germans claimed that Jews had gotten what they deserved, that they had provoked the outburst.

By the 20th of November, the head of St. Paul's Cathedral in London had written an article that declared: *"The Jews are using their not inconsiderable influence in the press and Parliament to embroil us with Germany!"*

At almost the same moment, the President of the Council of Churches in America announced: *"Though we as Christians are sympathetic to the plight of the Jews, we do not in any way support a political Zionism or the settlement of Jews in the British Mandate of Palestine."*

From that moment, mercy became tempered with practicality. Settling thousands of homeless people would take money. Whose money? Whose land?

Murphy brought the bad news home to dinner that night. It had all come in at once—the smashing of hope, the final revelation of the utter hypocrisy of the democracies.

He tossed a sheaf of paper down on the dinner table in front of Theo.

Theo looked up at him. He did not pick up the dispatches but waited instead for Murphy to recite the news out loud.

It took a moment for Murphy to find his voice. The roast grew cold on the platter as appetites waned.

"Alaska is out. The honorable Representative Dies from Texas and Senator Borah from Idaho have said that America will not take one more refugee than it has to. That Congress will vote down anything that comes through which even hints of enlarging the immigration quota." He paused as Theo's face reflected acceptance, but not surprise. "The Alaskans . . ." Murphy faltered in disbelief at what he had to say. "Well, they say that European Jews are not suited for settlement in Alaska. They would interfere."

At this, Elisa burst out angrily, "So what *are* we suited for? To die? Wasn't this enough? How can they—"

Murphy sighed and took his seat. "Now President Roosevelt is backpedaling as if his life depended on it. He says he didn't mean to imply that the United States would actually take in more refugees. No, sir. What he *meant* was that those 12,000 German Jews who are in the States on visitors' visas as tourists can have their visas renewed for another six months if they want."

"Visas renewed." Anna and Theo exchanged looks. Dieter and Wilhelm had just left for New York on visitors' visas as guests of Mr. Trump. They hoped to go to school there, out of reach of the turmoil of Europe. "Six months?" Anna said, her voice thick with emotion.

"Of course, that could change overnight." Elisa's eyes brimmed with tears of frustration. "After all, it has only been a little more than a week since Kristal Nacht. They have made themselves feel better by talking about compassion and mercy! They condemn the Nazis and then give Hitler the right to do what he wants. These people will not remember our suffering at all a month from now!"

"No homeland in Palestine," Theo repeated. "No support from the churches for Zionism. Then where shall we turn? Who will help us?"

Every news publication of the Western democracies was analyzed by specialists within the massive Reich Ministry of Propaganda. The experts assessed public sentiment based on what the democratic press published each day. They discussed demonstrations of outrage against the policies of the Reich and took propaganda measures to counter any disfavor.

Of course the Reich Minister of Propaganda, Joseph Goebbels, showed no surprise at the outcry against the pogroms of Kristal Nacht. What did startle him, however, was the speed with which that outcry subsided. Hitler was not at all taken aback. He recognized that the free press moved from one sensational story to the next, tiring of "yesterday's news" before the blood congealed on the sidewalks.

Goebbels brought several samples to the Chancellory to review with the Führer after the evening film screening of *The Big Broadcast of 1938*. Somehow it seemed fitting that they should gauge the effect of the press and radio broadcasts after watching the antics of Hollywood entertainers.

The Führer, in an excellent mood, sent his mistress, Eva Braun, up to bed and promised he would be along shortly. He was particularly jovial and uncharacteristically ordered a glass of beer.

Minister Goebbels felt that the clippings would not upset Hitler's charming mood in any way—with the possible exception of one small detail that could easily be remedied.

He threw open the leather portfolio containing the various newspapers. Hitler tossed several German magazines onto the floor and cleared the coffee table for action. His translator, Doktor Schmidt, read aloud the various condemnations in the articles, emphasizing the fact that the democracies were quick to add they could do little to help.

The last newspaper was from the TENS London office. A predictably critical article by Winston Churchill on the back page of the first section was none too alarming. But as the pages turned, photographs displayed various Christian pastors who had been arrested in Berlin—not just their photographs alone, but pictures of their families as well. Articles explained in detail why these men had been in disfavor within the Reich. Descriptions were given of their families. The question about their fate was raised. The implication was clear: these men were not Jews; they simply disapproved of the Reich. Was the Nazi party frightened of small voices of individual disapproval? Was the Führer so insecure that he could not tolerate dissension even from the pulpits of the churches?

Hitler frowned as Doktor Schmidt translated the lengthy articles. He leaned closer to stare at the smiling face of Pastor Karl Ibsen, his wife, and two children as they sat on the garden wall of New Church. This fellow had been nothing but trouble for the party. Since 1933, he had spoken out against every Reich policy designed to rid the state of beggars, cripples, and imbeciles. He championed the cause of hopeless causes! He proclaimed that every human life was of value. He decried the evils of euthanasia and forced sterilization.

Hitler tapped his finger on Ibsen's picture. "He is in custody?"

"Arrested for violation of the Nuremberg racial laws. Hiding Jews," Goebbels said in a positive tone.

"His family?" The Führer looked thoughtful. Too thoughtful. Perhaps he was disturbed by this display of German churchmen.

"Also in custody." Goebbels did not tell Hitler that the daughter still remained at large. He chose to overlook that small detail. Besides, he and Himmler had the best agent in the Gestapo working on that matter.

"Good." Hitler seemed satisfied. He sat back and sighed deeply. "You can see how it is, Goebbels. These sniveling democracies are not really worried about Jews, either. Ah! But the Zionists will find a way to stir up the pot over these Christian pastors. No one in the West will care if we eliminate every Jew between here and Moscow. But arrest a handful of preachers, and they scream like it is their own family. Immense hypocrisy."

Goebbels started to close the paper. The Führer put a hand on his arm to stop him. He wanted to look a moment longer at the photograph of the man who had caused him so much trouble.

"We handled the father of Ernst vom Rath quite well," Hitler yawned.

"Head of a racial office. Yes. He does not oppose us any longer." Goebbels could not see the connection.

"You see, Joseph, handling men is an art. Some you bribe with positions. Others you break with an iron rod. Some you simply persuade. Or torture." He smiled. "And then there are men like our pastors, here—paragons of German manhood. God and family come first. Honor, loyalty, and other admirable qualities fit in there somewhere." He motioned toward the photograph. "Do you understand me?"

Goebbels was not certain he did. It was late, after all. Past midnight. But he nodded.

Hitler tapped on Ibsen's photo again. "The Western press dotes on men like these. They make men like Karl Ibsen their martyrs."

"What can we do about it?"

"We get them on our side. Every man has his price. Money, prestige, position. Torture. A quiet word to the wise. These methods will work with nearly every man on this page. Pressure applied wisely will have them speaking out in public and proclaiming the greatness of the Third Reich. They will extol my rule and loudly denounce the West." He frowned. "Every one of them but this fellow, I think."

"Shall we simply kill him, mein Führer?"

"And make him an eternal martyr? No," Hitler laughed. "I know something about making martyrs. I would rather have Karl Ibsen on our side. One hundred percent."

"But you said yourself—"

Hitler raised a chin to silence Goebbels. "We will try all these other methods first with Pastor Ibsen. It will be best if we break him for reasons less noble than his love for his family. Save that threat as a last resort. If such a man succumbs for the sake of freedom, or perhaps good food, or a bribe, his own hypocrisy will forever make him say to himself that he really had not understood the justice of the Nazi cause. His self-hatred will make him ours entirely."

Goebbels nodded. It was better to use methods that appealed to a man's own selfish nature. The question was, of course, whether Karl Ibsen had such a nature. "And if such things fail to get results?"

"Keep his family on hand. We will use them as our weapon, if we must. A man like Karl Ibsen will say or do anything if his loved ones are threatened. We will own his soul one way or another. First, make it a goal to reeducate him. Eventually, I promise you, Minister Goebbels, we will have Pastor Karl Ibsen on the Reich state radio to broadcast the justice of the Aryan cause right back into the teeth of Churchill. Our own 'Big Broadcast of 1938.' "

———————

A blast of cold air hit Jacob's face as he opened the door leading up to the bell tower. He pulled his stocking cap down over his ears and ascended the stone spiral steps to the top.

The wind blew strong from the north. Flags on top of ministry buildings stood out stiff on their poles. Jacob ducked low and remained out of sight. He did not care if he could not see the traffic rolling by as long as he could glimpse the sky for a few minutes.

He sat on the floor of the round tower and watched a gray pigeon hop along the ledge above him. The great green bells were covered with pigeon droppings; the birds of Berlin had already lost their fear of the thundering bells of New Church. Like the voice of Pastor Ibsen and Jacob's father, the bells were silent now—no reminder to the consciences of the Berliners who had so easily resumed their daily life.

Jacob closed his eyes and tried to pray. In the end he could only tell God that he was afraid, that he was not ready to assume the responsibilities of manhood. How could he properly take care of Lori? He thought of her too much; he felt things for her that made being near her painful. He must steel himself, be brother and father to her, distance himself from those feelings. If he really was her brother, maybe he could fight with her and be angry with her the way he always seemed to be angry with Mark. She seemed so sad and alone. Jacob wanted only to comfort her, but to do so would be disastrous. It was difficult enough to sleep without the thought of reaching out to touch her.

He inhaled deeply, then let his breath out slowly. Cold air and the bell tower seemed to help him breathe easier.

He closed his eyes and listened to the hum of traffic on the street; the cooing of the pigeons and the hooting of horns . . . Then suddenly he heard the sound of voices in the yard below—people in the churchyard! Two men!

"I check it every night. No need to worry. Nobody will break in!" It was the old watchman.

"I just want to have a look around," said a pleasant-sounding voice. "Perhaps there is some clue about the girl's whereabouts. We have checked as many of the former church members as possible. No sign of her. No hint as to where she is."

Jacob's breath grew shallow with fear. He slid down the stairs, praying that Lori and Mark would be close enough to hide! Through the door and into the corridor he could hear the rattle of chains and locks stirring on the entrance doors of New Church. They were coming in!

He wanted to yell for Mark and Lori, but of course they would be caught if he made a sound. His shoes sounded like gun blasts to his ears as he attempted to move silently. He pulled them off and ran in his stocking feet. The chains still rattled behind him! He dashed up to the choir loft and met Lori pale and trembling at the top of the steps. Mark held open the door to the bellows room. His eyes blinked with his heartbeat.

A finger to his lips, Jacob pulled Lori into their hideout. They crammed into the bellows just as the laughter of the two men echoed into the foyer and permeated the walls of the entire church building.

"They went over this place with a microscope, Agent Hess," said the watchman.

"There may be things they missed that I would see," the second man replied without arrogance. He was not vaunting his ability; he was simply stating fact. "Certain leaders feel it is important that this girl be found. I have specialized in rooting out difficult cases."

Enclosed in the leather cocoon of the organ bellows, the words sounded distant and muffled, but the threat seemed more terrible than even the first day. *They had come back! Gestapo! They had not simply forgotten about Lori Ibsen!*

Lori wrapped her arms around Jacob's middle. He held her close against him, and suddenly felt the obligation of father and brother to protect her. Mark squatted down in a little ball. Footsteps ascended into the choir loft. *Only one set of footsteps,* Jacob thought. The agent was alone.

He smelled the bitter odor of cigarette tobacco. The agent stopped at the door of the dusty room and peered in. Lori, Jacob, and Mark held their breaths. They could hear the man mumbling as he stared in. Jacob prayed his lungs would not explode. He eased his breath out slowly as the man turned away and shouted down from the choir loft to the watchman below.

"Keep a sharp eye out for any light or movement, will you? If the girl comes back, no doubt she will look here for her family first. You will get a reward if we find them here, provided you are in on it."

The garbled reply of the old man was lost beneath the pounding of Jacob's heart. He prayed that Gestapo Agent Hess would find no sign. After all, they had been so careful; everything was left exactly as it had been the first time the Gestapo ransacked the church. The floor was littered with torn hymnals. Paper was strewn everywhere. The cross, which had been ripped down from above the baptistery, lay where it had fallen across the altar. The pinwheel of a Nazi swastika was painted on the pulpit. Jacob had prevented Lori from cleaning it off.

It seemed a very long time before the voices moved toward the door. Chains clanged against the heavy wood doors, sealing the church again. Only then did the trio relax a bit. Even so, Jacob insisted that they remain in the bellows until long after the sun went down.

Many of the prisoners arrested with Pastor Karl Ibsen and Richard Kalner were shipped by train or truck to the overcrowded prison camp of Dachau. The younger, stronger men like Karl and Richard were sent to a new place several hours to the east of Berlin.

Vast and still uncompleted, the nameless compound was being hewn from the forest that bordered Poland.

From behind the layers of barbed-wire fence, Pastor Karl could clearly see the Polish guards who patrolled their side of the fences in search of any desperate refugees who might have attempted escape from Germany.

Since Kristal Nacht, many such people cut through the wire in the night and carried children across the open field, only to be sniffed out by dogs or trapped in the long serpentine ditch just at the top of the rise. Most were caught and promptly returned to the German side of the line and handed over to the authorities. Men, women, and children were then brought by truck through the fortified gates of Nameless camp. Surrounded by gun towers and smirking guards, they were put to work building their own prison.

Only a dozen prison barracks had been completed on the day Karl and Richard stepped stiffly onto the frozen ground. Those dozen were crammed to bursting with thousands of prisoners judged fit enough to construct the remainder of the facility.

Heat and blankets were promised after the job was done. In the meantime, men in ragged street clothes, torn nightshirts and sagging trousers worked urgently beneath the watchful eyes of gray-uniformed men in heavy winter coats and boots. Gloved fingers curled around the triggers of machine guns pointed at the bare-handed prisoners who strung the barbed wire that surrounded them.

The whack of hammers echoed in the dark green forest from early morning until it was too dark to see the head of a nail. When the first snow fell, silent and beautiful against the evergreens, one hundred men died of exposure in a single day. A grave-digging detail was appointed the task of carting off frozen bodies and digging shallow graves for them in the frozen earth.

Even so, those who had come from other prisons before said that this was a virtual resort compared to Dachau. There was food here, at least—if a man could choke down rancid bacon and rotting potatoes. Most managed to eat. Those who did not were the next to die.

Although it was forbidden to call out another man's name during work hours, Richard managed to let every prisoner nearby know that Karl Ibsen was pastor of an evangelical church in Berlin—a man with a good position who really did not have to be here if he had only followed the Nazi doctrine against his Jewish parishioners. These facts caused others in the camp to look at Karl with an attitude of respect, even admiration.

Most were here because they had no choice. They were Jewish; they were anti-Nazi; they had said the wrong thing to the wrong person. Few at Nameless camp would not have gladly forsaken everything to get out of this place. They would have kissed the boot of a storm trooper and called Adolf Hitler blessed if only the gate of Nameless would swing open for them, and the border guards in Poland would look the other way. And then they would have run hard and fast and never looked back at those they left behind.

This was sensible thinking, logical for any man who loved life and longed to live past tomorrow. But this Pastor Karl Ibsen—now here was an unusual man, arrested while trying to convince Richard Kalner to come along and be hidden away from the Nazis!

Some said that Pastor Karl was a fool. A few encouraged him to claim that a mistake had been made; that he had only gone to the Kalners' apartment to collect on a debt when along came the Gestapo.

But Pastor Karl would not deny what he had done. It was a small thing. Small and pitiful and much too late.

"They will ask him to make a confession of his error," said a fellow who had been behind the wire for months. "And he will say he was a fool for helping lousy Jews, and then they will let him go back to Berlin. Maybe even back to his church if he is a good boy and promises to proclaim the wisdom of *Mein Kampf* from the pulpit."

"Pastor Karl will not deny us," Richard defended. "You will see. He is one with us."

Jacob strode from the charity room holding cans of tuna high in the air. He had found a treasure of foodstuffs in there, he declared— everything that had been collected since the beginning of the food drive in October.

"Tuna and canned meat. Flour in barrels! Salt and beans!"

There was even more than that, as it turned out—everything three people would need to survive for a long time. They could live here for months like three castaways on a desert island. The Nazis had sealed them in, but if they were careful, they could survive, and no one would ever know.

Mark looked less gleeful than his brother, Lori noticed. Maybe he was homesick and heartsick, as she was. At least Jacob and Mark had each other. *Family!*

She could not make herself care about the food. The prospect of being shut up inside New Church without Mama or Papa or Jamie seemed like prison. Jacob had already begun making rules:

THOU SHALT NOT LISTEN TO THE RADIO UNTIL THE WATCHMAN IS GONE.

THOU SHALT NOT TAKE BATHS IN THE BAPTISTERY LEST SOME-ONE HEAR THE NOISY WATER PIPES AND SOUND THE ALARM.

THOU SHALT SLEEP IN THE ORGAN BELLOWS ROOM FOR QUICK ESCAPE.

The list went on and on.

"Well, what do you think?" Jacob balanced the canned tuna on his head and turned slowly as if he were modeling a hat.

She did not smile. Not that he was not funny—at least he had always been able to make her laugh before. But not now.

She shook her head and tried to tell him she was not in the mood for games.

"We're rich!" Mark crowed, producing a bag of hard candy. "I thought they looked everywhere, took everything not nailed down."

"You think these thugs will look in a room marked CHARITY when they just looted every fancy shop in Berlin?" Jacob still smiled, but not so broadly. He let the cans slip off his head into his hands. "Practically a miracle, eh, Lori?" He was trying to cheer her up, but it was no use.

She bit her lip and tried to keep from telling them both that none of this mattered, that she wished she had been arrested and taken away with Mama and Jamie. "It's just food," she said. "It doesn't matter unless Mama and Papa come back here. What's the use of any of it?" With that she fled the room, leaving them staring after her and wondering what more she could ask for in such conditions.

Down the darkened hall she heard Mark's voice: "Girls! I wish the Nazis had taken her instead of Jamie! We might have had a better time of it then."

Lori muttered through her tears. "I wish so too, you little brat!" But she was too far away for him to hear.

15

Prophetic Voices

The woman clerk at the Foreign Ministry office removed the envelope from a scuffed brown leather letter case and placed it on the desk
in front of Anna and Theo Lindheim.

"I am sorry," she said. "This was returned from Germany by diplomatic courier. The attaché in Berlin attempted to contact your sister,
Mrs. Lindheim, but apparently the family has . . . left town."

Left town. The very words carried the suggestion of doom.

"But surely there is some explanation," Theo began. "They have
just left Berlin? Their home? Work? How can this be?"

"Really, that is the only message I have for you." The clerk directed
her gaze to Anna. "We are not in the business of delivering personal
messages, you see. And your sister is a German citizen." She nudged
the letter across to Anna. "There is really nothing more our embassy
in Berlin or this ministry can do."

Anna took the letter and held it in her hands as though its return
to her conveyed a message too ominous to contemplate. "Certainly
there must be a way for me to contact my sister."

"Perhaps through the German Embassy?" The woman knew, of
course, that this was impossible. How could the Lindheims approach
the German Embassy and expect help?

"You will not assist us, then?" Theo took the letter from Anna. "What
about their children? Surely you understand the danger they could be
in because of our own efforts to aid German refugees."

The woman shrugged and looked to other work. "They are not
refugees, are they? They are full German citizens. Not Jews. Not involved in the pogrom, certainly. Mr. Lindheim, are you aware of the
caseload we are dealing with? Requests for visas from truly desperate
people. My heavens, our fellow in Berlin went beyond his duty in this

instance. He is not a mail carrier." She offered no sympathy. She was busy, and she let them know it as she thumbed through a stack of papers.

"If there is any word of my sister's whereabouts—" Anna tried again to find some spark of hope.

"There will be nothing more from *this* department," said the clerk abruptly. "Perhaps you should put in a request with the Red Cross. And certainly you must have connections still in Germany that might assist you in locating your sister and her family."

Anna told herself that Helen and Karl and the children must be safe. Perhaps they had simply taken a holiday from the terror of Berlin. Maybe even now they were in some quiet refuge in the Harz Mountains. A thousand times Anna had begged them to leave the new Germany. They had refused, citing their duty to remain and work even as the world seemed to crumble around them.

Anna had not written them for fear of jeopardizing their safety through contact with her. She and Theo were labeled as criminals by the Nazi government. A phone call or a letter from her to her sister might have cast suspicion on them as well.

Somehow, Anna had continued to picture Helen shopping on Unter den Linden, or playing the organ at church. As Anna and Theo descended the broad staircase of the government office, Anna wondered if she would ever again play a duet with her sister. Suddenly, nagging doubts transformed into full-blown fears—for Helen; for Karl; for the children. Anna knew well enough how caring Christian people had managed to fall through the cracks and then totally disappear from the face of the Third Reich.

———

Within the refuge of King Faisal's palace in Baghdad, Haj Amin maintained his own staff of bodyguards and servants as well as a late-model short-wave radio to keep in touch with his fighters in the British Mandate. Although reports from the majority of Jerusalem and the southern area of Palestine had been excellent, news from Galilee had been dismal. Holy Strugglers owned the roads after dark everywhere—except around Hanita. The pace of terrorist attacks against the English and the Jews was increasing everywhere—except near Hanita. German S.S. commandos were training Arab mercenaries; their success was undeniable throughout the Mandate—except near Hanita. And now its neighboring Jewish kibbutzim seemed to be gaining strength as well!

At last Haj Amin held the explanation of that success in his hands. A dozen notes, all written in the same English scrawl in green crayon, were signed by one man: SAMUEL ORDE, CAPTAIN.

Some notes were stained with the blood of those who had fallen in the fighting against this dangerous English officer. All of them served up the same message to the guerrilla fighters in northern Palestine. The resistance of the Jews in that area had suddenly become fierce and deadly! Where twenty thousand British troops had failed, this one English captain and his secret army succeeded.

And his success made Haj Amin extremely angry.

"This Samuel Orde—" He drummed his long effeminate fingers against the notes. "You call him the most dangerous man in the British Mandate, Herr Vargen." He narrowed his eyes and glared at the German commander chosen by Hitler to assist with the Muslim rebellion.

"Dangerous," Vargen repeated, his face betraying no emotion, "because he is not afraid to fight."

"We are not afraid to fight."

"You pay these men of yours ten pounds a month and promise them paradise if they die fighting Jews and killing Englishmen. But they are still not half the fighters this Orde has managed to bring in. Professional British commandos, I believe, dressed as Jewish settlers. Your peasants are no match for them."

Haj Amin flushed with anger at the insult. "Then perhaps if the British are bringing in more special troops, we shall put the question to the Führer as well. Is that what you are suggesting?"

"For a start. I have sent my recommendations to Berlin. But most of all, I believe it is essential that we eliminate the Englishman, Captain Orde. Perhaps we might issue a bounty for his head. And then, politically, we must have the Arab leadership remaining in Jerusalem file an official complaint. The Führer agrees. This is not a matter of self-defense any longer, but attacks." He passed a typed memo from Berlin to the Mufti. It had just arrived at the German Embassy in Baghdad and bore the official seal of the Reich. It was signed with the name of Adolf Hitler, and addressed to the Mufti of Jerusalem in exile.

> One cannot forget, my friend, that the British are basically political beasts, swayed by all political criticism, very conscious of public demonstrations and disapproval, and eager to please whoever is the most vocally unhappy. I would recommend a two-pronged attack on this one English captain in Palestine who is effective against us. Eliminate him physically, if possible. The Reich will transfer ten thousand pounds into your account for this purpose. Failing that, make certain that the Arab Higher Committee of Jerusalem in your absence files protests of outrage against Captain Orde's obviously pro-Zionist leadership.
>
> We work together in a common cause. Stand firm in your resolve and we will live to see the world rid of the troublesome Jews without fail. Warm greetings, A. Hitler.

Along with the personal note of encouragement from the Führer, plans were included that duplicated the concentration camps already built throughout the Reich. Written neatly in Arabic script at the bottom of the blueprint were these words: FOR THE ELIMINATION OF THE JEWISH PROBLEM IN PALESTINE.

This brought a smile to the lips of Haj Amin for the first time in days.

———

The study in the Red Lion House seemed uncomfortably warm to Theo. He tugged his collar and mopped his brow.

Murphy tossed another scoop of coal onto the fire. He was not perspiring. Elisa sat wrapped in a blanket. Anna wore a sweater. Perhaps the open threats in Hitler's speech made Theo sweat.

He looked up at the clock: half-past eight. The voice of the Führer, like a razor, cut away the self-righteous illusions of the nations. *"Nor can I see a reason why the members of this Jewish race should be imposed on the German nation, while in the nations so enthusiastic about these 'splendid people,' their immigration is refused with every imaginable excuse. I think the sooner this problem is solved the better, for Europe cannot settle down until the Jewish question is cleared up! It may well be possible that sooner or later an agreement on this problem may be reached in Europe, even between those nations that otherwise do not so easily come together. The Jewish race will have to adapt itself to sound constructive activity as other nations do, or sooner or later it will succumb to a crisis of an inconceivable magnitude."*

Elisa raised her head, daring to interrupt for the first time. "What can he mean by that? Wasn't Kristal Nacht enough? Can there be more?"

At the time, the violence of Kristal Nacht had seemed inconceivable to Theo. Now Hitler declared something more terrible, something that the human mind could not imagine. And he was stating his intention over the airways of the BBC.

"One thing I should like to say on this day, which may be memorable for others as well as for us Germans: In the course of my life I have often been a prophet and have usually been ridiculed for it. During the time of my struggle for power, the Jewish race received my prophecies with laughter when I said that one day I would take over the leadership of the state and the nation and that I would settle the Jewish problem. Their laughter was uproarious. But now they are laughing out of the other side of their face! Today I will once more be a prophet!" Here, he paused as the world waited to hear the prophecy he would utter to the Jews of Europe. Anna took Theo's hand and glanced fearfully at him as Hitler boomed: *"If the international Jewish financiers in and outside Europe should succeed in plunging the nations into a world war, then the result will not be the bolshevization of the earth and the victory of Jewry, but the annihilation of the Jewish race in Europe!"*

Annihilation. The word was simple enough. It was, indeed, inconceivable, and yet no longer did Theo doubt what the Führer of Germany was saying.

"He means to kill them all," Theo said quietly.

Eyes raised to look at him, to study his face, to see if Theo truly believed such a thing was possible.

Theo cleared his throat. "He means it. And he has made the German people ready." He wiped beads of perspiration from his forehead. "In 1933, the year he came to power, one million babies were aborted in Germany. Then came permissible euthanasia, mercy killing of the old. That led to *selective* euthanasia, the murder of those who were mentally unworthy, racially unworthy. And then there were the children like Charles—the killing of babies who were considered imperfect." He looked each member of his family full in the face. "Annihilation of the Jews of Europe. His excuse for that will be war. The inconceivable is not only possible, he means to do it."

Murphy no longer needed convincing. The Kristal Nacht reports had eliminated all pretense that Germany was still a basically civilized country. "What do we do now, Theo?" Murphy asked. "What will it take before people believe this?"

"They believe it already." Theo rose and walked slowly toward the window. He looked out on the sleepy little square. "They have heard it. Who can doubt that the threat is real? Most do not care to think about it. But those who do hear and think and have a conscience must also have a plan."

"We can't wait for the British government," Murphy said, leaning heavily against the mantel. "And no one in America is any better as far as the government is concerned."

"Then I say we go back to doing things the old way." Elisa raised her chin defiantly. "Passports smuggled in. Forged papers. Why do we need to play their game? Hitler is right. The democracies are barrels of hypocrisy. The churches will not help. Why don't we go back to doing it the way it was done before?"

Anna answered. "Because we are being watched. Your father has been warned that if he works outside the immigration laws and quotas, he will be deported back to Germany."

Anna did not need to explain further. The group fell silent once again under that ominous reality.

Minutes passed. The speech of the Führer continued. Crowds roared their approval of his policies. *Yes, he is a prophet,* they seemed to say. And they were all quite willing to fulfill his prophecies.

The telephone call from Sir Thomas Beecham, conductor of the London Philharmonic Orchestra, issued a call to arms for every musician.

"Yes, yes!" he said to Elisa. "It is already arranged with the BBC. We begin rehearsal in an hour. Bring your fiddle and be ready to work!"

And so the musicians who had fled Germany for the safe haven of Covent Garden prepared for their first battle cry against the horrors of the Night of Broken Glass. Every face was grim; many eyes were red with tears of anger and fear for loved ones who remained behind in Germany. But their hands did not tremble as they held their instruments and listened to Sir Thomas as he explained the message he intended to send straight to the Chancellory in Berlin.

Standing tall and bull-necked on the conductor's stand, Sir Thomas directed his steely gaze to those musicians he knew had suffered the most under Nazi policies. He had heard Elisa's story of the fall of Vienna. He knew well the part her Guarnerius violin had played in that struggle to save the lives of Jewish children. He also suspected that the darkest days were yet to come.

"In Germany, those of you who are Jewish are forbidden to play the works of Beethoven. But we shall throw this music back in the teeth of Adolf Hitler!" He paused and thumbed through his music folder. "We had planned to open our season with Mendelssohn tonight, but since this is to be broadcast also in Germany, it occurred to me that Beethoven's Fifth might be a better message to send, eh?"

No one smiled. Elisa looked from face to face and pictured where old friends might have been sitting on the stage of the Musikverein. She felt homesick for them and angry.

Sir Thomas Beecham continued. "For those of you who are not familiar with Morse code, I will tell you that the letter *V* is three dots and a dash. The opening notes of Beethoven's Fifth are. . . ."

One at a time, faces broke into smiles as the musicians remembered the score and Sir Thomas held up his fingers in the V-for-victory sign. Simple. Three dots and a dash put to music. The letter for victory had been written by Beethoven long before Morse had invented his code.

"We must speak to the persecuted who remain trapped in the Reich, my children!" Sir Thomas held his fingers higher and answering hands rose among the orchestra. "Hitler thinks he has refused you victory, but we here in England will send the message back to Germany. Your friends and family will hear it on the BBC and have hope tonight!"

Peter tuned Herr Ruger's radio with the delicacy of a safe-cracker. Suddenly the static gave way to clear, elegant tones of Sir Thomas Beecham's voice.

"Among the musicians of the London Philharmonic are men and women driven from the orchestras of Germany by policies of racial madness which transcend any since the Dark Ages. Intolerance by Ger-

many has blessed the democracies with great talent; for this we may thank the German leaders with all our hearts! These talented people belong with us now, and through their instruments we send a message of victory yet to come to those who still cringe beneath the lash of the tyrant!"

It was a good speech. Peter and his mother took turns translating the best of it to Marlene, who was not really interested.

England! For Peter, the voice of the BBC was like water in the desert of last night's destruction. Through forbidden music, a sermon of hope was preached, and for an hour tonight, he did not think of the smoldering ruins of the Turnergasse Synagogue or the prisoner lorries that had taken his friends away. He found himself looking at Herr Ruger's photograph of Hitler and feeling strangely triumphant, as if a prophecy rang out in the notes, as if victory lay nearly within his reach.

———

The Nazis had searched New Church from top to bottom, and a miracle had occurred. Not only had they passed by the organ bellows, they had also overlooked the cupboard in Pastor Ibsen's office where the radio was kept. God had somehow blinded the eyes of their pursuers to keep them from finding the radio.

For Lori, food did not seem half so important as that link with the outside world. Tonight, in the nearly total blackness of the church, she led Jacob and Mark to the windowless study and ordered them to sit. She did not need to switch on the light.

She groped along the wall of cabinets to the one containing the radio. Jacob closed the door of the study as she turned the knob and a low whistle announced the first words from the outside.

"Papa kept it tuned to the BBC," she said in a hushed voice. "The only real news."

The voice of Sir Thomas Beecham crackled over the radio. Lori, a shadow by the light of the dials, turned down the volume.

Jacob spoke impatiently. "How will we know the news if this fellow is talking in English only?"

Lori translated the little speech given by the British conductor about Beethoven and victory. The words made them all feel better. *Someone in England knows what happened in Berlin! And now they tell us to have hope!*

Jacob had never cared much for classical music, but he sat spellbound as the forbidden music of Beethoven signaled that the sound of smashing glass had been heard beyond the borders of the Third Reich.

———

Lucy lay in the dark on her bed and listened to the faraway music of London's BBC. It was forbidden, of course, but everyone with a radio listened to England all the same—for this reason the authorities had demanded that all Jews turn in their radios. Hitler did not like the thought of Jews taking comfort from the self-righteous pronouncements of the British against the Reich.

Tonight Lucy felt especially sorry for the Jews of Germany who could not hear this musical condemnation of the riots against them.

Beethoven's Fifth. Music and victory. Only an Englishman would make such a connection and have the audacity to announce it over the radio. Three dots and a dash, indeed! According to rumor, Hitler himself listened to the BBC to hear what the British were thinking. Maybe tonight he had heard the English conductor thank the Führer for sending England the finest musicians in the world. Perhaps Hitler paced and raged while the London Philharmonic Orchestra gave his nasty racial laws a good stiff slap in the face! Lucy hoped so. She hoped that Sir Thomas Beecham had ruined Beethoven's Fifth Symphony forever and always for the Führer! From this night on, Beethoven's Fifth would be Lucy's secret theme song.

16

Death by Politics

The wind blew high above Jerusalem, pushing the clouds across the sky like sailing ships. The British Union Jack strained against the flagpole; metal clips on the flag clanged like a warning bell as Samuel Orde strode up the steps of the British High Command.

Soldiers on either side of the door saluted, their neatly pressed uniforms and spit-shined shoes a distinct contrast to Orde's rumpled khakis. He returned their salute. *I haven't missed all this,* he thought as he caught some hint of foreboding in their manner toward him. *So. Here I am again. Up to my neck in hot water.*

"General Wavell will see you, Captain Orde." The adjutant led him into the small office that overlooked the Old City panorama across the Valley of Hinnom.

Wavell barely acknowledged Orde's salute. He motioned to a chair and studied his reports for a moment before he cleared his throat in an embarrassed way.

"Well, so you have been cleaning out the rats' nests in Galilee."

"Been quite successful. Night raids. Catching them off guard. Striking first."

Wavell slapped a hand down on his desk and leaned back, glaring at Orde. "And who are you using for soldiers, Orde?"

The general did not need to ask. He knew. Everyone knew what was happening in the north. A collection of ragtag Jewish settlers, trained and armed by this English officer, were beating the socks off a combination of Arab mercenaries from all over the Middle East who were armed with German- and Turkish-made rifles. It was a stunning success. Orde had written about it himself and sent the stories to Murphy's TENS office in London under a pseudonym.

Orde considered the red face of the commander opposite him. "I am using anyone who is available and not afraid to die."

"You are training Jews! Everyone knows it, Orde. Strictly against the policy of the Mandate! You are putting weapons into the hands of the Zionists, making them potentially capable of turning those weapons on us."

"Their weapons are captured German ordnance." He did not back away from the challenge. He had broken every rule in the book and yet had been right in doing so. "German-made. You know what that means." He leaned forward with urgency. "The Nazis have come here, just as they are fighting with the Fascists in Spain and calling the Loyalists who oppose them all Communists—"

"We are trying to keep a lid on this thing."

"The lid was off long ago. The Zionists are the only friends we have, General Wavell. And we have tied their hands and put them in front of a firing squad where Hitler is the judge and Haj Amin is the executioner!"

"We are protecting the settlements as well as possible. That was your assignment as an English officer!"

"And I have fulfilled my duty!" Orde replied angrily. "While Arab gangs have closed down the roads to British vehicles every night since the rebellion began, I have kept our roads open in Galilee. There have been murders all over the rest of the Mandate, but only two since I arrived in Galilee."

"You know most of the staff officers favor Arabs."

"A sentimental hangover from the days when Lawrence led the Bedouins against the Turks."

"And you fancy yourself another Lawrence of Arabia, eh? Orde of Palestine?" His eyes burned with the challenge. "Savior of the Zionist cause?" He held up a sheaf of articles Orde had written about his own exploits in Galilee against the gangs. "You are your own press agent—exploitation and egotism in the highest!"

Orde managed a slight smile. He never expected to fool anyone with his pseudonym. He had only wanted to shame the British High Command into training and equipping the Jewish settlers to fight a mutual enemy.

"We are defeating the enemy on the field of battle. There is nothing written in the articles that is not absolute truth."

"I will tell you the truth, Captain Orde, and the truth comes to me straight from Whitehall in London! The truth is that our government does not consider the Arab gangs of Haj Amin to be our enemies. They are simply discontented with the way things stand. They may well be future allies and the Arab Higher Committee does not consider it in the interest of future peace in this region for us to allow the Jews to fight at our sides. Arabs do not fight at our sides in this conflict, after all."

Orde managed to stifle his sarcasm at this remark. "No, sir. I do not expect them to."

"Well, then?"

Orde smoothed his mustache and took his time. "Well, then, I propose inducting the Jewish night squads into our military. It is not required that we state they are Jewish, simply that the men I command are effective in stopping ambushes on the roads and the blowing of pipelines from Lebanon." He inhaled with an air of satisfaction. "Regardless of what truth Whitehall sends us from London, we know that a bit of sensible muscle applied correctly here in Palestine is much more effective in keeping the peace than all the politics in the world."

"Jewish soldiers?" General Wavell shook his head as though he could not believe his ears.

"With proper training we could clean out a lot more nests than just Galilee."

Wavell looked out the window. The weary expression on his face indicated that he agreed. But there was something else. "The Arabs and our own colonial secretary are discussing the idea of a peace conference. Talking."

"Ah. And they cannot talk if we fight."

"They say you must stop fighting before they will even talk about talking," he said evenly. Regret filled his voice. "You have done too well, Orde." His eyes met Orde's. "I must order you now to defend your perimeters and nothing else." He frowned. "Is that clear?"

"Clear. Politics—and dirty politics at that," Orde said angrily. "You and I both know the intentions of Haj Amin. He would be king here and take over every good thing the Jews have done for this rock. Great Britain is the biggest loser in this political game. We may well be handing over Palestine—first to Haj Amin, and then to Hitler."

"We are soldiers, Orde. Bound to obey." The general seemed to sink down in his chair. "Even when we cannot agree." Tapping his pipe against the ash tray he considered just how much he could say. "You have been tagged the most dangerous man in Palestine by the Mufti's henchmen. Watch your back, Orde. You're a fine soldier. I would hate to lose you to a dagger through the ribs."

"That might be preferable to this slow death by politics."

———

The story would rate only a couple of columns on the back page of American newspapers, but in London, it was front-page news.

Murphy scanned the text of the cable one last time as gale-force winds howled against the windows of his office.

LONDON: *At least twelve persons were killed in the winter's first gale, which at one time today reached a velocity of 108 miles an hour.*

For some U.S. publications, that one line would be all the news printed on the subject. *So who cares about a little storm in England?*

For those who lived through it, however, every other news in the world seemed to recede into the background. Winds howled down the English Channel, tossing the huge battleship *Royal Oak* like a champagne cork on the waters. Waves eighty feet high smashed sea walls and tore the steeples from cathedrals. Twice Murphy looked out the window and thought he saw the spires of Parliament bending like trees.

The *Queen Mary* was unable to reach Southampton and was forced to spend a long night bobbing at anchor off the Isle of Wight. Bridges and homes were swept into the sea. The funeral procession of Queen Maud of Norway, who had died on a visit to England, was abandoned as royal mourners were threatened by the force of the storm.

A flock of fifty sheep were blown off a cliff into the sea. Murphy wondered if this last incident might be some sort of divine warning to the political sheep of England that a much more terrible storm was brewing.

Just as he mentioned this idea to Elisa, the electricity winked off for the rest of the night, leaving the entire nation in a total blackout. Another portent of things to come?

The storm created quite a bit of inconvenience around London. Only total fools and taxi drivers dared to brave the roads. Business was virtually locked up tight—every business but that of gathering the news, that is.

Ordering doors at home locked and windows taped, Murphy cast his lot among the fools and went to the office hoping, like Prime Minister Chamberlain, that peace was at hand.

But there was no peace. It began to snow, and word came in from Southampton that the TENS Paris correspondent was stranded on the English side of the Channel. This was especially bad news; the English Prime Minister was in Paris with the French appeasers attempting to get in on the latest diplomatic maneuvers by the Germans.

Every reporter was safe at home. As Murphy prepared to close up shop, the telephone rang. He stared at the receiver for a moment, astonished that the telephone was still working. Then he picked it up. "TENS head office."

A nasty crackle hissed into his ear, telling him that the phones did not have long before they would be gone as well.

"Operator . . . Jerusalem . . . Palestine . . . personal to . . . John Murphy."

Jerusalem! It was a miracle; while the water of the English Channel sent British battleships running for cover, the cable beneath eighty-foot waves was still intact!

"Right! Murphy here!"

Another long vibration ran through the line as words pulsed through

Paris and Budapest and Istanbul and then on to Jerusalem. The faraway voice of a Britisher broke through. "Hallo? Are you there, Mr. Murphy? This is your Jerusalem correspondent on the line! Hallo? Are you there?"

Captain Samuel Orde! TENS' anonymous correspondent in Jerusalem! Lately, he had filled the wires with glowing reports of battles against the Arab gangs in Galilee. He mentioned his own name in every article as the daring British captain who led the troops to victory. Not a modest man, this unnamed correspondent. He managed to get credit for the skirmishes even if he did not get his name on the byline.

"Orde! A lucky break! We just got word about the Arab-Zionist conference! What's the reaction there? Any hopes for peace?"

Silence seemed louder than the crackle on the line. "Word is that the plan comes straight from Berlin. Rerouted rather like this phone call through the Mufti in Baghdad."

"What's the point?"

"They are hoping to tie the hands of that dashing Captain Orde who is smashing them in Galilee," Orde said with a laugh, the words suddenly as clear as if he were in the next room. "The Arabs are coached in every word. I'm afraid the Zionists are about to be sold out. Another Munich." His voice faded. "A hefty price on his head . . . wanted you to have the straight story in case. . . . Tell Winston that—"

"Tell Winston what?"

The crackle turned into a roar, and the phone went dead. So much for a modern miracle.

Murphy scribbled notes from what little he had gathered from Orde. There was a price on his head. There was a plan behind this offer of peace from the Arabs. The British High Command in Palestine was also in the mood for appeasement. Sam Orde might have been winning battles, but they were all in danger of losing the war.

Murphy stared thoughtfully at the downpour and then picked up the telephone to call Churchill. No luck. The lines across London were down.

Otto smelled the woodsmoke of his mother's kitchen stove before he topped the rise. The air was still, broken only by the jingle of harness bells and the rush of the runners across the snow. On either side of the road, fences and pastures were concealed by a thick carpet of snow that banked the edge of deep green forest. Above the trees, the rocky peaks of the Tyrol were lost from view behind the clouds.

He snapped the reins down hard on the back of the mare. In spite of the cold, she was sweating after an hour's hard pull over the snow. Still, at his urging, she picked up her pace, giving the harness bells a ring of urgency.

At the sight of the farmhouse, Otto swallowed hard and brushed his eyes with the sleeve of his coat. The tears were only from the wind, he told himself as he resisted the temptation to cry like a homesick child.

Snow was almost to the eaves on the right side of the chalet. A thin ribbon of smoke rose up from the chimney, carrying the scent of baking bread into the crisp afternoon air. "Home," Otto whispered, suddenly certain that he would not go mad after all!

Papa stepped out of the front door. Tall boots topped his baggy trousers. His heavy coat was buttoned crooked and his hat was off. He lifted his chin to gaze with alarm at the distant sleigh. Who would be coming up to the farm after such a storm? Maybe a lost tourist? Maybe Gestapo? Karl Wattenbarger's posture conveyed suspicion and then, after a long moment, the stiff back relaxed with delight as he recognized his son!

Otto could hear the call back into the house: "Mama! It is our boy! Otto is home! Marta! You hear me? It is Otto!"

The Wattenbarger farmhouse was full of guests. Nineteen in all, none of them tourists.

Children hung on the banister and peered down at Otto like stone carvings that had come to life in the care of the Austrian family. Those same faces had been gray and unhappy when Otto had brought them here. There had been so many over the months that he could not remember every name or the exact circumstances of their desperation.

"We cannot take in anymore," Karl said sadly to his son.

"But, Karl—" Marta started to argue as she poured hot cider for Otto.

"No." Karl silenced her. "When there were nine and the first snows closed the passes through the mountains, we said, 'Well, we have nine guests for the winter.' Ja. And then there were eleven, and then fifteen. Now nineteen. We have food enough if we eat twice a day. Porridge in the morning and milk for a snack. But nothing to spare. We must pray that the snows melt early and the pass opens before the Nazis come up here to steal our pantry clean."

"They have taken seven cows," Marta added, sitting down beside Otto. "Gert and Ilse and Buttercup, who gave the most milk, as you know. Yes, I think the Nazis will let us alone now. They will let us feed the livestock through the winter, but in the spring they may take everything into their own pastures."

"Do the neighbors have any room?" Otto asked, not willing to let go after what he had seen in the cities throughout the Reich.

Karl shook his head sadly. "Most are as crowded as we. At least those we could trust to ask. Here in Kitzbühel alone there are over two hundred children hidden." Karl's brow furrowed with concern for the thousands of children outside the tiny circle of safety. "Maybe the Americans troopers and the English will come through now, after what the storm troopers did."

"It wasn't just troopers, Papa," Otto said. "It was everyone. Friends. Neighbors. Everyone turned out, as though hell had taken over and turned men inside out." But he looked at his cider and wondered if he should tell them about the empty hospitals. He could not make himself say it out loud. Here on the farm some illusion of peace and beauty remained. The brutality of the world outside was measured only in missing cows and homeless children. The reality of it had not yet penetrated, and Otto would not speak of the darkness as long as some light remained here.

"Surely there are people in Vienna who will help, ja? Just until spring when the snow melts and we can take them out." Karl was torn by his inability to offer a solution. "And maybe by then the English government will have a plan."

Otto nodded. Some families would never be allowed to leave the Reich no matter how wide any nation opened the gates. Children of political prisoners were as despised as their parents. These were the people Otto would face when he returned to Vienna. He would be forced to look into the eyes of Michael Wallich's children and tell them there was no room for them. No escape.

Karl seemed to read the unspoken pain in his son's eyes. He put a leathery hand on Otto's arm. "You must think of the Holy Family, ja?" He gestured toward the crucifix above the table. "Only they escaped from Bethlehem when Herod's soldiers killed the little ones. Even the angels of Almighty God could not warn every mother to flee."

Marta nodded. "We do what we can, son. And God does not judge for what we cannot do."

Emotion crowded Otto's throat again. "There is so much I must do that I hate. And so much I want to do that is impossible." He listened to the clatter of young footsteps above them. "There will be a terrible slaughter . . ." He did not finish. What was left to say? *Save a few while multitudes perish, and pray you made the right choices.*

"You are not judged, Otto," Karl replied quietly. "Do what you can and know the angels wept also in Bethlehem."

The Jews of Vienna, forced to clear away the debris of their own broken lives, swept the streets and sidewalks clean. Shop windows were boarded over, never to open again.

But Lucy Strasburg's life remained littered with the shards of her shattered illusions. They cut into her heart, then sealed into tough, impenetrable scars. She saw no one's misery but her own. She grieved for no one but herself.

Sometimes she felt drawn to walk again on Stephanie Bridge, to look longingly down at the brown waters. But in those moments, certain of hell, she glimpsed her own judgment. To die now would mean that she would take a second life, the life of her unborn child. Could she add murder to her roster of sins?

Twice she wandered into the great cathedral of St. Stephan's. Wolf did not like her to go there; the Catholic church labored under the heavy scrutiny and disapproval by the party. But she was a woman, and so he overlooked her weakness for religion.

She did not tell him that she came here like a starving child going to a bakery to smell the baking bread. Like a pauper who looks at a grocer's stand and longs for what he cannot buy, Lucy sat in the back of the great cathedral and wished that she had whatever was for sale in such a place. But she had nothing with which to buy her salvation. She had given everything good in her for the sake of Wolf's passion.

Priests and nuns with worried faces moved about St. Stephan's. The Nazis had stoned the residence of Bishop Innitzer, declaring war on Catholics as well as Jews in Austria. Maybe the priests had no comfort left to offer Lucy. With that thought in mind she left the cathedral without asking for help. There was, it seemed, no help left for anyone. *Look out for yourself,* her heart whispered. *You are the only one you can count on.*

Lucy walked a precarious high wire with the ravenous Wolf waiting below for her to slip. She teased him and she baited him. She made demands on him and then scorned him when he failed to meet them.

When he brought her the fox coat, she pretended that it was not good enough quality. "The sort of thing a junior officer would give his spinster sister," she mocked.

He had responded with anger, perhaps even with disappointment. She remained unmoved, and so the fur had been returned and replaced by one of richer color than the first. She rewarded him with her passion and left him happy that he had pleased her.

Only a few weeks before, she would have been ecstatic about the first coat, of course, but she did not let him know that. It was a game. Sometimes she rewarded him with her approval, but not always. And so he began to work at pleasing her without ever knowing that she did not still love him. Power filled the void love had left in Lucy's heart.

Secretly she called Wolf her little hound, uttered with the same disregard with which he had once called her his cow. She made him beg for her and try to please her. He never knew that all she wanted was to escape from him, to carry this baby far from the beautiful hands of Wolfgang von Fritschauer and his dutiful little Nazi wife. She determined that the thing he wanted most from her would never be his. How to accomplish that, however, was still a problem she grappled with. Even in their most tender moments that thought occupied her mind. As she smiled and whispered his name, she thought of trains and obscure places beyond the borders of the Nazi Reich.

One single beam of sunlight broke through the overcast sky and filtered through the window of Lucy's apartment. Somehow that shaft of light lifted her spirits.

She sat alone in the elegant little parlor of the apartment. From left to right, according to value, she laid her assets out on the cushions of the pale yellow Queen Anne sofa.

The Swiss watch Wolf had given her came first, then a small gold and amethyst ring she had received from an aunt who had purchased it in Paris years before. An assortment of gold and silver bangle bracelets and a necklace lay next to the ring. On the far right she placed the large solid silver crucifix that she had inherited from her grandmother.

It seemed a pitiful little pile against the expensive furniture of the parlor. She had saved only a few marks from work; the rest she had squandered on clothing and handbags and shoes and treats that she had sent home to her younger brothers and sisters.

"I have been a fool," she said aloud to the empty room.

Few of these possessions could she sell. To sell the watch would incur Wolf's wrath and suspicion. To present the little ring to the appraisers might cause them to smile and toss her a handful of change. Bracelets and the necklace would bring nothing but outright laughter. *"Gold plated, my dear! Not real silver, only polished nickel!"*

Only the silver crucifix offered any hope. Lucy suspected that it was very valuable. She had placed it on the end of the row because it was the one thing she had which she dreaded selling. Still, it seemed that she had nothing else.

The cross itself was a full twelve inches from top to bottom and quite heavy. The metal was a work of art. Patterned to mimic the grain of wood, Lucy could almost see the rough splinters tearing into the flesh of the mourning Christ who hung on it. And silver spikes ran through hands and feet; a crown of perfect little thorns jammed down into the forehead. There was no wound yet in the side of Christ. Lucy's grandmother had explained to her many years before, *"He is not finished dying yet, you see, Lucy. The soldier thrust the spear into His side after He was dead. But this shows that our Lord still suffers for our sakes."*

Indeed, this was a different picture of Christ than the one Lucy had always seen above the altar of every church. Limp and pierced, those Christs were dead, indeed. Ah, but this one—His eyes looked right at Lucy, His mouth open as if He tried to make her hear His words. Every tiny detail was flawless. A picture of horrible suffering and grief.

Lucy had often contemplated that image as a child. It had hung above the dining table in the *Herrgottseck* of Grandmother's little house. Grandmother had often raised her eyes and spoken to the suffering Christ, as if He were an old familiar friend.

The sunlight inched across the cushions, finally resting on the gleaming silver crucifix and glinting back into Lucy's eyes. She looked away, unwilling to admit that there was nothing else of value which might provide funds enough for her to escape Wolf.

She shook her head. How could she sell the cross her grandmother had cherished? With an audible sigh, she stood and looked down at the delicate petit point embroidery on the chairs that flanked the sofa. Her eyes swept around the walls at the paintings which hung there. The paintings were ordinary, of the type sold by itinerant artists in the alleyways along the Danube. She looked back at the chairs. They were far from ordinary. Although Lucy had no knowledge of their style or maker, Wolf often touched their hand-carved gilded frames with an odd sort of reverence, just as her grandmother had touched the crucifix.

These chairs were of great value, as were the Persian rugs she stood on. But how could she sell such things? They did not belong to her, and Wolf would certainly notice their absence the instant he came through the door.

The bronze clock on the mantel struck four. The sunbeam that had raised her spirits for a moment slipped away as Lucy heard the clank of the elevator arriving on her floor.

Quickly she scooped up her treasures and carried them into the bedroom to dump them in the bureau drawer. In a moment, the sound of Wolf's latch key scratched in the lock, announcing his arrival.

He did not speak, but with a heavy sigh, pitched his hat at the bronze cherubs on the clock and then sat down on the sofa. He propped his feet on the coffee table, never noticing that she had entered the room. She hurried toward the kitchen to brew a pot of coffee. Removing a bottle of brandy, she splashed a bit into his cup as he always liked. Only then did he speak.

"No brandy." His words were clipped like commands. "The Führer is here, and it would not do for him to smell a whiff of it on my breath. He disapproves of strong drink."

With a broad smile, Lucy looked out from the doorway. "Well, Göring drinks, as does every other German general, I hear."

"I am only a major," Wolf replied. "When I am a general, then I will not fear the Führer smelling brandy on my breath."

She was disappointed. Wolf was always less harsh when he had a little to drink. She carefully poured it back into the bottle. She did not ask him how the meetings were going. "You will be a general soon enough," she said brightly.

"You are right," Wolf called to her. "If this matter deciding the boundaries of Czechoslovakia is settled correctly, I will move up quicker than I ever imagined." He paused, as he often did when he talked aloud to himself. "The Hungarians want a piece of the Czech territory, and that will give the Führer reason enough to march the rest of the way into Prague. Privately, that is all the talk. We will let the Hungarians make their demands, and then we will proclaim that what remains of Czechoslovakia needs the protection of the Reich. By spring we will march into Prague, and I will be a colonel, at least."

"Will you also go to Prague?" Lucy asked with a slight pout in her voice. She had been considering escape to Prague, but if what Wolf said proved true, she would have to find another place. "You know the baby is due to be born then."

"You will manage without me, I am certain," Wolf replied irritably. "Now fix me a sandwich. I only have half an hour, and then I must be back. We have not even taken time for lunch until now."

Lucy obeyed obligingly, grateful for the warning he had given her about Prague. Did everyone know what the Führer planned for the Czechs? Wolf had told her so casually. She frowned and asked a question in spite of herself. "What will the English say about it when we take Prague also?"

"They will say plenty, as always, but they will not do anything. As always."

17

Preparations

Chin-ups. Sit-ups. Jogging for miles around the pews! It was more than tiring; it was insane!

Jacob tied the spare bell rope to the banister of the choir loft and stripped off his shirt. Then he pulled himself up hand over hand and hung there, grinning down at Lori.

"See? Nothing to it. Like the angels up Jacob's ladder, eh?"

She had done all the rest, but she would not do this. Heights terrified her. She would not climb, no matter what he said.

"I won't."

He lowered himself down and dropped the last eight feet, landing upright beside her. "You will learn to do this, Lori, or you will not eat."

"Fine!" she said defiantly. "Then I *won't* eat! But I would rather die of starvation than by falling thirty feet on my head!"

"It isn't thirty feet." Mark tried to act as mediator. He had been doing that a lot lately.

"It's fourteen feet. Nothing," Jacob said. "I did not even use my feet or legs. You can use your legs if you—"

"I won't! This is the kind of stuff they make the Hitler Maidens do! Calisthenics! Burn books and spend your time developing muscles! You're as bad as any Hitler Youth leader! My arms and legs ache."

Jacob motioned with his head that Mark should leave. He could handle this himself.

Mark shrugged and left the auditorium, relieved that he did not have to climb the rope.

"Now, Lori," Jacob said in a patronizing tone, "sit down, will you? Let me tell you . . . sit down." He directed her to a pew. "Relax a minute. We are adults. We can talk this thing through. There are reasons why—"

Lori did not want to hear his reasons. She was tired of his endless bullying. She had done everything he said because he acted as if it was important, but she would not climb the rope!

"I won't."

"But you must learn." He stood behind her and rubbed her shoulders. "When we leave here—"

"You said we could stay forever," she protested. "I am not leaving until my parents return."

"Let's skip over that part." He did not sound as gruff with her as he had ever since they had been left here. "What I mean is, if we have to leave . . . suddenly . . . we need to know how to climb and how to run and . . . we won't be able to think about being tired, you see?"

He was telling her they could be pursued. They were certainly wanted by the men who held their parents! But she did not want to think about that, not today. There were things Jacob could not understand because he was not a woman. There were things about her body and her emotions that only Mama and her friend Susan knew about. She did not feel well. Jacob's hands on her shoulders helped her headache, but she would not climb the rope!

"I want to lie down," she said softly. "I don't feel like doing this today."

He pinched her hard. "You're too soft!" He sounded angry. "You will hold us back and get us all killed if we have to make a run for it!"

"Then *run*!" she cried. "And I will stay here!" She stood up and whirled to face him. "And don't touch me! I won't climb your stupid rope! I . . . I wish my mother was here! I want a hot bath and a cup of tea! I want to be left alone!"

She stormed from the sanctuary and took refuge in the ladies' room, the only place she could be alone. There she wept until she thought she had no tears. An hour passed, then two. Finally a timid knock sounded on the door.

"Lori?" It was Jacob.

She did not answer. Her eyes were bloodshot and puffy. She looked as though she had been hit in the face.

"Lori? Are you in there? It's Jacob."

"I thought it was the Gestapo!" She could not help saying it.

"Yes." A long pause. "Well, I was hard on you today."

"Every day you are hard on me!"

"I thought maybe . . . I was thinking that . . . perhaps," he stammered. She could almost hear him blush through the door. This was not at all like Jacob Kalner. "At home . . . there were times when Mother would want a cup of tea and an aspirin." He cleared his throat loudly. "And Father ordered us to be gentlemen. I have not been a gentleman. And I am, well . . . open the door. I made you tea."

"I won't climb your rope!"

"All right . . . I mean, not now. But here is your tea."

She raised her head and replied regally, "Leave it at the door. I don't want to talk to you no matter how sorry you are!"

It was a miserable, rotten thing to say to him on one of the few occasions he had been sensitive. She regretted sending him away, especially when he was just beginning to figure out that she was not an eleven-year-old rowdy anymore.

It would have been nice to talk to someone. To Jacob. To tell him how very much she missed her mother, especially at a time like this.

Opening the door a crack, she pulled in the tepid cup of tea. Two aspirin lay in the saucer, along with a stack of crackers. It was not Mother. It was not a long soak in a hot bath, but it was something, at least. This small kindness made her cry again. Maybe later she would try to climb Jacob's rope.

Shaved heads and filthy black-and-white striped uniforms; a bowl of watery soup and a place on the straw of a crowded bunk—within the walls of Nameless camp, all men were created equal. Entitled equally to suffer. Entitled equally to endure. Entitled equally to perish at the whim of beasts in military uniform who considered themselves more equal than other men.

Grief was the great leveler of men—rich or poor, wise or foolish, or just ordinary. None of that mattered anymore. Even goodness at times seemed to be lost in a mottled shade of gray, blended into the mist of human misery. But for the most part, the difference between light and dark seemed distinct. Some men, like Pastor Karl Ibsen, were candles; other men were the wind that would snuff out their light.

From the high view of the watchtower these rows of striped uniforms did not seem human or distinct in any way from one another. But each faceless form was an individual of untold value and unmeasured worth. In this way the pastor saw his fellow prisoners. *A face. A name. A man. A soul.* He counted them all as worthy of love. He loved them all in the name of his Lord, no matter how light or dark the shadows that fell across their hearts.

In this terrible purgatory, Karl Ibsen found a flock that needed him more than all the filled pews in Berlin. For his own suffering he thanked God, because many men found the truth while Karl suffered among them.

This morning the north wind penetrated his thin cotton uniform. His hands were broken and bloody from cold and from the work he did without gloves. He looked like any other man in the assembly yard.

Kapos with sticks in hand prowled the rows as the roll call was read. Sometimes for no reason at all they stopped to level a blow across the back of a prisoner. Cries and thuds punctuated the calling of the roll. It lasted for hours.

During this time, Karl prayed. The guards and their dogs could not see that he prayed, and so they could not stop him. Karl prayed for his wife, Helen. He thought of her in every pleasant way, and inwardly he smiled because her goodness was real and her love was eternal. He prayed for his children, for Lori and Jamie, that they would remember all he had taught them and not be afraid.

Beside him a man fell coughing to the ground. Karl stooped to help him and was kicked hard in the stomach. The man who had fallen thanked him, blessed him with a look, and then the S.S. officer kicked him as well. When the man could not rise, he was shot. His blood splattered on Karl's uniform.

Karl stood slowly. He wept silently, but he did not stop praying.

The members of Orde's Special Night Squad listened quietly to his report of his meeting with General Wavell. He concluded by restating the general's order that they confine their actions to defending their perimeter.

Larry Havas stood behind Orde in the little knot of men. He shrugged and remarked to Zach, "Just what we expected all along. Jews who strike back rock the British boat, if you know what I mean."

Captain Orde rounded on him savagely. "And just what do you propose to do about it?"

"Do about it?" queried Havas. "Me?"

"Is that your only response, Havas? 'Oh well, it was good while it lasted?' "

"But, Captain Orde, what other response can there be?" inquired Zach. "To continue means that we will soon be asked to make the short trip to Acre prison and then the even shorter trip to the end of a British rope!"

"That is the trouble with you Jews!" Orde snapped. "Always so patient, worrying about trouble that might find you. You might as well go lie down on your bunks and wait for the Arab knife that cuts your throats, because it will come far more certainly than the British rope!"

Moshe watched the exchange in silence. With a dramatic change of volume, Orde suddenly lowered his voice to a bare whisper, so that all the men had to lean in to hear what was said. "My own neck is more squarely in the noose than any of yours." His words were barely audible, but his eyes flashed fire. Startled, Moshe realized how much Orde looked like the image of an Old Testament prophet.

"We cannot afford to think about what we are not allowed to do," Orde continued. "Instead, we must take full advantage of what we are permitted."

Quizzical glances flew around the group. No one dared to respond to the challenge in the flaming eyes to ask what he meant. Orde answered the unspoken question.

"You are permitted to go freely on the roads of the Mandate, are you not?"

"Yes, but what—" questioned Zach, then he stopped abruptly as Orde continued.

"And to defend yourself if attacked?"

"Yeah," grunted Havas. "So what?"

"So," concluded Captain Orde, "let's get busy defending ourselves."

Piano lessons! The steady tick-tock of the metronome matched the patter of raindrops but clashed with the unsuccessful attempts of nine-year-old Deborah Harding-Smith to attack the musical scales one octave at a time.

"Once again, from middle C." Anna positioned the child's rigid fingers on the piano keys for the eighth time. "Try again, Deborah. One and two and. . . ."

Deborah began again, banging down on the keys as if she were at war with the keyboard. The constant rhythm of the metronome had no more meaning to this exercise than the howling of an alley cat on a back fence. In fact, Anna often thought that it would be easier to teach a cat to dance the rumba than to guide this one child into the wonderful world of tempo. Tone deaf and totally without rhythm, Deborah hated these hour-long lessons. The time here was wasted. She knew it. Anna knew it, although she did not say it. And everyone who heard this horrid banging also knew it. Everyone, that is, except for the child's mother.

Mrs. Harding-Smith believed her pigtailed daughter had the potential for great talent. She was, as yet, uncertain of what that forte was. *Maybe ballet?* Deborah got stuck with one leg on the bar and tore her tights—not once, but twice. *Perhaps tap dancing?* Ah well, the poor thing could not remember heel from toe or hop from shuffle. The tap teacher developed a nervous twitch in her right cheek and declared to Mrs. Harding-Smith that Deborah could not even march in step, let alone learn to shuffle-hop!

Deborah's untapped talent was not to be found in the art of dance. The search for Deborah's undiscovered genius continued through cello, flute, and clarinet lessons, as well as several other instruments that wheezed, whistled and bawled like dying animals. The piano was a last resort, Mrs. Harding-Smith confessed. It was difficult to make a piano sound like anything other than a piano, no matter how badly played it might be.

Anna supposed that this was meant to comfort her on the long journey through the land of fractured whole notes and stuttering scales.

This afternoon, Charles and Louis peered out from the hallway to investigate what had happened to the poor piano. Anna waved them away and sat down on the bench beside Deborah, who suddenly burst into tears of frustration.

The lesson became a time of consolation. The child sobbed in Anna's arms and confessed that she hated all musical instruments and that she would rather be playing cricket with her six brothers, or hiding out in the club house, or anything at all besides this.

Anna knew how she felt.

"Well, then, perhaps we should tell your mother together."

"Oh no! Mother will be most unhappy! She will think I am an utter failure. I have not even learned to play the scales properly. I try, really, Mrs. Lindheim! I do try! I am not so absolutely stupid as all that!"

"So you want to keep trying, do you?" Anna asked as Charles and Louis peeked around the doorjamb again. She narrowed her eyes, a clear sign that they were intruding on an emotional moment.

Deborah wiped her nose on her sleeve and nodded miserably. Anything was better than facing her mother with another failure. "Yes, I want to try. I *will* try."

Anna felt sorry for the little girl, but after so many weeks, she was also sorry that the torment must go on to avoid the scowling disappointment of Mrs. Harding-Smith.

"All right then. Trying is the same as winning." Anna took a deep breath and stared at the big black notes on the instruction booklet. Pretty boring stuff.

Anna closed the book. "If we are going to go on, we must find *something* about the piano that you can enjoy, ja?"

"I like it when *you* play." Another big sniff.

"But what do *you* like about the instrument?" Anna danced her fingers over the keys. Beautiful, clear and alive, the notes covered the serious conversation of the boys as they discussed the unhappy female on the bench.

"Well . . ." Deborah screwed up her face. "I can send my brother Harry signals on it when he is upstairs and I have to practice."

"Signals?"

"Yes. Mother thinks it is part of the lesson, you see." Deborah lowered her voice. "Mother can't tell one note from another." Her lips turned up in a sly smile. "So I send Harry messages. In code. I learned it from his Scout handbook."

Anna rather liked this new twist in the concept of music as the language of the heart. "And what sort of messages do you send?"

Deborah's eyes brightened; her face grew firm with determination and expertise. "You see, two dots, like this—" She banged hard twice on middle C. "That is the letter *I*. You see?"

Anna nodded. She was impressed—at least interested. "Go on."

"Four dots—" Deborah banged four times on the key of D. "That is the letter *H*. You see?"

The letter *A* was a dot and a dash. *T* was one dash only. *E* was one dot. Put all together, the message was, *"I HATE..."* Deborah went on to spell out two more complete words, *"PIANO LESSONS."*

She could also signal things like, *"MOTHER IS A CRANK TODAY,"* and *"ONLY TEN MORE MINUTES AND I CAN GET UP."* The potential for communication on the piano was endless, much better than the other instruments that merely squeaked and did not cooperate at all with Deborah's skill as a telegrapher.

At Anna's urging, the child went forward through the entire alphabet, then as Anna played a series of chords in the treble clef, Deborah repeated the performance on one note with skill and undeniable talent. The result was a new composition, impromptu, and quite nice in its simplicity—something bordering on a simple jazz tune. Anna laughed and said she knew an American jazz trio who might perform Deborah's remarkable new song.

Half an hour later, Mrs. Harding-Smith returned to fetch her daughter. Anna and Deborah treated her to a duet, a jazz composition called, "Telegraph Alphabet."

The mother laughed and cried and blew her nose loudly into her handkerchief. No matter that Deborah played one note only during the course of the song! Her child had *at last* discovered her forte! She was a prodigy in the true sense of the word!

Anna Lindheim closed the door behind her departing pupil and the ecstatic mother. She sank down into a chair with a sigh of great contentment. At last she had helped Deborah Harding-Smith find her true calling. No doubt the child would grow up to operate a telegraph key for Western Union.

———

The storm passed, leaving behind an unusually clear night. Brittle starlight outlined the silhouette of Parliament. Such grand beauty only reinforced the notion of those who believed, like Chamberlain, that Britain was the center of the universe. Beyond the boundaries of her mighty empire, the stars seemed dull in comparison.

Tonight, Theo and Murphy donned their formal dinner jackets. Anna and Elisa dressed in elegant evening gowns. Charles and Louis eyed them with childish envy and sat sulking in their pajamas beside the radio.

Freddie Frutschy and his wife Hildy came up the steps precisely at seven o'clock from their newly refurbished apartment on the ground floor.

Charles loved Freddie, of course. So did Louis. And they also liked Hildy very much. Hildy was also from Germany, but that had been a long time ago, she explained in English. She spoke English with an accent much worse than the freshest immigrant, and yet she refused to speak German to the boys. *"Great Britain my home ist. Und English now I am speaking!"* Hildy was very happy in the new apartment, happy to work as housekeeper while Freddie doubled as bodyguard and chauffeur for the household. *Und happy she vas to sit on the babies also,* she declared.

As pleasant in temper as Freddie, Hildy had wispy gray hair, braided and woven like pretzels on her head. Her face and figure were both round. She wore false teeth, which clicked and clacked in her mouth whenever she spoke her garbled brand of English.

The couple filled the doorway. "Ach, Eleeeza! Beauuutiful you ist tonight! Never mind you the boys about. Tonight a fine time ve ist having for sure!"

Charles could hardly understand a word she said. He imagined that her mouth was something like the telegraph key, and if he could only learn Morse code, everything would suddenly make sense in her exclamations of ticks and tocks and dots and dashes. In the meantime, no German would she speak, and her brand of English was undecipherable.

The two boys reluctantly rose and gloomily embraced the two elegantly dressed couples. Hildy dashed off to tune in the BBC to her favorite radio program. *"A pathetic British imitation of a pathetic American soap opera,"* Murphy had described the show.

Elisa cupped Charles's face in her hands and leveled her clear blue eyes at his. "Don't send us away unhappy, Charles," Elisa whispered. "Tonight is a very important night. You must be happy for us to go to this meeting. Maybe we will be able to help those children we dreamed about. When you say your prayers tonight . . ."

"I will," he agreed. No need to say more. He knew enough about this topic that he could tell the grown-ups a thing or two. But tonight they were doomed to stay home and listen to Hildy's radio programs until eight o'clock when they would be sentenced to bed by the extension of her stubby finger and a series of garbled clacks. "But I wish I could come too."

At that, a sympathetic Freddie hoisted Charles up on one broad shoulder and then Louis on the other. "Ah, come on, lads," he said. "We fellows'll leave the old woman to 'er BBC whilst we play with the tin soldiers, eh?"

Charles could touch the ceiling when he sat on Freddie's shoulder. Life seemed much more pleasant from such a great height.

The dinner party at the London home of Dr. Chaim Weizmann had an impressive guest list. Several sympathetic members of Parliament were in attendance with their wives—including Winston Churchill, Anthony Eden, and Harold Nicolson, who were known for their opposition to the Chamberlain appeasement policies. Weizmann, dressed in his black dinner jacket and stroking his scholarly goatee, leaned in to whisper in Theo's ear.

"There they are." He nodded his head toward the English politicians. "Our jury."

By this, Theo understood that every other guest had been invited to testify. Theo, in addition to his internment in a Nazi prison camp, had seen much in Berlin on Kristal Nacht. Anna had firsthand experience with the thousands of homeless refugees in Prague. Elisa had lived through the horrors of Vienna and could also testify as to the desperation of the children of Germany as seen through the lives of Charles and Louis Kronenberger. As for Murphy, he was an American. His perspective completed the circle of world opinion in favor of the rescue of the Jews of Germany. The roll call of witnesses included other prominent refugees from Hitler's new Reich. In all, a dozen Englishmen and an equal number of witnesses attended.

Testimony was given one on one as members of the jury were placed strategically between witnesses. The clatter of conversation hummed throughout each course of the meal, and Dr. Weizmann presided regally at the head of the long table. There was no need for him to direct the conversation. In an hour, over prime rib and Yorkshire pudding, more factual information was passed along than in several days of official meetings.

Over dessert and coffee, the discussion became more focused. Harold Nicolson, British writer, back-bench member of Commons, and staunch backer of Anthony Eden, spoke first.

"We are simply outnumbered," he said simply. "On both sides, labor and conservative, the debate was clearly sympathetic, but pathetic as far as the will to do anything at all."

Winston Churchill puffed on his cigar and morosely swirled his whiskey in his glass. "I heard the figure of 10,000 children from Germany and Austria mentioned. We took in as many from Belgium in the late war." His lower lip extended in thought. "You must not allow yourselves to be backed into a corner of anachronistic talk about moral responsibility and past obligations of Great Britain," he warned. "Talk is cheap."

"And that is coming from our finest orator," Anthony Eden quipped.

A twittering of polite laughter subsided into silence as the guests waited for Churchill to finish. Murphy contemplated the slouched bulk of the bulldog statesman with amusement and respect. He was, in physical appearance, the exact opposite of the handsome and dapper Anthony Eden. But both men shared the same views and the same disdain for the appeasers.

Churchill continued. "Lord Halifax"—he cleared his throat as if the name had stuck there—"has quite bluntly defined the interest of the government in ensuring that the Arab states would be friendly to us. In other words, we must not only invite the devil to tea, but must serve up our friends to him on his plate."

"And our children," remarked Weizmann.

"Yes." Churchill cocked a watery eye at the leaders of Zionism. "If this goes unchallenged, then you might as well return forever to London and build a house with three floors in it. One could house the government of smashed Austria. The second, the government of Czechoslovakia. And the third, all your hopes of a Jewish homeland."

"Well and good, Winston," added Eden, "but what is to be done?"

"This meeting between the Arabs and the Zionists has been called to give the appearance that the government is really doing all it can do to maintain the peace in Palestine. They are, in fact, giving the Mufti everything he wants, like Hitler in Munich. Therefore, I could recommend that the Zionists refuse to attend *unless* the rescue of ten thousand children in Germany is immediately undertaken." He nodded toward Murphy. "Such a reckless gamble should be widely publicized, of course, to demonstrate the desperation of the cause."

Silence filled the room. It was indeed a desperate move. To boycott such a meeting could mean losing everything. "There are seven hundred thousand Jews in the Reich," added one distinguished scholar from Heidelberg. "Only ten thousand?"

"It is the very number mentioned in the Commons debate," Theo interjected. He understood the reasoning behind the figure. "We will simply quote that number back to Chamberlain and Halifax as the number they mentioned."

Churchill raised a thick finger. "And as the number of children rescued from Belgium in the Great War, it is a precedent. We must ask ourselves if our fathers were more moral and decent than we are." At that he smiled briefly, knowingly, then sank back into the enjoyment of his reeking cigar.

Perhaps there was a method in the madness, after all. To rescue ten thousand was something, anyway. It was still not a Jewish homeland, still not a standing-room-only Zionist state. But it was ten thousand lives.

———

The other guests had left two hours earlier. The mantel clock in Chaim Weizmann's study chimed two A.M. Cigar smoke hung in a thick haze across the room.

Murphy's eyes sagged, heavy with sleep, as the conversation continued. Only Winston Churchill seemed entirely awake. Theo looked exhausted but attentive. Anna rested her head against his arm. Elisa looked pale and thoughtful as she listened to Winston's plan. She turned down Mrs. Weizmann's offer of the spare bedroom. The Lindheims were a family of concert musicians, she explained. Late nights were a way of life.

"Censorship in the Reich is a difficult problem." Churchill looked at Murphy, who could only nod his agreement. "How long did they keep your reporter locked up?"

"Three days. And now his reports are about the new construction sites and the autobahns. Nothing meaningful. His phone is tapped. Every word coming out of Germany is screened by propaganda officials; photographs as well. Anyone transgressing the rules of the press is liable to be arrested and executed as a spy." Murphy smiled as he thought of Timmons, the ex-sportswriter. "Timmons is not cut out for it."

"Since we cannot get answers the normal way, the best thing for us to do is to ask questions." Churchill lifted his chin and stared at the clock. "Time is running short for Europe, Murphy. People seem content to accept Chamberlain's version of the world. I propose we challenge that version on the radio. A political mystery program, if you will. The Trump Broadcasting version of 'War of the Worlds.' " He grinned. "We will ask about the fate of individuals, like Anna's sister, who have vanished, perhaps. And about policies. Nations. The plans of leaders. Questions may stir our people from their apathy."

"What about the answers?"

"We still have friends behind the gate in Germany. We must put the machinery in place to bring the truth back to us. I have some thoughts about how we might achieve that with the help of a certain piano teacher." He tapped his cigar on the ash tray. "Let Timmons send his reports about the autobahns. And let Herr Hitler wonder about how TENS gets the answers to our questions so soon. I think the censorship problem is about to be solved, my friends."

18

The Mouse and the Serpent

Money.

Never before had money been such a concern to Lucy. With enough money, she could break free from Wolf. Without it, Lebensborn became a certainty.

She remembered the whispered concerns of her mother and father as they struggled to feed nine children during the desperate days in Germany before Hitler had brought promise of order and prosperity to the German nation. With so many mouths to feed, Lucy took a job as a housemaid and a waitress, with every pfennig pooled into the family finances. She had never minded giving up her paycheck to help the family. It had seemed natural and right; there were still younger brothers and sisters at home in Bavaria. Even now, Lucy faithfully sent home half of her salary and spent the other half on little luxuries for herself.

She looked at her paycheck. For the first time she would send none of it home to Bavaria. For the first time she would not walk by the shop windows on the Kärtner Ring and pick out a new hat or handbag or pair of shoes to buy for herself. The check was for a hundred marks: twenty-five dollars a week. Lucy calculated that she would need at least a thousand marks before she dared to leave Wolf. Such a vast sum would take her two and a half months to save, even if she never spent a pfennig for anything!

She sighed and walked into the bank, wondering how she might acquire the needed sum in less than ten weeks.

The bank clerk, a sweet little man with big cow eyes, recognized her and smiled. She had told him all about her family back home and the reason for the weekly money order.

"Guten Abend, Fräulein Strasburg." He pulled out the money-order book automatically. "Will you be sending your usual again this week?"

"No, danke." She signed off the check and shrugged self-consciously, knowing he would wonder what had happened to make her change her pattern. "This week I will just keep the cash."

"All of it?" Surprise and concern raised his thick eyebrows in an arch over his brown eyes.

"All of it, danke," she replied with a smile.

He seemed almost hurt as he tucked away the money-order book. "In cash?" This was most unusual.

"Ja. Danke." She pretended to study the grain of the marble counter. "Ja," she said again, searching for a lie that would salve his curiosity. "Mama wants me to send packages home now instead of money. The products here in Vienna are still much better than in Germany," she added with a conspiratorial whisper. Then she pretended to worry that her words might be overheard. She winked at him, giving him the all-clear. "So. Heil Hitler, ja?"

At this revelation, he brightened, genuinely relieved. He counted out the Reichmarks. "You are a devoted daughter." He slipped the bills beneath the cage. "Grüss Gott. Until next week then!"

Lucy tucked the bank notes into her handbag and strolled happily out of the bank. She was glad that the little clerk had liked her illusion. If he had known the truth, she mused, he would have said, *"You are a faithless lover and a terrible S.S. mother."*

She let out a sigh of relief. She would pick another line to stand in the next time she came to the bank.

At the meeting in the big cathedral there were almost a thousand people, Anna said. Charles wondered if he and Louis counted because they were so short. He hoped that children did not count at the meeting because that would mean there were really a lot more than one thousand.

Men stood at the podium and spoke. Women also seemed angry and determined.

Elisa and the string quartet played music and everyone sang together.

When it was over, stacks of the yellow papers were handed out and places were assigned for people to distribute them. Charles knew that he counted then, because he carried a thick stack of yellow flyers on his arm. He liked helping; it made him feel better.

It was cold this afternoon. He waited at the top of the long stairs that led down into the Trafalgar underground entrance. He and Theo were in charge of the handrail on the *UP* side of the stairs. Anna and Louis were in charge of the *DOWN* side.

The policeman told them they could not go down into the tube even though it would have been much warmer than standing out in

the wind. There were rules they had to obey about where a person
could stand with a petition and how to hand out the handbills. A pastor
and four others had been arrested in Blackpool, so everyone had to
be careful. The government did not like this, but it was not like Germany. Charles was glad of that.

Crowds pushed up and down the stairs. Most of them looked the
other way when Theo and Anna spoke to them. It was cold, after all,
and no one wanted to stand outside and sign anything. Charles passed
handbills to as many as he could. People folded them and put them
in their pockets, and Charles hoped they could read them when they
got home by the fire.

A man in a black coat and Homburg hat stopped and put his face
close to Charles's. He read the writing on the handbill and smiled a
smile that was not altogether nice.

"Would you like to sign?" Theo asked. "For the children."

"You already got me," said the man. "But I could use a handful of
your leaflets. Put them where they belong."

Theo thanked him and gave half of Charles's stack to him. Charles
watched him walk down the sidewalk. He paused for a minute, shook
his head, and tossed the leaflets into the garbage can. Then he walked
quickly away before Theo could reach him.

The leaflets were ruined, covered by grease from a half-eaten sausage and ashes from a pipe.

"Over a hundred!" Theo looked angrily at the man who crossed the
square. "A very small fellow."

Other people had been nicer. An old woman brought Charles and
Louis peanuts and handed out their papers while they ate. Some days
the sun came out; more people stopped to sign and talk than on the
dark days.

This part of it was slow going, as Murphy said. But every day he
wrote for the newspaper, and three times a week there were radio
broadcasts that Murphy said could be heard as far away as the German
Reich. He said he hoped the broadcasts gave Hitler indigestion, and
Jewish people hope.

———————

D' Fat Lady had a name, which Charles learned to say. "G'bye, Dell."
He felt sad the trio was leaving.

"You remember t' pray for ol' Delpha Mae, honey." She took
Charles's face in her big hands and kissed his forehead. She could see
the worry in his eyes. The Nazis did not like people who were any
other color than white. What would they do to these black American
singers as they toured through the Reich? "You listen to yo' daddy's
radio station every Thursday, honey, 'cause ol' Delpha Mae gonna be
sending you love through the wires. Huh?" She gave Louis a kiss. She

called him Louie and shook her finger at both the boys. "We gonna teach old Beet-hoven a thang or two! Gonna teach them Nazis all about bein' hip!" At this, she threw her head back in a big laugh and hugged both boys one last time.

There were hugs for Elisa, Murphy, Anna, and Theo while the taxi driver loaded steamer trunks and Hiram Jupiter's silver horn for the trip to the ship.

Philbert, the piano player, gave Anna one last word of advice. "You 'member now, you don't *need* no music written down when you play! It's different *ever* time, Miz Anna! By the time we gets back t' England, I 'specs you gonna be playin' jazz as good as Fats Waller, and that ain't no jive!"

"We'll play a duet then," Anna laughed. Then with serious eyes she took Delpha Mae's hand. "God bless you. Be safe, ja?"

"Don' worry none 'bout us!" Delpha Mae said loudly. "We is too noisy to jest diss'pear! Them Nazis would cause a *war* if'n our program didn't come on the radio ever week like *clockword!*"

Charles figured she meant to say *clockwork*. *D' Fat Lady Trio Program* was broadcast every Thursday over TBS like clockwork. Ivory soap was the radio sponsor and Charles had learned to sing the advertising jingle when he had been in New York. It was almost his favorite radio program, except for Charlie McCarthy. He liked the jazz because most of the times the lyrics were *"Bippity . . . bop, bop, hey dah-dah!"*

With such words in their songs, the trio did not need to know German. They had already made a big hit in Paris. Three months of live broadcasts from France to America had put Ivory soap in the same league with French perfume. The trio had wowed sedate society in London, and now Elisa predicted that Mozart and Schubert would be dancing the jitterbug in their graves.

As for the Führer, it was well known that he publicly disapproved of modern music, even while he privately screened American musicals. In regard to black musicians, he considered them to be a curiosity, "like performing bears," and he looked the other way when groups toured the cabarets of Hamburg and Berlin and Vienna. Trump Broadcasting Service had specially arranged the tour of European capitals with Murphy overseeing the link-up through the BBC in London to New York. This was the only broadcast from Germany that did not require the approval of Nazi censors.

Delpha Mae was right. The group was so popular in the States that not even the Nazi leader would dare insult them or discourage a warm reception in the Reich. Besides, he rather enjoyed this contrast of the great German culture to that of the culture of the United States. Delpha Mae had heard Hitler's description of the corrupt and primitive music of "former slaves." She simply shrugged it off and said that she reckoned the trio would add a little color to the entire tribe of goose-stepping prison wardens! *"Ain't that so?"*

Delpha Mae was not afraid of anybody!

"You be listenin', you two!" she called as the taxi pulled away. "I'll blow you kisses from Vienna, babies!"

———

Wolf rummaged through Lucy's closet, at last pulling her most austere black dress from the rod—long sleeves, ankle-length hem, and high neck. It was the dress Lucy hated above all others.

"I wear that to funerals," she snapped, "not luncheon receptions."

He tossed it on the bed. "This could be a funeral—your own, if you do not wear the dress."

"You told me he wanted to see beautiful German women. How can he tell if we are all made to wear black shrouds?" she pouted as she pulled up her stockings.

"Haj Amin Husseini is a Muslim leader in exile, expelled by the British. He is here as a guest to the Führer. His idea of beauty does not include low-cut dresses and bare ankles and shoulders. Women are meant to be covered—veils and such."

"Then what's the point? How will he be able to tell beauty? Take him on a tour of Rome and let him look at the Sistine Chapel. Michelangelo painted some lovely nudes."

"Vatican City will not appeal to the leader of the Muslims in Jerusalem." He buttoned his tunic and smoothed his hair. "He is more interested in touring prison camps for Jews than seeing great paintings, I hear." Wolf watched her in the mirror as she dressed. "The Mufti considers women as window-dressing. You may smile, but don't talk."

"Like a basket of flowers," she said cynically. She did not like playing this role for the Mufti. She had heard he was barbarous and effeminate at the same time. Haj Amin was nothing like the sheik portrayed in the movies by Rudolpf Valentino. Rumor among the secretaries in the Foreign Ministry said this Mufti fellow was actually more interested in pretty boys than women. The thought made Lucy's skin crawl.

This was one reception she wished Wolf had not asked her to. He explained that the Reich was courting the Arab factions in the British Mandate with the aim of acquiring Palestine as a colony of the Reich. The Jewish problem was as vital there as it was in Germany itself. And now those self-righteous Englishmen were campaigning to reopen the gates of Palestine for ten thousand Jewish waifs. British officers were leading Jews into battle! Haj Amin had come here for some reassurance that Germany would make such immigration impossible, as well as silence Jewish guns, Wolf told her. The Führer desperately wanted to drive the wedge deep between the Arabs and the British in Palestine.

The Jewish issue provided an ideal wedge, as long as it did not also damage relations with Germany.

Wolf believed that Lucy could not fully understand these lofty matters. But she understood the politics of dividing one group against another. Such tactics were used every day in friendships and marriage. Jealousy, dissatisfaction, anger—all these things could be used in getting what one wanted. Arabs and Jews had lived side by side for centuries. Now Hitler wanted Palestine; Haj Amin wanted Palestine. Together, Haj Amin and Hitler would have it—a simple matter of the eternal triangle, not to mention strange bedfellows. The Nazis and the Muslims had crawled into bed together, and together they plotted the end of the Jews.

What is so difficult to understand about that? she asked herself as she caught her first glimpse of Haj Amin arriving in his black Mercedes at the Hofburg. He had a light complexion and blue eyes, which no doubt made it easier for the Nazis to accept him. Whispers around the room told of the Mufti's Crusader ancestors. He wore long robes and a fez on his head. He was small boned and indeed glided with a feminine walk into the room.

He took Lucy's hand as she moved through the reception line. He smiled, appreciating German beauty, no doubt. Lucy smiled back without speaking, feeling queasy at his touch. She attributed the reaction to her pregnancy and the strange excitement of coming near to someone so important. But then again, there was something about this man that reminded her instantly of the poisonous snakes she had seen in the reptile cages at the Schönbrunn Park zoo. Nothing at all about him even vaguely resembled Rudolph Valentino.

The afternoon was a social occasion. All the women were dressed like Quakers, and the men like peacocks. Haj Amin's arrival had been well publicized in the state press as well as the international press.

Haj Amin stood before the journalists of the world and said quite firmly that this drive for the immigration of ten thousand children into Palestine would have to be silenced. Otherwise those Englishmen who ruled Palestine with such tyranny would be startled at the violence they faced from the Muslim populace. There would be no peace, he warned. There would be no peace conference between Jews and Arabs and the English until this idea of ten thousand homeless Jews in Palestine was stamped out once and for all! *No immigration!*

Lucy listened to the BBC at night when Wolf was not at home. Some, like Churchill, also saw the snake inside Haj Amin. Churchmen and plain people all said something must be done quickly, but it sounded to Lucy as though nothing would be done in the end. The success of

Jewish fighters in Galilee was discussed at length. That, too, seemed doomed to failure.

At times Lucy walked past the ruins of Jewish shops or the long bread lines where the Jewish women came with their children; she wondered what would happen to these people. They looked like sad-eyed mice huddling in the corner of a reptile cage. The jaw of the snake was unhinged, and through the clear glass Lucy watched them being devoured whole. Everyone watched. There was no attempt now to hide anything. But what could anyone do?

Lucy did not like asking herself that question. Why should she do anything, after all? Maybe she was one of the mice. How could she help anyone when she could not even help herself?

————

The smoking truck sputtered its way through the village. The men of Hanita knew this place sheltered several Arab terrorists from across the Jordan. Only two days earlier the terrorists had sniped at another Jewish settlement, killing one man as he drove a tractor and seriously wounding the first of his friends who had run to help him.

Orde's Special Night Squad had tracked the attackers back to this village, but done nothing further—nothing until now, that is.

Moshe had no trouble looking genuinely nervous as he wheeled the truck past the village in the gathering twilight. "Come on, come on," he muttered to the complaining engine, "don't break down here!" Missing the right front fender and headlight and sporting four unmatched tires, the ancient Dodge flatbed was used to haul seed and stock fodder around Hanita, but was seldom trusted off the settlement's property. Its sagging springs were even now loaded with a neatly stacked load of grain sacks.

Moshe's shoulders hunched over the steering wheel as he urged the truck to continue running with all the strength of willpower he could muster. He threw a glance sideways as he clattered past the headman's house. Against the doorjamb leaned a keffiyeh-crowned man with a hawklike nose and a permanent scowl because his lower lip was missing.

Moshe thought the man looked mean enough to have bitten his lip off himself. The man narrowed his eyes as he watched Moshe drive by, then spat loudly enough to be heard over the rattling engine. The view in the cracked rearview mirror through the missing rear window showed Moshe that the terrorist had abruptly ducked inside the house.

Relieved at having successfully passed the village, Moshe thought ironically that the villagers would probably be as pleased as the Jews of Hanita to see the last of this man.

A scant quarter-mile beyond the Arab community, the narrow dirt track began a sudden steep grade. Midway up the climb out of the sandy wadi lay a hairpin switchback that could only be turned by successively going forward and back a few feet at a time—a turn that would slow down any traveler.

Moshe painfully maneuvered the complaining truck around the corner, gears clashing. The truck's whole body shuddered like a prehistoric beast dying. Giving a last bellow that ended with a slowly spinning whine, the truck's engine died. Only halfway around the turn, the truck stood squarely across the road.

Moshe jumped out of the cab and hastily grabbed a rock with which to block the wheels before the truck rolled backward into the wadi. Then he backed toward the truck's hood, all the while staring intently down along the road. He raised the hood on its lone remaining hinge and propped it open with the stick tied there for that purpose.

He was busy for a moment, reattaching the two sparkplug wires that had become disconnected. He might have done it faster had he watched his hands instead of the road, but his hands were shaking as he wiped grease from them onto the legs of his coveralls.

When he straightened up he was not surprised to see three shadowy forms in checkered keffiyehs striding toward him up the road. They came boldly, making no attempt at caution or quiet. The man with the disfigured face took the lead; the other two flanked him a few paces behind. All three carried rifles slung over their shoulders.

Partway up the hill they stopped as they saw Moshe gazing down at them. "What's the matter, Jew?" called the leader. "Has your machine breathed its last?" The other two men snickered into their beards.

"Just a little trouble," replied Moshe in carefully measured tones.

"More than you think, dog," said the lipless one. "You are in a puzzle. If you run like the cur you are, I will shoot you down like I did that Jew farmer the other day. And—" He paused ominously. "If you stand still I will cut out your heart." He reached into the sash knotted around his waist and drew out a short gleaming knife.

Moshe mumbled something, but in a voice too low to be heard. "What was that, Jew?" called the leader of the terrorists, stepping a few paces nearer.

Moshe's lips could be seen to be moving, but the three men still could not make out his words. One of the mutilated man's companions called out mockingly, "He must be praying!" The trio advanced a few more steps.

In a voice suddenly so loud that it made the three stop in their tracks, Moshe called out, "You are right! I am praying *right now*!"

As he shouted the last two words, Moshe lunged under the front axle of the truck. On the truck bed, a tarp that had covered the top of the load of grain sacks was thrown off. Zach and Larry Havas stood up, German-made rifles in their hands. The weapons lay across the barricade of sacks pointed down the slope at the startled Arabs. Havas' first shot dropped his man in his tracks.

Zach Zabinski fired, missed, then worked the bolt and fired again before his mark had finished shrugging the rifle off his shoulder. The second terrorist also crumpled in a heap on the road.

The leader of the cutthroats didn't even try to bring his rifle to bear. Instead, he threw himself forward at the first shot, screaming his anger and defiance. He brandished his dagger overhead as his charge carried him almost to the side of the truck before Havas and Zabinski each fired again, both shots striking the man. The impact of the blows spun him completely around, so that his robes twirled in the twilight like the frenzied dance of a religious fanatic.

A moment later and the hillside was quiet again, and Moshe crawled out from under the truck. "I cannot tell you," he said, "how glad I am you fellows have been practicing."

When they had returned to Hanita, Orde met them at the gate. "How did it go?" he asked dryly.

"No trouble at all," replied Havas, grinning. "Of course, we had to defend ourselves once, but honestly, it was no trouble at all."

Alfie did not even bother to duck tonight when he spotted the light of the old watchman come around the corner of New Church. The watchman never looked for anyone in the tombs. He only whistled and hummed and looked at all the boards on the windows and doors. He would not have been very good at playing hide-and-seek. He did not know any of the good places for hiding. He walked very slowly, shuffling his feet. This was not the other watchman who was at New Church before. Alfie did not like the new man's face. His eyes were squinty and his mouth turned down. He had a little mustache just like Hitler and he wore an armband with a crooked cross. If it had not been for that, Alfie might have tried to make friends with him. But Alfie especially did not like the armband.

Soon enough the watchman went away. Alfie was glad. He went down the stone steps into the underground room. It was all dark; Alfie did not light his candle until the watchman had come and gone each night.

He felt along the stone bench for his matches and the candle. He had practiced, and now he could light the candle with only one match. Mama had let him have the broken candlestick for his clubhouse when he had asked her. The light made the room seem warm and he whispered thanks again to Mama with the same happy feeling he had when she gave him the candlestick so long ago. Maybe Mama had known how much he would need it. Maybe he had known it too, in a way, even though he had not thought about it then.

The smooth stone walls shone golden in the light. On the right and the left were benches made out of stone. Alfie made his bed up neatly and smooth on the right bench. Stacks of sardine cans and cans of beans and peaches sat on the floor below the left bench. Alfie put them in rows that looked like a town with buildings and streets, and even a park. Sometimes he stacked two cans of peaches up to make a tall building like the Opera House. With sardine cans he made the Brandenburg Gate. He put his tin soldiers on top and liked his city very much. He used the empty cans for houses where people lived. His apartment was all shiny and bright because he took the labels off the empty cans. And over there was Friedrichstrasse and the Jewish church like it used to be, and then New Church where everyone came and sang and prayed and Pastor Ibsen talked about good things like Jesus loving children no matter how smart or not smart they were.

The Hitler-men had not liked that talk. They stood in the back of the church with angry faces when Pastor Ibsen talked about God looking inside at souls to see who was really perfect and who was deformed. Alfie played out that Sunday morning again and again, because he remembered how good he felt that Pastor stood up for Alfie and the other children who were being taken from their families and sent away out of the sight of the German people. That day a lot of other Christians came to New Church. The Hitler-men wrote down their names on lists and said they had not heard the last of this!

Alfie made his tin Hitler-men stomp away and climb to the top of the shelf to report to Hitler; then they slipped and fell all the way to the floor. Sometimes he liked to make up his own ending.

The story he liked best of all was the one he performed tonight. In the back of the bean-can New Church with the candle for a bell tower, Alfie put *this* place. *His* place. Home with Mama. It was a sardine can with lots of sleeping tin men in it. Alfie was an infantry soldier in a handsome blue uniform. Sometimes his Alfie fought off troops of Hitler-men who came to take him. Sometimes he tapped through his imaginary city and visited people and shops. Tonight, Alfie put the tin-man Alfie to bed and sang songs from New Church and prayed and pretended that it was dark even though it was not really dark because of the candle. Last of all he put the general on his tin horse and then put them both on the candlestick.

"I am Jesus, King of everything," the general said. "And you don't have to be scared, Alfie." Then the candle and Jesus swooped through the air.

"Here I am!" the tin Alfie said, waking up. "I want to fight with you! Make me smart like other boys, and I will not be a dumbhead! I will fight the bad men!"

Jesus flew down and the candle was bright on the silver can where Alfie lived with Mama. The horse rode slowly into the can and Jesus touched Alfie with His sword. "You are smart!" Jesus said. "And I will make you fight good for me!" And Alfie was not a dumbhead anymore.

"Please wake up Mama, too!"

The sword touched sleeping Mama and she woke up and hugged Alfie. She was so glad to see him that she hugged him and hugged him, and Alfie had trouble getting away to knock the bad men off the Brandenburg Gate and rescue Werner and Dieter and Heinrich.

Alfie scooted back to look at his little world. He would be glad when things really happened the way he imagined. He stared hard at the pretend Alfie who stood before Jesus. He wished he could really be smart and fight a good fight for others the way Pastor had fought a fight for him.

"How did I do, General Jesus?"

"Well done, Alfie." Then Alfie lifted up the horse and rider back in the air and they flew away to watch everything in Berlin from heaven.

19

Night Visitors

The empty cans of Alfie's city clanked and clattered down in the dark.

It was pitch black. Alfie sat up in his bed. He was afraid. Something had knocked over his cans! His heart was pounding fast, and he could not breathe because he was so scared.

"Mama?" he said to the darkness.

A deep sound of breathing answered him. For the first time Alfie thought about ghosts.

"Who is there?" he shouted. He was afraid to reach for the candlestick. He was afraid to run for the steps. Whatever was there stood between him and the steps. He heard it! It kicked his city and maybe crushed his tin men with its big feet!

"Is it . . . Jesus? Jesus, I hope it is you! *Jesus?*"

Alfie was shaking all over, just like when he figured out that Werner was dead and that they would kill him too. He pulled his blanket over his head and scrunched way back in the corner, hugging his knees and pressing his face against his legs. He tried not to cry; but it would hear him and get him.

"Go away!" He took a deep breath and tried to sound brave. "This is my place!"

More cans clattered down from the shelf. The breathing made a soft rumbly noise. Alfie closed his eyes tight, expecting a blow.

A can rolled across the floor. Then something pounced and landed lightly on the edge of the blanket. Alfie gasped and screamed in terror. He struck out and hit something soft and furry. With a hiss and a meow, it whisked up the steps and away.

By the light of the candle, Alfie twisted open the sardine can. It hissed, and the aroma of fish filled the place. He went up the steps where the cat had run away and placed a sardine just inside the iron gate.

He dripped a little juice a few steps back and laid the next sardine on the marble floor. He decided he would not give him more than two sardines unless he came down the steps. Alfie broke a third sardine in pieces and left one bite on each step all the way down into his room.

Animals were nicer than people. Alfie remembered what the lady said on the day after Berlin was smashed. It would be nice to have a friend!

He prayed as he laid the little trail across his room and climbed back into his blanket. He put the sardine can right on his chest and left the candle burning.

———

Bare light bulbs hung from the ceiling of Barrack Seven at Nameless camp, high out of reach from even the highest tier of bunks to prevent suicide by electrocution.

In Barrack 7, however, there had been no suicides since Pastor Karl Ibsen had come among the prisoners. Sometimes smiles were exchanged between the men. They were kinder to one another than the prisoners of Barrack 14, where stealing and beatings were rampant. The difference was duly noted; it was not liked by the camp commanders.

Prisoners were not supposed to act humanely toward one another. The retention of dignity was a sign of inner resistance. Even silent resistance sent a tremor of fear through the ideology of oppression, the mastery of strong over the weak. It raised terrible questions. Who is really strong? And who is really weak?

Karl Ibsen and Richard Kalner shared a place with ten other men on the top tier of bunks. There was just enough room for them to lie side by side like sardines in a can. Their heads faced out toward the narrow aisle; they were not safe even in sleep from the blows of their captors.

The lights blinked once, a warning that all prisoners must now be in place for lights out. In the most remarkable minute of each day, one man on each bunk recited a scripture for the group to think on before sleep. The ritual had begun with Karl and Richard on bunk 49. It had spread from tier to tier, embraced by many and rejected by some, until these brief scripture lessons became the high point of each day. Men who had not spoken a word of scripture since Bar Mitzvah searched their memories to recall passages memorized in their youth. Those who had never read one word from the Bible sought out others from across the barracks.

"It is my turn to say something tonight. Have you a short verse I can learn?"

"The joy of the Lord is my strength."
"Look upon my suffering and deliver me."

There was no lack of supply, it seemed. Newcomers who scoffed at first soon found themselves as eager as their comrades to learn a new verse. After a while no one could remember who had started the tradition.

Karl did not admit that this was something he had picked up at a church camp when he was a boy, or that he had memorized complete books of the Bible one verse at a time.

"May my tongue sing of your word,
for all your commands are righteous."

From the bunk below, Karl heard the quaking voice of a young man who had come from Austria a week before. He declared he was an atheist, and asked Karl for the shortest scripture in the Bible. Now he repeated that verse in a mocking voice.

"Jesus wept."

Silence below. Then, *"Why did He weep?"*

"Because He knew what men could do to one another."

"He saw us here. It broke His heart."

A longer silence followed as each man considered the tears of Jesus. There was no great theological debate, no need for it. The Lord's tears spoke to the heart from the shortest verse in the Bible.

Throughout the barracks, guards with rubber truncheons shrieked for silence. The lights went out. Then, the young atheist who had offered the scripture in jest wept also.

———

Since the church picnic last summer, Lori had often daydreamed about being alone in a quiet place with Jacob Kalner. She had even imagined what it would be like to kiss him. Now such thoughts seemed foolish. She looked at him with resentment and anger.

The tiny bellows room of New Church was cold. Lori's teeth chattered as they placed the pew cushions on the floor to serve as mattresses. The heavy red velvet draperies from behind the altar had been taken down and would serve as a blanket for the trio. They dared not attempt to keep the furnace burning or sleep in a more comfortable room in case the Gestapo returned for a surprise search of the premises. The bellows room was the safest place, Jacob reasoned. At the first sound of trouble they could kick the cushions and the drapery into a corner among a stack of other items that had fallen into disuse around the church. And then they could slip back into the bellows to hide. Comfort was of small consideration compared to safety.

This thought in mind, they climbed into their makeshift bed. Jacob lay closest to the door. Lori lay next to the bellows and Mark slept in the center. It was still early evening, but not even light from the street-lamp penetrated the black cubicle.

Lori lay awake a long time as she listened for imaginary footsteps in the church beyond. Her breath mingled with the frigid night air in a steamy vapor. Jacob and Mark breathed with the even cadence of deep, untroubled sleep. Lori took some comfort in their ability to sleep. It was hard for her to close her eyes. Hard to give up watchfulness, in spite of the fact that they had rehearsed and drilled their escape a dozen times. *What if they come and we do not hear them?*

Every pop and groan of the rafters became the imagined footstep of a Gestapo officer coming to search the tiny church for fugitives. The wind against the roof, dry leaves tapping on the windows—the slightest sound became the harsh whispers of their pursuers. Even beneath the heavy fabric of the curtain, Lori trembled with fear. Mark curled warmly at her back. Jacob slept against the door so he could hear if they came. But he slept so soundly! *What if we do not hear them in time?*

She thought of her family and prayed for them one at a time. But those thoughts made her so sad that she considered slipping out of the church and marching to the nearest Gestapo office to give herself up. It was better not to think too much. Better to be afraid instead of locked in despair for Mama and Papa and Jamie. And so she let herself tremble, let the churning fear keep the sadness away.

It was very late when her eyes finally grew heavy with the exhaustion of terror. At last she drifted off into an uneasy sleep where the sounds of Mama's arrest replayed over and over again in her dreams. Somewhere far off, she thought she heard the thin, high wail of her brother's cry as he was carried away.

"No! No! Mama! Don't let them take me! Mama!"

She felt an urgent tapping on her head! *The signal!* Jacob wordlessly slipped from beneath the blanket, on his feet in an instant. He pressed his ear against the door and then, without explanation, tore the heavy fabric off Lori and Mark and tossed the cushions against the wall.

Lori jerked wide awake at the first sign of danger. Without waiting to listen, she grabbed Mark by the arm and guided him back into the giant bellows of the pipe organ. Only seconds passed before Jacob followed into the cramped space. Lori wiped her face with the back of her hand. Her cheek was wet. She had been crying in her sleep.

She listened, trying to hear what had awakened Jacob; trying to make out the imminent danger that must be ascending the steps to the organ loft.

But she heard no sound except the thump of her heart in her ears, the rapid breathing of her companions.

Jacob exhaled loudly, as if with satisfaction. "All clear," he said in a voice that seemed too loud for the tiny hiding place.

Neither Mark nor Lori dared to believe him. *How could he know?*

He said even louder, "Come on. Back to bed! Just a drill!"

Lori groaned with audible relief. All this fear wasted on a drill! What gave him the right to say when they would have a drill? She had just fallen asleep, and now she had to do it all over again!

"We have drilled enough!" she said angrily as she dusted herself off. "I just washed my face before bed, and now I'm all dirty again!"

Jacob grabbed her by the arm as she reached for the doorknob. "You're not going anywhere. I told you. Use the toilet before we go to bed, because once we're here for the night, we're here!"

"You can't make laws about such things," she argued angrily. "Unless you're a . . . Nazi!"

"I told you—" he began.

"You did not tell me you would wake me up in the middle of the night for nothing!" She pushed past him and jerked open the door. He did not try to stop her, but set to work reconstructing their bed.

"We needed a drill," he muttered to Mark. "You don't go running off to the toilet every time we have a drill, now do you, Mark?"

Mark was too tired to reply. It seemed like a very long time since they had been able to sleep a whole night through.

Lori grasped the cold metal banister and worked her way cautiously down the dark stairway to the foyer. Groping along the wall, she found the door of the women's room and slipped in.

They had agreed that lights must never be switched on in the church, and so she moved blindly to the sink and splashed ice cold water over her gritty face and hands and arms. She could not find the towel; she shook off the drops and wiped the dampness on her slacks, aware too late that her clothes were also filthy and she would have to wash her hands again.

Silently fuming at Jacob, she repeated the whole process one more time and then searched for the towel. Then she heard it . . .

In the pitch blackness of the tiled room, Lori heard the sound of shallow breathing. She stood rooted at the sink, blinking in the darkness toward where she knew the mirror would be. Was that her own pale face staring eerily back at her? Was she imagining? Why could she not move?

Her mouth went dry with fear. She held her breath, hoping that perhaps she had only heard an echo, her own echo against the tiles. But it was not so. The breathing was real; human, but not human. She opened her mouth and tried to speak the name of Jesus. But her lips could not form the word, so she simply stood there, clutching the cold porcelain of the sink.

There could be no doubt that whoever . . . *whatever* . . . was there with her had heard her clunking around. Why did it not speak? Why was the breath so shallow and . . . so *frightened* sounding? She drew a breath. Was it Mark? Had he slipped down here ahead of her to frighten her as a terrible prank, to teach her that she must obey Jacob?

Resentment gave her courage. "Who . . . who is there?" she demanded.

A little cry answered her, resounding off the tiles of the little room. "*Lori?* Sister? *Lori?*" It was the unmistakable voice of Jamie, sniffing through tears and calling with joy all at the same moment. *"Lori?"*

"Jamie!" She said her brother's name again and again as she patted the wall in search of the forbidden light switch. "Oh, Jamie!" she cried, no longer caring who heard her. It *was* Jamie! The light slammed against their eyes, making them both squint and blink as they took in the sight of each other in astonishment.

Jamie was dressed in the black uniform of the Hitler Jugend. His shoes were new and brightly polished, and he wore a heavy warm coat and gloves. His clothes looked new and strangely dark against his fair skin and hair.

He embraced her, holding tightly to her as he explained his escape from the Hitler Youth dormitory after dinner and his return to the dark and deserted church by way of a streetcar. "And then I came in through the window! And I was sitting in the basement for a long time, but then I had to use the toilet so I came this way and then I heard something . . . something . . . I don't know. I thought maybe a ghost or Gestapo. I ran in here and hid up on the toilet tank, you see, but then you came in. You didn't turn on the light . . . I thought the ghosts had followed me!"

She stroked his back gently as he rambled wildly on. And then, mindful of the lights, she reached up and flicked them off again. Only then did Jamie fall silent and let her simply hold him close.

"We must be careful of the light," she said softly. "I don't think they'll come back—not with all the signs. But we cannot go turning lights on, or someone will notice." She smiled in the dark, touching the fine, soft hair of her brother as Mama used to do.

"Where is Mama?" Jamie asked after a moment.

"They took her. I . . . I don't know where. Or Papa either."

"I saw our auto," Jamie said, as if he were telling of meeting an old friend. "It is parked not far from the Kalners' flat. The streetcar passed it, and I looked at it very hard. It was Papa's auto . . ." He sighed heavily. "I wish I had gone with Papa. Oh, Lori! What could have happened to them?"

Lori held her emotions in check. She was the older, the more responsible. She would not cry like a little baby, even though she wanted to. She had asked herself the same questions a thousand times, but she had no way of knowing the answers. "They will let them go," she replied in her most reassuring voice. "You will see. Mama and Papa will be released in no time. The Gestapo won't hold them. They can't.

Papa hasn't done anything. Mama is innocent. Don't worry, Jamie," she said.

"Are you alone?" he asked, drawing away and stiffening at the sound of footsteps against the flagstones of the foyer.

A muffled voice called through the door. "Lori? Are you all right?"

"Jacob!" Jamie said triumphantly.

Hand and hand the two went out to tell him Jamie had come home.

Alfie called his new cat Joseph, because his coat had so many different colors. Alfie knew the names of colors: orange and yellow and brown and tan. And Joseph had a little white on his pink nose and three white paws.

Alfie was glad that Joseph had come to live with him and keep him company. He did not mind sharing the sardines. Joseph was very fat but did not eat a lot. He was no trouble and slept on Alfie's feet every night. Joseph helped keep Alfie warm.

The best thing about Joseph was the way he purred and buzzed all over when Alfie stroked his soft fur, almost like laughing. It made Alfie feel happy inside that the cat liked him.

At first Alfie worried when Joseph hopped up the steps and slipped out between the bars of the gate to disappear over the fence of the graveyard. Alfie hung on to the bars and looked out to the very spot where Joseph had jumped. He watched the place for hours and hoped that Joseph would come back. But Joseph sneaked back another way, and suddenly Alfie felt him rubbing against his legs and buzzing hello.

After a while Alfie quit looking at the spot where Joseph jumped over the fence; he decided that Joseph was just playing a trick on him. Alfie gave Joseph an extra sardine every time he came back and let him lick the tin while he stroked his back. Alfie hoped Joseph would not go away forever. Such a terrible thought made Alfie's heart beat fast with fear. He didn't want to have to get used to loneliness again.

"You are such a good friend, Joseph," Alfie said to the cat. "Will you still come back when I run out of sardines? There are not very many cans left, but I will feed you all the same. But you must not forget me when there are no more sardines to eat."

Joseph purred as though food made no difference to him. He smiled a cat smile and cleaned his whiskers and lay down in a ball on Alfie's big feet. Alfie sat very still for a long time because he did not want to disturb Joseph. He did not wiggle his toes or say anything at all, even though he was thinking how much he loved this new friend and how glad he was that Joseph shared his warm coat even though there were not many cans of sardines left.

Lucy hoped to slip out of the room before Wolf awakened. She dressed in the dark, ran a brush hastily through her hair, and groped in the top drawer of the bureau for her Mass book. Today was the day of her patron saint, St. Lucy. It was also Lucy's birthday—not that she expected anyone to remember. As a final gesture of an innocent past lost forever, Lucy longed to sit in the pew of St. Stephan's Cathedral and hear the familiar words of the one Mass she remembered well.

She quietly slid the drawer back into place and put a scarf over her head as she inched past the bed where Wolf lay sleeping like a guard dog dozing on the threshold.

Her heart beat faster as her coat brushed the side of the bed. *Help me; help me get out, and I will light a candle and—*

Wolf's hand shot up and clamped hard around her wrist, pulling her down to her knees beside him. "Where are you going, little fox?" he asked with a too-sweet voice that betrayed his anger at being awakened.

She cried out with pain at the strength of his grip. "Please, Wolf! You're hurting me!"

"Where are you going at this hour?" He did not reach up to switch on the lamp. He could not see the Mass book she held up in the blackness as proof.

"I . . . I am going to confession! To early Mass!"

"Or have you been somewhere and are just sneaking back into the room?" He twisted her wrist. "Eh? Have you been out with someone?"

"Wolf!" The pain shot up her arm. She thought her wrist would snap. "No, Wolf! I am going to church! To Mass! Turn on the light, and I will show you!"

He hesitated, then switched on the lamp without letting up on the pressure of her wrist. Blinking against the brightness, he peered at the little leather book she continued to hold up like a flag of surrender. A cross, an open Bible, and the communion cup were stamped in gold on the cover. He snatched the book from her free hand as she moaned softly, not trying to argue with him. "Parish Mass Book and Hymnal," he read; then he flipped open a page marked by a red ribbon. He laughed as he read the writing at the top of the page. "St. Lucy. Virgin. Martyr! *Innocence!*" He roared with laughter, released her, and hurled the well-worn book against the wall.

Lucy sat rubbing her wrist in the pool of light as he lay back on his pillow, laughing at the idea of his Lucy sneaking off to honor such a saint!

She did not raise her eyes, but remained, shamed and humiliated, on the floor. "I . . . always go to Mass on this day," she managed to say, although the words nearly choked her.

"Well, you have nothing in common with this dead Catholic, let me tell you!" Lucy had never seen Wolf so amused. "St. Lucy's Day! Virgin!

Martyr! Innocence! Nothing you could claim!"

She felt some desperate need to explain, to stop his ridicule. "It is
. . . my birthday, Wolf. You see . . . I was not trying to . . . I mean, I
know I am not . . . should not go, but every year . . . I have never missed
a year."

He jabbed her under the chin with his thumb, lifting her head with
the painful pressure until her eyes were forced to look at his mocking
smile. "Your birthday is it, St. Lucy? My innocent virgin! My long-
suffering martyr!"

Tears stung her eyes. She held her breath, not wanting to dissolve
into weak emotion in front of him. In one instinct of self-defense, she
slapped his hand away and scrambled to her feet.

"All right! I know what I am—I am the creation of your holy Reich!
I know who I belong to! But I am going to Mass because it is my
birthday. Even whores have birthdays!"

His mouth still curved upward in a smile, but he shrugged and lay
back, surprised at the sudden show of fortitude. He waved a hand as
though brushing away a fly. "Go on, then. You women! All the same.
You and your church! Every prostitute from the highest level in Berlin
to the lowest level in Vienna has a crucifix above her bed."

She picked up the book and moved toward the door. She did not
want to give him even an instant to change his mind and order her
back to bed.

"Be back before eight o'clock!" he shouted after her. "And bring
me a pastry from Demel's on the way back!"

She slammed the door behind her as if she had not heard his words.
Then she ran down the dark stairs and out into the cold, deserted
streets of sleeping Vienna.

———

Lucy was late. She stepped off the nearly empty streetcar on the
opposite side of Stephansplatz and jogged quickly across the slick
cobbles toward the Riesentor, the giant gate. She hoped the entrance
was unlocked. Breathless from running, she threw herself against the
massive doors beneath the first arch. They did not yield. She ran to the
center arch and pushed. Again, the doors resisted her.

It would be a small Mass, Lucy knew. St. Lucy was not a very
important saint, as saints go. *The priest will probably be in some little
side chapel,* she reasoned, running down the stone steps and making
her way to the side and rear of the towering edifice.

Clambering down a flight of steep steps, she pushed against the
tarnished bronze handle of a wooden door. The hinges yielded, opening in welcome. Lucy lunged into the church, and found herself in a
small, nearly deserted niche where a handful of old people knelt to
receive Communion.

The priest did not look at her as he held the host and blessed it, but certainly he must have heard the tardy worshiper clatter in!

Lucy stood rooted, cradling the tiny book in her arms. *Too late! I am too late even for this day!* She knew the words by heart, but she dared not utter them. She had not been to confession; had not laid the hell of her sin before the black-frocked priest who now ministered to the ones who had been on time. *Princes persecute me without cause, but my heart stands in awe of your word. I rejoice at your promise as one who has found rich spoil....*

Yes, Lucy knew the words. She had no need of the Mass book to read from today, but even as she listened, she knew that for her to speak such words was blasphemy! To speak the words of an innocent martyr, unabsolved, would heap more darkness on her soul. Lucy stood in silence. When the priest had passed down the row of kneeling communicants along the altar rail, he looked up at her questioningly.

Lucy simply stared back in confusion and then she hurriedly shook her head and looked toward the door as if to say she had stumbled in by accident. A convincing performance. The priest glanced away toward his early congregation and did not notice Lucy even when she stepped back into the shadows and turned to slip out the way she had entered.

20

Christ Among the Suffering

Names of the missing drifted across the frontiers of Germany first by the hundreds and then by the thousands. Businessmen and scholars, former politicians and clergymen, all had been swallowed up in a single night.

Those in the free world could not hope to discover the fate of all of them; they could only hope to alter the fate of a few.

The list for tonight's TBS broadcast at the BBC in London contained only ten names—German priests and pastors who had been arrested on Kristal Nacht and had not been heard of since. Murphy carefully interviewed anyone who had known these men in the pre-Nazi days in Germany. Each page of the typed script bore a photograph of the missing clergyman and some biographical information, including family members and the possible reason for the arrest.

The program would be beamed from London to Amsterdam and then into the heart of the Reich. If it reached the right ears, perhaps there would be answers.

Two and one half minutes was allotted for each man and his family. An average of thirty seconds per name.

Murphy reread the short descriptions and wondered how it was possible to cram an entire human life into two and a half minutes.

The inner circles in Berlin knew that the original concept of the order came from Reichsmarschall Hermann Göring himself. Göring had no real sympathy for the weak and ineffective German Church, but his sister was quite open about her disapproval of Nazi tactics against the clergymen. Her vocal expressions of that disapproval were an irritation to Göring. At last he decided, *"Anything to shut her up!"*

The case was brought personally to Adolf Hitler with the explanation: *"The foreign press is not as concerned about our treatment of the Jewish question as it is about the crackdown on the clergy. Such a move would also quiet the murmurs from the Vatican."*

The Führer listened and remembered that his own strong resolve was born out of his days in prison. Too much pressure against the German churchmen might, in fact, create a diamond out of a lump of coal.

Based on that conclusion, a plan was formulated and the command was issued from the highest authorities in Berlin.

The smell of pine boughs filled the cold morning air. The clean, sweet aroma cleared Karl's head of the foul odor of nights inside the prison barracks.

Three dozen men worked on the line, stringing thick rolls of barbed wire on the inner perimeter of the compound. Within a week the wire would be electrified, they were told. Even to touch the wire would mean instant death. But for now, bloody hands and nicked clothes were the only penalty they paid.

The layers of wire seemed formidable enough without electricity, Karl thought. Even if a man somehow managed to get past this barrier, two more lay beyond it—not to mention the machine-gun towers above.

He scanned the mile of fence that followed a gentle slope down and then a level stretch for another half mile before the fence turned a corner. The camp was enormous. How could they expect to fill it? Why was it so big, and who were the potential prisoners waiting on the Nazi lists?

Karl looked up at the towering white clouds piling up over Polish territory. In the distance, he could hear the shrill whistle of the German express train as it slipped over the Polish border on its way to the free port of Danzig. Karl hesitated just a moment too long for the young guard who watched him.

"What are you looking at?" the guard demanded. He did not beat Karl, probably because he knew of Karl's vocation. A few Nazis still hesitated to beat a pastor.

"I was listening to the train whistle," Karl answered, as if he were carrying on a normal conversation on a street corner in Berlin.

"A lonely sound," the young dark-haired guard said as he lit a cigarette.

"A lovely sound," Karl contradicted as he returned to his task. "A free sound."

The whistle blew again, and a flock of birds rose up from the trees that bounded the track on the German side. In a spiral swirl they circled and then swept across to the Polish side of the frontier. *The sky has no boundaries,* Karl thought, as he watched and envied their flight.

"Karl!" Richard's voice came as an urgent reprimand, a request that he pay attention to their job. Maybe the guards thought twice about beating Karl, but Richard's bruises were evidence that they did not hesitate at all to club him down for any imagined offense.

Karl looked back, first at the sharp barbs, then at the bloody nicks in Richard's hands. With every drop of blood spilled here at Nameless, Karl thought of crowns made of woven barbed wire and iron spikes driven through innocent hands. The image somehow made this suffering more bearable.

"Karl!" Richard whispered again, raising his eyes for Karl to follow his gaze.

Four soldiers tramped toward them through the mud. Only their eyes seemed visible beneath heavy helmets and warm trenchcoats with the collars turned up. Their eyes were fixed on Pastor Karl Ibsen.

"You are Pastor Karl Ibsen?" asked the fellow with his rifle slung over his shoulder.

Karl did not stop his work, but replied with a silent nod.

"Then you will please come with us." They stepped apart, leaving him room within their inner square.

Richard's eyes met Karl's steady gaze. *So this is it. They intend to shoot you or turn you loose,* Richard seemed to say in that look. "God bless," he whispered as Karl turned away. The soldiers did not hear him, or they would have knocked him down with the butt of a rifle.

The camp commandant of Nameless was a small, waxy-faced man with worried, red-rimmed eyes. No one had ever seen him with his peaked cap off, and now Karl knew why.

The thin, balding head was covered with scabs. Except for the Nazi uniform he wore, the fellow could have easily been mistaken for a prisoner with an advanced case of ringworm or eczema.

He looked through the file marked with the name and number of Pastor Karl Ibsen. He scratched his ear. A dusting of dandruff flocked the shoulders of the proud black uniform.

Karl stood silent before the desk of the little man in an office that was no more than a shack warmed by an iron stove. He did not mind the wait, nor was he intimidated by the shabby little man in the grand uniform. Karl enjoyed the warmth. It was the first time since his arrest that he had felt any warmth penetrate his clothes and body. It made him pleasantly sleepy.

"So." The commandant began at last. "You are Pastor Karl Ibsen of New Church, ja?"

"Pastor Karl Ibsen of Nameless camp." Karl gave a gracious bow.

The officer was not amused. He wanted to get right to the point. His little nose twitched as the warmth of his stove began to awaken the stench of Karl's body.

"It seems there may have been a clerical error."

"Is there such a thing in the Reich?" Karl said, amused, guessing what was coming.

With a wave of his hand the officer dismissed the comment as a jest. He managed a wan smile. "Yes. Well, sometimes even the Reich can make mistakes, given confusion and chaos of rounding up these vermin."

"Vermin?"

"The Jews. The Jews you were arrested with." He cleared his throat and studied the folder again. "It seems that one of the prisoners has reported that you had come to his flat in order to collect a debt he owed you. You were then arrested and brought here. If you are willing to swear to such a thing, you will be released . . . under certain conditions and restrictions, of course."

So, Richard had told his tale. He had lied for the sake of securing Karl's release. "Was the prisoner Richard Kalner?"

"Yes. The former professor. Richard Kalner."

"Where is my wife?" Karl jumped to the question uppermost in his mind. "Helen. My wife?"

"She is also . . . in detention. As is the wife of Richard Kalner. We will see to it that they pay you what you are owed. Jews cannot take advantage of—"

Karl raised a hand, interrupting the officer. "And what about my children? Where are they? Also arrested?"

"Naturally you are concerned." The officer seemed almost solicitous as he scanned the report. "Son, James, taken to Hitler Youth school in Berlin. Daughter, Lori . . . at large." His lower lip protruded as he said it again. "At large. Still . . . somewhere. Possibly with relatives?"

Karl did not reply. Each beloved face came up before him now as he considered his choices. And what were those choices? "You mentioned certain conditions and restrictions."

"Yes. I have been instructed to inform you that this is a simple matter, really. You simply sign a paper saying that you have been well treated and that you will not slander the Reich. Your future sermons must be submitted to the local authorities for censorship. No different than every other church in the Reich nowadays."

"And may I preach from any part of the Scripture that I feel led to?"

The officer laughed. Karl Ibsen surely was joking again. "Within the established guidelines of the State Church, you know."

"And what about those in my congregation who are of Jewish heritage?"

"Well?" The officer became suddenly impatient. What sort of foolish question was this? "What do you think? If just going into a house to collect a debt got you arrested, then what do you think?"

Karl did not have to think hard. "I want a public hearing," he said coolly. "I am a citizen of Deutschland, and I request a public hearing."

"But . . . you are . . . I am telling you—" He held out the slip of paper that Karl was to sign. *Good treatment. . . . Do not hold the Reich responsible. . . .* "There can be no hearing, you see. If you sign this, you are free to go." He smiled hopefully. "All you must do is denounce your associations with these Jews, and you are as free as any man in Germany."

"I was at the home of Richard and Leona Kalner because I owed *them* a debt."

The commandant laughed with relief. So that was what this was all about! "You do not know the laws? No Aryan owes any debt to a Jew. Your debts and my debts to the Jewish moneylenders are all erased, a gift from our Führer to the German people! So . . . it was all a mistake. You went there to pay this swine, and . . . well, here you are."

"Not that kind of debt." Karl looked at the man with pity. Here was a creature who could be purchased by the Führer's laws.

"Debt. You did say you owed him a debt."

"The debt that love requires of all men; the debt that demands that we do good to others, not harm; that we not look the other way when the innocent are persecuted. I owe them much more than money. I owe my life."

The eyes of the scabby little man hardened. He understood, and the words of Pastor Karl Ibsen convicted him. He did not like it. "What about your family?"

Again and again this terrible question had played in his mind. *What about Helen? What about Lori and Jamie?* Should he go against everything he knew was right for their sake? Would they hate him for staying here to minister as one dying man to other dying men?

"I love my family," he said.

"Then sign."

To sign was a denial of the Christ he served. Karl trembled as he considered it; he longed to take the pen and sign his name and walk out of hell.

"Jesus died for my family. Should I not be willing to die for His children?"

"You are a fool." The pinched face grew more pinched. High moral issues disgusted him. Life and death were enough to deal with every day. "You can return to your home in time for church next Sunday, your wife and children at your side."

"I will spend my Sunday here," Karl said softly, "where Christ dwells among the suffering."

After a moment of hesitation, a rubber stamp slammed across the unsigned paper. "You are dismissed, prisoner Ibsen."

———————

Sunday morning. Each week on this day, the emptiness of New Church haunted Lori. The colored glass of the high windows made patterns on the empty pews. Iron pegs in the wall where the Nazis had torn down the wooden cross seemed marked with blood-red reflections from the rose window.

The pews where row on row of families had stood together in praise and worship were empty. Papa was not in the pulpit, Mama not at the organ. No song. No Bible readings. No request for prayers of healing. Healing people. Or healing this broken land.

Jamie knew what Lori was feeling. He came to sit beside her in the choir loft. Together they smiled down at the memories that crowded the vacant sanctuary. He took her hand and they hummed softly, "A Mighty Fortress Is Our God."

First Mark came and sat behind them, then Jacob. Jacob sang the words of the song, although his voice was off-key. Lori smiled. She had always loved listening to Jacob's voice. She had pretended not to notice two years ago when it had croaked and cracked and eventually slidden into manhood. It was wonderful to hear him sing; she would not tease him as she used to.

"Where do you suppose Papa is?" Jamie asked when the song was finished.

"Your father?" Jacob said, voice echoing into the rafters. "Maybe we don't know where he is, but I can tell you what he is doing."

Jacob was right. Pastor Karl Ibsen would be preaching or praying on this day, no matter where he was, no matter what they did to him.

"And your father will be helping the sick," Lori said, turning to face Jacob with a tender look. She caught him off guard.

Jacob nodded. Frowning against the emotion, he stuck out his lower lip. "I hope . . . they are *together*," he managed to whisper. "We should pray for them, especially today, I think."

The congregation of four joined hands, and for a moment the empty pews of New Church seemed full again.

———————

Snow fell throughout the day, covering all of Vienna with the illusion of peace.

The charred remains of synagogues and shops lay concealed beneath a cold, white shroud. Jagged heaps of dynamited walls took on soft, smooth contours, easing the memories and consciences of those who passed by. It seemed as though no great synagogues had ever stood in the city. After the fires of Kristal Nacht died away, nature completed the eradication begun by the Nazis. Already the Reich and the world beyond had begun to forget.

Only the trapped, the imprisoned, the hopeless seemed to remember clearly the terrible vision of what the future held for the Jews of Germany.

Peter pulled the collar of his coat close around his chin. The north wind spit freezing flakes against his cheeks and obscured the end of the street in a white, swirling veil. It seemed the safest time to check on their home.

He tucked his hands deep into his pockets as he trudged past the boarded-up shop of old Frau Singer. Other pedestrians darted into buildings for shelter. Automobiles pulled to the curbs, leaving the streets nearly empty except for an electric streetcar that rumbled by. The car was nearly full of bundled-up passengers, and another half-dozen people waited at the corner ahead of him. Stamping cold feet, they glared impatiently toward the approaching car. A placard above each door proclaimed clearly, *Juden Verboten!* Even if he had the fare, Peter could not ride it. He looked away as it stopped for passengers. Pretending not to notice or care, he hurried past, envying the closeness and warmth of the Aryans inside it.

He traced the steps he had taken to the Fishers' apartment during Kristal Nacht. Nearly every shop window on this street was boarded over. Heaps of rubble still blocked parts of the sidewalk.

Peter looked up to the window from which the old man and his wife had been thrown. He shuddered, more from the memory than from the bitter cold. Then, with that image fresh in his mind, he hesitated at the corner, afraid of what he would find on the street where he had grown up.

Where once organ grinders, peddlers, and beggars had strolled beneath the facades of the stores and houses and long blocks of flats, there was only silence, emptiness. He shook his head, reprimanding himself for expecting to see friends and neighbors instead of planks and cardboard nailed across shop fronts. He told himself that no sensible person would be out on a day like this, that people still lived behind the boards which shut out the light from their homes and businesses. And yet the old neighborhood, once so alive in the shadow of the Turnergasse Synagogue, seemed haunted and strangely eerie.

He could not make out his own apartment building through the billows of snow. He hoped the windows of their apartment had been boarded over. He wondered about his collection of books. Boxes of novels and volumes of history had been donated to him by fleeing friends. Had they survived intact? He longed for a good book. The world could fall apart and Peter would not notice as long as he had his books to read.

Quickening his pace, he strained to see. Thoughts of his little library drove away fear. Suddenly nothing seemed as important as knowing the fate of those books. For half a block he did not think about the friends he had watched being herded onto the Gestapo prisoner lorries. For two hundred paces he was warmed by the memory of summer evenings with a novel open on his lap as he had looked out over this teeming street from the window of his bedroom. *Children playing, women gossiping below as they leaned on their brooms....* Life had gone on even after the Nazis had come. But now . . .

Automatically, he looked up at the telephone wire where the ragged tail of Marlene's kite still dangled. He had laughed at her when the warm winds had stolen the kite from her. She had stood in the street and wailed as Herr Temko rushed from his confectionery shop to console her with a piece of hard candy. Had that been only six months ago?

The remains of the kite flapped, tangled up on the wire, smashed and broken and torn to pieces—a grim reflection of the broken lives below.

Peter stopped mid-stride and gasped as his own building came into view. Only two charred walls remained of what had been a three-story apartment building. The window that had been his room gaped open with the harsh white sky behind it.

There was nothing to go home to. Almost the entire block was destroyed. Perhaps no one was left alive behind the boarded windows, after all. Perhaps those who had not fled or been captured were now ashes, like the books. Peter shook his head. *Ashes!*

Why had he not filled his pockets with the books, saved something at least? But he had not known, had not believed that it could come to this. No one was left from Turnergasse. Maybe no Jews were left at all in Vienna.

———

Shivering in the cold, Lucy walked slowly past the Hofgarten greenhouses near the Imperial Palace. She dug her hands deep into her pockets and tucked her chin down inside the collar of her coat.

Through the glass she could see the gardeners busy at work on plants that would be placed in flower gardens throughout the city. Sometime in March, the people of Vienna would go to bed on a winter's night and wake up to an instant spring. The world would bloom without anyone being aware of how it happened. Lucy had watched them planting the bulbs in the Rathaus Park—red tulip bulbs, a bent little man had explained to her. When they bloomed they would match the flags of the Reich. Hitler himself had imagined it and had given the command for a million bulbs to be brought in from Holland. It was likely to be a very pretty sight indeed, Lucy thought, and one she hoped to miss. By then, she would be somewhere else—far away from the gardens of the Imperial city. Soon afterward, she would have a baby to hold in her arms.

It all seemed like a distant dream, and yet, as she touched her stomach through the lining of her coat, it seemed frighteningly real as well. A little someone to feed and clothe and care for. Lucy shuddered with cold and fear. She needed money. She needed a miracle.

It was a short walk from her office in the Rathaus to the six-story baroque building at Number 17 Dorotheergasse. Taking up an entire city block, the structure housed one of the world's largest last-resort banks for the financially desperate of Austria. First established by a Hapsburg emperor to benefit impoverished subjects, the place had stood since 1707 as the only government pawnbroker and auction house in Europe. Clients could present almost anything as collateral for a loan and walk out with at least enough cash to purchase bread for a day. Hitler, rumor said, might have starved to death without this service. Mozart had been a frequent visitor between symphonies.

The name clearly set in stone above the broad double doors read *DOROTHEUM*. The Viennese called the place *"Tante Dorothee"*—Aunt Dorothy—as if it were a benevolent relative they could occasionally tap for financial assistance. This sense of kindness and familiarity had been driven from the place, however, by the new Nazi overseers.

Desperate Jews arrived at the door with the wealth of their worldly goods. They left with only a small fraction of the actual worth. Diamonds, furs, precious paintings, and antique furniture all disappeared, swallowed down the maw of the Reich's financial need.

In her handbag Lucy carried her grandmother's silver crucifix, the only thing she owned of any real value. It seemed a small matter to part with it when she considered the value of what she carried within her.

Lucy looked to her right and saw a beautiful grand piano, upended and wheeled through a freight door. How many times had she heard Wolf speak of the bargains he had bought here at the auctions? Everything had been shipped back to his home in Prussia, she assumed, just as he would try to ship her baby back to Prussia. Precious things vanished easily in the Reich nowadays.

She squared her shoulders and walked in, careful not to look anyone else straight in the eye. Austrian police stood guard in the foyer, their uniforms unchanged from the pre-Hitler days—with the exception of a swastika armband that branded them as loyal servants of the Führer. To her right, a guard sat at a large desk munching a bratwurst sandwich. *INFORMATION* read the placard beside his thermos bottle.

She felt suddenly nervous as she approached him. Fingering her handbag, she did not speak until he swallowed a big mouthful and looked up at her. His expression communicated impatience for her to get on with it so he could finish his lunch.

"Bitte?" she asked hesitantly as she gestured toward the long corridor with dozens of doors opening to each side. "I have something . . . to sell." She fingered her handbag and smiled nervously.

"Everyone who comes here has something to sell, Fräulein." He wiped his mouth on a clean linen napkin. "And everyone has something to buy, we say here. So. Where may I direct you? You have a piano in your handbag? Or maybe a radio?"

"No. A . . . this . . ." She pulled out the velvet-wrapped crucifix and showed him one end of the gleaming silver.

He seemed unimpressed. "I don't know. Fine arts, maybe. Or religious artifacts?" He shrugged. "Up the stairs to the appraisers. They will know best. Two flights up." He returned to his sandwich, and Lucy climbed the marble stairs to the offices of the appraisers.

The office for the Appraiser of Religious Artifacts was the first door to the left of the stairs. Lucy entered, surprised that no one was there except the appraiser himself, who busily scrutinized the gold work on an eight-branched menorah. Behind him on a desk lay dozens of such items, Jewish treasures, Lucy assumed. Were they sold for their weight in gold and silver, she wondered? If so, her crucifix seemed small in comparison.

She bit her lip and closed her eyes for a moment, asking forgiveness for what she was about to do. There was no other way. To sell the watch Wolf had given her would invite his wrath.

Lucy held the handbag against her heart and waited for the little man to finish his investigation. He glanced up at her, startled to see that someone had come into the room.

"Bitte." He laid down his magnifying glass and smiled, revealing a row of gold-capped teeth that would no doubt be worth a fortune at the Dorotheum. "I did not know anyone had joined me." He cleared his throat. "Lovely, is it not?" There was, Lucy thought, a hint of sadness in his voice as he gestured toward the menorah. "From a fine Austrian family." He shrugged, as if to dare her to disagree. "The authorities wanted to melt it down. But it is worth much more than the metal." Rubbing a hand over his bald head, he shrugged again. "I have been here a long time. So? How can I help you, Fräulein?"

Lucy stared hard at the candelabra and then at the rows of tagged artifacts behind the appraiser. "I want . . . to sell . . ." She faltered. She did not want to sell the crucifix. "I *must* sell . . ." She started to open the handbag and then stopped and pulled up the sleeve of her sweater to reveal the Swiss watch. A few seconds ticked off. "This watch. Where do I find the appraiser for watches, please?"

The old man looked relieved. Certainly he had the saddest of all appraisal positions in the Dorotheum these days.

"Ah. Good. You have walked up one flight of stairs too many, I'm afraid. Next floor down. End of the corridor."

Lucy did not need to lie to the watch appraiser, but she lied anyway. "Money to send home to my parents in Bavaria."

It made no difference to him why she needed money. He simply considered the collateral and determined how much it might bring at auction. "Three hundred marks is the retail value," he informed her. "A very fine timepiece, but we have many fine watches coming in every day." He himself was from Bavaria, his accent like that of everyone Lucy knew from Munich. She commented on the fine clocks made there, and he smiled appreciatively. "For a citizen of the Reich, I am authorized to lend one-third of the value."

Lucy frowned and sat back in real disappointment. Was it worth facing Wolf for a mere twenty-five dollars? "That is not very good." She looked searchingly into his eyes. "My parents . . . you see . . . they are in desperate need of funds."

"Well then, if you sell it, I can offer you two-thirds of the price. If it brings more than that at auction, we deduct our fees and you get the rest."

"Yes," she agreed instantly. "Two hundred marks is good." It was not as good as Lucy had hoped, but she placed the sum in her handbag with the crucifix and hurried happily back to work. It was a start, anyway. And if the situation became truly desperate, she still had the cross that she could take back to the sad-eyed man at the Dorotheum.

In the meantime, however, she would have to think of a way to explain the missing watch to Wolf.

21

One Righteous Man

The envelope arrived through the mail slot of Red Lion House right along with the regular mail. From the outside it seemed harmless. Elisa, Charles, and Louis paid no attention to the large brown envelope sandwiched in with two letters from Leah Feldstein in Jerusalem. Nothing seemed quite as important as Leah's letters that arrived on the regular mail ships from Palestine twice a week.

Elisa opened them right away and read out loud. She skipped over some parts, but shared the most exciting stories with Charles and Louis. *It is not as bad in Jerusalem as you might be hearing. Be sure to take the news about Muslim riots with a grain of salt, because living with a newspaper man you should know how things are exaggerated to sell papers!*

This kind of jibe, directed at Murphy, made Elisa laugh. Things really were bad in Palestine, but at least Leah could still joke about it. Letters from Leah were the best part of the week. *God never promised us that life would be without difficulties,* Leah wrote, *but He did promise that we will overcome them as He has.* Such words of encouragement like these made all of them nod their heads and say again that no matter what happened, the best news yet was that they would all be in heaven together for sure!

Such words made Charles think about Mother and Father. It made him wish he could hurry and be with them, too. Sometimes he felt as if he were trying to straddle a creek—one foot in heaven and the other foot here with all the new people he loved. He missed Leah very much, and thought of her in the Promised Land the way he thought of Mama and Father in heaven—except that Leah was able to write letters from Jerusalem. He wished his parents could also write letters from heaven. He asked Jesus to give them little messages since there was no post office in heaven.

When Elisa finished, Charles and Louis asked her to read the part again about Shimon cracking walnuts in Tipat Chalev with his plaster cast. They liked hearing about the way Jewish boys could go to their own schools and there were no Nazis to beat them up or make them get out. It was good to know that the same English uniforms Charles and Louis saw on the soldiers around London were also right in Jerusalem, protecting boys and girls from the Arabs who liked Hitler. *Better than that,* Leah added, *we are all part of God's kingdom. One family. One nation in His eyes. The people who want to destroy the world for their own reasons will find in the end that darkness must always fall back in retreat when there is light—even the light of one tiny candle! Each of us must fight the darkness in our own way. Some are soldiers who struggle against force. Some are preachers who raise their voices. Some pray. Some play music of praise. Shimon and I fight by simply remaining here in Jerusalem. God promised that we Jews would return to the land. Our battle is to believe His words and stay put, even though the Arabs would like to drive us back to the sea. . . .*

Louis asked Elisa to read all of Leah's words. But Charles did not need to know everything. He clung tightly to the words of hope she sent to them in London. *We will win! We will make it! Don't worry or be afraid!*

All of this seemed to be written just for Charles, because sometimes he wondered if they would win. And he *was* afraid!

He drew pictures of the house on Red Lion Square and put his smiling face beside that of Louis in the crooked crayon windows. Leah would be able to tell which face was Charles and which was Louis because there was still a line marking the scar on Charles's mouth. That scar worried him lately; his imperfection frightened him. After all, that scar made him different and hated in Germany. Because of his mouth, his father and mother had died. He thought about that a lot, and only Leah's letters made him feel better. Somehow he, too, wanted to fight the darkness, but the darkness felt too strong for him. He did not talk about these things, but they rose up in him every day as he struggled to learn to speak. The fears were with him when he smiled and someone's eyes flitted down to the pink scar and then back to his eyes.

Elisa gave each of the boys one of Leah's letters to hold. They studied the stamp from this faraway part of the United Kingdom. Part of the same empire as London, but so very far away!

And then, just as she had done every day, Elisa divided up the remaining mail between the boys and they helped her open it. Charles slit the big brown envelope, and the darkness came into the room and flooded over him, driving away the good words of Leah, making him remember in one quick glance the things they had run from.

Color drained from his cheeks. His eyes were riveted to the picture that was only half out of the envelope.

"Charles?" Elisa took the envelope from his limp hands. She gasped, and pain filled her expression. "Dear God," she said, tossing the envelope across the table and gathering Charles up in her arms. "Oh, Charles! Charles! Who would send us such a thing?" She began to cry. She buried her face against Charles's shoulder and repeated his name again and again.

Louis had not seen the black-and-white image of the man nailed to the planks, and yet his face, too, reflected fear and grief. Elisa did not stop crying. Charles stared away out the window. It was very bad, this picture, whatever it was.

Louis ran to the telephone and rang up Murphy at the office.

————

The S.S. commandant called Karl out from the long lines of prisoners. "You have a visitor," he announced loudly.

A ripple passed through the ranks of men. No one had visitors. Such things were not permitted, unless . . .

"They will work on him," said the atheist. "He will go over to them. You will see."

He muttered the words at great risk. Others also whispered among themselves. The guards must have heard, yet they did not beat the convicts for resenting Karl Ibsen.

Karl marched off, surrounded by four guards, to the office of the commandant. Richard watched as the striped uniform entered the office. "He will be back. You will see. He is the only righteous man I know."

————

Even with his eyes closed, Karl would have recognized the Rev. Gustav Dorfman by the scent of his hair pomade. Today, in preparation for this visit, Dorfman had groomed himself a bit more heavily than usual.

The distinguished pastor of the First Lutheran Church in Berlin was handsome, in a posed sort of way. In his late forties, he was tall and thin, his suits always tailored to meticulous perfection. His wavy gray hair was always neatly trimmed, always in place. This afternoon was no different.

Dorfman was well known within the church long before Hitler came to power. Widely recognized and respected as a man of God, his mellow, fluid, convincing voice packed the pews of Germany's largest Lutheran church every Sunday. Karl knew him on a handshake basis only. He had not been surprised when Dorfman had been among the first churchmen to join the Nazi movement as the wave of the future, declaring National Socialist doctrine as "the hand of God to punish evil."

Dorfman did not offer to shake Karl's grimy hand. It was just as well, Karl thought. Dorfman waved the guards from the room and indicated where Karl should sit. This man expected respect and received it in some measure from those who followed his teaching. Karl, beneath the filth and stench of his ordeal, viewed this shallow, empty man with pity rather than respect. Some of the men in the bunks of Barrack 7 grasped more knowledge of the Scriptures than this self-proclaimed spiritual leader. The young atheist who had wept at the thought of the Lord's tears had infinitely more spiritual depth.

However, Karl was glad for the chance to sit down in the warmth. No doubt the Nazis who respected Dorfman's authority and the size of his congregation also believed that Karl would respect a clergyman as prominent as this.

Dorfman took the chair farthest from Karl. He smiled. Perfect teeth gleamed. Manicured nails drummed the table.

"Well, Pastor Ibsen. Karl?" The voice was smooth. "Tell me why you are here."

"I was ordered to report to the office," Karl replied. "I assume it is to speak with you."

The perfect smile twitched. Was Karl playing a game? "No, what I mean to ask is, why were you arrested? And why are you still here in prison?"

Karl cut to the heart of the matter. "I was arrested when I attempted to help my friends . . . my brothers."

"And who are these brothers? You can't mean the Jews?"

"There are others as well, also brothers. But, yes, I suppose I am arrested for standing for the rights of Jewish Germans."

The phrase *Jewish-Germans* sparked resentment in Dorfman. Jews were Jews in his eyes, and Germans were Aryans. He had been asserting that since his seminary days. "Karl," he said in a patronizing voice, "aside from the fact that the Jews have been scientifically proven to be subhuman, was it not the Jews who killed Christ?"

It was a trivial, ridiculous argument, laughable in its ignorance if it were not so dangerous and deadly. The reply came not from Karl but from the scripture verses he had memorized on his sixteenth birthday. *"Then the governor's soldiers took Jesus into the Praetorium and gathered the whole company of soldiers around him. They stripped him and put a scarlet robe on him, and then twisted together a crown of thorns and set it on his head. They put a staff in his right hand and knelt in front of him and mocked him. 'Hail, king of the Jews, they said.' "*

Karl paused for a moment to respond to the astonished look on Dorfman's face. "These were Roman soldiers. You may check if you doubt me. Matthew, chapter twenty-seven. *They spit on Him and took the staff and struck Him on the head again and again. After they had mocked Him, they took off the robe and put His own clothes on Him.*

Then they led Him away to crucify Him."

Karl managed a slight smile. "Sound familiar? Easter service. Seems to me that the death of the Lord was the reason He came to this earth. I know you discount the Old Testament Scriptures, but Isaiah 53 speaks of the Messiah being offered for the sins of all mankind. Not just Jews—even pure Aryans like you may be saved, a free gift from the greatest Jew who ever lived."

Dorfman's face clouded with resentment. How dare this filthy criminal quote scripture to him, a leader of the State Church! So this was the result when renegade Protestants strayed from church doctrine.

He pulled up his seminary teaching to counter this heresy. "The church leaders believed the Jews should be slaves to Christians. Martin Luther himself—"

"Is a sad example of the reality of human fallibility. Speak to me through the Scripture and we will have a match, Reverend Dorfman, but please do not quote Martin Luther to me. Or Saint Augustine. Or any of the rest. By now those men know how badly they erred. When the Day of the Lord comes, I do not want to be found quoting them."

The Rev. Gustav Dorfman called in the guards to return Karl to his rightful place among the sinners and tax gatherers of the Reich. Perhaps he would come again one day, but he had not been prepared to meet such a skillful adversary.

"You are still with us, preacher," called up the young atheist from below Karl's bunk. "What did you meet in there today?"

Karl sighed. "I met a man who was wearing the robes of a great religious leader when Jesus came to Jerusalem. He saw the Lord and hated Him because Jesus was truly righteous."

The young man called up to Richard, "What is he saying?"

Richard did not reply. He rolled over and fixed his dark eyes on Karl. "Tell him what you mean, Pastor Karl," he said.

"I mean that the religious leaders who crucify the Lord exist in every generation. They have been present in every age. I met a man today I can only pity. In the end his suffering will be much deeper than ours."

The mocking tone was tempered by the edge of sadness in Karl's voice.

"And yet you tell us that God loves even a man like that," said the atheist. "Even the Nazis He loves, you say?"

Karl considered the challenge. It was a real question, worthy of reply. Could a just God care even for evil men? "He sees them as they will be if they don't repent, Johann. He pities them. Remember your verse, 'Jesus wept.'"

Winston Churchill looked more like a bulldog than ever. His lower lip protruded angrily as he scowled down at the photograph on the coffee table in front of him. He picked it up by the corner and then let it fall back again.

"It is good to see the sort of men we are dealing with," he growled under his breath to Murphy. "I shall take this image with me into battle at the House of Commons."

Murphy passed him a long list containing the names of prominent men and women arrested in Germany on the night of November 9. Included on that list was the name of Anna's sister and members of the Ibsen family. The list had been enclosed with the photograph of Thomas von Kleistmann. The implication was clear: the same sort of horrible death awaited those people who opposed Hitler unless they could be ransomed and released. Some names were already crossed off, killed by the Gestapo or yielded to Nazi pressure. Others were checked with a note that read:

FAMILIES OF THESE PRISONERS ARE ALSO MISSING. SPOUSES AND CHILDREN ARE HELD RESPONSIBLE FOR THE CRIMES OF RELATIVES AND SUBJECT TO THE SAME PUNISHMENT AS THE "GUILTY."

This long list, obviously taken directly from secret Gestapo files, had been sent to John Murphy at great risk to whoever had sent it. The photograph had not been intended to harm Elisa or the children, but to warn Murphy. The envelope was addressed to Murphy. It was not meant to be seen by anyone but him and those he trusted.

Churchill sighed and shook his head. Such a sight made even the Old Lion speechless. "Is the little boy all right?" He imagined the terror of a six-year-old in seeing such a thing.

"Charles has seen too much already." Murphy spread his hands in a gesture of helplessness. "There are a million Jewish and Christian Charleses living through this kind of thing, Winston, the children of men who are willing to die for the right even though nobody on this side of the line seems to care." He stared at the image of Thomas and suddenly felt sorry that they had never met. "They must have someplace to go. *Now.* No more talk. It is too late for talking." He slammed his fist down on the list. "Here is the picture of reality. This is the evil England is making peace with!"

Winston Churchill's eyes brimmed with emotion and resolve. "Bring Charles to the debate in Commons. For the sake of the ones he left behind, he must hear the final debate on the refugee question in Palestine. Even if we do not win, Murphy, one child must be a witness to his generation that we did battle against this blinding darkness."

———

This time Wolf was not late to Cafe Sacher. Lucy kept him waiting—

not too long, only five minutes; but she made certain that her entrance was noticed. She did not look toward their corner table as she swept into the room. She played to the eyes of other men, certain that Wolf would notice their interest as well.

He stood and pulled out her chair. His face displayed his jealousy as he resumed his place and finished off the wine in his glass.

"You are late!" he snapped.

She displayed her empty wrist. "The catch on my watch broke. I lost it today somewhere on the Ringstrasse."

"Lost it!" he leaned forward. "That was a very good watch! Expensive."

"Not good enough, or it would not have broken."

"You will not get another one."

"Then I will be late, won't I, Wolf?" She could see that she was having an effect on him. His tanned complexion reddened with anger toward her. She knew she must be very careful in her game. "I thought of you . . . of who I belong to . . . and when I looked at my wrist, the watch was simply gone." She shrugged. "I was disappointed, of course. But you see, I think of you even without it, Wolf."

At this, he softened a bit. The hard line of his mouth curved up at the corner as he pondered her compliment. "Then you do not need another one."

"I need nothing at all to remind me," her voice was soft as she leaned in toward him and touched the back of his hand. "After all, I carry a little Wolf inside me."

At this, his indignation vanished entirely. She had played her cards well and he rewarded her with his approval. "In that case, maybe you should have a new watch so you will never again keep *this* Wolf waiting, ja? I got the other from an old Jew on Franz Josefs Kai. He was selling out. Said it was the finest. He was lying, no doubt, and I would have him arrested—"

"Will you?" She tried not to let her concern show as he directed his anger to the old Jew who sold him the watch. Would her lie cause the arrest of an innocent man?

"The fellow is already arrested. Rotting away somewhere."

"Because of me?" She was horrified.

He laughed. "Such concern, Lucy! No. The fellow was accused of trying to smuggle diamonds, I think. Something like that. A fabricated charge, but reason enough for his entire stock to be Aryanized. I could have gotten your watch for nothing had I seen it coming." He poured himself more wine. "That will teach me to trust a Jew."

Lucy's conscience was relieved. She had not been the cause of an old man's arrest. Of course, the old fellow was in prison anyway, no matter what the reason. Still, Lucy decided she would be more careful about her lies to Wolf. She sat silently, feigning interest as he continued his monologue of hatred against the Jews of Vienna.

"They are worse here than in Germany, as a rule. At least at home they acted the part of German citizens. I had not thought much about them at home. But here in Vienna! It is no wonder the Führer hates them so. They laughed at him when he was a hungry student in this place, and now he is laughing at them." The waiter placed onion soup before them. He inhaled the aroma and then cautiously took a spoonful. He might as well have been talking to himself, but Lucy continued to hold him with her gaze, to nod and smile at all the right pauses. She had learned to be the perfect audience. "Some fellow in the Gestapo is tipping them off, we think. We come to the door of a prominent Jew and find that he has slipped out the back the night before. Several rich ones have gotten away. Who knows what they have smuggled out with them? Himmler has taken the case away from the Gestapo and put it into my hands. I will find him, whoever he is."

"Well then, you will gain another rank before the baby is born," she said brightly, flattering his dreams of glory.

"Yes. Yes. That is true." He sipped another spoonful of soup. "I have narrowed the field down to half a dozen." His eyes narrowed as he pictured the suspects and savored the flavor of an arrest. "Himmler says that ruthlessness is a quality to be admired when duty calls for it. And so I will cultivate that. Himmler will notice such a thing. Not even friendship matters compared to the good of the Reich." He directed his preoccupied gaze to Lucy as if he had just noticed her presence across from him. "You see how important this is to me." The eyes hardened. "You would not ever betray me, lie to me. Would you, little fox?"

She managed an indignant laugh. They had discussed this before. Wolf was not speaking of political betrayal or loyalty to the Nazi cause. "No man could come close to you," she replied coyly. "Here, I promote you! You do not need to arrest any traitors to please me. I promote you to general of my bed. No, field marshal! Or, more true, you are my führer, the leader of my country, Wolf."

He relaxed a bit, sitting back and swirling the deep red wine in his glass. "I did not like the way men looked at you when you came in."

"I cannot help how they look."

"Or the way you looked at them."

She shrugged. "Soon enough men will look at me and say, there goes another mother for the Reich!" She patted her stomach. "They can look all they like, and I will still be pregnant with your child."

"When you begin to show, then you go to the Lebensborn," he announced sternly, though seemingly satisfied with her reply. She had managed to fend off the attack once again.

Lucy considered the warning and the growing life within her that would soon enough lead to her own imprisonment at Lebensborn. The thought of gaining weight made her cautious about eating. She only nibbled at the vegetables and did not eat the roast at all. And tonight, for the first time ever, she refused even a taste of Sachertorte.

Homemade British leaflets in support of the immigration of child refugees dominated the conversation over dinner at the Führer's table. BBC broadcast appeals to the British people had brought minimal public response, and the Führer was convinced that the hypocrisy of the English leaders ran in the grain of the common people. No one wanted a homeless, filthy tribe of paupers invading their cities and homes. This effort, he insisted pleasantly, would fail like all the others.

"The voice of dissent is always stronger than the voice of weak Christian charity. And this is what makes our race strong. We are the only people on earth who are not swayed by the weakness of this false mercy. Let the English talk and weep and plead! Those idiots! What is the difference?"

Himmler picked at his vegetables and remarked, "It is a pity we have emptied out the insane asylums, yes? We might have sent them ten thousand imbeciles in answer to their leaflets!"

The guests laughed at the idea. "Let the English hypocrites see how far their mercy extends when it comes to drooling idiots, eh, Himmler?"

It was too late to speculate on such a marvelous practical joke. The do-gooders did not seem to have room for healthy children, let alone inferior ones. The German institutions had been cleaned out, but it would have been a great joke to send over a batch of imbeciles and cripples to these whining English nannies.

There was, of course, a slim possibility that some British aid might be extended to refugee children. If that was the case, Himmler said sternly, steep fines would be levied on the parents of such children and they would leave the Reich without so much as one mark tucked into their shoes!

This information would no doubt slow the beating hearts of compassion and silence the criticism. Mercy would put on a more practical face and show up this sentimental nonsense for what it was.

The Führer based his actions on the basic premise that all men were equally motivated by greed and selfishness. This time would be no different.

Joseph, cat of many colors, was sick. He did not eat his sardine. He lay curled on his blanket in the corner and watched Alfie, who watched him back unhappily. Joseph panted when he breathed and made his mouth into silent meows of pain.

Alfie was afraid. He hugged his knees and studied Joseph in the candlelight. It looked as if the lid was closing on his furry friend. The long soft tail flicked nervously. Joseph did not move his tail like that unless he was unhappy. Things were very bad tonight.

Twice more Alfie laid the sardine beside Joseph, but the cat looked away. It was no use dragging the ruby necklace across the floor. Joseph did not want to play. He would not pounce on it or smile his cat smile at Alfie.

"Don't die," Alfie moaned. "Please, Joseph. Everyone here is dead but you and me. Please get well, Joseph." Then he reached his hand out to pet Joseph, but the cat growled at him and showed his teeth. He did not want to be touched. He only wanted to lie there and hurt while Alfie watched him sadly.

22

Life Amid the Gravestones

From the bell tower of New Church, Mark and Jamie could clearly see the brown-clad workmen as they drove the posts into the soil of the flower bed outside the iron gate.

"What does it say?" Jamie squinted and tried to make out the lettering of the sign.

"It is the same as the one in front of the synagogue, I think," said Mark. "So now we know why they wanted to close your father's church."

"But Papa told them he liked New Church where it was." Jamie remembered the day his father had been approached by government officials with an offer to relocate New Church and build a big new building. "Papa told them that New Church was not so big and maybe not new anymore, but that it had stood through two hundred years of storms, and he would not move." Jamie frowned. "They did not like it."

"So they got it anyway." Mark read the sign.

ACHTUNG! ATTENTION! A GLORIOUS NEW CENTER OF GERMAN CULTURE WILL BE CONSTRUCTED ON THIS SITE, BY ORDER OF THE MINISTER OF THE INTERIOR. TRESPASSING FORBIDDEN. HEIL HITLER!

"You suppose that is why they arrested Papa?" Jamie wondered aloud. "And why they burned the synagogue, too?"

"Your papa was arrested because of us," Mark replied impatiently. "Because we're Jews. And the Nazis burned the Temple for the same reason. If they want a house or a church or a store or a whole city, they don't ask anybody. They just take it. That is what my father said the day they arrested him. They wanted our fathers because they are friends. The church doesn't have anything to do with it."

When the public works truck drove off, the boys clambered down the spiral steps, relieved that they could report no one left within earshot. But Lori and Jacob were already arguing in the basement over what was left of their food supplies.

"Once I even thought I liked you," Jacob tossed a can of tinned beef down with a clatter. "Now I see you are the most stubborn girl who ever lived."

"And you are nothing but a bully! It is no wonder you got into a fight every time you walked into the street! You can't even get along with—"

"With *you*? Ha! *Impossible!* I wish I had taken Mark and run the opposite direction!"

Mark and Jamie exchanged looks of disgust. This sort of discussion had become a daily occurrence—whispered anger followed by steely silence between Lori and Jacob. Jacob thought he should be the boss. Lori argued with him about everything from sleeping arrangements to how much each person should eat each day in order to preserve their food supply. After all, she reasoned, she had been the one to discover the case of meat tins.

"We cannot go on forever." Jacob sat down hard on an empty wooden crate. "You think that night watchman isn't going to come inside some night and catch us by surprise?"

"Not with all your drilling!" Lori exclaimed.

"You want to stay here for the rest of our lives?" Jacob grabbed Mark by the sleeve of his sweater and pulled him close as if choosing sides for a battle.

"And if we leave, where will we go?" Lori demanded.

"Prague, where your father said we should go all along! There are people there. That pastor he knows. I say we get out of the church!" Jacob was adamant.

Lori gestured at the tin of beef and the boxes of communion wafers. "But we can make it last another month if we're careful."

Jamie looked at the boxes of flavorless wafers and grimaced. "Breakfast, lunch, and dinner," he said mournfully. "And besides, we can't—"

Lori interrupted him. "My mother and father will certainly be released by then. How would they know where to find us?"

"We can sneak out the basement window," Jamie interjected.

"Brilliant." Lori silenced him with a dark look. "Doors and windows chained and padlocked. The Nazi seal across every door. Sneak out the window and go where?"

"Prague, I'm telling you!" Jacob shouted, arguing over the heads of Mark and Jamie.

"We are safer here!" Lori insisted.

"No . . ." Mark began, trying to tell Jacob and Lori.

She would not let him speak. "With those signs no one will come snooping. We can wait it out. Even if it takes longer than a month, we can wait! We have water. Coffee and tea in the kitchen. If the Gestapo comes again we will hear them rattle the chains and have time to hide." Her voice was so full of pathetic hope that Mark and Jamie exchanged looks. *Wait until she hears . . .*

"Besides," she continued, "they would take one look at us and arrest us on the spot. We look like we have been mining coal. Or rolling down a mountain. You think we would not be noticed dressed like this?"

This much of her reasoning was accurate. She was the only one among them who looked halfway clean. She even washed her hair in the dark bathroom once a week.

Mark caught their reflection in the glass of a cupboard. They looked terrible, smelled worse. Their clothes clung to them. Their hair was combed, but badly in need of a trim. They looked precisely like boys who had been hiding out for nearly a month.

Mark eyed Jacob, hoping for help to silence Lori. "They are going to tear down the church," Mark blurted out.

"That's right!" Jamie added. "We saw the sign. They are going to build a cultural center. Over the synagogue, too."

Disbelieving their grim report, Lori simply glared at them and shook her head.

"We aren't making it up," Mark protested. "We saw the sign."

Jacob cuffed his brother angrily. "You were in the bell tower again!"

"But, Jacob!" Jamie backed up as Lori and Jacob suddenly became allies against the two younger boys.

Lori grabbed Jamie by the shirt and yanked him to her.

"You were in the bell tower?" she echoed. "They could have seen you!"

"They're going to tear down the church!" Mark cried as Jacob shook him again.

Finally Jacob and Lori heard it. *"Tear down—"* Lori's anger and disbelief turned to concern. She raised her head as if to listen for the sound of a wrecking ball against the silent stone walls of the little church.

"What did you see?" Jacob demanded!

They told him once again, repeating the words of the sign.

Lori finally spoke over their heads to Jacob. They were almost friends again. "They warned my father that New Church would not stand in the way of the master architect's plan." A smile of bitter amusement came to her lips. "I guess you were right, Jacob. We have to leave."

"Yes." Jacob's voice held no pleasure. "I . . . I'm sorry. About this. About your father's church."

She chose to ignore his sympathy. She decided yesterday that she loathed Jacob Kalner. She did not know what she had ever seen in him in the first place. She did not want him feeling sorry for her now.

Her cool reserve surfaced again. "We will have to wash our clothes and underwear."

Jacob grasped his trousers at the waist as if to keep her from taking them. The arguing began again. "Nobody is getting my trousers off me," he scowled. "I saw the S.S. herding those poor schmucks around the streets in their nightshirts. Not me! If they get me, it will be with my pants on."

"Go ahead and stink then, Jacob Kalner!" Lori snapped. "But stay away from the rest of us! The Gestapo will smell you from Albrechtstrasse and say. '*Himmel!* Somebody must have died in New Church! Better go have a look!' " She lifted her nose haughtily and stepped back a few paces to make her point. "But the three of us will be clean, at least. They will not track us by our scent when we leave! We will be washed!" She wrapped an arm protectively around Jamie, who looked back at her suspiciously. "Won't we, Jamie?"

"Well," Mark replied, out of reach of Jacob's long arm, "at least we won't stink like Max!"

At that, Jacob's eyes narrowed in anger and he shook a meaty fist at his brother, who dodged him and joined Lori's camp.

"We will sleep in the choir robes tonight. And we will be clean enough to walk out of here and go to a movie," Lori finished triumphantly.

At this, Jacob's eyebrows went up and he smiled slightly. He would try a different tactic with Lori. If she insisted that they all be clean, there was another way to do it. "Or we can burn these clothes," Jacob said. He appraised Jamie, who squirmed uncomfortably beneath Lori's hand. "We will send Jamie back to your house. He can break in and get us whatever we need. I can wear your father's clothes—"

"No!" Lori said. "I *forbid* it! Jamie is not going out until—"

"I have some money hidden." Jamie darted back to Jacob's side. "I was saving it for Christmas. I can get that and clothes and—" His face flushed with the thought of such an adventure. "And the extra set of keys for Papa's auto!"

"He will be caught!" Lori wailed. "I am the oldest! I will not allow it!"

Jacob looked at her stonily. "And if he is caught? What then? They will take him back to the Hitler Youth school. And he will be fed and have a place to sleep. But if any of the rest of us are arrested, what then? I am sent to Dachau. You, you pretty little Aryan, will be sent to an S.S. breeding farm and produce little blond babies for the Fatherland and the Führer."

Jacob's last statement was too much for Lori. She burst into tears

and ran sobbing up the basement steps. *Let them do what they wanted!*
She was tired of fighting, tired of making decisions for these hateful,
terrible boys!

Even the boarded glass of the windows rattled when she slammed
the door. Slamming doors was forbidden by Jacob. Lori had the last
word, after all.

Once she was gone they made the plans without her. At least, Jacob
made the plans and the little boys agreed to them.

Jamie would sneak out of the church and raid the parsonage four
nights from now when the moon was dark. He would bring back
clothes, money, jewelry, and the spare keys to Pastor Ibsen's automobile.

During a Nazi party rally in Berlin, the foursome would make their
break. It would be a simple matter, Jacob explained to his compliant
comrades, as long as nobody made any mistakes.

———————

The prisoners of Nameless camp recognized the black, mud-splat-
tered Mercedes of Rev. Gustav Dorfman as it passed the main gate. No
one was surprised when special roll call was ordered before evening
meal.

Caps off, the men were forced to stand in the cold drizzle as Karl
Ibsen was once again called out from the ranks.

"You must be an important fellow, Prisoner Ibsen, to have such a
visitor."

By now the other prisoners did not blame Pastor Ibsen at this obvious attempt to drive in the wedge between him and them. They did
not blame him that there would be no shelter or soup for all the camp
until battle was done between Ibsen and Dorfman.

Karl left them, confident that they would pray for him, hopeful that
he would not be kept away long. They were his brothers. Together,
they huddled on a precipice of survival. They were learning that great
battles were won when their prayers silently went up for one another.
Although the guards led only Karl into the office of the commandant,
several hundred hearts went with him.

Gustav Dorfman came prepared. Dorfman had excelled in theological debate in his seminary days. He had learned early that winning an
argument often hinged on simply putting the right emphasis on the
correct syllable. From the pulpit, his melodious voice resounding from
the rafters, the emphasis he put on certain words and verses had led
a congregation and then an entire church into error.

In the days following their first conversation, the men in the barracks had questioned Karl:

"Can this man Dorfman really believe what he preaches, or does
he say it just to keep the people in line with the government?"

Karl had thought about those questions deeply before he attempted an answer. In the mud and suffering of Nameless camp he had looked at the prisoner uniforms: striped like prison bars, all the same. *Then God said, "Let us make man in our image...."*

So this was the image men like Dorfman saw of the Creator. They made the image a slave to serve their own ideas—identical, faceless, without color. Dorfman's god served the masters of the Reich. The basest clay had set out to change the image of the Potter.

"Dorfman's heart and mind were convinced of his own righteousness before he ever read one word from the Scriptures," Karl answered. "He has seen what he wants to see in God's Word. He believes what makes him feel best about himself."

"But how can he not see the truth?" asked Johann, who had found truth in the tears of Jesus only a few nights before.

"He is like a color-blind man gazing at the shining lights and colors of a prism. His view of God is gray. There is no love or brightness or beauty there, only gray. He has clothed God in a drab gray uniform. He has dressed the heart of the German people in that same uniform and ordered that they march in step. Look at their belt buckles, Johann. *Gott mit uns*—God with us! Pity them. They have never seen the glory of a rainbow reflected in one teardrop of the Lord! But you have seen it, Johann. So have I. Never mind that they try and make all men look alike and talk alike and think alike and march in step. They have failed before they began, because we are all splashed with the colors of God's great love for us. Let your heart run and skip with the joy of it, Johann! God sees the colors of your soul, even in this place. From the least among us, He counts us beautiful, made in His image."

This truth caused Karl to grieve for the grayness of Gustav Dorfman's soul as the man flipped open his Bible and smugly began his debate in support of conformity to the government policies he proclaimed in his church.

"So, you want God's word on the subject? Let us begin. Romans, chapter thirteen, is one that every Christian must heed. A command." He began to read aloud the words that Karl knew by heart. *"Everyone must submit himself to the governing authorities, for there is no authority except that which God has established."* He followed the words with his finger, *"Consequently, he who rebels against authority is rebelling against what God has instituted, and those who do so will bring judgment on themselves."* He paused and gestured toward the window where guard towers were clearly in view. *"Rulers hold no terror for those who do right.... For he is God's servant to do you good. But if you do wrong, be afraid, for he does not bear the sword for nothing. He is God's servant, an agent of wrath to bring punishment on the wrongdoer."*

Karl closed his eyes for a moment, then looked again at the bristling guard towers. He could clearly see the outline of the gray soldier and his machine gun trained on the backs of the men waiting in the field.

"A suitable passage for der Führer to seize upon. This has often been used as a club with which the ignorant have been beaten into submission to evil."

"The reason you are here is that you have disobeyed the God-given authority of the land. That authority is the Führer."

"The reason I am here is because I have obeyed the law of God that is written in that same chapter in Romans. *Love your neighbor as yourself. Love does no harm to its neighbor. Therefore love is the ful-fillment of the law.*" He paused. There was enough within those verses for several weeks of sermons, but his friends were standing in the rain, after all. "I saw firsthand the Nazi government's treatment of neighbors on Kristal Nacht."

"You call these Jews your neighbors?" He flipped open his Bible. "The Lord himself has said in Matthew 21, verse 45 to the Jews, '*There-fore I tell you that the kingdom of God will be taken away from you and given to a people who will produce its fruit!'* " Triumphant, he laid the book open on the table.

Karl simply quoted the rest of the passage. "Verses 45 and 46: *When the chief priests and the Pharisees heard Jesus' parables, they knew he was talking about them. They looked for a way to arrest him, but they were afraid of the crowd because the people believed he was a prophet.*" Karl inclined his head slightly, as if amused. "Chief priests and religious leaders throughout the generations have often sought ways to silence the true Jesus. They have arrested or condemned those who preach His word. And then they are afraid that the simple people in the crowds who hear and believe will turn against their authority. The first day they accused Jesus, the simple people in the crowds were Jews." Karl shook his head slowly at the expression of anger on Dorf-man's face. "He was speaking to men like you, Gustav Dorfman. Mat-thew twenty-three, *Everything they do is done for men to see.... They love the place of honor at banquets and the most important seats in the synagogues; they love to be greeted in the marketplaces and to have men call them Rabbi.... Woe unto you, teachers of the law and Phar-isees, you hypocrites! You shut the kingdom of heaven in men's faces. You yourselves do not enter, nor will you let those enter who are trying to!*"

Dorfman jumped to his feet in outrage. Like the Pharisees, he was indignant that Karl Ibsen was talking about him. "You! How dare you!"

"Not me! Hear the words of our only teacher . . . a rabbi! A Jew! The Messiah! Hear His words to you, Gustav, and tremble. *Woe to you, teachers of the law and Pharisees, you hypocrites! You travel over land and sea to win a single convert, and when he becomes one, you make him twice as much a son of hell as you are.* Listen to the voice of the

Lord, Gustav! *One of them, an expert in the law, tested him with a question—"*

"That is enough."

"Teacher, which is the greatest commandment in the law? Jesus replied, 'Love the Lord your God with all your heart and all your soul and all your mind.' First and greatest . . . 'And the second is like it: Love your neighbor as yourself. All the law and the prophets hang on these two commandments.' "

"You are insane," Dorfman said in a low, menacing voice. "Insane to talk to me like this! Do you know the power I have here? They will do what I tell them. If I say you are a hopeless case, then—"

"It is you who have lost your hope, Gustav. And you, and men of the church like you, have hidden the true Messiah from the people of the Covenant. From the Jewish people. You think God is not watching? Jesus is still there, still true and loving beneath all the molten gold you dip Him in! Hang Him in the churches, persecute the race from which He came, claim that you are the new Israel! But I tell you, He is not in your church, Gustav. No, He is here in this camp. He walks—alive— among the suffering! He has not forsaken His covenant or His people Israel! I hear His voice, and it calls me to obey *Him . . . not* you! Not your dark and twisted Führer!"

Karl stood to face Dorfman. Filthy and stinking in his uniform, his eyes revealed more life than those of this withered man inside his perfectly tailored suit.

Dorfman tried to speak. He looked at the Bible fearfully. Had he ever heard the warning of judgment before now?

Karl spoke. "Jesus wept because of men like you. He also died for all of us, Jew and Gentile alike. But I pity you more than most men, Gustav, because you have poked your bony finger in the eye of God, when you should have stooped to touch His hem and mingle your tears with His."

"Are you finished?" Dorfman backed up a step, regaining some of his aloofness. "No. I do not need to *ask* you if you are finished. I *tell* you. This is the last . . . last chance. I am ordered to say . . . if you repent your stubbornness . . ."

Karl smiled sadly. Dorfman still saw gray.

"You will not convert me to your cause," Karl said. "I will pray for you, however. You are in deep water. I would not trade places with you for all the riches of the Reich."

———

"No!" Alfie cried, his eyes growing wide with terror. Something very bad was happening to Joseph. The soft white belly of the cat tightened, and he growled miserably. And then Joseph jerked his head around to his tail and made a moaning sound.

"Joseph!" Alfie called the name of his friend. Tears splashed on the stone floor beside the untouched sardines. "Don't leave me alone, Joseph," he begged.

Again the cat moaned and his stomach tightened, and it seemed as if Joseph's insides were coming out. Alfie shrank back in the corner and watched what must surely be the last breath of his little friend. He sobbed and called for Mama and then for Werner. He wished he had not run away from the hospital; it might have been better to go with Werner than to be so sad and alone!

Then something amazing happened to Joseph. He licked and licked at the little something that had come from inside him. He did not seem to hurt anymore for a while. And that little something between Joseph's paws suddenly moved and made a tiny squeak and said *meow*!

This terrible thing was not so terrible. It was a kitten! It was wet and skinny and very unhappy-looking, but it was alive. Joseph cleaned the little yellow thing and then looked proudly at Alfie. *What did you think?*

Alfie wiped away his tears and dropped down on all fours to look closely at the kitten. Joseph let him look, but growled when Alfie tried to poke it with his finger.

"Joseph," Alfie said happily, "you are a mother!"

The yellow kitten nuzzled close to Joseph and, finding a faucet in the soft fur, began to nurse. Alfie had seen this before with his dog. He had seen puppies eat supper this way, so he was not surprised. He had not touched the puppies, either. Mama had not let him watch them be born, and he had always supposed that his dog had burped them up. This was something new. Alfie did not go to sleep all night as Joseph had five more kittens. A fat gray one, a little tiger-striped one, and one just the same colors as Joseph. The last one, black with white paws, did not move when Joseph cleaned him. He just lay there between Joseph's paws, very still and small. Joseph nudged the kitten away and turned his attention to the other ones who squirmed and squeaked and wiggled against Joseph's belly.

Alfie looked at the black and white kitten. It was no bigger than Alfie's finger. He asked Joseph's permission to pick it up, since Joseph did not seem to want it.

He placed it in his hand and sat back against the wall. It was wet and cool against his skin. Its little mouth opened in a gasp for breath—still living, but not for long. This kitten reminded Alfie of the boys in the ward of the hospital. Weak and thin, it could not compete with the row of strong and healthy kittens squirming against Joseph's belly.

"Ah, little cat." Alfie held it up to the warmth of his breath. "I would call you Werner if you would live."

The tiny body twitched and Alfie ran his finger gently over the paper-thin ribs. Back and forth he stroked the kitten. He held it close to him and spoke gently to it while his finger licked it in place of Joseph's tongue.

"Live, little Werner," Alfie whispered over and over throughout the long night.

The ribs rose and fell as the kitten lived on by the will of Alfie. It's damp fur dried into a fragment of fluff. The pink nose twitched, and the white paws began to stir weakly.

Alfie put the tip of his little finger into the mouth of Werner. The snap of suction rewarded him. Only then did he lower the kitten for Joseph to see again. The mother cat purred her gratitude and nuzzled the kitten. Joseph even allowed Alfie to find Werner a good faucet and plug him in for his first warm meal.

———

Peter had not left Herr Ruger's apartment since he discovered their home was destroyed. Nor had he allowed his mother to go out. Marlene, who had left her dolls at home, complained incessantly about the fact that she could not so much as look out at the snow, let alone go play in it. A self-centered ten-year-old, Marlene still could not believe that anything had happened out there since she had not been affected by it. No one had hurt her, and so, no one could have been hurt. This punishment of remaining in Herr Ruger's apartment was the only unhappiness she could perceive. Her whining left Peter on the verge of throwing her out the window.

Baby Willie was Peter's only salvation. A constant source of entertainment, the seven-month-old babbled and cooed and crawled and drooled in happy laughter when Peter held him high over his head or played peek-a-boo, or crawled after him in a game of infant tag.

Thankfully, Peter's mother had brought an entire basket of diapers along. Laundry lines crisscrossed the front room of Herr Ruger's elegant apartment. Clean diapers were placed on the radiators to dry. Socks and underwear draped on a line running from the dining room to the Queen Anne armoire like pennants on a ship.

Herr Ruger's flat had become a kind of ark for the little family. Kitchen cupboards were well stocked. Warmth hissed and rattled through the steam radiators. No one had knocked on the door or telephoned. News blared over the radio with typical Nazi party fanfare. Herr Ruger had not returned to claim his home from the little band of fugitives, and so they stayed on, eating the food cautiously, warming their hands gratefully, sleeping soundly in beds that were not their own.

Marlene, oblivious to all danger, finally shattered the tranquility of their imprisonment.

Her serious dark eyes locked on a piece of paper, she emerged from Herr Ruger's bedroom. "Mother, I have written a poem about the snow. It is very good, I think. And I have decided that I will be a poet.

I will write a verse every day until next year and then I will have an entire book."

She handed the paper to her mother with a flourish.

"Well, read it to me," Karin Wallich said, handing the paper back to Marlene.

Marlene shot a sullen look at Peter, who was prepared for the worst. "No," Marlene declared. "Peter will laugh at me." She reverently placed the paper back in her mother's hands.

Karin smiled benignly with the kind of patient look that mothers have when they must interpret a child's genius out of chicken scratchings. Her lips moved as she read silently. "Why, Marlene, this is really—" Then Karin Wallich's smile faded. The praise died on her lips. Color drained from her cheeks at what she held in her hand. She managed a whisper. "Marlene, where . . . where did you . . . get this stationery?"

"From Herr Ruger's desk drawer," the child declared blithely. "But do you really like my poem?"

"Show me!" Karin was on her feet now. Peter stood in automatic response to the alarm in his mother's voice.

"What is it?" He took the paper from her hand.

His eyes focused past the scrawled letters and ink blotches to the embossed letterhead of the sheet. The eagle of the Reich clutched a broken cross in its talons. Beneath that was the insignia of the Gestapo, the Vienna address of Gestapo headquarters!

Peter roughly grabbed his sister's arm. "Where did this come from?" he demanded, giving her a shake.

She began to cry. "It was in the desk. All I wanted was some paper. There was lots of it. Lots and lots. He would not mind a few pieces of blank paper. He would not even miss them."

"Show me where you found it!" He propelled her into the gloomy bedroom. A large credenza with a fold-out writing desk stood open. A stack of clean white letterhead stationery lay in an open drawer. Peter and Karin hovered over it, staring at the ominous emblem in disbelief. Neither of them dared to touch the paper, as though the insignia itself might harm them. Marlene whimpered her innocence in the background. They seemed not to hear her.

"Gestapo," Peter whispered.

"Where could he have come by it?" Karin could hardly speak.

"Stolen? Perhaps he has stolen it."

"If the apartment is ever searched . . . if he has stolen Gestapo letterhead stationery! Why . . . they will *arrest* him! They will execute him!"

"But why would he have it?"

"They will say he is a forger."

"Maybe he is." Peter frowned. He pulled open another drawer. The credenza had not been opened before. They had left the tiny drawers and compartments alone, just like the chest of drawers. Personal things, the belongings of Otto Ruger, had not been looked at. Herr Ruger's privacy had been respected . . . until now.

Inside the second drawer lay a framed photograph of Otto Ruger. The image made Peter gasp and blink with horror. *Otto Ruger in a Nazi uniform. Smiling beside Gestapo Chief Heinrich Himmler, who is speaking to Adolf Hitler on the steps of the Vienna town hall.*

Karin slowly picked up the photograph and held it for a moment, then tossed it back into the drawer as though it had burned her hand.

"Mein Gott! Herr Ruger . . . he is . . . *one of them!"*

A chill filled Peter, the same terrible fear he had felt during his walk through Vienna on Kristal Nacht. Suddenly the apartment felt heavy and dark around him, as though the walls had ears and eyes. *Like creatures on exhibit in the zoo,* he thought.

"We must not stay here," Peter said firmly, taking the photo from the drawer and looking closely at Herr Ruger as if to be certain that there was not some sort of mistake. *No. No mistake!*

"I always thought he knew too much. A strange character, our Herr Ruger. Showing up with news of your father after the arrest. He has planned this. He has lured us here. Probably there are listening devices to hear us talk, about your father and—" She lowered her voice and looked wildly around at the walls. "What shall we do, Peter?"

He put a finger to his lips, feeling the same paranoia. He pulled his mother into the bathroom and turned on the water to cover their conversation.

"We cannot stay here. You are right. This is some sort of trap. Not just for us, but for Father." Peter was convinced of it. "It is only a matter of time before they come for us here." He slammed his fist against the sink. "We have been idiots! We *trusted* him!"

Karin looked at her image in the mirror. She appeared years older than she had two months ago. Older than even a week before. She felt as if someone else was living through this nightmare. "Hurry, then," she said wearily. "I will pack our things. Clean up. We can be ready in half an hour. But where will we go?"

23

Friends in High Places

Half an hour later, the face of Peter's mother was still pale and drawn, a colorless contrast to her red hair. Then Peter caught a glimpse of his own reflection in the bedroom mirror. His skin was as pale as hers. His red hair stuck up. He, too, looked frightened.

Karin closed the door so that Marlene could not hear.

"What are we to do now?" she asked hoarsely.

"The entire neighborhood has been cleared," Peter said again as if to convince himself of the truth.

"I do not know what prison your father is in, where they have taken him. If anything happens, how will we know? And if he writes us, how will we get his letters?" Tears brimmed in her eyes. She seemed not to be thinking about Herr Ruger anymore or the possibility of listening devices planted in the walls. Peter hoped she would not cry.

She looked at their luggage, remembering again why their clothing was packed. But they had no home to return to; the old neighborhood was dead, stamped out in one night.

"The Nazis could not have arrested everyone. There must be others like us. If we could find them, get away from here before Herr Ruger returns." She wrung her hands and paced back and forth in the bedroom as Peter sat silent and thoughtful in the overstuffed chair beside the window.

He lifted the edge of the shade and peered out toward Frau Singer's shop. They had not seen any sign of the old woman. What had become of her?

Peter closed his eyes and tried to think what his father might have done. No answer came to him. He drew his breath slowly and gazed out over the snow-dusted skyline of Vienna. In spite of the cold, two birds perched on the telephone wire just outside. Peter traced that wire to another and another. Telephone wires and electrical wires intact throughout the city. With a half smile he turned and looked first at the telephone and then at this mother.

"Well, why don't we just ring someone up?"

She looked at him as if he had gone mad. They had not even dared to lift the receiver, for fear the lines might somehow be connected to some unknown Nazi at the telephone exchange. Once, when Willie had pulled the telephone off the table, they had both rushed to pick it up, and had stared silently at the thing as if a Gestapo officer might crawl out of it.

"Ring someone up?" Karin frowned at Peter. "You mean just like that? Telephone someone?"

"If the lines are still working—and I can't see why they wouldn't be. The storm troopers broke windows and furniture, but they did not pull down the telephone lines."

She opened her mouth to protest, but closed it again and sidled up to the phone. Her fingers rested on it, questioning the wisdom of such a brash move. After all, if the walls were bugged, certainly the telephone would be as well. "Maybe it doesn't matter," she said, finally picking up the receiver. "Who? Who should we call?"

"Frau Singer." Peter looked out the window again as he mentioned the name of the old corset maker.

"But her shop is closed."

"Everybody's shop is closed. That doesn't mean she won't answer the telephone if it rings."

"But is she there?"

"Call her and see." Peter continued smiling down on the little corset shop as his mother dialed. He could hear the ring of Frau Singer's phone. Once. Twice. And then . . .

"Guten Abend. Singer's corsets and—"

Karin Wallich cried out in astonishment. Could it be that easy? "Frau Singer! It is you!"

"And who else should it be? But who is—?"

"Karin Wallich! Oh, Frau Singer!"

"Mein Gott! Himmel! Mein Gott! We thought you were gone forever! Some said you slipped over the border into what is left of Czechoslovakia! Karin Wallich! But where are you, my dear? You are not calling from Prague?"

Peter put a finger to his lips, warning his mother not to mention that they had been in the apartment of a Gentile just across the street. Such juicy news would no doubt make the rounds and somehow end up in the ears of a party official.

"I am in Vienna," Karin answered with relief.

"With the children, my dear?"

"Yes. With Peter and Marlene and little Willie."

"Are you well?"

"Much better now. We thought the wind had blown everyone away."

The old woman's laugh crackled over the line. *"A strong wind blows from these storm troopers, but even the Nazi wives need corsets! They have broken my shop window, but as long as I have my two hands I can make what they need."*

The color returned to Karin's face. She smiled easily at the old woman's resilience, and the smile melted years from her face. Peter laughed to see it and slapped his thigh in delight. *All this time . . .*

"It is so good to hear your voice, Frau Singer," Karin winked at Peter. "We thought we were the only ones left."

"They arrested nearly all the men between sixteen and sixty. I was certain Peter would be taken as well. They destroyed the soup kitchens and left the women to clean up. There has been little to eat this past week, but today the first funds came from the Refugee Children's Committee in London. There will be food again tomorrow."

Karin covered the mouthpiece and whispered happily to Peter, "The soup kitchen will be open tomorrow! Imagine!"

There was much news to catch up on, but the telephone was not the way to do it. The thought came to Peter and his mother at the same moment, and their smiles faded as quickly as they had come.

"Yes, well, I really must not keep you any longer, Frau Singer," Karin said abruptly. "Perhaps we will see you soon."

As the old woman stammered her farewell on the other end of the line, Karin replaced the receiver. Enthusiasm was tempered by caution once again. Should they go to Frau Singer's apartment and ask for shelter? The place was only across the street from Herr Ruger's window. Perhaps they would put the old woman in danger by going there.

Wolf was proud of the thick Persian rugs he had acquired for the apartment. He had sent a number of similar purchases home to East Prussia, but these two he kept out purposefully.

The designs were of rare intricacy. There was a special name for each design. Lucy could not remember exactly what Wolf had told her about them except that they were exceptional and valuable. He had picked up the whole lot from a confiscated Jewish house not far from here.

On the cream-colored border of one of the carpets were four reddish-brown spots. They matched the color of the woven wool background, but the spots were some sort of stain.

"Blood," Lucy said firmly.

"Chocolate," Wolf said, unconcerned.

"It looks like blood to me," Lucy insisted. "And I will not walk on blood."

"Jewish blood."

"I . . . I don't care whose blood it is! I cannot bear to have it in the apartment, Wolf! How can I sleep with a stranger's blood in the house?"

"You are squeamish for the daughter of a farmer. Didn't you ever see the slaughter of a hog? Not much different than the slaughter of a Jew!" He laughed as she clutched her stomach and turned away.

"Stop it! I will not have even one drop in my house! Can you be so thoughtless?" She pretended to be near to tears. "I am expecting a baby! Can you be so heartless as to play such a cruel game with me? Such matters affect the unborn, you know."

Wolf's mocking smile vanished. He looked at her apologetically and shook his head. "I was only joking. Just teasing you! I am sure it is chocolate." He laughed nervously.

She shook her head defiantly and sank down onto the couch. "I don't believe you! And what if it is? I will look at the spots and imagine—" She gestured toward the second rug, which was smaller but just as beautifully patterned. "And how can I know they are not both stained with someone's blood? Look at the color!"

Wolf considered the rich deep red of his treasures and regretted that he had pushed the issue so far. "So, have them cleaned." He shrugged, then frowned. "But carefully. There are ways, you know. They must not ruin the color." At that he put his arms around her and pulled her close against him. He expected a reward for agreeing with her about cleaning the Persian rugs. Normally he did not give in to such frivolity.

Lucy remained stiff and unresponsive to his touch. He kissed her but she did not soften, as if the horror of the rugs had made her into a statue.

"What is it?" he asked.

"Roll them up," she commanded. "I cannot . . . not when those things are open like that. Roll them up so I will not have to look at them."

Wolf nodded impatiently and acquiesced to her desire, certain that when he yielded, she would then yield to him.

———

Frau Singer's shop was only across the street, but it might as well have been on the opposite bank of a raging river. Once again Peter looked out past the edge of the shade and then back to the luggage by the door.

Only two scuffed tan leather suitcases and a box of diapers remained of their possessions.

Baby Willie sat on top of the diaper box and drooled as he chewed intensely on a rubber duck. He was the only member of the family who was not waiting nervously for the sun to slip away so they could escape Herr Ruger's apartment.

Mozart, Herr Ruger's cat, eyed the baby coolly from a window ledge. *The cats will be glad to see us go,* Peter thought. *Then they will no longer have to dart past this tail-grabbing human kitten who seems to have invaded every corner of their house.* Peter had already decided to let the cats out when they left the apartment. It would not do to have Herr Ruger return home to starved pets and a stinking apartment. Perhaps the cats would hide out in the alley and come home when they saw their owner in the window.

"Another half hour, Mother," Peter said. They had a plan of escape. Down the back stairs, out the rear door, and then once around the block before they returned to Frau Singer's place.

"I should have asked her first," Karin fretted.

"It is better this way," Peter replied as he eyed the wall clock next to the photograph of Hitler. "She will not turn us away."

"I will be glad to go." Marlene pulled up her socks and sat primly on the edge of the sofa as if waiting for a train. "There is nothing to do here."

Peter was about to reply that he was certain Marlene would be unhappy no matter where they were, but the sound of footsteps made him forget it. There was no time to move, no time to speak. A key scratched in the door lock and then, as the cats leaped from their perches and ambled toward the door expectantly, Herr Ruger entered.

He looked up briefly, accepting the fact that there were people in his apartment. Then, stamping snow from his boots, he doffed his Russian beaver hat and entered.

"Peter!" He seemed genuinely relieved as he stooped to scratch beneath Mozart's chin. "And Frau Wallich! Are you coming or going?"

Karen Wallich was on her feet in an instant. "We were just leaving," she said through a cracking voice. "Only stopped by to—" She gestured at the cat.

"No, no!" Herr Ruger glanced at the luggage, then at Willie on the box of diapers. "You have been here a while? I was hoping to find you."

Peter moved toward the suitcases. "We are on our way to a friend's house." He placed the apartment key beside the telephone. "And so—"

Herr Ruger straightened slowly, his fair skin flushed pink from the cold. Golden-red hair fell over his forehead much like the dark hair of Hitler in the picture. He smiled at Marlene as though he was puzzled by this strange welcome and the haste of Peter and Karin Wallich to leave. "You do not want to go so soon, do you, Marlene?" he asked. "I have just arrived home. I would like a cup of tea. Do you know where the tea is, Marlene?"

"Oh yes," Marlene blurted out, basking in the attention.

"Then perhaps you would fix me a cup of tea before you leave."

Karin's shoulders sagged as Marlene hurried to comply. It had been simple for Herr Ruger to discover that they had been in his apartment long enough for Marlene to know where the tea was kept.

He picked Willie up and held him on a thick, muscular arm. "Have you found your way around all right, Willie? You do not seem to be in such a hurry to go."

The baby smiled and batted him on the chin. Herr Ruger grinned. He looked at Karin. "Children are seldom frightened unless they are given a reason." He paused, gestured for her to sit, and then pulled up a rocking chair and continued to hold Willie. "So, I can see clearly that you are not like Willie. You are afraid of me." He cleared his throat. "I am blunt. Straight to it." He directed his gaze to Peter, who sat rigid and silent on the sofa. "You did well, Peter. You were invited to come here. Have you been comfortable?"

Peter looked hard at him, remembering the picture of Herr Ruger standing beside Himmler and Hitler. He tried to pretend he had not seen it. "We . . . that is . . . I remembered you said we should come if—"

Karin interrupted, "And so the night of the riots . . . our own apartment was burned to the ground."

Herr Ruger nodded. "Yes. I saw it. So, you have been staying here. Why are you leaving?" he pressed on.

"We have other friends . . ." Peter shrugged, carefully avoiding looking into Herr Ruger's searching eyes. Such eyes seemed to know everything.

"Then who will watch my cats?" Ruger smiled. He stood and placed Willie into the arms of Karin; then he raised a finger, instructing them to remain where they were. With that, he disappeared into the bedroom and re-emerged holding the photograph they had discovered. Hanging it on an empty nail beside the clock and the photo of Hitler, he turned to face his guests. "My pride and joy, that photo," he said. "You see how close I am to the Führer. How trusted I am."

Karin trembled. Peter did not look at the terrible picture. He stared at his hands, picked nervously at his nails. "You are wise to be frightened by me," Ruger finished ominously.

"What . . . do you want with us?" Karin breathed.

He answered with a question. "Have you told anyone you were here, Frau Wallich?"

A look passed between her and Peter. They had not even told Frau Singer. "No one."

"Good." Herr Ruger smiled. "So, Karin, you look enough like me to be my sister, wouldn't you say? And Peter might be my nephew. It is the hair, you see. The red hair. I spotted it in the file photos."

"Gestapo," Karin whispered, looking up searchingly into his face.

"You are *one of them*. Why are you . . . why have you done this? Why? You know what we are. Surely you know what has happened to my husband."

Herr Ruger's face hardened. A strange half smile played on his lips. "Yes, I know what has become of Michael Wallich."

"What? *Where is he?*" Peter begged. "Where is my father?"

"He is dead, Peter." The smile remained. His eyes looked cold and unfeeling as he announced the news.

In the kitchen doorway, Marlene cried out and dropped the teacup onto the floor. "Mama!" she wailed. "Papa is dead!" She ran to her mother, who sat dry-eyed, unsurprised, as if she had known it all along.

"We wish to leave this place. Are we allowed to leave?" Karin's tone was emotionless.

"You mean leave this apartment? Or leave Vienna? Or Austria?" Ruger questioned, staring at the weeping little girl who clung to her mother.

Peter angrily jumped to his feet and shouted, "All of that! We want to get out! *Out of here!* Do you understand that?"

Herr Ruger put a finger to his lips, then gestured toward the ceiling. "The neighbors, Peter," he warned, still smiling. Then he sighed. "I am working on that. Getting you all out, I mean. There is a place I know in the Tyrol. Maybe there. But the snows have closed the passes already. You will have to stay here a while at least."

Silence filled the room for a few minutes, except for Marlene's sniffling. Karen stroked her hair. Baby Willie tangled his stubby fingers in her curls and pulled.

"Why are we here?" Peter asked wearily. "Why have you brought us here? Why help us if you are one of them?"

Herr Ruger shrugged. "It is not so simple as us and them, Peter." Now Ruger looked very sad. "You must all call me Otto. Uncle Otto. Do you understand? I am your Uncle Otto Wattenbarger from the Tyrol. Do you hear me, Marlene?" He caught the eye of the little girl. His stern voice stopped her tears. "I am Uncle Otto. And you will say nothing more than that, even to your mother."

"We do not have the option to leave here, I take it?" Karin's tone now became hard and resentful.

"That's right. It's gone too far, Karin. Sister." He turned to Peter. "Have you ever been to a Catholic church, Peter?" he asked, as though it was the logical progression of their conversation.

"No. And I will not—"

"Will not?" Otto raised his chin in amusement at this defiance.

"You are in this as deeply as we are," Peter spat. "I suppose you are not in danger if we are caught?" This was an open threat.

"Do not be ungrateful, Peter," Otto replied as though the words made him sad. "Or I will simply kill you myself and say you had it coming." He clapped his hands together. "Now. We must begin our catechism. You must learn to pray. Learn how to address a priest properly. And how to speak to the saints. All the saints." He seemed very pleased. "But first, Marlene, you must make me another cup of tea."

———————

Nightmares came fresh and vivid every night now for Charles Kronenberger. It did not matter that Elisa and Murphy left the light on and spoke of only happy things to him and Louis. Charles was still afraid. Would the bad men who had followed them to Vienna and killed Father also come here to London? The Englishmen did not seem very angry about the things Hitler was doing. Maybe they would not stop him if he found out where Charles was and remembered that this was one little boy who had gotten away from him.

Such fears came to him against his will. In the quiet of his new home, he would remember the frightened voices of his mother as she begged the Gestapo not to hurt Father. He would see the fist raise up and fall across her face as she fought to keep the doctor from taking Charles to the clinic. He would hear once again the clink of metal surgical instruments on the tray, and then he would awaken with a cry to find Elisa at his bedside.

Sometimes when the grown-ups did not know he understood, he would listen to them talk in English about what had happened on that dark night in Germany. The names of his father's friends were among the many arrested. *Pastor Karl Ibsen.* Charles knew the name well. Pastor Ibsen had helped his father fight when the Nazis said only perfect people were welcome in the Reich. He had spoken up for other boys and girls like Charles. Somehow he had survived a long time. But now Pastor Ibsen, like everyone else who protested, was gone. Timmons wired Murphy from Berlin. Murphy had closed the door and told Elisa and Theo and Anna. But Charles listened at the keyhole and heard what the grown-ups said. That night the dreams were worse than ever, and Charles thought that God had sent the dreams to punish him because he had been bad and listened.

Eyes looked worried even when faces smiled at Charles and Louis. Louis could speak more clearly than Charles, and so he asked the questions out loud. But Charles had just as many questions as Louis did. *What happened to the other children like me who are still in Germany? Will they get to come to England, too? Who is left to speak for them since Pastor Ibsen has disappeared? Will the Nazis come to London? Will they kill me while I sleep? Will they hurt Elisa if her baby is not perfect?*

Last night, as Charles lay in bed with his eyes closed, bits of Murphy's voice had drifted up to him.

"Not only is Ibsen missing . . . closed the church . . . your Aunt Helen

*and the children vanished ... Timmons is looking into it, but ... hope-
less. Dangerous situation. . . . Euthanasia . . . one hospital emptied overnight. . . ."*

Charles fell asleep after hours of staring at the closet door and
wondering if Nazis were in there waiting to empty out his bed forever,
too.

The next morning Murphy promised it would be a special day for
Charles and Louis. Mr. Churchill had gotten them all permission to sit
in the press gallery of the House of Commons. Despite the lack of
visible response to all appeals, the English government might find
some way to help the refugees, Murphy said, and it would be a good
thing for Charles to see how they would do it.

Charles put on his best brown tweed jacket and knickers. He
combed his hair carefully and then looked closely at the pink scar
where his mouth had been broken. His lower lip still stuck out a bit
farther than his upper lip, but the doctor said they could fix everything
until no one would notice. Even so, Charles thought that someone
might see where his mouth had been imperfect. Charles knew what
sorts of things happened to imperfect children, and it frightened him.
For the first time since his trip to New York, he wrapped a scarf around
his neck and carefully pulled it up to conceal his mouth. Until that
pink scar healed, he decided, he would hide it from the Nazis. He
would hide it also from the Englishmen who liked the Nazis. Otherwise,
maybe he would just vanish too and someone whole would get the
new bed and toys he'd gotten from Mr. Trump.

His serious blue eyes looked back from the mirror. In his mind,
Charles warned himself, *Do not get too happy, Charles. You were happy
with Father in Vienna, then the Nazis came. Everything could go away
and then you would feel worse.* He would not tell Elisa that he was
scared anymore, because that made her worry. But he would be careful
all the same. It did not pay to feel too happy.

––––––––

"Guten Tag, Pastor Ibsen," the camp commandant said pleasantly,
as if greeting him at the door after Sunday service. "Did you hear us
singing hymns in chapel this morning?"

Pastor Karl stared straight ahead at the wall map of Poland. He had
heard the singing, yes, and the sound of such music coming from the
mouths of men like this had sickened him. He did not reply.

"We sing quite well, I think." The commandant tapped a cigarette
on his desk and then held the open case toward Karl if he would care
to smoke. Cigarettes were highly prized by prisoners. The commandant
was hoping to thaw the ice of this stubborn iron-jawed churchman.
"You do not smoke?"

Karl stared over the officer's head toward the blue sky shining through the window behind him.

The commandant lit his cigarette and rocked back in his squeaking desk chair. "There has been a change in policy," he continued in his too-pleasant voice. "You are to be relieved of your work among the other prisoners."

A pause. Karl let his eyes flit down to skim the pock-marked face of the officer. "I told you. I will not sign your paper."

The commandant laughed. "Such strength of character we consider admirable. Of great benefit to the German people, if it is channeled properly."

"You will not cut a new path for this stream," Karl said softly.

"A man of conviction. A true German. A son whom the Fatherland does not wish to lose." He waved his hand in the direction of Hitler's glaring portrait. "Clemency has been offered. You are a Christian. A man of God. You should have a time of rest. A time to think and read and bathe . . ."

At the mention of a bath, Karl's eyes flickered with an instant of longing. In a split second he mastered that basic desire for cleanliness and masked his face with resolve again. But the commandant had seen that desire. It made him cheerful.

"I see you approve."

"I prefer to remain with the others," Karl said, regretting having shown even that brief weakness.

"We would not think of it. The Führer has given the order personally that you are to be treated well. You are a man of God, after all."

"I am a Jew," Karl said as though declaring his nationality. "Let me go back."

The cheek of the commandant twitched in a flash of impatience. But he also mastered his emotion quickly. He shrugged. "You are as Aryan as Adolf Hitler. We know this. That is why we are patient. You have been among the Jews too long. It is natural that you—"

"I am a Jew," Karl said again, firmly.

The commandant was determined not to lose before he had really even begun the process of winning back Pastor Ibsen to the German fold. He spoke to him as though speaking to a child. "Your race entitles you to a gift from the German people whom you have served as pastor. A little time out of the cold. It is cold." He tapped the ashes of his cigarette. "You still have friends in high places in Berlin, you see. People who wish to see you back home where you belong, preaching as you did before." It was a lie, meant to personalize the offer of warmth and a bath and a day of rest.

Karl saw through the lie. "I have only one friend in high places, and He is not of this world."

The commandant mashed out his cigarette and smiled less easily at this reply. "You are not above the law or the commands of the Führer. He is the highest authority in the land, and so we shall both comply with his offer of clemency." He pushed a button on his intercom and two armed guards immediately appeared to escort Karl from the office, across a snow-dusted gravel courtyard to the empty shower room used by Nazi soldiers and officers.

Karl hesitated a moment at the step and looked up to see five hundred of his fellow prisoners, row on row, beyond the wire fence. They were turned so that they might clearly witness the mud-coated pastor enter the building and emerge thirty minutes later as clean as any free man in Berlin.

24

Never Give In to Fear

Rain crackled down on ten thousand black London umbrellas. The broad picture-postcard view of Parliament and the river Thames was obscured from Charles as he clung to Elisa's hand and dashed up stone steps and into echoing corridors filled with people. His child's view was not of majestic stone arches and polished floors, but a forest of pin-striped pants and ladies' coats and dripping galoshes in the cloak room. This place where Murphy said the English ran their empire was very confusing.

Charles was afraid of being lost. Such a crowd and such noise reminded him of Vienna in the open square before he had lost Father forever. The big people did not see that he and Louis were down below and in danger of being stepped on. The endless babble of their voices was unintelligible. Charles tried to hear only Elisa's words.

"Up those stairs to the gallery? Mother and Papa came early . . . they'll be sitting with Dr. Weizmann. No, not in the press gallery."

He held desperately to her hand as she inched her way through the mob. Keeping his eyes on her face, he could see that she was attempting to smile pleasantly, although her eyes seemed worried. Murphy had said he would meet them there. But how would Murphy find them in such a busy place? The current of the crowd moved forward toward the steps.

"Hold the banister." Elisa looked down at Charles. Her blue eyes matched her hat and her dress, light and pretty like sunlight beaming down through a dark wood. Charles smiled back from beneath his scarf and then, behind them a voice harumphed and called out.

"Mrs. Murphy! Elisa!"

Charles knew the voice. It was Winston Churchill. Elisa stopped on the bottom step and turned. She raised her hand to wave, and Charles grasped the fabric of her dress. He did not take his eyes from her face as she looked toward the voice.

"Did you bring the little men?" Churchill asked. He could not see them either, so Charles raised his hand to mark his place on the lower step. People pushed impatiently past them, but they did not yield.

"Good morning . . . a day of hope for us all," Elisa called. Charles heard no hope in her voice. Still, his stomach churned with excitement. He did not think about the crush of trousers and shoes. There was something wonderful at the top of the stairs!

A big belly towered above him. The full-moon face of Winston Churchill beamed down. Watery blue eyes twinkled out from heavy lids, and the great man's lower lip jutted out in a crooked smile. Churchill bent at the waist and extended his hand first to Louis and then to Charles.

"How do you do? Master Louis Kronenberger. Master Charles Kronenberger."

"How . . . how . . . do you . . ."

Churchill focused his attention on Charles. "I am pleased you could come, young man." The chin jutted out in thought as he laid a thick hand on Charles's head. The face moved closer until that was all that Charles could see. Churchill pushed the scarf down, exposing Charles's mouth. "There. That's better." Charles noticed that Churchill's lower lip also stuck out farther than his upper lip, and he smiled. "A smile to give me strength," Churchill said. "You must remember, young man . . . *never* give in to fear. Never, never, never give in! I shall look for you in the gallery."

Another quick shake of the hand, and the big face was gone. Once again they turned their attention to the steep stairs. Charles did not think about putting the scarf back in place. He did not think about the pink scar on his lip. Something good was about to happen, and he let go of Elisa's hand and charged up the steps ahead of everyone.

———

An electric atmosphere permeated the hall of the House of Commons. Elisa could feel Murphy's tenseness as she took her place beside him in the press gallery. Several rows to her right, the faces of Anna and Theo reflected the same deep concern as the expression of the Zionist Chaim Weizmann beside them. Anna managed a smile and a small wave to the boys. Elisa wished they could have sat together; that she might have been able to hold her mother's hand the way Charles clung to her hand now. Elisa felt very young and small as she considered the importance of the coming debate. Thousands of lives depended on the results. The riots Leah reported in her letters from Jerusalem seemed to put all hope in jeopardy.

"Winston was looking for you," Murphy whispered.

"He found us." Elisa looked over the rail of the gallery as members of Parliament took their places on the long benches. Prime Minister Chamberlain and his Cabinet cronies sat facing Winston Churchill and the opposition party. Charles leaned against the rail and waved shyly at Churchill, who spotted him immediately and managed a lopsided smile of acknowledgment for his smallest fan.

Charles nudged Elisa and pointed downward. There was the fellow who would not give in. *Never give in!*

How grateful Elisa was that Winston had taken the time to seek out Charles and whisper such brave words. If the Old Lion had clapped her on the back and directed his comments to her alone, it would not have meant half so much as his kindness to Charles. She noticed that the child laid the scarf over the back of his chair as though he had brought it along by mistake and should have left it in the cloak room. Murphy also saw the discarded scarf and shared a sigh of relief with Elisa.

"So what did Winston say?" Murphy asked, his eyes lingering on the scarf.

"He said, 'Never give in to fear.' " Elisa repeated the words as if they were a prayer for Charles and for everyone who was threatened now. Such brave words made her think of Thomas and the photograph they should never have seen. The sight had made her fear—for herself, for her family, and for the many thousands who lived within the shadow of such brutality. Yes, she was afraid, but she would not give in to it. There was too much to do. They could not be paralyzed by threats.

The bulldog face of Churchill turned upward one more time to the gallery. He winked and gave Charles the V-for-victory sign. And then the battle began.

Elisa found herself more concerned with the reactions of the boys than with the debate. Louis fell asleep after a restless hour in his chair. But Charles sparked with interest, although he could not have understood most of what was being said. His eyes were intense. He stared hard at Winston Churchill, frowning when the statesman frowned, nodding his head when Churchill made a comment on the proceedings.

Elisa noted that Charles's lower lip jutted out in imitation of Churchill when Colonial Secretary Malcolm MacDonald took the podium. When the same look of defiance as Churchill wore filled the child's eyes, Elisa knew that Charles had found his hero. A sense of gratitude filled her eyes with tears.

MacDonald began to speak, and his words rang out the death knell for those trapped in Germany. But Elisa, like Charles, had heard a sermon on the steps of Commons. A one-line lesson in courage had been etched on their hearts.

"The tragedy of people who have no country has never been so deep as it is this week," MacDonald began.

"Hear! Hear!" cried Churchill and a handful of others.

"But I must sound a word of warning . . ."

Murphy leaned close to Elisa. "Here comes the blow."

"When we promised to facilitate a national home for the Jews, we never anticipated this fierce opposition by the Arabs."

Charles sat forward on the edge of his seat. His small, pale hands were clenched in tight fists on his lap as he listened and tried to make sense of what was being said.

Yes, it was true that the Jews had made the desert bloom in the Mandate. Yes, it was also true that the Arabs poured across the border at a rate of 35,000 a year to enjoy the benefits of that progress. But it was equally true that they had now begun to fear Jewish domination. The riots of the Mufti's men were purely a matter of protest against further Jewish immigration. England was being forced to pay attention. *How could the persecuted souls of Germany settle in a place where they would surely be slaughtered?*

The men on Chamberlain's side of the room cheered MacDonald as he finished. Such reasoning made sense. If the Jews went to Palestine and were slaughtered, then they were Britain's responsibility. If they remained in Germany, the blood was on the hands of Hitler. No one liked responsibility!

Churchill's turn came; Louis slept on, while Charles rested his chin on the rail to drink in every word and mannerism.

Churchill studied his notes in silence for a moment; then his glasses came off again and he shoved his notes back into his pocket. He would speak from the heart. In one final loving call to courage, he raised his eyes to Charles. The look was steady and unwavering, as though he were speaking to every child still suffering within the Reich. All of them watched him. Every mouth was marked with a thin pink scar, but every heart was guileless and innocent. A million young faces looked down through the eyes of Charles Kronenberger and asked for help.

Perhaps, Elisa thought as she observed the silent understanding which passed between the great man and that small boy, Churchill had invited Charles here as a witness to his own heart.

A moment later the resonant voice filled the hall with its measured cadence.

"People . . . children . . . are dying, meeting grisly deaths from day to day. Only two weeks have passed since the Night of Broken Glass devastated the persecuted of Germany, and we have already forgotten their misery! People are dying. While here—" He swept a hand toward Chamberlain. "All that is done is to have debates and pay compliments and above all run no risk of making any decision to help!"

The faces of the opposition stared back with open contempt as he spoke. "Never give in," Elisa breathed. Her heart beat faster as she realized just how unpopular these words were. *How much* this man risked to speak out!

"In regard to our pledge for a Jewish homeland, it is obviously right for us to decide now that Jewish immigration into the Mandate should be equal to Arab immigration each year. My honorable friend has put the figure of Arabs crossing the Jordan at 35,000 a year. Jewish immigration should be equal. It is just! If the Arab gangs refuse to accept this, then we should consider our obligation to them discharged!"

The outcry of the opposition filled the hall and drowned out the voice of Winston Churchill. Someone behind Chamberlain howled that the reason for the troubles in Palestine was the presence of the Zionists! *"The Arabs could be managed if it were not for the Jews! After all, that is why the Arab gangs attacked—"*

As the crowd shouted Churchill from the podium, Elisa regretted that Charles had come here after all. But then she looked at him. He brushed his blond hair back defiantly and raised his chin. His blue eyes blazed angrily and he stood up, holding his hand high in the air for Churchill to see. Little fingers were raised in an unmistakable V sign.

Churchill inclined his large head in thanks. *Never give in!*

It was the winter of Munich, the season of defeat and appeasement of evil, Elisa thought as she listened to the uproar of seared consciences. But here blazed the bright flame of one candle that had been passed on to another fragile wick. The battle must be won now, one life at a time.

The outcry of those opposed to the immigration of children to Palestine began to die away. But a louder, more insistent sound penetrated the high windows of Commons above the gallery.

Horns and voices mingled together. The faces of the M.P.s reflected confusion, then concern. The unmistakable outrage of a massive crowd could be heard.

"SEND PARLIAMENT TO BERLIN!"

"NO ROOM IN COMMONS!"

"COMMONS CONCENTRATION CAMP!"

At a stern nod from Prime Minister Chamberlain, MacDonald stepped to the podium. The roar of the crowd extended from the streets in an unending wave.

"There you have the voice of the people of Britain! Our honorable friends may see by their outrage that we must consider the needs of our homeland first! There! There is the British reply to those who would embroil us in a conflict which—" His words were almost drowned out by a fresh blast of horns from small boats and barges on the Thames.

Elisa lowered her head with a heartache at such a demonstration against a hand extended to help the innocent. Charles sat up and smiled, not comprehending the meaning of it. The light from the windows filled his face. Louis woke up and frowned at the din.

"What is it?" he asked.

On the floor, MacDonald continued. "The people have spoken, and now it remains for us to respond to their wishes."

At that, a small elderly man in a dark suit hurried across the floor to whisper in the ear of Prime Minister Chamberlain. Chamberlain's face reflected concern, then astonishment. He gazed up at the vibrating windows as if trying to understand.

"They want the kids," Charles said, holding up his fingers to Churchill again.

"No, Charles—" Elisa started to explain. Then the stirrings among the men on the floor stopped MacDonald midsentence.

More blaring horns. Voices shouted from bullhorns as the Prime Minister rose and MacDonald stepped down.

"It seems . . ." Chamberlain said with croaking voice, "we are asked not to venture out. There is a . . . a demonstration, you see. People. Fifty thousand?" He looked over his shoulder at the messenger, who nodded. Yes. At least that many.

They packed Parliament Square and blocked the traffic of St. Margaret Street. Rushing through the gates of New Palace Yard, thousands had stormed the entrance of Westminster Hall, threatening to invade the House of Commons itself! A young clergyman had climbed the statue of Oliver Cromwell to lead the cheering crowd.

A chant began outside: "LET THEM COME! OPEN THE GATES!"

Churchill raised his head. Had he heard right? A slow smile spread across his face. Fifty thousand British men and women had taken to the streets! And now their voices joined the few within the government who had cast a vote for mercy.

"LET THEM COME! OPEN THE GATES!"

A few men stood up and stared at the windows. They gaped at one another. Clearly they had misjudged. Could it be?

Murphy patted Elisa's hand and hurried down the stairs and out into the lobby. The crowd had pushed its way in. Their shouts resounded from the high vaults of the ceiling. Over the arched doorways of the lobby, the mosaic saints of the Kingdom gazed down serenely at the sight. Signs dripped wet from the rain:

SUFFER THE LITTLE CHILDREN TO COME UNTO ME!

THERE IS ROOM AT THE INN!

OPEN THE GATES!

LET THEM COME IN!

The faces of the thousands who crammed in, blocking the doorways, were not angry, merely determined. Blue-coated bobbies did not push them back into the rain. They faced the arched doorway leading to the Commons chamber. The thick oak panels did not keep their voices from penetrating the room.

As the masses waited outside, an emergency bill for child refugees from Nazi Germany passed within minutes. Ten thousand British families willing to take children filled a list in one day. There was a waiting list of others who longed to help.

The people of England had spoken, indeed.

───────────

The drab gray metal door was only one of fifty identical doors off a long, sterile corridor. There was no sound in the hallway except for the tramp of boots and the clanking of keys as cell number 17 was unlocked for Karl.

He stood outside, stubbornly refusing to enter until two guards nudged him firmly forward and then banged the heavy door closed behind him.

It was a red brick cell, constructed by civilian workmen to guarantee the strength and security of the structure. The cell had a concrete floor carpeted by a layer of straw, with a small drain hole in the center and a toilet in the back corner opposite the cot. The only illumination came from a light bulb screwed into a ceiling fixture far out of reach. Ventilation was provided by a barred window eight inches square.

As the sound of retreating guards echoed hollowly beyond the cell, Karl stared at this example of the Führer's mercy. This was, indeed, the cell of a favored prisoner. According to rumor, the former Austrian Chancellor Schuschnigg was somewhere in this cell block. Other high officials of the Nazi party had been brought to such a place when they fell out of favor with the Führer. Often they stayed just long enough to reconsider the error of their ways and appeal for pardon. Sometimes pardon was granted. Sometimes it was not.

Karl's eyes lingered on a small, rough wooden table at the head of the cot. On it were books, blank stationery, and a pencil for writing. For an instant his heart rose. *Was that a Bible on the table?* He rushed forward to retrieve a leather-bound volume from among the stack of pamphlets.

SELECTED READINGS FROM THE HOLY BIBLE. Karl opened it up and skimmed through it briefly. His joy left him. The readings, pulled from the context of their original place in the Scriptures, were arranged under headings like, *DUTY TO AUTHORITIES* and *WHAT GOD SAYS ABOUT THE JEWS.*

The title page of the twisted collection was emblazoned with a swastika and the symbol of the new Nazi state church. Shaking his head, he tossed the book onto the cot and picked up a pamphlet containing the virulent anti-Semitic writings of Martin Luther's old age. The spirit of Antichrist, it seemed, had been compiled in each of the booklets and writings selected to occupy Karl's hours in the cell.

Better to be filthy and stinking and hungry in the barracks with other men than in this place, Karl thought. For the first time since his arrest, a sense of loneliness overwhelmed him. He thought of Helen and Lori and Jamie. He remembered Christmas as it had been last year and the years before—the reading of the Christmas story from his precious, uncut Bible; the sound of voices raised to sing in praise of the little King born in a stable; the aroma of Christmas supper; and the look of delight on the faces of his loved ones as they unwrapped their gifts. Later, when everything had been cleaned up, Helen had lain in his arms and they had loved each other with the gentle passion grown from years of friendship, of knowing each other. And the children had slept a contented sleep.

Such memories rushed in on Karl with pressing grief. He dropped to his knees in the straw and moaned softly. *How much better to work beside other suffering prisoners! To struggle day to day, moment to moment, with cold and hunger and bleeding hands and then to fall exhausted on a plank bunk and sleep!* There was no mercy in this clean, bare cell. There was no comfort in the carefully chosen passages of the books left for him to read. In the barracks he had been comforted by giving comfort to others.

In this place there was no one to encourage; no one to help; no man with whom he could share his ration and say, *"I am here for this reason. . . ."*

In this cell, there was only Karl, and he knew that loneliness was the fiercest fire of all to try his faith.

The bathroom had been converted into a darkroom. Otto posted a sign on the door forbidding entrance until the passport photos were developed.

After rinsing the pictures, he placed them in the bathtub to dry. Otto brought them out for viewing after supper, and ignoring the moans from his subjects, he declared that the photographs were perfectly dreadful, just as all passport pictures were meant to be.

Willie was too young to be required to have his likeness on official identity documents. Babies changed too much from one week to another. Not even the rabid fanatics in the Nazi Ministry of the Interior expected that.

"His papers will be simple," Otto said cheerfully. "I can have them back in a matter of days."

"So what? He is not going anywhere without the rest of us." Peter watched lovingly as Willie pulled himself up to stand along the side of the sofa. He was trying so hard to walk! He looked at Peter as if to see whether Peter was proud of this latest accomplishment.

Otto did not answer Peter's statement. The truth was, it might be necessary to separate the family, to send each one out of the Reich a different way. Until that time, Otto was exploring the possibility of moving Willie and Marlene to families in Vienna who might be willing to shield Jewish children.

"How long will it take for my passport?" Marlene looked down unhappily at the pouting image of her face. "I won't show it to anyone."

"You'll show it when they ask you for it," Peter challenged. "Or they will arrest you and drag you off."

"But it doesn't look like me," she whimpered.

"Yes, it does. Ugly." Peter regretted saying it before it was out of his mouth. His mother insisted he apologize. Marlene made a face at him. Typical.

"We had better get our papers soon," Karin said to Otto. "Or I know two children who are likely to wake the dead with their arguing." She apologized to Otto. They had moved in on him, disrupted his life, and now he had to endure the bickering of Marlene and Peter. She knew he would be glad to be rid of them all.

"I will be glad when you are safe," Otto said quietly as he gathered up the pictures.

Peter eyed him from the sofa, where Willie happily pounded his big brother's leg, begging to be picked up. "Why are you doing this?" Peter asked.

"Maybe because I don't want to hear you and Marlene fight anymore." Otto smiled, trying to make light of the one unpleasant fact of their confinement.

"That's not what I mean," Peter said, picking up Willie and receiving a slobbery kiss. "I mean why—from the start—have you put yourself in danger for us? You don't owe us anything."

"Your father was a good man," Otto replied. "He died so that a lot of other men could live. This is just my way of fighting back. One small thing I can do. There are other men who also admired your father. I am getting help with your papers. You will seem as Aryan as Himmler himself when we get through." He still seemed cheerful, hopeful. "Just try, you and Marlene, not to kill each other before we get the details worked out."

Orde had not come to the evening meal at the Hanita mess hall. He had not spoken to anyone at the settlement all day. Moshe and Larry Havas walked together across the dark compound. The lantern in Orde's tent was still glowing. His shadow paced the length of the tan canvas, then back again.

"You think we should ask him if he wants to come listen to the radio?" Havas asked tentatively.

Moshe shook his head. "You ask him if you want. Not me. As a matter of fact, I want to sleep in another tent tonight. He is in one of those black moods."

Havas shrugged. "You can bunk with us if you don't mind the snoring."

"Better than growling."

The music from the old Philco radio filled the mess hall with pleasant echoes. It was American music from some big band at a New York hotel, someone said as Moshe and Havas took a seat beside Zach.

"Very mellow stuff," Larry said. "Too mellow. Depressing. What we need is a little Tommy Dorsey to wake us up."

"What we need," said Zach quietly as he stirred his coffee, "is for Captain Orde to snap out of it! He is like a dark cloud hovering over the entire settlement. We speak to him, and he grunts. Smile and wave, and he scowls. I was so happy this morning when I heard about the child refugee transports. I asked him what he thought about it. Ten thousand kids to England, and I thought he was going to hit me." Zach shook his head. "What do you think, Moshe? You bunk with him."

"I think you should shut up. Here he comes." Moshe jerked his head as the door swung back and Orde strode in. All conversation stopped dead. No laughter; nothing but a solemn awareness that the cloud was sweeping across the hall toward Zach.

Moshe did not look up. It seemed to him that the head of every man and woman in the room pulled in between hunched shoulders. Like a herd of tortoises, no one wanted to take the brunt of Orde's mood.

Zach pretended not to see Orde until he sat down beside him.

"Shalom, Orde."

"That means peace," Orde remarked sourly.

"Hello. Goodbye. Whatever," Zach tried to sound cheerful. It was the wrong move.

"What are you so happy about? Still gloating over ten thousand children going to England?" Orde scowled.

"Well, no. Although it is better than leaving them in the hands of the Nazis."

Orde glared hard at him. "Let me tell you what this means."

"Do I have a choice?" Zach still feigned lightness. The cloud darkened.

"You have been sold out by the British! Those kids are not coming home here to Zion! No, they are being torn away from families to be spread around like so many chicks from a hatchery! You have been paid off! Ten thousand children in England, and the Zionists will be expected not to bring up the issue of immigration again! Haj Amin and Hitler have won! The price for the nation of Israel is ten thousand children." He was fuming, his face flushed with anger. "There is dancing in Berlin tonight. The Mufti and the Führer are dancing on the graves of your people, and you expect me to smile?"

No. No one expected him to smile. But the feeling was that it would have been better if he had stayed in his tent.

"At least we can be happy that the children are saved," Larry ventured.

"Saved? They are consigned to the obscurity of wanderers and orphans! *This* is where they belong! *This* is the promised homeland for the people of the Covenant, and I tell you, we will do everything to bring them here!" He thumped the table. "Do you understand me? We will not be purchased with the lives of child-hostages! We will fight here, and everyone from England to Hitler and the Mufti will wonder what has gotten into us Jews in Palestine!"

No one dared to challenge his reference that he was one of them. "Don't forget, Orde," Zach said gently, "it is you who are on our side, not us on your side." Nervous laughter rippled through the room. "Come on, we are in this fight as one." Zach shrugged. "Although at times you out-Zion all the rest of us put together." He laid a hand on Orde's arm. "That makes you the most dangerous man in Palestine to the Mufti because you will fight, and to us Jews because you are a Christian who is fighting for us. And for Zion. It is a miracle we speak of among ourselves. It makes us think, you know?"

"Yes." Orde stared at his clenched hands and slowly relaxed them. "And we have the promise of His Word to back us up." He stood abruptly. "Well, then . . . I am tired. Shalom."

That was all. He left the settlers staring at one another, wondering at the odd man they called Hayedid, Friend. Moshe bunked with Larry, much preferring the snoring.

25

Treasures

The porter, a young peasant—thick-necked, short, and well-muscled—had dark features that made Lucy wonder if he was a Jew. He assured her he was Hungarian. After all, Vienna had been the capital of the Austro-Hungarian Empire. Many swarthy people who were not Jews lived in the city, and many Jews who were not swarthy. It was all very confusing to Lucy, at best.

Not wanting trouble, Lucy had checked his papers before she hired him. There was no *J* stamped on the page denoting a Jew. Only then did she offer him two marks for carrying the rugs for her.

As she instructed, he followed at a discreet distance, the rugs rolled and slung easily over his broad shoulders. He carried them as though they were not at all heavy and kept up with her quick pace.

DOROTHEUM. Lucy turned to make certain he was still behind her. Their eyes met, and he stopped and looked away. It was important, she had told him, that no one realize she was so impoverished that she must sell these priceless family heirlooms.

Lucy slipped in and climbed the stairs, pausing at the first landing to watch him enter after her and follow. A broad nod of her head told him that he was doing well. He followed her up to the fourth floor and found the appraiser's office identified by the sign *PERSIAN CARPETS*.

Once inside, the young man dropped the cargo where she pointed. Lucy paid him, gave him a pleasant smile of farewell, and hoped she would never see him again. He checked the coin in his hand and left without comment. These days it was common for people to sell off family possessions. His expression, which seemed to convey his amusement that such old rugs had any value at all, caused Lucy a moment of genuine uneasiness. Suppose she had paid two precious marks to have the things carried, and then they were of no value?

Suppose her ruse of faintness over the sight of brown chocolate stains was for nothing? She certainly could not repeat such a performance to gain Wolf's permission to empty the apartment of its furnishings.

Her palms were damp and cold by the time the appraiser turned his attention to her. He perched his spectacles on his nose and looked first at her and then at the rolled-up rugs beside her on the floor.

"Ah!" He smiled. "Kurdistani."

How did he know this from the bottom side of a rolled-up rug? "Yes," she agreed as if she knew. "Are they. . . ?"

He was already stooping beside them, feeling the texture and examining the closeness of the threads. "And a very fine example, too!"

This answered her question. "Family heirlooms," she said with just a hint of tragedy in her voice.

The appraiser looked up at her with a start. "Yes, I know." His voice was flat. His eyes narrowed slightly. "I knew the family."

She stared blankly at him. She was caught, and she knew it. Drawing a deep breath, she stared out the door and imagined this little man questioning her and calling the Gestapo. She thought of what Wolf would say.

Swallowing hard, she attempted a maneuver. "Not my family," she said softly.

He straightened and faced her with a hand on his hip. He dared her to lie, dared her to tell him that she knew the people who had once owned these rugs. His defiant and angry look pierced her defenses. "Would you care to explain?"

"I purchased them." She raised her chin. Why should she explain anything? "Now I need money."

"Surely you have a bill of sale for such fine merchandise." His gaze was steely, as if he spoke for the family they had been taken from.

Lucy looked desperately at the door. She wanted to run, to disappear into the crowds of the city. Tears, genuine tears, filled her eyes. "No. I have no bill of sale. I know nothing about these except they are supposed to be of value . . . and the truth is, I need money. I . . . they belong to my fiance . . . that is, he acquired them. I don't know how he got them, but he did."

"Is he a thief?" The appraiser seemed unmoved by this breakthrough of honesty.

With a shake of her head she replied, "No. He is an S.S. officer." She hesitated. "And he is not my fiance. And . . . I need . . . the money." Her words had fallen to a choked, pleading whisper.

The man reached around her and closed the door. Then he turned to face her. He was considering what this liar with the stolen carpets of his Jewish friends had to say.

He swept a hand toward the carpets. "These were taken . . . *stolen* . . . from the home of my friend. He asked that I might keep watch for them, just on the chance that they might show up." His lower lip protruded. The muscle in his jaw twitched angrily. "There are several others."

"No." Lucy was pleading. "He . . . he shipped them to Prussia."

At this news the appraiser gave her a sad, disgusted look. "Thief or S.S. officer—what is the difference?" He shrugged with resignation. "I could be arrested for that. And you, no doubt, would be arrested for stealing these from your S.S. thief. Therefore, you have something on me. And I have something on you. We are equal before the law." He gave a slight bow from the waist and managed a smile.

"I would not report you," she said. "I'll take them back and no one will ever—"

He held up his palm to silence her. "It is too late for that. You brought them here to sell them. Therefore, I will tell you that there is a reward for them. Not a big reward, considering their great value, but then, my friends have lost a great fortune here in Austria and elsewhere. So the reward is small. Two hundred marks each."

"Two . . . hundred . . . Marks? Each carpet? That is four hundred."

Lucy gazed at the rolled treasures in astonishment. She had not guessed! Could not have imagined! "But . . . won't the Reich steal them back again?"

He smiled briefly. "No," he said flatly, the simple word fraught with meaning. "My friend is out of the country on business. But I am authorized to pay the sum, and he will reimburse me. Therefore, are you in agreement with the reward?"

Lucy bit her lip, then frowned. Perhaps she had chosen the most valuable thing in the apartment to steal. "Well, I . . ."

"You will think of something to tell him. A bright Fräulein like you." He was already counting out the money, and the matter was settled.

———

Without questioning Otto, Karin Wallich had sewn their passport photos into the lining of his heavy, double-breasted camel's-hair coat. It was a fine overcoat. Worth a lot of money.

Otto did not wear it as he entered the Dorotheum; it was wrapped in paper suitable for storage. This was a wise procedure if a man wanted to pawn his best coat. Otto had also tossed in a handful of mothballs for good measure.

He entered the Dorotheum at the same moment as the tall, beautiful blond woman and her porter. He held the door open for them both and smiled at her obvious attempt to pretend that the rugs over the fellow's shoulders were not hers.

Otto knew this woman—or at least he knew *of* her. She was the mistress of Wolfgang von Fritschauer, now comfortably housed in the former flat of Elisa Lindheim—all thanks to Otto. It paid for Wolf to keep on Otto's good side.

His eyes lingered on her shapely legs as she ascended the steps. The rug bearer was also noticing the striking beauty of his employer. Heads turned everywhere in the Dorotheum. No doubt it was difficult for a woman like that to do anything without being noticed.

Otto had heard Wolf boasting about those Persian carpets. They were his best bargain in Vienna, Wolf said. So what was Wolf's mistress doing hocking the carpets? Maybe she just needed the money. Then Otto smiled at his own curiosity. After all, someone might look at him and wonder why he was pawning his overcoat.

At first the news of a home in England for refugee children sounded like an answer to the prayer of every Jewish mother in the Reich.

Peter watched his mother's face as she listened to the distant BBC broadcast. At first her eyes reflected joy; then the slow realization of separation from her children etched pain deeply into her expression.

"Those who may apply for the child transports must meet the following conditions. Applicants must produce a certificate of health demonstrating that the child has no physical or mental impairments—"

"That leaves Marlene out," Peter joked, but his mother did not smile. Marlene shot him a black look, although she could not fully understand the English words.

"Applicants between the ages of infancy and sixteen years of age will be considered. Passage through Poland to the Free Port of Danzig must be secured, and all economic conditions imposed by the government of the Third Reich must be complied with."

Those conditions included the payment of all fines and taxes owed by the parents of the children to the Nazi government. Papers must be current. Children of criminals against the Reich would not be allowed to immigrate.

At least twenty other conditions had to be met, but Peter did not hear them. Peter's father, Michael Wallich, was considered a criminal by the authorities. This one issue alone shattered any hope that they would be allowed to leave Vienna. They were hiding out precisely because they had no money to pay the additional fines that had been levied on them. Without cash to pay off the Gestapo, no papers would be issued. Beyond all that was the question of purchasing train passage to faraway Danzig.

Peter patted his mother on the back. "Well, Mother, you see? You can't sell us, and you can't even give us away! If you had money you could pay someone to take us to England but . . ." He shrugged. "It looks like you are stuck with us, yes?"

The pain did not leave Karin Wallich's eyes, even though she managed a smile for Peter.

All the sardine cans were empty.

"I'm sorry," Alfie told the mother cat, Joseph. "I don't have anything left but one can of peaches. I know you don't like peaches."

Joseph did not seem to mind. She flicked her tail and fed her kittens, then ran up the steps and disappeared. When she came back, she cleaned her whiskers as if she had just eaten a sardine, and then she fed her kittens again.

Alfie would have liked it if he could eat, too. He saved the last can of peaches for two more days and did not open it until his stomach felt as if it were chewing itself.

Now there was nothing left at all, and Alfie's stomach hurt again. He sat still because his head was spinning. The kittens were fat and round. Joseph had lots of milk for them and did not ask Alfie for sardines. This made Alfie think that maybe Joseph knew where to find food on the outside.

Joseph licked her babies clean while Alfie stacked his empty cans. He put his tin soldiers on top of one another but felt too weak to play with them.

"I am hungry, Joseph," he said. "Do you know where food is?"

The cat smiled a wide cat smile and licked her lips. She got up from her blanket and shook her babies loose. Then she walked toward the steps. *Yes,* she seemed to say, *I know where there is food.*

Alfie stooped and scooted all the kittens back into one wiggling heap on the blanket. He put a diamond ring in his pocket in case he might need to trade it for food.

Joseph waited patiently for him at the top of the steps and then dashed out from the gate while he fumbled with the lock.

It was daylight, clear and not too cold. The sky shone blue behind the jumble of bare branches, and Alfie looked up at the sky and laughed. It had been a long time since he had been out of the dead-Halder house. It felt very good to have sunlight on his face again.

He followed Joseph, who strolled toward the stone wall surrounding the churchyard. The wall was taller than Alfie's head, but the cat jumped over it easily. Alfie went back to the secret opening through the fence and crawled through. He took a deep breath and then looked around to see where Joseph had gone. She sat on a stone bench beneath a tree. She waited for Alfie, then bounced across the grass and then along the sidewalk in front of New Church.

Even though Alfie was hungry and light-headed, he smiled and waved at passing cars. It had been so long, and today was a better day than the day the men had put up the boards and signs all over New

Church. Things looked almost normal except for the black heap where the Jewish church had been.

There were city sounds and clanging trolley bells and people walking into shops up the street. Joseph looked over her shoulder at Alfie, her fur shiny in the sunlight. She walked straight toward the ruins of the Jewish synagogue, and Alfie saw a line of people waiting to go into a building just behind where the church had burned.

Alfie breathed a deep breath. He smelled food. Joseph smiled at him. He picked her up and held her as he crossed the street.

He took a place at the end of the line. The faces of the people did not look very happy. There were not very many men—mostly women, a lot of children, and some old men. All of them looked at him strangely; they knew he was different. Alfie was sure that they could see he was a Dummkopf.

"Is there food here?" he asked a pretty woman in a brown tweed coat and a black scarf. Her eyes were sad. She looked at Joseph and stroked her head.

"The soup kitchen is open," said the woman. "You have a pretty cat."

"Can I get food here?" Alfie's stomach growled. "I don't have any more sardines."

The woman looked down at two little girls who clung to her skirts. "This is the line for the children's transport."

"Where can I get food?" Alfie said. "I am hungry, and my cat said I could eat here."

She smiled slightly and stroked Joseph's head again. "You have a smart cat," she said. "Stay with me. I will make sure you get something."

"My name is Alfie. My cat is Joseph. She has kittens."

The lady smiled a little more, but Alfie could see that her eyes were still sad. "Where do you live, Alfie?"

He thought for a moment and decided it would not be good to tell her too much. "I live with my mother."

An old woman standing in front of the nice lady leaned in and whispered, "I didn't know there were any of them left on the streets."

Alfie knew what she meant, but he pretended not to notice the way the grandmother looked at him.

"Poor thing," said the young woman. Her children stared up at Alfie and the cat. They knew that he was a Dummkopf, but he smiled back at them in a friendly way.

"Would you like to pet my cat?" he offered. "Her name is Joseph."

"Are you going to England on the transport ship?" one of the little girls asked.

Alfie thought about it. "Yes. I will go."

"Mama, can he go?" asked the second girl.

The old grandmother shook her head and put a finger to her lips. "Only healthy children," she whispered.

She thought Alfie did not hear, but he did. She did not mean children who were not sick. Alfie knew that she meant no Dummkopfs could go to England on this ship.

"Maybe I won't go," Alfie said bravely, "because I do not want to leave my cat Joseph and her kittens. They would miss me. Maybe they would even starve if I was not here to feed them." Saying this made him feel better.

A short man in a torn sweater walked down the line. He handed out forms that everyone took and studied. Alfie took the white paper also and pretended he could read it. As the line moved closer to the door, people filled in the blanks and talked about what it said.

"Only ten thousand children . . ."

"It is something, anyway."

"Do you suppose there will be room?"

Alfie folded his paper and put it in his pocket. *No room for Dummkopfs,* he told himself. But it was all right. He was needed. Joseph needed him. God had brought him there to care for Joseph and to save little Werner's life.

Later, over a bowl of thin soup and a piece of bread, Alfie felt much better about things. He would come back here if they let him. These were Jews, he decided, and he was glad they shared their soup with him even though he was not smart.

The present site of the German Railways Information Bureau was at number 6 Teinfaltstrasse in Vienna. It had been taken over, Lucy heard, from a Jewish-run banking firm after the Austrian Anschluss. It was of suitable grandeur for the lofty aspirations of those who wished to travel within the ever-expanding borders of the Great Reich. It provided an atmosphere of elegance and prosperity as well as customary German efficiency.

Lucy stood outside and gazed longingly through the gold lettering. *Reichsbahnzentrale.* The eagle and the swastika were stenciled above. To the right, a large travel poster showed a photograph of a luxury hotel and spa in the newly acquired Sudetenland. On the left, an even larger photograph depicted a quaint row of old burgher houses with steep roofs and half timbers and a carved coat-of-arms on each door. The charming scene reminded Lucy of the lovely old houses in Munich. But this place was not in the Reich, in spite of the Teutonic appearance and the fluttering Nazi flag frozen in the corner of the poster.

"Danzig." Lucy repeated the name on the poster. "VISIT DANZIG." It looked like a place she might want to visit, a place to hide. Everyone in Danzig spoke German. This made it more appealing as a destination than France, since Lucy spoke only German. She had wanted to run away to Paris, but it occurred to her as she listened to Wolf order dinner in a French restaurant that it would be impossible. Belgium and Holland were likewise ruled out. Wolf could speak half a dozen languages and never failed to seize every opportunity to do so in front of her. The effect was intended to make her feel small and stupid. In fact, it made her consider ways to get around her limitations.

The travel poster advertised FREE CITY OF DANZIG—German to the core and yet not a part of Hitler's Reich. It was, Wolf had explained sourly to her one night, the last of the old-time city-states. Like the Vatican in Rome, it had its own government. It had once been a part of Germany, a part of Wolf's own Prussia. It had been vilely cut off from the Fatherland after the war, he said, to provide the one port to the Baltic Sea for Poland. The League of Nations administrated the 200 square-mile port, but the customs house was staffed by Poles. The police force and army were also Polish.

Wolf spoke about Danzig with fire in his eyes. He still considered it to be German, just like Austria and the Sudetenland. One day, no doubt, it would be reincorporated into the Reich. But for now, Lucy only cared that the language in Danzig was plain German and the politics were not. The swath of Polish territory separating Danzig from Germany would also separate Lucy from Wolf.

"Danzig!" She whispered the name hopefully and entered through the tall glass doors of the building. It still looked and smelled like a bank. Pillars of green-and-white-swirled marble supported the echoing ceiling. Clerks stood in cages behind the counters, and long lines of would-be travelers waited for the next available clerk. Oak racks along one poster-covered wall held timetables for steamship lines and railroads and attractive brochures depicting every possible destination within the Reich and without. Fresh new brochures had been printed immediately after the borders of Czechoslovakia had been eliminated. Under the heading Czechoslovakia few pamphlets remained. A forlorn row marked *Prague* had been picked clean. Lucy supposed that many German officers, like Wolf, knew that the next destination on the Reich map was Prague.

She shuddered, glad she had not decided to travel to Prague. It would be swallowed up soon enough, and then what would she have done?

Just below Czechoslovakia and to the right were a dozen different booklets showing the glorious sights of Danzig. Lucy picked up one and thumbed through it. She looked guiltily over her shoulder, wondering if anyone in the bustling office could read her thoughts. *No S.S. maternity home for Lucy Strasburg! A tiny room and a job in Danzig!* She would say her husband had gone to sea, and when she had enough money she would go away too. Maybe she would take French lessons and learn to speak so well she could move to Paris after all.

She gathered up the pamphlets and shoved them furtively into her handbag. Then she walked to the rack marked RAILWAY TIMETABLES and then on to the one labeled SHIPPING LINES.

A feeling of exhilaration filled her as she hurried out of the office. No one stopped her. No one cared that she might want to take a little trip and never come back.

She could hide her treasures from Wolf, and he would never know she was gone until it was too late. All his S.S. laws could not touch her in Danzig. Such matters were not addressed in travel guides, but Lucy knew that in the little port, *she* would be the mother of the baby she carried.

The news of child refugee transports whispered over the barely audible radio in the study of New Church. The four children sat in a tight semicircle around the receiver. They pressed their heads together and tried to breathe softly as the details and conditions for immigration were spelled out.

"Of course this changes everything," Jacob said when the news was over.

"It does not change anything," Lori insisted. "You heard all the regulations to get on one of those boats."

Jacob was adamant. He switched off the radio and scooted back on the floor to lean against the bookshelf in the darkness. "The regulations are—"

"No children of political prisoners," Lori interrupted. "That means us, in case you have not figured that out. They mean to hold us hostage here, threaten our parents with some harm against us. I have known that all along."

"The conditions are only for getting out of Germany and to Danzig with the official Nazi seal of approval on our documents," Jacob said.

"Which we and other hostage children like us will never get. Many are called, Jacob, but few will be going to England. The Nazis will never let us go."

"So what? They would not let us go to Prague, either, and we have been talking and planning all day. Listen! If we can get out of Germany at one border, why not another? And if we can get to Danzig, maybe the English will let us get on one of their boats, out of reach of marching armies. The German army will have to swim the Channel before they take England. I want to put as much distance as possible between me and them!"

Lori sat silent considering the logic of his reasoning. Maybe he was right. And yet, Prague was a certain refuge. Maybe Mama would be in Prague. Certainly the people there knew Aunt Anna and could contact her in England, tell her that Lori and Jamie were safe.

"Well?" Jacob demanded a response. "It's closer to the Polish border from Berlin. It makes perfect sense . . ."

She gazed intently into the darkness, trying to decide what they should do, trying to see what Mama and Papa would want them to do. One choice seemed as dangerous as the other. The Czechs were turning back refugees at every crossing. The Poles actually drove truckloads of prisoners to the German side of the frontier and deposited them in prison camps.

Lori had found an outdated map of Germany in her father's study and presented it as her credentials for participation in the planning meeting in the choir-robing room. Jacob accepted her offering with a reluctant nod. He did not want her to think a map would entitle her to make any decisions, especially not with word of the refugee transports from Danzig.

He spread the map on the floor and they knelt down to study it. Jacob, on the south, had the best perspective. Lori, to the north, read the names of cities and nations upside down. Jamie stared silently from the east and Mark glared in the west.

Tiny dots, pinpoints on thin paper, linked by a grid of black lines. Ten thousand children would be passed from one dot to another.

The four sat in thoughtful silence for more than a minute as they considered what lay between the dot of Berlin and the dot of Prague.

"Look," Jamie said at last, tracing his finger along the thick black line of the main railroad from Berlin to the east. "It is only two and a half inches from here to the border of Poland. And another half inch to Danzig and the transports."

Lori reached across the map to touch Prague in the south. "But it is still only two inches farther to Prague. We should not think about Danzig. They will not take us on the ships to England. Papa said we should go to Prague; that is where his friends are, where the refugee children's headquarters are. Aunt Anna started that program. I'm not going to Danzig!"

Jacob leaned closer to the map. "There are more Nazi storm troopers between Berlin and Prague since the Sudetenland has fallen. It will be a more dangerous passage for us. And these things . . . here, where the Czech border used to be . . . these are mountains."

"Not very big ones," Mark said.

"But there will be snow," Jacob tapped the mountain fortifications that were now firmly in Nazi control. "Snow and storm troopers between Berlin and Prague. I say we head north instead. We reach Danzig. Call your aunt in England."

Lori drew back, sitting on her haunches and clenching her fists angrily. "You heard the rules. We do not qualify for those ships to England!"

"To Danzig!" Jacob's reply was firm. He was the leader. If it was up to Lori, she would simply sit in the church until the Nazis knocked it down on her head. She still hoped her father would come back! What did she know? "Yes. To Danzig. It is closer, and there will be fewer troops to get past."

Her chin trembled as she searched for words to express her outrage. "No! I am not going to Danzig! Papa said Prague, and so Jamie and I will go to Prague! If we *must* leave here, we should go where Papa wanted us to go. That way he'll be able to find us. Besides, *you* said we should go to Prague!"

Jamie's face reddened. He did not like his sister making decisions for him. This was not for a mere girl to decide. "I am going where Jacob goes."

"You are going right where Papa and Mama wanted us to go—the refugee center in Prague! Otherwise, how will they find us when—?"

"There is no *when*," Jacob growled in a low whisper. "Stop thinking they are coming for us! They are in prison, or worse!"

"Shut up!" Lori cried. Her fist came from the north and glanced off his cheek in the south. "You always think the worst!"

The blow did not hurt Jacob. He touched his hand to his cheek and smiled wryly at the attack. "You hit like a girl. You think like a girl."

His amusement only made her more angry. With a strangled yelp she threw herself against him, her fists pummeling his face and shoulders as he fell backward on the floor and raised his arms to shield himself.

Quick-thinking Mark rescued the precious map from Lorie's scrambling feet. Jamie drew back in amazement at his sister's wrath. He had never seen such a thing from his sweet and gentle sister! Not ever! Now, here was Lori, slugging away while Jacob rolled back beneath the blows and tried to stiffle his laughter.

"Join the Hitler Maidens," Jacob mocked. "They will teach you how to fight!"

At that, Lori's eyes widened. She hit him harder, but still he laughed at her as her fists bounced off the shield of his big hands.

"Anything! Anything is . . . better—" She reached for his hair and pulled. He gasped with surprise and grasped her arm, angry.

"You little—" He jerked her back and down to the floor, pinning her without effort while she kicked and called him a filthy Nazi commando, a Gestapo slime, and an atheist.

"You are rotten! *Rotten!*" she hissed, kicking her legs hard as he sat on her and held her arms against the floor. "Let me go! Let me—" Tears of hot anger spilled over. "I won't go with you! Not ever!"

Her knees struck him in the back, but he held her firmly in place. "Now you listen to me!" Jacob's voice was just as angry as hers. "You have been nothing but trouble! You whine about your parents—"

"When Papa gets back—"

"He's not coming back!" He gave her a shake and then let her cry for a moment, then continued. "*So!* No one is coming to save us; do you hear me, Lori? It is up to us! We cannot survive if we argue—and you argue about *everything*!"

"You are . . . unreasonable!" The rage in her voice fell away to frustration and grief. "I cannot! I have not . . . you have not even let me have a bath! I want a bath! I want . . . my mother and father! I want to go to Prague so they will find us!"

Jacob glared down at his sobbing captive. She closed her eyes tight but tears still escaped. Her pretty face was red. Her nose was running. A flash of pity for her coursed through him. "Lori . . ." he began gently, but did not let her up.

"And you are so . . . brutal! I am glad to know!" She tried to raise her arm against his weight. "You hear me? I am *glad* to find out how mean you are, Jacob Kalner, because I . . . I didn't know how *mean* you were!"

The blow hit home. Jacob had not thought of himself as mean. He had only been cautious and careful. His rules and regulations had been for their safety. Somebody had to be the leader, and it certainly could not be this sniffling female. "I am the leader," he said defensively. "Somebody has to be the leader, and it's me."

"You're a bully. Like *Hitler!* If you weren't Jewish, you'd be a basher, just like they are! And I'm glad I know the real you because as soon as we get out of here I *never*—" She struggled against him. "I never want to see you again!"

Jacob looked up at Mark and Jamie, who watched from a safe distance. Mark shrugged as if to say, *What do you expect?* Jamie scratched his head in embarrassment at his sister's outburst. Neither boy seemed to agree with her. "If I let up, will you promise not to—"

"I promise nothing!" she sobbed back.

He pressed harder on her arms, and she winced with pain. "Promise. And we will talk reasonably."

"Let me up! Brute! Bully! *Adolf Hitler!*"

Fresh anger flooded him at her words. He bent down over her, his nose an inch away from hers. "Take it back!"

She turned her face away. He pressed his lips against her ear and whispered fiercely, "Take it back, or I will—"

"You will *what*? Hitler! Hitler! Hitler!"

"I should throw you out of here. Turn you over to the S.S.! I'm glad to see what a stubborn person you really are! All this time I was thinking you were such a—"

"Such a what?" she demanded, raising a knee hard into his back.

"Such a pleasant person! I am only glad to have this time to get to know the real you, that's all! Not the kind of girl a man wants to . . . be trapped with . . . that's all!" He scowled up at the boys who still watched the struggle with amazement. He addressed them as their leader. "If we did go to Prague, it would only be because I want to get rid of her, and she will not be gotten rid of any other way." He released his grip, but remained sitting on her stomach. She did not move for a moment. The print of his fingers showed red on the skin of her wrists. "You are a lot of trouble but I will take you to Danzig with us anyway," he said. As she sneered back defiantly, he rose and stalked out of the basement, pausing only to gesture to his troops that they should follow and leave the mutineer to herself.

26

The Only Way Out

Over a hot cup of tea, Lucy studied the travel brochures and time-tables as though every word contained a happy prophecy about her future. Within each paragraph she inserted her own name. In the frame of every photograph, she imagined herself smiling in the sun on the steps of the old brick Marienkirche cathedral, or sipping a glass of white wine in a little cafe along the Grosse Alle. She scrutinized the names of little shops housed in the gabled buildings of Langer Market. In one of those shops she would find a job and pass her days happily gazing out on that very street!

At this point Lucy frowned, sat back, sipped her tea, and looked away with a long stare of worry. *And what will happen if I do not find a job?*

She flipped to the part of the brochure that discussed in detail the currency restrictions for leaving the Reich.

The financial situation has made it necessary to limit the amount of currency of any kind that may be taken out of Germany. The maximum permitted as this is published is 200 marks.

The cold chill of reality set in. She stared bleakly at the rates of exchange. Two hundred German marks was equal to just under fifty dollars. One American dollar was equal to one Danzig gulden. Legally she could take not one penny more than that amount out of the Reich. To attempt to do so would result in arrest for smuggling and instant imprisonment after the first customs check.

Lucy had seen firsthand how thorough the Nazi customs officials were. Some months before, she had witnessed the arrest of a Jewish couple who had concealed currency in the lining of their coats.

The memory made Lucy blink. Jews, she knew, could take only ten marks from the country. She had thought their arrest was only right as she had watched them being led away. But she was considering the same crime against the state. Her cheeks reddened with a flush of shame at her former self-righteousness. She had raised her head in disdain as the pale woman had begged the officers to let them go. How unfeeling Lucy had been then when Wolf had haughtily uttered, *"Jewish swine! Trying to steal from the Aryan people!"*

With a shudder of regret, Lucy pulled her attention back to her own troubles. *HOTELS. Danziger Hof, 100 rooms (6 with baths) 2–3 guldens per day.*

"No," she muttered aloud. All her funds would vanish within two weeks at that rate, even if she gave up eating! "There will be no sipping of white wine in a cafe," she sternly warned herself as she skimmed down the list to the bottom. *Continental, 35 rooms opposite the Main Station. 1 gulden per day.*

There was nothing in the booklet any cheaper. Lucy mentally marked the place and resigned herself to the fact that even before she found a job, she would have to search for a boardinghouse where meals were included with a room.

Such restrictions made the matter of counting her assets seem foolish now. What was the purpose of selling her watch and rugs and her grandmother's silver crucifix if all the cash would be confiscated, anyway?

With a sigh, Lucy pushed away the brochures and timetables. She stared, unseeing, across the rooftops of Vienna. Perhaps this was all futile. Maybe she was, indeed, destined to be a prisoner in the elegant Lebensborn. Perhaps she should simply resign herself to giving up the baby. Certainly Wolf's arrogant self-assurance in this matter was his knowledge that she was trapped. How could she leave Germany? And if she did leave, how would she survive?

Her tea grew cold in the cup. She wanted to ask God for help, but she dared not. Why should she expect her prayers to be heard?

Once again the vision of Stephanie Bridge and the cold waters of the Danube coursed through her mind—a vision as easily imagined as the streets of Danzig. Perhaps it was the only way out, after all.

The obvious distortions and lies published by the State Church and pronounced by men like Gustav Dorfman did not threaten Karl Ibsen. He knew the Scriptures; he could recognize in an instant where whole passages had been lifted out of context and mutilated to suit the aims of the Nazi party. Reading the booklets and inwardly debating their twisted contents became a game with him, a mental and spiritual exercise. If other Nazi clergymen came to debate him in his cell, he would be ready for them. He could reply with the whole truth of God's Word.

At first, this confidence had made him smile. All these years he had preached the importance of memorizing the scriptures not by isolated verses but in the context of their whole meaning. He had not foreseen how valuable that lesson would be to him. But then, he had not ever imagined being locked in a tiny cell with no other company than a stack of printed lies.

The theology of the Nazi church was not the big lie that attacked Karl in the darkness of the night. The battle was much more subtle and much more dangerous.

As dawn crept through the tiny window of his cell, he lay beneath the thin blanket on his cot and listened once again to the whisper: *Once I was of use to God. Now what good is my life? What testimony do I have in this utter silence and loneliness?*

Karl could hear the distant whistle of the train to Danzig. The counterpoint of the prison loudspeakers echoed in the clear morning air.

He closed his eyes and pictured the groaning awakening in the barracks, the shouting guards, the growling dogs. The whisper came to him again: *You stayed here to help them. To minister to the suffering of this place. And here you are, locked in a cell. You are somewhat warm. You are fed. You have paper on which to write. And you are of no use to anyone here.*

Outside in the corridor, Karl could hear the rattle of the approaching meal cart. He would get thick, lukewarm porridge, a slice of bread, and a cup of tasteless coffee—an elegant meal compared to the breakfast given to Richard Kalner and the others in the barracks.

Karl sat up slowly as the meal slot at the bottom of the door slid back and the tray was shoved through. He stared at it, wishing he could give some of the abundance to those who needed it more than he did. The voice inside grew louder: *Maybe there was some reason for being a martyr when you could minister to the others. But this is pointless! You are separated from your family. You are more silent than you would be if you had signed the Nazi paper! At least you could do something if you left this place! Why not sign what they want and leave? You serve no one in this place.*

The meal slot shut with a clang. He stared at the food tray angrily, resenting the luxury of a meal that denied him the right to say, *I am here for Christ. I stay among the suffering and the hungry to serve my King, to share the comfort of God's love with others in need.*

A sense of guilt hung over him as he prayed over his meal. He ate it all, every bite, with the awareness that every morsel was precious. At the far end of the corridor the cart rattled back, picking up empty trays. Karl took his pencil and wrote the note he had written every morning since he had been placed in the cell: *LET ME GO BACK TO THE PEOPLE I HAVE COME TO MINISTER TO. PASTOR KARL IBSEN.*

He never received any acknowledgment of his request. The official answer of the Nazi state church was that it was not suitable for any Aryan to minister to a Jew. Karl knew that answer from the booklets. They were all lies, yes, and yet, still he listened to the whisper: *Why not tell them what they want to hear and go free?*

After lunch, Moshe lay back on the cot and watched Samuel Orde scribbling away at the desk against the back wall of the tent. It was not a desk, really, but two planks laid out on sawhorses pilfered from the Hanita workshop. It served its purpose.

When Orde was not training the young men of the Yishuv to fight like Englishmen, to march sixty miles a day and survive hardships in the desert, he spent his off-hours writing about it at this desk.

Does he ever sleep? Moshe wondered drowsily. His feet ached from last night's hike over rough terrain. His back and neck felt as though he had been trampled by a herd of elephants. He wanted only to stretch out and sleep. But there was Orde—writing, writing, checking notes like a bank executive, putting sections of paper to one side and shuffling other sections together.

The stack of manuscript pages grew day by day. While some members of the Special Night Squad returned to the plow during the daylight hours, Orde plowed through his *magnum opus*. Moshe had come to find out what it all meant.

"What is it?" Moshe asked at last.

"A training manual for the army of the future nation of Israel. And for the Haganah to use until there is an official army, of course."

It was an answer, but Moshe had not been asking *that* question. He wanted to know what drove Orde to work so hard. Why did he love the thought of Zion, the Jewish homeland, so much that he dedicated all his life and training to moving it nearer to reality . . . Or at least to helping keep the dream alive in these perilous times?

"No." Moshe tried again. "I mean, why are you doing it?'

Orde did not lay his pen down or turn around. He kept writing as he spoke. "It seems important for you to have a training manual, one particularly fitted to this terrain and these fighting conditions. Also, it seems important that I put down on paper what we are fighting for— the specific promises God has given in His Word about Israel and the return of your people to the land." He paused for an instant, the pen held just above the paper, poised to continue. "Also . . . I have the feeling I may not be here with you much longer."

This was not exactly the reply Moshe had wanted, either. The ominous foreboding in Orde's voice made Moshe sit up in alarm. "Don't say such things, Hayedid. It is bad luck," he said. He had already lost his brother and did not relish the thought of losing his English friend.

"Luck has nothing to do with it." Orde laid the pen down and turned to look at Moshe. His expression was kind, as if Moshe's concern had touched him.

"I am trying to ask you . . . not just about this book of yours, but about why you do this? Why do you care so much what happens to the Jewish people? You must be one of a handful. Other Englishmen resent the way you help us, resent your faith. We all see it, even when you slap a man for coughing when we are on a sortie, even when you are so harsh with us that we think we cannot walk another step. You keep on walking yourself, and so we must follow where you lead us. How do you have the strength? And *why*?"

"Ah. So that is your question, is it?" Orde seemed amused by this burst of emotion, confused though it was. "I can tell you this, Moshe . . . I keep walking to get back to Hanita so I can write this book for you!"

"You could get killed," Moshe challenged. "The Mufti calls you the most dangerous man in Palestine. There is a great reward for your head. Quit joking with me, Orde. I want to know why you are so interested in us!"

Something deeper filled Orde's eyes. He considered the question. "Your Messiah came through the root of Israel. He says His Covenant is with you forever, for a thousand generations. The Lord submitted himself like a lamb of sacrifice to pay the penalty of my sins. Mine. Samuel Orde. My many sins He took on himself."

Tears, real tears shone in Orde's eyes. "I am *so grateful* for His love and kindness. I really believe that He considers the people of the Covenant His own dear children. Satan desires that the promises God made to the Jewish people be broken, that you also be slaughtered like lambs. No Jews. No Israel. Because then God would be a liar."

He frowned. "Is that possible? Could evil stamp out the Covenant? I don't know. But there is a battle going on here to do just that. And I am a soldier. I understand battles; fighting for what is right. So I am here. This is a spiritual battle between good and evil, light and dark. Some men will fight it with prayers and words of peace. I am called to fight with my sword, as David fought the Philistines. It is the least I can do for my King. He died for me. Should I not be willing then to die for His beloved people?"

Moshe had no response. He had a thousand questions, but maybe he did not want to hear the answers Samuel Orde would give him. And so he lay back down and closed his eyes and pretended to sleep while the scratching of Orde's pen continued for hours.

The tickets came to Otto's box in a sealed envelope direct from the Berlin headquarters of the Abwehr, military intelligence. Inside was a note on the letterhead stationery of Admiral Canaris himself.

Officer Wattenbarger,

Congratulations on a job well done in Vienna. These tickets were purchased in advance with great difficulty. Our hope is that you will find some relief from the cares of duty in these most enlightening shows.

Admiral Canaris
Chief of Abwehr

There was no mistaking Canaris's meaning. The job well done was the matter of getting the cyanide tablet to Michael Wallich before the Gestapo staff butchers could make him talk. Michael's easy death had saved the neck of Canaris and every other high traitor to the Nazi cause. Canaris owed a debt of gratitude to Otto, but much more to Michael Wallich. A handful of tickets seemed a pitiful reminder that Michael had risked everything for a democratic Germany and lost.

Otto fanned the tickets out on his desk, twelve in all. Two for each Wednesday night performance over the next six weeks.

The seats for the raucous American jazz performance had been sold out in Vienna for a month.

D' FAT LADY
FAMOUS AMERICAN JAZZ TRIO
DIRECT FROM PERFORMANCES
NEW YORK—PARIS—LONDON—BERLIN

And now they were coming to Vienna. Posters and leaflets were everywhere. Every high Nazi party official and officer in Vienna was scrambling for seats—anything to provide some relief to the endless concerts and Strauss waltzes morning, noon, and night.

Tickets to hear American jazz, for Otto and a guest—pure gold, no doubt, worth a trunkload of fine china or a fine Persian rug. This was a strange and extravagant gift, considering that tickets were being resold now on the black market for many times the original price. Otto had heard yesterday that a certain S.S. officer had procured two seats by jailing an Austrian furrier until he agreed to pay bail with his tickets.

Otto gathered them up and stuffed them into the envelope. He was not particularly fond of American jazz. Reselling the tickets could make him mildly rich, but he also knew that Admiral Canaris was a frugal man. Such a wildly expensive gift said more than a mere *thank you.*

Light from the lamp over the dining table glinted in Karin Wallich's red hair. She ladled up the soup and then smiled tenderly at little Willie when he flapped his arms enthusiastically at the prospect of supper.

Taken all together—the soft glow of her hair, the warm and tender look from mother to child—the effect was stunning. Otto looked away quickly, uncomfortable to discover that the widow of Michael Wallich was a beautiful woman. Desirable. He did not look at her face again throughout the meal. She did not speak to him except to answer his questions in monosyllables. Perhaps that distance was better kept intact.

Peter, who did not like Otto, still managed to carry on conversation: science, art, great books he had read. The boy was obviously as brilliant as his father. Such intelligence added to the personal risk for him. Intellect in a Jewish child was interpreted by Nazi doctrine as sly and devious.

The truth was, Peter made suppertime bearable for Otto. He pulled his mind away from . . . other things.

And so it was a surprise to Otto when he raised his eyes from Karin's hands and asked her, "Do you like American jazz?" An odd question to ask right in the middle of passing the bread. Her mouth curved slightly upward. Almost a smile.

"No," she replied.

Silence descended as Peter considered the reason Otto would ask such a question. Whatever the reason, Peter did not like the tiny smile on his mother's lips.

"Ah. Well . . ." Otto stammered and looked away from her. He was glad she had answered no; otherwise he might have done something insane and actually asked her to go out with him. For an instant he had forgotten why she was here. Forgotten why she could not step out into the sunlight or go shopping. The men in charge of Michael Wallich's case had said:

"Husbands tell wives secrets."

"Certainly the woman knows what he knew."

"If she is still in Vienna we will find her."

"But how to make her talk?"

"She has children, doesn't she? Hang a child by its thumbs, and there is no mother in the world who would not. . . ."

Otto stared at his spoon. The memory of that conversation made the color drain from his cheeks.

"Are you all right, Herr Wattenbarger?" Karin leaned forward with concern.

He had told her she was in danger because of Michael's activities. He had not told her everything—not about the danger to the children or the fact that they were the weapon the Nazis could use against her. That was why the rule had been made about the children of political prisoners not being allowed on the child refugee transports to England. The children were held hostage. The children assured that imprisoned mothers and fathers would do or say anything they were told.

"Herr Wattenbarger?" Karin rose from her seat and took a step toward him. *"Otto?"*

She had never called him by his Christian name before. The sound of it jerked him back to reality. "I . . . had a moment. Not feeling well . . ."

Everyone was staring at him, even baby Willie. Otto looked at the baby, then at the delicate face of the mother. The Gestapo was right. They could probably break Karin to pieces and she would not tell what she knew. *Ah, but to hurt baby Willie—one blow to that sweet face, the twist of his chubby arm . . .*

Otto managed a nervous laugh as she put her hand to his forehead. "I am not a fan of American music, either."

"If it affects you so badly, I would not mention it," she said. "Do you need to lie down?"

Her hand was cool. He put his hand to her arm in a gesture of appreciation for her concern. "I'll be all right. Just a long day. Thank you."

This much conversation between Karin and Otto sparked a smoldering look from Peter. The rest of the meal was eaten in silence.

Ronacher's Establishment had been known as the most prominent place of amusement among the wealthy of Vienna before the Anschluss. Located at number 9 Seilerstätte, just off the broad boulevards of the Ringstrasse, the place had always been packed with barons and dukes and a fair mix of their female counterparts.

The clientele had changed since the coming of the Nazis. Now peasant boys who had risen through the ranks to become high Nazi party officials sat in the velvet chairs of the elegant supper club. The food was still the best in Vienna. The entertainment was the most lively and modern in Europe. Backstage, electronic equipment was in place to broadcast live shows to other cities in Europe.

Tonight, holding tightly to Wolf's arm, Lucy walked through the double doors of Ronacher's and into the room she had only dreamed of as a child. Never had she imagined herself here at the finest nightclub on the Continent.

The glitter of medals and jewels did not hide the fact that most of the audience had humble beginnings, like Lucy's. Wolf looked over the other guests with a distinct air of disapproval. Noting table manners and wild laughter and the copious amounts of liquor being consumed, he leaned forward and muttered to Lucy, "All the plow horses have come wearing their racing silks tonight."

Once his disdain had intimidated her. It had also impressed her. Tonight she smiled back at him.

"Those of us raised on a farm have a certain respect for the plow horses. I think that these would be better called *sows' ears*, Wolf darling. Sows' ears who have come to Ronacher's in hopes of turning into silk purses, yes?" she beamed.

He swept his arrogant eyes over her and took her hand. "And what are you, my little peasant?"

"A fine brood mare, I think. Deserving of good food and comfort so my master may have a more pleasant ride."

Once again she surprised him. He appreciated wit, even in a farm girl. He had not suspected she was capable of such repartee.

"Give me a strong colt, Lucy, and one day I might give you Ronacher's as a gift."

"This one seat is enough." She turned her head toward the stage and dance floor where *D' Fat Lady Trio* would soon begin their performance. "I know how difficult it is to get tickets. I am the envy of everyone in the office, Wolf."

Champagne corks popped at nearly every table. Wolf ordered French champagne, the best on the list. Then he proceeded to name the various politicians and military men around the room. He knew the minute details of their low beginnings, and he recited facts with the attitude of an aristocrat scraping manure from his riding boots. Suddenly he paused in his monologue and laughed out loud at the sight of a red-bearded man seated at a table next to the stage.

"And will you look at that!" Wolf poured himself another glass of champagne. "There is the fellow you wanted to meet, the man who managed to find your apartment. And that peasant has the best seat in the house, too!"

"Gestapo?"

"Special investigations."

"He seems young." Lucy eyed the broad shoulders of the man dressed in an outdated blue serge suit. He was seated with a buxom, plain-looking young brunette in a cheap black dress right off the rack. Both of them looked out of place, and the woman seemed a bit drunk as well. She babbled on incessantly while the man with the red beard sullenly stared at the curtain.

"I wonder who he arrested to get such seats," Wolf said. "It pays to know this man, I tell you. Apartments. Furniture. Furs." He flipped the sleeve of Lucy's new coat. "Well, I manage all right. But look at Otto, will you? Sitting there without pretense in his blue suit. And all the medals and diamonds in the room do not have as good a seat as he has!"

There was, at least, some respect in Wolf's tone as he said this.

"Otto?" she asked.

"As much a peasant as you, but no racing silks, eh? Like the Führer. Yes, that is what I admire in the Führer. His plainness. A plain brown uniform. He does not attempt to conceal what he was, like Hermann Göring with all the tinsel on his chest. A plain and honest man, Hitler. He knows something about duty."

Wolf was speaking to himself; Lucy might as well have not been there. The man named Otto was simply a jumping-off place for Wolf's Prussian monologue about duty and discipline and the Aryan way of doing things.

Very boring stuff after the tenth time. Lucy tuned him out. She preferred staring openly at the tasteless display of new and stolen wealth that adorned these hopeful sows' ears.

Wolf had finished off almost an entire bottle of champagne by the time the curtain came up and *D' Fat Lady Trio* blasted away at every vestige of aloofness, duty, and Prussian reserve.

This black woman, with her wide white smile and a glittering dress plastered to her enormous body, rocked the place like a Munich beer hall. Even dressed in their finest, the peasants who attended this performance could not conceal their origins.

Lucy loved it. And when D' Fat Lady singled out the reserved and austere Otto, she laughed and applauded wildly with the others. Stiff and grim-faced, Otto was hauled into the spotlight, caressed and crooned at to the tune of "I'd Rather Be Blue." She twirled his hair around her big black finger; wrapped a silk scarf around his waist to pull him close. Only when he blushed a deep red and smiled with embarrassment did she finally let him go. He headed for his seat, and she pulled him back again!

It was delicious. Lucy only wished she might have seen such a woman pull Hitler onto a stage in his plain brown wrapper! *Could the Führer blush?* Lucy wondered. *And would Wolf still admire him if he actually showed some human emotion?*

This strange question replayed in Lucy's mind as she turned to watch Wolf's response to the show.

His eyebrows raised slightly, he smiled at D' Fat Lady as she wrapped the silk scarf around Otto's neck. But Wolf's smile was not pleasant. Lucy had seen this smile a thousand times, cold and filled with resentment and mistrust as the black hands tied a big bow in the bright pink scarf.

With a shrug Otto bowed slightly and returned to his seat amidst thunderous applause. Lucy thought she could see envy on the faces of the men around the room. After all, they had worn their medals to catch the spotlight. But the plain blue suit now wore the racing silks.

Wolf's eyes narrowed as the applause died away. "That will teach him to get tickets so close to the front." He was not amused.

D' Fat Lady gave a deep bow, then straightened up, clicked her heels together and raised her arm silently in a rigid Hitler salute. Then after a long pause she smiled and said in accented German, "That is how high my dog can jump!"

The crowd roared with laughter. The woman across from Otto nearly fell off her seat. Only two men in the room did not smile. Otto's face was hard as he removed the scarf and tucked it into his pocket. Wolf simply glared at D' Fat Lady and poured himself the last of the champagne.

Otto emptied his pockets onto the bed. The note D' Fat Lady had slipped him during the evening's performance was tied into one end of the scarf.

Instructions were simple. Each week he would stop by the box office of Ronacher's and pick up a fresh program sheet. He was told to tune in to the BBC broadcast on Monday night at eight o'clock. A number of rhetorical questions would be asked. Otto would listen, and then through information channels, answer those questions as specifically as possible—names, dates, future plans of the Führer in central Europe. All these things must be reduced to a series of dots and dashes inserted along the dotted border that framed the picture of the jazz trio on the program. Simple telegraphic code. After that it was a matter of enjoying the Wednesday night show at Ronacher's and leaving the program on the table.

Otto burned the note and flushed its ashes down the toilet. As simple as this all sounded, Otto knew what even a single scrap of paper left lying around could mean if the plan fell apart.

The highest sources in the German command were involved. They would provide him answers, he was certain—information he could not possibly be expected to know. Other things he would find out on his own.

For the most part, however, he played the role of courier between the head of military intelligence and the American jazz trio. It was an odd arrangement, indeed, but Otto had long ago ceased to be surprised by methods of passing information.

27

Breaking the Silence

Winston Churchill's bulk seemed to take up most of the glass sound booth at the BBC. After seeing him at his fiery best on the floor of Commons, Anna thought how much he now looked like a caged bear on display.

A sheaf of notes lay in front of him. To his right a cork bulletin board held the photographs of Helen and Karl, Lori and Jamie, as well as eight other prominent Germans who had spoken out and now had vanished.

The warning light came on. Thirty seconds to air time. Churchill nodded slowly, cleared his throat and glanced through the questions he must put to the world, and to one man within the Reich in hopes of getting necessary answers.

The link to New York was strong—no sunspots or unpredictable atmospherics dulled transmission to the West. The link to Europe, however, was weaker. Blank spots were reported in transmissions to Amsterdam, Prague, and Paris. There was no way of checking the reception in Berlin and Vienna, however, since the BBC was supposed to be banned there. Murphy did not look worried as he raised his hand to signal ten seconds.

Anna gripped Theo's hand and prayed that the question would be heard and an answer would come quickly about Helen and Karl and the children.

The red light blinked on as Murphy's hand lowered. Churchill looked up, then down, and began.

"I avail myself with relief at the opportunity of speaking to the people of the United States and to people whose hearts are free in spite of imprisonment. . . ."

He sounded awkward and uncomfortable in these opening lines.

Anna prayed for him. Everything must be right and strong!

"I do not know how long such liberties will be allowed. The stations of uncensored expression are closing down; the lights are going out in men and in nations alike. Let me, then, speak in earnestness and truth while time remains. . . ."

————

Baby Willie played with a pan and a wooden spoon in front of the radio set. Peter thought that his baby brother preferred music to the forbidden speech of the Englishman Churchill. But these words were better than food to Peter, who sat beside Otto and leaned in to hear the speech.

Otto took endless notes, pausing to run his pencil down the page as Churchill moved from one question to another.

"Have we gained peace by the sacrifice of the Czechoslovakian republic?"

Otto underlined this question and the next one as well.

"The question which is of interest to a lot of ordinary people is whether that sacrifice will bring upon the world a blessing or a curse."

Otto underlined the word *curse* twice. He held up his finger sternly to silence Marlene as she strode cheerfully into the room and demanded that music be put on.

"We must all hope it will be a blessing, that as we averted our eyes from the process of liquidation of a country we will be able to say, 'Well, that's out of the way. Let's get on with our daily life.' But we in all lands must ask ourselves, 'Is this the end, or is there more to come? Has any benefit been achieved by the human race by submission to organized violence?' "

"Why do you listen to this, Uncle Otto?" Marlene chirped. "Boring stuff. And aren't you supposed to be a Nazi?"

Peter gave Marlene his most deadly look. She stuck her tongue out at him and retreated to her room to sulk and mumble.

Peter's mother brought tea. She sat down at the far end of the table and fixed her attention on Otto. It seemed to Peter that he had seen her look at his father with that same odd mix of respect and fear, during similar moments when Michael Wallich also scribbled notes, or when he had talked in hushed tones to strangers who came to the house.

Peter had not paid attention to the undercurrents then. Now they pulled him along as well.

————

The words of Winston Churchill whispered in the dark study of New Church. Lori held tightly to Jamie's hand and wished that Papa could hear this man.

"We are confronted with another theme. It is not a new theme; it

leaps upon us from the Dark Ages—racial persecution, religious intol-
erance, deprivation of free speech—the conception that a citizen is a
mere soulless fraction of the state. To this has been added the cult of
war. Children are taught from their earliest schooling the delights and
profits of conquest and aggression. A whole, mighty community has
been drawn into this warlike frame. They are held in this condition,
which they relish no more than we do, by a party several million strong.
Like the Communists, the Nazis tolerate no opinion but their own. They
feed on hatred. They must seek a new target, a new prize, a new victim.
The culminating question to which I have been leading is whether the
world as we have known it should meet this menace by submission or
by resistance. . . ."

Then the speech took a remarkable turn. Suddenly Winston Churchill began to speak about the men in Germany who had chosen to resist
the Nazi ideology and had paid for it with the sacrifice of homes and
work and even lives. Some of those men had simply disappeared without a trace. Their families were also missing.

He recited names, told stories of individual courage. And then, as
Lori held her breath, she heard the story of her own father flood the
room.

"Involved from the beginning against the euthanasia and infan-
ticide commonly practiced in the Reich, Pastor Karl Ibsen and his entire
family have simply disappeared from the scene in Berlin. His home has
been turned over to the state. His church is condemned. His wife and
children have not been heard from!"

"Here we are!" Jamie cried. "Hey, Herr Churchill! We are still here!"

———

In the mess hall of Hanita settlement, the words of Churchill were
translated into half a dozen languages. Orde simply sat among his men
and listened without comment—until this moment.

"We shall meet this aggression with resistance," he replied, as
though Churchill were there among them. He smiled and scratched his
head thoughtfully. "Is he talking about Hitler or Haj Amin, do you
think?" he asked with a wave of his hand. "Ah well, all dictators have
the same boot maker from hell. Some wear bigger boots than others,
but the effect is identical, eh?"

No one was listening to the BBC anymore. Did Hayedid, their friend
and commander, mean that they were to go out again? Moshe noted
the eager faces of the men who had flocked to the settlement with just
such a thing in mind.

Orde glanced at his watch. "Winston would be the first one to agree
that resistance does not mean self-defense alone, lads. There is no
moon tonight. Are you well rested?"

———

Anna had not stopped praying for the impact of Churchill's speech to reach the ears of those who needed to hear. Karl and Helen, along with a handful of others, represented the few who had been willing to speak out. Not enough people had joined them, and now the question remained, *What could only one righteous man accomplish?*

Churchill's voice resounded with the same stirring sound that he spoke with in Parliament. He finished:

"It is this very conflict of moral and spiritual ideas that gives the free countries their strength. You see these dictators surrounded by their masses of armed men and vast arsenals. They boast and vaunt themselves before the world. Yet in their hearts is unspoken fear. They are afraid of words and thoughts! Words spoken abroad, thoughts stirring at home, in churches and schools—all the more powerful because they are forbidden—terrify them. A man chooses to speak what is right and decent; a little mouse of thought appears in the room, and even the mightiest of dictators is thrown into panic. And so that one man must be silenced. They make frantic efforts to bar words and thoughts. Men and righteousness are made to suffer. . . ."

Yes. Karl and Helen Ibsen were made to suffer. Thousands of others suffered now, as well. At the end of the broadcast, Churchill appealed for anyone with information about the missing families to contact the Red Cross or the local offices of TENS. Then the red light winked off, and it was all over. No applause—just Winston Churchill in the glass booth mopping his brow and gathering his papers.

———

"Don't even think about it," Jacob warned Lori as she looked thoughtfully at the telephone on her father's desk.

"But you heard it!" she cried hopefully. "They said to call the TENS office! I know about that. It is the American newspaper office. My cousin Elisa married the fellow who runs it in London, and—"

"London!"

"There is an office here in Berlin. A reporter who works for them called Papa once." She continued to stare at the forbidden telephone as she talked. The more she said, the more reasonable it seemed that they should contact TENS. "Listen, no one knows where we are, no one in the world but us! Now the BBC has broadcast our names and asked for help in finding us. Oh, Jacob! We can call, and they will help us."

He was adamant. "They will help us into prison. Or worse. You think the Gestapo is not interested in us as well as our parents?"

"Not you or Mark. They did not mention you! Just me and Jamie! So let me call and tell them where we are."

"And in five minutes there will be a Gestapo prison van at the curb! You are dreaming!" He was angered by her foolishness. "No one is going to get us out of here but us! If it had made any difference, we could have called the British Embassy, told them we were coming in for tea and political sanctuary! Lori, wake up before you get us killed!"

"Let me telephone! Maybe he can help."

Jacob took her by the arms. "Now you listen to me and understand what I am telling you!" He gave her a shake. "Do you know why our parents wanted us out of the country? Out of harm's way? I'll tell you! Because on their own, without us to worry about, they can hold up against any pressure. Torture, death even! They were not afraid for themselves! They were afraid for us! For what the Nazis can make them say and do if we are threatened!"

Tears tumbled down her cheeks. "The law of family guilt." She knew about it. This law above all others in the Reich kept the people in line. Papa talked about it, calling it the most cruel law of all. The law of hostages.

"Let me tell you what your father and mother could not stand! They could not bear seeing you . . . hurt." The Reich had devised a thousand ways to hurt a young woman like Lori. They would not have to break her arms to break her father. Consigning her to an S.S. brothel or to duty as a breeder for the S.S. Lebensborn would be enough. There was much more, but Jacob did not speak these things. The thought of them terrified him for Lori. He knew how Pastor Ibsen would react, simply because Jacob also wanted to protect her. It was a responsibility that had made him more stern with her than loving, perhaps—but the truth was, he cared deeply what happened to her.

"I . . . I just want everything to be all right again." She bit her lip and tried not to cry in front of him.

He pulled her close against him, wrapped his arms around her as he had longed to do every day since they had come here. Laying his cheek on the top of her head, he closed his eyes. He had to fill the shoes of her father now. He had to think logically and protect her even from herself if she was not able to think clearly.

"You know that man who searched the church? A Gestapo agent. I am certain of it. He was looking for you, Lori. I felt it when we were hiding." He stroked her back. She did not pull away from him. "I thought that if he found us I would have stayed and fought him until you got away." He frowned, hoping he was not telling her too much. "It is you they want. You and Jamie. My brother and I are Jewish. It is natural that we oppose them. But you see, your father is one of them, and it cuts them to the core that he will never really belong to them. A Gentile and a true Christian. Your father is more a threat to them than you can imagine. And you, Lori, are the only way they can get to him." He lifted her chin and searched her face. "Do you understand what I am saying?"

She nodded hesitantly and then leaned her head against his chest again. She had needed an embrace, and she was grateful for his show of tenderness.

All three boys were snoring. Lori got up quietly and tiptoed out of the bellows room. She felt her way down the stairs and along the corridor to Papa's study. Closing the door softly, she sat on the floor and pulled the candle and matches from her pocket.

To strike even one match after dark was forbidden by Jacob, but there were no windows in Papa's study, converted from an old storeroom ten years earlier.

The match flared. Lori touched the flame to the wick of the candle, then sat for a while as wax dripped in a little heap on the stone floor. Tall shelves of books ringed her, but not one could tell her what she ought to do now.

Everything Jacob said made sense, yet Elisa's husband was the head of TENS. Would they ask for information if they did not have some plan for helping the Ibsen family?

They could have called a hundred people in Berlin and asked for help long before now. Lori had not done so because Jacob trusted no one. But *this* . . .

She carried the candle to her father's desk and unlatched the secret cubby hole in the back of the center drawer. The address book was still there. She opened it and made this her gauge for making a decision.

"TENS." She thumbed through the sheets containing her father's neat printing. *"Timmons,"* the entry read. *"TENS. Adlon Hotel, room 122, telephone 3–6677."*

From there it was an easy reach for the phone.

At the rattle of the key in the lock, Karl Ibsen sat erect on his bed. It had been a long time since he had seen a human face.

The heavy door groaned a protest. Arthritic hinges opened reluctantly.

Framed in the doorway stood another prisoner—black and white stripes, eyes downcast, the thin six-foot frame stooped with the same suffering Karl felt. The face and features had been ravaged by that suffering, and at first Karl did not recognize the man.

Then Karl gave a small cry of joy. A hand shoved Pastor Nels Ritter into the cell and the door clanged shut behind them! Karl's prayers had been answered!

"Nels!" he cried, embracing the silent brother.

"Hello, Karl." The voice of his old friend was altered; joyless. *But no matter! They were together in their suffering for Christ! They had spent years upholding each other in prayer, and now they were brought to this moment . . .*

Karl wept with relief. Nels looked coolly around the cell. He stood with his hands clasped in front of him.

Nels did not seem pleased to see Karl. Arrested for opposing the laws and the enforced infanticide of sick babies in the Reich, Nels had always been a fighter. Karl knew instantly that something had broken in him; and was it any wonder? But together they could stand the pressure. Here was a gift of God that would make the Nazis wonder what power they were facing!

"Sit, Nels," Karl said gently, as though speaking to a child.

"No." Nels stood in the center of the cell. He did not embrace Karl.

"Nels? It's *all right*. Whatever they made you say—look at me, Nels. I know your heart. God knows."

"Don't you want out, Karl?"

"Yes. Of course. Yes."

"You know you don't have to agree with everything they say."

"What do you mean?" The first joy ebbed away. Nels had been sent here to convince him. "Please, *brother.*"

"Don't!" Nels raised his hand, a gesture like an axe being raised. "We don't have to say what they tell us *always*; just avoid saying what they don't like."

"Is that what you are going to do?"

"I am going home to my family. And you should do what they want and go home to your children! You think you are Peter or Paul? John on Patmos in solitary confinement? You have children! And . . . they . . . *need you, Karl!*"

"Yes." Karl sank down on his cot, crying openly. In all his weeks of solitary, he had never felt so alone. "And I need them. They are praying. Helen is praying—"

"Helen can't pray, Karl," he blurted out. *"She is dead!* You hear me? Helen is dead! Give it up and go home to your children! Helen, *Helen* . . . is *dead!*"

The rattle of night squad gunfire had silenced the last sporadic firing from the walls of the Arab stronghold. This did not mean that the fighters of the Islamic holy war were dead. No. They had simply melted away into the labyrinth of Palestine's deserts.

Captain Samuel Orde followed Zach Zabinski to the toppled stone fence where a dead man lay sprawled out.

"I thought you should see this." Zabinski shone his flashlight down at the face of the dead man. Blue eyes stared blankly up past Orde, the jaw slack in the relaxed grin of death. The hair was blond and the ash-colored skin was fair.

"European," Orde remarked. He shone the light into the man's mouth, illuminating three gold fillings. "His dentist doesn't live in Cairo, I can tell you."

"What do you make of it?" Zach asked grimly. "Tonight it seemed . . . different somehow. More organized. The grenades . . ."

"German made," Orde commented as he tore away the blood-soaked robe of the dead man. "Must have been the Nazi imitation of Lawrence of Arabia, eh?"

Zabinski smiled grimly at the joke. Captain Orde could make a joke at the oddest moments! "Not a successful one I would say, eh?"

The wound went clean through the heart. The foreign soldier died before he hit the stone he lay on. He wore black trousers beneath the robe, and heavy hobnailed boots. Orde had little doubt where the man had come from, but just to make certain he raised the limp white arm.

"Look at that, will you?" whistled Zach. "What do you make of it, Captain?"

A small tattoo of twin lightning bolts next to the letter *O* marked the soft underside of the dead man's arm. "Come, now. Are you telling me you've never heard of this before?" He let the arm fall back.

Of course. It was stupid even to comment on such a thing. Quite obvious, with all this business of secret signs and sacred mottos and dark rituals. Even his blood type.

"He's an S.S."

"Well done." Orde sniffed with disgust and wiped a fleck of blood from his hands with a handkerchief. "One of the master race in the flesh. Only now he's just dust, eh?"

"Quite dead."

Orde walked away a few paces and called to his men. "Load the bodies in the truck, lads!"

There were twelve dead among the Arab fighters. Reports from the Arab Higher Committee invariably denied that any Jihad Moquades were ever required to take the quick road to Paradise while fighting the Jews. News of actual deaths might dampen the enthusiasm of even the most dedicated Holy Struggler. Orde, therefore, continued his practice of hauling the bodies of his foes to the nearest Arab police station where he dumped them off with a note pinned onto their clothing: *I SHOULD HAVE STAYED HOME.* This always had a sobering effect on potential Jihad Moquades who might have otherwise happily joined the marauders of the Mufti's terrorist forces. Attacks tended to slow down for a few days after Orde conducted his own body count in this manner.

"I'd send this one back to Hitler with a note, but I'm sure der Führer would find a way to blame the Jews of Germany." Orde stepped over the body and made his way to where his men held three prisoners at gunpoint.

———————

A tiny mouse of independent thought had appeared within the great halls of the German Chancellery, and the Führer was trumpeting his fury at Churchill's broadcast.

It was not Churchill's reference to Czechoslovakia or racial persecution that angered him; it was the fact that once again the obstinacy of Pastor Karl Ibsen shook the fist of spiritual warfare in the face of the whole Nazi Reich.

Hitler's blue eyes turned black with rage. His translator wondered if the Führer's pupils had dilated completely or if some other dark presence had simply taken control of Adolf Hitler's human body. It made Doktor Schmidt shudder as he relayed the challenge of the British statesman.

Minister of Propaganda Joseph Goebbels did not look up to follow the pacing German leader. Goebbels was frightened. As propaganda goes, the news he had for his Führer was not good.

"Report to me the progress we are having with the reeducation of the German clergy," Hitler demanded. He paced and turned, snapping his fingers impatiently as he brooded.

"Reverend Gustav Dorfman is solidly with us, publicly denouncing the falsehood of the pastors who remain stubborn."

"I do not care about Dorfman! The man is something I clean off my shoe! Yes, he is with us because it benefits him! What about the others?"

Of course there were others. Goebbels calmed the Führer with stories of those who had recanted their former views of national socialism and now applauded its mission from God. Many now stood in their pulpits, reinstated, ready to preach according to the doctrine of the state.

"We have had particular success with a Protestant pastor, Nels Ritter. He is quite vocal on your behalf now, Führer, and he was quite close to Pastor Ibsen in the old days."

This news did not cheer Hitler. He spun on his heel and fixed his dark stare on Goebbels. This was the mouse! This was the name and the man he feared. *A truly righteous man,* they said. *A man who could not be compromised!*

"And what about Ibsen?" he demanded. "When shall I have my broadcast? When will he tell them in England what they must hear? When will he say that we are right and just? Tell me where Ibsen is!"

"In a prison at the border. We are making progress, mein Führer. He remains unchanging in his stubbornness. He does not know of the interest in his life from the West, of course—nothing to encourage him in his obstinacy. He is . . . we are slowly breaking him, Führer."

Hitler lowered his chin and glared out from beneath his forelock. He swept it back with his hand. "Break him quickly, Goebbels," he ordered. "I want him on the radio, repudiating all that Churchill has said. He will say that we are good and just in our battle. He will say that the Almighty has blessed our cause! I want him to say it out loud! They make him a martyr, and he is not even dead. They wonder where he is, well, we will let them hear his voice speaking on our behalf!"

"Such things take time."

"Time?" Hitler raged, striking out at Goebbels. "I do not have time to waste. They focus on this insect of a man as if he matters. And through his voice we are accused of crimes. You know where he has stood! I want every one of his stands reversed in our favor! I do not care what you do! You and Himmler. Only do not kill this man! I want him on my side." Suddenly Hitler remembered the faces of Ibsen's family: Helen, Lori, Jamie. "I told you we would use his family as a last resort. So. Now it is time to move on. Tell Himmler! Make Ibsen beg for the lives of his family! Make him promise anything for their sake! I want this matter settled!"

28

Betrayal

It was Timmons on the phone from Berlin, all right. His voice sounded excited, an octave higher than usual. He shouted for Harvey Terrill to quit kidding around and go get Murphy.

Harvey waved at Murphy across the din of the newsroom. Murphy thumped Adams on the back and took his time sauntering back to his own office.

"It's Timmons from Berlin," Harvey said laconically. "Frantic, as usual. Says he has something for you about Elisa's cousin?"

Murphy eyes widened. He shoved past Harvey and lunged for the phone.

"Timmons? Timmons! This is Murphy!"

No reply. Murphy thought he could hear voices in the background behind the usual long-distance static.

"Hello! Hello, Timmons? What have you got? Are you there, boy?"

The sound of guttural laughter sifted across the miles. Maybe Timmons was talking to someone in his room. Had he called and then left the phone hanging off the hook?

Murphy tried again, this time with a more formal tone. "Hello? This is Murphy. TENS London on the line."

Heavy static intruded into the connection; then suddenly a voice broke through clearly. A thick German accent replied cheerfully. "Ah. John Murphy. The newsman? Ja. This is Officer Alexander Hess. Write the name down, bitte, in case you should need it. No doubt you will have questions. Your embassy may relay them to me personally at the Reich Ministry of the Interior. Gestapo, ja?"

Murphy stammered, trying to keep the man on the line. "What? Is this a joke? Let me talk with my employee. This is a private conversation. Put Timmons on the line."

"*Nein*. No private conversations here, you know, Herr Murphy." Hess laughed. "I regret to inform you that your reporter is detained for questions, possibly conspiring to harbor fugitives from the law. Yes? You understand? Okay, then. You have questions? Call the Ministry of the Interior."

At that, the receiver clattered and clicked dead.

People at the soup kitchen had begun to ask too many questions, like, "Why doesn't your mother come here?"

Alfie told them that she was home sleeping, and then they said, "It must be the sleep of the dead, because she is always sleeping."

Such things made him feel nervous. As the time came closer for the children to leave for the transport, sometimes Hitler-men would come to look at documents and take people away. So far Alfie had managed to slip out before they stopped him. But they were at the soup kitchen and looking for people to close the lid on.

It was time for soup, but Alfie did not go. He had not gone the day before either, and he was hungry. There was no way to get around it; he would have to buy food and bring it here, or he would starve and the kittens would not have anyone to watch over them.

Alfie picked out his jeweled necklace. It had a green stone in the center as big as his thumbnail with diamonds shining all around. *Such a pretty thing ought to buy a lot of sardines,* he thought as he shoved it into his pocket.

He decided he would go to the grocery store around the block from New Church. Sometimes he and Jamie had gone there to buy chewing gum or hard candy. The grocery man knew them and was nice sometimes, when he was not too busy.

Alfie's stomach was rumbling by the time he hurried across the busy street, then past the shoemaker's and the toy store and the ladies' dress shop where Mama had gone shopping for her clothes. He stopped for a minute in front of the window like Mama always used to do. He could see himself in the glass, and imagined her standing beside him.

"Hello, Mama," he said. "I wish I could buy you a dress." But he knew that Mama would want him to buy food instead, and so he walked on, rounding the corner to where Niedermeyer's Grocery was.

Herr Niedermeyer was dusting the top shelf with a feather duster as if nothing had changed at all since the last time Alfie had been in. He did not look up at Alfie, which meant he was busy thinking and would probably not be nice today.

That was all right. Alfie did not need help. He got a basket and went right to where the sardine cans were stacked up high. Alfie took a lot. Then he scooped in some cans of milk, because the kittens would be needing to learn to drink milk properly from a bowl. They would not always be babies crying for their mama.

After that, Alfie got a loaf of bread and some chewing gum and peaches. He had enough to fill two boxes. He could carry two boxes without trouble. Mama used to send him to the store because he was big and strong. She would call ahead and place her order, and Alfie would go pick it up.

Alfie put the basket on the counter by the register. "Hello, Herr Niedermeyer," Alfie said.

The feather duster went up like a flag. Herr Niedermeyer looked as if he were seeing a ghost.

"Mein Gott! Is it . . ." He snapped his fingers, trying to remember Alfie's name. "I have not seen you in a long time! Good heavens! Not since—" He frowned. "What is all this?"

"Food," Alfie told him. It was strange that Herr Niedermeyer did not know what Alfie had in the basket.

"You want all this?"

"If it will fit in two boxes for me to carry."

"It has been a long time since you were here with that other little boy. What was his name?" Niedermeyer began ringing up the items on the register. One by one he put them in boxes.

"Jamie."

"Ah, yes! The Ibsen child." A strange look crossed his face. He was thinking of something unpleasant. Alfie watched his eyes squint down. "Do you know where Jamie is?" he asked.

"I think they took him away."

"Yes, but he got away and men have come round looking for him. If you see him you will tell me, won't you?"

Herr Niedermeyer was being nice, after all. He pushed the keys on the cash register, making a lot of numbers behind the glass window. Alfie stared at them.

"You have money?" Niedermeyer asked. He did not like the way Alfie looked at the numbers. Alfie had never bought anything but chewing gum before.

"Yes, I can pay you. If it is not enough, we can put something back." Alfie dug in his pocket and placed the jeweled necklace on the counter.

The grocer opened his mouth in astonishment. He looked at the necklace and then glanced from side to side to see if anyone else was looking. He scooped it into his hand, mumbling something all the while.

"Not enough? You want to buy half the store?" Then he went pale and scared-looking. "Where did this come from?"

"I picked it up in the street. Pretty, isn't it? My cats like it, but I am hungry."

"You did not steal it?" Niedermeyer whispered and let it drop into his pocket.

"No. If I did, I did not mean it." Alfie stacked the boxes on top of one another.

The grocer was staring hard at him. "You . . . I remember now. Jamie's friend. The Dummkopf. They took you away, ja? To—" He did not seem nice anymore. "You caused all sorts of trouble for that pastor, too, I remember! It is quite clear now. And they took you to the sisters of Mercy asylum, and . . . How did you get back here?"

Alfie felt scared. Herr Niedermeyer looked angry, like people looked when they would shake Alfie or hit him on the face. He picked up the boxes and started to back away.

"I am going home now."

"Home? Home where?" Niedermeyer snapped his finger and mumbled something about a reward. "Wait!" he called to Alfie. "Wait here. I'll get you some candy. I . . . just a minute!"

Alfie stopped just inside the door. "Only a minute. I got to go home."

"Sure, sure." Niedermeyer grabbed a pack of mints from the rack and put it on top of the boxes. "Now just wait; I have a surprise for you, ja?" He hurried through a curtained door just behind the register.

Alfie heard him dial the phone and ask for the police, please. Herr Niedermeyer was calling the Hitler-men to come after Alfie!

The bell above the door jingled as Alfie slipped out. He carried the boxes down the alley and ducked to hide behind garbage cans. Alfie did not move when the green police car wailed up in front of Niedermeyer's Grocery. He listened to the men talk about Alfie and Jamie and how Herr Niedermeyer had always suspected that the Dummkopf was stealing while the other diverted his attention. He was certain that the Dummkopf ought to know where Jamie Ibsen was because the two had been fast friends. He wanted to know if he could have the reward if they were brought in.

Alfie stayed in the alley until long after dark. It was only a short walk back to the churchyard, but now he was afraid. They were looking for the Dummkopf! And looking for Jamie!

From now on, Alfie knew he would have to be very careful.

———

Goebbels stammered as he faced Gestapo Chief Heinrich Himmler and Special Agent Alexander Hess.

"I did not tell him about the situation with Ibsen's family. He was too angry, Heinrich. You know how he can be."

"The official records show that Helen Ibsen died in prison. The Führer need not know anything but that. And as for the children, Officer Hess has good news for us today." He motioned to the round-faced plain-clothes officer who tugged his earlobe thoughtfully. He looked more like a pleasant, balding shopkeeper than a Gestapo officer.

"We know the children are in Berlin," he said casually. Such momentous news, and he acted as though it were nothing.

"Berlin? *Where* in Berlin? With whom?" Goebbels asked incredulously. All this time, and the Ibsen children might have been walking past him in the street.

"Where? We do not know exactly." He shrugged.

"Really, Heinrich," Goebbels protested to Himmler. "This is not good news. The Führer is demanding action with the family of this man."

"Just listen." Himmler was cool, confident.

Hess began again. "We discovered them quite by accident. We had the lines of the American reporter Timmons tapped. Usually there is nothing of interest coming or going over that line, but there was a phone call. A young woman. The girl Lori, we are certain. She thanked Timmons for the broadcast. Said that she and her brother and the children of"—he checked his note pad—"Richard Kalner were all together. Here in Berlin. Timmons agreed to meet them. The man is a dolt. He cannot possibly grasp what it means to them." Hess broke into a slow, sleepy grin. He yawned as though bored. "We have men stationed at the place of rendezvous, near Brandenburg Gate. Timmons offered to pick them up in an automobile. Anyway, they do not know what this Timmons looks like. We detained him about an hour ago. I will take his place and meet them."

Goebbels wiped his thin face with a white handkerchief. This was great news—the clear hand of providence! So at least a part of the Ibsen family would be available for use to convince the recalcitrant pastor of his error. Goebbels hoped to have the broadcast arranged quite soon, after all.

————

The inside of the streetcar was illuminated by three light bulbs in the ceiling. By this light, passengers could read the advertisements above the windows and the latest rules and regulations about who could ride and who could not. *NO JEWS ALLOWED* was stenciled in unnecessarily large letters above the driver and then again on the fare box.

With the rain outside, the car was crowded almost to capacity. Lucy took the only remaining place beside an old woman just behind the driver's seat. There were many Nazi uniforms on board, but the old Austrian woman next to Lucy still carried on a loud and animated conversation directed at the nervous driver.

"And so"—she gestured toward the sign about Jews—"you see, it is this sort of thing I am talking about!" She did not seem to notice when Lucy sat beside her and the car lurched ahead. "Look! Look at what they have posted all over my Vienna!" She clucked her tongue for the shame of it. "All my life I have lived in Grinzing, which as you know is just outside the city. And now I come to shop and I hardly recognize the shopkeepers anymore. Everyone is leaving, and can you blame them?"

The driver glanced nervously in the rearview mirror to see a dozen grim, stern faces beneath peaked Nazi caps looking back toward the old woman. The man was sweating. It would have been humorous had it not been so dangerous.

Lucy looked out the window at the darkening city in an attempt to ignore the indignant monologue against the Germans who stomped in and took over everything so that a native could not even find her way around anymore! Coins and currency were different! Even the names of places around Vienna had been changed to honor the conquerors! "It is a crime." The old woman's lower lip protruded defiantly and Lucy felt sure she was purposefully speaking loud enough for everyone on the car to hear her.

They stopped and started, clacking past the Stadtpark. Uniformed passengers got off, but not before giving the old lady an icy stare. New German passengers got on, took their seats, then sat rigidly as she began her tirade against the government all over again. In spite of the cold air rushing in from the open door, the driver wiped beads of heavy perspiration from his forehead.

Lucy simply stared at the passing lights and sights of the city. Just ahead, across from the canal that wound through the park, loomed the enormous central railway terminal. Lucy's head turned with involuntary longing as they passed it. Somewhere at the end of the line was the freedom for an old woman to complain on a street car without fear! Between that magic place and this, however, stood uniforms and stern faces and rules and customs inspections that would take Lucy's survival money and pitch her into prison in the bargain. The thought of such a journey made her shudder more than the open defiance of the Austrian woman who blasted the Nazis with such disregard.

"And now you will see what I am talking about!" The old woman nudged Lucy and held up a ticket stub for everyone in the public car to see. "Look here!" She shook the stub at a round-bellied Wehrmacht officer who managed to retain a complacent, cow-eyed look of innocence. "You see what you and your Führer have done!" She held the ticket higher. "I bought this streetcar ticket to travel to Am Heumarkt! But I thought you renamed it Adolf Hitler Platz and so I bought the ticket for Adolf Hitler Platz! Now he tells me that the place you renamed Adolf Hitler Platz is really much farther up the route, and so here I am!" Her sagging cheeks reddened with rage as she fixed her gaze on the innocent officer. "I have spent too much on this ticket! It may be only a few pfennigs to you, but it means a lot to an old woman!"

So that was what this was all about. As simple as that. She had paid fare for a place up the line and now would lose the unused portion of the ticket. Relief flooded several faces.

The Wehrmacht officer stood up, managed a smile, and clicked his heels politely as the car stopped at Am Heumarkt.

"A simple error," he said on behalf of the Reich. "The driver will no doubt refund the unused portion and then, perhaps, you will know that we Germans have come to make life better for our brothers and sisters in Austria, ja?" At that, he plucked the ticket stub from the old woman's fingers and presented it to the startled driver. "Refund the fare to Adolf Hitler Platz, if you please."

"Danke! Danke!" the old woman said. "So gracious, so polite, so just!" Two copper coins were promptly refunded, and the old woman limped down out of the streetcar.

As other passengers boarded and counted out their change and pulled their tickets from the roll, Lucy Strasburg conceived the answer to her dilemma.

"Wait!" she cried as the doors banged shut. "My stop! I'm getting off here, too!"

With an exasperated roll of his eyes, the driver opened the doors and let Lucy off to rush past the mumbling old woman. Just across a narrow bridge lay the train station—and, she hoped, the solution to her financial problems.

———

Haj Amin Husseini, exiled Grand Mufti of Jerusalem, defender of Islam and herald of Jihad, advanced majestically to meet Adolf Hitler. Haj Amin was dressed in a flowing blue cape over an expensive white silk robe. His perfectly starched white tarboosh sat poised above his red-bearded face like a crown of state. Of the two men, Haj Amin looked more like the monarch of an Aryan nation than did the dark-haired, drably uniformed Hitler. Even so, Haj Amin was coming to beg favors of the German Führer, and both men knew the reality of the relationship.

Haj Amin touched his fingertips to his forehead, his lips, and his heart in a sweeping gesture of salaam. Hitler bowed in acknowledgment, then extended his hands in welcome. The Führer directed the Grand Mufti to a pair of formal chairs drawn up before a stone fireplace. Haj Amin's retainers had not been permitted to enter with him, and with a short wave of his hand, Hitler dismissed his own aides as well.

Haj Amin spoke first, in excellent German. "Herr Hitler, how it pleases me to meet you at last. Your assistance to our struggle is such clear evidence of your far-seeing wisdom."

"And how is that struggle progressing?" inquired Hitler quietly, even though he already knew the answer.

"Well, extremely well! Of course you know my poor troops have neither the equipment nor the training to even compare with your legions, whom we strive to imitate. But with additional funds—"

Hitler interrupted. "It has come to my attention that the efforts in the north of Palestine have suffered some setbacks. Even some of our . . . advisors . . . to your cause have disappeared. Can you explain this?"

"It is the perfidious British," replied Haj Amin, bristling. "They say they will not tolerate these Jewish murderers, but they wink at this man Orde and his gang of commandos."

"So because of one man your campaign falters?" asked Hitler, fixing his gaze on Haj Amin's eyes.

The Mufti shifted uncomfortably in his chair. He had noticed that the Führer had not said "our campaign." "We have placed a price on his head. It is only a matter of time until—"

The Führer answered kindly, but his firmness admitted no further argument. "You are in error. No Jews, no British must be allowed to think that resistance is profitable, or even possible. They must be allowed no time to reflect on what one man can do."

"But how can we stop him immediately?"

"Isolate him. Have your envoy tell the British that the sole reason for the Arab riots is their wayward officer. Tell them that there can be no peace until he is removed, that there cannot even be peace talks until he is out of the way." The Führer's voice was patient, instructive.

Haj Amin blinked. "But we have used the peace talk issue to prevent further Jewish immigration to Palestine."

"Exactly," Hitler confirmed, as if recognizing a bright pupil. "They have met one demand. Now is the precise time to escalate those demands. Tell them it is not enough."

"I see, I see," nodded Haj Amin. "And if they refuse to discuss the matter?"

"Promise them unending demonstrations, riots, and bloodshed, and then have your representative walk out of the room!"

"And will the British sacrifice one of their own, their best fighter?"

"My friend," said Hitler jovially, "you must study the lessons of the history of your own region more thoroughly. The British are in the precise spot to bring you his head on a platter, if you know how to ask for it."

Later that evening the Führer of the Third Reich and the Grand Mufti of Jerusalem appeared together publicly. They spoke of mutual admiration and cooperation in overcoming mutual problems. The Führer and the Grand Mufti posed for photographs together as Herr Hitler presented a personal token of friendship to Haj Amin. It was a bullet-proof vest.

It had been a discouraging week for Otto. His notebook carefully hidden away, he had taken all the names and facts from John Murphy's broadcast with him to the offices of the secret police.

Claudia, the thick-trunked, surly secretary in his outer office, scowled at him reproachfully when he gave her two names to look up in the cross files.

Returning an hour later, she smiled at him and tossed the folders onto the *IN* basket.

"These priests," she said. "Somebody twists an arm and they howl they didn't mean to offend the Führer! Ach! They are neither one with us nor steadfast in what they are supposed to be. Not worth the bullet to kill them nor the food to feed them, eh?"

Without comment, Otto leafed through the records. Both men, painted so sympathetically by Murphy, had confessed the error of their ways and recanted their foolish stubbornness against the Reich. Blessed saints for the Nazi cause now, they were both being restored to their pulpits. No doubt they would soon be making public statements that would make the newsman look like a fool around the world.

He shuddered at what the Ministry of Propaganda could do with this. The people in England and America would have to choose their martyrs carefully. Many men would gladly praise the devil and go free than suffer even a small discomfort. Otto knew this to be true from personal experience. Tragically, it seemed to be the most self-righteous men who yielded first when proper pressure was applied. Somehow they convinced themselves that they could still serve God and the Reich at the same time. Claudia's cynicism about the clergy was correct. The only ones they fooled were themselves.

Three more from the original list had recanted by the end of the week. Two elderly priests had died within days of their imprisonment. This left three men unaccounted for, somewhere within the vast prison system of the police state.

On Wednesday morning Otto called the Berlin Gestapo headquarters with the rumor that two children matching the description of Karl Ibsen's son and daughter were reported in the Vienna area. Would a complete file be forwarded immediately in the event the two were captured? His fabrication worked. The file was sent by air. By noon a thick folder lay on Otto's desk.

IBSEN, KARL HENRY. Doctor of Theology. Age 41 years. Married 1924 to MERSER, HELEN IRENE—deceased, Ravensbrück, November

28, 1938. The file provided pictures of the couple and their children, facts, and data going back to 1933. The information painted a portrait of integrity and courage. Otto read it throughout the afternoon. It was also a record of suffering and tragedy.

29

Ivory Palaces

The wind blew hard again, shaking the radio antennas high atop the BBC in London. Murphy paced nervously, raising his eyes at the sound of the wind. Would the Vienna broadcast penetrate the weather closing in over Europe?

The performance was supposed to be recorded and rebroadcast to the States at a later time. If the American public was deprived of their weekly jazz ration, there was no telling what sort of backlash might come to the advertising sponsors. These European performances had made a smash hit back home. Billed as D' FAT LADY TRIO IN IVORY PALACES, BROUGHT TO YOU BY IVORY SOAP, the official figures showed that sales of the floating soap had jumped by 50 percent since the tour began. No other jazz trio would do. Americans wanted the music straight from Europe's ivory palaces.

The American radio listeners were not the only ones praying for a clear connection to Vienna tonight. In the studio with Murphy sat Winston Churchill and the head of the British Secret Service. Anna, Elisa, and Theo lined one side of a long table opposite a small, mousy-looking telegrapher who had come with the intelligence chief.

The questions asked by Winston Churchill on his own radio broadcast were about to be answered, entirely in the syncopated rhythm of D' Fat Lady. These questions had been carefully formulated by members of the Foreign Office as well as British Intelligence, the plan conceived by Anna Lindheim and a certain piano student who preferred sending coded messages to practicing her scales.

The great recital was about to begin.

"He will be sending the signals entirely in the bass," Anna explained patiently to the telegrapher, who could not imagine that this system would work. No uncensored news had come out of Germany for years, and he did not believe that an American black man at the piano could break that barrier.

"I told you," he said dryly, "I am no musician. If it is in the bass or the basement or the attic, I still cannot tell one note from another. Just write down the little dots and dashes as you hear them, and I will translate the code for you."

"It will be recorded, Anna. If we miss anything, we can play it back," Murphy explained. "You can do this."

Elisa came along as a backup musician. She also had a notebook open. Provided Philbert could play the rhythm of short dots and sustained dashes as the German contact wrote them down, there seemed to be little chance of a foul-up. Of course, there was this matter of the weather. Now that Timmons had been arrested by the Gestapo in Berlin, it seemed more important than ever that this work.

The phone rang. Murphy snatched it from its cradle. His face reflected relief, then delight. *"The connection is through!"*

Moments later, recording technicians in a glass booth in another part of the building began to record the thunderous applause that greeted the trio as they stepped onto the stage of Ronacher's in Vienna. The technicians did not know how important their efforts would be tonight. Like the telegrapher, the rest of the world would hear the music they had come to recognize and love. But Anna heard the first staccato message of the piano even before the applause died away.

"Four dots. Break. Two dots." The telegrapher read over her shoulder.

"That spells *Hi,*" said the man sourly.

As the tinkling keys continued in the background, D' Fat Lady greeted her listeners. "Well, hello-o-o-o, my babies! And hello-o-o-o, Charlie and Louie, wherever you is! D' Fat Lady gonna sing ever' song fo' you t'night!"

More applause. Anna as well as Elisa could hear the tuneless background music of the piano continue to tap out a constant, unwavering code. No matter that the notes might be played from one octave to another, it was there! Unmistakable. Half note. Half note. Quarter note. Break. Half note. Half note. Half note. Break.

"From the ivory palaces of Vienna, Ivory soap presents..."

Quarter. Half. Half. Quarter. Break. Quarter. Half. Quarter...

"And here's a song that'll tell the folks back home jest what we is a feelin'..." At that, the full rich voice of Delpha Mae broke into the familiar tune of "Ain't Misbehavin'."

The piano never missed a beat. Half. Half. Break. Quarter. Half... The date *March 15* was spelled out. And then the name *Prague.* Followed by *Invasion.*

Churchill had asked what had been gained by the sacrifice of Czechoslovakia. The answer that was relayed from German High Command: S-C-O-R-N.

And was this destruction of the one central European haven for minorities a blessing or a curse?

C-U-R-S-E.

Could peace, goodwill, and confidence be built upon submission to wrongdoing backed by Nazi force?

N-O. Y-O-U M-U-S-T F-I-G-H-T O-R D-I-E.

And so the messages came, clearly more troubling than any that had come out of the darkness of the Reich until now. Prague would fall on March 15. All the sacrifice of Munich meant nothing. More suffering was yet to come. Hitler intended war. No matter what he said publicly, there was always one more reason for him to march forward, one more manufactured injustice that he would right with his iron fist.

"Puttin' on the Ritz" mentioned other players in the drama whom Churchill had not named in his broadcast. H-A-J A-M-I-N. P-A-L-E-S-T-I-N-E A-T-T-A-C-K.

How far was far enough for the Führer? After Prague, what would come upon the world? Then Poland. The excuse would be Danzig. Then Russia. Then France. Belgium. Holland.

A-L-L W-O-R-L-D.

Twenty minutes of doom was passed through the light joyful music of D' Fat Lady. In between every telegraphed announcement of Nazi intentions of conquest and terror, the audience applauded. The message was clearly in the air, filling their heads, but nobody heard it!

At last the name of Karl Ibsen was tapped out in the sweet melody of "Taking a Chance On Love." Before the song was finished, the pen had fallen from Anna's hand. She leaned her head on Theo's shoulder and cried as word of her sister's death in prison reached her for the first time.

Tiny drops of wax on the floor. Jacob picked at them absently while they listened to the syncopated rhythm of D' Fat Lady Trio over the radio in Vienna.

He could not catch the strange lyrics, but the beat made him tap his toe and think of England and America and child transport ships leaving for freedom from Danzig.

Lori had been strangely preoccupied all day long. She seemed not to hear the music. Perhaps she was still considering making a phone call to that reporter.

He dug his thumb into the wax, scraping it off the floor. *Candle wax?*

Jacob looked toward Lori, studying her profile. Her eyes were downcast, her mouth in a tight line. She had not looked him in the eyes all day. *Why?*

"There is candle wax on the floor," he blurted out.

She jerked her head up. A moment of fear and guilt crossed her face before she mastered it. Yes, it was guilt. No use trying to pretend. "So?"

"What did you do?" he sprang to his feet and looked at the desk top. *Drops of wax.* And then at the dial of the telephone. *One tiny drip.*

In a flash Jacob knew: she had gotten up and come down here in the night. She had found the number and called. For a moment he wanted to grab her and shake her. Instead, he towered over her. Why did she not look at him?

"Tell me," he said in a quiet voice as the music played in the background and Mark and Jamie gawked at them without understanding any of it.

"All right!" she replied defiantly. She jerked her face up. "I called. So what? I called, and the Gestapo did not come! Jamie and I are going to meet him at the Brandenburg Gate. Come if you want. Or don't come. But you are not telling us what to do anymore!"

Jacob stepped back from her. His arms hung limp with fear and resignation. "There is not one newsman in the whole Reich who does not have a tapped telephone. If you go to meet this man, you condemn yourself . . . Jamie . . . and your parents to defeat—maybe death."

The look on her face was adamant. She knew he would say these things. But the plan was all worked out. She was going and he would not stop her!

D' Fat Lady crooned something gentle—an American love song, Jacob supposed, but it was lost on the listeners of New Church. He was certain that if she left, it would be the end of her. He would never see her again. Pastor Ibsen would end up leading a Nazi congregation in the praises of the holy Führer.

"When are you leaving?" he asked.

Momentary surprise flashed in her eyes. She had not expected him to give in so easily. "Tonight."

Jacob glanced at Jamie, her accomplice by birth. Jamie shrugged as if to indicate he had no choice.

"What time do you meet this fellow?"

"Midnight."

"Very cloak and dagger, Lori. Commendable. You think the police won't notice a young woman getting into a man's car at the Brandenburg Gate at midnight?"

"Well, I didn't want to say where we were! I knew you would do this. If you and Mark don't want to go, then fine. I respect that. I did not give away our hiding place."

Jacob sighed with exasperation. He glanced around the room and fixed his gaze on the closet. The lock was conveniently on the outside.

"Jamie!" Jacob snapped. "I am the leader. You are not going."

Jamie nodded agreeably. He never wanted to cross Jacob. "Sure," he said, too quickly.

Lori shot him a venomous look. "Traitor!"

"No." Jacob reached down and grasped her wrist. "He is smart. And so am I." He yanked her to her feet and in one quick motion threw her into the closet and locked the door as she screamed at him and pounded her fists against it.

"You can't! Let me out! Let me go! I will call him again!"

Jacob jerked the phone line out of the wall. He crossed his arms and stared at the door.

"You can come out for breakfast. We have been through too much, Lori Ibsen, for me to let you get hurt now. Whether you like it or not, I am your father and your brother for the time being."

"I hate you!" she screamed. "Let me out!" The shouts dissolved into tears.

Jamie smiled at Jacob. "A smart move," he said. "Papa would have done the same."

"The apple does not fall far from the tree," Officer Hess remarked to the commandant of Nameless camp. He brushed his finger across the pictures of Lori and Jamie Ibsen and then touched the picture of their father. "They look very much like him, don't you think?"

The commandant smiled sourly. "In such a place as this, one's appearance changes drastically."

"As should one's state of mind. But you have not been able to alter the state of mind of this pastor," remarked Hess in an accusing tone. "So, the Führer has asked me to take charge of the situation here as well."

"I thought you were on the job of finding the little apples from Karl Ibsen's tree." The commandant took offense at the accusation of failure in Hess's words. Hess had not yet met Ibsen and so did not know what he was up against. "Found them yet, have you?"

"It is a matter of time. But we don't need them. Not now. Ibsen is just a man like any other. Soon he will be marching in step, singing in tune."

"So you think?" The commandant scratched his scabby head. "He is your patient, Herr Doktor."

Karl's arm and two of his fingers were broken. He wrapped them the best he could in strips of cloth torn from his blanket. Still, the ache was unending. It kept his mind focused. *"Fear not those who can kill the body. Fear not those who can kill."*

Again and again he repeated those words. When the new S.S. officer strode into his cell, Karl was not afraid of what he might do to him. He would welcome an end to this. The torture had not ended since the hour Nels Ritter had left him.

Officer Alexander Hess played the role of one sympathetic to Karl's situation. He had a chair brought in, and he sat across from Karl and talked gently to him at first.

"All right, you have made your point. But you cannot win, Pastor Ibsen." The round, shop-clerk face seemed sad. "Look at you! I was just looking at your picture. You and your wife Helen." He paused while the knife found its mark. "And your children. Lori and Jamie. Beautiful children. They haven't changed. Only taller."

Haven't changed? How did this man know? Did he see them? Talk to them? The knife twisted. Karl dared not answer.

Hess continued. "They miss you, of course. They cannot understand why their own father has abandoned them."

Silence. An ache filled Karl's heart, a pain much greater than the broken bones.

Hess extended the photograph of the family. *Helen, sitting in the sunlight, her arm linked with his! And Lori and Jamie hugging each other. Karl's hand lay on Jamie's shoulder—this same hand with the broken fingers.* Karl could remember what it was like to touch the faces of his children.

He caressed them with his eyes instead. His throat tightened with emotion and longing for that moment, and he prayed that God would help him not to show his longing to this new man. A miracle. Karl's eyes remained dry and his breath even.

Fear not those who kill the body. . . . Oh, God! They use love to try to kill my soul!

"Why don't you just admit your errors? Then all will be well again. You can see your children. Embrace them."

"I cannot embrace anyone," Karl said. "My arm is broken."

"Bones heal. Broken hearts do not. You are leaving your children as orphans. By your choice."

"The Lord . . . says . . . 'I will be father to the fatherless.' "

A flicker of anger flashed through the officer's eyes.

"You have suffered here." He maintained his patience. "I am certain they have made it very hard for you."

Fear not those who can kill the body.

"But are you willing for Lori and Jamie to suffer—maybe to die—for the stubbornness of their father?"

Could words so cruel be spoken in such a gentle voice? Such a question should have been asked with a chorus of shrieking demons.

If Karl listened, perhaps he could hear the wailing of hell behind that question.

An answer, Lord! An answer! Fear not! Fear not those who kill the body, only those who kill the soul!

Karl closed his eyes and listened to the answer in his heart. He looked up at Hess, who sat waiting. "My children are both saved."

"But they are not safe."

"They are safe."

"They are in the hands of men who may use them as weapons against your stubbornness. Are you willing—"

Karl jerked his head up. He had heard the Voice tell him what he must ask. "You say my children have grown?" He smiled.

"Life in the Hitler Youth is very good. Good food, exercise, and . . . they are well. For now."

"May I see photographs of them?"

Karl saw the surprise cross the man's face. "Photographs?" He looked at the picture of the family. "There you have—"

"I want to see how they have grown."

"Well, I . . . that is, we—"

Karl smiled. "You cannot provide me with photographs because you do not have my children. No, Lori and Jamie are not in your web."

"You will see—"

"My children are saved," he said again. Then he closed his eyes and did not hear the rest. He listened to the sweet whispers and was unchanged. Unmoved. Unafraid.

The din inside the vast railway terminal was deafening. Voices, hissing train engines, and loudspeakers emitted an echoing roar.

The ticket lines were all long. From the bits of conversation gleaned from around her, Lucy guessed that nearly everyone here was trying to get home for the holidays.

The queue inched slowly forward. It was thirty minutes before Lucy finally found herself face-to-face with a ticket clerk.

She hesitated a moment too long with her question and the man burst out impatiently, "Yes? Well? Well?"

She carefully gauged how she might ask the question without rousing the man's curiosity. There was certainly something illegal in what she hoped to do. The trick was not getting caught.

"Yes. For Christmas, I want my brother to come to Vienna to visit me," she began.

"Yes? Well?" He wanted only details necessary to sell her the ticket so he could get on to the next customer.

"He will not come unless it is a round-trip ticket back to Bavaria."

"Round trip, Bavaria . . . that would be Munich. The fare is—"

Lucy interrupted him. "What I need to know is this: If I convince him to stay on with me in Vienna, might I obtain a refund on the unused portion of his ticket?"

There was nothing to think about. "Certainly. Return the unused portion, and you will be refunded. Yes." He paused as he figured the fare. When he looked up through the wire of his cage, the beautiful blond woman had vanished.

———

Seven hundred marks. Lucy laid the bills out on the bed in neat piles of twenty mark notes. It was not the full one thousand that she had hoped to have, but it was enough, and much more than the limit she could legally take out of the country.

She patted the money with the joy of a child who had been saving a long time for something special. *"Danzig!"* she said aloud as she slipped the notes into a long brown envelope and then into her purse. A shudder of excitement and relief coursed through her.

On the radio in the front room, martial music blared as a prelude to some official Reich announcement. The people of the Reich and the people of France had just signed a mutual non-aggression treaty. Lucy paid no attention to the details. Soon, she would be out of Germany, and she had found a better place to hide than France. "Danzig," she said again as she hurried out the door and made her way back to the bustling railway terminal.

The lines were longer, the clatter more resounding; the movement of people through the building seemed constant.

Lucy took care not to stand in the same line she had when she asked her question an hour before. She had too much at stake to risk the first man recognizing her.

The ticket clerk, an Austrian civil servant with a drooping mustache and a cap so old that the visor was cracked, smiled at her through the cage. The smile seemed to say that he had been around a long time and was not threatened by the German workers who had been brought in to replace so many.

"A long wait, eh? And how can I help you, Fräulein?"

"Danzig." Lucy pulled her envelope out and laid it on the counter.

The ticket seller looked down his nose at the envelope. "Danzig, ja. You are traveling alone?"

The blessed question filled Lucy with happiness as she answered it. "No—I mean, what is the fare?"

"How many tickets to Danzig, bitte?"

Lucy had forgotten the most important bit of information. "Well, they must be round-trip tickets. From here to Danzig and then back again to Vienna, if you please."

"And how many are traveling?" The man was not impatient. Travelers were often a bit confused about travel plans. But he could not tell her how much until she told him how many.

"How much for each passage, bitte?" she insisted. "I need to know if I have enough for all of us, you see."

That was a different matter—counting her pennies. Of course, there must be cash enough for each traveler, or someone would have to stay behind. "Round trip. Vienna to Berlin to Danzig. Back the same route." He checked a printed sheet. "If you get a Polish travel visa, the cost is only sixty-five marks, Fräulein."

A Polish visa. Lucy had forgotten all about that. "Polish visa." She said the words carefully, as though she did not understand.

He answered patiently. "Ja. You must, if you enter Danzig overland through Poland, go to the Polish consulate and obtain a travel visa. That is the least expensive manner of travel."

Lucy did not care about least expensive. This was, after all, merely a banking transaction for her. She would put all her extra money into round-trip tickets. At the first stop, she would cash in the unused portion and convert it to ready cash.

"What is the other way?" she stammered too eagerly.

He seemed amused. He cocked a bushy eyebrow and leaned forward with advice. "Many people do not wish to be troubled with the Polish visa. Yes. I understand." He smiled, revealing tobacco-stained teeth that gave him the appearance of an old horse. "If you purchase a ticket directly to Danzig only, you may go in a sealed car across the Polish frontier and never have to go through Polish customs. And then, Fräulein, you do not need a visa."

"That sounds like a very good idea. How much?"

"One hundred marks," the old fellow said. "And will all want to travel together?"

The line behind Lucy was restless with the slow Austrian way of doing things. There were impatient murmurs as she counted out the bills. "Five round-trip tickets," she said, figuring that she could easily carry out the extra cash and never be questioned by the German authorities.

"You will be traveling when?"

Her smile faded. "When?"

"It is important to know when you will come to catch the train." His smile widened. "Otherwise you will miss it."

She exhaled nervously. "I . . . might I make the decision later? We have not all settled on the date yet." She looked toward the platforms as a train chugged slowly out from the train shed. For an instant she thought how easy it would be to buy her tickets and get on the train right now. But she had not packed. She had brought no clothes. No baggage.

The ticket seller stuck out his lower lip and gestured toward the number of his cage. "I will write out the tickets, Fräulein. And when you decide, make certain you come to my counter the day before. We will fill in the date, ja?"

She nodded gratefully and slipped the money to him as he filled out all the details on the tickets. Everything but the actual date and time. As he finished, the amusement in his eyes faded to a serious concern. "Good luck, Fräulein," he whispered. "This counter, remember. Grüss Gott." The voice was so low that only Lucy could hear it above the noise of the terminal. Until this moment she had not guessed that others fleeing the Reich currency regulations might have tried the same method of concealing funds.

Slipping the tickets into her handbag, she raised her hand in a halfhearted *Heil.* A question filled her mind: *Is it safe?*

"This counter *only*, Fräulein," he said. "Remember." With that warning, he looked past her and called loudly, *"Next!"*

There was so much to do. Ten thousand homeless children were coming to England soon. Stacks of letters and applications piled up on every table at the Red Lion House, and even higher stacks cluttered the house of Anna and Theo.

"You would think we could have no time for grief," Elisa said to Anna.

Charles heard them talking in low, sad tones as he walked through the front room toward the stairs with Louis. The two boys sat on the landing just out of sight and listened. Things had been gloomy indeed since the broadcast of D' Fat Lady in Vienna. Charles and Louis had been ecstatic about their names being mentioned over the radio. They had run up to hug everyone when the adults came home. But Anna had only hugged them tightly, the way mothers hug when they do not want to cry but might do it anyway. And then she had really cried.

Louis put a finger to his lips to warn Charles not to make a sound. They might get to the bottom of this somber mood that had undermined all the excitement.

"We can't give up on Lori and Jamie, Mother," Elisa consoled.

"No. But the message said they were in hiding, being hunted as well. I was hoping they made it to the charity in Prague. But there has been no sign. And who knows what will become of Karl now that Helen is dead? We must pray that he does not give in to them, Elisa. He is . . . a man like your father. You know how deep the goodness goes. The kind of man that evil men envy and destroy." She paused. "I was just thinking about that family. All of you children playing in the backyard. You were more like a big sister to Lori than a cousin."

"I played with her like a little doll—and she was."

"Helen and I used to watch you both and imagine what it would be like to be grandmothers together, in Berlin, to take our babies for long strolls in the Tiergarten, to the zoo." Anna's voice broke. "I wanted to tell her you were expecting . . . she was the last of my family. Somehow having her gone makes me miss my mother and father as well."

"Not the last, Mother. We must think of Jamie and Lori, and not give up hope. There was that message from Timmons in Berlin."

"Yes." Anna sounded stronger. Louis exhaled loudly with relief as she lightened her voice.

Elisa abruptly held a hand up to silence her mother. "Charles? Louis?" she called. "What are you up to?"

"Listening," Louis said honestly. And that was the end of the conversation.

Elisa and Anna returned to the forms and endless applications, all from mothers hoping to send their children far away to safety.

The evening gown was too tight. Lucy strained to hold in her stomach as Wolf tugged at the gaping zipper.

"You cannot go to the concert in this," he said impatiently.

"I will wear the other one," she said. "The red one you like so well."

"You look like a prostitute in that!" he snapped. "The general is visiting from Berlin. The entire commission will be attending tonight. How would it look if I show up with a fat-bellied whore at my side?" He glared at her stomach, which did not show her pregnancy at all in everyday clothes. Only in the skin-tight evening dresses was her condition noticeable.

"Well then, I will keep my coat on." Lucy fought to keep the emotion from her voice. She had been looking forward to the concert of Christmas music at the Musikverein. It was the only occasion Wolf had invited her to for the holidays.

"You will not keep your coat on," he sneered, "because you are not going. You are too fat. Fat pregnant women belong at the Lebensborn. Generals expect their junior officers to be discreet about such matters. That is why the Lebensborn has been provided. I have not been discreet."

Lucy did not push the argument further. Better to let the matter drop before Wolf arrived at the conclusion that she should be confined at the Lebensborn immediately. Lately he had become more and more impatient and irritable with her.

"Then I am not going." She shrugged as though it did not matter. Slipping out of her dress, she pretended to look at herself in the mirror. She was, in fact, watching Wolf look at her. Out of the restrictive dress, Lucy looked no different than always. She hoped that Wolf noticed; that thoughts of sending her behind the walls of the Lebensborn would vanish as he appraised her. She turned to face him. "You know I do not dress to please your generals, Wolf," she chided. "And if you prefer me this way, then I simply will not dress at all."

The seductiveness of her tone melted his impatience with her. He grabbed her by the wrist and pulled her close. "No one else must be able to look at you." He kissed her.

She pushed him away and raised an eyebrow in surprise. "Who would look at a mother of the Reich?" she teased.

"Everyone looks at you. Don't pretend you don't know that." He held her wrist too tightly, and she did not struggle.

"Then maybe you should keep me pregnant from now on," she smiled.

"I intend to try."

"But tonight you have already succeeded and so you do not need to stay. You will be late," she warned. He kissed her hard, angrily. "Your general will not approve if you are late to the concert."

He pushed her away and stepped back, looking at the soft, subtle roundness of her belly. "Too many Sachertortes," he remarked. "Put your dress on. You may go with me." He glanced at his watch. "Hurry. We have a stop to make." He smiled again, as though he had some secret triumph he would not share with her.

"What should I wear? What would please you?"

"The red dress." He changed his mind just that quickly. "It is near Christmas. Red is a suitable color."

————

Wolf cradled a bottle of champagne in his arm. The bottle was wrapped in red cellophane and tied at the neck with a red bow. He placed it on the seat of his car between him and Lucy.

She supposed that the champagne was for some general or other, but she was wrong. As they drove through the snowy streets of Vienna, Wolf explained.

"You remember the task I have been given? To find the leak among the Gestapo staff? To find the one tipping off the Jews?"

Of course she remembered. Within the context of that conversation Wolf had spoken of ruthlessness and duty as one quality. She had heard a threat to herself on that night.

"You have found him?"

He jerked his head in reply. Lucy studied his profile as the lights of decorations on the city hall gleamed through the windshield of the car. The brilliant Christmas decorations of Vienna seemed an unreal contrast to the subject they spoke of. Lucy looked away as a streetcar loaded with Christmas shoppers rumbled past. The smoke of burning fires rose up from the open-air bazaar in the park in front of the Rathaus. Everywhere were uniforms. Nazi uniforms. All those in civilian clothes wore swastika armbands plainly visible on the arms of their coats. Every building was draped with enormous swastika flags illuminated by blinking lights. This was Austria's first Christmas under those flags. Somewhere in all this, Lucy imagined the man whom Wolf now pursued. Did the fellow browse through the stalls of the Christmas bazaars? Or was he off somewhere saving a Jew and sealing his own fate in the bargain?

Such thoughts made Lucy depressed. She did not smile and nod as usual when Wolf explained how he had managed to track down his culprit.

"A friend of mine—as a matter of fact, he is that fellow who managed to find your apartment for me." He laughed. "You said it right. It pays to cultivate the Gestapo, especially if such cultivation leads to the arrest of a Gestapo traitor and a promotion for me." He patted the champagne bottle. "And so, just to be certain, we will drop in on him tonight. Bring him a gift of our gratitude. If there are Jews in the apartment, so much the better."

She looked at him stupidly. "But it is nearly Christmas."

"So? What has that got to do with anything, my soiled dove?"

He was right, of course. The season of the year had nothing to do with being ruthless. On the contrary, arrests had been stepped up during the holidays.

"It just seems strange to bring him a gift, and then—"

"We will not arrest him tonight," Wolf said irritably. "As a matter of fact, we must hurry so we are not late for the concert. There will be time enough. He will not expect it. No, I know this fellow. He will not see the handcuffs until they are on his wrists."

30

Social Call

On this block of once-elegant flats, even the glass of the streetlamps had been broken. Boarded windows made the place look like a neighborhood of ghosts as lights glimmered out from between the cracks. The worst had been done here to the Jews of Vienna. Those who remained clung tenaciously to the remnants of their lives.

Wolf's black car turned the corner onto a street less marred by Kristal Nacht. Here and there was evidence of what had been, but for the most part, the buildings appeared normal and unscathed.

It was easy to spot which home or shop was owned by a Jew. As Wolf slowed and pulled to the curb, Lucy looked with interest at the nailed-up shop window displaying a freshly painted advertisement: MADAME SINGER, CUSTOM-MADE CORSETS AND UNDERGARMENTS IN THE LATEST PARIS FASHIONS. OPEN.

Lucy had heard of the Jewish corset maker. Even the wives of German party bosses bought her garments. Lucy made note of the address.

To her surprise, Wolf parked at the curb in front of Madame Singer's shop. He set the brake and took out a silver hip flask. Without explanation, he took a deep swig of the strong-smelling stuff and washed his mouth with it. He opened the door and spit into the street.

"He must think we are a bit drunk" he cautioned, handing Lucy the flask. "Drink."

She sipped tentatively and grimaced. The liquor burned her throat and brought tears to her eyes. "Terrible."

"American whiskey." He snatched up the wrapped champagne. "Otto will not feel threatened by our dropping in if he thinks we have drunk enough to disregard our manners."

At that, he slipped out of the car and came around to open the door for Lucy. This sort of propriety had first attracted her to him. Unlike the peasant boys of her village, Wolf had seemed the very model of chivalry. She had not suspected that underneath the public Wolf a private one lurked—a Wolf who differed very much from her first impressions.

She took his arm and he held her securely as they walked toward the entrance of the white stone apartment building across the street. His eyes turned upward to the lighted window of an apartment that looked down onto a small courtyard. Through the tan window shade, Lucy thought she saw movement, and a surge of fear coursed through her. Behind that shade Wolf believed there were Jews hiding—enemies of the Reich, Communists and Socialists, bent on the destruction of the German people. These were the types of criminals he spent his life pursuing, and now Lucy was part of the hunt.

"Remember," he warned as he opened the door of the lobby. "We have had a bit too much to drink. We just happened by. Smile, my fox, and the huntsman may have a reward for you tonight."

Lucy smiled and held tighter to Wolf's muscled arm as they walked across the black-and-white tiled floor of the lobby to the antique elevator cage. "Are they dangerous?" she whispered.

"Smile," he said again and the whiskey on his breath reminded her of the charade.

———

If anyone in all the world had a little sister more stupid than Marlene, Peter could not imagine it.

He hurried to button his trousers as the knock sounded on the door a second time. His mother lay in bed with a headache. That left Marlene and Baby Willie only a twist of a doorknob from disaster.

"Wait!" Peter whispered harshly as he stumbled from the bathroom.

Too late. In an instant, Marlene threw open the door and stood gaping in dumb horror at an S.S. officer and a woman in a red dress and a fox fur.

Baby Willie squealed happily and crawled toward them as Karin emerged too late from the bedroom.

"Who are you?" The officer's words slurred slightly as he peered at Marlene and then into the flat. His smile faded. He squinted drunkenly at the number on the door. "Well, Lucy, have we got the right place?"

The woman did not reply. She looked at the baby on the floor and then at the frightened little girl in front of her. The smile remained frozen on the woman's face, but there was something in her eyes . . . *something* . . .

Peter composed himself. He forced himself not to look at the twin lightning bolts on the collar tabs of the black uniform. Pulling up his suspenders, he nudged Marlene out of the way.

"This is the apartment of my uncle," he said. "Otto Wattenbarger."

Confidence. The terror they all felt must not be evident to this man.

"Otto! Yes!" The officer pushed past Peter into the apartment. "Then this is the right place. I thought so, Lucy. I told you this was it."

The woman hesitated a moment, looking embarrassed; then she entered as well. Peter could smell alcohol on their breath. He did not close the door, but stood beside it as the officer stepped over Willie and leaned close to stare at the photograph of Otto beside the Führer.

"Yes! Here he is! I told you this was it!" He held up the champagne bottle. "For Otto. Where is he?" He patted Peter on the shoulder, not waiting for an answer before he plunged on to another question. "And who are you?"

Karin stepped out of the bedroom and stooped to gather Willie protectively in her arms. "I am Otto's sister." She extended a hand. "Karin Ruger. These are my children. Otto did not tell us to expect company."

"We were just in the neighborhood. Came across this bottle of champagne, a fine vintage. A little something for Christmas." He glanced toward the woman, who was not looking at anyone. "Right, Lucy?"

As if on cue, the woman looked at Karin as though she were surprised by something. "Yes. A gift for your brother. He managed to help us acquire our flat, you see . . . and—" Her eyes seemed to lock on Baby Willie, whose red curls framed a round and brightly joyful face. At her look, the baby tucked his chin shyly and laid his head against his mother. His thumb went to his mouth in a gesture so innocent that the woman's look became tender and human. The expression seemed out of place in the red dress and fur and perfectly coiffed hair.

"Well, maybe we should wait for him." The S.S. officer headed for the sofa and sat down, then patted the place beside him for the woman.

"Our manners," the woman said. "Forgive us. Wolf . . . you have not made an introduction." She did not move to sit beside him.

The officer nudged back his peaked cap. "Right. I am Major Wolfgang von Fritschauer, at your service. And this is Fräulein Strasburg."

"Fräulein Lucy Strasburg," the woman added with a touch of embarrassment in her voice. "We were just on our way to a concert . . . and I . . . have wanted to meet Herr Wattenbarger to thank him. Are we disturbing. . . ?"

Of course they were disturbing everything and everyone except for the baby, who considered them with a coy interest as he slurped happily on his thumb. Karin shook herself into action. "Would you like coffee? My brother may be a while, he said. Business, you know." She was already moving toward the kitchen, gathering the still-gawking Marlene up and shoving her ahead. "Come help me, Marlene."

Peter closed the door. They were not leaving after all, these intruders. The Fräulein sat down and crossed her long legs, which poked out from a slit in the dress. Her shoes were also red. The major helped her off with her coat and tossed it over the arm of a chair. His boots were tall and perfectly shined. Peter had seen boots like that, proud and brutal boots, kicking his father, kicking other men. Peter had not imagined ever getting within range of S.S. footgear with a smile on his face.

"My mother will prepare your coffee," he said, sitting stiffly in a chair opposite the couple.

"You speak with a Viennese accent," the officer said pleasantly. "Otto did not tell us he had relatives here."

Peter shrugged. How was he supposed to reply to that? Had the officer also noticed that Karin's accent was quite different from that of Otto, her supposed brother? "You are not from here." Peter turned the conversation back to the officer.

"Prussia. Northern Germany."

The fellow looked Prussian, Peter thought, hating him politely. The military bearing, close-cropped blond hair beneath the peaked cap, ice blue eyes peering with arrogant amusement from beneath the visor, straight Greek nose—all like the statue of a god come to life. Peter pulled himself into a straighter posture and nodded.

The woman spoke with the low accent of Bavaria, but she seemed the female counterpart to this Prussian Adonis. Smooth chiseled marble in a red dress, she was perfect as long as she did not open her mouth to speak.

But she did speak. Her broad peasant accent was not so lofty as that of the officer. "You did not tell us your name," she urged. That look appeared in her eyes again—human, almost pained.

She was more difficult to hate, but Peter managed. He knew what she was, sitting there in her red dress showing her perfect legs. The officer did not keep company with such a woman for her intellect. An ignorant Bavarian peasant, so low that the only way she could raise herself was to hold on to the coattails of the devil. An insane urge ran through his mind. He wanted to ask her if the apartment Uncle Otto had found for her was in a Seventh District brothel. The thought made him pale.

"You have a name?" she asked kindly, and Peter knew that she was not drunk like the officer.

"Peter," he replied, tying to avoid staring at her legs. It was hard to concentrate; she was looking right at him, the way his geography teacher had looked kindly at him when he got the answer right.

"Peter! Well, I have a brother at home named Peter also. And you look about the same age. How old are you?"

"Fifteen." Peter did not want to give her any more information. Why did she ask such cheerful questions? He was afraid she would ask him about school, and then what would he say?

"Do you go to school, Peter?"

Yes, he had gone to school until *they* had invaded Austria. Now schools were closed to him and Marlene, to all Jewish children. How he longed for school! "Yes. The new Hitler Jugend school in our district has just opened. I will go there after the holiday break."

She seemed surprised at his answer. "Oh," she said, and he felt confident that he had fooled her.

"You Austrian children are quite behind the children of Germany," the officer remarked, eyeing him critically. Did that perfect Greek nose smell a Jew nearby?

"Uncle Otto says it will not take me long to catch up. Who knows, maybe I will also be an S.S. major one day." The game gave Peter a dangerous thrill.

The officer's expression became momentarily thoughtful. "Such a thing would please your uncle, I am sure."

"My brother Peter is also in the Hitler Youth," the woman blurted out. "I have an older brother as well, in the Pottsdam garrison. Everyone is in the military, now days, ja?"

At her interruption the officer became instantly surly. He looked away as if her friendly attempt at conversation disgusted him. His look made Peter pity her.

"The Wehrmacht for some. But the S.S. for me," Peter said. "It is the motto, you know. '*Meine Ehre heisst Treue.* My honor is loyalty!'" Peter repeated the motto enthusiastically. He raised his arm. "Heil Hitler!" he said, as if it were the "Amen" to a prayer.

"Heil Hitler," repeated the officer with a sneer fixed on his face. He no longer looked drunk. "Your uncle has taught you well. No doubt *we* will have to catch up to *you* in the Hitler Jugend." He stood suddenly, leaving the bottle of champagne lying on the couch.

Karin, looking worn, brought the tray of coffee into the room. Marlene followed meekly behind, carrying Willie and not looking at anybody.

"You are leaving," Karin said. It was not a question. Peter hoped the unwelcome guests did not hear the relief he knew was inherent in the comment.

"Yes. We are late. Nearly late for the concert." The officer did not seem drunk at all now. Every movement was clipped and preoccupied. "Come, Lucy," he snapped his fingers as if the woman were a dog to follow after him. She rose, looked at the baby and then at Karin and the coffee cups on the tray. "Your son is a very bright boy. I am sure he will do well in the Hitler Youth."

Karin smiled with genuine relief. "I do hope so. Thank you for coming. Come again when you can stay longer. I will tell Otto you waited for him."

"Heil Hitler," Peter said again in confident farewell, and everyone repeated the words except for Willie, whose thumb returned to his mouth.

———

Again and again the Wallich family replayed the encounter with the S.S. major and his woman. Beginning with Marlene's stupid mistake, they progressed through the first moments of their terror at the sight of lightning bolts and the fancy dress of the beautiful woman from Bavaria. Everyone remarked at Peter's remarkable composure as he fended off questions and fabricated a future career in the S.S.!

When they came to the end of the story, they all howled with laughter. Even Marlene laughed after sulking for a while, saying she could not help opening the door.

Hours later Otto came home, his cheeks were red from the cold. He carried little gift-wrapped packages in the deep pockets of his trenchcoat. Laying them out on the coffee table, he said he should have gotten a tree, but they would not be here long enough for that, anyway.

Then he listened to the story of the champagne bottle. He frowned and stared at the red bow tied around the neck. He asked questions about their behavior, nodding his head in approval at Peter's replies.

"They did not suspect anything, I am certain," Peter said.

Otto drew a deep breath and sank down on the sofa to consider what he had heard. "The day after Christmas I am driving you to Czechoslovakia myself. You will have to make your own way from Moravia to Prague, then on to Danzig. You will be out of harm's way there." Again he stared at the champagne bottle. "You must accompany me to Mass. If we are being watched, it will be expected that my sister and her children go with me to Christmas Mass. Yes. They may be watching."

Later as everyone was sleeping, Otto gently shook Peter's shoulder and called him into his room.

"Listen," Otto whispered, "there is something you need to keep for me . . . and for your family." He opened his wallet and produced a pawn ticket from the Dorotheum. He gave it to Peter, then stuffed a handful of bills into an envelope. "If something should happen to me—"

"What do you mean?" Peter spoke too loud. Otto put a finger to his lips to silence him.

"Just *listen*, will you? Maybe it won't be necessary, but if . . . if I can't make it home . . . *this* is your ticket out of the Reich." Otto grasped his arm. "Take this in to the Dorotheum. Pay off the loan."

"What is it?"

"Just *pay off the loan*, and bring the bundle back to your mother. She will know what to do."

Peter's drowsy expression changed to one of sadness as he looked down at the pawn ticket. "I . . . hope nothing happens because of Marlene being so stupid."

"That's enough," Otto sighed with relief. "Just a precaution. Now go back to bed."

————————

The holiday concert was held in the gilded hall of the Musikverein. Lucy listened to the music with a dull ache inside her. Later, at the dinner in the gold-and-white hall of the Imperial Palace, she sat between a Russian and a Frenchman who talked around her. Did anyone notice that she hardly smiled?

The clear, bell-like voices of the Vienna Boys' Choir brought tears to her eyes. Red and green candles decorated the tables. The great Christmas tree evoked an awed murmur from the crowd when it was unveiled. But it did not seem at all like Christmas. She had difficulty playing the role of Wolf's carefree courtesan.

Wolf was not pleased with her as they drove away from the brightly-lit palace. "You were surly tonight!" he snapped after they passed the guards and he could be himself again.

"I learned surliness from an expert teacher."

He slapped her—not hard, just a startling backhand across her full red lips. "I will teach you—" he said menacingly. "I should have left you home."

"You needed me to help you spy." She daubed a speck of blood from her lip and smiled. "Terrible criminals they are!"

She had never mocked him openly before. He took her words as a challenge.

"You saw what they are!"

"Yes, I saw. A frightened woman and three children."

The simplistic response made Wolf laugh incredulously. "You couldn't see that they are Jews?" he cried. "Yes, they were afraid! And I knew the minute the girl looked at me that these are Jews. Probably rich ones. I knew we had them before we even went into the apartment!"

Lucy had also known, and had pitied the little family and longed to ask them not to hate her for what was about to come upon them. *It is not me! There is nothing I can do about it! I am just along for the ride!* She wanted to get to know the boy named Peter who looked at her with such polite scorn. He was a Jew; she was the mistress of a Nazi. Both were prisoners.

"They weren't Jews," Lucy argued. "I don't think they are Jews or smugglers or any such thing! Not black marketeers or . . . or anything like that. I believe them. This Gestapo man has his sister visiting for the holidays, and—" She paused for effect. "Really, Wolf, I would be careful until you are certain. You might arrest the sister of a Gestapo agent, and then he would find a way to take back our apartment."

At the streetlamp Wolf gave her a withering look. He clenched and unclenched his fingers around the steering wheel. Had she succeeded in planting a doubt? "I have told you before to keep your mouth shut, you Bavarian slut! You chat with that boy like he is an old neighbor in your village, and now you tell me maybe they are not Jews."

"I'm simply saying you should check the story. Have them watched for a day or so." She pouted, staring out the window. "I just think you should be careful. How would it look on your record if you arrested the family of a Gestapo agent after coming drunkenly to their door and imagining you smelled Jews inside?"

Wolf pressed hard on the accelerator to show Lucy his displeasure at her. He had not been drunk earlier, but now he definitely felt the endless rounds of schnapps and wine. Her words made him doubt, and he did not like to doubt what he had been so certain of only a few hours before.

"They are Jews. Otto is no doubt taking bribes to protect them. He should go to prison right along with them."

She mocked him again. "Oh? The Reich has prisons for babies, does it?"

He ignored her remark as they moved slowly toward the domed Burgtheater, which was bathed in floodlights and draped in banners. He snapped his fingers. "Ha! He could be living with her, eh? She is an attractive sort. A racial charge would knock him into the clink and toss away the key."

Lucy snorted in scorn at such a wild thought. "Or, she might be his sister. In which case you will be court-martialed for slandering a loyal servant of the Reich."

"Why . . . why do you argue with me?" Her way of undermining his every idea made him furious and frustrated. "You are a fool to believe such a thing. The woman might pass for an Aryan. And the boy and the baby. But that girl—Jew was stamped on every feature."

Lucy shrugged as if the matter bored her. She grew more silent and sullen as he mumbled his theories as though they were fact enough to hang this Otto Wattenbarger fellow. Well, she had warned Wolf. Was it her fault if he did not listen? Maybe he would be the one arrested and then she could walk away from Vienna a free woman. She had not seen criminals in the flat—just a woman with weary, fearful eyes. Everyone had eyes like that in Vienna. "And so what if they are Jews?" Lucy regretted saying the words even as she blurted them out.

Wolf roared the question back at her. "If they are Jews . . . if they are not his family, as they claim, then a high-ranking party member is taking bribes to help rich Jews! Personally profiteering—and who knows what else he might do for money?" He glanced at her with all the disdain he could muster. "In a few days I will have your proof! Everything I shall need to send Wattenbarger where he belongs. You will see. Irrefutable . . . Jews in his apartment!" His cold blue eyes glinted steel and ordered her to be silent. Her involvement in the matter was finished.

The message came by early post to Murphy. He read it without surprise and passed it across the lunch table to Theo and Chaim Weizmann, head of the Zionist movement. The two had just been extolling the effectiveness of Captain Orde's campaign against the Arab gangs in Palestine. Orde and his training manual were the last, best hope for members of the Yishuv to withstand the pressures of politics and terrorism combined.

RE: THE MOST DANGEROUS MAN IN PALESTINE
Dear Murphy,

I am disturbed to hear there are rumblings of discontent in several branches of the government with regard to the tremendous successes of our Captain Orde. No doubt those news dispatches he has written with anonymous pen were not in the least exaggerated. If anything, he has concealed most of his accomplishments beneath the dry jargon of a journalist. The truth is, however, that neither the Nazis nor the Arabs like our friend in the least! Messages have been sent—stern messages—that he must be taken out of the picture in the Mandate, or there will be no peace conference in London next month. The Arab Higher Committee has vowed that they "will not attend as long as Great Britain is supplying favor, arms, and ruthless officers like this Captain Orde to aggress against our peace-loving people!"

Thus spake the leaders of assassins, cutthroats, and butchers who write history with their own particular twist. They further insist that this Captain Orde is not a captain at all, but a full general incognito.

The last is a compliment, but believe me, no one within our government or the army is smiling or in any way pleased. Sam Orde is in trouble with the High Command. He has done too excellent a job. His results speak for themselves. There is talk that he may be posted back to England and given a desk job out of harm's way. A tragedy, although it may save him from assassination by the Arabs.

You may be losing a great correspondent in Jerusalem; England is punishing a loyal servant for offending those who would murder British subjects in their beds, and a great victory may be won for the Mufti. It reeks of appeasement once again. . . .

There was much more to the letter, but that was the meat of it. Theo placed the paper almost reverently on the table. "So the rumors are true."

"If we were a nation, Samuel Orde would be the head of the War Department. And no one would ask if he was a Jew."

Theo smiled cynically. "Oh, they would ask. And they would challenge his right to be there doing his best." He had lost his appetite.

Chaim Weizmann nodded at the reports he had heard about Orde from the Jewish Agency. "A fellow so single-minded and dedicated makes people around him a little . . . ill at ease, I think. A few thousand years back in our history, we might have called him a prophet."

"And stoned him."

"Or called him a great general."

"And made him king."

"There is a fine line that a man must walk in his success," Weizmann finished.

"He reminds me a lot of my brother-in-law," Theo said.

"Ibsen? The German pastor?" Weitzmann seemed surprised by the comparison. "He is a soldier?"

"Why not? A true man of God fights darkness with prayer and good deeds. A soldier in a right cause fights darkness by drawing his sword and putting an end to men who kill without conscience. All darkness comes from the same source. And all truth comes from God."

"Then we really are fighting a holy war," Chaim laughed.

"At times I hear invisible swords crashing above my bed and behind me as I walk down the street." Theo smiled, too, but his eyes were serious. "This aim of the Muslim Council and Hitler to kill the Jews is pure evidence in the flesh that the real war is between Light and Darkness. And every living human serves one side or the other." He looked squarely at Murphy, who had been silent during this exchange. "Maybe if Orde is posted back in England, you should point at his enemies and tell him to rejoice. Frankly, we can savor the fact that Herr Hitler hates us. It makes this life difficult, certainly, to lose everything one worked for. But that is not the point. When the devil looks at Sam Orde and Karl Ibsen, he shakes in his boots, because he sees men who have not given in."

"A worthy aim," Murphy remarked. "Churchill said it to Charles."

Weizmann raised his glass in a toast. "As the poet said:

Here's to unknown generals of light,
unsheathe their swords of truth and right!
With prayers and deeds together fight,
and put the evil hosts to flight."

"To Samuel Orde," Murphy said.

"To Karl Ibsen," Theo added.

"And to the unknown soldiers."

31

Christmas Eve

Lucy could not help raising her eyes toward the window of Otto Wattenbarger's apartment as she ducked into the courtyard of Madame Singer's corset shop.

An old basket maker and a maker of votive candles shared the same courtyard. They stood talking over their Dutch doors and looked up when they saw Lucy. Both men smiled and nodded, hoping that she was a customer come for last-minute shopping on Christmas Eve. They seemed disappointed as she passed them, pausing instead before the closed door of the old corset maker.

"She lives upstairs," called the candle man. "Ring the bell and she will come."

At least they were not jealous of the business Frau Singer attracted. Lucy pulled the red and green braided bell cord. Upstairs she could hear the faint jingle of the bell.

The window opened a fraction. "Coming! Coming!" the woman called down. Then the window shut tight and the two men began to talk to each other again about the things they had sold at the bazaar in the Rathaus Park and how the Germans had nearly cleaned Vienna out. Things were better since the Nazis had come, but how was anyone to restock now that the merchandise was sold and shipped back to "the Big Brother"?

Lucy pulled the collar of her plain brown woolen coat up around her ears as she waited. It was cold in the courtyard; an icy wind whistled down the steep eaves of the building.

"Ring it again," laughed the basket maker, and at that moment the stately, refined figure of Frau Singer appeared in the doorway. "So sorry, my dear." The woman spoke in a soft Viennese accent. She stepped aside and let Lucy come in from the cold. "I did not mean to keep you waiting. The tea kettle whistled, the phone rang, and at the same moment you came."

Lucy stamped the clinging snow onto the mat and then smiled and nodded as if it did not matter at all. She wondered what Wolf would say if he knew she had come here to a Jewish shop? "You are the corset maker?" Lucy asked, looking around.

"I am Madame Singer." The woman extended her hand. "My stocks are somewhat depleted—" She waved her hand around at the broken shelves of what had once been the finest corset shop in Vienna. "I have moved everything upstairs for safekeeping." The face was kind, softened by a fan of fine lines at the corner of each eye which pleated when she smiled and nodded. "It does not really matter. My ladies still know where I am."

Lucy tried not to stare at the obvious destruction in the room. "I have heard that you are the best at your craft."

The old woman laughed. "Painless corsets," she said, and Lucy knew that the woman did not blame her for what the other Germans had done to her beautiful shop. "Painless corsets cannot be bought off a shelf, now can they? They must be fitted and handmade. That is why I am still here, my dear." She took Lucy by the elbow and directed her to a steep flight of stairs leading to her living quarters. "What are you in need of, a pretty and well-proportioned girl like you? A brassiere? Something for a strapless evening gown?"

Lucy followed after, feeling an instant kinship with the woman. She was so much like the women of her village—without pretense, welcoming everyone readily.

"I am expecting," Lucy said bluntly, "and I would like to keep my figure as long as possible."

At the top of the stairs, sunlight made rainbows through the beveled windows of the old woman's main room. Silk negligees hung on racks beside the tea cart. Bolts of silk and cotton lined up in a row on the fat, friendly blue chintz sofa. An old-fashioned treadle sewing machine stood center stage in front of a warmly hissing gas stove. Brassieres lay stacked in neat lines on top of the lace-covered dining table. It was whispered that Hermann Göring's wife bought her underthings here. She had been angry when she heard that rowdies under her husband's orders had demolished Madame Singer's shop.

The old woman pulled open Lucy's coat and appraised Lucy's figure an instant. "Off with the coat, if you please," she ordered. "Let's see what we've got to work with."

Lucy obeyed, not feeling at all self-conscious. She held her arms out to the side as Frau Singer circled her slowly.

"Very good," said the old woman. "You are long in the waist and so will carry the child well. How far along are you?"

"Nearly four months."

At this information, the thin penciled arch of the eyebrows rose in surprise. "Gottenyu!" *Yiddish,* Lucy thought, *the first signal that the old woman really was a Jew.* "You hide this very well naturally!"

"I need some time . . ." She faltered, unable to explain why she could not simply wear maternity clothes and waddle about like other pregnant women.

"Yes? This is not a time for corsets, my dear. Soon enough you will simply blossom, and there will be no hiding of a thing like that."

"I will lose my job," she said, a half-truth. "You know how they are."

Frau Singer eyed her with a knowing look. She did not need to say any more. "Well then, I will do my best. You will have to wear plain skirts and jackets straight at the sides, thus—" She demonstrated. "Bring your skirts, and I will adjust the waistline for you." She smiled and the lines fanned out across her face. "It is like a magician. Sleight of hand, all in the angle. I once helped the mistress of a duke remain out of confinement for the full term. Everyone thought she had just put on weight. Too many pastries from Demel's, they said. And then, poof! She lost the weight and had a baby boy suddenly appear on her doorstep. Or so she said. Everyone knew the truth, but that is really the way it happened."

Madame Singer did not ask questions; Lucy was grateful for that. Pins in her mouth, the old woman measured and hummed pleasantly as she figured how much of this fabric and that she would use. "We will make adjustments as your body changes, my dear," she promised. Then she fixed tea and the two women sat at the window and chatted as the afternoon sky grew dusky. "I will not offer you a pastry," Madame Singer remarked in a motherly tone. "That would be too cruel, and someone would accuse me of making my customers fat so that I could sell corsets."

Lucy paid a remarkably small amount and promised to return in three days to pay the rest and pick up the special corset. She left the shop feeling refreshed, as if she had just had her hair curled and her nails manicured. No wonder the wives of the Nazi officials still patronized the little shop.

The candle shop and the basket maker's shop were locked up tight when Lucy walked from the courtyard. She looked up at the lighted window where the doomed little family lived unsuspecting of Wolf's plans for them. A cold blast of air swooped down from the gables, and the warmth Lucy felt blew instantly toward the Danube.

Standing on the corner in the freezing wind, she held tightly to the scarf around her hair. The streetcar trundled past, but she did not run toward the stop. Still she looked up at the window. A cat sat on the sill, placidly looking back at her.

She could not explain why, but she found herself rummaging

through her handbag in search of blank note paper and a pen. Leaning against the streetlamp, she thought of the sweet baby sucking his thumb, the frightened face of the chubby little girl, the weary look of her lonely mother . . . and the anger that seethed just beneath the surface of the boy named Peter. "Heil Hitler, indeed," she muttered, shaking her head. She wrote the note, then darted across the street and into the building. Wrapping her scarf close around her face, she planned to pretend to be on the wrong floor if they happened to catch her.

The groaning metal cage of the elevator lifted her up. Her heart pounded. She was breaking the law; she could be executed for such a simple act. And yet, who would ever know?

It was Christmas after all. Lucy hoped that someone would do something nice for her if she was in such a fix.

She pushed the brake button, locking the elevator, then folded the note, ran to the apartment door, and shoved the paper under it.

Lucy was back out on the street again, waiting at the streetcar stop before her heart slowed to a normal rate. Only then did she shudder at the thought of what Wolf would do and say when he found that the rabbits had escaped from his snare.

She looked back toward the lighted window of the apartment. The cat still sat silently on the window ledge as if nothing unusual had happened at all.

———

The holidays had come to London, filling the streets with music and lights and smiling faces Charles and Louis had never seen in all their short lives. Together they climbed the Victoria Memorial in front of Buckingham Palace; from this perch they watched the changing of the guard. Red coats and tall black shakos on the heads of the soldiers made them seem like nutcrackers come to life! The clop of horses' hooves against the cobbles of the street was better than the toy cavalry horses sent from Macy's by Mr. Trump!

It was a magic time. Charles could not remember Christmas as a time of real happiness. All their lives they had lived under a shadow of fear that made the singing of carols sound brave and defiant, but never joyful.

A shadow reached here, as well, but it no longer threatened the boys. Charles saw the sadness cross Anna's face sometimes. He knew what she was thinking without being told . . . she was thinking of the children in the photograph on her piano. Lori and Jamie Ibsen. She was wondering about their Christmas—where they were, where their father was now.

Charles understood such sadness. When his own father had been in prison, his mother had carried such thoughts in her eyes as well.

With so many children coming to England, they had much to be happy about. But Christmas would be much better if these two could come, too. Lori and Jamie were lost somewhere. Anna smiled and said Merry Christmas, but Charles could see the worry in her eyes.

———

Jacob hoped the Gestapo had forgotten about the Ibsen family and New Church. He had somehow imagined that people drove past and pictured the building as deserted and condemned. The urgency of fleeing had been lost in the midst of planning for escape. There was so much to think about. Every plan must have a backup; every eventuality must be explored and thought out. He worked his troops with calisthenics until even Lori could climb the rope as quickly as Jamie or Mark.

She was angry with him now, of course. She believed that he had destroyed their one chance of getting out of Berlin without having to climb ropes or scale walls or run for miles. But today, she was proven wrong.

All the gear was packed and ready for the escape, stowed away behind stacks of Communion plates in the cupboards behind the baptistery. Jamie and Mark were playing checkers on a homemade board in the choir loft. Lori was sulking in her father's study. Jacob was studying maps.

Then the chains on the doors of New Church began to rattle. A terrible groaning sound reached their ears; the wooden planks nailed across the entrance were being pried loose.

Mark and Jamie were first into the bellows. Jacob waited at the top of the stairs and prayed for Lori to come soon. She slid to the base of the stairs. Clutching her shoes in her hand, she half-crawled, half-stumbled up toward Jacob. He pulled her up, dragged her to the bellows and into their cocoon just as the entrance doors swung back with an explosive clang.

Then, far away, they heard the echoes of footsteps and voices resounding throughout the building.

"They said not to waste anything . . ."

"You take that side of the building. I'll inventory the offices and storage."

"Wilhelm, take a look at the pipe organ! *Mein Gott!* We should be able to pull it out and install it in that new ice skating rink planned for the—"

"*Nein!* The Reichskulturbund has put their stamp on it for the new opera building. Such a fine instrument! What a waste it has been in this place."

They were taking inventory—finding out what was usable in New Church before they knocked down the walls. Lori swallowed hard and tried not to cry. It seemed like the autopsy of a loved one. She found herself trembling with sorrow rather than fear as the fellow with the harsh lowlander accent examined the massive organ. Then the unthinkable happened. He switched on the motor that powered the bellows. The wooden support above them began to move down. Jacob raised his hands and braced himself hard to hold it up. His face grimaced with the strain of it; then agony as wood cut into his hands and finally broke into splinters at his resistance.

Lori could hear the clicking of the mechanism and the tapping of key and pedals. A terrible wheezing sound groaned from the pipes as the right bellows worked to do the job of both. Dust filled the space. Lori pulled her collar up and squeezed her eyes shut tight.

Just as suddenly, the storm ended. The electric motor whined off. The clear voice of the attacker called to his comrades from the other side of the partition. "Someone will have to look at this. I think there is something wrong with the bellows."

Mark coughed. Not a big cough. A strangled, garbled cough. Jacob clamped a bloody palm over his mouth. He coughed again.

"Listen to that, will you?" called the workman. "The thing sounds like it is dying!"

"They'll go through it next month," someone shouted up. "Just take a photograph and describe what you see. You're no Bach, anyway!"

For three hours the workers combed the building. When they finally left, Jacob rushed down to see if their supplies were still intact. They were there, tagged and moved to a larger pile labeled *MISCELLANEOUS*.

The boom of the wrecking ball against the stones of New Church seemed very near.

———

All day the Wallichs practiced the things Otto had taught them. When to bend the knee and cross oneself, how to clasp hands properly and kneel and stand and kneel again, the simple Christmas carols they had known before. Such songs were always being played this time of year by the Beidermeier bands on the street corners. Before the world had fallen apart, Peter had seen his mother pass by a cold group of shivering musicians and drop coins into the open empty case of a trumpet player. The songs were the best part of the complicated ritual of Otto's Holy Catholic Church.

"St. Stephan's," Otto had remarked cheerfully as he left them this morning. "We will hear the Vienna Boys' Choir. Don't be nervous. It is not so very different from the synagogue."

It was going to be quite different, Peter was certain of that. His mother and Marlene practiced the lessons of Gentile worship with some enjoyment. For Peter, the requirements of passing for a Gentile rankled him to the core. He hated it all. He often considered striking out for the border on his own and slipping through the Nazi patrols into Czechoslovakia.

Relieved when Otto finally set the date for their departure from Vienna, Peter only regretted that he must now play out this charade of Christmas in St. Stephan's. It was easier for him to raise his hand and say *"Heil Hitler"* to an S.S. man and his bimbo than to bow the knee to the Gentile God. He hated their Christ. He detested the sign of the cross and all it represented. Such things, he believed, had taken his father. The sky had shattered on Kristal Nacht, and there was no God, no heaven there when he looked up. He learned the catechism like the pages of a survival book he would discard once they crossed the border of the Reich.

Peter eyed his sister with disgust as she primped before a mirror. "Uncle Otto" had brought her a new dress to wear to Mass. Her stringy brown hair was plaited and pinned like snail shells over her ears. She looked too fat, as usual, as she batted her eyes at herself and rehearsed the curtsey she must perform to priest and plaster saint alike. But Peter kept his mouth clamped tight. To tell her what he thought would be to call down upon himself a storm of wails and sobs and then the wrath of his mother.

"Didn't Uncle Otto buy a pretty dress, Peter?" she simpered, not turning away from her reflection.

He grunted a reply and turned away. Needing some moment of pleasantness, he scooped up Baby Willie who had crawled beneath the coffee table to chew on something.

"What have you got now, little street sweeper?" Peter sank down on the sofa and pulled a gooey slip of paper from the tight fist.

Willie tried to put the paper back in his mouth and squealed an indignant protest when Peter wrenched it from him.

"What is it?" Karin looked up from her studies at the dining table.

"Nothing. Paper. He could choke."

Karin nodded, then sank back into concentration over the Mass book.

As Peter wadded up the paper to toss it at Marlene, one word caught his eye. *JEWS.* The ink was smeared a bit, and yet here was Peter's true identity shouting back at him. He unfolded the paper, careful not to let the dampness smear any more letters.

JEWS,
YOU MUST LEAVE THIS FLAT IMMEDIATELY OR BE ARRESTED. YOU
ARE DISCOVERED. GRÜSS GOTT.
A FRIEND

Peter stared hard at the words as the blood drained from his face. The baby reached out for the paper with sticky fingers.

"NO!" Peter shouted. He was shouting at the note, but Willie thought the harshness was meant for him and puckered his face to cry.

"What now?" Karin asked. "Peter, really, he is just a—" Karin's words stuck in her throat. The look of stark terror on Peter's face passed to her. She rushed to take the note from her silent, frightened son.

She read the words once, unbelieving, then again, then a third time as realization of their peril filled her.

"Oh, dear God! What are we to do? What?"

Peter sprang to his feet as Marlene finally turned away from her reflection to gape at her panic-stricken mother and brother.

"What has happened?" she cried. Real tears filled her brown cow-eyes. She could cry at the drop of a hat; this seemed more like the drop of the sky.

"Get your things," Peter ordered, looking at the door. Were the Gestapo even now entering the building? Did they climb the stair or ride the elevator?

"But . . . but . . ." Marlene stuttered. "But . . ."

"What about Otto?" Karin took Willie and held him to silence his crying. The room filled with terror, an electric spark that flicked from one person to the other and back again.

"He is probably already arrested," Peter said, grimly looking around the room to decide what to take and where they could run—tonight, of all nights.

"What?" Marlene stamped her foot and screamed.

Peter turned on her angrily. "I'll tell you what! Those people you let in! That's what! You stupid little brat! You've hung us all, and your precious Uncle Otto in the bargain!"

His words were too cruel for Karin to stand. She stepped between them and ordered them to gather their things quickly. *Now!*

"But what about Otto? What about Christmas at St. Stephan's?" Marlene whimpered.

"No Christmas." Peter rushed past her to throw his clothes into a suitcase. "We are Jews again."

Ten minutes later the little family had managed to cram all their belongings into two small suitcases.

"What about Otto?" Marlene asked again. "We should warn him they are coming."

"He knows already," Peter said, wanting to strike her for her stupidity.

"But, Mother," Marlene whined. "He will wonder where we have gone!"

"Your brother is right," Karin said. "It is no doubt too late."

They switched the lights off. Karin placed the rumpled note into her pocket. They would dispose of it far away from here.

Marlene threw herself at her mother, grabbing her around the waist, begging to leave some word for poor Uncle Otto who had been so kind.

"Shut up!" Peter slapped Marlene across the head. "We are going outside! Out of here! Do you know what that means? Only Jews weep in the streets of Vienna. Now shut up."

"Go wash your face," Karin instructed her daughter with a voice so weary that it was barely audible.

Marlene suddenly fell silent, as if Peter's warning had finally turned off the spigot of her hysteria. She hurried to the bathroom, closed the door behind her and switched on the light while the others waited in impatient fear.

Marlene looked again at her own reflection—the sad brown eyes, the perfect hair now mussed by Peter's slap. The face was more angry and defiant than heartbroken. Marlene raised the note she had stolen from her mother's pocket. She read the pretty handwriting and then, so Otto would know why they left, she tucked the note into the frame of the mirror.

"Hurry!" Peter called to her.

Marlene splashed water on her red face and smiled as she emerged.

———

There had been no time to formulate a plan, yet Peter and his mother said the same name at the same instant: *"Frau Singer!"*

The corset maker's house was just across the street, a few quick paces from Otto Wattenbarger's door. Where else could they go?

Karin hesitated a moment, aware of the danger in which they might place the old woman.

"There is no place else," Peter whispered as he took his mother by the arm and decided the issue. "You take one suitcase and Marlene. *Go!* I will bring Willie and follow by a different route."

The plan evolved just that quickly. Karin and Marlene slipped out the back door of the building. Peter, lugging his bundled-up brother and a satchel full of baby things, left by the front door.

He stopped outside on the sidewalk and tugged Willie's cap down around his ears. The baby shuddered and looked surprised by the cold air against his cheeks. Peter dawdled a moment longer, glancing nonchalantly along the shadowed facades of the buildings for some sign of a watcher. He saw no one, and he hoped that his mother and sister were not being trailed as they left the alley.

For just a moment, he considered walking directly across the street and into Frau Singer's shop. The green car of an Austrian Schupo passed by, and Peter thought better of it.

He tried to look lighthearted. *Big brother taking his baby brother out for a stroll to look at the Christmas lights of Vienna.*

"It is cold, isn't it, Willie?" Peter remarked, and the words rose up in frosty puffs as he walked carefully over the icy sidewalk.

As if in agreement, Willie tucked his head against the warmth of Peter's coat and gazed in wide-eyed wonder at the sights and sounds of the street. It had been so long since Willie had been out, Peter wondered if he even remembered the outside.

Peter talked constantly to Willie, pointing to this shop and that building as if the infant could somehow comprehend Vienna. The baby tried to suck his thumb through his mitten and got a mouthful of coarse wool for the effort. Only then did he begin to fuss. Peter tugged off the tiny mitten and let Willie have the precious thumb as they rounded the corner onto the broad Ringstrasse.

A brass band on the street corner played Christmas carols. Lights shimmered everywhere. In the windows of a thousand apartments candles were lit on the Christmas trees.

It was beautiful, but Peter was not part of it. He could not think of the beauty, only of the danger he felt pressing at his back; threatening Baby Willie—perhaps snuffing out their lives as easily as the candles on these trees would be extinguished. Stronger than any desire he had ever felt, Peter wanted to protect Willie from such a thing.

Peter stopped a moment as a streetcar rumbled by on shiny wet tracks. He put down the satchel and shifted Willie's weight, kissing him on his ruddy cheek. Willie smiled up at him without ever taking the thumb from his mouth. The baby did not know, could not realize, the desperation and love behind that kiss. Peter looked back to see if anyone followed them.

Beyond the enormous public buildings of the Ringstrasse, Peter could make out the spires of the churches of Vienna. Distant church bells began to clang joyfully, announcing the first services of the evening. Peter hefted the satchel again and hurried through the last-minute shoppers as he made his way back toward Frau Singer's shop. *So much for the Mass book. So much for Marlene's Christmas dress and her dream of being one of them!*

He had walked far enough. If they were being trailed, Peter had not spotted their pursuers. He exhaled a long, relieved breath and turned down the first side street. The noise of traffic at his back, he walked faster, in a hurry to be inside, to see if his mother and Marlene had made it safely to Frau Singer's flat.

———

There were churches somewhere, Lori knew, where families stood side by side together in the pews and sang Christmas songs without fear of who might be watching or listening. Echoes of her own memories replayed in her mind as the shadows of evening dissolved into the darkness of deserted New Church.

No lights shone this year—no garlands, no manger scene or clumsy church pageant. No choir sang songs of praise and joy. Only four small voices whispered the soft melody of "Silent Night."

In memory of Christmas Past, each of them had chosen something small from New Church to carry away. They wrapped their own gifts and laid them on the dusty altar. Lori read the Christmas story, and each of them prayed for their mothers and fathers and all the others who were not at New Church tonight.

The service completed, they opened their gifts. Jamie had chosen his father's silver filigreed letter opener, the one Pastor Karl had brought home from a pilgrimage to Jerusalem ten years before. He held it up in the gloom. A faint glimmer of light struck its dagger-like blade. Jamie had always admired it, he explained, but Papa had never let him touch it. His prayer was that by next Christmas he could give it back to his father.

Mark had searched the church from top to bottom for something— anything—that might make a present for himself. He came across a packet of twelve yellow pencils and a box of clean white stationery with envelopes. It seemed an elegant gift to give himself from New Church.

Lori found her father's hidden Bible, the one that remained whole with both Old and New Testaments intact, even after the huge bonfires in which every vestige of the Jewish Scriptures had been taken from the churches and burned. As Papa had explained, the Old Testament held all the prophecies about the coming of Christ. Without them, the story was only half told, and told incorrectly at that. Lori was uncertain if any complete Bibles remained in Nazi Germany. But this last one she would take with her so she could read the words in her own language.

Jacob took the red velvet altar cloth, the one with the embroidered gold letters on it: *HIS FAITHFULNESS WILL BE YOUR SHIELD AND RAMPART.* Jacob did not say that tonight, especially, he felt need of a shield and rampart, even though that was the reason he had removed the cloth and folded it carefully. He said he liked the color of the velvet and he could not think of anything else to take. A nice memento, he explained gruffly. He would not allow any sentimentality to creep into his voice, although he was as homesick and heartsick as the others.

They sang one more carol, then sat in silence on the floor in front of the altar. Images of shining lights and roasted turkeys and Christmas trees played in each mind.

"Well," Lori said feebly. "Merry Christmas, then."

Jacob cleared his throat too loudly, the sort of sound that announced he had something to say. "One more present." He reached out for her hand and laid a small oval paper-wrapped something in her palm.

"But we weren't supposed to—"

"This is for you to use here." Jacob sounded strangely shy, like a little boy—maybe even hopeful that she would not throw the thing back in his face.

"Here? But we are leaving tonight."

"Well, I have been so . . . strict . . . difficult about certain things," he stammered. "Open it."

She held it up to her cheek. A faint floral smell escaped the wrapping. She tore open the paper and felt the smooth, round surface of a new cake of soap. Not just any soap, but the guest soap her mother had kept in the basket by the sink in the bathroom at home.

"Mama's soap!" she cried with delight. "But how. . . ?"

Jacob shrugged. She did not see the gesture of embarrassment. "I remembered it. From when I visited."

Jamie piped up. "He told me to bring it back."

"Oh! It is . . . wonderful!" She inhaled its fragrance. It seemed so long since she had smelled anything so wonderful. "I will take it with me and . . . find a bathtub!"

Jacob cleared his throat again. "Well I . . . that is . . . we thought maybe since it is our last night . . . maybe you might want a real bath now."

She laughed. *A bath! After six weeks? Could there be a better gift?* "But *where?*"

"We filled the baptistery for you," Mark said enthusiastically.

"It has been heating all day long," Jacob added in a matter-of-fact tone. "We will stand guard out here. The curtain is closed, so . . ."

The baptistery. It almost seemed a sacrilege. Lori hesitated as she wondered what Papa would say.

"But in church—"

"We got the idea from Grandfather Kalner," Mark explained helpfully. "In a Jewish church, you see, that is where everyone used to take a bath. I can't remember the name, but Grandfather swore it was true."

"Well then—" Holding the sweet-smelling bar up to her nose, Lori hurried past the altar and through the door that led to the baptistery. She climbed the steps, not minding the profoundness of the dark.

The air was warm and steamy from the water the boys had prepared. This tank was something Papa had made as a special project for the church. *Heated water.* It was a wonder and a marvel—and a necessity, since old Herr Gruber had gotten baptized one Sunday and died of pneumonia the next from the shock of the cold water. Papa had not wanted to send his flock to heaven quite so soon as that.

Lori laid her clothes aside and brushed her toe across the warm, soft liquid. She heard herself sigh with pleasure as she stepped down into the tank and let six weeks of bone-cold discomfort melt away. Beyond the curtain where the boys waited for her, she heard them laugh with delight at her pleasure.

She untied her thick braid and let her hair float on the water. Clutching the soap like a treasure, she lathered herself from head to foot. She held her breath and slipped her head under the water, surfacing only when her lungs began to sting.

"Why didn't we think of this sooner?" she called.

Did they hear her? It did not matter. This was nearly heaven, one memory she would have with her from New Church every time she took a hot bath!

And then, through the curtain, she heard them singing. They were caroling softly to her, apologizing in their own shy way for six weeks of harassment.

It was hard to remain unforgiving while floating in the scented luxury of a warm, soapy baptistery.

"Thank you," Lori muttered into the water, "I love you all."

32

Flight

The drive north through Palestine toward Hanita was long and dangerous. Sandwiched between armored transports, Orde was grateful for the protection of the convoy. His vehicle was not government issue; Orde's enemies within the politics of the British military had seen to that. He was using transportation provided by the scrounging efforts of Larry Havas and maintained in what was wryly referred to as "operational order" by Zach Zabinski.

The car, of uncertain parentage, may not have had one original part left on it, but as Zabinski said, "It runs more than it doesn't." Orde was returning from an unsuccessful attempt to get his Special Night Squad supplied with more modern weapons, including explosives.

"Can't be done," he was told. "Out of the question." The belligerent Jews must not be given the means to take action against Arabs except in strictest self-defense.

It did not matter that the Jihad Moquades, the Holy Strugglers, were provided with German-made weapons, or that they recruited mercenaries from nearly every Islamic nation in the Middle East. It did not matter that they were promised ten pounds a month if they lived, and instant admittance to paradise if they died battling the hated Jews and the infidel Christian Britishers. What mattered was that British policy required nothing be done to antagonize the Arabs any further. Offensive weapons for Jews? Unthinkable!

Orde was disappointed, but not surprised. His continued appeals for more equipment and official British sanction for his squads was partly a ploy. Orde reasoned that if he stopped asking, the political wizards would begin to question why. He did not want them to examine the stores of captured weapons with which the Jewish troops trained and fought. The convoy sped up slightly, taking advantage of a slight downgrade.

Captain Samuel Orde tried at all times to understand the minds of his Arab terrorist opponents. True, they fired their weapons wildly at times, expending more cartridges in an aimless show of emotion than Orde's troops would go through in a month of training and combat combined. But the sermons of their leaders acted upon them like a drug, driving out fear of death and making them a formidable foe.

Driving northward, Orde's little car eventually parted company with the convoy as he turned off toward Hanita. He mulled over the other reason for this trip, hoping that it might prove more successful than the appeal for arms.

In a recent action against Arab infiltrators, one Holy Struggler, an Iraqi, had been wounded and left behind. Through gritted teeth he explained to an interrogator that he hated all the British and all the Jews. He was angry that he had only been wounded, because he had lost both his ten pounds a month and his place beside the prophet Mohammed.

The Iraqi prisoner had warned darkly that the battle was only beginning. New men were coming from the north, he promised, more every day. Soon the stinking British would all be rotting in hell beside the cursed Jews. Haj Amin Husseini and the great German leader Hitler had both promised that it would be so!

Orde had transported the talkative captive to the British Mandate's government offices in Jerusalem. Hopefully, he reasoned, somebody in charge would figure out that there was more than just Arab unrest at stake here, that the only possibility of retaining a democratic toehold in the Middle East was the establishment of a Jewish homeland.

Orde downshifted as he rounded a corner and rolled into an Arab village that sprawled across the abruptly narrowed road. Maybe, just maybe, after the information was reviewed, the British government would realize that it was already at war with Germany. Just as in Spain, Nazi Germany was flexing its muscles, challenging a ruling government while pulling the strings of manipulation from just barely behind the scenes.

Captain Orde downshifted again, then braked suddenly as an Arab boy leading a donkey loaded with a bundle of sticks walked directly into his path. Orde instinctively thumped the steering wheel as if to honk the car's horn, but the horn was one piece of equipment that had never worked.

Having made his sudden entrance onto the road, the donkey apparently decided that it did not wish to make as quick an exit. It stood with its ears laid back in an elaborate show of sulky displeasure. The Arab boy first tried to pull the donkey into motion; when this failed, he went behind the animal and gave it a shove. It merely shifted its weight from one foot to the other, but continued standing in the middle of the narrow lane.

Orde scanned the road to see if it was possible to go around the balky creature, but one side was bordered with a low stone wall and the other blocked by a roadside produce stand. Orde hoped that the proprietor of the stand would assist the boy in moving the donkey, but the owner was nowhere in sight. No one else seemed to be around, either.

Orde did not want to get out alone in the middle of an Arab village, but he had nearly decided that he was going to have to help when the beast suddenly moved. The boy took a stick from the bundle on the donkey's back and tapped it lightly on a hind leg. Both boy and pack animal moved rapidly out of the street. As he slowly accelerated, Orde watched the pair disappear from sight; from behind the houses, the boy stared back at him. He had not given Orde a single glance during the struggle in the road.

Why is he watching me? Orde wondered. *And why did the boy suddenly remember the secret to making this particular donkey move after several minutes of struggle? It is almost as if he received a signal that it was time to move on.*

A tiny pebble of suspicion dropped into the pool of Orde's mind, and its ripples spread out through his every fiber. Orde's nerves and the hair on the back of his neck stood on end—a thin wisp of white smoke was coming from the back of his car!

At that moment Orde ceased to think, and his reflexes took over. He braked the little car hard and turned its wheels into the low stone wall for good measure. The immediate stop almost threw Orde into the windshield, but he turned the motion to the side and lunged out the car door. He rolled over the stone wall, smashing his shoulder heavily as he fell.

The bomb planted in the rear of the car went off with a deafening roar. A great ball of flame rolled up as the gas tank exploded. His head covered by his hands and his face pressed into the dirt of Palestine, Samuel Orde could feel the concussion of the blast and the intense heat that burned his hands and the back of his neck.

Pieces of the auto began to rain down like shrapnel, but Orde was already up and moving. He ran in a low crouch along the stone wall, and, miraculously, none of the spinning pieces of jagged metal touched him. He ran desperately, expecting any minute to be pursued.

By the time the frightened villagers came out to view the smoking remains of the assassination attempt, Orde was already more than a mile away, heading for Hanita. As he covered the ground in a rapid hike, he alternated between thanking God for sparing his life and apologizing for having been so stupid that he needed divine intervention.

Orde would never have forgiven such inattention on the part of one of his troopers, and he resolved to never again be guilty of it himself. *Especially not now,* he thought. *There are miles and many Arabs between here and Hanita.*

Not even a strong cup of coffee could remove the chill from Karin Wallich.

Peter stood by helplessly as his mother trembled uncontrollably beneath Frau Singer's thick Eider quilts. Every moment of fear she had felt over the last weeks suddenly broke loose. She did not cry. Peter would have liked it better if there had been tears in Karin's eyes, but there were none. She simply lay there, staring at the ceiling and shivering as though she lay in a pool of icy water.

"There now, Karin my dear. My *dear* . . ." Frau Singer stroked Karin's forehead. "You are safe now. No harm will come to you here."

Peter knew that Frau Singer's words of reassurance were only a whisper of hope. Harm could, indeed, come to them here. Nowhere in Vienna was any Jew safe.

Marlene huddled in the corner of the bedroom beside a large dark chest of drawers, her brown eyes wide with fright. Finally she realized the seriousness of the situation. *At last,* Peter thought as he stalked past her, *Marlene figured it out!*

Mercifully, Baby Willie had fallen asleep in a bed made up in the bottom drawer of the chest. Peter stooped over his baby brother and found some comfort in the fact that he could sleep so peacefully. He wanted to reach out and brush back the curl on his smooth forehead, but instead he contented himself with simply gazing at the child. Peter did not look at Marlene. He knew that if he looked at her, all comfort would vanish. He blamed her somehow for what had happened. He could not explain his anger, not even to himself, but he knew for certain that Marlene's actions had led to their discovery and the note and this.

He looked at his mother again. He wished she would cry. "We are finally at Frau Singer's after all, Mama," he whispered, hoping to remind her that they had wanted to be here all along. She did not acknowledge his words or even look at him.

Once more Peter looked mournfully at her, then stalked out of the room. He picked his way around the bolts of material that littered Frau Singer's once-spotless front room. The light was out. A soft glow emanated from the gas heater. Peter went to the window and leaned against the frame. He pulled back the shade a fraction until he could see the street and the entrance to Otto's apartment building. Soon *they* would come. They would come in their cars and go up the stairs and break in the door in their search for a mother and three children.

He did not have long to wait until the first act of the drama took place. They came on foot, the tall S.S. Major Wolfgang von Fritschauer and three other men. *The couple who had come to bring their champagne and Christmas greetings!*

The sight of the major made Peter want to shout at Marlene to come and see what she had done! He wanted to shove her fat, simpering face through the glass of the window and scream at her. But he simply watched in silence. Was there any hope of warning Otto what he was coming home to?

At the thought, Peter's heart beat faster. Perhaps he could run down the stairs and wait across the street to call a warning when Otto came home.

The instant the thought came to him, he spotted two more men in the shadows flanking the doorway. No doubt others would be at the back door and still more watching from either end of the street. The awareness of how near they had come to their own arrest made Peter sweat as a wave of fear and nausea washed over him. The trap had been set only minutes after they had found safety. Now Otto Watten-barger would pay the penalty for all of them.

Peter waited, hearing the kind murmuring of Frau Singer in the bedroom. He could not understand what she said. His attention fixed on the solitary figure of Otto Wattenbarger as he rounded the far corner. He passed beneath the ring of a streetlamp, his step cheerful, unsuspecting. He carried a shopping bag in one hand and a very small Christmas tree in the other.

So he decided we must have a tree after all . . .

"Turn around," Peter whispered, desperately willing Otto to hear the danger. "Go back. They will not know it is you if you go back now."

The words made a round circle of steam against the windowpane. "Go back . . ."

Otto walked on, unheeding the warning of Peter's heart. And then, for just a moment, he paused and looked up at the window of his flat. It was dark behind the shade. Mozart the cat sat like a black shadow on the sill. "Yes, it is dark!" Peter urged. "We are not there! Something has happened! Go back! Do not go home, Herr Otto!"

Another few seconds passed; then Otto started forward again. The spring returned to his step. Whatever whisper of dread he had heard was gone now. He did not notice the men in the shadow. He did not see the man walking half a block behind him. Propping the little Christmas tree against the door of the building, he shifted his shopping bag and stepped into the trap.

Peter groaned audibly and hung his head as the glass door swung back, reflecting the men who waited in the street. A minute passed until the light behind the shade came on. Mozart jumped from his perch, and Peter knew that it was finished.

He shook his head slowly as he imagined the startled look on Otto's face; the accusation; the denial; the arrest.

Peter slammed his fist against the wall and leaned his head against the window frame.

A moment later he heard a sniffle. *Marlene!* She stood at his elbow, staring up at his face when he turned to scowl down at her.

"It's all my fault," she said. "It's my fault, isn't it, Peter?"

For an instant he was filled with such hatred for her that he wanted to answer her with a smack across the mouth. He thought better of it. No need for that. He simply answered honestly.

"Yes. Yes, Marlene, it is all your fault. Except for you we would have been on our way across the border tomorrow. Now we are trapped here." His rage almost choked him. "And now, because of you they have arrested Herr Otto. Because of you, they will throw him into prison and torture him!"

Marlene gave a strangled sob and covered her face with her hands. She did not argue. She did not beat her fists against Peter in resentment. It was true. All her fault. Marlene sank to the floor with a groan and sat there very quietly in her pretty Christmas dress while Peter stepped over her.

Standing in the long queue of last-minute shoppers waiting for the streetcar transfer, Lucy at last considered the implications of her impulsiveness. The thought of warning anyone to run from Wolf filled her with a mix of giddy excitement and fear. She also felt strangely pleased at what she had done; it seemed like a Christmas present to the Jewish family. She hoped beyond reason that young Peter and his family had escaped and that the traitorous Otto, who had helped them, was also on his way to safety somewhere.

Perhaps curiosity made her board the streetcar back to Frau Singer's, or perhaps the warmth she felt when she considered her good deed. She did not consider the possibility that a raging fire of danger behind that good deed threatened her as well.

Lucy smiled as she stepped off the car in front of the boarded-up shop. She had already thought of a good excuse for her return: she would simply claim to have dropped her lipstick and then come back to look for it. Maybe she could look out the window of the old woman's apartment and watch Wolf enter in search of people who were long gone.

She did not need the basket maker to show her the way this time. Lights blazed pleasantly from the old woman's upstairs windows. Most likely she was already working on Lucy's corset.

Glancing back toward the street, Lucy pulled the braided bell cord and waited. The old woman did not call down to her. Lucy rang again, a little longer this time.

At the first ring of the doorbell, a chill coursed through Peter's body. Cold perspiration beaded from every pore. It made no sense that such a simple sound in this safe place would blast away his composure like a cold wind. He had remained calm through everything until now. He told himself that they were safe and that he was glad to be away from the tyranny of Otto's lessons and warnings. He had said it did not matter that Otto was arrested as long as the rest were safe. These were, at best, fragile self-delusions that enabled him to accept what had happened. But the second ring of the doorbell shattered his hopes and plunged him into an abyss of fear for the first time in weeks. The sound of the ringing, urgent, insistent, demanded that the door be opened.

"It's the Gestapo," Peter said to Frau Singer as she rushed past him to peek out the window.

She paled visibly and repeated the word "Gestapo" as she peered down through the tiniest of slits.

The silence grew so intense that Peter could hear the old woman's breath against the fabric. Then a distant, cheerful voice came from the street below.

"Madame Singer! Madame . . . I have come back . . . I forgot something. Won't you let me in?"

Frau Singer let out an exasperated sigh. "Peter!" she exclaimed. "Gestapo, indeed! It is one of my clients, and you have frightened the life out of me!" She cracked open the window and cupped her hand to call down, "One moment, bitte! I will let you in, just one moment!" The window slammed shut and the old woman whirled to face Peter. "Go back with your mother and sister."

Peter, chagrined by his cowardly reaction to a doorbell, glanced toward Willie, who still slept in the bottom drawer of a chest in the parlor. "Should I take Willie?"

Frau Singer clapped her hands at him, ordering him to leave the room. Willie was sleeping. He would be fine. There was a very cold client waiting downstairs for her to come, and Peter must stop this nonsense!

"Coming! Coming! Coming!" she called as she tramped down the steps to the side entrance of the shop.

The corset maker's pale face greeted Lucy as the old woman unlocked the door and stepped aside to let her in.

"I am sorry." Lucy began walking toward the stairs. "Have I disturbed your mealtime?"

"No, indeed. But, Gottenyu! It is Christmas Eve, and you are back? You were just here. Your order cannot be ready."

"No, I . . . you see, I am certain that I dropped my lip rouge on the floor. May I . . ." She gestured up toward the apartment.

"I am watching the child of a friend. He is sleeping, and . . ." The old woman hung back. She did not want to go upstairs with Lucy in tow.

"Just a quick look, Frau Singer. I am sorry." The woman took a conciliatory tone. "I got home and looked, and . . . it is the only color I have that will match my dress tonight."

The old woman gave a hesitant nod. Surely it was all right—just a moment to look. "I have not seen it. Of course my eyes for distance are not so good. If it is there, we will find it."

The parlor looked just as it had this afternoon—perhaps a bit more cluttered. The gas heater glowed red; the room was almost too warm. A little suitcase was beside the dining table—for the baby Frau Singer was watching, no doubt.

"It must be here somewhere." Lucy pretended to look around the floor as Frau Singer searched beside the sofa.

Lucy knelt and ran her hands over the carpet. Then she looked toward the open bureau drawer, where Willie lay soundly sleeping.

Her eyes widened. She sat back on her heels and stared at the child. "The baby," she whispered. "How did he—?" She looked at Frau Singer, whose ashen face betrayed everything. Lucy crept nearer to the makeshift cradle. She reached her hand out as if to touch the red curls that tumbled over Willie's forehead. She had seen this child once, and she could never forget him!

Frau Singer stood very straight. She did not look at Lucy. She did not speak as she attempted to regain her composure. "The child . . . of a neighbor. A neighbor. I . . ."

A strange smile played on Lucy's lips. She was glad they were here, but she wished they were farther away. No use to pretend she did not know. "Are they all here?" she asked with unconcealed amusement.

"All?" The old woman was still trying to pretend. She was not a good liar. "I cannot think what you mean."

"Willie." Lucy jerked her head toward the sleeping baby. "Peter. Karin is the mother's name, I think. And—" She snapped her fingers as the name of the girl escaped her.

A shudder visibly passed through Frau Singer as she denied everything. No Peter. No Willie. No . . .

Lucy stood slowly and fixed her gaze on the bedroom door. Silence hung like a pall of thick smoke in the room. Lucy walked toward the door, only to be blocked by Frau Singer. "The toilet is not there," she insisted. "Please . . ."

Lucy reached out, grasped the doorknob, and opened the door.

The three of them huddled together on the bed. Karin lay beneath the blankets, dark circles of strain beneath her eyes. She wearily gazed back at Lucy.

Peter sat clutching his mother's hand, defiant and angry.

Marlene, who tried to hide behind Karin, was simply terrified.

"So you are here," Lucy said with a laugh. "Imagine!"

"What do you want with us?" Peter demanded as he stood to block the others from her view. "We have not hurt anyone! What do you want?" For a moment Lucy thought he might strike her.

Stepping back, she glanced toward Willie. "I wanted to see if you got my note."

His rage dissolved into astonishment. *"You?"*

Lucy bowed slightly. Peter stepped aside, revealing the grateful face of Karin gazing up at her. "I thought I might have a better look from here." Lucy shrugged, embarrassed by her lies. "Forgive me, Madame Singer. Your view . . ."

Frau Singer did not reply. She opened her mouth and closed it again.

No one could speak. Lucy backed up another step. Frau Singer shook her head as if she were coming out of a dream. "Do you still want your corset?" she croaked.

"Indeed," Lucy said. She looked at Peter and frowned. "What did you do with the note?"

Before he could answer, Marlene rose up on her knees and blurted out, "I left it for Uncle Otto. I left it on the mirror of the bathroom!"

Peter swung around and slapped her hard across the face. "Now Otto is arrested and so will she be for helping us! You think that S.S. officer will not know her handwriting?"

Lucy felt giddy. She looked from the sobbing child to Peter. Finally she turned her eyes back on Baby Willie who slept, undisturbed, through everything. She put a hand on her stomach and hoped her baby slept as sweetly now. The sky was falling. All her plans were crashing down around her head, and yet the baby must not be afraid . . . must not feel what she was feeling in this terrible moment.

Frau Singer took Lucy's arm, guiding her to a chair.

"Sit. Here, before you fall down."

———

With the handle of his spoon, Karl Ibsen had scratched out a crude calendar to mark the day of his imprisonment. Although there was no mention of the date, no hint from his jailers, Karl knew that tonight was Christmas Eve.

Cold wind whistled around the corner of the red brick building and in through the high window of his spartan cell. Karl closed his eyes, imagining the voices of faraway carolers on the wind. But it was just that . . . imagination. From there it was only a short step back into memories of last Christmas.

Helen sitting at the piano in the parlor. Lori rearranging packages beneath the tree. And Karl hefting Jamie up on his shoulder to place the angel on the very top . . .

"Higher, Father! Lift me higher!"

In the darkness of the cell Karl laughed out loud, repeating the laugh of that moment. And then the laugh dissolved into a sob of aching loneliness. He pulled his knees to his chest and buried his face to conceal the sounds of his grief.

Where are my children now, Lord? Without their mother ... without me? What will come of them? Oh, God! If the Nazis press me at this moment, I will say anything! God, do you hear me? Do not let them come here tonight!

No sooner had Karl finished that prayer than the sound of a key scraped and clanged against the lock of the cell door. As it was thrown back and light flooded the room, the exultant face of the camp commandant grinned drunkenly down at Karl. The strong smell of schnapps entered the cell with him. Four guards hovered in the corridor behind him.

"Well, Prisoner Ibsen! Happy Christmas to you! Of course, we do not call it Christmas any longer. No more little babes in the manger, ja? No one has even noticed the changes. Except maybe fools and old women. Which are you, Pastor Ibsen? A fool or an old woman?" The smirk of derision dissolved into unconcealed hatred. "Your stubbornness has cost me a leave. Every other commandant in the system got a break but me. We're waiting to welcome your two brats to Nameless, you see!" He kicked at Karl, causing a spray of straw to fly up in Karl's face. "Now get up!" He screamed the command, then whirled and left. Two soldiers with bayonets on their rifles rushed into the cell. They leveled the points in Karl's throat, prodding him to his feet.

Did they notice the dampness on Karl's cheeks? Had they heard that prayer somehow and broken in to mock it?

It did not matter. God sent a different answer to the heart of Karl Ibsen than the one he had expected. A sudden peace filled him as he staggered out and then down the stinking corridor. Would they kill him now? he wondered. He was unafraid of death. To die would be merciful *. . . to spend Christmas with Helen in heaven!*

They pushed him through three separate corridors, down a flight of metal steps and out into a courtyard blazing with the yellow glow of floodlights. The wind tore through the thin fabric of Karl's uniform. He shielded his aching eyes from the searing light. His arm was slapped down by the butt of a rifle as the voice of the commandant screamed at him again. *"ACHTUNG!* PRISONER IBSEN!"

Karl snapped to attention, eyes forward. Directly before him was a wooden gallows complete with three waiting ropes that swayed eerily in the wind.

"Death," Karl said with a half smile. Once again the butt of a rifle slammed into his stomach, knocking him to the ground.

He lay gasping for breath. The polished boots of the commandant strolled to his head. Karl could see the reflection of lights and gallows distorted in the shining leather.

"Yes, Prisoner Ibsen. Death." A short laugh. The reek of schnapps.

"But not your death. Ah, no. The Führer does not want your death; he wants your approval. And if not your approval, then at least your acceptance, ja? You understand?"

Karl, still fighting for breath, shook his head. No. Not approval. Not acceptance. Not ever.

"And if I told you your children will be here tonight to dance from our little Christmas tree? Like angels on a string?"

Karl's head jerked up. He looked in horror at the platform where two figures were being led up the steps. *Oh, God! Not my children! Jamie! Lori!* His eyes focused on the prison uniforms. No. Not the children. No. These were men. Skeletons with striped rags covering their bones.

Another laugh. "Well, Pastor Ibsen. So you see we have our little joke to wake you up. Not your two little brats. Not tonight anyway. But . . . *your children,* all the same. Here you see we have brought two of your converts."

Karl struggled to stand. And again he was shoved down. With a snap of the commandant's gloved fingers, the bayonet was placed at Karl's throat.

"Now we will all rise for the benediction, eh, Pastor?" More laughter from all the guards. "Would you like to pray for your children who are about to die? Eh? For Prisoner Richard Kalner? For this young man beside him? Johann . . . Johann something. Ah, well, what's in a name?"

The courtyard seemed to be in motion. Karl swayed as he stared up at the faces of his friends . . . indeed . . . his family!

"Why?" Karl begged.

"Because you will not confess, Prisoner Ibsen. You will not take the oath of allegiance to our Führer. *You* are the reason they are dying."

Karl looked from the face of the commandant to the face of Richard Kalner. Hands tied behind his back, Richard stepped forward to the rope even as his gentle eyes sought Karl's face.

The doomed man shouted, *"Home for Christmas, Karl!"* Boots slammed into his legs and he tumbled down. Still he shouted. *"Stay true! Stay true, Karl!"* A final blow to the stomach silenced him.

Then young Johann cried out, *"Jesus wept!"* There was no more time to speak. A fist to the cheek and then the noose was dropped around the slender neck. Richard's limp body was dragged up and the second rope was put in place.

"But there are three ropes!" Karl cried. "Let me! Let me go with them!" He lunged forward, arms extended as if to embrace them. "Let me go too!"

"Stay true! Auf . . . auf Wiedersehn!"

The commandant raised and lowered his hand. The trapdoors sprung open beneath the two men.

And they danced from the barren branch of the Nazi Christmas tree while Karl Ibsen sobbed in agony too deep for sound.

The excitement of their imminent escape suddenly vanished from the face of Jacob. Even in the gloom of the church Lori could see his skin grow pale as though he had seen a ghost.

She touched his arm. He gasped, started, then managed to turn his eyes away from some horrible thought and focus on her concern.

"Jacob?" she asked gently. "What is it?"

It took him a moment before he found words. "I . . . I know what we are running from," he stammered. "But what are we escaping *to*?"

"Freedom," she answered simply.

"I was . . . it is Christmas, you know . . . and I . . . could not help but wonder . . ." He looked away from her gaze. "Our parents. My father." He fought to explain. "I thought for a moment I heard him say my name." He covered his eyes with his hand.

Was Jacob Kalner crying?

Lori touched his cheek with her fingertips. *Tears.* She put her arms around him and pulled him against her. He laid his head on her shoulder and wept. He did not know why the tears came, but he cried all the same. He wept quietly so the younger boys sleeping a few feet away would not hear him.

In the solitude of his cell, Karl had no one to comfort him. He, too, wept quietly, keeping the satisfaction of his pain from his captors.

He did not question God any longer. God had not done this thing. God had not arranged for Karl to be here in this stinking cell or for him to preside over the deaths of Richard and Johann.

Karl stared at the red brick wall opposite him and remembered the grief and troubles of Job.

"Curse God and die. . . ." The wife of Job spoke to Karl now.

Karl replied aloud. " 'Though He slay me, yet will I trust Him!' "

And then the voice that whispered in his ear changed to an accusation. "*You* killed those men. One word from you and they would have lived! And the Nazis will do the same to Lori and Jamie! When they are captured they will be strung up before your eyes!"

Karl groaned and covered his ears, but he could not shut out the voice. He cringed on the floor of the cell against the weight of the accusation.

"Lord!" he cried loudly, no longer thinking of the eavesdropping prison guards. *"Help me!"* Again and again he called out the name of Jesus. He could no longer recall the scripture passages that had carried him through so much. *"Please!"*

Once again the warm peace filled him. He sat up slowly and drew a ragged breath. Tears stopped instantly.

And then he knew . . . he saw it clearly and he spoke, his voice strong. "I know who you are."

He waited but there was no reply.

He spoke again. "You accuse me before the Lord, do you not? I know your name. The Accuser. Yes. I heard your voice. You wound me with your darts. But I tell you this!" He shook his fist at the empty air, certain that a dark presence saw his defiance. "My strength is in the Lord! In the Spirit of the Almighty! I have no faith in myself! You think you will have some small victory over the Lord if I give in? Is that what you think? Is that why you accuse me? I tell you that if I fail, then the Lord will have another and another who will fight for Him! Speak for Him! Remain true to Him!"

Karl's voice was ringing against the walls of the tiny chamber. The slit in the cell door slid back, but Karl was not aware of the eyes that watched him.

He shouted, "The Lord is my strength! I will not be afraid of you! Of what men can do to me! I know who you are! I know my enemy! I will fight you! *FIGHT YOU! And you will be ashamed!*"

He managed to climb to his feet. He raised his hand to the howling wind outside his window. "It is Christmas! God has come among us! The miracle is accomplished! *YOU! YOU CANNOT CHANGE IT NOW!* The Gate is open!"

———

Through the loosened boards of the basement window, the sounds of the Nazi Christmas procession drifted into the cold underbelly of the dark New Church.

By the glow of one tiny candle, the fugitives checked one another's clothing one last time.

Jacob wore warm traveling clothes belonging to Lori's father. The trousers were slightly loose around the waist, but a belt and suspenders held them in place. Pastor Ibsen's hiking boots were one size too big, but this was remedied by two extra pair of wool socks.

Lori was dressed in a red dirndl skirt trimmed in green lace. It was appropriate for Christmas, of course, but beneath her dress she wore short leather pants, *Lederhosen,* in case their flight should force them over rough terrain. She also wore her most sturdy shoes, hoping no one would notice that she did not wear her Sunday shoes with her favorite dress.

Jamie and Mark also wore leather knickers and wool socks beneath heavy alpine jackets and sweaters gleaned from Jamie's chest of drawers. They had only one pair of hiking boots; Jamie wore the boots, and Mark wore his old sneakers. Wisely, Jamie packed another pair of sneakers in his small rucksack, along with extra socks and woolen underwear, two more sweaters, and mittens for everyone. He had heard that Danzig was very cold this time of year. With all of that, he rolled up the black uniform of the Hitler Youth. He had wanted to leave it behind, but Jacob had grabbed it up and stared hard at it as though he heard some whispered message in its fabric. Then he had thrust it at Jamie and demanded that the vile thing be taken along.

Outside, the crowds sang more songs, but not songs of peace on earth, not songs about the baby in Bethlehem. Ancient carols of pagan legends filled the air of Berlin tonight as the torches of the masses lit the facades of buildings with a hellish glow.

"It is time," Jacob said, looking up at the ladder they had made out of old boxes. The crates leaned against the damp stone walls of the belly of the church and led up to the broken window.

Lori held Jacob's eyes with her own fearful look for a moment. He blew out the little candle and touched her gently on the arm.

"You go first," Jacob instructed Jamie. It made sense. If Jamie were caught climbing out the window, he would simply say that he had run away from the Hitler Youth and come here. They would take him back, but the others would have time to hide before the church was searched again.

Jacob hefted Jamie up and then held the groaning crates steady as the boy cautiously picked his way up toward the sliver of light shining through the boards.

Seconds passed slowly before Jamie called down in an exultant whisper, "At the top."

The sound of creaking followed as he pushed against the boards, hesitated to look, then slipped out into the cold night air.

Jacob's hands sweated as he waited a full minute before Jamie called in through the boards: "All is calm!"

Jacob tapped Mark on his shoulder and sent him clambering up the pile next. The barricade creaked and the sound of singing increased as Mark escaped to the outside with Jamie.

"My turn?" Lori asked with a hesitant excitement. Jacob could hear her voice shake at the thought of being outside again after so long. Did she also regret leaving their refuge in some way, as he did?

"Good luck," he said as he took her hand to help her up.

She did not move for a moment but stood there beside him, holding his damp hand. Then she stood on her tiptoes and brushed her lips briefly against his before she began to climb.

He listened to her breathe as she reached in the dark for handholds and scaled the fifteen-foot heap much more slowly than Mark or Jamie.

"Come on!" urged Jamie impatiently through the crack in the boards. "Hurry up, will you?"

At this she slipped and cried out as a box tumbled down, narrowly missing Jacob.

"It's all right," he assured her hoarsely. "Go easy, Lori. I will catch you if you fall."

He did not tell her that he would not be able to see her if she slipped and fell from the top of the dark pile. Probably he would be covered by the rubble before she hit him. All the same, his words seemed to reassure her. Moments later she called down that she had reached the window and then she, too, squeezed out through the space.

"Come on, Jacob!" Mark chided him. *"Alles ist klar!"*

As Jacob scaled the heap with ease, it swayed precariously beneath his weight. He reached up, grasping the ledge of the broken window just as the boxes rumbled and spilled away out from under his feet. He punched at the last of the boards over the window with his fist and then pushed through the space. Their only retreat now lay on the bottom of the basement floor!

There would be no going back. Mark and Jamie and Lori surrounded him as the rumble emanated up from the basement.

"The ladder has fallen!"

"We can't get back!"

"And so we press on," Jacob said, brushing them off and creeping forward from the wall of the church to the bushes that surrounded the building. The others followed—first Lori, then Mark. Jamie brought up the rear. Like a clumsy parade of waddling ducks, they crept through the flower bed, careful not to get their clothes dirty. They must not look the part of children who had escaped through a hedge and then a muddy churchyard!

Jacob peered from between the branches of the bushes. The graveyard was dark. Headstones, lopsided from the sinking earth, rose up as gray shadows before them. Crosses and square above-ground crypts made silhouettes like the unlit buildings of a deserted city. Beyond that was the iron gate they had passed through on Kristal Nacht, a lifetime ago.

He hesitated a moment too long for Mark, who tugged impatiently at his jacket.

"Hurry! The *watchman!*" he warned.

But Jacob knew the watchman would not make his rounds of the desolate place until eleven o'clock—still nearly an hour away. He waved his hand, warning Mark not to attempt to instruct him. Then Lori gasped and pulled at his arm. Jacob looked up and saw the watchman's light swing around the corner of the church and leap from boarded window to boarded window at the far end of the building. Only a minute and the old man would be shining his light on the foursome!

Jacob broke from the bushes and ran for the cover of a headstone. He did not think of the knees of his traveling trousers as he lunged behind a tall black marble obelisk.

Like foxes breaking from a hedge, the three followed after him, each finding his own gravestone to crouch behind. Jacob could not see the others, but he could hear them breathing, panting with fright as the footsteps of the watchman quickened and moved toward the bushes.

Do not breathe! Be quiet! Oh, God, make the fellow deaf! Jacob thought as he leaned his cheek against the cold stone and tried to melt into its inscription.

The watchman jogged toward the broken basement window and the loose boards that hung there. Someone had gone through them, broken the Nazi taboo!

The blood drummed so hard in Jacob's ears that he could not hear the others breathing against their own headstones. Like an evil finger, the light of the watchman probed the shadows surrounding New Church, touching the bushes and the frostbitten plants, scrutinizing the walls of stone; less than ten feet from where the four lay curled in fear on the dirt of sunken graves.

I will have to kill him, Jacob thought as he closed his eyes as if to hide from the light! He was an old man, Jacob knew, but Jacob had never killed a man before. How to do it?

His fingers closed around a stone as the old man swept the light up the wall to an arched window in the main auditorium and then down again to the broken window of their basement escape hatch.

"Himmel!" cried the old man in alarm. And then again he whispered, *"Himmel!"*

33

TOR AUF!

Kill him! Kill him! Kill him! The blood pounded in Jacob's ears as he clutched the stone and crept forward to strike the old watchman down. He slipped behind Lori, who gasped at his unexpected touch. The watchman whirled around at the sound and stared in terror at the black tombstones.

At that moment, a flock of upraised torches fluttered by in the street. The old man looked at them once and shouted for help. Then he raised his whistle and blew a shrill alarm, halting the torches. It was too late to kill the old man. Too late to run for the gate.

"HELP!" The old man ran back along the path to open the gate. *"Someone has broken into the church! Thieves have broken into the—"*

Lori grasped Jacob's hand. Mark and Jamie scrambled to huddle with them.

Jacob watched as the torches seemed to multiply. They saw no retreat back into the church, no escape from the churchyard. It was over for them.

"I'll try to draw them away," he said. "Run for it!"

"No!" Jamie cried. "I know a place!"

With no more explanation than that, he leaped out from behind the tombstone. "Come on!"

They followed without question. No one else had any ideas. Lori fell in the mud. Jacob grabbed her arm and dragged her up. He held tightly to her as they ran blindly toward the back of the churchyard, toward the white family crypts that formed a tiny community for the dead beneath the trees of New Church.

Behind them the swelling voices of a mob surged through the open gate. They had only seconds before the light of the torches would pierce the covering safety of this darkness.

"Here!" Jamie cried as they reached the square stone crypt of the Halder family. "The key is above the gate!" He jumped up and tried to reach the ledge where the key was hidden. The lights behind them moved along the sides of the church, dipping down to examine every boarded window.

Jacob reached up and ran his hand along the stone ledge in search of the key. It was not there. Jamie cried out and shook the rusty iron bars of the crypt gate.

"It was here! The key was here!" His words were lost beneath the shouts of the men who called out to one another and broke down the boards over the doors of the church. Their guns drawn, they peered into the darkness beyond the torchlight. Two men swept their torches near the ground in search of clues. As the doors of New Church crashed open, Jacob dropped to his knees with Lori to sift through leaves and dirt for the missing key.

Jamie laid his face against the bars. The hiding place. So close. No one had ever found him and Alfie in this place. And now the key had vanished! Tonight, when hiding was not a game, but a matter of survival—of all nights, the key of the crypt was not to be found.

Lori prayed as they searched. *"Tor auf!* Oh, Lord, please. *Tor auf!"*

The thump of footsteps circled the outside fence. No use trying to scale the stone wall. Too late now for Jamie to take them out through the break in the fence. Every escape was cut off.

"Lord," whispered Jamie, *"Tor auf . . ."*

In his restless sleep, Alfie heard the sound of leaves and footsteps and whispered voices that penetrated his dreams. The angels stood beside him again as they often had throughout the weeks. He felt their light through his closed eyelids. He did not open his eyes. They were there. He did not need to see them.

The kittens stirred in their box. They knew the angels had come back as well. Alfie did not need to wake up and check them. The dreams were too nice; he did not want to wake up.

"Alf . . ." The light glowed brighter as the angel spoke his name like Mama used to do.

"Yes?" he whispered with a smile.

"Alf . . . they cannot find the key."

"Huh?"

"Tor . . . the gate." The voice was more urgent than gentle.

Alfie frowned in his sleep. The angel wanted him to do something. "What?"

"Alf . . . Alf . . . Tor . . . Alf . . . Tor auf! Open the gate!" The angel touched his face and told him to wake up.

Alfie breathed in deeply and opened his eyes as the bright light dwindled to a small star and vanished. He was awake. The sounds of scratching and whispered voices sifted down the steps.

"Where is it? *Where?*" It was the voice of Jamie. Clear as anything, it was Jamie!

———————

Torches moved deliberately up the path toward the Halder crypt. Light scoured the other tombs and probed the stones for signs of the living among the dead. The men who searched did not seem to be in a hurry. While shouts resounded from inside the church building, the flames of the torches sniffed nearer the crypt. Jacob rose from his knees and stood with clenched fists. He would fight them when they came, but it would do no good.

As they stood to face their fate, a large, clumsy hand reached out from inside the crypt and touched Jamie's shoulder. Jamie dropped to his knees in terror, but did not cry out.

"Is that you, Jamie?" the old familiar voice of Alfie asked softly. "Are you playing hide-and-seek, Jamie?"

"Alfie!" Jamie could hardly whisper. *"Tor auf!* Open the gate, Alfie! Do you have the key?"

"I got the key, Jamie," the voice said too slowly. Then Alfie's giant hand pawed the air between the bars and with unwavering accuracy, the key slid into the lock and the gate swung back.

The fugitives tumbled into the crypt. They scrambled between Alfie's legs as he slowly swung the gate shut and turned the key in an unhurried fashion.

"I'm glad you came, Jamie," he said, his voice frighteningly loud.

"Shut up!" Jacob snapped.

Jamie was gentle. "We have to hide now, Alfie. They are—" He pointed at the swaying torches.

"Oh. Shhhh." Alfie put a finger to his lips and then spread his arms wide to herd them to the back corner. "Down there. In the basement."

The square hole in the floor blended into shadow. Jamie slid down first, showing the others where to go. The blackness was heavy and palpable, the air thick with the smell of old sardines and mold. Alfie was last down the steps. He slid the stone hatch over the opening just as the voices of the pursuers swept into the crypt.

"I thought I heard—"

The hollow clunk of stone sliding into place cut off the words.

"Shhhh," Alfie said with a sound like escaping steam. The voices outside penetrated the stone floor. The iron gate rattled loudly. Lori leaned her head against Jacob's arm.

"Shhhh," Alfie warned again. A thin line of light penetrated the seam around the stone hatch. Within that square, the figure of Alfie stood framed on the steps. His face glowed with excitement, and he smiled as he stared up at the light. The big, clumsy hand reached up to where the brightest beam gleamed through a chink. And then as though he were brushing it away, it suddenly vanished and the blackness was complete once again.

Never was there such a Christmas tree as the tree in the center of the big room in the Red Lion House. Charles Dickens himself could not have imagined a more green or full or fragrant tree as he sat by the fire and wrote *A Christmas Carol.*

Or so Murphy said as he stood tiptoe on the stepladder and placed the gossamer angel on the top. Branches bowed down under the weight of candy canes and gingerbread cookies and a hundred colored lights that winked on and off as Charles and Louis watched with wonder.

The lights were new, sent from Mr. Trump in New York. He had purchased them at Macy's in New York and sent along a note explaining that the same sort of lights were used on the tree in America at the White House.

This bit of important information gave the lights an aura of magic for the boys. Charles and Louis had never believed in Santa Claus or elves working at the North Pole. Such fantasies had faded early as they had witnessed photographs of Hermann Göring dressed in a Santa suit, handing out gifts to good little members of the Hitler Youth. But Charles and Louis did believe in America and the White House!

Cabled all the information about the prisoner Pastor Karl Ibsen, the White House had made appeals to the German government on his behalf, and on behalf of his missing children. This lifted Anna's spirits. Every day she and Elisa walked across the square to the little church to pray for them. There was still hope, in spite of news of Helen Ibsen's death.

It was, at long last, Christmas Eve. The lights of the Christmas tree reflected on the polished wood floor of Red Lion House. Dinner dishes were cleared away and stacked. Everyone had tasted the puddings and pies, and the adults savored the very last of the Viennese coffee.

A warm fire crackled and glowed in the fireplace. Charles and Louis sat Indian-style on the hooked floral hearth rug as Murphy and Theo read *A Christmas Carol* in the very room where some said Dickens might have written the story.

Curled up on the sofa, Anna and Elisa listened to the story for the first time as well. Theo read the part of the narrator and sometimes paused to interpret the unclear passages from English into German for the struggling language students in the group. Murphy embellished the speaking roles with all the terror of Ebenezer Scrooge as he came face-to-face with the dark-hooded Ghost of Christmas Yet to Come.

Theo raised his eyes to make certain the boys had caught the mean-

ing of the English words. The terrified expressions of their faces confirmed that they understood perfectly. He pressed on with the story:

*"They reached an iron gate. He paused to look round before enter-
ing. A churchyard! Here, then, the wretched man whose name he had
now to learn lay beneath the ground."*

"Kirchhof!" Louis uttered the word for graveyard.

At this point, Charles covered his eyes as if he did not want to see
what Theo would read next. But the picture of the graveyard remained,
so he uncovered his eyes again and held tightly on to Louis' hand.

Theo continued with a slightly quavering voice. *"It was a worthy
place. Walled in by houses; overrun by grass and weeds, the growth of
vegetation's death, not life ... choked up with too much burying; fat
with repleted appetite. A worthy place!"*

Charles knew that the churchyard was not really a worthy place.
This terrible graveyard of Christmas Future was a place so forsaken
and forlorn that even the weeds died on top of one another for lack of
rain. He squeezed Louis' hand and stared hard at the coals on the grate
as Theo continued.

*"The Spirit stood among the graves, and pointed down to One. He
advanced toward it trembling. The Phantom was exactly as it had been,
but Scrooge dreaded that he saw new meaning in its solemn shape. ..."*

Louis' eyes grew wider, and he whispered the word for gravestone,
"Grabstein!" He shuddered and leaned closer to Charles.

*"The Spirit stretched his finger out toward the granite slab that
marked the former existence of a human being—"*

This was a terrible time for the story to be interrupted by the sound
of the doorbell ringing like an angry bee. Everyone jumped. Charles
grabbed Louis around the neck and they both squealed. Then everyone
laughed and sat back and breathed easier.

The doorbell rang again.

"Probably carolers," Elisa said. She went for the platter of cookies,
and Charles raced Louis to the window to look.

"Not carolers," Louis said with disappointment. "It is some old
beggar woman!" Their story had been interrupted not for music, but
for charity. Murphy told them that this was just the sort of twist in plot
line that Dickens would approve of!

At first Anna did not recognize the woman who stood in the halo
of the porch light and pressed her finger so urgently to the bell. Her
brown coat was badly worn, torn at the sleeve and mended. Her hair
was concealed beneath a tan scarf, her hands bare. Her shoes were
run down at the heels and her woolen stockings were mended in several places.

Anna frowned through the window, pitying the beggar who had
come to the door on such a night. Then the finger pressed hard again
on the buzzer and the face turned to look up, beseeching heaven;

praying that Anna Lindheim would answer the door!

Anna gasped and put her hand over her mouth in an instant of recognition. The face of this once-beautiful thirty-eight-year-old woman had visibly aged, but Helen Ibsen gazed up at her as though from the grave.

"Helen!" Anna cried through the glass, and Helen's face broke into a broad smile. Reports claimed she had died in prison in Germany, but here she was! *Dear God, a miracle!* Helen Ibsen standing at Anna's door in London!

Charles Dickens' *Christmas Carol* was laid aside, probably until next year.

Presents did not matter. The lights on the tree in Red Lion House seemed dim compared to the joy of the reunion of these two sisters. And yet, tears were shed there as well. One of the Ibsen family was here, one of four faces in the photograph on Anna's piano. This reality, like a white-hot flame, turned their joy into a molten gold . . . beautiful and bright, but still untouchable.

Murphy thought they should call a doctor, but Helen asked only to be taken to the home of Anna and Theo. She would be fine, she said, she was only tired, very tired.

The three of them left and it was bedtime for Charles and Louis. There would be presents in the morning, Elisa promised after prayers, because they were very good boys.

Long after the lights had gone out, Charles lay awake in his bed.

"Louis?" he said softly.

"I'm awake too," Louis answered.

"Thinking?"

"Uh-huh. I was thinking about what surprise I want on Christmas morning. How about you?"

"I would like to see our mama again," Charles said. But he knew that miracles only happened sometimes, and this one would not be there when they awoke in the morning.

———

The teakettle shrieked. Helen turned toward it as though she had never heard that ordinary sound before. The thick blond hair beneath the scarf was matted; dirty. Anna ran a hot bath for her and brought her tea to sip in the tub.

Clean clothes were laid out for her—a pretty blue dress that matched her eyes, real stockings, and slippers for her feet until new shoes could be purchased for her. She bathed and dressed.

For a long time Helen did not speak. She wept in Anna's arms and then sat quietly as she tried to remember everything that had happened since the night of November 9. And after she remembered, how could she sort it all out?

"I'm sorry, Anna." She sat up and wiped her eyes. "It has just been so long. A miracle, I suppose, that I am here. A miracle. But I would rather be back there with my children, Anna, and with Karl, you see."

Walking through Helen Ibsen's ordeal took a long time. First came the terrible night in New Church, the last time she saw Karl, and her arrest with all the others the next morning. Lori escaped, she thought, as did the Kalner boys. Again and again the Gestapo asked her where Lori was. She said she did not know, and they beat her until her back was bloody.

She showed Anna the still-pink scars of the lash. "But I prayed, Anna!" she said in a soft whisper. "I remembered the Lord and His silence. And I prayed."

Weeks in a cell had followed and then, without explanation, she had been released with three prostitutes—simply given her coat and her papers and turned out on the street.

"New Church is condemned. Leona Kalner has disappeared." A strange smile played on her lips. "It was so easy to leave Germany; it had to be a mistake. My papers were all in order. I caught the train to Prague. I hoped . . . we had told the children to go to the Protestant home in Prague." Tears came again. "But they were not there. No one has heard from them. Oh, Anna, if they made it out, they would have gone to Prague!"

A series of small miracles had resulted in a visitor's visa to England. Helen was not Jewish, and she was the wife of a pastor. The British consulate had granted her a temporary visitor's visa the first afternoon. From there she got Anna's address and borrowed ship fare from a pastor in Prague. "I came on a freighter. I have not got enough money left to pay for a cup of tea."

Anna pulled her into her arms. Anna had not let herself believe that they would ever meet again on this earth. "You do not need money for tea, Helen. You must stay here. We will do everything we can. And we will pray!"

"Hey, Moshe, Zach, get a load of this!" Larry Havas sounded excited as he ran toward them, waving a scrap of notebook paper.

"What is it? Some news about Captain Orde?" asked Moshe.

"Have they made him king of Palestine or something?" kidded Zabinski. He stopped joking when he saw the grim look on Havas's face.

"What is it really?" asked Moshe again.

"Judith was monitoring British military radio traffic and she picked this up: part of an army convoy was diverted to investigate the report of an explosion in an Arab village."

"So this is news?" demanded Zach. "Some Arab making pipe bombs has blown himself up?"

"Shut up and let him finish! Go on, Larry," instructed Moshe.

"The unit that checked it out found what was left of a car, but there wasn't anybody in it or around it."

Zach looked concerned. "And this was on the route Captain Orde would have been traveling?"

"That's just it: Orde had been traveling with that convoy until he reached the Hanita turnoff; he should have reached here by now!"

The first light of Christmas morning crept over the damp cemetery of New Church. Jacob cautiously raised the stone hatch to peer out and listen. He was grateful for the fresh air. He sucked it into his lungs voraciously, as though he had been under water for a long time.

Only hours had passed since their detection by the watchman, and yet it seemed much longer than that. Jacob had thought they would be well on their way across the border to Poland by now. But here they were, a few dozen yards from where they had begun, and in a much worse place than they had started from.

The advantage they had hoped to gain by leaving in the midst of a rally was now gone. Although all government buildings stayed open on Christmas Day, most of the shops closed their doors in some remembrance of Christmas Past. Traffic would be light. Chance of detection would be greater today than ever. Although Jacob could not see clearly from this place, he could hear the vague murmur of voices. There were still searchers around New Church.

Maybe tonight, he thought, letting the hatch slide down quietly into place. Maybe tonight they could sneak through the hole in the fence, separate, and meet at Pastor Ibsen's car!

Alfie played with the kittens and let Lori and Jacob talk. He was polite, like Mama taught him. He did not interrupt while Lori and Jamie argued with Jacob.

"We cannot take him with us." Jacob sounded angry.

"We cannot leave him here!" Lori's anger matched his.

"Maybe we cannot get out of here, either," whispered Jamie fearfully.

"We'll get out, all right." Jacob made a fist. "If they haven't found us now, they won't find us. We'll sneak out and follow our plan."

"We are taking Alfie," Lori said again.

"He is not in the plan." Jacob stared at Alfie. "Look at him. Sitting there with his kittens. He doesn't even know what we are talking about."

"If we leave him here, it is murder."

"To take him is suicide. There is too much at stake to take along this Dummkopf."

Jamie stood up and clenched his fists as if he wanted to fight Jacob. "Take it back!"

"Well, what else—" Jacob raised a hand to hold back Jamie's hitting.

"Shhhh," Alfie warned them when they got too loud! Maybe the men were still out there.

Jamie and Jacob looked at him. They lowered their voices again.

"He is smarter than you think," Jamie said. "And he saved our lives. *Your* life. If you leave him, you are leaving me and Lori, too, because we won't go without him. My father wouldn't leave him, I know that much! He would say that it is a miracle that Alfie was there to open the gate for us! And you don't spit in the eye of a miracle!"

Silence. Joseph the cat purred as Alfie petted her. Maybe it was time for Alfie to tell them about the angels and also about the grocery store. Which first?

"You have to be careful, Jamie," Alfie said, now that it was his turn. "The Nazi-men are looking for you."

"How do you know that?" Jacob snapped.

"I went to a store to buy food, and the grocery man asked questions about you. Then he called the police and I heard them talking. They talked a long time. Don't go to the train station. Or the bus. They were going to pick you and Lori up." Lori grew pale and Jacob sat up straight. He smiled at her and raised his eyebrows as if he knew something she did not know.

Jacob stared at Alfie, smiling strangely. "Maybe you're not a Dummkopf after all," he said. The words were mean, but the sound of his voice was not. "All right, then. Alfie is our miracle. We won't spit in his eye. We will take him, God help us."

Alfie was glad. "God will help us," he said. And then he told them about the angels who told him to open the gate.

34

Plan for Escape

Lucy awoke to the quiet gurgling of a baby. For a moment she could not remember where she was, and then it came to her with a flash of fear. *Christmas morning!* She had not gone home to Wolf last night. Surely by now he knew what she had done!

Strong, bitter coffee helped Lucy to think. Cradling the cup in both hands, she inhaled the aroma. Somehow it calmed her. The girl, Marlene, begged her to forgive her for leaving the note. Strangely, Lucy felt no animosity. The child had simply forced Lucy to a final decision— a decision to do something good for the first time in too long.

"Wolf knows who you are—" She leveled her eyes on Karin. "Wallich, isn't it? Karin Wallich?"

Karin replied with a single slow nod. Had Lucy ever seen such depth of sorrow in any woman's eyes? Such a look marked the face of Mary, the mother of Christ, in the fresco above the altar of Lucy's church in Bavaria. Such a thought crowded out all other thoughts for a moment. She imagined shouting at Wolf that he was hunting down the family of Christ! In the eyes of Karin Wallich, Lucy found the woman at the foot of the cross, watching the torture of the innocent.

"Fräulein Strasburg?" Madame Singer touched her gently, as if to draw her back into the present moment.

Lucy sipped her coffee. She must not let herself slip into such fantasies. They made her want to cry out how sorry she was for what was being done! Such images made her want to beg forgiveness. Like the prostitute Mary Magdalene, she longed to step into the fresco to weep beside the mother of the Lord. *It is the strain of the day*, she reasoned.

"Where was I?" Lucy pressed a finger to her temple.

"I am Karin Wallich," Karin replied. "And they know it."

"Yes." Lucy cleared her throat. "Wolf figured that out. And from there he came to the conclusion that Otto Wattenbarger was a friend of your husband. To arrest you and be able to condemn Otto as a traitor all in one day, Wolf will do whatever is necessary."

"We are not caught yet," Peter said.

"Thanks to you, Fräulein Strasburg," added Karin gently.

How kind and grateful were Karin Wallich's eyes. Lucy could not meet her gaze or respond to her thanks. "You are not safe yet. Please. You are only across the street. We must get you out of Vienna. Out of the Reich."

"Perhaps we can find a way to place the children on the transport list," Frau Singer offered.

"No. He will be checking every list." Lucy frowned. "Do you have your papers, Frau Wallich?"

Karin produced them, the old documents—the Wallich name, the photographs, the enormous *J* for Jews inscribed across the pages of the passport. "This is hopeless. You would be better off to burn these than to carry them."

"Otto took our photographs." Karin blinked back tears at the memory. "But no passports. He was going to . . . what does it matter now?"

Lucy opened her handbag and pulled out five tickets, train tickets from Vienna to Berlin, Berlin to Danzig. "Maybe . . . if we could find some other way to get you to Berlin. Catch the train there. Then it would not matter so much if you carry Jewish documents as long as they are in order. But Wolf will have men on every train platform looking for Karin Wallich. And Peter and Marlene. And Willie."

"Tickets to Danzig!" Peter touched one on the corner as though it were a ticket to Paradise. "I have dreamed about a ticket to Danzig," he said wistfully. "And there it is. Magic. But no good to us."

"We can thank my dear Wolf for the tickets. I hocked his rugs at the Dorotheum to buy—"

"Hey!" Peter sparked and fumbled in his wallet. "Here it is. Otto gave this to me the night after you and Wolf showed up." He flashed it around the small circle of intense faces.

"A pawn ticket." Lucy took it from him. "Dorotheum. I guess I am not the only one."

"But you see," Peter explained, "Otto said if something happens to him—which it has—that I am supposed to go to the Dorotheum with this." He spread the fold of his wallet to display the bills. "The Nazis keep it open even on Christmas Day."

Lucy shook her head. "Yes, but there are Gestapo agents at every entrance picking up Jews right and left." She bit her lip. "I will go. If he has me arrested, you will have my train tickets. Somehow, maybe—"

"But, Fräulein—" Karin started to protest.

"You really should call me Lucy. We are in this thing together, Karin.

Don't worry. Wolf will not have me killed. Not even tortured, I think. I am carrying his child, an S.S. baby. If I do not come back, you must remember that and not worry. He wants this baby, you see."

———————

"If he's coming he will have to understand!" Jacob paced the small space like an angry schoolmaster.

"Well, at least talk nice to him," Lori said.

"I *am* talking nice." Jacob inclined his head with mock graciousness to Alfie who was trying very hard to understand the plan of escape. "Aren't I being nice, Alfie?" He did not wait for a reply. "All right, now. For the tenth time, tell me how it works, Alfie. Go ahead. Repeat it!"

Alfie's brow furrowed in thought. He wanted very much to get it right. "The train," he said doubtfully.

"Yes, yes, yes, and what about the train?"

"It will come to the border?"

"Yes. It will stop at the border check on the German side of the big fence." Jacob swept his hand over Alfie like a musical conductor pulling the notes from his orchestra.

"And what will happen on the German side of the fence?" Lori gently urged.

Alfie smiled at her. He liked it better when she asked him questions. "Nazi-men with guns and dogs will look all over the train inside and outside for people who try and sneak by. Yes?"

"Good, Alfie!" Lori said. Then she shot Jacob a hard look.

"And then they will open the big electric gate and the train will go through very slowly . . ."

"Yes"—Jacob resumed again—"into no-man's land. And as the train slips through, we must each roll under the train and grab the metal rods on the bottom. Hold on very tightly, and it will carry us into no-man's land."

Alfie nodded his head enthusiastically. It was a dangerous game, like jumping onto a trolley, but he could do it!

"And then the train will stop inside the no-man's land, because there is another big electric fence on the Polish side!"

"Very good! And then what happens?" Jacob was looking relieved. Alfie seemed to have grasped their plan at last!

"When the train stops in no-man's land, the Nazi guards get off the train and the Polish guards get on, yes?"

"Yes! And we slip on the train when the doors are open! Then the doors will be sealed and the train will start up and the Polish gate will open! We will ride all the way to Danzig in the bathrooms!"

Lori put a hand on Alfie's arm. "Now you see why we cannot take your kittens, Alfie! They would be hurt."

He looked at the kitten box and then at Werner kitty. "Except for

Werner. I have to take Werner because he will die if I leave him. Jacob promised I could take Werner!"

"Don't get him upset," Jacob ordered Lori. "Why did you have to bring up the cats again?"

This addition of another person to their plans caused Jacob to want to rehearse everything again—walking to the car, seating arrangements, the trip out of Berlin on the Autobahn. He rummaged through his knapsack in search of the road map. There were train schedules and a street map of Berlin and Danzig, but the road map was missing.

"The map!" he muttered angrily. "Where is it? Mark, did you do something with the map?"

No one had seen it since their last rehearsal. Somehow it had not made it out of New Church with the rest of the gear. Lori consoled him that perhaps it did not matter anyway, since he could probably sketch the entire map of northern Germany and then across Poland to Danzig by heart!

Jacob did not tell her that he had never driven farther than a few blocks in the city with his father, and around the Tiergarten Lanes after begging his mother to let him get behind the wheel. Somehow, staring at the straight wide lines of the Autobahn on the road map had made him feel more confident. *Just get on the Autobahn and drive straight to the border....*

Yes, he had it all memorized, but all the same the road map had been the closest thing to having his father sit beside him when he drove.

Jacob sat on the stone seat like the statue of *The Thinker.* He hoped the others could not see how frightened their leader was as the minutes ticked toward departure. He had put it off for weeks, but suddenly there was no more putting it off. *Key. Clutch. Gear. Starter. Gas. Autobahn....* They all believed he could do it, map or no map!

Lucy drew a deep breath to bolster her courage as she stepped out of Frau Singer's shop. The curbside where Gestapo cars had been parked was vacant, and the line for the streetcar was short. She climbed aboard and paid her fare, then sat to watch Vienna slide past as though in a dream.

Every policeman and every uniform on the street seemed a threat. She fixed her lipstick and brushed her hair, trying to act normal. She practiced a quick smile in her compact mirror and prayed that no one would see on the outside that her insides were churning like a paddle wheel on a Danube River steamer.

The bell clanged and the streetcar started forward, then slowed, then lurched on again from stop to stop. Men and women got on and off. The men looked at Lucy curiously, as they always did. Some smiled, but she looked away, aloof. Now there were more reasons than the displeasure of Wolf to remain distant.

She stepped off the streetcar one block from the Dorotheum. Then she walked away from it, turning the corner and doubling back to approach it from the opposite direction.

Those extra steps did nothing to make the uniformed guards at the doors of the Dorotheum vanish. The swastika flag still flapped noisily above the entrances. The walk had served no purpose except perhaps to give Lucy a few extra minutes to compose herself before she entered the building.

She faced the stairs she had ascended to pawn the carpets. She knew which floor to go to for rugs and watches and even religious artifacts. But this ticket—what had Otto hocked? What department should she go to in this entire vast complex of rooms?

Lucy held the ticket in her fingers and frowned up toward the stairs. Would it not look suspicious if she asked the concierge where she should take the ticket? He would ask her what item she wanted to redeem, and she could not even tell him what it was.

Her heart thumped wildly. People pushed past her, in the doors and out again. A man in a crisp blue uniform walked toward her. He was not smiling. She turned to go, but he called to her.

"Fräulein?"

Lucy stopped. She felt herself grow pale. He was staring at the ticket in her fingers.

"I . . . I am . . ."

He took the ticket from her. "This is such a confusing place." He studied the numbers for a moment. "I get lost myself sometimes. Coats. Men's coats." He pointed down the hall. "Down there. You will see this number on the door, Fräulein."

"Danke." She managed her most charming smile, the "helpless-female" one which always made men feel good about themselves and grateful to her that she allowed them to help.

Her composure regained, her confidence restored, Lucy took the ticket to MEN'S FINE COATS AND CLOTHING.

ITEM: 1 OVERCOAT
STYLE: DOUBLE-BREASTED CAMEL'S HAIR
SIZE: 42 REGULAR
QUALITY: EXCELLENT
MAKER AND YEAR MADE: ROBERE, PARIS, FRANCE, 1938

A dollar value had been put on this coat, of course. Lucy paid its redemption with the funds Otto had left with Peter. She gathered the package into her arms. The scent of mothballs was strong. An overcoat. Perhaps nothing more than an inheritance from Otto to Peter Wallich, whose own coat was ragged.

Or perhaps there was something else. The coat felt hot through the wrapping. Lucy wondered if everyone could see that the paper concealed something dangerous. She tried to hold it casually, as one would carry such an item home from the dry cleaners. *It is nothing. Just a coat* . . . But she hugged it to her when she sat down on the streetcar. *Value? Maybe priceless.*

The remaining hours waiting in a tomb made Lori feel as if the walls and the Nazis were closing in on her. At last she wondered if her nerves would hold.

"It is Christmas Day," she moaned, "and look at us!" She closed her eyes and laid her head back on the damp stones. She missed her parents; she longed to sit in the sun again and laugh again, to walk in a street without being afraid.

From his place beside his city of tin cans, Alfie watched Lori. Mark and Jamie played with Alfie's soldiers and complimented him on the construction of towers and spires and tin-can castles. But Alfie was not listening.

It was Christmas! Alfie had forgotten all about that. He felt sorry for Lori and ashamed that he had forgotten about the presents he got for her and her mama. Lori looked worried and unhappy, as if she might cry. Her eyes were too pretty for crying, and so he told her to close them. He had a surprise for her.

Then he put the jewels in her hands. "Merry Christmas, Lori. Open your eyes." She gasped and looked at Alfie and then at the treasure. "I got them for you and . . . for your mama . . ." He frowned. "Where is she?"

"I don't know, Alfie." Her voice was soft and nice, as it always was when she talked to him. "But where did you get such . . . things as these?"

"In the street." She liked them, he could tell. "I got them for you and your mama. And now maybe you can buy a ticket to . . . Where are we going?"

"Somewhere safe." She patted his hand.

"The Promised Land? America?"

"Maybe. And when we get there we will buy a house for all of us to live in together. We will buy it with your jewels, Alfie, and no one will bother us again."

Alfie looked around at the dripping stone room that had been his home for so long. "I will like to live where there are windows. Clear windows to see through, and no bars—like it used to be. And my cat Joseph, and her kittens will have a room all of their own." He looked at Joseph who was feeding her babies. "I can take her, can't I, Lori?"

"No!" Jacob said from the steps. "We are taking you, but the cats are staying here! We're leaving tonight, like I said. The five of us, and no cats!"

————

Almost safe! Still no Gestapo vehicles in front of Otto's apartment.

Lucy hesitated a step to scan the street on either side. Clutching the package tightly, she lowered her eyes and walked on toward Frau Singer's shop. These last few yards seemed more frightening than all the rest. It was here, after all, that Wolf would come. This small stretch of shops and apartments had been the focus of his attention for weeks. Possibly months.

No sooner had that thought crossed her mind than his automobile rounded the corner ahead of her, heading toward her. Unmistakable through the windscreen of the convertible she saw Wolf's grim face.

Run! Lucy's mind screamed to her. But it was too late to do anything but keep walking. He had already spotted her. The car sped up, sliding past Otto's building and screeching to a stop beside her.

Lucy managed a smile. She raised her hand and tried to look glad to see him. Maybe he had not seen the note in her handwriting on the mirror. Maybe he did not suspect that she had spoiled his hunt and flushed out the game before he had opportunity to fire.

"Where have you been?" he demanded.

"Where have *you* been?" she spat back.

"Working."

"All night?" she demanded, taking the offensive. "And what is her name, eh? Who were you working on? Is she pretty?"

Jealousy, even pretended, took him off guard. "Get in!" He slung open the passenger door and tapped his fingers impatiently on the wheel as she slid in beside him. "Working on my prisoner!" he snapped. Apparently he had not had much success, judging from the angry look on his face. And did he know about her note?

"You should have called," she accused.

"The Jews got away. All the Wallich brood have gotten away. And now Otto denies that there were any Jews! He maintains that the woman was his sister, says they went back to the Tyrol! He is impudent in his defiance of us!" He banged a hand on the wheel, then made a U-turn and parked in front of the building. "Agent Block and his assistant went over the place with a fine tooth comb . . . found nothing. I will search myself." The steely gaze turned on her. "So . . . You did not tell me what you are doing here?"

She laughed. "You told me to have a corset made," she said coyly. "And I thought if I came, I might find you here . . . or *there.*" She pointed at Otto's window. "I am sorry you have lost your Jews, Wolf. I do hope you find them again so we can go out for dinner."

Exasperated with her flippancy, he sighed and shook his head. "That would be nice."

"I need to visit the ladies room," she said absently. Do you mind if I come up with you? Too much coffee. Too much baby."

He shrugged. "Why not?"

———

Peter watched Lucy enter the apartment building beside Wolf. The S.S. officer seemed preoccupied, angry; but his anger was not directed at Lucy. She placed the bundle under her arm and smiled.

"What is happening?" Marlene asked contritely. "Is she coming?"

"She is with him. The officer." Peter rubbed a hand over his eyes in fear for her and astonishment at her self-control. "I don't think he found the note yet. He could not have found it. She would be arrested if he knew about it."

Behind him he could hear Marlene mumbling on the bed. He glanced at her. Tears streamed from her closed eyes. Marlene was praying.

———

She did not want to seem too eager to leave Wolf. Lucy wandered around the empty apartment while he dumped out drawers and pawed through Otto's belongings. Mattresses were slit open, carpets pulled up. *Nothing!* Wolf thumped the closet walls and broke the hanging rod in half in case something was hidden within its hollow center. *Nothing!*

Lucy stood patiently beside the radio as Wolf ransacked the second bedroom. She had found what she came for; it had slipped down between the wall and the sink. *A miracle!* Wolf tore through the bathroom; opening the toilet tank, then using the heavy lid to break the sink from the wall.

Lucy browsed through the program for this week's D' Fat Lady concert. She thought of Otto at the stage. She pocketed the program, then, noticing that the radio dial was set to receive the BBC, she cranked the knob once.

Wolf gave a cry of frustrated rage. *"NOTHING!"*

Lucy remained calm, complacent. "Wolf, darling, I'm going on to my errand now. You smash a while, and I'll meet you back home."

He appeared in the doorway, his shirt dark with sweat, his hair falling over his forehead, and his eyes wild.

"I can smell it! They were Jews!" he shouted. "That Wallich woman! I know who they are!"

"Wolfie," she said patronizingly, "I hope you are right. Otto will not like what you have done to his flat . . . and after he found ours for us, too. This is not a way to return a favor!"

He threw a dish at her head. It crashed against the wall behind her.

She glared angrily back at him. "All right! I have had enough! You are a child, and I am leaving! I will meet you at home when you are finished with this pogrom against your rival!"

Wolf lifted his chin. Eyes narrowed. "I will wait for you." The anger dissolved to confusion. "I . . . I need you tonight. It has not been . . . this has been a most difficult . . ."

Lucy's heart sank. He would wait in the car. *Oh, God!* She had to go back with him! *Another hour, another night of this!*

"How long will you be?" she asked quietly.

"Half an hour." He sounded contrite. The prospect of promotion was slipping away. The child she carried was now his best asset, the surest means of advancement.

"Then I'll meet you at the car." She hefted her package.

"Wait a minute. What have you got there?"

The answer hung in her throat for a moment. "Clothes to be altered." She walked past him and out the door.

———

"Where are they?" Lucy cried as she slipped into the shop of the reluctant corset maker.

"Mein Gott! We thought you were arrested!"

"Get them!" Lucy charged up the stairs. The parlor was empty. "Where are—?"

"In the bedroom. She is alone," Frau Singer called to Karin. "The package is here!"

Lucy tore the paper off the coat as the Wallichs pressed in around her. "What is it? What?" She searched the pockets and turned it inside out. "What did he want you to get?"

Karin reached in and lifted the hem of the coat. She looked at the stitches that bound the silk lining to the camel's-hair fabric. Then with a soft sigh, she plucked scissors from Frau Singer's sewing basket and tore out the thread. Four brand new, perfect official passports fell out onto the floor. Marlene's pouting image stared up from her documents. Ugly, yes. But beautiful. She laughed and picked it up. *MARLENE ANNE RUGER. ARYAN.*

All right, so there it was. The priceless documents. Surely Wolf would suspect that such documents had been made. Perhaps he would have men on duty at every station to check photos and passports against the Gestapo pictures of the Wallichs.

"Listen to me," Lucy took Karin's arm. "I have to go with him now. But *listen*!"

Karin nodded; her smile of relief vanished. She could see plainly that it was not over. They were still across the street. "What should we do?"

Lucy frowned and ran her hand through her hair. She did not want

Wolf to come looking for her. So little time. If he finished early . . . She groped in her handbag, pulling out the railway timetables. "Danzig . . . *Danzig!*" There it was. Two trains leaving Vienna. One tonight at 9:30. The other at 3:08 tomorrow morning. "You cannot leave together. They will be looking for four of you. Understand? Not even on the same train."

Karin blanched at the thought of separation, but agreed. "Willie and I?"

"No." Lucy said it before Peter could. "You and Marlene."

"But my baby—"

"The boys must stay together. If you are caught with a circumcised baby, they will arrest you, and . . . you know what that will mean to the child. No. You and Marlene. They will search you. No doubt of that. But they will see women, not Jews."

"What about Peter and Willie?" Marlene looked fearfully at her brothers. She was no longer thinking only about herself.

"They will go with me, as my nephews. I can handle these Gestapo types." Lucy spoke with a confidence that made everyone believe her. "You and Marlene leave tonight. Take your tickets to the ticket clerk in the third window of the central train terminal—the one opposite Stadt-park. You must see no other clerk but this one fellow. Can you remember?"

Peter was at the window. "Wolf is coming out."

"The third window!" Lucy repeated. "His name is Kurek. He has a drooping mustache. He will stamp in the date and time on your ticket. *Say it!*"

"Kurek. Third window. Central," Karin repeated.

"Wolf is standing by the car," Peter reported. "Leaning on the fender. Angry. Arms crossed."

"Yes." Lucy was breathless. "Peter. I will meet you at a quarter till three tomorrow morning, you and Willie, beside the drinking fountain to the right of the ticket window. Be there early. Kurek is off duty at 2:00 A.M. You must get the tickets stamped before then! *Say it!*"

"Kurek. Third Window. Central. Before two," Peter repeated. "Wolf threw down his cigarette. He is coming."

Lucy turned and embraced Karin Wallich, then slipped something into Marlene's hand. It was the note from the mirror. "Go now and rip it into a thousand pieces. Down the toilet with it, and no mistakes!"

Marlene smiled and ran to obey as Lucy hurried down the steps to meet Wolf at the curb.

35

The Last Pure Heart

Jacob was right. Alfie knew he was right, but still it did not make it any easier.

Big tears rolled down his cheeks and onto Joseph's face as she sat purring on his lap.

"I can't take you, Joseph," he said sadly. "You can't go with us. We are trying to get away from the Hitler-men. These fellows do not like Jews like Jacob and Mark. And they don't like Jamie and Lori because they are real Christians." Joseph put her paws on Alfie's chest and rubbed her face in his salty tears as if she understood. "And they don't like Dummkopfs like me."

She purred loudly as though to say she liked Alfie a lot. This made Alfie blubber more.

"But the Hitler-men don't have anything against cats. At least I don't think they do. I think they like cats, because cats are just cats and don't argue with them, you know?"

She purred louder.

Alfie looked up at Jacob, who was looking somewhere else and pretending not to notice Alfie and his cat Joseph. But Alfie could tell Jacob heard them talking.

"You have to stay here with your kittens. They need you a lot. Except Werner." He frowned toward the little black-and-white kitten who tottered about on unsteady legs. "Werner is like me, Joseph," Alfie explained to the mother cat. "He is not as strong as your other babies, and so—" This was difficult to explain to a mother. "So Jacob says I can take Werner with me and take care of him. Otherwise he will die if I leave him."

Joseph did not seem to mind. She curled up on Alfie's lap and blinked sleepily at her kittens. *Maybe she understood and maybe she didn't,* Alfie thought, but either way this was a very sad day.

Jacob let him pack some cans of milk and even sardines for Werner. Alfie had very little else to take for himself. He packed a few tin soldiers, especially Jesus and His horse. And then Lori held out the jewels Alfie had given her and told him he could use some of them to buy whatever he needed when they were out of Germany. This made him feel better. He promised Joseph that he would buy Werner a nice pillow to sleep on and lots of good food to eat.

Dressed in his black Hitler Youth uniform, Jamie ascended the steps of the crypt first to reconnoiter. Jacob hoped their pursuers had given up after a day-long search and had gone home to hot cider and a warm fire by now.

The churchyard was pitch black, although it was not late. He could not even see the silhouette of the church building as he peered out from the hatch, listened, and then slid it back fully.

"Be careful," Jacob warned. Jamie inched past him and emerged in the upper chamber of the crypt. He crawled forward, clutching the key, and waited. No sound—only a slight breeze rustling dead leaves among the headstones. *So this was it!*

"Come on." Jamie reached up and fumbled with the lock. Clumsy in the dark, he could not open the gate.

"Tor auf!" Jacob demanded. Alfie took the key from Jacob and in one deft movement opened the gate.

It groaned back on its hinges. The fugitives huddled just inside the arch like partridges waiting to be flushed out. There was still no sound, no movement in the blackness. They slipped out and waited, moved forward a few paces and halted. Alfie locked the gate behind them. He reached through the bars and scratched Joseph's chin, and then joined the crouching procession as it wound through the tombstones toward the break in the wall behind the gardener's shed.

Tonight there were no shouts, no alarms, no running footsteps or fluttering torches—only deathly silence. Leaves crunched beneath their feet; hands in the darkness reached out to make certain there were five in the line. Five together. Five slipping through the secret break one at a time.

It was easy, as easy as Jacob had envisioned it should be when they first thought of the plan. Still, their hearts beat the uneven rhythm of fear. Their breath came shallow, rising up in little locomotive puffs of steam in the cold night.

One, two, three, four, five through the churchyard fence! And Werner the kitten in Alfie's pocket.

Peter could not watch as his mother held the baby in a last embrace. He focused his gaze on bolts of cloth and the glowing gas heater, and finally, on Marlene's brown hat. It was her best hat; it matched her coat and her eyes and hair. She was proud of it. Peter had teased her, telling her it looked like an upside-down soup bowl. Now he regretted saying so many mean things to her.

She was quiet and sad, not the usual primping, fussing little Marlene. Peter saw regret and sorrow on her face, and suddenly he wanted to tell her things he had not known he felt until this moment of parting.

Mama stood framed in the doorway of the bedroom, her arms full of Baby Willie. She rocked him and whispered quietly against his cheek, telling him things she might not ever have a chance to say to him again.

Peter knew there were things he must say to his sister, in spite of the fact she had been the bane of his existence. He took a step toward her. He towered over Marlene. She looked up at him with those chocolate brown eyes, a single tear poised in each eye, as if stuck there. Words were stuck also.

He straightened her hat. A shudder coursed through him. He wished she did not look so Jewish. He hoped that Lucy Strasburg was right. He prayed that when the Gestapo at the border checks examined Karin and Marlene that they would see only mother and daughter, not two Jewesses.

"Do I look all right?" she ventured. "In my soup bowl?"

"Very nice . . . in your . . ." Peter swallowed hard. How he hated this emotion, this longing to hold on! It was so much easier to want to punch her! So much easier to cringe at every word. But now that *goodbye* might mean forever, nothing could shield him from loving her. Even her. Sister. Marlene. He could not say more. He reached out and pulled her close in a hug—awkward at first, then a warm merging of the emotion they both felt.

"You know, Peter," she whispered, "maybe someday I will grow up . . . and be like Mama. And you will like me." Such hope filled her voice!

"Until then," he whispered, "you keep me on my toes, ja?"

She laughed and sniffed. Tears of relief came. "You and Willie will be careful? I'm not worried about me. I would rather something happen to me than you and Willie, see?"

"Nothing will happen to any of us, Marlene." He tried to sound reassuringly gruff. He patted her back. "Just believe that. We will meet at the Danziger Hotel day after tomorrow. Like we planned." He lifted her chin and kissed her lightly on the furrowed brow. "Don't worry. Just take care of Mama . . ."

His words trailed away. He felt his head grow light. Mama stood at his elbow, pulling a string from his jacket, straightening his hair, stroking his cheek. He was almost grown now, and Mama was trying very hard to say goodbye to him as if he were a man. But the expression in her eyes when she looked at his face was the same as it had been when she looked at Willie. How he wished she could rock him, too, and whisper against his cheek! He wanted to lay his head on her shoulder and hear her say that everything really would be all right. But now it was his turn to embrace her, to comfort her, to say all the things a man of courage must say. Papa would expect it of him! *So why was he crying?*

"There, there, son," she said quietly, smoothing his hair and letting him rest his face against her shoulder. "You must not worry. We have not come this far to fail now. We will believe!" A mother was expected to kiss away her child's hurt. Even for a child as tall as Peter.

He straightened and wiped his wet cheeks on his sleeve. "Yes, Mama." He cleared his throat. "We will meet at the Danziger Hotel. And don't worry about Willie. I will take good care of him. You know he is as happy with me as anyone. You and Marlene . . . have a safe trip, then."

Peter watched them from the dark window until they boarded the trolley, paid their fare, and sat perfectly framed in the lighted car. Marlene smiled, excited about making such a long trip. Then those brown eyes began desperately searching the facades of the buildings, finally fixing on the window where Peter stood in the blackness. The small gloved hand rose up; fingers curled slightly down in farewell, and Peter saw her lips move: *I love you, Peter. . . .*

They had planned even this. Lori walked alongside Jacob. She held his hand and talked to him about last Christmas as they strolled along the sidewalk.

Jamie and Mark flanked Alfie, who looked out of place between them. He towered over them both. *The sore thumb,* Jacob thought, praying that they would not meet any old acquaintances on the streets of downtown Berlin tonight.

The neon lights and blaring traffic assaulted their senses after weeks of enforced silence and nights without light. Lori tried not to look spellbound; she kept her eyes on Jacob's face, pulling at his sleeve when he, too, gawked at the marquee of a cabaret that blinked on and off in red and yellow lights.

"Where was the car?" he called to Jamie when they were out of earshot of three drunken middle-aged couples.

"I think . . . just up there—" Jamie jerked his thumb. "But maybe not anymore. Who knows?"

Alfie knew. "Pastor's car?" he asked with a broad, childlike smile. "I saw it. It needs a wash." He raised his nose in the air as if to take his bearings in the cacophony of the city streets; then he pointed. "It is still there."

Lori squeezed Jacob's hand to slow him down. Let the trio cross the street first. They must not walk too closely together. There was a policeman on one corner. And there was another . . .

The five had to walk separately; if policemen were looking for Jamie and Lori as Alfie said, then they must not present their faces like photographs off a wanted poster.

A uniformed officer walked toward them. He looked at Lori's face, letting his gaze slide down her once and then up again. He looked away, frowned, and then looked back.

"Laugh," Jacob said softly; then he looked at her and guffawed loudly. She mimicked him, her laughter bordering on the hysteria of terror. *Two young people out for a walk, having fun . . .* The officer did not recognize her after all. He brushed past them and they hurried, still laughing, to cross the street.

There stood the car, caked in dust, its windscreen dull gray. The tires looked low. Jacob casually unlocked the door, opening it for Lori. He was keenly aware that it was at this point the trap might be sprung. Had Pastor Ibsen's car been identified? Had it been left here just for such a moment as this?

Lori slid into the passenger side. Her father's glasses lay on the dashboard, his gloves still on the seat. She could not suppress a groan as she reached over and unlocked Jacob's door. He jumped behind the wheel, and the three others crammed into the backseat.

Key! Clutch in! Gearshift in neutral! Turn the starter, and—

"What is wrong with it?" Lori gasped.

The engine groaned and moaned, trying to turn over. Then it died.

Jacob pounded a fist on the steering wheel. This far, and now the battery was dead! Could it be?

He prayed and tried again. *Key. Clutch. Gear. Starter.*

The moan sounded more pitiful than before. Jacob sat staring through the filth of the window. Lights from the neon signs blinked in weird patterns on his ashen face.

"Dead," he said dully. "Dead battery." He bit his lip and then instructed, "Stay here!"

They could see him as he struggled to open the awkward latch and lift the hood. It creaked open like a gaping mouth. Jacob pounded on the terminals of the battery in hopes . . . *Maybe just corroded?*

Cars whizzed by him. He left the hood open and then climbed back behind the wheel. *Key! Clutch! Gear! Oh, God! Starter!*

This time there was a slight groan and a click. Jacob's frightened breathing fogged the window. He was breathing like someone very frightened.

"Hey, Max!" Mark asked, calling Jacob by the old nickname, "what do we do now?"

Then the unthinkable happened. A green police car slipped in along the curb in front of them. Nose to nose, the vehicle hemmed them in.

An officer got out of his vehicle and walked slowly up to Jacob's window. His finger twirled, indicating that the window should be lowered.

Lori prayed, certain that the car had indeed been left here to trap them. Now there was nothing more they could do. No more running. No place left to hide.

Jacob did not look at the police officer as he rolled his window down.

The officer peered in, a strange look crossed his face. He glanced at them, then looked hard at the raised hood.

Alfie blurted out, "Hey, I know you! You are the . . . the policeman who . . . at the corner when I was lost."

Doubt crossed the face of the officer. He squinted into the backseat at Alfie. Same cap. Same coat. Same face. Were there any left in Berlin like this one?

"Yes, I remember you. Ah! Yes. I see you have gotten use from your clothes, ja!" He tipped his hat at Jacob. "Your brother?" he asked.

Jacob managed an astonished nod. "Yes . . . my . . . my brother."

"We are old friends." The officer opened Jacob's door. "He is the last honest fellow in Berlin, I think. I have thought of him often. So"— he thumped the car—"what is the problem? Aside from a layer of dirt?"

"Battery," Jacob managed to stutter the word twice.

"I can give you a jump-start," said the officer with a wave of his hand. "But you will have to keep the engine running until you get where you are going."

The beads of perspiration on Jacob's forehead reflected the colors of the neon lights. In the backseat, Mark and Jamie sat frozen and silent, not believing that a German policeman was hooking cables to the battery of their stalled automobile and advising them to keep going and not turn off the engine.

Jacob cranked the starter one more time. The engine coughed and rumbled and vibrated to a thundering start.

"Let her run a few minutes," advised the officer. "She has been sitting quite a while."

Was that a smile on his lips?

"Yes."

"I checked the license and registration, since it is on my beat. I was hoping someone might pick her up." He looked past Jacob, directly at Lori. "You are leaving Berlin?" he asked.

She nodded. Should she tell him anything? *Anything?* Should he know they were leaving?

He rubbed his hand across his jaw and peered up the street and then down again. "Listen to me." He lowered his voice. "There are roadblocks across the bridges, and on the main Autobahns from Berlin in every direction. They are looking for lots of criminals; among them a brother and sister . . . ja?"

Lori's mouth went dry as cotton. "Ja," she managed. "Bitte?" she asked. *What were they to do?*

"Gut. You understand me." The officer looked hard at Jacob. "I do not know who you are, but if you do not want to end up in prison, you must take the side streets out of the city."

Jacob could hardly make his mouth work. "Which. . . ?"

"Do you know Landsbergerstrasse?"

"Yes."

"It runs past Friedrichshain. The park."

Jacob knew the place well—a wooded area, filled with streams and small lakes. He had gone swimming there with friends. "Yes. I know it."

"Leave the city by that direction. If you are followed, drive into the park. Abandon your car and run into the woods. They will not catch all of you that way at least." He looked at Alfie's innocent face with concern.

Alfie held up his kitten. "You see what I have?" Alfie asked.

A moment of pain and pity flashed across the man's broad peasant face. "Yes, boy. And it is a nice kitten. Did you find it in the street also, like your clothes?"

"No. He is Werner. His mama and brothers are back in the Halder grave at New Church with my mama. Please . . . will you take care of them?"

The officer exhaled loudly. This appeal was more than he had bargained for. Danger at every turn, and this poor boy was thinking about his kittens, at home with Mama. *The purest heart in Berlin. Maybe the last pure heart?* "Yes, boy. I will see to them."

With a curt nod, he backed up a step and turned from them. Unclamping the cables, he slammed down the hood.

"Now get going before someone arrests you for illegal parking."

"We are certain that they were hiding out in New Church like little mice," Officer Hess explained with a shrug. "Gone now, of course. But they left us an itinerary."

"And this is what you have found of the Ibsen children in all this time?" Minister of Propaganda Joseph Goebbels slapped his hand down hard on the road map that had been found beneath the window at New Church. "A road map! My own press prints these. What is that supposed to mean?"

Officer Alexander Hess was a patient man. Because of his patience he had earned the reputation of achieving his goals. He traced his finger along the blue ink that followed the line of the new Autobahn from Berlin to the train crossing at the Polish border.

"You will notice two things, Reichsminister Goebbels," he said. "They intend to cross *here,* where the express train to Danzig passes the border."

"Maybe this is nothing! *Mein Gott!* Such a line could have been drawn by Pastor Ibsen years ago and the map discarded by the children."

Hess smiled. Patient and clerk-like, he had reasoned it all out. "If one is going to cross into Poland at the train crossing, it would be customary to *board the train* in Berlin, you see." He waited for that ordinary fact to penetrate the irritation of Goebbels. "However, the children have marked the *Autobahn*. They intend to drive from Berlin to the border and cross into Poland just *there*. They will abandon their car, no doubt."

"*What* car? What? They have a *car*? Why haven't we heard about an automobile before?"

"After I saw the map, I checked vehicle registrations in Berlin. There have been no thefts; however, there is an automobile registered to Pastor Ibsen. It is missing." He slid his finger along the marked route to indicate that the vehicle should now be heading north and east toward the Polish border. "I have sent out a description of the Ibsen children to all the towns along that route—and a description of the vehicle, of course. Nothing could be simpler. A reward is offered. They will be picked up within hours, and we will transport them to their father's prison, a mile from the border crossing. You will have your statement from Pastor Ibsen. The world will have it." His matter-of-fact attitude reassured Goebbels.

"I will give the Führer *your* word on that." A thinly veiled threat lay behind the comment. If Hess failed to find the children, he would also fail to break Ibsen. And the Führer wanted badly to add the Ibsen name to his roster of faithful churchmen.

———

Lucy lay staring up at the dark ceiling. Wolf's heavy arm stretched across her as if to hold her here beside him even as he slept. When she tried to turn, the arm tightened, a prison of flesh and desire that kept her chained to him like a slave.

Hours ticked past slowly. When the clock tolled nine-thirty, she imagined Karin Wallich and Marlene on board the train leaving Vienna at that moment. She wanted to pray for them; to remind the Lord of His mother's eyes. She wanted to ask that everything would go well. There was no question about the authenticity of the passports. She only hoped the mother and daughter had not been pulled aside for questioning.

The night slipped by and Lucy found herself thinking that at this hour, the train would pass through one city or the other. Perhaps tomorrow she would also be passing those checkpoints. But it was a long way from Wolf's bed to tomorrow.

Lucy was afraid. Alone with him like this, she knew what he would do to her if he suspected. She had told Frau Singer that he would not beat her, would not kill her. In reality, she knew better than that. And if, by some miracle he only had her locked up in the Lebensborn, he would have her eliminated after the baby was born.

The baby!

A gentle butterfly fluttered briefly in her womb. She felt it every day now. It filled her with the purest love she had ever known, and the deepest grief as well. Mothers like her who had lain in bed and wondered about the mystery of life within them now said goodbye to the children they had borne. Everywhere in the Reich, women like Karin Wallich sent their babies away on trains and hoped that one day they might be together again.

Lucy did not want to send her baby away to be raised by another woman. She wanted to hold him, to feel him turn his face to be nourished by her. She longed to hold his little hands and praise him when he took a step. She wanted his smiles and kisses to belong to her heart, his tears to fall against her shoulder.

She had witnessed the sorrowing eyes of the mother of Christ in the face of Karin Wallich. And in that moment her own fears and sorrows had somehow bonded inextricably with the grief of every woman in the Reich who was forced to say goodbye . . . forever.

Jewish women had their children torn physically from their arms. Christian mothers who had remained steadfast watched as their children were spiritually poisoned, growing finally as dark as the masters of Germany. This sort of separation was just as real; the grief, though different, just as profound. The end was just as final. *Eternal.*

Lucy wanted to pray, but she did not know how. Like Mary Magdalene at the foot of the cross, she longed to talk to the Son of that sorrowing mother.

"Jesus!" her heart cried as the clock chimed 1:00 A.M. *"Lord of hurting mothers . . . hold our babies close. The wolves are at our heels."*

She silently whispered other awkward words. She did not pray for herself, but for her child and the children of other mothers. And then, a small miracle—*Wolf rolled over!*

Lucy rose quietly and dressed in the dark bathroom. She could not take her clothing. No chance to pack. But she rummaged in her drawer and stuffed a change of underclothes into her largest handbag and found her grandmother's crucifix as well.

Wolf groaned softly from the bed. Lucy stood, unmoving, in the blackness. Peter would be at the station by now. He would have the tickets stamped. The train would be turning slowly, pointing north toward Berlin, and then to Danzig.

Suddenly the light flashed on. "Where are you going?" Wolf demanded, scowling at her in the bright light.

"I . . . I didn't mean to wake you." She felt like weeping. Now he would never let her go!

"What is that in your hand?" He stared hard at the crucifix.

Lucy held it up for him to see. "My grandmother's—"

"Ah. You are going to Mass again." He switched off the light without looking at the clock and lay down heavily on his pillow. "You and your God of hopeless causes. Pray that I find the Jews, will you? And bring me back a pastry from Demel's."

36

Freedom Ride

The clashing gears of the Ibsen car resisted when Jacob did not push the clutch pedal in far enough. Lori glanced nervously at him. Her father's automobile had never made such terrible noises before. *Maybe from sitting so long without use?*

The missing road map was emblazoned like a neon sign inside Jacob's skull. Streets spun off of Alexanderplatz like spokes from a wheel. Some led away to Gestapo roadblocks, spot checks, and certain arrest. Jacob correctly turned onto Landsbergerstrasse. At first it was well lit and broad, later dwindling down to two lanes and eventually flanked by fields and farms and thick woods.

This was not as he had planned—no straight highway to set his course and carry them north and east two hundred miles straight to the border at Firchau! The back road they traveled was poorly marked, unlit, and often in need of attention. But some consolation lay in the fact that there was no traffic to contend with.

They passed the Hoppegarten racetrack eleven miles outside of Berlin. *Only eleven miles!* And yet, Jacob felt a sense of exhilaration. *He knew exactly where they were!* He had driven this complaining car eleven miles closer to the border and had not yet been stopped, had not even seen a police car on the way.

He was driving hunched forward over the wheel.

"Can you see?" Lori asked, noting his uncomfortable position.

"The dirt on the windscreen," he replied.

"Well, you can't drive two hundred miles to Firchau like that," she said. "Your back will be broken."

He had not realized she was commenting on the awkward way he was sitting. He smiled self-consciously. She was right. His back and shoulders ached after only eleven miles. He sat back against the leather. He tried to relax his death-grip on the steering wheel and look casual about this, like his father used to look when he drove. Head slightly raised to peer down his nose at the road. Fingers limp as he gently guided the car. Yes. That was better. He could do this. He looked toward her as if to speak, and as he did, the wheels also turned with his head.

The car swerved to the right. He over-corrected, crossing the center and brushing the gravel of the left shoulder like a drunken driver.

Cries of alarm rose up from the backseat. Lori sat rigid with her legs braced hard on the floorboard, her mouth open in a noiseless scream. And then Jacob brought the car back on the road again.

"Sorry," he muttered when he could breathe again.

"Jacob?" Lori stammered his name. "Have you driven much before this?"

"Some." That had been a long time ago, he wanted to tell her, before the state had confiscated the family car. Their Jewish-owned car had been Aryanized and now belonged to the family of some minor Nazi official. Jacob did not explain all this to her. He had never mentioned it. The humiliation of it was too painful.

"Well, listen," Lori suggested. *"Don't look at me,* but listen. I learned to drive with this car. I passed my driver's test, and . . . maybe I should drive and you navigate?"

He did not speak for a long time. The road was straight. He wanted to ask her if she had guessed he could not really drive. But he did not. He knew she knew. It was easier to pretend that she did not.

"A good idea," he said, braking raggedly and pulling to the side of the road.

She took the wheel and shifted the gears effortlessly; the brakes did not grab or squeal. The three boys in the backseat fell soundly asleep, and for the first time since he had imagined this desperate flight from Berlin, Jacob actually believed they might get out safely.

The great steam locomotive panted and drummed beneath the train shed. The sound was not half so loud as the pounding of Lucy's heart as she hurried into central terminal!

Peter Wallich stood by the fountain. He leaned against the wall and propped Willie up to face him on his knee.

In a tweed cap, matching knickers, and jacket, Peter no longer looked ragged. He had replaced his old coat with Otto's camel's-hair overcoat, folded on top of his suitcase.

He did not seem to see her at first, although she raised her hand when he looked her direction. He lifted Willie high above his head and smiled and talked to him as a gendarme strolled past. The policeman gave the brothers a warm glance. The officer paused a moment as if to speak to Peter, but Peter did not look at him and continued to make Willie giggle. No chance to talk. He walked on.

Only then did Peter look at Lucy and then up at the face of the huge bronze clock on the far end of the station. She was late; it was nearly three o'clock. He had been fending off the wolves for fifteen minutes longer than he wanted to! All these things were obvious in the hard look he gave her as she approached.

"Where have you been, Aunt Lucy?" he muttered under his breath. "We are the only passengers this morning. Everyone else at the station is Gestapo."

"Are we boarding yet?"

"We could have been snug inside the train ten minutes ago," he remarked sourly. He seemed to have forgotten who had purchased his tickets and rescued his passports.

"I told you," Lucy replied, taking his suitcase in hand, "I have a brother named Peter. He was your age once—a rotten age. I could handle him, too." She shot him a threatening glance. "Manners, bitte, and we will get along nicely." She smiled sweetly. "Is that clear?"

With Jacob as navigator and Lori as pilot, they skirted the tiny walled city of Custrin and struck out through rolling farms toward Landsberg.

At times Jacob thought he heard the distant shrill of a train whistle across the land. The tracks, he knew, were not far from the road they now traveled.

The city of Landsberg cast a soft glow on the predawn horizon. It was still hours before sunrise, and in the absolute stillness of the sleeping country, the fact that they were running for their lives seemed unreal.

Just beyond Landsberg, the coughing and sputtering of the engine jerked them back to reality. Then it clattered loudly and died.

"What's wrong with it?" Jacob slapped the dashboard as though he could wake up the machine. "Has it ever done this before?"

Lori's face was tense as she steered the dying vehicle to the side of the road. "Once," she said quietly.

"What is it?"

"Papa said its head broke." Lori winced. "I think that's very bad."

Lucy Strasburg's stern remark served as a warning shot over Peter's bow. It took him by surprise. He liked it, and suddenly decided he liked her, too.

He shrugged his agreement to her peace terms, then stepped back as she proceeded to waltz them through three different passport checks. None of the officials ever even looked at Peter or Willie. They were too busy looking at Lucy, listening to her talking about her nephews here beside her, and her sister who had sent them to Vienna to keep Lucy company over the holidays.

She talked and talked, spinning such a story that Peter had to shake his head in order to keep himself from believing her as well. The pressure was off, and he suddenly felt very tired.

Everyone on the platform knew all the details of their stay in Vienna within minutes—what parks and museums and concerts they had attended; how long they had stayed, and what they liked to eat best.

Astonished, Peter listened as Lucy named off all the places he had wanted to visit in a lifetime of living in Vienna, but had never had the chance.

He heard tales of himself patting the nose of a Lipizzaner stallion and being invited to watch the training.

"All this in just two weeks!" Lucy exclaimed.

The passport officer smiled pleasantly as she finished her recital. Only now did he look Peter full in the face.

"And how do you feel after such a vacation in Vienna, young man?"

"Tired," Peter answered truthfully.

The officer laughed uproariously. "Indeed! Who would not be? Sleep all the way to Danzig then, eh?"

"No, no!" Lucy linked her arm through Peter's. "He has to keep me company!"

Peter thought she would have stood and chatted another few minutes with this uniformed officer. Did she know that this was a fellow who had people locked up at will? If she was aware, she did not seem to care. He was an excellent audience. And she, perhaps, was the finest actress Peter had ever seen.

The train whistle shrilled the three-minute departure warning. Lucy had become old friends with a man who would cut Peter's throat if he had bothered to take him through the customary physical body search. But the search had not been requested. She had talked until the last possible instant they could board the train.

Peter decided that she was either the dumbest woman he had met or the smartest. She was fearless, he was sure of that.

———

Four o'clock in the morning. No one was up except perhaps for dairymen milking their cows. Soon enough, however, there would be farmers driving this road to market. They might notice the abandoned car and ask questions. Maybe someone would even call the police and give the location. Then it would be easy for the officials to check the registration and discover that the car was the property of a certain Pastor Karl Ibsen.

"We'll have to hide it," Jacob said, trying to find a suitable place to stash the vehicle.

Alfie inhaled deeply. "There are lots of big trees over there. And a river too, I think. Let's put it in the water."

Jacob no longer felt like questioning Alfie Halder. As Jamie said, Alfie was smarter than Jacob thought.

With Lori steering and Werner the kitten comfortably on the dash, the boys pushed the useless vehicle toward the sloping banks of the Warthe River. Deep enough for good-sized ships, the Warthe would easily swallow up the car.

After an hour of muscle, they grabbed the kitten, then gave one final heave, sending the derelict car to a watery grave.

They could see the dairyman in the light of his swinging lantern as he walked slowly toward the barn.

Ducking low behind the hedge, Lori brushed the dirt from Jamie's black Hitler Youth uniform and straightened his hair.

"All right, you know what to say to him?" Jacob asked Jamie.

"Yes." Jamie recited. *"Heil Hitler."* He hated that part especially. *"My friends and I are traveling, and we would like to sleep in your barn a little while and then have breakfast. We can pay you well."*

"Good," Jacob said, thumping him on the back. It was always important to know your lines. "If he says no, then walk that way, back toward the river. We will meet you."

They were all exhausted. Days of preparation and anticipation had left them without energy. Now that the car was in the drink, it seemed that they deserved a little sleep in some fresh straw. Lori prayed that this farmer would be a kind man. Papa always said that German farmers were the best people on earth. He had said it even after Hitler had come to power. Plain people, they did not change with the winds of politics . . . they simply grew more seasoned with their land.

This was an older man, his gait was stiff and slow in the early morning cold. Maybe he would not like to hear Jamie give the salute, but it was best to be prepared.

Jamie struck off across the yard and met the farmer at the door to his barn.

Up went the arm. *Heil!* The farmer did not respond in kind. This was a good sign.

Snatches of conversation drifted to them amidst the crowing of roosters and the impatient bellowing of cows wanting to be milked.

"Why did you want to stay here?" the farmer bellowed also. A no-nonsense man. "There is a Hitler Youth camp just over that hill. Go stay with them, why don't you?"

"Ummm. Not all of my friends are . . . Hitler Youth. And, ummm

. . . your barn is a better place for us."

Silence. A big laugh from the farmer. "It's hard to know who to give the stiff arm to, isn't it, son?"

Moments later, Jamie beckoned them to come at a run. Within fifteen minutes the farmwife had brought them blankets and all five were tucked in the sweet-smelling straw.

They had only four hours' sleep among the belching, cud-chewing milk cows belonging to Herr Schöne and his wife, but it was their best sleep since Kristal Nacht.

They awakened to the voices of the old couple as they argued at the door of the barn.

"They cannot go out. The Hitler Youth will see them, and—"

"Those little black-beetle swastika wavers," growled the farmer in his quietest whisper. *"I thought these children were part of that mob. But they can't be. Did you see the big one with the kitten?"*

"Shhh!" scolded the farmwife, Frau Schöne. *"They will hear you!"*

Wide awake, Jacob rolled over to see if Alfie had heard the comment about him.

Alfie's eyes were open, and he smiled broadly. He held up Werner and whispered to Jacob, "They are talking about my kitten. They like Werner. They like us too, I think."

It was another miracle, Alfie said—thick slices of fresh, warm bread with lots of butter slavered on top, a pitcher of fresh milk, then another, and a third! None of them could remember when they had eaten anything so wonderful! They shouted their thanks to Herr Schöne, who was mostly deaf, as Frau Schöne explained. And the couple would not hear of taking payment!

Little Werner lapped up milk from Alfie's cup until his furry belly bulged. Even the kitten's eyes looked as if they might pop. Alfie told them all he would have to be careful and not squeeze the kitten after such a meal.

A second miracle followed the bread and milk. Herr Schöne smoothed his drooping mustache and peered down at his guests.

"It is not safe for you to travel on foot around here in daylight. Not even in the dark. Not with that camp of Blackshirts over there. They'd think nothing of popping that kitten and then going after you."

"Not so harsh," protested the Frau to her husband. "You will frighten them!"

"They need to be frightened. Terrible days, these days. So—" He lifted his chin. "Where are you going?"

Lori and Jacob exchanged looks. This was not in the plan. They had vowed to trust no one!

Lori shrugged. Jacob told him. "Northeast to Firchau," he said.

"You hear that, Mama?" shouted the farmer. *"North to Firchau!"*

Jacob imagined that the Hitler Youth could probably hear it as well.

"Sehr gut!" exclaimed the old Frau. "Today Papa is heading just that direction. Cabbages and chickens is going north as far as Schneidemuhl. Would you care to ride?"

———

The train to Danzig chugged into the enormous new Südbahnhof train terminal in Berlin, a glass and steel cathedral of technology and modern engineering. At this latest structure of the Reichsbahn, Nazi party members in good standing disembarked during the layover for the usual document checks. Murals and sculptures displaying the mythical bodies of strong Aryan workers adorned the place with the perfect ideals for the race.

The steam of the locomotive billowed up and cascaded from the domed roof, and Peter thought they had entered a new version of hell. He did not want to tour the building in spite of the hour layover. Lucy stayed with him as she had done throughout the long trip from Vienna as passengers had gotten on and off all along the way. She had faced them all with her dazzling personality. Those who had been reluctant to talk with her, had, nonetheless, done so.

Not one of the strangers who had entered their lives along the way would even remember what Peter and Willie looked like. When they looked back on their trip, they would remember only that the compartment had been shared with a garrulous blond from Bavaria.

The Berlin terminal was crawling with police and agents. The Biedermeier friendliness of Vienna was nonexistent on the faces of the plainclothes officers who scrutinized everyone from behind their newspapers. Peter had not imagined that the atmosphere of heaviness could be darker anywhere than it was in Vienna, but here in the north every face looked grim and fixed. Perhaps it was the close proximity to Hitler and the policy makers of the Reich; everywhere arms flipped up and lips formed the *Heil Hitler*. Hello. Goodbye. *Heil Hitler*. The stuttering blasphemy echoed in the air. In Vienna, Otto had taught Peter how to cross himself like a good Catholic, but here, the religious genuflect was that stiff arm! In Berlin there was no god but Hitler.

A sharp rap sounded on the door of the compartment. "Fräulein?" the porter called. "Everyone is getting off the train."

"Come in." Lucy fixed a smile on her lips, but even that was wearing thin. Perhaps she felt the heaviness, too.

The porter opened the door a crack. "I am ordered to say . . . to tell all passengers . . . the train will be delayed another hour." He gestured toward their windows. "You see?"

A uniformed band filed into the station. Behind them came the Blackshirted security forces of the S.S. They stood in long rows from the entrance of the Bahnhof to a smaller platform where a train with only four cars waited.

"The Führer?" Lucy asked.

"He will be coming soon," the porter said. "The Ministry of Prop-aganda has told us to tell everyone in Bahnhof. The Führer has a political guest—some foreigner. We need to make an impression. If you and your nephews will join the crowd, bitte. There are flags pro-vided."

Unconsciously, Peter touched his passport in his coat pocket. The door closed and Lucy made a face to show her distaste of these things. "Cheer loud, Peter," she instructed. "Young men your age consider the Führer their hero."

Peter held Willie in his arms so that he would have a reason not to give the salute. One could not be expected to stand at attention and say those words with a baby in one's arms.

The railway official passed out miniature swastika flags at the turn-stile. Hundreds of people came from out of nowhere, then thousands. The band began to play a military march. Peter was given two flags to wave, as though Willie could also hold one of them. Then in the jostling crush and the hum of excitement, they were somehow pushed forward to the front of the mob.

As "Deutschland über Alles" played, Hitler appeared, surrounded by an entourage of Reich officials. Goebbels and fat Hermann Göring came behind the Führer, and even the brutal schoolmaster Himmler, the man Peter's father called a butcher. All the men who had destroyed their lives.

Peter raised his little flag and screamed *Heil Hitler* along with all the rest. The Führer reached out to touch the hands of his adoring people who had come to worship him. He came nearer down the line, at last, horribly, locking eyes on the sweating, frantic face of Peter holding Baby Willie.

"Heil Hitler!" Peter managed to snap to attention in spite of the baby in his arms.

"A fine example of young Aryan manhood!" the Führer said. He took Willie into his arms, and the bulbs of a hundred cameras popped to capture the tender moment.

God! Oh, God! Help!

"*Heil!* Yes. *Heil ... Heil ..."* Peter stammered. The men around the Führer laughed with amusement at the young red-haired Aryan so over-come by the attention of his lord.

"Your name?" the Führer demanded.

"Peter ... Ruger ... Mein Führer."

More laughter.

"This is your brother?"

"Ja. My brother."

"You must both grow up to serve the Fatherland. Ja?"

"Ja. Ja. Mein Führer."

All this was caught by the camera's eternal eye. Someone scribbled down Peter's name. The Führer returned the infant prop and then passed on to the next target of his attention.

Peter could scarcely breathe as the ceremony ended with echoing chants of *"Sieg Heil!"*

Lucy, ashen with fright, guided him back to their train. They were allowed to keep their flags, and all along the way people patted Peter on the back and rubbed Willie's soft curls for luck as the Führer had done.

He could barely answer questions during the document check, and when they were allowed back into their compartment a fellow in a black S.S. uniform filled the space across from him. It was still a long way to the border.

———

From within their hollowed-out nest among crates of chickens and cabbages, Jacob could clearly hear the voices of the young men who manned the roadblock.

"We will have to take a look through your cargo."

Farmer Schöne replied with his usual flair. "EH? SPEAK UP! CAB-BAGES AND CHICKENS, THAT'S WHAT."

The youthful soldier replied with equal volume. "WE ARE LOOKING FOR FUGITIVES KNOWN TO BE HEADING THIS—"

"NO! CABBAGES AND CHICKENS. YOU CAN LOOK, BUT THEY HAVE BEEN LOADED SINCE LAST NIGHT, AND YOU HAVE TO PUT THEM BACK."

The soldiers talked among themselves. "Himmel! Gottfried, will you look at that pile of crates? Like the Eiffel Tower with feathers. It will take us hours!"

They addressed the old farmer again. "WE ARE LOOKING FOR TWO CHILDREN. A BOY AND A GIRL TRAVELING IN A TAN CAR."

"EH? TWO CHILDREN? NEIN! WE HAVE EIGHT CHILDREN. THIRTY-THREE GRANDCHILDREN."

"The old fellow doesn't even know what we're talking about."

"AND ON THE TRUCK IS CABBAGES AND CHICKENS. YOU CAN LOOK, BUT PUT THEM BACK RIGHT, AND IN A HURRY. THEY ARE FOR THE GARRISON IN SCHNEIDEMUHL, AND THE GENERAL DOESN'T LIKE TO BE KEPT WAITING!"

After a few seconds more of mumbled conversation, the guards waved the old farmer through the line without the usual *Heil*.

———

The locomotive whistle howled farewell to the demons of Berlin as Peter leaned back in the corner of his seat and let weakness wash over him. The devil, clad in brown, had touched him and burned the energy out of him. He was exhausted.

Lucy was already talking familiarly to the S.S. officer.

"I loathe these stiff-collared tunics." The officer unbuttoned the top button. Peter thought this round-faced man looked more like a shop clerk than an S.S. "But there are times when duty dictates . . ." He frowned. "I know you! Vienna! You keep company with a certain major . . . *Wolfgang von Fritschauer!*"

Lucy giggled with pretended delight. "What a memory!" She leaned forward. "I confess . . . I do not remember you."

"I was not in uniform." He snapped his fingers. "Your name is . . . Lucy. Lucy, is it? Who could forget you."

This was the penalty she paid for talking to everyone from railway porters to street peddlers. "What a mind! I don't have any memory at all."

The officer extended his hand. "No matter. My name is Alexander Hess. Special investigations."

"Lieutenant Hess."

"Alex, please. We are old friends, although you do not know it."

She tilted her head slightly and brushed her hair back from her forehead. "And how far are you traveling?" she asked the lieutenant.

"All the way to the border of Poland," he replied, warming to the look in her eyes. "An unpleasant duty. Dealing with traitors."

"I am *so* relieved we will be traveling together," she said in almost a whisper. "My nephew . . . I have worn you out, haven't I, Peter?"

Peter nodded. The words sounded as if they were coming from a deep canyon in the Alps, echoes in his head. He was too tired to be frightened of the skull-and-crossbones insignia on the uniform. The lightning bolts looked harmless enough. Baby Willie had already drifted off to sleep on the padded bench beside Peter.

Lucy laughed and tucked her arm beneath that of the officer. "You see? He can't even keep his eyes open. I need a little company. I am best late at night . . ." Her smile dazzled the officer.

"Ja? You are?"

Lucy looked patronizingly at Peter. "Just close your eyes and go to sleep, Peter. We won't pay any attention to you, and you don't pay any attention to us, eh?"

As Peter leaned back against the seat and the train lurched forward out of the station, Lucy asked the lieutenant if he had any schnapps in that little silver flask of his.

37

The Angels' Gift

When Peter opened his eyes, the reading lamp was on above the head of the S.S. officer. Lucy was not in the compartment. Willie was gone.

The S.S. lieutenant sat across from Peter. His tunic was unbuttoned; his boots off. His face was unshaven and his hair disheveled. He smelled strongly of schnapps. And he was staring.

It was a hard, curious sort of stare, the kind of stare which asked, *Haven't I seen you someplace before? Someplace besides where you say we met?* The look instantly sent a shot of adrenalin through Peter. He sat up, suddenly wide awake.

"Where is my aunt?" he asked in a croaking voice.

"Took your baby brother to the washroom. Change his diapers."

"Ah," Peter looked out the window. The expression on the face of the officer did not change. Peter prayed that he would look somewhere else, or that Lucy would come back. No one ever looked at him when she was around. Why had she taken Willie out to change him? Why had she left Peter alone with this iron-jawed S.S. officer? Then Peter remembered. Willie was circumcised. One look at that, and the lieutenant would know everything.

"So, what Hitler Youth unit are you in?" asked the officer, the smell of schnapps sour on his breath.

"You mean Aunt Lucy didn't tell you everything about me?" Peter wished now that he had not slept through her conversation. No doubt she had told this fellow all about Peter—details that Peter did not know.

"No, she didn't. So—"

"Pardon, bitte. I have to use the toilet," Peter said. He fumbled with the door, pushing against it instead of pulling.

"Pull." The man's voice held an edge, even in that one word—some doubt he wrestled with when he looked at Peter. Had he seen the photographs of the Wallich family? Was he trying even now to put the name and place to the face?

Peter escaped the closeness of the compartment and leaned heavily against the wall of the corridor. *Where was Lucy?*

The train rattled hollowly over a trestle bridge as Peter walked toward the washrooms. Why had Lucy left him there alone and given the officer time to look at him, time to *think*?

The door of their compartment swung back and the officer emerged, following Peter. The corridor light glistened on the man's close-cropped blond hair. Shadows emphasized the pocked skin. His blue eyes looked bloodshot beneath a jutting brow. The train rocked off the bridge and settled into an even rhythm again just as Peter reached the line to the men's room. It was a single compartment. *Thank God!* More Jews had been discovered and massacred in men's rooms than any other place in the Reich.

The lieutenant stood without speaking in line behind Peter. Peter grew more nervous as each man moved forward into the stall. He imagined the lieutenant breaking down the door after him, shouting to everyone that here was another circumcised Jew! Peter Wallich had been hiding at Otto's so long that he had forgotten the terror of public toilets.

"You want to go ahead of me?" Peter asked the officer.

The strangeness of the question reflected in the man's expression. "Not especially," he smirked.

"Well," Peter bumbled, "it's just that you had so much schnapps to drink, and . . . I thought maybe . . ."

The S.S. chin went up slightly in response to such stupidity. Peter felt the eyes of the man boring into the back of his head. If this fellow knew Wolf, did it not stand to reason that he had seen the photographs of Karin Wallich and her children? Maybe every S.S. officer in Vienna had seen them!

Nauseated by the time he entered the stall, Peter threw up, then stared at the door for five minutes, fully expecting the hinges to come crashing in any instant. He left the stall without ever unbuttoning his trousers. He would wait to use the toilet until Lucy came back to preoccupy the officer. Then Peter would come back. Alone.

———

There was a thirty-minute layover in Landsberg—time enough to stretch the legs and breathe a bit.

But Peter did not wish to see the Bahnhof when S.S. Lieutenant Hess asked him. Nor did Lucy wish to accompany him for a quick snack. She would stay, she said, and feed the baby. The layover was just long enough to get the child settled for the long journey ahead to Danzig.

Both Peter and Lucy gave an audible sigh of relief when the officer buttoned his tunic and stepped off the train. Lucy had done a magnificent job of talking and drawing attention away from Peter and Willie, but still she saw that same nagging *something* in the man's eyes.

The fact that he knew Wolf was terrifying to her. Wolf would find out where she had gone. Even without the note on the mirror, he would figure out who had sprung his prey from the trap!

"We will not reach the border for hours yet," Lucy said thoughtfully. "I will try to get him out of here—in the saloon car or the dining car— until then. When we come back, the light must be off. Pretend to sleep. I will hope it does not come to him where he has seen you before."

So there it was. She said it. It was not Peter's imagination. "And if he remembers?"

She looked at Baby Willie, who slurped noisily on his bottle. "He is getting off at the border station. After we cross the border into Poland, the train compartments will be sealed, locked on the outside, until we get to Danzig. We will be safe then."

"That is still a long way."

Lucy smiled knowingly. "I will do what I can to keep his mind off you and Willie. If it comes to it, the doors will not be sealed until we reach Poland. We might jump . . . but then again, it would be better if *we stayed* on the train and *he left.*"

They were comrades in arms, indeed. Peter decided once more that he liked Lucy Strasburg very much. She knew exactly what she was saying; every word and gesture was calculated. Some other time, such ability might be despicable. Right now, it was admirable.

"He asked me what unit I am with in the Hitler Youth."

"And?"

"I told him to ask you."

"Good. And I told him . . . to ask you! You are a clever boy. I told him about your visit to Vienna—the same stuff—but you may write whatever autobiography makes you happy. You did well enough with Wolf the other night. All that nonsense about the S.S. motto. Very good. Be whatever you want to be. I did not tell this jackal anything. But it is better to stay out of his attention and to sleep, ja?"

For ten hours Peter would be cooped up in a very small cage with a hungry tiger. Yet Lucy seemed to believe they could manage even this, even if they had to boot the S.S. lieutenant out of a moving train. Peter had misjudged this woman the first night he had seen her at the side of Wolfgang von Fritschauer. Now he grinned at her as she fussed with the baby. Maybe Lucy was really an angel beneath her lipstick and rouge. For the first time in his life, the story about Rahab, the prostitute in ancient Jericho who hid two Hebrew spies, no longer seemed shocking to Peter. He found himself hoping that if and when the walls came down, Lucy Strasburg would be spared just as that harlot had survived long ago.

"What are you looking at?" She colored slightly at his stare. *Had she never been admired, one soldier to another?*

"You are a righteous woman," Peter said simply. Then he excused himself and hurried to use the toilet before the tiger got back on the train.

When Peter returned, the S.S. lieutenant was sitting next to Lucy. Her arm was draped over the back of the seat. She touched his face with her finger, and the man did not even look up at Peter as he entered.

Lucy could only pray that the uncertainty she felt about their chances was not transmitted to the sensitive adolescent across from her. They must exude confidence, or this Nazi would smell their fear and know.

Like Wolf, this S.S. lieutenant might be fooled for a while by sheer bravado, but if the facade of her courage ever slipped, the passage to Danzig would end in leg irons.

Peter had not seen the S.S. officer enter the phone booth on the Berlin platform. The boy had been busy looking at Lucy, deciding she was some sort of saint. *Ah, well, if it made him feel better . . .*

But from her position, she had been able to see the phone booth, watch the S.S. lieutenant flip through his little black book. She had seen his expression change from confusion and suspicion to a sinister pleasure at whatever news he heard on the other end of the line.

Had he called Vienna? Had he contacted Wolf and casually mentioned that Lucy Strasburg had not gone to church to pray after all, that the trip to Demel's for a pastry was actually a journey to Danzig?

She brushed her fingertips familiarly against the man's cheek, playing for her life. But perhaps this fellow was also playing a game with her. What did he have to lose, after all? It was a long way between here and the border; she was amusing company. He could simply have her and the children arrested at the crossing. Until then, she touched his cheek and made pleasant conversation to pass the hours.

———

Inside Jacob's head, the neon road map flashed: a hundred and ninety-seven and one half miles from Berlin to Firchau. Between farmer Schöne's barn and this deserted spot in the woods outside their destination, the truck had been halted at seven different roadblocks. The Nazis had orders to search for other things besides Lori and Jamie, but not once was the cargo of cabbages and chickens inspected.

"It was a miracle," Alfie said without surprise. They stepped out of their hiding place like five feathered clowns emerging from a giant cake.

It was dark. For once the old farmer was quiet as he spoke, cautious, apologetic that he could not get them closer to their goal.

"Over there is the big new prison they are building—" He pointed to a rise. "They don't want anyone to know it is there, but it is. And we do."

Jacob spread out his mental map and tried to take his bearings. Which way was the border? And where was the customs house where the train would pass through the gates into Poland?

The farmer answered that question without waiting for him to ask. "Fifty yards through the woods is the railroad track. Follow it. Stick close to the wooded side. Straight on to Poland. You can't get lost. Just don't get found. They patrol with dogs, I hear."

With that, the old man passed them a sack of provisions and wished them godspeed. Patting each head, including Werner's, he left them there to travel ahead on their own.

———

"What are you trying to do? Get me drunk?" Peter could hear the coarse laughter of Officer Hess. "Oh well. A long way from here to Firchau. Time enough to sober up after a little fun!"

The voices of Lucy and the lieutenant penetrated the door of the compartment. He reached up quickly and switched off the light, then leaned over and pulled his cap down across his eyes. Sleeping. He must be sleeping—just sitting there like a piece of luggage while Lucy and the S.S. officer talked around him and over him.

Hours would pass before they would be at the border. She could handle the passport and customs officers easily after this.

The door burst open, and light from the corridor flooded the compartment. Lucy and Officer Hess were laughing. He was drunk. Peter could smell it on his breath; hear it in the slurring of his words as he lunged for the seat.

He patted his lap for Lucy to sit. "Come on! *Come on!* My lap is more comfortable than the seat." He pawed her crudely.

"Wolf would have you shot if I did!" Maybe Lucy had been drinking, too. Peter frowned beneath his cap, the movement exposing his eye slightly. He did not like the way the S.S. lieutenant was touching her. Only a dead man could sleep through this.

"Wolf might have you shot anyway, eh?" he asked, pulling her against him.

Lucy was not drunk. From the corner of his eye, Peter caught an instant of fear in her expression. *Sober fear.* And then it was gone again. She struggled as the lieutenant yanked her down.

It was a playful struggle. The officer tried to kiss her. She pushed him back. "Please . . . you will wake my nephews."

"Let them wake up," he slurred, holding her wrist.

"But . . . *please* . . . Herr Lieutenant . . . Wolf will not—"

"So who cares about Wolf? You are not afraid of Wolf. You have left him, eh?" The voice became harsh. Demanding. The hand clamped harder on her arm, and he threw her back on the bench. "Call me Alex, remember? Old friends. *Lucy*. I never forget."

"You are . . . hurting me . . . *Bitte!* Alex! Herr Lieutenant!" There was no charade in her appeal. She struggled harder. The man held her down beneath him on the bench.

Peter could not pretend to sleep. He sat up and switched on the light. His cap fell to the floor. He glared hard at the angry officer.

"Leave my aunt alone," he said, standing slowly to his feet.

Lucy lay where the scowling officer had her pinned. She shook her head at Peter. *He must not interfere!*

The officer did not let her go; he simply sneered at Peter as if he were an insect to crush when he was not busy with the woman.

"Get out of here!" the lieutenant snapped. "And take the brat out with you."

"Let her go, I said!" Peter threatened. "You are drunk!"

"Yes? *Drunk?* In a few hours I will be sober, but you will still be a Jew! You should pray I do not remember the way you order me around!" He sat up. Lucy did not move. Her face reflected all the things she had dreaded. *He knew!* Maybe he had known all along.

"I . . . I don't know what you mean," Peter stammered.

"Oh yes?" The officer pulled his pistol from its holster and waved it at Peter's face and then at the still sleeping Willie. "You don't know?"

"Bitte, Herr Lieutenant." Lucy tried to pull his attention back to her. She laughed as though this was a drunken fantasy. "Don't play such games. He will leave . . . *won't you,* Peter? Leave us *alone*, Peter! *Take Willie.*"

Peter clenched and unclenched his fists. He would not let Lucy do this for him and Willie. *"I will not leave!"*

"Too bad." The officer pulled back the hammer and put the barrel behind Willie's ear.

"Oh! Please . . . Herr Lieutenant! *Don't,"* Lucy begged.

He pushed her back hard. "You see, boy, this woman and I were about to strike a bargain. She was going to give me something in exchange for your life. You see?"

Peter licked his lips. He stared at the gun against the baby's head.

"All right!" Peter cried, looking from his brother to Lucy. "Just let me take him and get out!"

"Sure, sure." Lucy tried to sound soothing, but her hands trembled. The usually smooth voice cracked. "Let them go, Herr Lieutenant."

"Too late!" The gun pointed back to Peter's face. "I am out of the mood for love! I prefer to *hunt* now!"

"Don't do this," Lucy whispered. "You will be sorry. My nephews . . ." She tried to recapture the illusion.

"Nephews?" His voice was low, barely audible. "Wouldn't Wolf be surprised that your nephews are the Jews he has been looking for?" He laughed explosively. "Ah, you are going to be in a lot of trouble—"

"Please . . . just too much schnapps!" She sat up slowly, trying to reason with him.

"Imagination, is it?" The lips curled down. He jumped up and pressed the gun into Peter's heart. "Drop your trousers, Jew! If you aren't a Jew, prove it!"

Peter looked at Lucy. Such agony on her face! Why had he interrupted this sloppy drunk? Why hadn't he let her take care of him?

"Did you hear what I said, you circumcised swine? Drop them!" The gun pressed hard into Peter's chest but he did not move. He would not do it! Let this evil man shoot him through the heart! He would not take down his trousers in front of Lucy . . . or anyone!

He lifted his chin in defiance. "You are the swine, not me," Peter said evenly, daring the man to pull the trigger.

Instead, the Lieutenant simply reached down and grabbed up the baby, who wailed unhappily in sleepy confusion. The gun went to Willie's mouth. The baby waved his arms in pain as the officer jammed the barrel into his throat. "Suck on this, you little *Judenschwein*!"

"All right!" Peter cried, fumbling with the buttons of his trousers. *"Don't!* Put him *down!"*

The drunken lieutenant then pointed the gun at Peter and smiled.

In that moment, Peter glimpsed Lucy's handbag raise up behind the S.S. lieutenant and come down in an arch on top of his head. There was a loud thump, and the officer's eyes rolled back as a trickle of blood dripped down the side of his head. The gun fell from his hand. Willie hit the seat with a thud and gasped for breath before shrieking with rage and indignation. Officer Hess hung in the air an instant longer before his knees buckled and he fell back on top of Lucy.

They ate in silence as they walked the first miles in the center of the railroad tracks. The oak ties across the gravel snagged the toes of boots and shoes, causing each of the children to stumble in turn. Mark tripped on a crosstie and fell, bloodying both knees. He did not cry out, but Lori could see the black stain of blood seeping through his trousers. Jamie stepped into a hole and tumbled down, biting through his lip. Even within the narrow borders of the straight track there were small traps on the roadbed.

Only Alfie seemed never to trip. Lori walked behind him and watched as he held the kitten carefully and walked in a high marching kind of step.

To the right above the treetops shone an eerie white glow. *The prison camp,* a nameless enclosure where men were caged. Although Lori could not see the guard towers or the electrified fences that stretched for miles, this unnatural light illuminated their path and cast shadows which hid the dangers of uneven places.

Somewhere Lori could hear the steady, distant drone of the generating plant that powered the floodlights and made the fences here and at the border deadly to touch.

It reminded Lori not of the true Light but of the power Darkness had to distort their vision. That ominous hum encircled all of Germany, keeping some people out and others in. The unnatural light pursued them at this moment. She felt it above her and behind her. It sought to close the gate to their freedom, sealing them in this gray, colorless world, where blood was black and flesh was ashen. It distorted what was real, raising small depressions in their way to make them fall and concealing bumps to make them stumble. The light of Darkness made even their straight path treacherous and painful.

As never before, she felt the nearness of personal Evil tonight. It lurked there, in the shadows of the woods, in the iron-gray light of the prison, in the small puddles of blackness beneath their feet.

"Is he . . . *dead?*" Lucy shuddered as Peter propped Hess into the corner of the seat.

"Only sleeping like a dead man," Peter replied with grim amusement in his voice. He pulled the peaked cap down over the officer's forehead, then stepped back to study the effect. *Not dead, only sleeping. Yes. Drunk and sleeping.* Peter crossed the officer's legs at the ankles, giving the overall impression of a man who was very comfortable.

"You were very brave," Lucy said firmly. She did not scold him for being too brave, although that was implied in the tone of her voice. "My knight."

Peter hefted the handbag at her feet; it must have weighed twenty pounds. "What have you got in that thing?"

"My inheritance." She smiled and opened the bag, allowing him a glimpse of a large solid silver crucifix.

"Ha!" Peter cried. "The only weapon against vampires and demons, I hear! Now all we need is a wooden stake through his heart . . . providing he has a heart."

Lucy cradled Willie, whose bottom lip was split and swollen. He frantically sucked his bottle and looked wildly around the compartment for any sign of other monsters. At last his eyelids drooped. He breathed a ragged sigh; his little body relaxed, started awake, then relaxed again.

It was a dilemma they had not anticipated. Peter sat on the edge of his seat and considered what to do with the unconscious S.S. lieutenant.

"Very natural-looking like this, don't you think? At the passport check we tell them he is drunk and asleep. Give them his papers, then dump him out the window on the Polish side."

"If he wakes up, we are dead."

"Too bad we did not kill him."

"I do not relish the idea of being arrested for murder," Lucy said.

"You think they will punish you less for helping Jews? Why don't we get rid of him?"

"Because if we throw him off and he wakes up and manages to stagger to a telephone . . . he will call ahead and—" She frowned. "He is *S.S.*! One phone call, and we are arrested."

Peter examined the tall shining boots of the officer. The boy had always wanted a pair of boots like that. "Let me handle it," he instructed Lucy. "Go to the dining car with Willie. I can handle this."

"I am not going anywhere until you tell me what you intend to do." Lucy was adamant.

"You know what makes this fellow an S.S.?" Peter replied as the officer moaned and stirred slightly. Peter pointed the pistol at him as a precaution while they talked.

"He is waking up," Lucy said in a frightened voice.

"Yes. The S.S. lieutenant is waking up. If we throw him off the train like this, he will crawl to some farm and terrorize the farmer and telephone the border guards. Then we will be arrested. A very frightening thing, this skull and crossbones, these lightning bolts. They make a very homely, stupid fellow like this feel man enough to rape women and jam guns into the mouths of babies."

For a moment Peter looked as though he might shoot the officer.

"What are you getting at?" Lucy's heart was racing. The lieutenant was going to wake up and they would have to fight him again!

"It is the uniform, you see. What happens when you take those clothes off a man like him?"

"Disgusting."

"A naked, barefoot Nazi," Peter continued. "I, for one, would never let any naked barefoot stranger come to my door and demand to use the telephone." Peter smiled slyly. "Herr Lieutenant Hess and I have much to talk about between here and the Polish territory. Now take Willie out. I do not want my brother to be frightened again by this monster."

First Peter threw out the S.S. tunic from the window. He counted to sixty and tossed away the cap, the trousers, and then the army-issue underwear and socks. The small hand-carried suitcase followed. Finally, at gunpoint, Peter instructed the naked officer to lay the briefcase on the opposite seat.

Peter dumped out the contents. A small handgun tumbled out. Peter tucked it into one of his new boots and sat back with the luger pistol pointed squarely into Hess's face.

Peter had donned Otto's overcoat; he was chilled, but not unbearably so. "Now shred your papers," he ordered, "and out the window with them."

Hess obeyed in jerky, uneven movements. "There are more where these came from," he snarled, at last picking up his own identity documents.

"Small pieces." Peter lowered the aim of the pistol toward the man's abdomen. "Very small."

The fragments of passport whipped out of the officer's hand. "Now close the window," he stammered. "I will freeze to death."

"No. I want to make certain you are sober before I kill you," Peter said with a grin.

"You are a smart young man." Hess managed a smile, but it quickly disappeared. It was too cold to maintain this illusion of a man in control. "Smart like your father was smart. You don't . . . need to kill me. We can make a deal, ja!"

"What kind of deal?" Peter mocked him. "You expect me to let you go free in exchange for my own life so that you can turn in Wolfgang von Fritschauer?"

For an instant, Alexander Hess looked very sober indeed. "Wolfgang von Fritschauer? No. I swear I would not!"

"You think I will let you go so you can undermine their operation? Exchange my life for Lucy and Wolf? After what they have done for me? For hundreds like me? *My honor is loyalty,* Herr Lieutenant Hess. Wolf has been like a brother to me. No! I would not think of giving a man like you a chance to ruin it all. I am afraid I will have to shoot you and throw you out the window like your clothes, eh?"

"You won't shoot." Hess looked panicked. "You are . . . too young to murder a man . . . like this." He held up his bound wrists. Hands clasped together, he seemed to be begging for mercy.

"You mean in cold blood?" Peter was smiling. The freezing wind held Officer Hess in a much stronger grasp than either the pistol or the belt on his wrists.

"Give me your coat . . . *bitte.* I will pay you . . . I swear I will not have Wolfgang or . . . Lucy arrested. Untie?" His skin took on a definite bluish cast.

Peter pushed him a bit further. "It was you who killed my father, wasn't it?"

"No! I swear it!" Now Hess had something to argue against. "I never met your father!"

"I do not believe you! Justice has delivered you into my hands, Herr

Lieutenant Hess! I will not have long before I can avenge the blood of Michael Wallich."

"No! *Really!* This I am not guilty of! I swear it! Someone else! Not me!" Again the trembling arms rose up to beg. Hess was altogether sober.

Peter had created his own story, as Lucy suggested. The result was enjoyable. He was in no great hurry to end the play.

"There is still some time before the whistle blows."

"The whistle?" Hess's teeth chattered violently. "So? The whistle?"

"I do not want anyone to hear the gunshot that takes your miserable existence."

"Just listen to me—"

"There is time. Tell me, why should you live, Herr Hess—a cockroach like you?" Peter smiled as Hess proceeded to renounce all his former associations with the Nazi cause. He was doing this, he said, because it was the law of the land, and he must obey. But really, the system was corrupt, he said.

"And what about the Führer?" Peter asked.

"Rotten. Evil and dark! He has brought me to this! The Führer should die."

"Not the Jews?"

"No! Never! The whole Nazi party! Corrupt. Rotten."

"But not you?"

"No, I tell you . . . please . . . close the window." The voice was pitiful.

"Not yet." Peter said as the wind mussed his red hair. "I have not decided yet whether to let you live."

They had been following the tracks for hours when the light of the Danzig train appeared like the giant eye of a cyclops behind them.

A wide field fringed with fir trees bordered the right side of the track. Jacob took Lori's hand as they scrambled down the berm and the others followed.

They stepped into the trees to watch as the train—their train—thundered on toward the border checkpoint. The lights several kilometers up the track made a faint, pleasant glow against the night sky. They had fixed their hopes on this point—until now.

"Well, there it is," Jamie said gloomily.

"We will never make it now," Mark added.

"If we hurry—" Lori cried, as the headlight on the train sprayed a circle of track and gravel with illumination.

Locomotive. Coal car. Dining car with candles and waiters and passengers sipping wine. Then the sleeping cars and the first-class compartments, and then . . .

Like a spirit on the wind, something shot out of the window and flew up in the air. Then another object—and another, and another—swept out on the updraft. Like bats, they flapped and floated to earth.

Gathered all together, the clothing tossed from the window of the Danzig train made up the uniform of an S.S. lieutenant. Everything was there except the boots. Jacob tried on the tunic. It fit a bit snug across the shoulders. The trousers were too loose around the waist. But in the moonlight, at any rate, the effect was impressive. Beneath the peaked cap visor, Jacob could easily pass for twenty-one. His crooked nose and his fighter's physique completed the deception nicely. Mark found an extra pair of size ten boots inside the suitcase. Perfect!

The train could delay for several hours for an examination on the German side of the border. They were not too late, and now they had a Nazi lieutenant as well as a Blackshirted member of the Hitler Youth among them!

Jacob had not yet figured out what use he would make of his marvelous costume, but Lori declared it must be another miracle. Alfie said that the angels had sent them the clothes.

38

The Gate of Liberty

"TEN MINUTES TO FIRCHAU! NEXT STOP FIRCHAU! ALL PASSEN-
GERS FOR FIRCHAU! CUSTOMS CHECK FOR THE POLISH FRONTIER!
PLEASE HAVE ALL DOCUMENTS READY!"

Peter and Hess could clearly hear the instructions of the porter
through the door. In spite of his shivering, spasmodic muscles, Hess
managed to look relieved. Hopeful. Maybe he had convinced the young
Jew not to shoot him, after all.

"Close the window," Hess begged. "Untie my hands. Let me have
your coat!"

Occasional lights from isolated houses slid by.

"I don't think so. I still do not trust you. If I let you live, and Wolf
is arrested, I could not forgive myself. No. It is best if an insect like
you does not live."

"Don't shoot me, please. I was just—"

"And I don't like the way you treated my brother, besides. Or Lucy."
Peter raised the gun as if to ready it for the shrill of the train whistle.

"Just a . . . a little joke. Too much schnapps."

"But you are sober now."

The head bobbed in wild agreement. "Yes!"

"Good. Now sit on the window ledge."

"Mein Gott! Don't shoot me!" He crawled up to crouch on the window ledge.

"I am going to blow your brains out when the whistle blows, Herr
Lieutenant Hess. And then I am going to push your faceless body out
on the tracks." Peter was smiling. The hammer on the luger was cocked
and ready.

"No! Please, no! Bitte! I am begging! I promise!" He no longer
noticed the wind or the smoke from the locomotive.

"When the whistle blows. . . ." Peter raised his voice as the train rounded a curve and began to slow. "Unless—"

"*Anything!* Please, yes!"

"Unless you prefer to jump."

Hess's eyes grew wide as he stared for a brief instant at the gun in Peter's hand, then out at the passing countryside. He raised his arms as if to dive, then launched himself out of the window like a stark white ghost into the night.

The curtains flapped in the dark compartment where he had been. Peter laughed out loud, then stuck his head out to watch the body of Herr Hess tumble like a stone down the gravel embankment into a hayfield.

"AUF WIEDERSEHEN!" Peter called, and closed the window.

"Herr Hess will have a hike," Peter said to Lucy as the train slipped into the electrified enclosure and up to the platform in front of the customs house. "The night air will clear his head."

Lucy still looked worried. On the platform two matrons sat inside glassed cubicles flanking separate entrances into the German customs house. One door was marked MEN and the other WOMEN.

Peter followed her eyes and blanched. *The physical search!* Here Gestapo doctors randomly chose passengers for complete physical examinations. Those wishing to cross into Polish territory from the Reich were required to submit to this, if asked, or face arrest. The obvious reason given for these searches was to make certain that nothing of value was smuggled from the Reich. It was impossible, after all, to conceal currency or valuables in such a condition.

The main side benefit for the Gestapo was the apprehension of male Jews masquerading as Aryans with false passports. Like the men's room, these examinations had become the gauntlet through which every circumcised Jew must pass to freedom. Not everyone was selected for this indignity—only those who seemed suspicious to the matrons in the glass booths. Lucy was counting on the possibility that once again she could talk their way out of it and the trio could pass with a superficial customs check.

They were close enough to see the dour expressions on matrons on the customs platform. Voices rang out distinctly in the night air.

"*Schnell! Schnell! All passengers disembark! Have your documents and all luggage ready for examination!*"

It was perfect except for one minor detail. The train had rolled through the massive wire gates without stopping. The gates had been instantly closed and re-electrified. Train and passengers were now imprisoned inside an enclosure that could not be entered or exited until the deadly current was switched off long enough for the train to slip through the gates on the Polish side of the compound.

Customs and passport examinations when leaving the Reich were the last chance the Gestapo had to apprehend those they considered criminals, whatever the charge might be. Every offense, real or imagined, was considered one final time within this massive barbed-wire enclosure. Every passenger was considered guilty until proven innocent. The electrified fence assured that no one could run away.

There was still a chance for Jacob to retreat from their position thirty yards outside the fence. The gate did not keep them in; it kept them *out*! It prevented their passage through the other side.

As Jacob watched the examination of the train, he realized that perhaps it was no accident that they had been locked out. The flashlights of Nazi soldiers probed the huge iron hulk of the Danzig train. Every inch was being explored, from undercarriage to roof, for possible stowaways.

They all watched the procedure with sinking spirits—except perhaps Alfie, who seemed untroubled by the fact that they were on their bellies in the underbrush within shouting distance of those who would most like to throw them all into prison. Outside the fence uniformed guards stood every few feet. There seemed no way that Jacob could casually stroll up in his newly acquired S.S. uniform and order the gate to be opened so that his friends might enter and board the train.

No one dared ask the question that lay heavy on Jacob's mind. They had come all this way—for what? And now it was only a matter of time before the guard dogs caught their scent and flushed them out.

The platform bristled with soldiers and Gestapo inspectors as Peter and Lucy stepped from the train. She held Willie. With her impeccable Aryan looks, it was less likely that she would be asked to strip or ordered to undress the baby for a search.

Willie was miserable. Lucy had deliberately left his diapers soiled so that the inspector would not be eager to examine the child for circumcision.

"Males here!" barked a matron. "Females in this line! Schnell! The train is waiting, please!"

Passengers shuffled onto the cold platform. Some faces were sullen, some fearful. The fearful faces were pulled aside and ordered into the examination rooms.

In the meantime, Nazi officials ransacked luggage; experts who knew every smuggling trick probed the compartments. Up and down the lines officers pulled out suspects, and roughly ordered them to comply.

Behind Lucy and Peter a slight commotion arose as a man and a woman resisted feebly and were handcuffed and immediately shoved out of sight into the room marked DOCUMENT VERIFICATION.

"You! To the examination!" the matron said to a timid-looking man three places in front of Peter in line. She skipped the next fellow, a round-bellied Bavarian in Lederhosen and tall woolen socks. She scarcely looked at the man in front of Peter; instead, she blinked in amazement at Peter. *"It is you!"*

The color drained from Peter's face. He looked behind him, hoping that she meant someone else! But she was staring right at Peter!

She grasped his arm and pulled him out of the line. Then, whirling around, she spotted Lucy and Willie. *"And there is the little brother! Himmel! Look! It is the two brothers!"*

She was shouting at the top of her lungs. Soldiers and plain-clothed Gestapo men looked away from their charges. Peter considered running, leaping from the platform and diving into the shadows that flanked the tracks, but he was certain he would be shot full of holes. He prayed they had not captured his mother and sister at this same checkpoint.

Lucy gazed miserably at him. They had tried . . . they had come *so close* to making it!

"Look, everyone!" the matron's voice rang out in the night. *"Here are the brothers from the evening paper! Look! The boys who know the Führer!"*

Peter's mouth dropped open. Another matron rushed toward him, carrying the front page of the Nazi party newspaper in her hand. There, beneath the banner headline announcing the formal signing of a non-aggression pact with France, a photograph showed the benevolent Adolf Hitler holding a baby. *That very child! Willie Ruger!* The one with the stinking diapers! And there was this fine example of young Aryan manhood! *Peter Ruger!*

"Ach! To think we shake the hand that the Führer has touched!"

Peter glanced down at his own photograph. Could it be? Two adoring brothers within the circle of the Führer's admiration. Their names were given right there in the caption.

Peter noticed how pale and wild-eyed he looked in the picture. Did no one see that the expression on his face was a grinning, hysterical fright?

"Look! Look how much it looks like him!"

His heart pounded frantically.

"You would like to have a copy of this, I am certain," said the uniformed officer in charge of the station. He patted Peter on the back and greeted Lucy . . . *the boy's aunt!* He ordered a matron to go fetch two copies off the stack, because the family might have difficulty getting more once they crossed the frontier.

Lucy babbled on about what a delight it was to meet the Führer close up like that, how special that Adolf Hitler had singled out her own nephews for recognition.

Peter moved through it all grinning wildly, like a marionette who had no control over his own trembling legs. No doubt the facial expression he now wore was very much like the photograph in the newspaper.

———

Alfie pulled his toy general from his pocket as they lay hidden in the underbrush. While the others were too frightened by the nearness of danger to move, he played happily with horse and rider.

Lori watched him, taking a strange sort of comfort from his utter trust that they could not be harmed. He whispered to her, "The angels said it is all right. Don't worry, Lori."

She smiled at him and put a finger to her lips to remind him of the rule of silence. Instead, he tugged on Jacob's sleeve. He pointed far down the track. "There they are," he mumbled. "See them?"

"Shhhh," Jacob warned.

"But look—" Alfie's voice sounded too loud. "They are not stars or angels! Here come the dogs and their men!"

Five heads turned in unison to stare in horror at the approach of three German shepherd dogs dragging soldiers along behind them as they sniffed the undergrowth outside the compound.

"Headed right for us!" Jacob muttered, banging his fist on the ground. "I will try to distract them. You make a run for it."

"No!" Lori gasped. "We stay . . . together!" They had come too far for it to end like this. Tiny pinpoints of light probed the bushes. Jacob looked back wildly to see if they could make a run for it. Inside the compound, guards and other passengers were crowding around a young man on the platform. They called out his name, smiled and laughed with him. No one was looking this way. *Maybe now?*

Jacob jumped to his feet. At that instant a dog lunged against his leash, breaking the hold of his master. Barking and snarling, the animal ran full bore toward Jacob and then, twenty-five yards from where Jacob stood, a naked man screamed and dashed out of a shallow ditch.

Whistles trilled a warning! The celebration on the platform silenced. Jacob ran up the track toward the fugitive, shouting, *"Stop that man! Stop that man!"*

"Tor auf!" shouted the commandant from the customs building. "Open the gate! *Tor auf!*"

Someone threw the switch; the red warning light changed to green. Soldiers and guards poured from the compound in pursuit of the shrieking man who now fled to the other side of the tracks in an attempt to escape into the woods.

Dog handlers eager to try their well-trained animals issued the command and pointed toward their target. From a dozen directions guard dogs charged to the capture.

Passengers inside the compound crowded to see, pushing through the open gate to witness what was certainly the end of an escaped convict from the prison camp over the hill!

Alfie stood and slipped the kitten into his pocket. He reached down to help Lori to her feet as Jacob, in his S.S. uniform, jogged to meet them.

Alfie linked his arms with Mark and Jamie as Jacob had taught him in the drill.

"All right," Jacob said in a gruff voice. He herded them through the crush of spectators. "That's enough! Enough sight-seeing, now! An escaped criminal, no doubt. Back on the train! *Back on the train . . .*"

No one noticed as they passed through the gate. "The gate is *open!*" Alfie smiled at Lori. "They told me they would open it for us." He stepped into the train. "Did you hear them calling my name? They were cheering, Lori! *Tor Alf,* they said! *Alf* . . . just like Mama used to say my name!"

"A miracle, Alfie," Lori said softly. "Just like you said."

Epilogue

Captain Samuel Orde had trained his soldiers well.

"Halt, who goes there? Hands up, or I'll shoot!" In his excitement, Artur Bader had shouted the words in his native German. But the meaning was clear enough in any language: *I am deadly serious.*

Bader took no chances, nor did he wait to see what he had caught. He blew three sharp blasts on the signal whistle around his neck without once taking his eyes or the muzzle of his rifle off the lighter shadow on the hillside.

His alarm was answered by three whistles from the guard post on his left and three more from the right. The sound of running footsteps could be heard converging on Bader's position. When other guards were covering his flanks he ordered loudly in Arabic, "Come in slowly, with your hands high!"

A low chuckle came from the brush, followed by carefully enunciated English, "Don't shoot, I'm coming in."

Bader rocked forward on his feet at the sound of the voice, but still did not move or lower his gun. A figure detached itself from the darkness and walked carefully toward the fence surrounding Hanita.

Only when the figure stood beside the barbed wire with both arms raised overhead did Bader advance from his position to a gun barrel's length away.

"Well done, lads," remarked the man. "I would have bet a week's laundry detail that I could still sneak in this way."

"Captain Orde!" exclaimed Artur. "Is it really you?"

"Well, I'm not the Ghost of Christmas Past, if you follow me. Where's Zabinski?"

"Here, Captain," answered a voice from the left.

"Since you've caught me, better march me in proper," suggested Orde.

"Yes, Hayedid . . . Captain. You others, back to your posts."

"But, Captain," called Bader, "we thought you were dead. You've been missing for days! Where have you been?"

"Adding another chapter to the manual," Orde replied. "Now, are you going to keep me standing here all night, or will you hurry up and open the gate?"

If you would like to contact the authors,
you may write to them at the following address:

Bodie and Brock Thoene
P.O. Box 542
Glenbrook, NV 89413

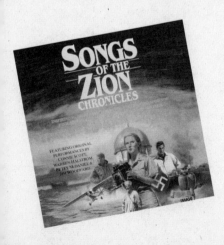

Warsaw Requiem

Warsaw Requiem

Bodie Thoene

Research and Development By
Brock Thoene

BETHANY HOUSE PUBLISHERS
MINNEAPOLIS, MINNESOTA 55438

With the exception of recognized historical figures, the characters in this novel are fictional and any resemblance to actual persons, living or dead, is purely coincidental.

Cover illustration by Dan Thornberg,
Bethany House Publishers staff artist.

Copyright © 1991
Bodie Thoene
All Rights Reserved

Published by Bethany House Publishers
A Ministry of Bethany Fellowship, Inc.
6820 Auto Club Road, Minneapolis, Minnesota 55438

Printed in the United States of America

Library of Congress Cataloging-in-Publication Data

Thoene, Bodie, 1951–
    Warsaw requiem / Bodie Thoene.
        p. cm. — (The Zion covenant) ; book 6)

    1. Jews—Poland—Warsaw—History—20th century—Fiction.
2. World War, 1939–1945—Poland—Warsaw—Fiction. 3. Holocaust, Jewish (1939–1945)—Fiction. 4. Warsaw (Poland)—History—Fiction.
I. Title. II. Series: Thoene, Bodie, 1951–   Zion covenant ; 6.
PS3570.H46W37   1991
813'.54—dc20   91-36674
ISBN 1-55661-188-9   CIP

In thinking about the dedication of this book,
I have worried about whether it gets old being an editor and
having multiple books dedicated to you.
All the same,
there is no one else who will do for me in this but

Carol Johnson

. . . And so, *Warsaw Requiem* is for my friend.
My dear, one-and-only
Carol-Annie,
who, after Brock, has read
my soul and manuscripts before anybody
and who I love a lot . . .

(Do not edit this, please.)

Books by Brock and Bodie Thoene

The Zion Covenant

Vienna Prelude
Prague Counterpoint
Munich Signature
Jerusalem Interlude
Danzig Passage
Warsaw Requiem

The Zion Chronicles

The Gates of Zion
A Daughter of Zion
The Return to Zion
A Light in Zion
The Key to Zion

The Shiloh Legacy

In My Father's House
A Thousand Shall Fall
Say to This Mountain

Saga of the Sierras

The Man From Shadow Ridge
Riders of the Silver Rim
Gold Rush Prodigal
Sequoia Scout
Cannons of the Comstock
The Year of the Grizzly
Shooting Star

Non-Fiction

Protecting Your Income and Your Family's Future
Writer to Writer

The Authors

BODIE THOENE (Tay-nee) began her writing career as a teen journalist for her local newspaper. Eventually her byline appeared in prestigious periodicals such as *U.S. News and World Report*, *The American West*, and *The Saturday Evening Post*. After leaving an established career as a writer and researcher for John Wayne, she began work on her first historical fiction series, The Zion Chronicles. From the beginning her husband, BROCK, has been deeply involved in the development of each book. His degrees in history and education have added a vital dimension to the accuracy, authenticity, and plot structure of the Zion books. The Thoenes' unusual but very effective writing collaboration has also produced two non-fiction books, *Writer to Writer* and *Protecting Your Income and Your Family's Future*, as well as a new frontier fiction series, The Saga of the Sierras. Along with their prolific writing schedule, Brock and Bodie make a home for their teenagers.

Contents

Prologue

January 19, 1991

All the reading lamps had gone out, leaving the cabin of the jet muted by the soft twilight of recessed lighting.

Through the small window of the El Al passenger plane, the stars above the Mediterranean seemed hard and cold, unblinking in the thin atmosphere of 35,000 feet.

David Kopecky stared out across the moonlit wing, watching as a red light winked on and off with a steady rhythm. Closing his eyes for an instant, he remembered his own longing as he had watched lights like this pass over the night sky above Russia. Always he had craned his neck to watch, dreaming of the freedom that must surely lie at the end of the journey. He had imagined men and women encased in the sleek silver cocoon of a passenger jet high above his head. *Where are they going?* he had wondered. *And how are they so privileged that they can leave Russia?*

The freedom, the flight, the tiny red beacon on the wingtip had always been for others, not for David Kopecky. Not for his wife Eva, who slept soundly against his shoulder. But on this night, all his dreams and years of longing had at last made him one of those much-envied travelers.

He was sixty-three years old, and this was his first trip on an airplane. But he was unafraid. His son Mikhail had embraced him and begged him to reconsider, to think of the missiles that exploded in Tel Aviv. Was it not possible that one of those missiles might strike the plane before it landed? Could they not delay just a little while after so many years of waiting patiently? Gas masks. SCUD missiles. The cheers and threats of men like Yasser Arafat and Faisal Husseini as explosions rocked the civilian sectors of Israel and sent Israelis running for sealed rooms. *What kind of life is that?* David's son had asked him. Certainly remaining in the Soviet Union was a sensible option now that there was a war going on.

David had patted Mikhail on the cheek and replied quietly, "We are not flying into a new war. We are simply continuing our journey into a very old war."

David did not need to remind his son that Arafat and Faisal Husseini were both blood relations of Haj Amin Husseini, the Muslim leader in Jerusalem who had blocked the immigration of Jewish refugees from Europe before the Holocaust. Mikhail knew well enough that the same family which had terrorized the Jews of Palestine in the time of Hitler was still in the business of terror, still claiming to be the voice of the Palestinian Arabs.

The old war had continued without a break in stride, even after Hitler had perished and the courtroom of Nuremberg had pronounced the last sentence against the mass murderers of the Reich. But the terror of the PLO did not seem so dark as the future David saw for the remaining Jews of Russia and Europe. He felt the evil stir again. Once again he had seen the banners at public rallies declaring: *JEWS TO THE OVENS! FINISH WHAT HITLER BEGAN!*

The banners, the whispered words and the shouted slogans were being accompanied by blows. In Europe men were beating Jews, murdering Jews because they were Jewish. *Again. Once again.*

"You must come soon to Israel, Mikhail. You and Ivana must bring the children and come join us in Israel as soon as your papers are in order."

Mikhail's eyes had betrayed his skepticism. What man would take his wife and children into a land of sealed rooms and gas masks and falling debris?

It was natural that his son would feel that way. After all, David had not spoken to Mikhail of the horrors that had happened in Poland. He had not told his son that he was Jewish until the first breeze of freedom had given him some hope. And then the letter had come from Israel, written in Polish. For the first time in fifty years, David Kopecky learned that he was not the only survivor of the once proud family of Rabbi Aaron Lubetkin!

My maiden name is Rachel Lubetkin. . . . Grew up in Warsaw . . . My family perished in the occupation. My youngest brother Yacov survived and is here in Jerusalem with me . . . our brother David Lubetkin possibly rescued by a Polish family named Kopecky . . . Could you help us locate . . ."

Thus the deception of over fifty years had ended. Only his wife Eva had known, and she had kept silent, guarding his secret, guarding his heart.

He smiled and put his hand on her cheek. She sighed in her sleep and shifted slightly in the cramped seat. She was not Jewish, and yet here she was beside him, leaving her son and grandchildren behind in Moscow to start over again in besieged and troubled Israel.

She, too, felt the hot wind of violence that had sprung up in the Soviet Union. She had left Russia for the sake of her son and his family. "To pave their path," she whispered through her tears. "If we do not leave, then they will not leave. Mikhail will come. He will bring Ivana and the children if we are there."

In that moment David realized that he had married the bravest woman in Russia. Like his own mother, he had married a woman who loved her own child enough to give him up in order to save his life. "Mikhail must come! There are gas masks for the Jews of Israel!"

David looked around the crowded cabin of the plane. Men and women and children of all ages slept leaning on one another in awkward positions. *Are they dreaming sweet dreams,* David wondered, *or the nightmare memories that come to me when I sleep?* He dared not sleep among these strangers for fear of crying out and waking with a start as his mind carried him unwillingly back to Warsaw—to the old war, to the fall. There were no gas masks for the Jewish children of Poland. The flight of refugees was not on bright silver wings, but within a thick, black cloud of fear. The roads were blocked by an endless mass of people—women and children, old men, weak and feeble. The very rich and the very poor mingled together in a groaning tide. That day, Polish Gentile and Polish Jew marched together. They marched *away,* somehow believing that they were fleeing from Death. And yet for anyone who looked closely, it was plain to see that Death was marching along patiently beside them.

Even now, as David Lubetkin Kopecky gazed out over the wing of the passenger plane, he could remember the drone of Stuka engines as they swung over the long columns like vultures. The road had erupted. Villages collapsed. Smoke had drifted across the gentle landscape as if to obscure the retreat of the helpless. David had seen those same images replay in his mind when the first news footage of Kuwaiti refugees had been broadcast. *Not running into a new war. Simply continuing the endless journey....*

David had no fear of coming face-to-face with an Iraqi missile. No, that was not the nightmare which woke him from his sleep. The terrible dream that haunted him was the memory of that first moment when this very old war began for him. That day when he and Samuel had left for school; when the bombs fell, there was no shelter to run to.

Six-thirty in the morning. Hundreds of children laughed and

talked as they clattered over the cobbled streets toward the school air-raid shelter. Then there came the high, useless howl of Warsaw sirens as the bombers began their Blitzkrieg on the far end of the Jewish section of town.

In that moment childhood was irrevocably destroyed. Screams were drowned by the whistle of bombs as children ran away from something that could not be outrun, toward a safety that did not exist.

The bigger ones ran faster. Little ones like Samuel were knocked down and trampled. David had thrown himself over his little brother and kicked back the rush of panicked feet. He had stayed with Samuel and so had not died with the others who reached the school just as the first bombs crashed through the roof.

That day, David had lain in the street beside Samuel and wept at the whistle of falling bombs, cringed at the roar of explosions, the grumble of collapsing walls and gutted buildings. *Gottman's Department Store. Menkes' Bakery. An apartment building. The Foundling Home. The school* ... Blasts shook the foundations of Warsaw. Buildings puffed out and then tumbled down onto the sidewalks all around the two brothers.

And then came the silence—an eerie and profound silence, disturbed only by the sobs of David and Samuel. The shattered bodies of playmates littered the street. There was no more childhood. No more illusions. All dreams vanished forever in that moment.

When it was over, only David and Samuel had survived the bombing of that street. Together they groped their way back through the debris to the frantic embrace and cries of joy waiting at home.

And this was only the first day of the war!

He remembered his family: Mama, named Etta. She was beautiful and good. Papa, Rabbi Aaron, wise and strong. David's sister, Rachel, at thirteen, was a duplicate of Mama. And baby Yacov. Little Yani, they called him. Could that little one be fifty-six years old now, with children and grandchildren? How could he ever bridge the gap of a lifetime of believing they had all died in the bright red ditches of Poland?

Always that first day, the first attack, was the memory that wrenched David from his sleep with a scream of terror. But they had all survived that terrible moment. David lived with indelible images of horror that in the light of day seemed far worse. And yet the hardest memory of all was the one which had blasted away his innocence forever.

And now he was going home once more to see his family. *Little Yacov. Rachel. Beautiful and brave Rachel.* They were alive! The children of Aaron and Etta Lubetkin would once again embrace one another in joy!

Over fifty years had passed, and still the whistle of bombs might mar their reunion. But at least now there were gas masks for Jewish children.

BALTIC SEA

Danzig

EAST PRUSSIA

GERMANY

POLAND

NORWAY

SWEDEN

BALTIC SEA

ESTONIA

LATVIA

NORTH SEA

DENMARK

LITHUANIA

EAST PRUSSIA

POLAND

GREAT BRITAIN

• Hamburg

• Berlin

Warsaw •

• London

NETHERLANDS

GERMANY

SOVIET UNION

BELGIUM

Prague •

• Paris

CZECHOSLOVAKIA
(before Munich Agreement)

FRANCE

Munich •

Vienna •

SWITZERLAND

(ONCE AUSTRIA)

HUNGARY

RUMANIA

YUGOSLAVIA

ITALY

BULGARIA

SPAIN

CORSICA

• Rome

ADRIATIC SEA

ALBANIA

MEDITERRANEAN SEA

GREECE

1

When a Sparrow Falls

"May 30, 1939"

Karl Ibsen repeated the date three times in order to remind himself that all days were not exactly the same. There was a world beyond the dark confines of his cell where dates meant something more than burned oatmeal for breakfast and thin soup sipped from a dirty tin bowl.

He had counted the days of his imprisonment by scratching rows of tiny notches on the bricks of his cell. Like a calendar, each month was represented by a brick. Six bricks were filled. He carved another notch on the hard red clay of May.

Somewhere it was spring, with flowers blooming in gardens and couples sitting together at sunny tables in sidewalk cafes.

"It is spring," he said aloud.

As if in answer to his words, a small bird fluttered to the bars of his high narrow window and perched on the ledge. It carried a fragment of string in its yellow beak. Only a sparrow, the kind of bird Karl's father had paid him to shoot with a slingshot in the family peach orchard many years ago. Karl had been paid one Pfennig for every ten sparrows he killed in those days. His heart was filled with remorse as he eyed the tiny brown creature and prayed that it would stay to keep him company. The killings were clear in Karl's memory as the bird cocked its head curiously and gazed down upon this man in a cage.

One thousand sparrows fell to my slingshot. I bought Harold Kiesner's old bicycle with my earnings. Forgive my cruelty, little bird . . . and stay.

The sparrow shuddered, dropped its string and hopped three steps before disappearing off the ledge with a momentary flutter.

"Gone," Karl said aloud. And then he groped for the words in the gospel of Matthew. The ones about the sparrows . . . something about God caring even for sparrows, knowing when even *one* sparrow fell to the earth!

Like a knife in his weary heart, he thought about the Thousand and wished he had known then how much more precious they were than the used bicycle! What he would not give to have even one little bird perch on his window ledge now!

But Karl had nothing to give, and so such thoughts were useless. He stared at the barred fragment of blue sky as though his longing might bring the sparrow back. The sky remained as empty as the window ledge.

Karl sank down onto the dirty straw and stared at his calendar. Brick by brick he kept a mental diary of the gray days he had passed in this prison.

Four and one-third bricks had slipped by since the Gestapo agent named Hess had threatened to harm Karl's children if the pastor did not bend his beliefs to the Nazi will. Karl had not yielded in all that time. He was certain now that his children had somehow eluded capture by the Gestapo, or Hess would have made good on his threat to use Jamie or Lori against him. *Perhaps then I would have broken. Ah, Lord, you know how weak I am. I could not remain steadfast and be forced to watch . . . if they hurt my children.*

His gaze skipped back to the notch which marked the day he had heard that his wife had perished in prison. *Helen . . . Helen . . . it must be lovely where you are now. I don't begrudge you that, but I am sorry I can't see it with you.*

Other marks represented days on which news of a less personal nature had been passed along to him. This litany of Nazi victories in nation after nation had been intended to convince Karl that there was no use in one Christian pastor holding out when the whole world capitulated to the Führer's iron will!

Seventeen notches into the January brick, Denmark and the Baltic states of Latvia, Estonia, and Lithuania signed a nonaggression pact with Germany. These tiny nations gave their pledge that they, too, would look the other way no matter what else happened in Europe!

Why do you not see, Prisoner Ibsen, that the Führer has been given a free hand? Do you think it matters to any country that one insignificant man remains stubborn in his beliefs?

On the first mark of February, the government of Czechoslovakia ordered all refugee Jews to leave the country within six months.

The Czechs have at last come to their senses about the Jews. That leaves only you, Prisoner Ibsen!

On the twenty-second notch, the German-American Bund of Fritz Kuhn held a demonstration of 22,000 strong in New York to block additional immigration of refugees to the United States.

And who do you think will speak up for you if you continue to speak up for people no nation will have? Troublemaker! You are despised and forgotten here! Confess your wrong-mindedness and come back to your own people, who will forgive you and welcome you!

With March, the rains had come through Karl's cell window on a strong, cold wind. And with the wind had come news that made him tremble for Jamie and Lori!

On the fifteenth mark of March, the German Army had swept across the line of the Sudetenland, which France and England had offered Hitler in Munich to save the peace. All that remained of the Czech nation had been swallowed up by Germany in one unresisting bite. That night the prison guards were exultant. Hitler himself had ridden into Prague and spent the night at Hradcany Castle! The swastika flag waved proudly over Old Town Prague. German soldiers danced on the Charles Bridge as the Führer's voice rang through the streets announcing that Czechoslovakia was now under the "protection" of the Third Reich. And not one shot was fired. Not one German soldier fell in battle.

Now you will see, Prisoner Ibsen! You will see what will happen to those refugee Jews of yours! Now you will see!

Karl had continued to carve away the days. At night he lay awake and dreamed of Lori and Jamie running from the Gestapo, who smashed the Protestant soup kitchen in Prague. Karl had told his children to flee to Prague. He had sent word ahead to the Refugee Relief Committee to warn them that his children were coming. And now Hitler slept in Hradcany Castle! Those refugee Jews who had been ordered out of Czechoslovakia in February were fleeing for their lives to escape the force that had hounded them throughout central Europe. Karl prayed that Jamie and Lori were not among those masses of desperate humanity.

The notches of March ticked by. Nameless camp was packed to overflowing with human flotsam washed up on the Nazi shore with the sinking of Czechoslovakia. And Karl waited. He waited for his guards to slam into his cell and drag him to a room to watch the torture of his children. He waited, knowing he would say anything they wanted— *anything!*—if only they would not hurt Lori and Jamie!

On the twenty-second notch, the guards came to tell him that Germany had also taken the Baltic seaport of Memel from Lithuania. *Certainly Prisoner Ibsen must see that it is useless to resist the righteous Aryan cause! The Führer has traveled by sea to Memel!*

Karl had smiled with relief because the news was not about Lori and Jamie. The guards had taken his smile as a sign that perhaps he was coming to his senses. They reported his reaction to the warden.

Karl was given an extra ration of bread to celebrate the Nazi occupation of the Lithuanian port.

The next day he was interrogated. His smile was questioned. He answered that he had only wondered if the Führer had gotten seasick. For this answer he was beaten, but when he regained consciousness he found that the smile within him had not died. *Somewhere Jamie and Lori were still free!*

In that same month, Spain finally fell to the German-led forces of General Franco. One million had died. Britain and the U.S. recognized the new Spanish government immediately. *Soon the whole world will be Fascist. Everyone but you, Prisoner Ibsen!*

On the first notch of April, the rattle of tin plates in the corridor announced breakfast. Karl heard the guards talking outside his door. England's Prime Minister Chamberlain did not much like the fact that the Führer had taken all of Czechoslovakia without asking. The English and the French were now saying that they would go to war against Germany if the Führer set his sights on the Polish port of Danzig. In reply, the Führer had renounced the British-German naval treaty, telling the English, "Who cares what you do?" Maybe there would be a war after all! Maybe it would come at last . . . over Poland! Even little Holland had mobilized.

The guards sounded pleased. They sounded hopeful. The metal slot in the door clanged open and the plate of burned oatmeal was shoved through.

"Feeding time at the zoo," a voice cried. Amid much laughter, the slot clanged shut again.

Once again Karl smiled. He, too, had been hopeful that day. Perhaps at last the democracies had drawn a line across the pocked face of Europe and said, *"No farther!"* So little Holland had mobilized its army to fight if Germany should, in fact, step over the line! *David against Goliath!*

From that first day of April until today, the thirtieth mark on the brick of May, there had been no further news. No interrogations. No laughter in the outer corridor. Prisoners on either side of Karl's cell had been moved. The silence was complete. His meals were passed to him without comment, his latrine bucket emptied in the dark by a faceless Kapo who entered the cell when Karl slept. The straw in his cell remained unchanged. His confinement became totally solitary. He prayed. He recited scriptures to himself. He let his mind walk through the past again and again until that mental path became worn into a groove that was easy to follow. He called out questions to his captors as they passed him his rations, "Was there a war?" They did not reply. They did not seem to hear him.

Could he be the only man left, as they had warned? Had everyone else gone off to fight in Poland?

Until today, the thirtieth of May, he had found himself slipping into such morbid thoughts. *But today the sparrow had come to his window!* Today he was reminded once again that it was spring! Somewhere there were gardens with flowers blooming. Maybe Jamie and Lori . . . maybe . . . maybe they were out walking—looking at colors, wondering about their father, hoping they would see him again someday soon . . . .

For months in France, important visitors had been picked up at their hotels in Paris and driven through the peaceful countryside of Alsace-Lorraine to tour the great concrete wall of defense, the Maginot Line. Politicians and industrialists, and celebrities such as Charles Lindbergh had all been invited to "take the tour." They had descended into the maze of concrete bunkers and gun emplacements; they had spoken with the French soldiers who manned this fortress; they had emerged again into the bright sunlight of the peaceful French country-side, convinced that there would be no war waged by Germany against France, not with such a massive line of defense to get through.

Today it had been American journalist John Murphy's turn to tour the Maginot Line. He was the logical choice for this week's guest list. As the head of Trump European News Service, he was establishing one of the most successful newspaper and radio news agencies serving America from the Continent.

Added to that, Mr. Murphy was a personal friend of the venerable British statesman, Winston Churchill. The two had crossed the Channel together, stayed at the Ritz in Paris for a day, and now walked through the steel and concrete caverns beside the French captain, Edmone Perpignon. Forty years old, with an erect carriage and snapping brown eyes, Captain Perpignon's entire career in the French Army was tied to the Maginot. He loved its smooth gray walls and bristling gun turrets, which pointed across the Rhine toward similar German fortifications.

"You see," the captain said to Murphy in a soft, thick accent, "General Gamelin said that perhaps you are the sort of person who should *see* the Maginot. Perhaps you will then understand it."

Murphy understood perfectly well how much stock the French put in this cement marvel that stretched from Switzerland all along the border to the lowlands of Belgium. Certainly the German Army would not want to confront such an obstacle. But wasn't it possible that the Germans might simply go around it? The government of Belgium had just announced that it would remain strictly neutral *if* war should break out; Murphy and Churchill had discussed just how much such a declaration would mean to Hitler. A few hours' march across little Belgium, and the German divisions could simply go around this hulking wall like a quarterback doing an end run.

Murphy considered using this analogy with the French captain, but then remembered that the French had no Rose Bowl football games which they might compare to war maneuvers.

The captain was ecstatic. "And if anyone in America doubts for a moment," he said, waving a hand at the long tunnel, "that peace is our only war aim, and defense is our only strategy, tell them this: We have anchored all our millions of dollars worth of great guns in five hundred million dollars worth of concrete!"

Murphy exchanged an uneasy glance with Churchill. Churchill had just been saying that the strength of the German war machine would lie in its mobility. Against armored tank divisions, concrete was indeed a barrier—provided the Germans attempted a frontal attack.

The French captain was in love with the Maginot; he was also in love with the history that had inspired it. "You must promise me you will do an article for the American newspapers about Lorraine! This place was the gateway used by the barbarians to invade France since the time of Attila the Hun."

Churchill broke his long and thoughtful silence. He paused and relit the stub of his cigar as he eyed the captain. "Yes. I can see the similarities between the barbarians and the Nazis. Herr Hitler would make a commendable Attila." He cleared his throat. "But are you *sure* they will try to come through this way again?"

The captain also paused a moment. He shrugged. "They always have before," he answered.

"Last time they came through Belgium," Churchill remarked dryly.

The captain raised an instructive finger. "We have urged the Belgians to see to their own defenses, and soon we will be extending the Maginot along the Belgian border."

"Why hasn't it been done before now?" Murphy dared to ask. "The crisis is imminent."

No doubt more important men than Murphy and Churchill had asked similar questions. The Frenchman had a ready answer.

"Partly because of cost. Partly because of time. But mostly because if the Belgians see our guns and forts facing them, they might think that we French are as aggressive as the Germans."

"Even though the guns are in concrete?" Churchill asked.

"It will be remedied in time." The captain was undaunted. His faith in this wall was not even scratched by the cannonade of doubts that exploded within Murphy.

They proceeded through enormous air-conditioned galleries linked with rail tracks and separated at various points by fireproof sliding iron doors. Casting all unpleasant thoughts away, Captain Perpignon showed them the floor that could drop inward, hurling any enemy who penetrated so far into pits fifty feet deep. The great guns were on the first floor, the control and chart rooms below them, then the plentiful supply rooms, overflowing with food and medicine and racks of shells, like the honeycomb of a beehive. A maze of oil tanks, machinery, and electrical generators were all duplicated for backup in case one of anything should fail. All of this was indeed impressive. Provided, of course, that Hitler followed the footsteps of Attila the Hun.

Once again Murphy rolled an uneasy thought over in his mind. The Germans were smart. Very smart. What did they know about the Maginot that the French and the Western world could not see? What secret did the strutting German Führer have tucked up the sleeve of his plain brown tunic?

Churchill looked at his watch as if he, too, were considering the same doubts as Murphy. "You are an excellent and convincing guide, *Mon capitaine,*" Churchill complimented, still looking at his watch. Hitler was to broadcast from Germany soon, and both Churchill and Murphy wanted to hear what he had to say tonight. Perhaps the success or failure of the French line of defense would be hinted at by some small word or phrase in the Führer's speech.

"Je fais mon métier," the captain replied with false modesty. "I am just doing my job."

He was doing more than that, Murphy knew. He was loving this monument to future death and past stupidity. He was waiting and praying for the moment when the guns of the Maginot would boom across the river into Germany. The thought of splintered German tanks and broken bodies filled him with premature pride. "They will come this way," he said. "The Germans are stupid. *Oui!* They will come!"

The German occupation of Czechoslovakia on March 15 had put Theo Lindheim back in uniform.

At the orders of Hitler, the German Army had rolled beyond the boundaries of the Sudetenland to smash what was left of Czechoslovakia. In the same hour, the divisions of the Czech Army and Air Force were ordered to abandon their weapons and equipment to their Nazi conquerors.

Instead, the handful of unmarried men who had been a part of Theo's air command had donned their flying gear, fueled their aircraft and headed for England. They hoped they might live long enough to fight for their country one day.

Hitler slept unconcerned in Hradcany Castle while troops marched into Old Town Prague and arrested the men and women who ran the refugee soup kitchen. *Subversives,* the Nazis called them. Hundreds were arrested and executed for resistance.

Hitler toured the great factories of the Skoda Arms Works—quite a prize for Hitler's war machine. Planes considered to be the most modern in Europe were handed over to the German Luftwaffe. Tanks, rifles, machine guns, and artillery from thirty dismantled Czech divisions were given to the Nazis, and now they pointed at the heart of Poland!

One by one, escaping Czech aircraft flying on fumes made it to a dozen little airfields in England. The pilots collapsed on the ground. They begged for political asylum, just as Theo had done the night England and France had first betrayed Czechoslovakia to Hitler's Munich Agreement.

The night of the Munich Agreement Chamberlain had vowed to fight for Czechoslovakia if Hitler moved any farther than allowed by the treaty. Now, Hitler swallowed the nation in one gulp. Czechoslovakia was no more. Every promise had been broken; men and women dying; the Czech people abandoned.

And Chamberlain did nothing to help.

Members of the exiled Czech government slipped out quietly. Some fled to England, where they were granted asylum like this small group of pilots with Theo tonight.

But England did not fight to save Czechoslovakia. Instead, the British Prime Minister vowed that *this* time he would guarantee assistance to Poland if Poland was attacked.

Days later, the Nazis discovered that the former government of Prague had deposited several tons of gold bullion with the Bank of England for safekeeping. Hitler wanted this gold. He wanted it immediately. After all, Czechoslovakia was part of the Reich now, was it not?

The British government handed the gold over to Hitler, who promptly put it to good use building more tanks.

March had been an amazing month for broken promises and broken lives, Theo thought. The refugee ships had arrived regularly, carrying their loads of brokenhearted children. Many of them were still at the house in London. How sad they were, how quiet. This is what bad politics and stupid politicians had brought them to.

As for the few Czech airmen who had managed to escape, they, too, were grim and bitter. They had saved these precious aircraft for what they saw was soon coming to England. They looked around for former officers who had fled like them.

And they found Theo Lindheim. "They will need us soon enough, Officer Lindheim!" exclaimed a young man whom Theo had trained to fly. "The English gave away our country, but we will stand with them to fight for theirs!"

Would Theo join them? Would he come and train young Czech students to fly?

The time to mourn was past, Theo reasoned. The fight was all that would soon be left for them. He put on his uniform that very day and joined the dozens who had fled in hopes of fighting another day.

The rich, newly plowed fields of France smelled warm and fragrant in the night air as Murphy and Churchill were driven back along the road they had taken that afternoon.

Beyond the dark boundaries of the hedges Murphy could make out the silhouettes of haystacks. In the daylight he had just been able to see the snouts of field guns protruding from the golden heaps. Everywhere for miles and miles of apparently tranquil countryside, machine gun nests hid in half-built cottages. Just beneath the tender shoots of grass, camouflaged pill boxes lay on the hills like snakes waiting to strike. Tank traps bristled with deadly iron spikes. And far away, across the uplands, unbroken coils of barbed wire waited for the return of some reincarnated barbarian to find his path back this way to a quick death in France.

Three hundred yards across the river into German territory, both Murphy and Churchill had seen the figures of German soldiers leisurely digging rifle pits—*in case the French should try to invade?*

Every bridge across the swollen Rhine had been mined. Loyal Frenchmen waited on duty with the button within reach . . . *just in case!* All of this, and yet Europe was at peace! There was no quarrel between Germany and France, or Germany and England! The Führer had said it. *All he wanted now was Danzig!*

Churchill sighed heavily. The moonglow shone on his waxy complexion. "And so it has come to this," he said sadly. "As though babies were born to grow and be hurled into the breach."

Murphy did not reply. He stared silently out the window and thought of Elisa, of their baby. *What kind of world would that little one be born into? Trenches and wire and concrete bunkers. Gas mask drills and . . .* He shook his head as if to force away the images of dead children he had seen in Spain.

"We have been brought to this abyss," Churchill continued with melancholy eloquence. "Germany rearmed in violation of a solemn treaty. Air superiority cast away by us. Just across the river back there they reoccupied the Rhineland. Their Siegfried Line built to match the Maginot. The Rome-Berlin Axis. Austria devoured. Czechoslovakia dismembered by the Munich pact. The mighty arsenal of Skoda now turning out munitions for the German armies. Thirty Czech divisions cast away."

Churchill's match flared, illuminating his round face in eerie light and shadow. "Yes," he finished, "we shall hear it tonight. Poland is next. By September, I believe; before the rains can stop the tanks of

Germany. By September, there will be war." His slow, certain drawl sent a charge of dread through Murphy as he listened. "The folly of great nations will be paid for by children and mothers. It has come to this at last."

2

Love Like Iron

Thousands of years had passed since Jewish mothers first heard the grinding of Egyptian swords being sharpened for the slaughter of their babies. As the first howls of grief had pierced the morning, a young mother nursed her baby one last time, placed him in a tiny cradle of reeds, and cast him adrift on the waters of the Nile River.

What mother over the centuries did not hear the story and *admire*? To step back from the murky water and watch that fragile ark rocking on the current required love like iron, heated in the fires of anguish and hammered against the anvil of desperation.

In 1939, the grinding wheels of Europe were heard rasping against Nazi swords. Jewish mothers nursed their babies and *knew* ... They braided the sweet, soft hair of their little girls and they *did not doubt*. . . . They tucked in their little boys and listened to prayers; they tied shoes and doctored scrapes . . . all the while the steady buzz of blade against wheel drifted through the nursery windows. And the little boys grew while mothers waited for the day when they would say goodbye.

Tonight, the docks of Southampton were illuminated in anticipation of the arrival of the ship. But there were no bands, no eagerly waiting husbands or wives, no whistles or shouts or excited waves or confetti. Not for this ship.

Over the weeks, the arrivals of the big passenger liners carrying refugee children from Danzig had been unlike any that Elisa Murphy had ever witnessed—refugees: joyless, homesick children!

Elisa's mother, Anna, and her sister Helen stood shoulder to shoulder on the quay. Their heads slightly tilted toward each other as though they wanted to tell a secret but had forgotten it. Faces were pained, and yet the eyes of both women were eager and hopeful as they scanned the solemn group of refugee children who stared down from the decks of the liner.

Little tugboats nosed the ship toward the dock, much in the way a terrier might nip at the feet of an elephant to make him move.

Little hands clutched the railing. Wide, frightened eyes peered out and wondered what sort of people would take them in. Where would they sleep tonight? Would they be warm and well cared for as their tearful mothers had promised them? Were these English people good and pleasant? Or might they be cross if broken hearts could not remember how to laugh for a while? Would they be sorry when the first tears came, that they had volunteered to take children into their homes?

Elisa looked back at them. She smiled and waved as though they were all old friends. She called out loudly in German, *"Guten Abend, Kinderlach! Willkommen! Willkommen!"*

With that, she turned back to the group of ten musicians who had traveled from London to Southampton for this solemn occasion. And they began to play their instruments. Classical musicians all, they played the brightest snippets of Mozart that they could think of. And finally that drew hesitant smiles from the children.

All the while, the child Elisa carried within her rested quietly, as though sensing the nearness of heartache. These little visits of welcome to Southampton seemed to be the only time the baby was still.

Anna Lindheim and Helen Ibsen had come to assist as interpreters for the homeless children. But they also came with the hope—the prayer—that Helen's children might somehow be found among these who had managed to escape. *Lori Ibsen, age sixteen ... No, she just had a birthday, didn't she? That is, if ... if she is still alive. And Jamie Ibsen, ten years old. Last seen being carted off to a Hitler Youth school. That was the last time his mother saw him. Nearly six months ago, it was.*

Aunt Helen showed the photograph of her missing children to several workers who had made the crossing with the few lucky ones. *"No, Mrs. Ibsen. So very sorry ..."* Aunt Helen looked at the photograph one more time—a longing look, a look that made Elisa put her hand on the baby in her womb and pray that her own life would never come to such a moment.

And each of these little ones who walked down the gangplank represented a mother like Helen who had said goodbye!

All the ships had come quietly into England in exactly the same way. And every arrival caused a lump of gratitude to hang in Elisa's throat. *These few are safe, at least!* But coupled with that gratitude was the uneasiness that comes when grief is very near and real ... when something in the world is terribly, *terribly* wrong!

Helen Ibsen had never cried before tonight. But she knew there was only one boat left that could bring her children from the Reich to the haven of England. Only one more chance for Jamie and Lori to be on that boat. One more chance.

Elisa looked at the face of her aunt Helen and thought how much she looked like Anna. Sisters. And she remembered how very much Lori Ibsen resembled Elisa when Elisa was that age. Cousins. There were still whole chunks of their hearts that Adolf Hitler held captive. That was true for these little ones, as well. They brought their lives and a future with them tonight. They would start all over again at the age of five or six or ten. But could anyone ever know what great love they left behind?

Only the mothers who let them go could answer such a question. Love had loaded them on this great ship; love had waved goodbye and thrown the final kisses. Love remained behind and watched the ship drift out of sight.

No one on this side of the Channel could replace that.

Elisa had some idea of what it meant. *Love like iron!*

Someone else to tuck him in. Someone else to braid her hair. Someone else to kiss the hurt away....

But these were hurts that could not be kissed away.

————————

The moon was full, bright as a searchlight over the Mediterranean. If he could have done it, Captain Samuel Orde would have shot it out of the sky in order to bring the lads into shore under cover of total darkness. The freighter was supposed to bring them in when there was no moon at all. But engine trouble and endless delays had resulted in the exact opposite result.

Orde and a dozen other members of his Special Night Squad huddled behind the dunes. Just below the lip of moon-drenched sand, a shadow curled over them like a dark wave. There they waited for the signal from the tiny lifeboat that had cast off from the freighter several miles from the coastline of British Palestine.

On the beach, a group of teenaged young people from the kibbutz sat around a roaring bonfire. They sang, they laughed, they roasted bratwurst on long sticks. Their voices seemed a strange counterpoint to the drama of thirty other young men of their own generation who struggled to guide the boat toward the signal fire.

A British military jeep roared up over the sand. Orde thought he recognized the voices of his countrymen as they demanded to know what sort of party was going on here!

A young, unafraid voice replied in concise English, "A birthday party! For Sasha." Then there was laughter and applause as a girl from the kibbutz stood and bowed in acknowledgment.

"You have no chaperon?" demanded the Englishman.

"We left them all in Europe," someone in the group said caustically. This was the sort of remark Orde had warned them against making. He grimaced and glared at the youthful offender from behind the dune.

"But *you* can be our chaperon," called Sasha. She skipped across the firelight and grabbed the arm of the reluctant officer. She pulled him into the group. "Come on! Give me a kiss! It's my sixteenth birthday! No one is serious tonight!"

Good girl! Orde silently cheered her. *Smart girl!* Then he prayed that the lifeboat would not choose that instant to flash its signal as it moved toward the shore!

"No. No. Can't join you tonight. Duty . . ." The Englishman was clearly embarrassed.

"Are you married or something?" asked Sasha, who gave him a kiss amid more shouts of encouragement. "Afraid your general will find out you had a little fun on the beach?"

The other soldier hung back. Orde could see the ramrod-straight back of the Englishman as he decided that he had certainly misjudged the meaning of this gathering. *Just kids, you know. A little party on the beach . . .*

More taunting banter drifted on the wind, half-obscured by the heavy pounding of the waves. The tide had shifted. Not good. High tides and heavy seas would make it impossible to bring in the boat without capsizing it. And could those illegal refugees, a handful of lads from landlocked Poland, swim? He doubted it. That was a terrifying thought added to a long list of unpleasant possibilities tonight.

"Hey! If you come back, bring us some of your English cigarettes, will you?" The request followed the retreating military jeep down the beach to the crude road that led through the dunes.

"They did it," Moshe Sachar hissed and nudged Orde in the ribs.

Orde glared at him in reply. Total silence had been the order. The only voices tonight on the dunes were to be those of young people as they tossed driftwood onto the blazing fire and pretended that they were really just a bunch of kids.

Nearly three hundred young male refugees had been brought in illegally this way over the last four months—escaping Germany, Austria, Czechoslovakia, and now beginning to slip out of Poland as the winds of Hitler's ambitions shifted to blow the inferno ever nearer. But none of those young people had ever landed in this ancient homeland under such threatening circumstances. *The moon. The heightened patrols. And now the tide.*

Orde let his breath out slowly, like steam escaping a pressure cooker. The scheme was to smuggle in young men over the age of sixteen. He had pictured building an army from the ground up, and these young refugees were to be his foundation. Papers could be forged once they arrived; it was much simpler than waiting for the slow wheels of governments to grind these strong, healthy lads to fine dust.

Others were being smuggled in illegally as well, of course. But Orde pretended not to notice them. Old men and women. Little children. They were not the stuff a future fighting force was built from.

The British government knew that simple fact as well. That was why they made it so difficult for young males over the age of sixteen to immigrate.

Well, here was Orde's answer to that—and the answer of the Yishuv! Like the mother of Moses, mothers in Europe darned the socks and underwear of their sons. They kissed them tearfully on their cheeks where the beards of young manhood sprouted, and they sent them off with strangers—with men called Zionists, who spoke of the Promised Land, of the covenant of Zion!

On leaky steamers they came. Under the scornful eyes of bribed captains they vomited over the rails of the ocean's most unseaworthy tubs. And then, nearing this shore, they were once again cast adrift in doubtful little scows, piloted by local fishermen, to run the gauntlet of the English patrol boats!

Their beacon light was a bonfire, a birthday party. Their signal was the voices of other young people who could remember the same long journey.

And when they landed, their shaky legs falling out from under them, they were greeted by men in uniform, led by a British captain named Orde who first terrified them and then astounded them and taught them to be men and Jews returned to their homeland!

It was all a very worthy enterprise. It was also profoundly illegal and dangerous for all involved. Especially for Orde.

Orde did not think of his personal safety now. The voices around the bonfire suddenly grew silent. Orde lifted his head above the crest of the dune and looked out across the water to where a single light flashed. One, two, three short blips and then one long. The signal for V. The code for Victory.

One by one, those around the bonfire stood to watch. They brushed sand from their trousers and shorts. They looked at the rows of breaking waves that rolled up on the sand between the fire and the little boat.

The lifeboat was in trouble. Orde and a dozen of the Special Night Squad joined the young men of the kibbutz at the water's edge.

"Who is piloting tonight?" Moshe Sachar asked the tallest of the young men, who had already stripped to his waist and pulled off his shoes.

"Julian," the fellow answered. The roar of waves nearly drowned his voice.

Orde could see the silhouettes of the refugees as the boat slid down the face of a swell and into the silver reflection of the moon.

"Julian knows what he's doing," Orde said, but he pulled off his shirt and shoes and stripped to his shorts as well. Yes. Julian was a good man. A fisherman, he knew the tides and currents of these waters. No doubt Julian knew his boat was in trouble.

A dozen inner tubes from the farm tractors had been threaded through a life rope like donuts on a string. In all the landings of refugees on this beach, the inner tubes had not been needed. Run aground during low tide, the passengers of earlier boats had simply jumped out and waded the hundred yards to shore.

Orde took up the makeshift lifeline and looked around him. Every other man had stripped as well, and now they waited only for Orde's instructions as the lifeboat was thrust up on the boiling foam of a breaker and then spun sideways.

Trouble! Were those cries of terror that echoed above the rumble of the surf?

"Only the best swimmers out! The water will be chest high for fifty yards and then drop away! Hold tight to the tubes and the rope. Don't be afraid, lads! Follow me!"

Like a commander leaping from the safety of a trench into enemy fire, Orde plunged in. He grasped the tube beneath his arm, using it as a shield against the pounding water. He never looked back to see who had come along. They were there. His men were all there. Through hell first and now high water, they would not retreat!

The icy water made his legs and feet and groin ache with pain. But as a boy he had always been first to dive into the frigid waters of the English Channel. Soon enough he would be numb to it.

There were shouts from the men behind him as they jumped into the waves. Lungs and body rebelled against such cold. The mind raged against the folly of stepping into the dark force that pummeled them.

A wave began its slow, crushing curl to Orde's right. He spotted the white flag of its crest and was certain that the wall of water would crash down on him. "Dive under!" he shouted, hoping that the man behind had seen the wave and heard his warning. He plunged into the black wall, dragging the reluctant inner tube after him; then he bobbed up on the other side.

Gasping for air, he could see that two men along the line had been swept back. They struggled to stand and move forward to take their place on the rope again.

Where was Julian's boat? Orde's toes barely brushed the sand. The water was much deeper than he had expected this near to shore! The moon and the tides had formed an alliance against the fragile little boat and the men who fought to reach it!

Orde let the buoyancy of the tube hold him a moment as he searched for the boat. Had it capsized? Were they already too late?

And then he saw it! The bow rose up and slammed down hard as it sledded down the face of an enormous swell. Water pushed it from behind, threatening to swamp and then capsize it. Still fifty yards away and to their left, the screams of terrified young men were clear above the tumult!

Orde kicked hard, aware that he had felt the last of the sand. He dragged the lifeline under yet another bone-crunching wave and swam to where he thought the boat should be.

He had cursed the moonlight before; now he prayed for the moon to light the scene! Julian was in trouble. Thirty young lads were in trouble. Orde was tired, but he fought on, unwilling to admit that he might also be in difficulty.

Ten yards forward! Then the waves pushed him back eight. He caught momentary glimpses of his men, their heads bobbing along the line they grasped as desperately as any drowning man. Behind them rose the eerie orange glow of the watch fire. It spoke of light and warmth and life . . . a distant world from the swirling water!

Yet another wave exploded just in front of Orde. He ducked beneath it but was again pulled back. His inner tube bumped against the man behind him. *Moshe?*

Moshe flailed a moment and then found his buoy again. He shouted, *"Over there! I saw it! She's gone over!"*

Capsized! The refugees would not last in this! Orde could not see where the boat had gone.

"Take the lead!" he called to Moshe who struck out left, directly parallel to the shore line. His stroke was sure and strong, his kick more powerful than Orde's. Orde gratefully took his place as second on the rope.

And then the belly of the capsized boat shone clearly in the moonlight! Julian was sprawled across it. Four others had climbed up beside him and now they reached out to grasp the others in the water who struggled to cling to the boat. Their forms were all light and shadow, like the negative of a photograph, and yet the terror on their faces was clear.

Then came the shout from the rescuers, *"Hold on!"* This was repeated in German, Czech and Polish. Julian turned his head, shouted and waved.

"I told you they would come!"

Those who could swim struck out toward the flotilla of inner tubes.

A dozen still clung desperately to the boat while Julian encouraged them.

"You see! Hold on! We're almost home now, boys! Not one will be lost!"

———————

The dossier that linked the political resistance in Austria with connections in Prague and Danzig and Warsaw was several inches thick. Compiled by Major Alexander Hess during his long recovery after being thrown from a train at the Polish border, it was a document that impressed Heinrich Himmler, chief of the S.S. and the Gestapo. For this reason, Himmler requested this private meeting with the Führer only two hours before Hitler's scheduled broadcast regarding the relations between Germany and Poland.

Major Hess, recently promoted from lieutenant, was in attendance this evening to explain the complicated web of connections between the perpetrators of what seemed to be a worldwide plot against the Führer. His facts and theories, listed in the cumbersome document on the coffee table of the Führer's private apartment, needed concise interpretation. Adolf Hitler had no time to read through such dossiers; he had barely enough time to listen. But tonight he was well in tune to talk of plots and possible coups planned against him by the German military and by foreign governments. Hitler did not need evidence to imagine that forces were intent on destroying him and his Thousand-Year Reich. He dreamed such things regularly. He listened to the voices that warned him where to go, where to walk, and whom to trust. Spirits guided him by night, and human voices like that of his Gestapo chief warned him and verified by their research that what the spirits spoke was true! For such a meeting as this, the Führer would delay his broadcast. Tonight the pieces of an unsolved puzzle continued to drop into place, clarifying the picture the Führer claimed to have glimpsed in a foggy dream.

After his ordeal at the border of Poland some months ago, Major Hess walked haltingly, with the help of a cane. The fact that he could walk at all was impressive. The doctors of Berlin had not expected Hess to recover so quickly from the wounds inflicted on him by the guard dogs.

Some wounds would never heal, of course. Major Hess's left eye was gray and clouded across the iris, the result of a fang wound. Loss of vision was total on that side, and yet Hess had spent every spare moment at the pistol range improving his aim and training himself to compensate for the lack of depth perception. His progress was pronounced miraculous.

Tonight the Führer believed that Hess had been spared for the sake of the Reich, for the sake of the Führer and the German people. It was no accident that the man had recovered to be brought to this moment! His research verified the worst fears of Hitler, and the heart of the Führer was touched by the loyalty and persistence of this man.

Himmler adjusted his round wire-rimmed glasses and with a wave of his hand indicated that Hess himself must share the conclusions of the report with the Führer. Hitler's dark blue eyes were rapt with attention as the story unfolded.

Hess removed a front-page photograph of the Führer standing beside two brothers. He smoothed it out before Hitler on the table. Hitler frowned and stared down at their faces.

"Although the caption names the brothers as Peter and Willie Ruger," Hess began, "these two boys are the sons of the Austrian resistance leader, Michael Wallich." Hess then pulled out a picture of the family: *Michael Wallich. Wife, Karin. Son, Peter. Daughter, Marlene. Infant, Wilhelm, a.k.a. Willie.*

Hitler paled visibly. "What does this mean? How did they get so close to me? Where was the failure of security in this matter? This boy—" Hitler pointed to Peter. "He is not that much younger than the young Jew who killed Ernst vom Rath in Paris! It does not take age to make an assassin!"

Hess and Himmler exchanged looks. The Führer was clearly seeing the significance of this matter.

Himmler cleared his throat. "Those around you on the day the picture was taken at the Berlin terminal have been interrogated. It was the photographer who chose these boys as subjects for this photograph, mein Führer. At first he denied knowing them, but of course with the right persuasion, he confessed everything we expected. He died before we could extract names from him, however."

Hitler's eyes narrowed as he considered the significance of having his picture appear with the sons of the man suspected to have been the head of the Austrian resistance. Did this not prove to all who wished to assassinate the leader of the German people that it was possible— *simple, really*—to get close enough to do it?

And now came the most harrowing point of all. Himmler filled in the blanks. "Agent Hess had been pursuing the children of Karl Ibsen, as you ordered. They were on that same train, it is believed. Agent Hess stumbled upon Peter Wallich in the company of the mistress of Wolfgang von Fritschauer. They were escaping the Reich together." Himmler turned to Hess now to continue.

"When I confronted Lucy Strasburg, informing her that she was under arrest for aiding the escape of Jews, Peter Wallich pulled a gun on me."

"He had a gun?" Hitler stared wildly at the newspaper. "I knew there was something about him! I felt that there was some danger . . . ."

"Who can say why the boy did not use the weapon against you, mein Führer," Himmler responded in quiet agreement.

Hitler sat up very straight. His hands rested on his knees. He did not remove his eyes from the picture of himself holding the baby while the near-assassin grinned wildly at him.

The Führer came to his own conclusion. "It was because I picked up the child. His brother, you say? Yes. That was it. Again I am saved by a force that guided me to make even the smallest move. Peter Wallich did not shoot me because he did not want to hit his brother."

No one could argue with such a possibility. It seemed a reasonable explanation. Himmler nodded. Hess also agreed that was certainly the case.

"You have done well, Major Hess." Hitler was emotional in his gratitude as though the injuries Hess had suffered from Peter Wallich had somehow been in defense of Hitler's own life.

"There is much more, mein Führer," Gestapo Chief Himmler said coolly. He did not enjoy the fact that this little officer received such high praise when it was Himmler who had set the wheels of the Gestapo in motion in this matter. "Of course, there are other factors that the Gestapo has uncovered involving a number of conspirators in various capital cities."

Hitler stretched his neck and drummed his fingers on the arm of his chair. "I am aware that the so-called democracies want nothing more than to see me dead. Where does all this lead? What do you have in there?" He glared down at the dossier.

Himmler nodded for Hess to take the briefing again. "Here is the connection. We know that Michael Wallich was working with a double agent in our own department." A photograph of Otto Wattenbarger was placed on the table. The Führer knew the face well. Wattenbarger was among the best men serving the Reich in Vienna after the Anschluss. Hitler's face darkened at this further evidence of treachery against him in the highest echelons of government.

"Like Michael Wallich, Wattenbarger died before we were able to extract any information from him," Himmler interjected. "Since that time we have been watching the moves of Wolfgang von Fritschauer. Since Wolf's mistress is obviously part of the resistance, we believe that it is only a matter of time before he leads us to her . . . and perhaps to others as well."

"Wolfgang von Fritschauer." The Führer repeated the name of the young aristocrat. "He is suspected? Is it wise to allow him to remain free?"

"Until we trace all the conspirators who have fled the Reich, Wolf must remain at large. He is being closely followed, of course," Hess replied. "His request for transfer to duties in Danzig and Warsaw may well lead us to those who plot against your life, mein Führer."

Himmler pushed his glasses up on the bridge of his nose. "There is a good chance that Wolf is guiltless in this matter." Himmler glared at Hess. Hess had pushed his accusation of Wolf too far. There was no conclusive evidence. "It was Wolf, after all, who arrested Michael Wallich as well as Otto Wattenbarger. I personally am of the opinion that he was simply taken in by Lucy Strasburg, who used him *carte blanche* as a means of getting information and then passing it along."

Hess shrugged with surly reluctance to accept this thesis. He fully believed in the guilt of Wolfgang von Fritschauer. "All the same, Wolf is being trailed. His phone calls are being monitored by an agent who reports to me."

Once again the face of Himmler displayed irritation. "The result of that monitoring at this moment is that Wolf appears to be following orders to track her down. He is also fulfilling his duties in Danzig and Warsaw. Several thousand men are in place within the area of Danzig. Weapons are smuggled across the river nightly. He is performing as you would expect on behalf of the Reich."

Hitler flared. "But is he loyal to *me*? Every traitor claims loyalty to the German Reich. They have forgotten that the Führer is Germany, and Germany is the Führer." He turned to Hess. "Continue your surveillance."

Hitler shifted uneasily in his chair as he considered other factors in the matter of the Austrian resistance. He glared at Hess, who was not getting to the point fast enough to suit the Führer. "It was not your job to deal with the Austrian plotters. You were under orders to break the will of Pastor Karl Ibsen. A simple matter of returning his children to our control." The thought displeased Hitler as he considered that Hess had accomplished none of that. Hitler's mood of growing impatience was a dangerous current to be caught in.

Himmler interceded. "The two issues are inseparable, mein Führer, as you will soon see."

"Then let me see!" Hitler bellowed.

With trembling hands, Hess fumbled through the dossier again. He had not expected such a change of moods. With a sigh of relief he placed the simple diagram of a triangle into the Führer's hands. At the pinnacle of the triangle was the name: ELISA LINDHEIM (MURPHY). From that point, a list of names trailed down the lines on either side. Those who were dead were underlined in red.

"On this side of the line, mein Führer"—Hess ran his finger downward—"you see the players of the Vienna conspiracy."

RUDY DORBRANSKY: Anti-Nazi agent active in smuggling operations on behalf of Jewish children. Performed in Vienna Symphony

Orchestra with E. Lindheim. Close association with Michael Wallich.

MICHAEL WALLICH: Leader of Austrian resistance. Owner of bookstore that served as a front for resistance activities after the Anschluss. Bookstore known to be frequented by E. Lindheim.

OTTO WATTENBARGER: Double agent believed to have passed information to E. Lindheim on various occasions. Lindheim's flat was subsequently leased to Lucy Strasburg after Lindheim fled Austria. Wattenbarger is now known to have had close contact with both Wallich and Dorbransky. Wattenbarger protected the family of Wallich, who were then assisted in escape by:

LUCY STRASBURG.

Hess moved to the other side of the triangle. "There are many less important connections, mein Führer, but here are the most vital."

THOMAS VON KLEISTMANN: Lifetime association with Elisa Lindheim in her years in Berlin. Love affair believed to have been ongoing until his arrest and execution for the murder of Gestapo agent Georg Wand in Paris.

Hess slid his hand past the more obvious names such as Theo Lindheim, Elisa's father. He skipped to the one name that had been his first concern before he had fallen into the center of what he was certain was a vast conspiracy.

PASTOR KARL IBSEN: Uncle of Elisa Lindheim.

There was much more written beside the name of Karl Ibsen, but the Führer saw only that the pastor was a relative of a woman so obviously linked with treachery.

"I have traced the connections, mein Führer," Hess said proudly. "Like a family tree, those who have opposed you all seem to know this one woman. Or they are associated in some way with someone who has been close to her. Vienna on one side, and the Ibsen case on the other."

Hess tapped the dossier. "The Ibsen case is tied to the Lindheim brood. Elisa Lindheim touches Rudy Dorbransky, who leads us to Michael Wallich and, of course, Otto Wattenbarger."

"The links of the chain are tight, mein Führer." Himmler's eyes sparked.

"These are just the underlings, I believe," Hess continued. "They are subordinate to a larger web of deceit that perhaps reaches even here . . . ." Hess swept his hand around the room. "Here to those who surround you. Here, even in the Chancellery."

Hitler's skin grew even paler as he listened and tried to imagine who among his personal entourage might be among this conspiracy. "Then they will be found out!"

"Exactly," Himmler nodded. "It cannot be coincidence that the Ibsen children and the Wallich children escaped to Danzig on the same night. Possibly on the same train. There is some deal that has been struck."

Of course. It all made perfect sense. How could Hitler have missed something so obvious as this? There was a higher force at work to remove him from power. Obviously, disloyal parties were at work against him, and he would have them strung up when they were rooted out!

"So Ibsen may be more than a religious fanatic." Hitler's eyes narrowed. "He does not yield to interrogation."

"He has been tortured. He admits to nothing except that his ruler is not of this world. He has maintained from the first that his children are safe; that they will not be harmed," Himmler said. "Someone has told him this. A bargain has been made with Ibsen—if he does not talk, his children will remain safe."

Hess picked up the folder and hefted it. "He will not talk, will not betray the conspiracy as long as his family is unharmed."

Hitler nodded and snapped his fingers rapidly. "If they are dead and the promises of his confederates prove false—"

"I think Ibsen will crack. He will tell everything he knows. Every day he is of less importance to us as far as his stubborn belief in his God. But, mein Führer." Himmler leaned forward. "He knows more. I am convinced. He is connected to it all. Finding the identity of the traitors within our government may well make the difference of survival for you . . . and for the Reich. For everything you stand for."

"Then find the Ibsen children," Hitler said softly. "And the Strasburg woman. Put agents at the disposal of Agent Hess in London, Danzig, and Warsaw until this matter is laid to rest." His fingers drummed on the chair. "I have felt the nearness of treachery," he mused. "It all makes perfect sense. And I will find the German traitors who would bring me down. They will dance on the end of a wire!"

By now Hess knew that he had completely won the confidence of Adolf Hitler. But he had saved his trump card for last.

"There is one more question that needs to be answered, mein Führer." Hess took the diagram from Hitler and began to write. "If there is a conspiracy against your life, who might be the one political enemy associated with Elisa Lindheim in London who would like to see you dead?"

Hess passed the diagram back to Hitler. At the top of the triangle, written above the name of Elisa Lindheim, was the obvious conclusion. All the indications pointed to one man: *WINSTON CHURCHILL*.

3

Red Lights Over Danzig

The French captain did not speak German, so he drove without comment as Adolf Hitler's speech echoed over the radio of the staff car. He hummed a French tune while Murphy and Churchill listened with rapt attention.

As Murphy listened to the broadcast of the German Führer's speech, he had no doubt that he was hearing a declaration of war against England.

The chirping of crickets through the open window of the car provided a peaceful background to the growling voice of Hitler.

Winston Churchill sat unmoving in the backseat. His brooding eyes reflected the awareness that as Hitler professed peace, he was, in fact, justifying reasons for war.

Today President Roosevelt had sent Hitler an appeal that the issues which fractured Europe should be settled peacefully, without German aggression. Matters could be solved around a world conference table without the use of military force.

Great Britain, Hitler asserted, was the aggressor. England had made a mutual assistance pact with Poland. In the event that Germany—peace-loving Germany—should attempt to take Danzig back, then England would go to war against Germany! This, according to the German leader, was a provocation, an encouragement for the Poles to rise up and invade peaceful Germany!

He then turned his verbal attack on the foreign policies of Great Britain in other lands.

Churchill smirked as the direction of the speech turned. "Here he goes," said Churchill, as though he had been expecting it.

"Now," the voice of Hitler raged with righteous indignation, *"I have*

just read a speech delivered by Eamon de Valera, the Irish Prime Minister. He does not charge Germany with oppressing Ireland, or any other nation, but he reproaches England for subjecting Ireland to continuous British oppression!"

Churchill shook his head knowingly. "The people of Northern Ireland wish to be severed from England about as badly as the Czechs wanted to be invaded by German divisions."

The voice of Hitler continued. *"In the same way, it has obviously escaped the attention of Mr. Roosevelt that Palestine is not occupied by German troops, but by English."*

At this assertion, Churchill chuckled bitterly. "It is a pity our Captain Orde cannot reply to that, considering the number of German Nazi officers he has found lying dead among the Arab terrorists."

"The Arabs living in that country have not complained of German aggression, but they do voice a continuous appeal to the world, deploring the barbarous methods with which England is attempting to suppress a people who love their freedom and are defending it!"

At this Churchill scoffed. *"Indeed!* I was on the committee that created the Mandate. We penciled in its borders in 1922, giving the vast majority of the Middle East to Arab sheiks who loved their freedom so much they roamed from place to place with herds of camels. Back then the Arabs did not want the little crumb of Palestine. They said it was too desolate to settle in! When we earmarked that tiny fragment for a Jewish homeland, do you know why the Arabs protested? They said that the place was so poor that it could support no one." He lit his cigar and sat back for a moment of reflection. "And after the Zionists made something of the place, these freedom-loving Arabs, who are now so dear to the heart of the Führer, poured across the borders of their lands into the British Mandate at a rate of thirty-five thousand a year!" His eyes narrowed. "Now they fight us with German-made weapons."

Hitler finally reached the point he had been searching for through this long, rambling tirade against British aggression. Had England made a pact with Poland to help if Poland was attacked? Indeed they had.

"In reply to this," Hitler's voice rose as he made a holy pledge to assist the oppressed peoples of Palestine and Northern Ireland, *"the German government is prepared to give to these states the same kind of assurance of our help. Indeed, we are already allied with them or at least united by close ties of friendship."*

"That should raise some eyebrows in Parliament," Murphy said in a low voice. "In one breath, Hitler is admitting Nazi assistance to the IRA and the Arab terrorists. The great battle against British aggression."

Churchill reached out switched off the radio as *"Sieg heil!"* threatened to drown out the song of the crickets. "Herr Hitler fights like a contentious woman," he said. "From point A to point W and back to point S, T, R and G. He is a failure as a logician, I fear." He frowned. "The speech is an ominous vision of what may very well be terrorist warfare in the streets of London as well as Jerusalem. We have heard a man well-schooled in the ways of total evil, Murphy. And I am afraid we are not equipped to deal with it."

The patter of raindrops surrounded the great stone prison of Warsaw with the illusion of peace. Rain this late in the season was unexpected and unwelcome, as unwelcome as the news from Berlin that negotiations must begin immediately on the issue of the Free City of Danzig and its return to Germany.

Uniformed prison guards manned every entrance of the imposing fortress. They smoked and pulled up the hoods of their rain slickers to keep dry, but a strange chill made their hearts tremble as they looked to the south and west and knew that tonight the great army of the Reich surrounded Poland like the claws of a giant crab.

Endless columns of desperate refugees from Czechoslovakia still pressed against the gates, pleading for entry into Poland. They were being turned back at every outpost, returned to satisfy the German appetite for human sacrifice.

Perhaps the Germans will not attack Poland next.... Warsaw, of course, did not wish to offend Berlin when it came to the matter of handing over fugitives from Nazi justice. After all, why would people flee the German advance if they were not guilty of something? Even as the Gestapo in Prague cracked down with a violence that rivaled the smashing of the Jews in Vienna, the officials of Poland mimicked the actions of their voracious neighbor. When it came to Jews, Poland agreed with Berlin. Great friendships between nations had been founded on smaller issues than a mutual hatred of a despised race. In this one matter, Poland and Nazi Germany were inextricably joined. Hatred of Jews was preached on the street corners and in the churches. It was taught to children and babies in the nursery, lectured upon at the universities. And from this night forward, the Jews of Poland would look over their shoulders and sniff the air of Warsaw for danger before they ventured out of their own neighborhoods.

Thus it came as a surprise when the black automobile of the Catholic bishop of Warsaw drove to the gate of the prison compound and stopped.

The window of the vehicle slid down, revealing the face of the bishop himself. Beside him was an ordinary priest, a Jewish rabbi, and a Jewess cloaked in a pale blue shawl.

"We have come to see the warden," said the bishop.

The flustered guard stammered a reply as he looked from the priest to the rabbi, and then to the woman. At last the vehicle was waved through the stone arch of the main prison yard. *No one would believe such a thing!*

Tires crunched over the gravel. Other guards left their posts to stare after the bishop's limousine and whisper among themselves about the meaning of such a visit. *So late at night! And the bishop himself! Not an underling! And with an old Jew in the backseat, and a very striking Jewess as well! What could it mean?*

Two men recognized the diminutive form of Father Kopecky as he stepped from the car and assisted the Jewish woman over the slick flagstones of the courtyard. Behind them came the bishop and the rabbi. *Side by side! What should be the protocol in greeting such a group? Would the warden cross himself? Would he kneel and kiss the hand of His Eminence?*

Only seconds passed before the warden blustered out of the building. His face revealed astonishment, embarrassment, and . . . confusion! Behind him followed two Polish officers, their sword tips clattering over the flagstones as they bowed and stepped back to flank the unexpected celebrities.

The guards lit cigarettes and passed them around from hand to hand. Twenty minutes passed in speculation of what such a visit could mean; then the door of the prison was thrown open. An arch of yellow light spilled out onto the cobblestones. The Polish officers, coatless, hands on the hilts of their swords, emerged first and rushed ahead to open the doors of the limousine. The bishop followed, then the old rabbi, and last the woman, holding tightly to the arm of a prisoner with a blanket around his stooped shoulders. The little priest, Father Kopecky, stood at the elbow of the bowed man. He supported him on his arm and aided him as he shuffled unsteadily to the vehicle. The priest's jaw was set and angry. He glared at one of the officers, who crossed himself after the door was shut and the engine started.

The guards shrugged and speculated. *What was the world coming to when priests and bishops rode in the same car with Jews! And on such a night as this, when Poland walked a very shaky line between Germany and Russia, too!*

———

Mama had decreed it: *"Everything must go on as usual, Rachel— as if Papa is not in Warsaw prison. We must not interrupt the studies of David and Samuel. Your papa would not like that, and so we women will be brave and silent."*

And so it had been for the past months. Since Papa's arrest, the questions of Rachel's younger brothers had been deferred. *Yes. Papa will be home anytime now. But you must study your Torah school lesson, or he will not be pleased.*

Frau Rosen, the housekeeper of the Lubetkin home, was dismissed. Her gloom and unending stream of gossip became too much for Etta Lubetkin and so, for the sake of the children, she had dismissed the old Yenta.

Tonight Rachel had been left in charge. Although she was only thirteen years old, she was the eldest and entirely capable of tucking her brothers into bed after supper.

The clock struck nine. The kettle was steaming with water for baby Yacov's bath. *Warm, but not too warm.* Rachel tossed a thick braid over her shoulder and rolled up her sleeves. She tested a drop of water on her wrist as Mama had taught her to do. *Perfect.* Carefully she poured the water into the white enameled pan on the chest beside the baby's cradle. She was an hour and a half later than she should have been in giving Yani his bath, but there had been news on the wireless from Germany. Terrible news! Hitler's threats against Danzig kept Rachel rooted, wide-eyed, in front of the big radio. David and Samuel had fallen asleep on the floor as they listened. It was an easy matter to guide them to their bed and tuck them in when the program was finished. Now there was only baby Yani and the matter of his bath to finish up. Rachel hoped she would be done before Mama came home.

Yani screwed up his face and bleated his displeasure when she removed his diaper and the cool air smacked his little red bottom.

"It is not *so* bad," she laughed.

In reply, Yani let loose with an intermittent stream that soaked her left sleeve and arm.

"Who taught you that!" Rachel gasped. "You Polish peasant!"

Yani cooed happily and kicked his feet in a perverse little dance of freedom. His fists wagged in front of his wide blue eyes as he made ragged attempts to find his toothless mouth.

"I will speak with the Lord and Master and ask that he send me only girl babies," she muttered in disgust as she hefted him into the water.

The bleat turned into a wail of protest as the warm water washed over Yani's plump thighs and belly. "You see," Rachel said soothingly. "I get even with you. You'll think twice next time before you wet on big sister."

Rachel was tender with this little one as she had never been with David and Samuel. Perhaps it was because she was older now. It came to her often that in only a few more years she would, indeed, have babies of her own. Yani was better than the dolls she had played with as a child. He was real. He smiled at her, and laughed sometimes. He held her fingers and moved his eyes toward her at the sound of her voice. Such sweetness eased the stress that each new day seemed to bring to the household since Papa had been taken. When news from the world abroad became too frightening to think about any longer, Rachel fled to the baby's crib.

Here was innocence.

Here was perfection.

Rachel cupped her hand around the velvet soft head and lifted Yani onto the thick towel. She wrapped him up and put her cheek against his cheek to smell his sweet skin. Mama always said it, and it was true—nothing smelled better than a clean baby. And nothing worse than a dirty one. Well, Yani was clean and sweet-smelling. Rachel cradled him in her arms and plunked down in the rocking chair. His warmth seeped through the towel. His thumb popped into his mouth. He sucked on it in drowsy tranquility while she rocked him and hummed and told the Lord and Master that she had not meant what she said about having only girl babies.

The clock struck the quarter hour, and then the half. Yani was asleep, his thumb still crooked at the edge of his mouth. He was diaperless, still wrapped in the towel, when Rachel finally laid him in his crib. The sound of an automobile approached in the square outside the house.

Quickly she diapered him. He awoke with an angry protest and then fell instantly back to sleep as she pulled a gown over his head and wrapped him in an eiderdown quilt.

The front door opened downstairs in the foyer. Mama was home! Rachel rushed to the head of the stairs to call out to her mother, to ask what news about Papa . . .

The light of the foyer lamp cast a golden glow on the black and white tiles of the floor. Except for that, the world seemed colorless.

There was Mama, her face pinched, worried, exhausted beyond anything Rachel had ever seen. And there was the Catholic priest beside old Rabbi Koznon with his yellow skin and yellow beard. Together, Mama and the rabbi held up another old man. Thin and frail and broken . . . beardless and bald.

The stranger's eyes were dark and familiar beneath thick eyebrows. His back was bent as if his head were too heavy to hold up. And yet he managed to look up. Up the stairs. Up into Rachel's questioning eyes, and then his cracked lips smiled. He was missing teeth. The stranger raised a hand.

"Rachel!" The effort of speech was too much. He coughed uncontrollably.

Rachel gasped. She put her hands to her mouth. *"Papa?"* she cried and swayed at the top of the stairs. Had the horror of his appearance been evident in her voice? She tried to control her trembling as she clambered down to the foyer.

"Be careful, Rachel." Etta warned her not to come too close. "Papa is not well. He . . . he is not well," she finished. "Call the doctor."

Rachel stopped two yards away from her father. He smelled terrible—like the public toilets in Warsaw. Like the poorhouse. Could it be? Could this old man be Papa? But yes! Those were his eyes looking back at her, loving her!

"Call the doctor," Etta repeated sternly. "Come, Aaron, darling. These clothes! We will bathe you and burn these things." Rachel stood transfixed, staring. There were bugs on Papa. Tiny crawling things. Etta turned and snapped at her. "Rachel! Wake up! Did you hear me! Call the doctor!"

Rachel found her voice. "What doctor? Dr. Letzno is gone. Who shall I call, Mama?" She realized she was crying. What had they done to Papa? What had they done to make him like this? To change him from the rabbi of Muranow into this—

"Dr. Tannenberg, then!" Etta's voice was strained as she and the old rabbi led Papa to the downstairs bath in Frau Rosen's former quarters. Papa in the servant quarters? Yes. Yes. A good idea. He could not be near the baby.

Rachel ran to the study and clenched her fists, trying to make her fingers stop shaking. She could hear Papa coughing, coughing, coughing! He was very sick! If he was so bad from being in Warsaw prison, what would have happened in two more weeks? Or two more days? *He would have died!*

She found the number in Papa's address book, the name and number written in his firm hand.

The phone rang too slowly. One, two, three rings and then a sleepy voice answered.

"Hello, Dr. Tannenberg, please! This is the daughter of Rabbi Aaron Lubetkin of Muranow Square. My father is very ill. *Please!* Come quickly!"

Rachel could distinguish the voice of the Polish priest from that of the doctor. Here in Warsaw, even accent separated Jew from Gentile. It was easy to tell one from the other after the first word was spoken. How strange it was to hear the accent of the Catholic priest emanating through the bedroom door, addressing her mother with such urgency.

"Have you wired your father in Jerusalem about this, Rebbitsin Lubetkin?"

"Not yet. I did not want to worry him. I was hoping that Aaron would be released, you see and . . . my father is old and frail. Things are difficult in Jerusalem just now, as you must know. And so I have not written him about it all."

"You must do more than write him, dear lady," the priest was sympathetic but firm. "Your husband and your family are obvious targets of the political anti-Semites. If things begin to go wrong for Poland, people like your husband will be blamed."

Rachel frowned and stared hard at the toes of her shoes. She thought of what the priest said. This was the same warning she had heard from Eduard Letzno before he left Poland for Palestine.

Papa's furious coughing followed, drowning out Mama's reply to the priest. And then, in a thin, raspy voice, Papa spoke.

"He . . . is right, Etta." He stopped, seized by another fit of coughing. "You must wire your father . . . if not for me . . . then for the children. They . . . must not stay . . . in . . ." His words fell away into more convulsive coughing. Rachel trembled to hear it. Papa sounded as if he could not breathe. The words were so halting; so full of fear. Yet surely he could not think that they would leave Poland for Palestine without him?

"Yes, Aaron. Yes, my dear," Etta soothed. Then she said to the priest, "No more talk of this. Not tonight. This is not the time. Surely you can see—"

"Etta!" Papa's voice was barely recognizable in its strain and desperation. "Listen to—"

"I will carry a wire to the telegraph tonight myself," volunteered the little priest. "Write out what you wish to say, and I will take it now."

A moment of silence passed. Rachel leaned forward and stared at the wood of the door as if she could see through it and read what message Mama wrote out to send to Grandfather. What would such a message say that could make a difference? *Please hurry and get us papers to Palestine? Better to face Arab riots than Polish anti-Semites?*

Rachel imagined the words and knew that if this was, indeed, what Mama wrote out, then things had become very bad for the Jews of Warsaw! Before his arrest, Papa had refused to admit the possibility of any one of them going to Jerusalem. But now, through the croaking voice of a sick old man, he demanded that Grandfather be notified how desperately they needed to leave!

Rachel shuddered. A cold fear crept up and tightened the skin on her neck. In her memory she could hear the shouts and threats of the Saturday people as they had broken down the doors of the synagogue!

Breathing fast, she left her post in front of Papa's sickroom and ran to the window in the front room. The imagined shouts became louder. She stood before the curtained window and pictured throngs of them with hateful eyes and flaming torches and crosses lifted high above their heads! Would they break down this door, she wondered? Would they drag Papa out of bed and carry Mama away on their shoulders to do terrible things? *Terrible things . . .*

Behind her, she heard a door open. The sound of Father Kopecky's feet padded briskly down the hall toward the front door. *"No, no. I will let myself out."*

He passed the archway leading to the front room where Rachel stared at the curtain. He stopped and put on his hat and coat. Then he saw her.

"What is it, child?" he asked, pulling on his gloves and eyeing her pale face with concern.

"Are *they* . . . out there?"

Curses replayed in her mind. The faces of the wicked men who had grabbed Mama swam before her eyes.

"Who?" asked the priest.

"The men . . . who . . . *those* men. You know."

Now he passed under the arch and hurried to the window. Without thinking he pulled back the heavy brocade drape. The rain-slick cobbles glistened by the light of street lamps in the deserted square.

"There is no one out there, child." He glanced back over his shoulder at her with concern.

"I thought I heard them . . . lots of them. I . . . I thought I heard them."

He smiled a sympathetic smile. "There is no one there. Nothing happening." He gestured for her to come to the window, to see for herself. "Just Muranow Square. Everyone is indoors I think, drying their shoes by the fire. Tucked into bed, where you should be now also." He looked at his watch. "You will need to rest so you can help your mother, yes, Rachel?"

He pronounced her name differently than it was spoken among her own people. The sound of it startled her, made her wonder once again why this priest concerned himself with them. She was grateful, and yet uncomfortable at the sound of her name on the lips of a Catholic priest.

"I do not like the goyim," she blurted. "They are a cruel and barbaric people." She raised her chin, daring him to argue on behalf of his own race.

For another moment he looked at the silent square. Then, letting the curtain fall back, he simply nodded his agreement and wished her a good sleep before he hurried out of the house.

It was very late in the night when Werner the cat got up from his sleeping place on Alfie's pillow. The soft fur brushed Alfie's cheek and woke him up when he did not want to be awake. He lay there with his eyes closed and listened to the other boys breathing. Jamie Ibsen wheezed. Mark Kalner, in bed beside Jamie, rattled. Jacob Kalner breathed deep and even. Alfie could always tell just who was where, and which one got up to use the toilet in the dark by the way everyone breathed. He even knew the soft breath of Werner-kitten, who was not really a kitten anymore.

Alfie did not like it when the breathing at night was not like it should be. Sometimes Jamie dreamed unhappy dreams. Jacob tossed on his squeaking cot and fought with dream people who visited here all the way from Berlin. And now, tonight, when everyone was breathing fine and not dreaming at all, Werner was prowling across the bed, jumping on the chest of drawers and . . . sitting on the windowsill.

The cot squeaked when Alfie sat up. He swung his legs over and kicked off the covers. *Maybe Werner needed to go out?* Alfie stepped around the piles of clothes the boys left on the floor. He kicked a shoe that thumped against the frame of Jacob's cot, but Jacob did not wake up. Then Alfie joined Werner on the sill of the tall narrow window that faced north and looked out over Danzig. The city looked very small and dark tonight, compared to the sky!

Alfie pulled back the curtain and asked Werner if he wanted out. But Werner did not want out. He was looking at streaks of color in the sky. Far away, streaks of blue and gold and red moved and faded, then brightened like a curtain of fire across the sky in the north. *Northern lights.* Mama had told Alfie all about them when he was little. Lights like that had called Alfie's papa to go to sea, she said.

Alfie stroked Werner and watched the lights for a long time. They were pretty colors, but they did not make him feel happy inside his heart. The glow reflected in the dark windows of other Danzig houses and looked like fire—like the fire Alfie had seen in Berlin the night he had run away from Sisters of Mercy Hospital. That was never a happy thing for him to remember. It was the sort of thing he usually remembered when everyone was fast asleep and he could not be comforted.

Alfie frowned and bit his lip as the colors in the sky changed to a deep red. The white walls of the house next door, the lace curtains Lori made, Werner-cat's eyes—all were red. Holding up his hand, Alfie could see that his skin was also red like the color of blood.

He did not mean to, but he blurted out Jacob's name. His heart was pounding and he was sweating through his pajamas.

"What!" Jacob sat up straight in bed.

"There . . . there are *lights* in the sky," Alfie said. His voice sounded frightened, but he knew he could not explain why he was afraid.

Jacob moaned. "Stars. Just stars, Alfie." He sounded unhappy to be awake. "Now go to sleep."

"Not . . . not stars," Alfie stammered. The lights made him want to run away. Just like he had run from the ward of the hospital that night when everyone else had been taken. "It is like . . . *fire.*" He tried to swallow, but there was no spit in his mouth.

Jacob came to his side, peering over his shoulder. "Ah." Jacob patted him. "Not a fire; just the northern lights." He was relieved. "Pretty, huh? I thought maybe Marienkirche was burning down or something." Another thump on the back. "Nothing to be afraid of. You and Werner go back to bed." The springs of the cot squeaked and squeaked again as Jacob tried to find his favorite position again. He sighed and soon his breathing was deep and even.

But Alfie did not go back to his cot. He leaned his forehead against the glass pane and watched the lights dancing across the sky. Deep inside a little voice whispered to him, *They are coming here. Coming again. They will bring their fire with them. Run and hide, Alf! Run! They will come here, too.*

Alfie had seen the fire of the Hitler-men in Berlin, and now it played before his imagination like a movie on a screen. "Where should we go now?" he said loudly. Too loudly. The other boys moaned a protest to his voice. He heard Lori's bed creak in the other room and then her soft footsteps.

He knew she was in the doorway, but he did not turn around until she spoke.

"Alf?" She always talked gently to him, like her mama used to. Lori's voice was a lot like her mother Helen's voice. Frau Helen Ibsen had said his name soft like that when Alfie's own mama had died. *"Alf?"*

He turned around and wiped away the tears that had tumbled out of his eyes. "Uh-huh."

"Bad dream?"

"No."

"Are you feeling bad about something?"

Silence. "I heard on the radio. The Hitler-men want this place, too."

"But England will not let them—"

"They are coming here." He gestured toward the sky as though it held the answer. "We should go away soon."

Again there was silence. Alfie knew that Lori was really listening to what he said. Lori did not ever think he was a Dummkopf. He heard her draw a deep breath the way she always did when she had something important to say. "Maybe you are right," she said. "I . . . I will try again to contact my cousin in England. The one who married the American newspaperman."

"Now?"

"Tomorrow. I will write her."

"Now!"

Another deep sigh. "All right then. Now. But you must go back to bed, Alf. I will write the letter, and tomorrow we will send it together. How is that?"

Alfie looked at the fire in the sky and then at the shadow of Lori in the doorway. "That is good. It is *smart.*"

The light from Lori's room seeped through the crack under the door of the room where the boys slept. Alfie lay on his cot for a long time until the light went off. Then he closed his eyes and went to sleep because he knew the letter to England was written.

———————

Danzig is a jewel imbedded in the backside of the Polish troll. The Führer said so, frequently. He always added his intention to slay the troll and cut out the jewel.

Wolfgang von Fritschauer thought of this as he gazed out the window of the antiquated Danzig local train rattling over the moonlit lowlands of the pygmy state. Only 754 square miles in area, Danzig was a tiny fragment of all the territory that the Reich had claimed as treasure over the last few months. But the leader of Germany planned to use this scrap of land as steel and flint to ignite his final conflagration.

"The decision to attack Poland was arrived at in early spring. Our strength lies in our quickness and our brutality.... Poland will be depopulated and settled with the German people. The fate of Russia will be exactly the same. Then will begin the dawn of the German rule of the earth...."

Wolf had been privileged to be in attendance when Hitler had spoken those words. Following that, Wolf had requested transfer to duty in East Prussia, which bordered Danzig and Poland. He had mentioned that he wished to be where the ultimate actions were destined to take place. It would be convenient as well, he suggested, if he could work closer to his Prussian home. His wife and three children were there on the family estate, after all, and neither Vienna nor Prague were places where he felt comfortable.

And so it was Prussia for Wolfgang von Fritschauer. Since March, he had traveled back and forth between the German territory of East Prussia into Danzig with regularity. Through connections with Hitler's foreign minister, Herr von Ribbentrop, Wolf now assumed the role of a businessman—a wine merchant who had constant commerce in the port of Danzig.

Of course he no longer wore his uniform, but he was just as active as he had ever been, supervising the infiltration of agents into the Baltic seaport. When the order came to strike, Danzig would be thick with German soldiers ready to take over the harbor, the Polish Navy, the ship-building facilities, and the gun emplacements facing out to sea. It would be a simple matter of German battleships steaming into port and the Army striking up the Vistula River to Warsaw. A swift blow to the heart and Poland, with its vast resources, would belong to the Reich.

Not once did Wolfgang von Fritschauer mention that there was one additional reason he had requested transfer from Vienna. The matter of Lucy Strasburg and the child she carried would be difficult to explain. Wolf knew that his wife, a possessive and jealous woman at best, would not accept his affair with a woman like Lucy until he was able to put a baby in her arms and say, *"You see, a child for the Fatherland and the Führer! And you must raise him with that in mind. It is your duty. My duty."*

Wolf fully intended that the day would come when he would say those words to his wife. And then he would add, *"The woman who bore this child for you is of no consequence. She is dead, and the child is your own."*

Wolf would make certain that those words were true. Lucy had betrayed him, betrayed her country as well. Death seemed a small punishment considering the depth of rage Wolf carried for her. He thought often of the pleasure he would reap in returning her to German territory and presiding over her execution personally. It would be a small matter to arrange once he located her. And he *would* find her!

Even before Major Hess had mentioned seeing Lucy on the train to Danzig, Wolf had known she had fled to this place. He had found her travel brochures in the apartment. *Poor, stupid Lucy. So provincial. She had chosen the closest thing to Germany without actually choosing Germany.* Wolf did not need the raised eyebrow of Agent Hess and the questioning glare.

"I am certain it was your mistress on the train to Danzig. She was with two suspicious looking boys. Jews, perhaps? I would have spoken with her, but I was attacked by four Jews and thrown from the train a few moments after that."

Wolf did not attempt to explain. He did not tell Hess how she had no doubt warned the family in Otto Wattenbarger's apartment of their imminent arrest, or that she had plotted all along this betrayal of his attentions. He simply shrugged and sipped his glass of wine as though it did not matter. *"The whore. I grew tired of her and threw her out. She'll show up at the side of a general before long, no doubt."*

If Agent Hess knew differently, if he suspected the truth, he at least remained quiet about it. His recovery from the injuries he had experienced that night on the Corridor Express no doubt had occupied his mind more than questions about Wolf's former mistress and her traveling companions. But Wolf knew that his record was no longer untarnished; he could suffer no additional failure.

All of it had simply strengthened Wolf's resolve to find her and finish her once and for all. Danzig was a small place. He had checked the hotels. She had spent four days at the Danziger Hof with two boys she claimed were her nephews. Then she had checked out and vanished. There was no record of her departure on the steamship lines. She could have easily crossed into Poland, but Wolf knew her better than that. Lucy must stay where her own language was spoken fluently, where she could chat with bellboys and waiters and tell them the story of her life. No, she would not go to Poland. She would not go to Prague or Warsaw or France. And she could not go home to Bavaria where her family lived. Wolf had friends in Munich who double-checked that possibility. If she became desperate and contacted her family, he would know within hours.

Wolf was certain that Lucy, with her limited intellect, would see Danzig as some sort of promised land. It was German in character, but not Germany. The laws of the Reich could not touch her here, yet the familiar culture surrounded her.

On this journey, Wolf would stop by the local hospitals. She was near the time when the child would be born. There was no running from that fact. Wolf would simply show the doctors a photograph of his *sister.* He would explain that she was unmarried and ashamed and would no doubt use a false name, and he would offer a reward for a simple phone call . . . .

The shrill whistle of the train announced that the passage to Danzig was at an end. Wolfgang von Fritschauer, wine merchant from Prussia, pulled on his gloves and stared out across the platform of the quaint train station of the free city. His quick eyes skimmed every face, every form. Passengers hurried toward the train; men and women kissed in greeting and farewell. Wolf could feel that Lucy Strasburg was somewhere among the crowds of Danzig. He sensed her presence as a hunter might sense the nearness of a stag.

Lucy Strasburg turned her head to the sound of Peter Wallich's weary tread on the steep steps. The stairs to the fourth-floor one-bedroom flat were steep, but there was something more labored than usual in the sound of his ascent. *He has heard the news from Berlin,* she thought. *He has heard the reply of Poland that they will not give in.*

For some in Danzig, the ominous radio broadcast tonight made their footsteps light with anticipation. *If there is war, it will begin here!* For others, like Peter and those thousands who waited in camps to leave Europe forever, the news put a raging fire at their backs even as they faced the sea.

Lucy rose from her chair and turned up the flame in the sputtering gas lamp on the wall. She had prepared Peter's supper hours ago, expecting him to come home at his usual time. But she knew from the heavy cadence of his step that he had joined with hundreds of others in the streets and listened to the radio broadcast on the loudspeakers. Lucy had opened the window and caught echoed words and phrases from the announcement. *She had heard enough to know!*

Peter's food had grown cold, and so she covered it and put it on the warming shelf until he came home. She tried very hard to cheer Peter up since baby Willie had been sent away—good meals, pleasant conversation. But tonight . . .

It took him longer to reach the landing. Longer to pull out his key. Longer to fight with the stubborn door latch. When the door swung wide, he simply stood in the hall and looked into the room as though he were seeing it for the first time. *Or the last time?*

There was no smile on his face. His curly red hair stood up as though he had been standing in a great wind for a long time. His eyes met hers, and only then did he enter the flat. *Was that fear in his face? What had he seen? Could only words cause him to look so pale?* He closed the door quietly and locked it.

"I kept your supper warm," Lucy said, as though everything were fine.

"Did you hear about it?"

She gestured toward the window. The open window and a good breeze carried the news far. "Bits of it."

"Polish Foreign Minister Beck has told the Führer *no.*"

"Good. Someone should have done that years ago."

"Either way, it means we cannot stay here."

Lucy shrugged and turned to get his plate. "If there is a war over Danzig, then France and England will beat the Nazis, and all our troubles will be over." She smiled and put the plate on the table, pulling out his chair.

He did not move from the center of the shadowy room. "Your baby is due anytime. You cannot stay here in such a place."

"I'm fine. Now sit down and eat. The Nazis are not coming to Danzig without a fight."

Peter's eyes grew dull. He stared at the food. "They are here already, Lucy. Waiting for the word."

"They got the word. From Foreign Minister Beck. I think the word is *NO.*" She tried to go on as if his mood did not put a chill in her heart. "Sit down, Peter. Eat before you hurt my feelings, will you? Never hurt the feelings of a woman who is expecting. She is liable to cry, and then you will be . . ." Her voice trailed away. It was no use trying to pretend. Peter was the one who was crying. A single tear tracked down his cheek. He brushed it away angrily.

"How did it come to this?" His voice sounded much too old for a boy of sixteen. *"How?"*

4

The Specter of Death Guards the Door

The half-moon cast an eerie glow through the clouds as swirling vapors thinned to a glowing film. Dark shadows outlined the muted details of the ancient thatched-roof cottages and rough stone fences of Ireland that traced the road from Dublin to this place.

Inside a cottage half obscured from the road by a stand of trees, three men waited beside a fire. There was no furniture in this one room—only the three men, reaching their hands out for warmth from the flames. An orange glow reflected on their skin as if they, too, were part of the flames. Two of the faces were of middle-age, faces weathered by the harsh Irish winds. Their expressions seemed frozen in an unchanging intensity as they bathed their leathery hands in warmth. Their heavy wool trousers, coats, and thick-soled boots were caked with mud from the ride across the soggy fields.

The third face was younger by a generation. A boyish twenty-five, the eyes of the third man did not stare into the fire as if some message were written there. His eyes flitted from the flames to the faces of his companions and then back to the window which was covered by a flap of dirty canvas. His clothing was American—pleated trousers and city boots too thin for the beating they had just sustained. The hem of his dark blue overcoat was wet, and flecks of mud covered his face and cap.

Outside, their horses stamped impatiently as the wind howled around the corner of the house. The young man looked up sharply as he listened.

"Not yet, Allan," said the stouter of his two companions.

"He'll be here soon enough," said the other, inclining his head slightly with an amused smile as he studied the nervous young Amer-

ican. "He looks like your sister, Colin. Aye. I can see the resemblance."
He looked back into the flames and saw a thousand phantoms from
his past. "But Maureen was a horsewoman. Indeed. She could sit a
horse better'n any lad."

Colin chuckled at the memory and nodded his large head. He ended
his chuckle with a sigh. That had been long ago. "What d'ya expect of
the lad? Raised in New York City. No horses t' ride. Even the trams are
electric."

Allan sniffed, embarrassed by the frantic spectacle he must have
made of himself holding on to saddle and mane and lurching about
like a drunk man as they rode. He considered telling his uncle that he
had ridden a pony once in Central Park, and that there was a mounted
police force in New York . . . . Then he thought better of it. The New
York mounted police were also Irish, thick of brogue and quick of
temper as his mother had been. Allan did not reply. He was fool enough
already in the eyes of his Uncle Colin and the IRA captain who had
come with them to the meeting.

"You think he'll be able to handle the job?" asked the captain. John
Dougherty was his name.

Uncle Colin nudged Allan. The boy must respond to the challenge
himself.

"I will not be riding horses in London," Allan said. "And there is
not a man among all the IRA who can handle this but me."

Colin raised an eyebrow in approval. Allan had spoken exactly true.
American born and bred, the boy was nonetheless his mother's child.
And she had been as much a fighter as any man in Ireland in those
days of the troubles. A toss of her curls and a flash of a smile and she
had managed to get more from the British soldiers than twenty IRA
strong men with clubs could do.

"His mother raised him right. He knows what we're about."

Allan grew bolder. He touched the scar beneath his right eye.
"Raised in Hell's Kitchen in New York," he said. "I learned to fight."

"You're here to watch," said John Dougherty. "Not fight. Not unless
we ask you to."

Outside, the horses stamped and whinnied. The sound of hoofbeats
rose and fell on the wind. Colin raised his head to listen. "They're here.
He's brought them."

The three did not move from their spot, but turned to face the door
in case the visitors might be Englishmen instead of their expected
guests. They had come here tonight to talk treason against the new
King George. It would not do to be surprised.

Allan looked from the face of his uncle to the door and back again.
Colin showed no sign of nervousness at this strange rendezvous. A
slight smile played on his lips as the tramp of boots and the jangle of

bridles and D-rings announced the arrival.

"The boy speaks German?" John Dougherty asked, reconfirming what had been repeated three times.

Colin nodded and drew himself up as the door burst open, and three men came in with a wind that swirled ash from the open hearth around their legs.

The ritual slapping of hands against sleeves and trousers in an effort to knock away the cold was enacted before the three men advanced to crowd around the fire. No one spoke for a moment as the warmth returned to numbed fingers and lips.

Allan stepped back into a shadow at the far right of the fireplace. He looked over the newcomers. He could easily distinguish the one Irishman from the two long-faced Germans who looked around the room with a sort of amused arrogance. Allan recognized the face of Kevin Fahey.

"So, Colin, this is the boy, eh?" Fahey cast a long look at Allan. "Maureen's son?"

Allan nodded, although the question was not addressed to him. Allan had been raised on tales of Fahey, and now the eyes of the IRA hero were turned on him!

"He knows what we're about," Colin replied gruffly. "Maureen raised him right. A fighter."

Now the stern, quiet eyes of Fahey pierced through Allan. The man's expression was different from those of his rough cohorts. Allan knew that here was a leader of men.

"And a scholar, too, I hear?" said Fahey. He extended his hand past the Germans who stood unmoving between them. Allan took the outstretched hand as if it were offered by a god. He knew Kevin Fahey without introduction. The warm brown eyes were human, humble and real. The red hair was tinged with gray and the face was no longer young as it had been in the mind of Allan when his mother had recited the endless adventures of this man.

"I am Allan Farrell, Maureen's son," he replied with a half smile. His mother's name provided his credentials.

Kevin Fahey frowned into Allan's face and then cried out, "Sweet Mary! I see the resemblance plainly! I would see her in you if no one had told me you were hers!" He embraced Allan as though he were the prodigal son come home. Fahey's own emotion touched Allan. *Family. This felt so much like the family Allan no longer had!* Tears came to his eyes in spite of himself. A pang of shame shot through him; then he saw that the others of his blood had shining eyes as well.

Fahey clapped him hard on the back. "And so she's come back to us too, in a way. She always said she would. Or that she would send her sons home to a free Ireland. We have yet to see that day. We shall have the priest say Mass for her while you're here."

Allan nodded, not certain he could speak. From the moment his mother had died in New York General, he had been surrounded by men who, like her, had fled their native land for America with the British on their heels. Some said that the IRA was as strong in New York as it was in Belfast. When Allan had raised his eyes from her grave, he had been met with faces of men like his uncle who reminded him it was *not finished yet*!

Now, as he stood before his boyhood hero, Allan felt a part of some destiny much greater than his own life. *Maureen's son. Graduate of Johns Hopkins University. B.A. History. Fellow at Georgetown University. On his way to London, where he would complete his doctoral degree.*

All of that had seemed like quite enough until a few weeks ago. And then the call had come. In some small way he was needed for the cause!

"Well now that this is settled" came the thick, dry accent of a German. "We have some business to complete, yes? And then a long way to ride before daylight."

Allan saw that they were looking at him. He returned their gazes curiously. Kevin stepped back and leaned against the cracking plaster of the wall. The wind howled behind him.

"These are the fellows who will be your contacts in London, Allan." He jerked his head toward the two men who seemed like wax figures compared to the full expressions of the Irishmen in the room.

"My . . . contacts?" Allan frowned.

"Much safer for us. There's not a man among us that won't be hanged by the end of an English rope if we're caught in London. You will report to these men."

Allan's uncle stepped in. "Another case of strange bedfellows wrought by politics and such, Allan."

Allan nodded once. Somehow he had pictured himself within the warm circle of Irish camaraderie. But then, this was a small assignment—a simple matter of nipping at the heels of British John Bull. In London no one would remember or understand the significance of the fact that he was Maureen's son. He would just be another American.

"Well then." Allan stretched his hands out for warmth again. "What is it I am to do?"

Dry clothing. Warm blankets all around. A hot meal for the refugee boys who were not too exhausted from their ordeal to eat. Julian's words had proved true—not one from the little boat had been lost. Three had died in the long overland trek from Czechoslovakia, but twenty-eight had survived to make it here, to the kibbutz in the home-land.

There was one pleasant surprise when the twenty-eight had been herded into the boys' barracks. One of their number, a thin, aquiline-featured fellow, burst into tears and confessed that he was not a boy at all, but a girl named Rebekah!

This confession was perhaps the greatest shock of the evening to the band of refugees: *Frank is really a seventeen-year-old girl from Prague!* She had cut her hair and bound her breasts and joined a group of fugitives in the woods of Bohemia to travel to Eretz Israel. All this way she had come, and no one had ever suspected! Smaller than the others, she had been bullied and threatened and bossed and punched if she did not move fast enough. Only at the moment she stepped into the barracks and saw the communal showers did she begin to weep.

Rebekah, moved to the young women's dormitory, was being pam-pered and fed as she recited the gruesome tale of fleeing Prague on the very night Hitler arrived to take over Hradcany Castle.

"And all that was small potatoes compared to getting here unde-tected in the middle of a gang of boys!"

Three remorseful members of the fugitive band took their chocolate cake to the women's dorm and there presented it to Lady Rebekah with their apologies. How relieved they were to find that the one they called *Frank* was not really a feminine-looking boy. "She is quite pretty, you know. How did we not notice?"

Orde instantly forgave the fact that this young female had taken up space of a potential soldier for the Special Night Squad. "A girl so clever and brave," he said, "deserves to be made an honorary member of the Special Night Squad."

Rebekah politely declined the honor and laughed at the pale faces of her comrades. "Enough is enough, thank you!"

Some time after midnight a British military jeep arrived at the gates of the kibbutz and demanded entry. Two British soldiers ordered that any illegal refugees who had come into the kibbutz be brought out to face justice.

Instead, Captain Samuel Orde emerged from his tent to meet with them. Righteous indignation turned into resentment as Orde explained that he had been here all evening. "No one who should not come into the compound has come in—except for you two English intruders."

They left sullenly. Two hours later a message came over the wireless that Orde was summoned to Jerusalem to military headquarters. Per-haps it was coincidence; more likely, suspicion of Orde's protection of the Jewish settlements had finally boiled over.

"No matter," he said returning to his tent. "It can all wait until morning." He instructed the radio operator to transmit the message that the wire had been garbled.

The French village where Murphy and Churchill stopped for the night was still deep within *la zone des armée,* explained the French captain over dinner. "And yet you see how well we French officers dine."

By candlelight in the dining room of the one hotel, Murphy was forced to admit that no other army in the world fed its officers like the French Army. Hors d'oeuvres, salad, salmon, and chicken breast were served with artichokes, and all washed down with *le vin-spécialité: Champagne rosé.*

"Keep the menu for a souvenir," urged the captain. "No matter what happens to France, it will prove to your friends that her officers will always dine like kings."

The food was as fine a meal as Murphy had ever had set before him, but he only picked at it. After listening to the speeches of Hitler and the Polish foreign secretary in Warsaw, the sense of foreboding he felt robbed him completely of appetite.

Bits and pieces of conversation drifted by him. At this moment he could think of nothing but his wife and their child. Their children.

The French captain did not understand either the German language or that of the Poles. He devoured his dinner and drank copious amounts of champagne as he chatted on about the invincibility of the Maginot Line and the strength of one million French soldiers.

Churchill, like Murphy, had simply tuned this jolly babbler out. He, too, sat in solemn contemplation of the dark political shadow that had stepped off the wall to tower above them in three-dimensional terror.

Both Murphy and Churchill declined dessert and coffee. Declaring exhaustion from the long day, they retreated from the too-cheerful company of their French guide.

Churchill's lower lip extended gloomily as they made their way up the stairs. Only when they were out of earshot of the captain did he speak.

"When Poland is attacked," he said, glaring back down the stairs, "the French menu will remain unchanged. They will remain behind their concrete."

"And England?" Murphy ventured.

Churchill raised an eyebrow. "How is Elisa?" He seemed to change the subject. "The baby coming soon?"

"She's fine. At the docks tonight helping with refugee children." Murphy managed a confused smile. "Another two weeks before *the* baby arrives."

Churchill patted him on the back. "When that happens, I would recommend that you send your family promptly to America. The Maginot Line is not long enough or wide enough. The English Channel is not deep enough or high enough. Take them home, Murphy." He turned as if to go. He had, indeed, answered the question. Two steps farther down the hall he stopped and turned slowly as he reached into his pocket. He pulled out a small revolver and held it out to Murphy. "You do carry a weapon, do you not?" he asked.

"I left it home. For Elisa."

"Here." Churchill chewed his words like a cigar to be savored. "Take this one tonight. I have another." Once again he looked over his shoulder. "In England there are at least twenty thousand organized Nazis. Soon it will be open season on men like you and me. On our beloved families."

Murphy took the revolver and suppressed a shudder. "We have a bodyguard living in the flat downstairs—ever since you recommended it." Murphy hefted the weapon. "Thank you, Winston."

"The best bodyguard may well be the Atlantic Ocean." Churchill remarked as he inserted the key in his door and left Murphy staring after him. The door closed. The latch clicked. Moments later, Murphy could hear the groaning of the chest of drawers being pulled across the floor to rest against the door.

Never before had Murphy so strongly desired to take Elisa home to Pennsylvania as at that moment. Tonight he followed the example of the British statesman known as the Prophet of Doom. He slept with the revolver beside him and the chest of drawers on guard before the door.

Rachel slept in her clothes on the settee in the parlor. She knew that it was morning before she opened her eyes.

Soft light penetrated her eyelids and the voice of Dr. Tannenberg penetrated her consciousness.

"Not typhoid," he said firmly. "No, Rebbitsin Lubetkin, your husband does *not* have typhoid."

She recognized her mother's sigh of relief and then Rachel opened her eyes to see them framed beneath the archway of the foyer. "But what do we do?"

"Still very serious . . . rheumatic fever can be just as deadly, only it is not in itself contagious. No. You need not worry about the children. It is, you see, from the strep infection your husband had six weeks ago. But some symptoms are much like typhoid—it is no wonder the young prison doctor confused the two. The fever. The jerking. The rash. Nodules and lesions. Perhaps the young fellow even thought he was about to have an epidemic of plague." The doctor clucked his tongue in sympathy for the prison doctor. "It is definitely rheumatic fever. It attacks the heart valves. Quite deadly, but not contagious."

"Please," Etta exclaimed in exasperation. "What can we do for him?"

"Just give him the medicine as I told you."

"But there must be something else."

"No. Just the sulfa drug. It is hard on the kidneys, but it will arrest the heart damage." He pulled on his coat. "I will be back this afternoon."

Rachel watched her mother grasp the doctor's sleeve. "I . . . I do not want *them* to know it is not typhoid." She bit her lip and stared up at him. "If they know it is not contagious, maybe they will take him again and then he will die in prison."

Dr. Tannenberg agreed with a single jerk of his head. "Rebbitsin, I will deceive them in this small matter. But I tell you this, the rabbi may die anyway. There may be other complications. Arthritis. Perhaps an increase in the uncontrolled jerking. But the heart damage is the most severe danger. It may make no difference for your husband if he has *only* rheumatic fever instead of typhoid or plague—"

"But it makes a difference to *them*. They let him come home!"

"No doubt they are hoping he will infect the entire Jewish quarter of the city," he remarked cynically. Then he shrugged. "I will tell no one the nature of the illness. But I cannot make any promises about his recovery, either. You understand? And if it is his time . . ." Another shrug. Rachel stared angrily at Dr. Tannenberg from where she lay. She did not like this doctor. She missed the kind gruffness of Dr. Letzno. He would not have shrugged when talking of death, especially not the possible death of Rabbi Aaron Lubetkin. He would have stayed at Papa's side. He would have administered the medicine himself and made certain that Papa recovered. No, Rachel did not like this doctor.

Etta accepted the doctor's words with dignity. "We will pray that my husband may have full recovery. We thank you for your help. For the medicine. And I implore you to say nothing that might dissuade the people and the authorities from thinking the worst. I cannot help but think . . . the symptoms are so close to typhoid . . . perhaps the Lord and Master has sent this other sickness to my Aaron so he could come home."

"I cannot pretend to know the mind of God, Rebbitsin. However, if I had a choice between coming down with typhoid or rheumatic fever, I do not know which I would personally rather die from. You see?" He smiled a patronizing smile and placed his drooping hat on his curly gray hair. "And so . . . I will return this afternoon, yes?"

On that gloomy thought, the doctor slipped out. Etta stared after him and then closed the door and shuddered from his words.

Rachel coughed, letting Mama know she was awake. Etta looked at Rachel and spoke to her for the first time since she had ordered her to call the doctor last night.

"You heard it all?" Etta asked, remaining in the foyer.

"All of it." Rachel sat up and smoothed back her hair that tumbled from a disheveled braid. "What about baby Yani? And David and Samuel? Can we all be together?"

Etta shook her head. She looked back at the door and frowned thoughtfully. "Our friends will care for the boys. No one must know." She tossed her head as if she had a plan. "This doctor says he might die anyway, but I tell you, Rachel, we will make him well and pray him well and let the specters of infection and plague stand guard at our door. The goyim will not come here. Not to collect a bill. Not to ask a question. Not to take your father from his bed! Nu! And you and I will nurse him without fear of becoming ill. The doctor says rheumatic fever is not so easy to catch." Mama was almost smiling. *Almost!* "Let them think there is typhoid in the Lubetkin house! And let them tremble at the thought of having to interrogate a man so ill." She looked Rachel straight in the eye. "It will all be for the best." Etta smiled in earnest now. "You will help me, Rachel. We will make him well together."

The black bread in the tin bowl was flecked with spots of mold. Karl Ibsen held a chunk of it up to the light and studied the green spores.

The sight of them made him smile. He remembered that Jamie had collected two dozen different mold specimens for a science project in school. Was the mold from black bread different from the mold of rye bread? For weeks the boy had cultivated tiny fuzzy jungles in petri dishes beneath his bed. With these microscopic worlds he had terrorized his sister regularly.

Penicillium blossomed into a wonderfully hairy green bouquet that Jamie placed upon Lori's pillow just before bedtime. Her screams had no doubt awakened the slumbering dead in the churchyard of New Church. And then there was the fascinating experiment in which several dishes of mold were placed in the icebox among the Christmas puddings and mince meat pies. This was done, Jamie explained to his angry mother, to see if coldness inhibited the growth of certain specimens. Helen sternly instructed Jamie to take his entire collection out of the house and into the cold winter night of Berlin. On the back stoop of the parsonage Jamie's beloved miniature mold gardens met their end. Yes, coldness did indeed inhibit the growth of mold.

Karl sighed and shook his head in distant amusement. Here it was hot and humid. Maybe that was why all the bread served at Nameless prison was covered with a soft green coat of penicillium. Karl listlessly brushed at it, but it clung tenaciously to the crust. It would not be gotten rid of so easily in the warm, moist climate of a Nameless prison cell.

"I am not hungry, Lord, and yet I know I must eat. To eat is to hope. I will not give up hoping." He frowned down at the green stuff that sucked nourishment from Karl's bread. Every day he pretended that perhaps there was some vitamin in this spore which somehow was of benefit to his body. He forced himself to close his eyes and take a bite. "For that which I am about to receive, may the Lord make me truly thankful . . . " he murmured.

Chewing on teeth that were sore from malnutrition, he was able to feel warmed by the memory of Jamie and his petri dishes. Wouldn't the boy have delighted in the giant mold specimen that his father now consumed?

———

The storm clouds over Jerusalem had parted. A bank of thunderheads piled against the distant mountains of Moab, but bright sunlight gleamed down on the clean pink stone of the Old City Wall.

The air was fresh and cool; the slight breeze carried the light scent of orange blossoms that bloomed in orchards throughout the British Mandate. In spite of the Arab strike, in spite of the violence that had led to the destruction of tens of thousands of the Zionists' orange trees, the Mufti had failed to uproot them all. And he had failed to uproot the men and women who planted and tended the trees.

His failure, in large part, was due to the efforts of the British captain, Samuel Orde. In six months Orde had turned the meager defenses of the Jewish settlers into a force to be reckoned with.

Orde stood at the open window in the office of Colonel Hallum and looked out toward the Temple Mount where the worst of the riots had begun with the death of Eli Sachar. The ancient pavement was rainwashed, unstained now by the blood of the hundreds who had fallen throughout the winter. The violence had finally receded like the clouds, but there were many dead and broken in its wake. Gazing out over Jerusalem from British headquarters, it seemed impossible to imagine the horrors that had swept across the Holy Land these past few months.

As though he could read Orde's thoughts, Colonel Hallum said quietly, "There is nothing holy about this land. Always has been a bloody, violent hole. Always will be."

Orde pretended not to hear. He drew a deep breath, savoring the scent of the orange blossoms. "Smell that, will you? There will be marmalade in the tearooms of London, after all."

Silence. Hallum knew well that the survival of the settlements was due to Orde. Everyone knew it. From this office all the way to London, no one in the government had missed the newspaper accounts of Captain Samuel Orde and his Jewish Special Night Squads. Several thousand young Jewish settlers had been trained in combat according to British standards. They had protected the water pipelines in the north regions of Galilee. They had saved the skins of a British patrol ambushed near Hanita, and captured the criminals who had kidnapped and tortured to death three British civil servants. And that was only a partial list of accomplishments. General Wavell spoke openly about the benefit of the Night Squads. He supported Orde when others did not.

The scent of orchards in bloom, however, spoke the loudest praise. But that was not enough, it seemed. Not in a world where politics was seldom played by the rules of common sense.

Hallum began again. "The Mufti has been in Berlin. Quite welcome at the table with Herr Hitler, they say."

A slight smile crossed Orde's face. "Have they noticed in the home office that the Japanese ambassador is also at the German Chancellery quite a lot lately? Has anyone in London made the connection that whenever Hitler invites a scoundrel to dine there is inevitably indigestion in the British Empire someplace?" Orde clasped his hands behind his back. He continued to stare at the Dome of the Rock, but he was no longer really seeing it. "And who is der Führer and Haj Amin Husseini serving as main course, I wonder?" Orde knew. He had known for some time. But still he wanted Hallum to have to say it.

"Haj Amin Husseini is exiled from the British Mandate." Hallum's voice was clipped. He resented the game. "The Arab Higher Committee that rules in his place in turn is demanding that officials in our government be brought to some sort of justice."

"Justice." Orde whispered the word, but it rang like a thunder clap of accusation. The very concept of justice had been carved up and devoured by Hitler and his dinner companions.

"To save face, you see. A compromise. Distribute the blame for the violence of the last few months." He paused. Waited for the meaning to penetrate.

Orde understood perfectly. "A scapegoat. Roasted in proper English fashion and served with Yorkshire pudding. Traditional in all negotiations for peace."

"If you will." The colonel raised his chin slightly. "A responsible individual. Someone of high profile but low rank." He cleared his throat as if to give Orde an opportunity to challenge him.

Orde simply bowed slightly in acknowledgment. What did he expect, after all? He had written his own press releases—all under a pseudonym, of course. He had not guessed that he was setting himself up for this moment.

"And?"

"And, they have decided—"

"They?"

"London."

"And Berlin?"

Hallum ignored the jibe. "London. They have found that you were somehow involved in every battle. Every aspect of this fiasco. From the first day on the Temple Mount when Eli Sachar was butchered until now. And so the final blame . . . the only possible—"

Orde shook his head. Not the Victoria Cross for service above the call of duty. Not even a promotion. Not even a "thank you, now please pass the orange marmalade."

"So what is it to be?" Orde asked.

"Posted back to England. Some desk duty for a while until this blows over."

"This will not blow over." Orde finally turned to face the uneasy colonel. "We will need those trained Jewish soldiers to hang on to this hunk of rock once the real storm breaks."

"That may be. But it is not the case now. The Grand Mufti of Jerusalem is in exile!"

"And what is one little British captain? Is that it?"

"*Posted to England! That is all!* Jews and Arabs are dead. British boys are being shipped home in boxes. And when the beginnings are traced, there *you* are! *Captain Samuel Orde.* On duty, right in the bloody thick of the fray! The Arab Council will be placated no other way."

"Unless I am killed?"

"You and I both know you are lucky to be alive. Every headhunter in the territory is out for you. You are a stubborn idiot, Orde, to believe that you can go on like you have and not end up a martyr!" Hallum's eyes narrowed slightly as he scrutinized Orde's stony face. "Maybe that is what you had in mind—to die like some prophet in the Holy Land?" Hallum rubbed his hand across his cheek. Had he stumbled onto something, perhaps? "Well, you will be offered up on the altar of political expediency, Orde. But I, for one, will not stand by your grave in Jerusalem! Go back to England! Give yourself a rest from this *obsession* of yours! This is not supposed to be a war! We . . . *Britain* . . . are here to keep the peace! You have forgotten that goal."

Orde turned back to face toward the city, toward the golden onion-shaped domes of the Russian convent at the foot of Gethsemane. Victoria Sachar was still there, safe within those walls, mourning for her husband. There had been days when Orde had wished that he himself could have died that day on the Temple Mount instead of Eli Sachar.

Orde knew what it was to lose someone you love and then be forced to go on living life alone. Did Victoria Sachar look back over her days without Eli and trace the beginning of her sorrows to Orde? Ah, well. Perhaps this was to be his punishment. It seemed much worse than dying—to be shuffled off to England and a desk job, there to wither away in obscurity while other men made the *difference* in the world. It was much easier to fall in battle; Hallum was right about that. *A martyr in the Holy Land!*

Hallum broke the silence of Orde's unwelcome reverie. "Look, old fellow . . ." His tone was that of a friend. "How long has it been since you have been home?"

"Home?" Orde could not quite grasp the question. Did Hallum mean quarters, or . . .

"England."

Orde nodded. He knew exactly how long it had been. He had left England one month to the day after Kate died. "Four years in June," he said. He did not add that it was also four years since he had buried his wife.

Hallum frowned slightly. "Four years. It is four years since you lost Katie, isn't it?"

Orde resented the fact that Hallum remembered something so personal. So very painful. "You have a keen memory."

"I attended the services, Orde, the day after my fortieth birthday. You bore up well. Everyone said so at the time."

"Why bring this up?" Orde snapped.

"Because it has occurred to me more than once that perhaps you did not bear up as well as we all thought. I have watched you here and—"

Orde raised his hand to interrupt. "Thank you, Colonel. But . . . this is a personal matter. That is not why you called me here. Are we quite finished?" He paused and shook his head resolutely. "In one month my commission is up. I wish to apply for early discharge, if you please."

Hallum regretted mentioning Katie Orde now. It was the final straw. He had pushed too hard. "Think about it."

Orde blinked in the bright light. "I *have* thought about it! Right here I have thought about it!"

"You will not be permitted to remain here in Palestine." Hallum was suddenly stern. "This will do you no good."

"I am requesting early discharge." Orde's face flushed with emotion. What right had Hallum to link Katie to his performance here as a British officer?

"As you wish, then." Hallum took his seat and opened the file. "Your discharge will be effective the day you set foot in England again." He sniffed, businesslike and unmoving. "Any questions?"

"No. No . . . *sir.*" Orde snapped to attention and saluted.

"All right, then. *Dismissed.*"

Orde strode from the building and stood in the sunlight as the British Union Jack snapped on the flag pole above him. He looked toward the Muslim Quarter of the Old City with the certainty that even in exile himself, the Mufti would be very pleased at the news of Orde's disgrace.

He let his breath out slowly. He had not imagined that the betrayal could be so complete. Walking slowly down the steps of the building, he forced himself to acknowledge the salutes of men of lesser rank. Now his rank meant nothing at all. He was of less significance in Jerusalem than the lowliest private in the motor pool.

5

Music for the World

Three times each day, Etta Lubetkin washed and changed her clothes and hurried across the square to nurse baby Yani. Always when she returned, the strain in her face was lessened. It seemed that the baby had somehow nourished her, Rachel thought.

Rachel's chores included going to the teeming marketplace. She looked forward to the excursions, to the noise and the bustle after hours of counting the labored breaths of Papa. She bargained cautiously, as her mother had taught her. And when she returned with cabbages or potatoes or bread or a chicken and recited the price to Etta, she was rewarded with a smile and a nod of approval.

Daily, gifts of meals were also brought to the back doorstep by members of the congregation. Dolek, the milk peddler, brought butter and cheese with his tall gray horse. At least one hot cooked meal a day came from the community soup kitchen. But from his sickbed, the Rabbi Lubetkin had forbidden his flock to enter the house.

Each Sabbath, a regular visitor came. His face at the door had surprised Rachel so much the first time that she had stood speechless before him and had not moved to let him enter.

"Who is there, Rachel?" Etta had called from the kitchen.

The little Catholic priest had bowed his head in greeting. Rachel could not remember his name, only his kindness.

"Father Kopecky, child," he smiled and prompted.

Flustered, she called her reply and stepped aside. "Father Kopecky, Mama. The priest. The Catholic priest!" *Did he want to come in?* she wondered in amazement.

He brushed his boots on the mat. *Yes. He wanted in.*

"Good Shabbat," he had said that first day, almost as if he knew something about a Jewish household.

After that first visit, Father Kopecky came often. On Shabbat, he laughed and called himself the *Lubetkin Shabbes goy!* He built the fires and chopped kindling. He stacked wood and lit the lamps. He cooked—or at least he lifted the kettle onto the stove and made hot tea for everyone. All the duties Jews were forbidden to perform on the Sabbath, this strange, whistling little priest did. On other days he bathed Papa from head to foot. Papa even managed to talk sometimes when the priest came, although at first he had thought he was dreaming.

When Father Kopecky came, Mama had rest. Rachel had time to retreat to her chair and read. And on this particular day, the Catholic priest read to Papa from the Torah; offered him precious words of discussion that mere women were unable to do. "A Shabbes goy?" Mama exclaimed in wonder. "The man talks like a son of the covenant, not some Gentile servant come to build our fire! Did he go to Torah school, I wonder?"

In spite of herself, Rachel looked forward to his coming. She still felt herself stiffen at the sight of his priest's frock. Was he not from the *other side,* from the world of the Saturday people where plaster gods were prayed to and candles were burned to the dead Christ above their altar?

Rachel had never seen these things because she had not ever dared to set foot in one of those places, but she had heard about the great cathedrals. She had seen the drooping dead Christ leading parades and funeral processions through the streets. She knew what it was to be accused of putting that Christ to death. *Christ-killing Jew!*

These things made the presence of Father Kopecky suspect at times. Rachel wondered why he came and then came back, why he read to Papa in Hebrew. *Why?* And then she remembered the way he had helped Mama in the street the day the Saturday people had attacked them. She remembered, and she really liked him. When he was late, she worried that he might not come. When he had to leave early, she hoped she had not offended him by a puzzled glance or a frank, curious stare.

It should not have surprised her that Papa also looked forward to the company of this man. After all, Papa was known and sometimes disapproved of for his friendships with those outside the faith. Dr. Letzno was one such character, but at least the good doctor had been born a Jew and circumcised on the eighth day. Priests were not circumcised, Rachel knew. They were *goyim,* Gentiles, and so there was no ceremony for them when they were babies.

Still, through his croaking fevered voice, Papa called the priest *"Righteous! A righteous Gentile!"*

Rachel was convinced that Father Kopecky must be the only righteous goy in Warsaw. Maybe in the whole world. She hated every other Gentile. The Saturday people had done this terrible thing to Papa. They had broken down the doors and taken him and made him sick. He was in bed because of what the Saturday people had done.

Maybe Father Kopecky was repenting for all of them, she thought today as she watched him stoke the fire. She held her book so that she could watch him secretly and then turn her eyes back to the pages quickly if he glanced her way.

He was whistling again, sweeping up ashes from the hearth as he always did. Suddenly he turned his head to look at her sitting in the plump over-stuffed chair. She looked quickly down at the pages. She felt her face flush because he had nearly caught her staring. She could not focus her eyes and she raised the book a bit higher to hide her cheeks.

He stopped whistling and said, "Hmmmm. That is very strange."

Rachel's eyes widened as she heard his footsteps move across the flowered rug toward her. He stood in front of her chair, an arm's length away. "Indeed," he said again. "Very peculiar. Rachel?"

At the sound of her name, Rachel felt the color deepen. She pretended not to notice he was speaking to her.

"Rachel? Child?" he asked again, as if requesting politely that she look at him.

It was not very far to look up. He was a short man, shorter than Rachel herself. She raised her eyes. He was smiling at her. Amused. She quickly looked down again. "Yes, Your Honor?" she stammered.

He reached out and took the book from her hands. He held it up and turned it sideways as if to study the words at a strange angle. Then he turned the book over. "You were holding it upside down, child." He gave it back to her. "Is this some new way of holding a book on the Shabbat? Nothing I have heard of. Seems like *work* to me."

Her mouth opened and closed in speechless humiliation. She was caught in the act! *Spying!* And now he was laughing at her.

"Pardon . . . I . . . I was . . ."

"Watching your *Shabbes goy* clean the ashes?" He laughed loudly. "Perfectly all right, child. Understandable. Who would want a Shabbes goy who did not do good work on the Sabbath?"

"I was . . . just . . . I did not mean . . ." Tears stung her eyes. She did not blink for fear that tears might actually fall.

He saw her embarrassment and became instantly contrite for having noticed and commented that she was spying. "Think nothing of it." His voice was fatherly. Priestly. Kind.

"I was not." She stared unblinking at her hands and tried to explain. "It's just that you are so kind. And I was just . . . I do not know why you are so kind. And I was just . . . I do not know why you are so kind when the others are . . ."

"Not?" he finished for her.

But there was no time for him to answer her. Maybe there was no answer anyway.

Mama came into the room. "Your Honor," she gestured toward the big clock on the opposite wall. "Aaron is hoping you might stay this evening."

The priest frowned at the clock face. Had he forgotten that it was time for the BBC broadcast of the symphony from London? "Ah, Rachel, we'll miss it if we don't hurry." He scurried out of the room, leaving a wake of unanswered questions behind. The growl of the radio emanated from Papa's room.

Rachel put down the book but did not move from the chair.

"We'll miss the beginning of the concert," Etta said, searching Rachel's eyes for a moment. "What is it?"

Rachel bit her lip and tried to define just what it was that troubled her about the little priest and his weekly excursions to Muranow Square. "Are there others like him, do you think?"

Etta nodded in reply, and then brushed the conversation away like ashes from the hearth. "Come along now. You know how Papa loves the concerts."

The whine of the BBC in faraway London slid into focus. So she had not made them late for the concert by her silly curiosity. She entered the bedroom where Father Kopecky was chatting pleasantly with Papa.

"I heard this performed by the Vienna Symphony Orchestra at the Czech National Theater in Prague two years ago," the priest explained. "It was a different world then, was it not?"

In honor of tonight's BBC broadcast of Mozart's Prague Symphony, Murphy donned his black dinner jacket and had his dress shoes polished. He endured the starched shirt with a smile as he sat in the close atmosphere of the audience in the radio studio.

The gathering was small, just enough people on hand to give the live broadcast the added dimension of applause at appropriate moments.

At five minutes to air time, Elisa took her place as second chair violinist for what would be her last performance until after the baby was born. She had given up playing for the large concerts at Covent Gardens some months before. BBC radio concerts were plenty. Now she could barely lean forward far enough to turn the pages of the music on her stand. She could not place the precious Guarnerius violin on her lap because she had no lap—only baby Murphy thumping around in there, threatening to kick over the music stand or punch a hole in the priceless fiddle.

Elisa had managed to sneak a wink at Murphy, flanked by Charles and Louis. The six-year-old boys were also dressed in matching white dinner jackets. *A very impressive sight,* Elisa thought. Being here with the boys was a loving gesture on the part of Murphy, who in his heart would have much preferred a jazz performance in Soho by *D'Fat Lady Trio*, who were soon to leave for America.

Murphy responded to her wink with the sort of look that let her know he would like to be paid back in kisses from his favorite fat lady as soon as she was once again a performing musician. How far she had come since she had last played this concert with the Vienna Symphony Orchestra on tour across Europe!

Elisa didn't need to turn the pages of the music—this was one score she knew backward and forward! It was this very symphony the old gang from Vienna had performed in Prague on the night she carried Rudy Dorbransky's Guarnerius violin home to Berlin. *Rudy's fiddle.* She raised it to her chin and silently dedicated her last concert to Rudy, who had tried so hard to stop all that had now come upon Europe!

Today it was his birthday, she suddenly remembered. How could she forget such a date? He had gotten drunk and gambled all night, losing everything, including this violin. And then he had come to her in tears to beg for a loan with which he might redeem his fiddle. She had counted out the bills and sent him on his way, never knowing what Rudy was really up to on the back streets of Vienna!

Now she knew. She knew everything. She knew too much. She was going to bring a child into this world, and tonight she longed for the carefree ignorance of those days. *Shimon. Leah. Rudy. All the much-loved members of the orchestra—everyone scattered, or dead, or playing the tune of the Nazis in Vienna.* Ah well, Hitler had chased her out of the arms of Thomas von Kleistmann and into the heart of the lanky American jazz-lover who now sweltered in a dinner jacket in this summer heat because he adored her! *Be thankful for such lovely things!*

The concert master raised his violin. The orchestra tuned up as the seconds ticked by and the red light blinked a warning that air time was approaching. *Time to get serious here.* Elisa raised her bow in salute to Murphy, in salute of all the others who were not performing with her tonight. The introduction made, Sir Thomas Beecham strode out to a smattering of applause. He raised his arms above his big head, and once again Elisa played. *Mozart's Prague Symphony. With Leah. Shimon. Rudy. Happy Birthday, Rudy. Did you know the Nazis have taken Prague? Hitler slept in Hradcany Castle. But I'm playing the Prague Symphony all the same. Because I remember what used to be. I remem-*

ber it's your birthday, Rudy, and I still have your fiddle.

The radio was one thing the Danzig Gang had decided immediately they must have! How else could they know the current events? Or keep up with the latest music from America?

Their apartment may have been sparsely furnished, but the big radio against the wall gave it a touch of refinement. They had traded a small gold pendant from Alfie's treasures in order to purchase it. Lori often said it was worth an entire gold mine to know what was going on.

They had heard the regular broadcasts of *D'Fat Lady Trio* throughout the group's European tour. Now that the American jazz trio was bound for home, Jacob spent the evenings slowly twirling the dials in search of a replacement.

Tonight the low whine of the tuner howled and then suddenly dropped London into the sitting room of the flat. *"SIR THOMAS BEE-CHAM OF THE LONDON PHILHARMONIC ORCHESTRA . . ."*

Jamie and Mark groaned as Lori gasped and shouted for Jacob not to move the dial.

He turned and scowled at her. "Somewhere there is jazz playing. Or maybe Charlie McCarthy! Please, not this—"

"This is London!" She grabbed Alfie by the sleeve. "Alfie, listen!"

He raised his head as distant applause sounded very near.

"What?"

Werner-kitten pounced on Alfie's big feet, batting at the toe that protruded from his sock. Alfie was too absorbed in this battle to take Lori's side in the radio argument.

"Come on, Lori! Enough culture, already," Jamie sneered.

"You have been out of school too long," Lori snapped. Then, as Jacob's fingers twitched, eager to tune out Mozart's Prague Symphony, Lori whirled to face off with him. "You touch that, and I will never speak to you again! That is *London,* you idiots! London! Where our very own Cousin Elisa is now a musician! Maybe playing right now with that very orchestra."

Jacob melted back with respect at such a thought that Lori and Jamie had a cousin on the radio. Even if it was only classical stuff. "Well, then . . ."

So Lori won. Jamie and Mark still looked disgusted. Edgar Bergen and Charlie McCarthy were more entertaining than this. But . . . well, it was London, after all. And soon a letter from them in Danzig would arrive there—maybe opened by one of the musicians in the very orchestra that was playing now.

That much, at least, was something to think about while the music played.

There was only one radio in the entire apartment building where Lucy and Peter shared a tiny one-room studio tucked beneath the eaves of a once-magnificent house.

Bent and crippled from arthritis, the aged concierge of the building had but one pleasure in his life. Last year at Christmas his daughter had sent him a Philco radio from faraway America. The radio would have cost half a year's wages for the old man, and yet he would not have sold the radio for twice that amount. On nights like this, when the reception was especially good, he would turn up the volume and let all the tenants enjoy his great luxury.

Tonight the clear strains of the London Philharmonic Orchestra wound up the steep stairs to the garret where Lucy and Peter lived. The concise British accent of the announcer left no doubt that the broadcast did indeed come all the way from London. In this way the old concierge wordlessly declared the value of the gift his daughter had sent. Somehow his own worth was enhanced by this treasure.

"Tomorrow he will ask me if I heard it," Lucy said softly as she and Peter sat together beside the open window. The view was only the tiles of the adjoining rooftop and beyond that the stars. *These stars are also shining in London,* she thought wistfully.

"How could we not hear it?" Peter was amused. "A very good radio. Four flights of very steep stairs. Not to mention walls and floors, and here it is right in our own flat, as though the radio was ours."

"He is proud of it."

"He has nothing else to be proud of," Peter said with an edge of bitterness.

"Don't be unkind, Peter," Lucy chided as the music soared. Such gentle music. "Just listen. He is giving us a gift."

"Not a gift. He is only being proud."

"Stop." Lucy leaned against the windowsill and closed her eyes to inhale the sweet summer air. "Don't ruin it for me. I am dreaming of faraway places."

"This is the Prague Symphony." Peter's voice was still tinged with disdain. "I hope you are not dreaming of Prague. Hitler is there."

"Not Prague." Lucy still did not open her eyes. "Of London. Where this music is coming from." She opened her eyes. "And it is a gift, Peter. It makes me feel . . . hopeful."

He laughed and turned his back on the stars. "Hopeful? You know what this is? It is a requiem for poor Prague, that is all. It is the melody of what used to be and what has now gone away forever. A requiem for the dead."

"Go to bed if you don't care to listen." He was goading her again, pushing her to talk about things she did not wish to talk about. Every night since the last Hitler broadcast it had been like this.

"You are the one who is not listening," Peter said, taking her arm. "And the next sound you hear may be the tramp of jackboots on the pavement."

"Stop," she answered in quiet despair. "Please."

"And after that, Wolf will be on the stair and at the door."

"Don't!"

"You must come with me, Lucy! Soon the requiem will be for Danzig."

"I will not . . . cannot go with you to Warsaw." Why did he push her so? Why could she not have one night without this, one moment of pleasure listening to music? Just a symphony from London, and now Peter was at her again to go with him to Warsaw.

"If you do not leave this place, then the requiem may be for you, Lucy. And for the baby. There is no more time. No hope for us here. Do you understand?"

Lucy did not answer. She brushed past him and opened the door of the flat so that the radio of the concierge was even louder. With a backward glance over her shoulder, she stepped out onto the landing and sat down alone on the top step. She hoped he would not follow her. She wished only that he would leave her alone and go to Warsaw if he was so terrified of the future. But she would not go with him into Poland.

The mellow sound of cellos and violins wound up the stairs like green ivy covering a shabby facade with a living cloak. The facade of peace and security for Danzig was ready to crack and fall to pieces, but just for tonight, for this one hour, Lucy did not want to think about it.

She felt the presence of Peter at her back, yet pretended not to know he was there. She prayed he would go back inside and leave her to her dreams.

After a moment, he left, leaving the door open just a crack. Lucy closed her eyes again and thanked God for the thoughtful daughter of the concierge. The symphony of Prague soared above her and around her, finally covering her with its beauty.

For just that hour, Lucy did not think at all. She simply rested in the music and dreamed she was somewhere very far from this place.

Orde lay back on his cot as the dulcet tones of the symphony echoed in the stone chamber of his permanent Old City quarters. The BBC Home Service broadcast was delayed by several hours from the original performance. Still, Orde listened to the music and imagined the musicians at their stands as though they were on the stage at Covent Gardens.

Katie had loved the concerts of London. He had merely endured them for her sake. Wearing a stiff collar and cuffs, being stuffed into a dinner jacket, had never been his idea of a pleasant evening. While Katie had shimmered in the glory of such music as this, he had nodded off or put his mind to work on some problem or other.

Now those delayed broadcasts of London concerts had become his one tenuous link with her. In those brief hours Orde allowed himself to think of her as she had been on those evenings. So beautiful, lost in an enjoyment that he had not shared with her while she was alive. Yet now he relived those precious moments at her side as though he, too, had cherished this music. It seemed odd to him now that he had not heard the beauty when she was beside him. And tonight, when he was so very alone, he longed to tell her just exactly what it was about the melody that moved him.

The second movement of the symphony began. Orde stared up into the shadows of the vaulted ceiling of the ancient barracks. Surely other soldiers had lain awake in this very room throughout the centuries. Officers of a dozen armies had stared up at these same stones and dreamed of lost loved ones as some musician played a sad song in the courtyard. The tunes, like those men, had vanished in the dusty air of Jerusalem. *And I, too, am dust.* Orde covered his face with his hands. "Oh, Katie, what is left for me? I did not see you when you were with me. I did not hear the melody of your heart! *A selfish, preoccupied man!* And now what is left?"

He sat up slowly and unlaced his boots, the boots of an officer. "What I would give if I could trade these in for that starched shirt and one evening at a concert in London with you, Katie. But I have nothing to replace this uniform, do I? Nothing at all to come home to." His own voice mingled with the sweet strains of the strings like a prayer. "But now I hear what you heard, Katie. It is beautiful. Yes, love. If only I had heard it before . . ."

6

The Hunter and the Hunted

It was a hot night. "Suffocating," Elisa said, as she tossed uncomfortably on the bed. "Humid as only a London summer night can be."

Murphy moved the mattress through the French doors and out onto the roof garden while Elisa sifted through his jazz recordings, finally settling on the mellow tunes of Glenn Miller.

As the soft tones of a muted trombone drifted out from the house, they lay together beneath the stars and silently gazed over the London rooftops toward the lighted dome of St. Paul's Cathedral. Crickets in the planter boxes chirped in counterpoint to the music. The scent of gardenias and sweet peas filled the air. Far away a siren howled into the night as Murphy sat up to rub Elisa's feet.

"Nice," she said.

"Better?"

"We should move the bed out here. Sleep under the stars."

"The air is not so clean as Pennsylvania." Murphy stroked her ankles. "But the crickets remind me of home."

Elisa did not answer. He thought perhaps she had drifted off to sleep—or maybe she was thinking of the chirping of crickets in some distant memory. "This reminds me," she murmured, her voice soft and loving, "of the night we made love beneath the oak tree in New Forest." Reaching for his hand, she pulled him down beside her. She placed his hand against the steady thumping of the baby within her. "And look what you did that night," she laughed. "Ruined my figure."

Murphy's voice filled with wonder. "He has the hiccups. *Huh!* The little guy is in there tapping away! What do you know!"

Elisa fixed her eyes on the great bright dome of St. Paul's. "Murph?"

"Uh-huh?" He was still preoccupied with the steady tapping inside her belly.

"I know you want us to leave London when it comes—the war, I mean."

He did not take his hand from her, and yet the sense of carefree wonder left him instantly. For a long time he did not respond. "There's more than the two of us at stake here. Charles and Louis. And this little one."

"I won't leave without you."

Were the crickets still singing?

"Maybe we won't have a choice."

"There is always a choice, Murphy. I . . . I don't want to live even a day without you."

"I wish I could go home, Elisa; you know how I feel. But there is something here I have to do." He touched her face and lay close to her. "England may well end up fighting alone. The American isolationists need to hear what's going on over here."

"They won't listen to you."

"Somebody will. There is a story that will have to be told. And what kind of man would I be if I leave when it gets too hot for comfort?"

"But I can't . . . don't want to raise this baby without you. Murphy, haven't we given enough? Done enough?"

"Your parents are still working with the refugee kids in spite of threats from the government that they are far too involved in politics. Can I do less?"

Elisa rolled over on her side to face him. Her eyes were bright in the soft light. Her look said all the things she had no words to say aloud. "I won't leave you, then. No matter what happens." She looked up at the sky. "If the stars fall right through this roof, I'll be here with you."

The image of falling bombs was too vivid for Murphy. *Madrid. Barcelona. Rows of children with blank eyes staring up into the sky. Incendiary bombs falling on the cities like stars . . .*

"Don't." Murphy put a finger on her lips. Warm and soft, those lips smiled at his touch. "We'll talk about it another time."

She was eager to think of other things. *Crickets beneath the oak trees of New Forest.* "Did you like the way I played my fiddle tonight?" she whispered.

"Kiss me," he murmured, pressing his mouth against hers. Here she was in his arms, two weeks away from having a baby, and yet he wanted her.

She chuckled, amused by his desire. "Your tastes have changed," she teased. "I never knew you were attracted to omnibuses."

"Depends on where they take me."

"It's a short ride to New Forest," she smiled. "And you've already ruined my figure. What have I got to lose?"

———————

Major Alexander Hess looked out at the thick pine forests of Poland as the Corridor Express train sped toward Danzig. Providence was smiling on him after his ordeal. He had been given the order to pursue the children of Karl Ibsen as far as he must in order to bring that case to a successful conclusion, but it seemed that his pursuit might have unexpected dividends.

The Führer had taken Hess's mutilated hand in his own hand and had given him this mandate: "If you cannot bring Karl Ibsen's children back alive to face him, then bring back their heads in a sack." He had smiled, but Hess knew well that the Führer was not joking. "In the diplomatic pouch if all else fails, ja? To which you may add the heads of resistance leaders and traitors," he concluded significantly.

Of course the Gestapo had agents in place in London to report if any word came to Elisa Murphy about the Ibsen children. Those agents, in turn, would report to Hess, and when the capture of Lori and Jamie Ibsen was accomplished, Helen Ibsen would also be eliminated. All of this would be done in a way that left no doubt as to the accidental death of the woman, of course. Although she had made no public statements about the imprisonment of her husband, the very fact that she was alive and capable of speech was still a matter of concern to the Ministry of Propaganda. Heads had rolled when it was reported she had escaped. That aspect of the case, of course, was of little concern to Hess. He demanded only that the woman be left alive as a possible source of information regarding her children. If Hess did not find them in Danzig, then he would follow them to France, or England, or Poland. He had promised the Führer that unlike Wallich and Wattenbarger, Pastor Karl Ibsen would not be allowed the luxury of death until he had made a full confession of conspiracy against the Fatherland. And if he would not bend, then he would witness the breaking of his children as a penalty for his obstinacy.

Danzig also held promise of the conclusion of a personal matter that had plagued Hess. Wolfgang von Fritschauer had been assigned to the area, and Hess was quite certain that in some way the man was still connected to Lucy Strasburg. If they were both involved in a smuggling ring on behalf of Jews and political dissidents, then Hess was resolved that he would bring both of them to justice as well.

Hess could never let anyone know the truth that it was Lucy's young companion who had held him at gunpoint and forced him from the train. To have admitted that would have destroyed his career. It was enough for Hess to greet Wolfgang von Fritschauer at the officer's brief-

ing last month and tell him that Lucy had been on board the Corridor
Express on the same night he was attacked.

Wolf had paled. Was it anger, or guilt? Perhaps Lucy Strasburg had
betrayed Wolf as well as Hess for the sake of those two Jewish children.
If that was the case, Wolf did not speak of it. He spoke of his weariness
of her; his relief that she was gone. Why, then, was the man so pale
at the mention of her name?

Hess felt a kind of disdain for von Fritschauer, whatever the truth
might be. He had been involved with a woman more vile and dangerous
than the Jews she protected. There was, indeed, room for more heads
in the diplomatic pouch. Hess had decided long ago that he must
question Lucy and then kill her, rather than attempt to take her back
to trial. That was the safest way to keep himself from disgrace. She
must not be allowed to give her account of the true circumstances of
his leap from the train. With the first twist of Gestapo thumb-screws,
the woman would be screaming that she had traveled with an officer
named Hess who was knocked out and held with his own gun by a
Jewish refugee boy.

A junior agent had been assigned to Hess in Danzig. Between them,
Hess was certain that the Ibsen matter and the issue of Lucy Strasburg
and Wolfgang von Fritschauer could be settled permanently.

He let the shade fall back and opened the basket of food that had
been prepared and packed by the Führer's own chef.

A thermos of tea. Sandwiches. Fruit and cheeses. Hess had brought
along his own bottle of schnapps, which he nursed discreetly. Everyone
knew that the Führer did not approve of the vice of alcohol—and
drinking was, indeed, one of the many vices of Major Alexander Hess.
He shrugged the thought away as the whistle shrieked the approach to
Danzig. He was, after all, conducting his own private celebration in
compartment 17.

It was a miracle, thought Karl Ibsen joyfully when the tiny sparrow
returned to the window ledge of his cell. Just a small miracle, but a
miracle nonetheless.

Karl dared not move from where he stood in the center of the cell.
The bird cocked its head in puzzlement at the sight of this human
canary in a cage. A grizzled creature, this human. Did no one ever
clean this cage or give water for the human to wash his boney, feath-
erless wings? A pitiful sight, this prisoner. No real bird trapped in a
cage was ever treated so badly as this.

Karl knew that he was only imagining the pity he saw in the tiny,
unblinking eyes of the sparrow, and yet, even imagined pity made him
feel . . . Feel what? What was this emotion that pushed inside his hol-

low chest? Had loneliness so deep and profound caused him to forget the feeling that now gripped him?

He looked toward the edge of his straw mattress. His ration of bread was wrapped carefully in the remaining rags of his shirt. "Stay," he whispered to the sparrow. "Stay and I will give you the best crumbs of my bread."

Karl decided the bird was a female. Drab brown color. Plain, unpretentious feathers. The tender, sympathetic look. Yes. A female. Had the bird been a male, it would have looked at Karl with terrible scorn. It would have hopped a slalom course around the bars to taunt Karl in a display of its freedom. "See?" it would have chirped. "Nothing to it. One hop and I am in the cell. One hop and I'm out. Spread my wings and I'm back in the forest. Not like you, old man!"

The lady sparrow lifted her head and looked beyond her beak at Karl as if to ask, "Whatever is to become of you?"

Karl replied aloud, "I don't know. Not in this life anyway. If I could fly . . . if I could fly away like you, then I would. Through the bars . . . Away. I would not mind leaving this life, and that's the truth. Only Jamie and Lori . . . my children . . ."

His voice became suddenly too unnerving for the little sparrow. There was too much passion here in this man-cage. Too much grief to be contained inside the brick walls. Like a terrible wind, the pent-up emotion of the prisoner broke loose and blew the lady sparrow from the window ledge. One flutter and she was gone. It was just too difficult—even for the tiny heart of a sparrow.

"Her name is Lucy." Wolf extended the photograph showing Lucy on the steps of St. Stephan's in Vienna. "Lucy Strasburg."

The stoop-shouldered doctor of the Marienbad Women's Hospital studied the slim and beautiful image for a moment and then shook his head slowly.

"I would remember such a patient. Your sister is very beautiful, Herr von Fritschauer. But—"

"Of course she won't look like this now, Herr Doktor. She is . . . her time must be very near."

"I would remember such a face." The doctor gazed a while longer. "Such innocence in her eyes. It is always the ones like your sister who end up being hurt by some fellow, yes? Pregnant, you say?"

Wolf bit his lip and stared at the picture of Lucy. He had never noticed the childlike expression on her face until now. *Innocent?* He had always imagined it was stupidity and country naivete. The doctor's words sent a fresh surge of anger through him. Lucy Strasburg was neither innocent nor stupid. She was clever and devious. She had made a fool out of Wolf, had she not?

Wolf was pale with emotion. The doctor touched his arm. "Are you unwell, Herr von Fritschauer?"

"This is an ordeal," Wolf mumbled, still staring into those wide eyes. "I have looked at every clinic. Every private doctor. No one has seen her. And you are right; she is not a woman one forgets easily."

"You were certain she was expecting when she disappeared?"

"Yes. Nearly four months."

"The father?"

"A lieutenant in the Army."

"He would not marry her?"

"He is married . . . an affair, you see. He has offered to care for the child, support my sister. She was ashamed. We know she came to Danzig. I have checked steamship lines, offered rewards. This picture . . . you may keep it. I have more. My name and telephone are on the back. If you see her . . . please . . . just call me. Do not attempt to detain her; she will only run again. Our mother is grief-stricken, of course. We only wish to help Lucy."

The doctor nodded slowly as he listened as though he were making a thoughtful diagnosis. "Yes. I will alert my nurses to the situation as well. If she is nearly full term, she will show up. It is certain. No woman would remain alone at such a time."

"That is what we have been praying for." Wolf returned the photograph to the doctor.

He glanced at it. "Where was this . . . taken?"

"St. Stephan's Cathedral in Vienna."

"She is maybe religious, your sister?"

It took a moment for the significance of the question to penetrate Wolf's consciousness. "Yes. *Yes!* Extremely. One of her little quirks."

The doctor laughed a short, knowing laugh. "Take it from a man who works with women. When a lover deserts a female, you will find her grieving one of two places—either to her physician or to her priest. If she has not been to one, then . . . ."

Wolf stared at the anatomy chart on the wall of the office. The doctor was right. Lucy the dreamer! Lucy the one who crossed herself before a meal or when passing a shrine on the street, or whenever she heard good news and bad alike! Why had Wolf not gone to the churches of Danzig before this? He had been a fool! He had been looking in places where she might find physical comfort, when he knew she was always looking wistfully at the spires and bell towers of churches they passed! He had teased her once that he was thankful she had not chosen the life of a nun because it would have ruined his pleasure. That remark had made her weep and admit that she had dreamed of such a life when she was a little girl.

He had laughed at her then. And he was laughing as he left the medical clinic and stared out over the spires of Danzig's great churches!

He was close now. Very close indeed! His city map had a directory of the port's many churches, listed by denomination. He ran his finger down the list as he whispered her name, "Lucy, Lucy, Lucy . . ."

Catholic churches. French. German. Polish.

The choices narrowed down to six German parishes scattered throughout Danzig. It was so simple! It was so certain! Wolf could not imagine that he had not thought of it himself. It had taken a healer of the body to remind him of Lucy's overworked concern for her soul! And now the scent was strong.

The train station of the Free City of Danzig was built to match the medieval architecture of the entire town. It looked like some ancient printer's woodcutting; a fifteenth-century engraving come to life.

Lucy Strasburg held Peter Wallich's hand as they walked in the shadows of the tall narrow houses of the old town. Sea birds played on the Baltic winds above the steep gables of the tall tight-packed buildings. A lone cloud scudded across the sky and threatened to impale itself on the spires of the enormous brick church known as Marienkirche.

There were flowers everywhere. Geraniums tumbled from the window boxes on every windowsill. In a small park opposite the train station, hundreds of tulips were planted to create the coat of arms of the last of the city-states; two yellow eagles flanking a red tulip shield.

This was not really the last of the city-states, Lucy thought as she looked at the flowers nodding in the breeze. Danzig and the Vatican City were the only two remaining historical oddities. Peter had told her all about the history of the place where they had fled four months before for refuge. Danzig flew its own flag over a tiny territory consisting of slightly more than 400,000 residents. The multitude of refugees who camped in shanty towns to the south were not counted in the population. The Baltic seaport issued its own currency, had an elected parliament, and was under the protection of the League of Nations. Danzig had a customs union with Poland and provided that great nation with its only access to the Baltic. The times when Danzig was not an independent state, it had been batted back and forth between Germany and Poland like a tennis ball. The Treaty of Versailles after the Great War in 1919 had wrenched Danzig from defeated Germany and brought it to its present precarious condition—claimed by Poland, coveted by Germany.

Lucy looked up to where a dozen Nazi flags spilled out from windows where flower boxes should have been. Even though the mailboxes were Polish and the uniforms of the customs officers were Polish, there was a nasty stirring among the German youth of Danzig. The Horst Wessel song was becoming quite popular. Even Sprinter's ice cream parlor with its glass-topped tables and immaculate wrought-iron chairs was becoming a gathering place for imitators of the Hitler Youth. On Thursdays there were Nazi rallies in the main square, and there was talk among the German population of returning to the Fatherland.

Peter warned Lucy that it was more than talk. Last week, he had placed his baby brother Willie in the arms of a stranger on a children's refugee ship. Then tearfully he had turned to Lucy and said, *"There. I have sent my heart away to England. Willie will be safe now. But there is no reason for me to stay here in this place. My mother and sister are never coming. I do not know what happened to them, but there is no use waiting here in Danzig for them to show up. They might have gone to Warsaw. We have old friends in Warsaw. Come with me, Lucy. Soon it will be as bad here in Danzig as it was in Vienna. Come with me to Warsaw to look for my mother and Marlene."*

Lucy had smiled and shrugged. How serious and concerned this boy sounded! Ah well, he was not really a boy any longer, was he? Peter Wallich had grown up since they had crossed the border of the Reich through the Polish corridor and gone on to Danzig. He was taller, still lean, but his face was fuller and tanned from his work on the wharf. He had done his part. He had taken care of his baby brother. When Lucy was too far along in her pregnancy to continue work as a shop clerk, Peter had managed to provide food for them both. But she could not go with him to Warsaw.

"I want you to come with me, Lucy," he said again. The sun glinted on his copper-colored hair. He looked toward the train station, then back to search her eyes.

"If you were ten years older I would say yes, Peter." She tried to keep her voice light.

"It is not safe here for you—or for me. And your baby is due. Come with me. We will find help in Warsaw, even if I do not find Mother and Marlene."

"You will find them. I am certain of it." Again the half smile of regret. "But, dear Peter, do you know what the Polish name for Danzig is? *Gdansk.* I can barely say it. I could never find work in Poland. The language is so—"

"You are German to the end."

"Ja. And so I'll take my chances here. We run from the same darkness, but for different reasons. My world cannot fit into your world. I have no friends in Poland . . ."

He pressed a slip of paper into her hand. "You do now, Lucy. You have me." He blushed a little at his own boldness.

Lucy knew he was in love with her, this tall, sensitive teenaged Jewish boy. It was flattering and touching, considering that she was unmarried and nearly nine months pregnant with the child of a Nazi S.S. officer. She opened the paper, half expecting some written declaration of his love. But Peter was more sensible than that. He had neatly printed the name and address of his Warsaw destination.

"Thank you." She kissed him lightly on the cheek. "You are a good friend to me, and I will not forget."

He looked away as the train whistle shrilled. "It seems to me they are playing our song again, eh?" He smiled to hide his emotion. "We said hello to that. And now goodbye." He took her hand and shook it as though she were a soccer teammate. "Well . . ."

"Auf Wiedersehen. And . . . *Grüssgott*," she said in her best Viennese accent. Then she held up the note. "I will write you. When the baby comes, ja?"

Again the whistle. If he didn't hurry, he would miss the train. Maybe he wanted to miss the train. His hand raised. His eyes lingered on her face as he stumbled up the steps. And then, he was gone. Peter Wallich was gone to Warsaw.

And Lucy Strasburg was alone—alone with the unborn child of Wolfgang von Fritschauer.

She almost wept, but then she squared her shoulders and turned away. "There are some things much worse than being alone," she whispered to herself.

————

The posters were everywhere it seemed—pasted on the news kiosks of London, on the walls of Victoria Station, in the subways, on the markets and stores of Oxford Street.

GAS ATTACK

Big white block letters splashed across a green background—there it was, right here in London: *HOW TO PUT ON YOUR GAS MASK: Always keep your gas mask with you, day and night. Learn to put it on quickly. Practice wearing it.*

It had become a regular drill in the house on Red Lion Square. On Monday, Wednesday and Friday evenings Murphy would unexpectedly call out, *GAS ATTACK!* This sent Charles, Louis, Elisa, and whoever happened to be around scrambling like mad to pull their masks out of the canvas pouches and put them on securely before Murphy shouted ALKA-SELTZER!

"If the mask is not in place by the time I call 'Alka-Seltzer,' " Murphy explained, "you lose."

To lose meant that everyone else got a piece of hard candy, while the loser had to practice putting on his or her gas mask five times in front of everyone else. Charles and Louis and Elisa never lost anymore. But sometimes company did. Charles enjoyed having company. Tonight, Dr. Patrick Grogan, speech therapist and English teacher to Charles and Louis, stayed for dinner, as he often did. He had never stayed for dinner on Monday, Wednesday or Friday, however, and so he was not prepared, even though Elisa warned him that there was likely to be a gas attack after dessert.

The alarm was given, and the mad rush for masks began . . . .

Everyone else sat happily around the table like a family of locusts while Dr. Grogan fumbled and blushed, his face matching his red hair.

"Sorry, Doc," Murphy said from behind the mask. His voice was muffled, as if he were talking into a tin can. "The word is ALKA-SELTZER! You lose!"

Charles and Louis clapped their hands with delight. They ripped off their nasty-bug masks and pointed at Dr. Grogan. Now they could get even for all the times he had made them do it again! *Practice! Practice! Practice! Come now, Charles, once again!*

Grogan was embarrassed. His round face flushed as he accused Murphy, "You planned this! You and these two little heathens! To get even with me. Come on now, admit it!"

Both boys nodded eagerly. Yes, they had planned it. That is why Charles had asked Elisa if Doc might eat with them tonight.

"Yes," Louis laughed.

"Yesssss," Charles agreed, giving the speech therapist a few extra *s's*, since they were a difficult sound for him to make. "Show us . . . how . . . to put it on, Doc!"

Dr. Grogan laughed. His big head rocked on his narrow shoulders and he laughed until his chubby belly ached. Wispy red hair, thinning on top, stood straight up from his first attempt in the Alka-Seltzer drill. He looked like a pudgy little leprechaun in from a windstorm.

Charles liked him, even if he did make him drill hour after hour. Elisa liked him because he was good with the boys. Murphy liked him for a lot of reasons, one of which was that he was American like Murphy.

Murphy passed out the cherry candy while Doc struggled to put on the mask.

"Say it, Doc Grogan!" Louis demanded. "Say the steps!"

"Okay! Okay! Little *heathen*! *Mary and Martha!*" This was Doc's way of saying *good grief*, Charles knew.

"Put it on!" Charles plopped his candy into his mouth and sat back to watch the show.

Doc nodded his big head. "One. *Hold your breath!*" He held his breath and fumbled with the mask. His face got redder. He let out his breath and exclaimed, "How can I hold my breath and recite the blasted steps of this torture?"

"Okay. We'll *say* it," Murphy instructed. "You *do* it." Then Elisa held up her hands like a conductor and they all recited the process together:

"One. *Hold your breath*. Two. *Hold mask in front of face with thumbs inside. . . . INSIDE*, yes. Like that . . . straps. Three . . ." Three was always Charles's favorite part to watch because people who did not practice always made such awkward faces.

"*Thrust chin well forward into mask.*" Out went the chin that was hardly a chin at all. Doc Grogan was mostly shoulders from the ears down, like a bulldog. *Like one of Winston Churchill's bulldogs,* Charles thought. He stuck out his lower jaw and bit his upper lip as he struggled to fit his face into the mask. This was the best-ever after-dinner entertainment! The absolute best!

Elisa laughed and held her big pregnant belly. She begged Doc not to be so funny because it hurt to laugh now that she was so far along. Murphy raised his eyebrows and made his best donkey laugh. A sort of *Hoo-haw-haw-hoo.* Charles and Louis hung on to each other lest they fall out of their chairs at the sight of their taskmaster being taken to task!

At last the bright red face was secure behind the googly eyes of the locust mask. Orange hair protruded from the straps like antenna. Doc Grogan tugged the straps secure to complete the instruction of number three. Then, because everyone else was unable to speak, he completed the process.

"Number four!" he shouted through the mask. "*Run finger around face-piece, taking care head-straps are not twisted.*" He crossed his arms in satisfaction and turned to address Charles and Louis. "Wait until your next lesson, me boy-o's."

They were not intimidated. Still, they hooted on as the eyes of the gas mask fogged up.

"Can I take it off and have some candy too?" Off came the torture device, leaving a flaming red crease around Doc's face. Murphy tossed him a candy as he smoothed his hair and glared at the thing. "Don't make me do it again. I beg you. *Mary and Martha!* What a torment! They would be laughing at us in Berlin if they could see what we do in London for entertainment!"

Tears of glee were wiped away. *Would the grown-ups talk politics again tonight? Of course.*

"Not that we will ever need these things," Elisa said as she stacked the dishes. "But at least the British government is finally taking Hitler seriously."

Ever since the Nazis had taken over Czechoslovakia in March, the sandbags around the government buildings in London had been sprouting, multiplying and finally towering like great lumpy heaps of laundry.

They were there around the Houses of Parliament, at the steps of Whitehall, and the foreign office. They protected the trenches dug in Kensington Park and Hyde Park and Grosvener Square, to name just a few.

It was not as if most people really expected war, or actually believed that Germany would press the issue of taking Danzig and the Polish corridor from Poland. Herr Hitler would not go that far, would he? "You bet he would," Murphy said. That was why he took the gas masks seriously. But for most of England, all of this was just precaution, a way to soothe the nerves of the more jittery types in government. And when the sandbags split after the spring rains and weeds began to sprout, there was a big row in Parliament about the matter. After all, there was supposed to be *sand* in the sandbags, not just ordinary garden soil! Then a member of Prime Minister Chamberlain's party suggested that the sandbags serve double duty. Why not plant a few carrots and turnips in the things?

This idea got the biggest laugh the House had heard for weeks.

That same week it was decided that something must be done to demonstrate that England was serious about defense. Murphy was among a troop of fifty journalists who set sail on board the aircraft carrier *Ark Royal* with the earl of Stanhope, first lord of the admiralty, and Colonel Beck, Poland's foreign minister.

As the ship plowed across the Channel, tours were given of the bridge and the galleys, the officers' quarters and the engine room. The day was crowned with an exclusive showing of *Snow White and the Seven Dwarfs.* Midway through the film, two dozen officers hustled out. The movie was stopped in the middle of vital action. The first lord then stood before the image of Dopey the dwarf and announced that the order had been given to put the entire British fleet on alert. "That explains these empty seats," he said calmly as Dopey looked down from the screen.

Murphy felt certain that Walt Disney would be relieved that no one had walked out on his epic by choice. . . .

Photographs of the first lord of the admiralty being upstaged by an animated dwarf made the front pages of a number of publications. *Life Magazine* dedicated a whole page to it, and the British government could almost hear the great guffaws of the German Reich.

Maybe Britain and France were finally taking Germany seriously, but it was a sure bet that Hitler no longer felt that either great nation was much more threat than a band of Disney dwarfs on the rampage.

"You think there will be war then?" Dr. Grogan asked with a hint of disbelief in his voice.

Elisa hustled Charles and Louis up the stairs and out of earshot from Murphy's answer.

He sipped his coffee and waited until their bedroom door was closed. "Unless you want to be in the thick of it," Murphy replied quietly, "I'd start looking into fares back to the States." He raised his eyes toward the room of Charles and Louis. "When it starts—"

"When?"

"When it starts, I'm sending them home. To my folks' place in Pennsylvania. London is a two-hour bomb run from Berlin. I saw what the German Air Force did in Spain, and they were not even officially there." He made the slow whistling sound of a bomb dropping and then the thud of an explosion as he gestured out the window.

Grogan inclined his massive head thoughtfully. "You can't think it will come to that. Chamberlain has given the Führer *carte blanche,* hasn't he? As long as jolly old England is not involved?"

Murphy shrugged. Nobody ever said that a thirty-year-old speech therapist was supposed to understand what was going on. "You'd better make all the notes you can about the structure and use of the English language. Unless something happens, Hitler figures that the whole world will be speaking German. You get me?"

Doc opened his mouth as if to argue the point, but a heavy knocking at the door interrupted what was proving to be an interesting discussion.

With a raised finger, Murphy warned Grogan to hold his thought while he answered the knock.

Harvey Terrill, the overworked night desk editor of TENS burst through the door. Waving an envelope, he pushed past Murphy.

"This came by special courier, Boss! Look! Look at this! Addressed to Elisa *Murry,* care of TENS London!" He slapped the envelope into Murphy's hand. He stammered on, pointing to the return address. "Lori Ibsen! Ain't that the kid who got Timmons into trouble in Berlin? The kid you been lookin' for all these months?"

Murphy turned to call for Elisa, but she was already rushing down the stairs.

"Yes!" Elisa was laughing. *"Lori!* Murphy! Call Mama! Call Aunt Helen! Oh, *Murphy!"*

7

Never Too Much for God

Charles and Louis banged on the steam radiator with a wooden spoon. This was the signal to Freddie and Hildy Frutschy in their apartment below that they were needed.

Freddie was sent in the automobile to fetch Anna and Theo and Aunt Helen while Murphy telephoned Winston Churchill with the news that the children of Pastor Ibsen were alive and well in Danzig. From there calls were made to the British home office and the decision was made that the children should be contacted through the British Consulate in Danzig.

While Hildy Frutschy made pots of coffee and tea, Harvey Terrill hurried down to the cafe to purchase a chocolate cake. Then an unplanned celebration began.

Pastor Williams arrived, and people from the church came to embrace Aunt Helen and see the letter with their own eyes. It was a miracle, it seemed, after so long! *And was there any word of Pastor Ibsen as well?*

No. The miracle was only partly complete. Lori and Jamie Ibsen had escaped Germany along with three other children, Jacob and Mark Kalner and Alfie Halder. They were all quite safe, but the letter asked if Elisa had heard from Pastor Karl and Helen Ibsen or the Kalners.

> *We thought to travel to Prague as Father instructed us, but now that the Nazis are there as well, we do not know where to go. There is no office for TENS news here in Danzig or we might have gone. The people here in Danzig are German, and many among them now favor Hitler. We have heard the threats of the Nazis against Poland, and although we are well and not threatened personally, we fear what may be coming here to Danzig. I pray that you will receive*

this letter if you are still in London, as you were when Mother spoke
of you. I am not certain of the spelling of your last name but pray
this will fall into the right hands and be directed to you. We miss
our parents very much. Have you any word. . . ?

Helen Ibsen sat in the rocking chair by the window and read the
letter from her daughter in English to whoever wanted to hear it. Always
at this place in the writing she cried as she had the first time.

"My children are alive," she said. "You see? The Lord is still in the
business of miracles!" Pressing the letter to her heart she added softly.
"And if Jamie and Lori are safe, then perhaps also my Karl, ja? It is not
too much to hope for. Not too much for God!"

———————

Lodgings had been arranged for Allan Farrell in the Bloomsbury
district of London. Mills University Hotel at 107 Gower Street was located not far from the British museum. The charge of fifty shillings a
week for students still would have been steep for Allan had it not been
for the supplement of his meager income by a modest bank account
from the IRA.

The money was transferred weekly from New York as though he
had some caring benefactor in the States. *"A small stipend,"* Colin had
told him. *"Call it a reward for your assistance, if you like."*

In truth, Allan's assignment was so insignificant that he felt almost
ashamed. He was nothing more than an errand boy, a messenger of
sorts. It was not what he had expected. It seemed almost beneath the
dignity of a son of Maureen Farrell. The stories of her exploits were
still fresh in the long memories of the Irish. She had made orphans of
many Englishmen's sons in her day and had rocked the corridors of
Parliament at the mention of her name!

Sheepishly, Allan argued with the proprietor of the Mills Hotel over
an extra weekly charge for boot cleaning and the washing of bed linen.
For the princely sum of fifty shillings a week, such amenities should
be provided as part of the service.

The proprietor cocked an eye at him and mumbled something about
rich Yanks wanting everything for nothing. Allan explained that this
service was listed in his guidebook and that anything less would be a
breach of the printed promise. And so his still-muddy boots were
placed outside the door to his small corner room. Clean sheets were
promised every Monday provided the fifty shillings was paid one week
in advance. One bathroom was shared by five other tenants of the
boardinghouse, although Allan did have his own washbasin. Rules and
regulations of the establishment were printed and posted on the door
of each room. Breakfast and dinner were included in the charge. Luncheon and tea were a matter of the lodger's choice of various plain

restaurants about the neighborhood.

Allan felt as though he had landed in high society after a lifetime of wondering where his next meal was coming from. All of this, and his only task was to meet with a couple of fellows who needed to exchange notes!

Allan frowned, certain that this job had been manufactured just for him because he was the son of Maureen Farrell. Like an orphan's pension, the egg-head scholar-boy was being taken care of because his mother had been a great woman.

It was a disgusting thought, one which brought a flush of shame to Allan's cheeks. *How could it be anything else?*

"I am a postman, Mother," he mumbled as he gazed out over the foot traffic of Gower Street. "Well paid for it, too. Room and board, with my boots shined each week like a gentleman."

He touched the scar beneath his eye, the scar he had gotten in Hell's Kitchen as a boy. He had worn that scar like a badge of manhood, never hinting that it had been a girl who hit him with a brick to cause that scar. Asthma had kept him small and weak as a child. Books had kept him company, filling his mind with dreams of adventure.

So here he was, the son of Maureen Farrell—an errand boy.

He shook his head slowly, certain of how this had all come to pass. *"You wrote Uncle Colin, didn't you, Mother?"* he whispered against the glass. *"Told him to look out for me?"*

It was the truth. There could be no other explanation. She was like that, Maureen was—a strong woman who got her way, even from the grave. He could almost hear the letter she must have written: *Young Allan is going to London to study. I've saved a bit ... not a well boy, even now ... For the sake of his pride, Colin, as a favor to me....*

They had all commented on how much he favored her, had they not? She was small and delicate-looking herself. *Ah well,* Allan thought as he looked around the room, *I will do what they asked and pretend it matters to the cause all the same.* He had spent his life pretending, wishing ... remembering he was the son of Maureen.

"I sense the imagination of the lovely Mrs. Murphy behind this request," commented Winston Churchill. "You, Murphy, are only the messenger. Isn't that so?"

"Right as always, Winston. Elisa doesn't travel far these days. As much as she enjoys coming here to Chartwell for visits, she would rather not have the baby here."

"I cannot understand why not," rumbled Churchill. "Most of my brilliant ideas are hatched right here. Why not a little Murphy? In any case, tell her that I will be very pleased to speak at a rally in support of the plight of Pastors Ibsen and Niemöller and the others. Even in their imprisonment, they continue to shine as beacons of righteousness amid the Nazi dark, and we must let them—and more importantly, Herr Hitler—know that they are not forgotten. Have you selected a location?"

"We hope that there will be an enormous turnout, so we plan to use one of the great churches. Perhaps even St. Paul's."

"And the date?"

"Elisa would like to participate in the orchestra, so she wants to allow some time after the baby's arrival—around the end of August, say."

Churchill thrust his hands deep into the pockets of his dressing gown and thrust out his jaw as he nodded. "We must trust that the Nazi terror has not given birth to the child of war before then," he said.

———

These were the days of arrivals and departures in Warsaw. Across the rooftops of apartments and houses, the train whistle would scream beneath the tin roof of the *Umschlagplatz*. Only a short time later the first groups of newcomers would straggle up Niska Street or Pokorna Steet to arrive with their bundles in Muranow Square.

Some came in search of relatives or old friends. Some came to Warsaw because they could lose themselves among the hundreds of thousands of Poland's Jewish community. All the same, they had a different look about them than Polish Jews. Ragged bundles and cheap suitcases were carried by the lucky ones. Those less fortunate arrived wearing all their possessions. Even in the heat of summer, they bore coats slung over their shoulders or tied onto the top of a valise. The more experienced among the refugees knew that it might be hot now, but that surely a cold winter was coming for every Jew in Europe.

Rachel was sweeping the front steps when the shrill cry of the train whistle announced that shortly new people would come to Muranow Square. Over the rooftops she could see the thick gray haze from the locomotives, as though this dark cloud had come with the wanderers, following them into Warsaw to pollute the blue sky with gloom.

She was watering the rhododendrons when the first family groups reached the square from different routes. Father, mother and two little boys arrived from Niska Street. From the cut of their clothes, Rachel could tell that they were from Czechoslovakia. Only secular Jews from Prague wore caps such as the man had on his head. The woman carried a coat with a silver fox collar. *They must have been wealthy before the Germans came,* Rachel thought.

An overweight man and woman and two teenaged girls limped around the corner of Porkorna Street. *German.* It was as plain as anything. The man was red-faced and had the look of an overworked owner of a beer cellar. The faces of his wife and daughters were flushed from exertion, their mouths twisted downward with disdain and bitterness. They looked around the square at trams and trees and benches. Everything was quite different from Germany and so could not be quite as good. The girls watched as a black-coated Hassid walked by twirling his earlock thoughtfully on his finger. They stared. Such sights were not common in Germany. *Perhaps some grandfather has fled the tyranny of Orthodox life in Poland, bringing his family to live in civilized Germany,* Rachel mused as she leaned against her broom and considered them. *And now look what German civilization offers them in return! Papa says they all would eventually come back to Poland, a thousand times worse off than when they had left!*

Behind this portly German family came a tall, lean red-headed young man, his frame tilted sideways as if the weight of his battered suitcase was going to pull him over. He wore no cap. By this, Rachel knew that he was a secular Jew. Those among her people who were religious always covered their heads with some sort of hat. But this drawn-looking young man had a bare head. His red hair stuck up wildly as if to emphasize his rebellion in this small tradition. He wore a heavy camel-hair overcoat, which added some size to an otherwise thin frame.

Rachel followed him with her eyes. He was the most interesting of the new refugees. He was not much older than she was, yet he was alone. No family. No companion. So youthful, and yet alone. Such a visage spoke of tragedy and ill fortune.

In his free hand, he held a crumpled piece of paper—probably with an address or a name written on it. Had his family sent him out of Germany to the safety of relatives in Warsaw? Was his father in prison perhaps, or his mother too sick to flee the Nazi regime with him?

He looked from the paper to the street sign on the corner and then back again at the paper. His face puckered in thought. His eyes narrowed as he mopped his brow with the sleeve of his elegant coat. A fine coat, a man's coat, not originally cut for him. Rachel wondered who had owned the coat before this red-headed young man. Perhaps his father? Or his uncle? Maybe someone dragged off in the terrible pogrom of November?

Beyond them, the trains of the Umschlagplatz whistled their farewell to Warsaw. On the departing trains were Jews of Polish origin who knew Warsaw too well to consider it safe to remain. Rachel knew that they would soon be playing out this same scene on the other end of the rail line. Straggling into a city square, checking their scribbled addresses against unfamiliar street signs, shifting luggage from one weary arm to the other. . . .

By the time they realized that every place in Europe was the same for a Jew, the homes and flats they had vacated in Warsaw would be filled by these.

Rachel looked up at the slate roofs of the buildings of Muranow Square. Like the set on a theater stage, everything looked the same. The parts were simply to be played by different actors.

She turned away and looked at the facade of her home. Big and yellow, it was a bright flower among lesser blooms in the garden. She had been born here; it was the only home she had ever known. Happy times and sad times had been played out within the safety of those walls. She had looked out her window and seen the first snowfall, the first bud on the great elm trees in the square. And yet now, her mother and father dreamed of leaving this place forever—boarding a train that would carry them far away from Muranow, far away from Warsaw and Poland! But were not all places the same when the tracks finally ended and the last whistle blew?

Such thoughts filled Rachel's young heart with despair. In his fevered dreams Papa moaned about sending them away to Palestine. *"Leave me, Etta!"* he cried to Mama. *"Take the little ones before it is too late!"*

Then Mama soaked a cool cloth and dabbed his forehead, assuring him that there was still lots of time for him to get well.

Rachel traced the path of the red-haired young man, the solitary stranger with no one to walk with on the crowded street. The sight of him made her shudder, as though his visage carried some portent of her own future. *Oh, Eternal!* Her heart cried out with pity for him and pity for herself. *I do not ever want to be like him! Please! Never alone! Alone in a strange land!*

It was better to stay, she decided that afternoon. Better to sit at Papa's bedside, to know the fate of every member of her beloved family! If she were ever given the choice to flee for her life or stay in Muranow Square with her mama and papa and little brothers, Rachel knew what she would do!

She watched the young wanderer until he dodged behind a clanging train and disappeared up Niska Street past the young couple with the two small sons. Only then did she retreat to the safety of the big yellow house on Muranow.

———

There were only thirty-six men in the meeting room of Albert Forster, Danzig's top Nazi official. Wolf stood before them with Gautleiter Forster at his side. He considered the expression on the face of each man. Age and features were all different, and yet the hardness of the eyes, the nodding of heads, the sense that each man was a coiled spring gave the group an almost identical look.

"You are the core of all that will come to Danzig," Forster cried as though he were speaking to thousands. "Only thirty-six men, and yet you are chosen to represent a thousand! You thirty-six will change the history of Danzig and so the history of the world as we know it forever!"

Forster paused, just as Wolf had heard the Führer pause for his audience to fire themselves further with applause and cheers. *Albert Forster is good,* Wolf thought. Berlin had made the right choice in this man. He had mastery over his officers. He lit a fire in their hearts with the promises he echoed from faraway Berlin! *They would make a difference! They would rid their world of Untermenschen. Danzig—and indeed all the East—must be scraped clean and purified by fire for the New World!*

The cheering died reluctantly, and Forster introduced Wolf as the personal emissary of the leaders of the Reich. More cheering erupted. The thirty-six hooted as if they were thirty-six thousand strong! Wolf let them yell, let them break into the Horst Wessel song and scrape back their chairs to stand at proud attention. He sang with them. He raised his arm to the swastika flag on the standard at the front of the room. Among these men he was not the quiet wine merchant on business in Danzig. He was the personal representative of the Führer. Wolf enjoyed the heady feeling of his own power.

The song ended. The thirty-six Brownshirts took their seats and waited in utter silence to hear what the spirit of Hitler would say through the mouth of Major Wolfgang von Fritschauer. Wolf let them wait. . . .

"In the name of Adolf Hitler, I greet you. *You,* who have been waiting here in Danzig for this final release! *You,* who have watched from afar the slow progression of the Reich across the land. I tell you now that *you* now are given the key of all power to unlock the door for the German race and their leader!"

The silence was profound, as though a holy rite were taking place.

Wolf began again. His Prussian accent was closer to the dialect of these men than to that of the party leaders in Berlin. Wolf recognized the profound effect this had on the thirty-six.

"The Führer has declared that Danzig must be united with Germany. Poland and England and France now say that such an event will result in war." Again he paused, letting the word *war* take effect. Stronger than love, stronger than hate, war stirred the passion and imagination of young men like nothing else, just as the idea of motherhood for the state had captured the hearts of the young men as their rite of passage. Bad music and bad reasons all sounded good and righteous and able beneath the banner of race and blood-brotherhood! To savor the bread broken with comrades made the values of war not only acceptable, but desirable. The Führer knew the hearts of his people well.

"For the sake of the German folk and German culture, the Führer sends you this promise: There will be war! War against the enemies of the Aryan people! It is inevitable, comrades. And it will begin here. With *you! In Danzig!*"

And so it was said. The Port of Danzig was not negotiable. Poland and England and France had thrown down the gauntlet. They had finally drawn a line, faint and uncertain though it was. The Führer had determined to step over it, and soon. These thirty-six, and thousands behind them, would provide the front line division when the moment arrived.

The certainty of it was a relief. All the youth of Germany had been impregnated by the great god of war. And now, here in Danzig, the bloody child of Death was about to be born.

It was a moment of deep reflection for the few gathered in the little room. Like apostles, they had been chosen to stir the hearts of their young soldiers to follow the crusade! There was no man in attendance who did not feel blessed by some vast force at that moment, filled by some unexplained power, lifted by the dark glory of blood and death!

"You have heard the words of the Führer. If there is to be a war, then let it begin on this issue . . . *Danzig!* Even as he meets the challenge of our enemies, he looks to *you,* depends on *your* loyalty and dedication!"

The rest of the meeting drifted into the practical mechanics of beginning a war. Demonstrations must increase within the Free City of Danzig. The summer must be marred by wave after wave of boycotts and strikes by dock workers and transit employees. Those who did not cooperate must be dealt with severely. German deaths must be attributed to the Polish government and, above all, violence must be pushed to such a degree that Poland would be required to act with force against these leaders and their men.

Yes, they would face death. They themselves might be martyrs to the cause of *One Reich, One Folk, One Führer!* In that they would find a kind of eternal life; eternal memory.

Planned demonstrations must appear spontaneous and widely separated throughout the territory. When Poland stepped in, the German battleships would be standing ready in the gulf of Danzig.

———

Once again the wine merchant, Wolf slipped out the back door of Albert Forster's offices. The long, low bellow of a foghorn sounded in the dark harbor. The port was quiet, but Wolf knew that even now an entire fleet of U-boats prowled beneath the Baltic Sea just outside of Danzig.

The streets of the city seemed deserted as well, and yet Wolf felt the presence of something . . . *someone* . . . watching him from the shadows. *British agents? French? Polish?* It did not matter. Let them watch and speculate on the late-night meeting of the German wine merchant with Albert Forster. Let them put whatever meaning they desired on it. If it stirred them to action against the ever-growing Nazi party in Danzig, then that act would only speed the beginning of the war. So much the better. Wolf was impatient. All of Germany was impatient. The baying of hounds had gone on too long for the liking of any hunter. It was time for blood to color the landscape. Let it come quickly.

All that was left was the title page. Orde stared at the blank sheet of paper for a moment and then printed in block letters the title of his *magnum opus*:

MILITARY TRAINING MANUAL
JEWISH DEFENSE FORCES
OF THE NATION OF ISRAEL
Compiled by
CAPT. SAMUEL ORDE, *In service to his King*

Never mind that there was no nation of Israel. Never mind that British Parliament had gone back on every promise it had ever made to the Jewish people since 1917. Parliament was not the last word, and the King whom Orde served was not the king of England.

No training manual for any army had ever been written quite like this one. Not only was it filled with practical firsthand knowledge about the art of desert warfare, it was reinforced with passages of Scripture, reminders of ancient battles in this same land and the covenant an unchanging God had made with His chosen people.

Now it was finished. Orde laid down his pen and wrapped the two hundred hand-written pages in butcher paper from the Hanita kibbutz kitchen. He tied up the precious package with twine and scrawled across the front: *For my brothers and sisters, my adopted family by the great blessing of our one Lord and King.* He signed his Hebrew name, *Hayedid. The Friend.*

Orde took one last look around the tent he had made his headquarters. He had known what was coming. His heart had warned him, although his mind had resisted. Every additional day he had spent with his men had been a gift. But now the gift of time had run out. Orde felt somehow that all his life had been spent in preparing him for these few months with what he believed was the foundation of an army for a nation yet to be reborn. This was the beginning for them. But what was it for him? What purpose would his life hold now?

He tucked the manuscript under his arm as though it contained orders from the highest general. Perhaps it did, he thought, tugging his beret into its proper angle.

At any rate, the manual was his legacy—his gift of every minute scrap of knowledge he had gleaned from his career as a fighting man. He closed his eyes a moment and prayed that it would be enough to sustain these men he loved, as well as those who followed after them and fought for the survival of the Jewish people. In his prayer, Sam Orde offered back to God what had been given to him. He asked no further blessing on his own life. He felt that he had been set aside by his King; now his life had no further purpose except to float and spin away the time he had left to live.

The skies above Galilee were bright, but Orde felt only darkness above him as he passed down the long line of his troops. They stood proudly at attention as he had taught them the first day he was with them. Now, instead of ragged work clothes, they wore clean pressed khakis for the occasion of their farewell. On their heads were the jaunty Australian bush hats that Orde had demanded from British ordnance and gotten after months of badgering.

Zach Zabinski called for the troops to salute Hayedid a final time. Orde returned the honor and then passed the manuscript into Zabinski's hands as one dying soldier might pass a standard to another.

"It is all there, Zach," he said in a low voice. "God willing, I will come back someday and review the troops of a proper nation." He managed a smile. *"Baruch Hashem."*

Zach saluted again, then tucked the manual beneath his arm as Orde had carried it. How everything had changed because of this one man! They had survived the most terrible of all winters and then a bloody spring because of Samuel Orde.

"Baruch Hashem, dear Hayedid. Shalom to you."

———

Charles carried Elisa's violin case into the TENS office. Murphy had told her not to carry anything but the baby, and so the boys had enthusiastically taken their chief at his word. They fetched glasses of water, cleared the supper table of dishes, swept the steps and, today, took turns cradling the cherished violin on their way to meet Murphy for lunch.

Murphy's face looked *growly,* as Elisa described it. Charles could clearly see him through the glass partition of his office as they moved through the bustling desks of the journalists.

"Lousy news from Palestine, Mrs. Murphy," one of the younger men called.

"What's with you, Jack?" chided another. "You always have to be the first with the bad news? That's sick!"

"That's why he's a journalist!"

"Ah, you're all sick!"

Smiling through the barrage of American banter, Elisa guided the boys past hands that reached out to muss their hair and sticks of gum tossed their way.

She knocked timidly on the glass door. Murphy was talking angrily to Harvey Terrill and waving a slip of paper in the air.

"So get hold of Mike Tracy in Cairo, that's all!" Murphy said, and then he motioned Elisa and the boys to enter as Harvey slipped out past them with a pained look on his face.

"What's all this about?" Elisa asked, giving him a kiss as he hefted the boys onto his desk.

"Nothing. Well, *something*, but we'll manage."

"Palestine? Jerusalem?" Elisa asked anxiously as Charles looked at Murphy's face for a clue. Leah and Shimon Feldstein were in Palestine. There was a war in Palestine. Just this morning Elisa had read them some parts of a letter from Leah. She had skipped others, in spite of the fact that Charles and Louis had begged for every word to be read. And now the men in the newsroom had mentioned Palestine.

"First the good news. There's a truce. Temporary to be sure, but the fighting has stopped. The bad news is strictly business. We've just lost our best correspondent in Palestine."

"You only have one."

"Right. Samuel Orde."

"Dead?" Elisa gasped.

"Not killed. Just reprimanded and posted out of Palestine by the British Army. He'll be on his way back to England at the strong insistence of the Arab Higher Committee."

"Oh. I'm sorry." Elisa did not sound very sorry, Charles thought. She sounded more relieved than anything. She was smiling again, talking about a BBC concert rehearsal and ordinary things like how she and Anna and Helen found perfect wallpaper for the baby's room. But Charles and Louis knew the big secret!

Murphy took his coat and hat from the rack and herded them out to the maze of desks where Freddie waited beneath the awning while a steady rain pelted the slick cobbles.

"Will y' be long, sar?" Freddie shook drops of rain from the shoulders of his slicker. "The missus has a few things for me to pick up."

Murphy gladly released their toothless giant to the task of running errands. Freddie's wife, Hildy, had taken up the additional duties as cook for them for the last few weeks, while Freddie had provided an imposing wall of protection for Elisa, Anna, and the boys. This arrangement seemed ideal.

"Take the rest of the afternoon if you like. I'll see Elisa home."

Freddie was granted use of the automobile, and the hungry foursome hugged the facades of the buildings on Threadneedle Street as they hurried through the pouring rain. It was a short walk to the one pub in London where nearly every patron spoke American and thought American and was, in fact, American. Murphy liked the place because of its familiarity to his homeland. Elisa and the boys liked it because it was quite different from any other atmosphere in London.

The publican was an Irishman who had multiple cousins in America, and so was forever up-to-date on the latest stateside news. He had letters from nearly every major U.S. metropolis and could pull them from under the counter at will to recite the home-front news to homesick Americans.

As the foursome entered the close-packed room, the publican was reading the latest news about the IRA bombing. He looked up and spotted Murphy, then hailed him as one Irishman to another.

"The British hate us, y' know, brother Murphy!"

"Can you blame them?" Murphy called back cheerfully.

At that, a dozen greetings were shouted out from various booths which lined the dark paneled wall, separated by wood partitions inset with beveled glass. Brass gas lamps had been converted to electricity and illuminated each table with poor light and shadows that concealed the faces of the diners. The whole place buzzed like a Waterloo railway station, and the smells of smoke mingled with the aroma of fish and chips and warm ale.

Everyone towered over Charles and Louis. People whom they had never met before greeted them as if they were related. Elisa explained that this was not bad manners, but simply an American eccentricity. It was okay with Charles. He had decided long before that he liked Americans a lot. He just smiled a gap-toothed smile and shouted "Hi'ya" right back at them. Helen, Theo, and Anna sat in the back corner booth. Their faces in shadow, it was hard to see them until Theo shifted in his seat and the light brushed over his amused features.

Murphy raised his hand and inched toward them as a stranger brushed by and remarked, "Hey, we got Krauts back there now. Whole place is being taken over by the Nazis, wouldn't you know?"

Murphy ignored him and pushed on. Now he could see that Anna was smiling broadly. It was an expression Murphy had not seen on her face for a long time.

"What's up?" he asked as they slid into the booth.

"Good news!" Theo proclaimed. "Or . . . maybe you have already heard?"

"I'm the last to hear anything. You know that." It was clear from the smug expression on Elisa's face that she also knew the news but had waited until now to share.

"*I* know," Charles giggled.

Murphy feigned unhappiness. "Everybody knows but me, then. Not a good recommendation for the chief of a news bureau, is it?" He had already guessed that the news concerned Helen Ibsen's attempt to contact her children. Smiles all around could mean only one thing.

"Tell him, Helen," Anna urged her sister.

Helen opened her mouth as if to speak, but tears of joy and gratitude choked off the words. "Anna?" she asked.

"All right then." Murphy put on his best newsman scowl. "We've got a deadline, you know. An hour for lunch. Somebody tell me."

Charles raised his hand as Doc Grogan had taught him when he had the answer. Louis' hand went up higher.

"Okay, Charles."

The news exploded from him. "The kids!"

Louis followed. "In Danzig!"

"They was on the telephone!"

"All the way from Danzig."

Suddenly everyone was talking at once. They were all fine. Not hungry or ragged. They lived in a two-room apartment in the older district of the city. Terribly homesick for Helen, they wanted only to get to England as quickly as possible. Theo had already wired funds through American Express to take care of steamer tickets the minute their papers were in order.

"I know Karl has been praying for them," Helen finished the story softly. Her hands trembled as she fingered her soup spoon. "He has prayed, and soon our children will be home."

8

By Dying I Conquer

Before today, Sam Orde had not realized how many prized possessions he had accumulated in three years of service in Jerusalem. Now, each precious item he had purchased in the souks or unearthed on Mount Zion posed a problem for him. How could he take them all with him to England?

Two packing crates were allotted to him. Two were not enough. They sat open and empty on the stone floor of his quarters in the Old City barracks. His cot was cluttered with an assortment of notebooks and rare volumes, ancient maps and parchments gleaned from the antique shops. The smaller things were of no concern. Arrow tips from the archers of Rome. Half a dozen coins from the time of Christ. A stone inkwell discovered near the ruins of an ancient synagogue. Orde stuffed these items into his empty boots.

But how to carry the two rare Persian prayer rugs? And the shofar in the inlaid mahogany box? And the silver menorah candlestick cast in the shape of an oak tree by a long-forgotten Jewish silversmith? His carved desk?

He sat down heavily and sighed. His gaze lingered on a square hand-hewn block of Jerusalem stone against his wall. Long ago marking the resting place of some fallen Crusader, the stone was carved with a cross and bore the chiseled Latin inscription *BY DYING I CON-QUER LIFE*. Orde had found it face down among the boulder-strewn rubble at the foot of the Mount of Olives. With the permission of Mother Superior at the Russian convent, he had carried the stone away, cleaned it, and spent many long hours wondering about the man who had lain beneath it. This odd reminder of his own mortality had become his most cherished possession. At one hundred pounds, its weight alone exceeded the limits imposed on personal shipping for the military. His Majesty's government could not be expected, after all, to make room for personal goods on military shipping. Otherwise, every retiring staff sergeant and major would be returning home with enough goods to open an antique store in Bloomsbury.

Somehow, Orde had not imagined that the stone would ever be a problem. He remained in Jerusalem with the feeling that he would be buried here one day, that the ancient Crusader stone would mark his grave as well.

"By dying I conquer life," he whispered, feeling the sting of being singled out as the example of British military folly for the Arab Council. Indeed, at this moment, he considered how much easier it might have been to have died with honor, to conquer unjust life by falling in this undeclared war. He ran his fingers through his close-cropped brown hair and looked around the small room that had been his home for three years. Nobody ever said that life was fair. Better a captain than a colonel, after all. And banishment back to England and the end of a military career was not the absolute end of everything.

Orde glanced over his things and considered his alternatives. The Army might rob him of his occupation, but he would not be forced to leave his belongings behind. He would travel by private freighter rather than military transport. Tomorrow he would buy a steamer trunk and purchase his own passage. By the time he reached England, his commission would be up. He would step onto the soil of his homeland as an ordinary citizen. No use spending another two weeks saluting and *yes-sirring*!

The decision made, Orde relaxed a bit. He fixed himself a cup of tea on a small camp stove, then set to work packing his books.

An hour passed, and a timid knocking sounded at his door.

"Cap'n, sar," called the melancholy voice of the Irish Corporal Hobbs. "Thar's an ol' rabbi here t' see y', sar!"

Since hearing the news about Orde's misfortune, Corporal Hobbs had gone about his duties with a catch in his voice and a tear in his baleful eye. This overdone sympathy irritated Orde, and so he fixed a broad smile on his face before throwing open the door. Hobbs towered over the diminutive form of Rabbi Shlomo Lebowitz. The old rabbi looked past Orde at the cluttered mess and the packing crates behind him. Hobbs shrugged, half saluted and left the rabbi and Orde alone.

"Come in, Rebbe Lebowitz. I cannot offer you a place to sit, but perhaps a cup of tea?" At the sight of the old man, Orde was filled again with a sense of regret. How he had grown to love these peculiar people of the covenant!

The rabbi's face registered dismay. "You are going someplace, Captain Orde?" He stepped into the small cubicle and swept his eyes over the disarray.

"Home to England," Orde managed to say lightly.

The rabbi was silent for a long, awkward moment. "We heard. Hermann Sachar was notified by the British high commissioner's office that the investigation proves you are at fault in some way for the death of his son Eli. A good boy. But noodles for brains to go to the Temple Mount on such a day, God rest his soul." The rabbi extended a crooked hand in sympathy. "The boy was meshugge. Herbert does not blame you. We in the Old City do not blame you. A letter has been sent to the high commissioner telling him so. You have been a good man here, Samuel Orde."

All pretense melted away. Orde stood grim but grateful before the old man. "You sent a *letter*?" he said quietly.

"And such a letter! You should unpack! They would not send you away after such a letter!"

Orde did not answer for a moment. "Yes, Rebbe Lebowitz. I fear they have made up their minds. It's England for the likes of me."

"But how can they—" the old rabbi sputtered indignantly.

"It is not for the sake of the Jewish community that I am blamed. The Arab Council, you see. They cannot carry all the fault for the riots. It is not politically wise."

Rebbe Lebowitz let his breath out in a slow, indignant sigh. He tugged his beard. "I thought the Englishmen were above such things."

Now Orde smiled. "Why ever did you think that?"

The rabbi tapped his temple. "I am crazy also, nu?"

"Well, I appreciate your craziness. And your support. I shall ask for a copy of your letter. Perhaps it will help me feel better, at any rate." Orde lit the camp stove and placed the kettle on to boil. Then he cleared a place on his cot for the old man he had come to consider a friend.

Rebbe Lebowitz sat stiffly on the edge of the cot and frowned at the packing crate. "What will you do? More soldiering? Somewhere else?"

"I'm afraid that option is not open to me."

The old man's eyes flashed with indignation. British injustice was full-blown, indeed. "Well then. The Lord and Master must have something else in mind for you." He pressed his lips tightly together. "Yesterday I was coming here to ask you for help when I heard what they had done to you. Such a man should not be treated so badly, I said. But what is right is often forgotten by what is convenient."

"Well spoken, Rabbi." Orde poured the tea and set a bowl of sugar on the crate before his guest.

"So the English are not in the mood for mercy or justice, eh?"

Orde noticed that the rabbi's hands trembled as he spoke. No doubt the old man had also heard of the decision of the Woodhead Commission to limit Jewish immigration to a mere handful each year until 1945, when immigration was scheduled to stop entirely. Had the judgment affected the old man's hope of bringing his family to Palestine?

"Any word about your daughter in Warsaw?" Orde asked gently.

The old man nodded once. He placed his cup back on the crate and pulled a long white envelope from his coat pocket.

"The quotas are filled. Imagine." He shook his head slowly. Orde's situation was momentarily forgotten. There were other matters of justice to discuss. The rabbi's face was pained. "My son-in-law was accused of plotting. He was in prison in Warsaw. He is just a rabbi, but they call him a threat to the community. He was released because of illness. England will not have him here in the Mandate. It seems . . ." His voice fell. "There is no appeal. Like for you, nu? Somebody always has to be accused. Otherwise the guilty will be discovered."

The old man absently opened the envelope and removed the useless passport photos of his daughter and her family. He held them reverently in his hand for a moment and then placed them one by one on the crate beside his teacup. He sighed as he looked at them, and Orde sensed that he was witnessing a private moment of longing in the old rabbi's eyes.

"My Etta." He tapped the photograph of his daughter. "Of course you cannot see how blue her eyes are in a picture, but I tell you . . . such blue."

Orde smiled in agreement. "She is lovely." There was no exaggeration in the statement. Orde did not need to agree out of mere politeness. Even with the austerity of a black-and-white photo, Orde could see how beautiful Etta was. Her slender neck and finely sculpted face were framed with raven black hair. Her skin was pale and smooth.

The depth within the clear gaze of her eyes made him think that in a moment her lips would form a word and she would nod her head and smile at him. He touched the corner of the photograph with his finger. "She is a real person," he muttered, amazed at the thought that this same woman was indeed flesh.

The rabbi smiled. The Jewishness of Orde's statement amused him. "Yes," he agreed, "Etta is a person. A *mensh,* my Etta is." He tapped the other faces in turn, "And these are also little persons. Here is Rachel, the oldest. Samuel. David. And our youngest, little Yacov. Yani, they call him. Here is the papa, Aaron. Before his arrest. Even a rabbi they make to shave his beard in Polish prisons, I am told." He shook his head. "Ah, well. The Poles may tear out our beards, but they cannot steal what is in here!" He thumped his chest defiantly. "There must have been many Jews in prison who need a rabbi, nu? Even one without a beard." He was not speaking to Orde but to himself and to Etta and her children. He fell silent. His eyes were moist. "I would like to hold the little one while he is still a baby," he finished. "But maybe these days they are safer in Poland than in Palestine." He managed a *who-knows* shrug and reached to gather up his little family.

Orde put a hand on the old man's arm to stop him. It was an impulse, probably foolish, but Orde did not want to see the matter fade away in the dusty archives of British immigration files. "I know some people in England." He paused, checking the impulse for a moment, not wanting to raise the hopes of the old man unless there was a possibility. "Perhaps I could put in a word for your daughter's case. After all, she was born here. Your son-in-law was educated in British Palestine. They have some claim, some right, it seems to me."

Rebbe Lubetkin raised his chin as if in thought. He nodded slowly and smiled from behind his beard. "This was the very matter I was coming to discuss with you yesterday. We should not let this matter die, I said to the Eternal! Maybe Captain Samuel Orde could help to find a way! After all, he is an Englishman and can navigate the hidden tracks of the English mind! So! I was hoping for this. Praying for your help." He reinserted the photographs into the envelope and then pulled out a thicker envelope from his pocket. "All the papers are here, you see. I brought them . . . *just in case.*"

The day was warm in Warsaw. Etta Lubetkin opened the windows wide and let the scents and sounds of summer into the house on Muranow Square.

Rachel looked out at the green leaves on the trees that lined the square. She had not noticed when the trees had bloomed or when the leaves covered the branches. It was as though Mama had opened the window and suddenly it was summer. Had spring ever come this year?

Sunlight filtered through the trees, dappling the cobbles like light dancing on the waters of the Vistula River. Trams and autos moved like ships. People skipped along like little sailboats scudding through the traffic. Suddenly Rachel wished she was out among the bustle.

Did Mama hear her thoughts?

"Rachel, your papa has said he would like a sugared roll from Menkes' Bakery. Nothing else will do for him at all, he says."

This was a good sign. Papa's favorite treat had always been the sugared sweet rolls from Menkes'. He had not even asked for one since his release from prison. When Mama had put one on his tray, he had not touched it or commented on it. And now, it was as though his appetite had blossomed like the trees, without any explanation. Just like that! A sweet roll from Menkes'!

Rachel sailed out into the sun, watching her own cheerful shadow with pleasure. Up ahead two Hassidim chatted as they strolled together,

their black coats flapping like the wings of birds. When Rachel looked
at their shadows she could imagine that the coats were a dozen bright
colors, like the cloaks of patriarchs. Like Joseph's coat of many colors.

And what color should she paint her shadow? Maybe her skirt was
bright red instead of dull and somber blue. Or maybe yellow with
orange flowers on it? Such thoughts were not fitting, perhaps, but they
seemed to match the brightness of the day.

Here and there mothers pushed their babies in prams, while other
children clung to their mother's skirts and sucked their thumbs. Two
bent old men shuffled past a group of young boys on their way home
from Torah school who stopped to pet the milk-cart horse.

David and Samuel would be returning from school to Frau Groshenki's house soon. Rachel fingered the coins in her pocket. Mama had
instructed her to purchase enough sweet rolls for the boys, to drop
them off, in honor of the return of Papa's appetite.

Every few paces someone called her name, asking how her papa
was and if anything was needed.

"I'm going for sweet rolls at Menkes'!"

"The rabbi is feeling better, then!" Everyone knew what Papa's favorite treat was.

Rachel pushed through the door of the warm, yeasty-smelling bakery. His hands full of a flat tray filled with warm bread, the baker looked
up, surprised to see her.

"Sholem aleichem, Rachel." He slid the tray onto a rack, then wiped
his flour-coated hands on his likewise floured apron.

"Aleichem sholem," Rachel said. She felt like laughing. Baker
Menkes had flour even on his bald head. His big ears stuck out like
wings. Had she ever noticed that he looked more like a prize fighter
than a baker? She decided that she had never noticed anything at all
before today. She had been asleep her entire life, but now it was almost
summer after a terrible winter. . . .

"Did you forget something?"

She had been here only yesterday afternoon. Had she noticed how
good it smelled then? "No," she answered, looking at the buns stacked
in neat rows along the top rack. Their tops were thick with a crust of
glistening sugar and cinnamon. "Papa is better," she said and his eyes
followed her gaze to the rabbi's favorite treat.

Baker Menkes clapped his powdered hands together. He had sent
home a sugared roll free with every purchase each time Rachel had
come for bread. It had always been untouched by Papa, and so Rachel
and Mama had shared it. *But today!*

"The Eternal be praised!" the Baker exclaimed. "A dozen for the
good Rebbe Lubetkin! *No, no!* Put away your money! This is for your
papa with my blessings!"

Mama would not like it if Rachel did not also buy something from Baker Menkes after such a generous gift. She studied the rows of cookies. The eclairs. The strudels. She would buy something wonderful to take to David and Samuel.

Baker Menkes' eyes flitted up and out the window. His pleasant gaze clouded slightly; the smile faltered, vanished, and when he looked back at Rachel, a preoccupied expression remained on his face. "Anything else?"

She looked over her shoulder as a freight wagon loaded with expensive furniture rumbled past. Muranow Square was filled with such wagons these days. People moving away. People moving in from all over. Why had Baker Menkes made such a face?

The wagon passed like a curtain. On the other side stood the young man in his heavy camel-hair coat. In this weather? His red hair stuck up wildly. His face was thin; too thin for the broad shoulders of the coat he wore. In his hand he carried a scuffed valise. He was staring hard through the window of the bakery. That was why Baker Menkes had frowned. *Hunger* was standing on the sidewalk across from this house of plenty. It was common, but disquieting all the same. The young man was not dressed in the fashion of Poland. He certainly did not fit the pattern of a Warsaw Jew. Maybe German? There were plenty of them streaming into Warsaw these days.

"German," Rachel muttered, suddenly noticing that her own feeling of lightness had vanished, just as Baker Menkes' smile had done a moment before.

"He was out there three days ago," said Menkes. "And then day *before* yesterday. *And* yesterday. His face keeps getting thinner until now there is not much there but hair and eyes. I gave him bread yesterday." He shrugged. "Told him to go to the Community Center at the synagogue. He said he was not religious and did not believe in a Supreme Being. Therefore, how could he take charity from the synagogue, he asked?" Menkes shrugged. "I told him if he was hungry one piece of bread was as holy as another. So here he is again. I won't feed him. He can go to the Community Soup Kitchen. Either that, or I will end up with a stray on my step forever more."

Rachel did not look at the stray again. She sighed and pulled her attention back to the display of strudel. Something for the entire Groshenki household would be suitable. After all, the Groshenki family had put up baby Yani, David, and Samuel ever since Papa had come home. "There." She tapped the glass. "That big one."

Baker Menkes pulled out the largest of the strudels, wrapped it happily and said he had been saving it just for her today. For this, he let her pay. But he would not take one penny for the sweet rolls.

The transaction complete, Rachel left the shop. The scarecrow redhead who had been across the street was gone now, as though he had sensed Baker Menkes' comments to Rachel. She scanned the crowded square in search of him. He would have been easy to pick out, but he had melted away and suddenly Rachel noticed that there were many more just like him all around. Some sat on curbsides. Others leaned against lamp posts or shaded themselves beneath the awnings of shops. Certainly all had the same lean and hungry look as the red-haired young man. Why did they torture themselves by loitering so near the mouth-watering smells emanating from the bakery? The baker was right not to feed just one. He would have soon taken over the job of the charity soup kitchen.

The package of rolls and strudel felt heavy in her hand. There was so much in her package, and so many hungry eyes looking at it!

She quickened her pace and looked at her dancing shadow again. It was just a shadow after all. Like the new green leaves on the trees, the homeless beggars seemed to have suddenly bloomed in Warsaw.

———

Tutoring sessions had taken on an interesting dimension since the children's ships had begun to come to England. On Thursday afternoon, Dr. Grogan gathered not only Charles and Louis under his wing, but a dozen other sad-faced young boys and girls as well, herding them off to the weekly scheduled London field trips.

Charles and Louis, who had been almost everywhere in London at least once, were at the head of the double line. Following Doc Grogan like newly hatched ducklings, the silent group entered the enormous courtyard of the British Museum. Of the dozen new hatchlings, not one spoke a word of English. Their eyes reflected the heartbreaking wonder of children who had spent a lifetime being shut out of public places in Germany.

Grogan walked backward, waving his hands like a conductor over their heads as he explained everything first in their own language and then in English. Charles and Louis enjoyed the introduction of the German language to their tour. Doc had always spoken to them only in English. It was much easier to understand everything when it was explained twice. Charles decided that this would be his best visit to the museum ever.

The broad steps and high double row of columns of the entrance were reminiscent of the great museum in Berlin. A dozen heads turned in fearful unison to gape at the blue uniforms of the bobbies on duty at the top of the steps. Were they there to keep Jewish children out? Were the wonders beyond the doors for English school children only?

"It is free to get in," Louis called in German over his shoulder, as though he were the guide and giver of this great gift.

"Now tell them in English, Charles," Doc instructed as he tipped his hat to the guard and smiled.

"It . . . don't cost—"

"*Doesn't* cost . . ."

"Uh-huh . . . It's free and everybody can go in." He felt as if he owned a piece of the museum when he said that. It was a good feeling.

Still, the ducklings looked worried as they entered the vast portals of the British Museum.

"It is the greatest in the world," Doc said with dignity. So much for Hitler's claims about Aryan culture being the greatest! The museums in all of Germany put together did not have even one-tenth the Egyptian mummies that were right here!

"Let's take them . . ." Charles pronounced his words very carefully, even though their companions could not tell if he was speaking exactly right nor not.

"Take them where?" Doc knew where, but he insisted that it be said.

"To see the mummies."

"To see Ginger!" Louis cried.

So much for the ancient Greek urns, Roman busts and Etruscan bronzes. Pottery, seals, and hieroglyphic characters of the Hittites held little fascination to a tribe of homesick six-year-olds.

It was enough to troop through the endless rooms of ancient artifacts. The sheer enormity of carved pillars from the walls of Assyria were impressive without having to be understood.

Charles and Louis were correct in their assessment of what was guaranteed to make a smash hit for the day. Proceeding straight on to the main staircase and the Northern Gallery, passing through the second Egyptian room and turning left, they entered *Ginger's room.* . . .

All eyes suddenly brightened with fascination. In case A lay *Ginger,* a favorite mummy of Charles and Louis. As withered as a piece of old shoe leather, the little man had a shock of ginger-colored hair and was billed as "the oldest dead man on earth."

Impressive! Now this was a museum worth visiting! Certainly the greatest on earth—who could argue?

Dr. Grogan explained that the fellow had been found buried in the sand; quite possibly he was one of the Hebrew slaves in Egypt. Or perhaps the fellow Moses had killed and buried?

This filled the air with a series of *oooh's* and *ahhhh's.* It gave the exhibit a familiar feeling, because everyone knew about Moses killing the Egyptian. That was back when Egyptians were like Nazis.

Jews were in trouble then, too.

So this was the fellow? Mummies, mummy cases and coffins were all on display in cases around the walls. Not exactly what the ancient

Egyptians had in mind when they sketched the blueprints for the pyramids, to be sure. *A nice Thursday afternoon outing for the young
descendants of the slaves who built the great monuments of Egypt....*

Doc Grogan was Moses for the afternoon, guiding them in two hours
through a museum where a person could wander forty years if he made
a wrong turn.

The most important lesson of the day was the introduction of the
lavatories at the end of the tour. *G-LAV for gentlemen. L-LAV for ladies.*

All of *this,* and no officer ever once questioned their right to be
there! Afterward, there was ice cream for everyone and a short ride on
the London tube.

It was here all along, just across the English Channel. Right here,
a few hours from the German Chancellery and the offices of the Gestapo!

There were reminders of Germany all around London, of course,
from the sandbags against the sides of the museum to the civil defense
posters on the monument to Lord Nelson in Trafalgar Square. But it felt
quite different here!

In Germany, the beggars and poor people had been rounded up
and shipped off to camps. Today, everyone noticed the blind beggar at
the entrance to the tube. He stood with his cup in his hand and a sign
around his neck, *I AM BLIND*. In Germany it would have been an offense
to place money in his cup. And so it was an amazing thing to see Doc
Grogan press a bill into the beggar's hand and wish him good luck.
The group of ducklings watched the blind man tap his way down the
sidewalk, right under the nose of a policeman! *And the blind man was
not arrested!* This was as interesting as Ginger, the mummy Moses
killed! Indeed, England seemed to be the promised land to every child
that afternoon.

"Maybe next week," Charles said to Doc, "we will go show them
the zoo."

———

From his vantage point in the reporter's gallery, Murphy looked over
the heads of the members of Parliament and suppressed a yawn. Prime
Minister Chamberlain had been droning on at great length, defending
his government's inability to put together a defense agreement with
Soviet Russia.

Murphy wondered how Chamberlain could speak so much about
not doing something. The thrust of the speech seemed to be that complete inactivity was preferable to false starts. The Russians, Chamberlain suggested, wanted a broader mutual defense agreement than Great
Britain should entertain.

His attention wandering away from the bland speech, Murphy's gaze traveled the seventy-five-foot length of the hall and up to the clock on the south wall. Around the clock face were grouped nineteen coats of arms—an odd number, to be sure.

Murphy had once asked Winston Churchill what the decorations meant. Churchill had explained that the crests honored the memories of the nineteen members of Parliament who had given their lives in the Great War. Churchill had added, with a loud clearing of his throat, that he hoped that the brave men who had paid the highest sacrifice for their country's stand against German aggression would not be "revolving in their sepulchers" as their banners overheard the present government's shilly-shallying.

Thinking about Churchill's comments made Murphy scan the chamber for him. The statesman was drumming his fingers on the bench beside him as he waited for Chamberlain to finish.

When the Prime Minister at last concluded his prepared remarks, Murphy expected Churchill to jump to the attack. Instead, Churchill deferred to his old mentor and colleague, David Lloyd George.

Lloyd George began by saying that Chamberlain's foot-dragging did not come from reasonable caution, but from a continued reluctance to antagonize Germany by being friendly toward Russia. The older statesman drew both chuckles and hisses when he hinted that Chamberlain's policy owed more to snobbery than to practical considerations.

So far, it was pretty mild criticism in Murphy's opinion, but Chamberlain's critics were just warming up. Lloyd George added that Russia had been willing to sign an agreement for months and was only waiting for a signal that Great Britain was ready to be serious. Anthony Eden firmly pointed out that any alliance intended to prevent aggression which did not include Russia would not be strong enough to prevent a war. Others continued attacking the lack of progress.

Finally Churchill rose to speak. In measured phrases he intoned, "Should war come to Europe, the success of a western front cannot be guaranteed without an eastern front, in which Russia must take part. No eastern front means no western front, and perhaps . . ." He paused ominously. "No west."

Hisses and cries of "Shame, shame" erupted from the benches of Chamberlain's supporters. When the hubbub died down, a voice behind Chamberlain demanded, "How can we trust Moscow?"

Churchill's reply was delivered over the top of his reading glasses, with the air of a master correcting an erring pupil. "In Moscow," he said, "the question is, 'How can we trust Chamberlain?' "

9

The Gifted Ones

Elisa sat beside Helen Ibsen in the small, cramped office of Harold Weyland, case officer in charge of the immigration of Lori and Jamie Ibsen.

Weyland was a bulky, bespectacled man with gray strands of hair combed over the top of his bald head. He wore a blue bow tie and a brown suit that looked as though it belonged to someone of a much smaller size. His white shirt strained at each buttonhole as if one more bite of the half-eaten sandwich on his desk would explode a volley of buttons around the cluttered cubicle. His eyes blinked like a telegraph as he studied the sheaf of information regarding the case. Except for the distant clack of typewriters penetrating the frosted glass of the office door, his wheezing breath was the only sound in the room.

Elisa sat very straight, as though she were in concert. Baby Murphy was doing his usual tap dance along the bottom of her rib cage. She folded her hands on what remained of her lap and silently wished the interview were over.

At last Weyland scanned Lori's letter from Danzig. He raised his eyes, looked at Elisa's stomach suspiciously and frowned, as though he feared she would have the baby right here in his cramped office.

"Mrs. Murphy . . ."

The silence was at last broken! "Yes?"

"You are married to an American." The tone was clipped, impatient.

"That's right. Bureau chief of London TENS. American news—"

He held up a hand to cut her off. "And this is your aunt?" He nodded toward Helen. "And these are your cousins?" He waved the letter and let it float to the top of the stack.

"That is correct," Elisa answered, suddenly self-conscious of the slight tinge of an accent in her voice. Weyland obviously had no patience with foreign accents. For this reason Elisa had come along to help Helen with the interview. Elisa's English was nearly flawless; Helen spoke English with the thick heavy sounds of one who had lived her entire life in Germany.

"Since you are an American by *marriage*—" Weyland cleared his throat to let her know that he knew where she really came from. "Then perhaps this matter of your family . . . these children, Lori and Jamie Ibsen, would be better handled by the American Embassy." He closed the file folder and stared with watery blue eyes.

Was this a dismissal? Helen clutched Elisa's hand and looked at her for explanation. Elisa shook her head in disagreement. "Our entire family is . . . we are in London, you see. My mother and father came with President Beneš from Czechoslovakia, invited by your government. They are here by special arrangement, and . . . the Prime Minister himself . . ."

Weyland drew back and opened the file again. *Why had no one told him this before? The Prime Minister?* "Ah. Well . . ."

More silence passed as he reconsidered the documents with this new information in mind.

"My dear Mrs. Ibsen." He faced Elisa, even though it was Aunt Helen he wanted answers from. Helen's mastery of the English language was acceptable in most circles, but Weyland demanded an interpreter be present in case there was difficulty. "I understand about your own children. And about those other two, the Kalner boys—although Jacob Kalner is over-age. Seventeen, is he not?" He paused to let this fact sink in. "But now there is this other matter . . . Alfie Halder. Tell me again . . . slowly . . . who he is and where he comes from."

Helen understood everything. Elisa did not need to translate. She and Helen exchanged resigned looks, and Helen began again. "He is a child who . . ."

The thought gave her a chill of fear. "He grew up in our congregation, you see. A sweet child . . ." How could she explain?

Weyland pursed his lips in thought. "There are so many thousands of requests these days. The cut-off age is sixteen. And for those who are younger, we have strict standards of health and intelligence that we check for. Children are being rejected, for instance, if they have decayed teeth or physical ailments, you see."

Helen blanched. Lori and Jamie had good teeth, healthy minds and bodies. But what about Jacob and Mark Kalner? And how could she ever explain about Alfie Halder? She looked to Elisa for help.

"Both parents of Alfie Halder are deceased; he has no family. No one to care for him. My husband and I will sign an affidavit of financial support, of course."

Weyland sniffed and looked down his nose at Elisa and Helen. "My own parents died when I was fifteen," he declared proudly. "And as you can see, I survived on my own quite well. Educated myself, and—" He swept his hand around the tiny cubicle as if to display his achievement. "You can see. You shall have to give a good reason for bringing a fifteen-year-old boy in the place of a younger refugee child who is truly in need."

"But Alfie is . . . *special.*" Helen leaned forward. How could she explain how special he was when children with cavities were rejected?

"Special." He chewed the word. "Ah. I see. Gifted, do you mean?"

"Yes. Gifted. A *gift*, Alfie is, to all who know him."

A new interest sparked in Weyland's dull eyes. "On occasion we do make exceptions for young people who might benefit from our educational system."

Elisa jumped in, grateful for even this impossible hope. "Good! Alfie Halder is special. My husband hopes to employ him."

Weyland frowned and stuck out his lower lip. "*Employ?* Dear me, no. He cannot be employed. Take the place of a British subject in London?"

"As an interpreter." Elisa gulped. "He speaks several . . . uh . . . unusual languages. Exceptional." She could not look at Helen's pale face.

"And Jacob Kalner?" Helen was flushed. It was warm in the office. Too warm. She felt light-headed. "Perhaps a student visa?"

"Kalner." Weyland frowned and chewed his upper lip. "Seventeen. A man by all guidelines. But perhaps . . . is he also exceptional in intellect?"

Both women spoke at once. "*Yes!*"

"Such visas are dependent on school records from the country of origin."

"Those remain in the Reich. In such a case one cannot call up Berlin and simply ask for them."

"Quite." Weyland was softening some. "Then you must understand that retaining the visa depends on how well a student performs here. And you will guarantee financial support for him as well?" Weyland shuffled through a stack of papers for the correct forms. He looked at them doubtfully. "The final decisions are always made at the consulate of origin. Danzig. All I can do is pass along the information from this side of the Channel. Due to the circumstances of your family situation, there is hope for your daughter, even though she too is seventeen. But the others . . ."

A student-visa application was pulled from the file. Weyland looked as though he was relieved to be done with this matter. Time to move on. Time to finish his sandwich. He clapped his hands together. "Fill out these. Four copies each, as you can see. And for the other children as well. I can make no promises. There are hundreds of thousands of these applications being submitted at every British Consulate on the Continent." He frowned and gestured toward the metal file drawers that lined every wall. "As you can see."

Both women left the office and stood stunned, in the center of the drab corridor. The sound of typewriters and voices echoed around them, but they heard nothing but the replay of Harold Weyland's unpromising words.

———

The telephone call from Holland came in to the London TENS office just as Murphy was rolling down his sleeves and searching for his hat. It had been a long day, with news breaking like a line of dominos clacking down one after another. Murphy was ready to turn the operation over to Harvey Terrill, ready to go home to Red Lion Square, to look at Elisa and the boys and *think on whatever was true, whatever was noble, whatever was right, whatever was pure. . . .*

Murphy, at the suggestion of his father-in-law, had been putting that scripture to a lot of use lately as the news leaking out of Europe grew increasingly grim. For a while, Murphy had begun to believe that there just weren't any good things left in the world to think about. Lately he had come to see that as the darkness had gotten darker, the little pinpoints of light had gotten stronger. There were fewer of those lights, to be sure, but the harder the blackness squeezed, the more vibrant the light became.

With that in mind, Murphy had given Timmons, the Berlin correspondent, the assignment of reporting on those bright spots in the Third Reich. *Who was left in Germany? What were they doing?*

Mindful of the impossibility of getting such a story past the Nazi censors, Timmons had carried it in his mind to Holland, where he placed the trunk call to the TENS bureau chief.

Night desk editor Harvey Terrill looked annoyed as he poked his head into Murphy's office. "Sorry. It's Timmons on the line from Amsterdam. Says he has to talk to you. Just you. Nobody else but you," he said with a shrug. "Doesn't trust me to get it right." It was only the first few minutes of Terrill's shift, but already he was edgy, Murphy thought as he picked up the receiver.

On the far side of the English Channel, the boyish voice of Timmons sounded frantic, as usual. The kid was learning journalism the hard way, after all. He had been picked up and interrogated by the Gestapo in Germany twice already. He did not want to take a chance on another stay in Himmler's resort.

"Must be some story," Murphy said, dispensing with the usual greeting.

"Probably the last we're going to see any of those little lights shining in Germany, Boss," Timmons said. His voice sounded as if he were shouting through a garden hose. "This morning two thousand Christians gathered outside the rubble of New Church. Nine pastors read the names of their colleagues who are now in prison, including Pastor Karl Ibsen and Martin Niemöller. Hitler is saying publicly, *It is them or me....* You know what that means around here. It will be them!"

"Let me get a copy editor. You've got the whole story?"

"I watched from across the street. Not close enough to get arrested. Professor Bauchin spoke for fifteen minutes before the goons moved in and rounded everyone up. There were trucks waiting on the side streets. Nobody tried to make a run for it. Everyone was arrested. An announcement was made by the Gestapo that the German Confessional Church will transfer the use of the cathedrals to the Hitler elite guard for that body's neo-pagan ceremonies. This is the penalty of the church's *Jewish influence* and *the political degenerations of Christianity.*" He paused. "Those are exact quotes, Boss."

"They aren't trying to hide their true purpose anymore, are they, Timmons?"

"Don't have to. The visible church in Germany is dead. No Bibles in the bookstores. I think we've just seen the last two thousand *open* Christians trucked off. Those lights you were looking for have all gone underground, Boss. A certain official from the German press told me that Ibsen is being held because he refuses to accept the *Aryan paragraph* that excludes all Jews and Jewish influence from the German church. Unless he accepts the Nazi version of Hitler's church, they say he's going to rot in there until he's forgotten."

"Forgotten." Murphy repeated the word as though it were the biggest threat to Karl Ibsen and the others who suffered in the same cause. *Whatever is true, whatever is noble, whatever is right, whatever is pure, whatever is admirable, excellent, or praiseworthy ... think about such things!*

The men within the walls of Hitler's prison camps were all of the above, Murphy reasoned, and then he added *courageous* to the list of things to think on as Timmons dictated the full story of the last Christian Alamo in Berlin.

Murphy was two hours late getting home to Red Lion Square. In that time, he had revised his interpretation of what Scripture meant when it said to *think on these things.* The apostle Paul had written those words while he was in prison, had he not?

Men like Karl Ibsen embodied all the qualities of what was noble and right and true and just. These were the qualities the Führer wanted the world to forget; these were the principles he wanted to rot away in prison so he could continue his plan unopposed. He had promised Ibsen full restoration if only Karl would remain silent! But because he would not compromise, Karl was locked away in the darkest of Nazi holes.

But Ibsen was not silent, Murphy realized. Behind those thick and terrible walls, his heart was still true to his God. His example rang out like a shout from the rooftop of St. Paul's!

Think on these things. . . .

With that in mind, Murphy called Anna and Theo Lindheim, Helen Ibsen, and Winston Churchill. They walked together on the roof garden and looked over nighttime London to where the great dome of St. Paul's Cathedral glistened in the spotlights like a moon rising over a mountain range.

Where the voice of a few brave men had been silenced, the bells of ten thousand churches should toll, reminding the world to *think on these things. . . .*

Allan Farrell read his morning edition of *The Times* as he sunned himself on a bench in Parliament Square. The headlines were all about Hitler. Troop buildups on the borders. Poland. Danzig. Editorials screamed about despots who gobbled up other peoples' land like a hyena tearing the flesh of a wounded animal.

Noble sentiments, considering their source, Allan thought. *Noble and full of hypocrisy.* Like English political philosophy for four hundred years, these words about the German Führer were colored by what was best only for England.

Allan raised his eyes to the weathered stones of Westminster Abbey where Protestant Queen Elizabeth lay buried in the same crypt with her half sister, the Catholic queen known as Bloody Mary. Catholics and Protestants had been slaughtering one another since before the reign of those two sisters. There had been a continuous and brutal war going on a long time before the strutting German Führer appeared on the scene.

James had succeeded Queen Elizabeth as Monarch. He had commanded the publication of his Bible at the same time he ordered English and Scottish Protestants to settle the ancient land of Ireland. In the name of religion, the executions and murders had begun in the early years of the 1600s. The troubles were that old. Seasoned in the keg of bitterness, three and a half centuries had not mellowed the hatred of Irish Catholics for the Protestant usurpers in Ulster. Allan could recite his family tree from the list of those hanging by nooses on its branches. There were no monuments to those men in their own land. Ah, but here in England there were monuments everywhere to the rulers who had hanged them!

Just across St. Margaret's Street, Allan could make out the bronze statue of Oliver Cromwell standing on the green outside of Parliament. Now *there* was a blood-soaked tyrant for the ages! He had plunged England into a civil war for the sake of his religion. He was responsible for the execution of King Charles I just a few miles from this spot! Cromwell had taken the government into his own hands, and melted down the crown jewels to pay his armies. He had smashed the Irish revolt with an iron fist and titled himself *Lord Protector of the Realm.* And now, Cromwell, who had cried out against the graven images of the Catholic church, was himself a graven image on the green of Parliament.

Despots had only to be victorious, Allan thought, *and all their brutality acquired the status of a holy crusade!*

Allan studied the statue of Cromwell for a moment, then looked back at the front-page photograph of Hitler and Mussolini. All these two modern-day dictators had to do was *win*; then they would also be cast in bronze to stand as Europe's most recent graven images. They were no better or worse than all those of any nation who had gone before them. Weapons were more advanced, to be sure. Evil could be refined to an art. But evil had always existed within the lofty world of politicians and kings.

Allan looked at his hands. They were too much like his mother's to be called strong and masculine. He had always been ashamed of his hands, tucked them into his pockets or stood with clenched fists. But her hands had been strong. She had used them to wage war against the oppression three centuries of her kin had suffered. Why, then, were Allan's own hands not strong? Why had Colin and the others marked him as a messenger for the cause, but not a fighter?

He looked at Cromwell. "They have made you a saint, you bloody butcher. You're worse off now than the men you killed, and there's nothing to be done about it, is there?"

Glancing away, Allan sighed. "There is one Irishman sitting across from your shrine, Lord Cromwell. They think I am too weak to do anything but shuttle messages to and fro, do they?" He raised his eyes to Big Ben as the hour hand slid into place and the great bells began to chime noon. He let his gaze glide over the piles of sandbags that were stacked thick and deep along the facade of every public building. The Houses of Parliament, Westminster Abbey, St. Margaret's Church, all looked as if they had been prepared for a flood . . . or at least a heavy German-sent storm.

Sandbags, ditches—all in preparation for what might come from the belly of a German bomber. But what about the damage one lone fighter might do behind those barricades?

Allan's eyes narrowed as he spotted his German contact snapping photographs like a tourist across the square. For now their common enemy, England, had made them allies. On this one point they could agree—it would be a lovely sight if the walls of Parliament came tumbling down. Did it matter if the weapon fell from the sky or came from within?

Allan pulled a small envelope from his coat pocket and folded it into his newspaper. Leaving *The Times* on the bench, he strolled away from the approaching contact. He paused for a moment as if to study the statue of the Earl of Derby. The German took his place on the bench and opened the copy of *The Times*. It was that simple. That antiseptic. Allan did not even know what message the note contained. The secret business of his unlikely allies.

There was nothing in the process that had given him one moment of excitement or nervousness. *Room and board. Clean sheets and polished boots. Good payment. And for what?*

Allan walked slowly along the sidewalk; past the sandbags and the statue of Cromwell. He thought that perhaps the old Lord Protector was worthy of a more active opponent.

Tucking his hands in his pockets, he quickened his pace to catch the red omnibus at the corner.

A fluttering poster nailed to a tree caught Allan Farrell's attention:

REMEMBER THESE MEN!

A list of names followed, as well as the explanation that these men were currently in prison in Nazi Germany. A great rally, a Remembrance Service, was to be held on their behalf on September 1. The bells of all the churches in England and America would ring out a message to the Nazis that those unjustly imprisoned were not forgotten.

Allan pulled the paper from its nail and studied it carefully. At the top of the list of those scheduled to speak was Winston Churchill. Allan frowned. Like Cromwell, Winston Churchill was also an opponent of everything Allan believed in. A hypocrite of the first order, Churchill had opposed the turning over of naval bases to Ireland. He argued on behalf of keeping Ulster chained to the leg of the British Empire!

And yet, Winston Churchill was going to speak on behalf of martyrs imprisoned in Germany! The irony of it was almost too much for Allan. He folded the paper and angrily shoved it into his pocket.

————

Extra sugar. Extra butter. Extra coffee. The cupboards of the Lubetkin house were overflowing with little bits of this and that brought from the members of the congregation to the rabbi's family. All those little bits had accumulated into so much that there was room for nothing else.

Mama stood in the pantry with her hands on her hips. "You would think we are having a Bar Mitzvah, Rachel!" she called over her shoulder. "So much! Go get David's wagon. Bring it to the kitchen door. We should take most of this to the soup kitchen. Your father says. So go."

Rachel hated pulling David's wagon anywhere. The left front wheel wobbled drunkenly after an unexpected collision with an elm tree in the square. Pulling the wagon was like taking a rabbit for a walk on a long leash. The wagon went its own way no matter which way Rachel tried to guide it. Why had Papa ordered that she should show up at the shul with this thing in tow? Everyone would be there. The members of the congregation who manned the staff often fed their own children there as well. They would all see Rachel in the undignified task of fighting a little red wagon up the street.

"Can't I go later?" She looked at the kitchen clock. Later would be after dark, and after suppertime as well. The kitchen would be empty, or nearly so. No friends or schoolmates to see her—nearly a grown woman—tugging a child's wagon!

Mama looked irritated at the suggestion. "So look at the clock. If you can't tell time, then look at the sky. Later will be dark. You can't go out these days after dark. You know that. Get your brother's wagon and quit kvetching. Your father said *now* take the stuff to the shul!"

Reluctantly, Rachel retrieved the offending vehicle from beneath the shade tree in the back. It was covered with pigeon droppings! *Humiliation heaped upon humiliation!*

It squeaked and resisted all the way to the door. Mama heard it coming. Everyone would hear it coming. Mama was waiting behind the screen with her arms full. She gasped at the sight of the wagon. "You cannot go with it covered in bird droppings," she scolded.

Rachel smiled slightly in spite of the tone of Mama's voice. Here was an unexpected reprieve. She blessed the birds who roosted in the tree! "It is a mess," Rachel said cheerfully.

"Soap. A little water, maybe! So wash it! And hurry, if you please!" *Bang!* The door slammed shut.

Rachel grumbled and scrubbed the wagon. Red paint chipped off in big flakes beneath the brush, giving David's wagon the appearance of something that had been pulled by refugees coming to Warsaw and other refugees going back to Cracow and still others back to Warsaw again.

"They will think I am a refugee," she moaned when the task was completed. She thought of the rag pickers and beggars roaming about Warsaw even now. None of them would stoop to pulling such a pitiful cart.

"Mama, it is not dignified," Rachel said as the last of the food was crammed between the slats, and then bundles of old clothes were placed on top.

"Dignified!" Mama scowled at her. "Five hundred homeless arrived only yesterday in our neighborhood, and you speak of your own dignity! Your father sick on his bed is not thinking of himself! He is thinking about those down at the shul. What would he say about your dignity? I should tell him you don't want to take our contribution to the shul because your pride would be wounded maybe?"

After Mama's speech about dignity, the loud squeaking of the wagon wheels was a pleasant relief. At least until Rachel reached the main street to the shul.

The rhythm was a steady *grooooan, clunk, shriek!* Rachel pulled right and the wagon rolled left. When she went around the streetlamp, the wagon stopped like a dog looking for a place to lift its leg. The thing was alive! An evil spirit seemed to have possessed it.

"Hello, Rachel!" called Frau Potemski from her stoop. "The rabbi, your father, he is better?"

Rachel felt her face color. "He is sending charity to the soup kitchen."

"They won't want the wagon," she laughed.

Rachel forced her lips to smile politely. "Good-day, Frau Potemski." The wagon lurched toward the stoop as though it wished to greet the good Frau.

"If you're going to have a pet, you should teach it to heel." The moon-faced housewife gave the wagon a nudge with her toe.

"Yes, Frau Potemski." Rachel's cheeks were bright red.

She did not look to the right or the left as she struggled up the next block. Friends hailed her and asked after her father. Strangers stared at her with the same curiosity with which she had stared at the red-haired young man in Muranow Square. She looked like one of them! Old clothes bundled on top of a cart. *Why* had Mama not been content to only send food?

"Well, good evening, Rachel!" It was Herr Menkes, the baker. "Running away from home?"

Clunk . . . shriek . . . grooooan . . . clunk . . .

"I am sorry, Herr Menkes, I cannot hear you! This assassin of a cart is making too much noise." She raised her nose slightly and struggled on. "And I cannot stop to talk because I am running away from home."

"You won't get far with that beast you are pulling!" he called after her. "Are you pulling it, or is it pulling you?"

She chose to ignore the jibe of the baker. He was more filled with sarcasm than a jelly donut was full of jelly! She would think especially hard before she went into his shop next time so she could have something clever prepared to say in reply when he teased her.

She approached the corner of the street, its curb looming up like the brink of a steep ravine. Rachel paused. The beast rolled up on her heels, then veered to the left, toward the curb. She tugged back on the handle, jerking the rusty axle around. With a loud moan, the wagon reared up on its hind wheels and then threw itself upside down!

Old dresses! Undergarments! Stockings and worn-out shoes! Papa's old trousers. Mama's old dresses. Rachel's old blouses and three nightgowns flew out across the sidewalk.

This motley collection of faded finery was followed by the real treasure: butter wrapped in waxed paper. Sugar in a paper bag. Salt. Pepper. Extra loaves of bread. Extra sugared rolls. Extra this and extra that. A little of everything that amounted to quite a lot of mess there on the busy street corner.

"Oh! You terrible monster!" Rachel wailed as the crooked wheel spun around happily in the air. "Now *look* what you've done?"

She stooped and jerked the wagon into a lopsided upright position. It had emptied all of its burden, and before she could stop it, it rolled away, off the curb.

Rachel sat back on her heels as the wagon splintered to a noisy death under the wheels of a taxi. The cab squealed to a stop, and a great commotion arose as men and women appeared to see what had happened.

Rachel covered her face with her hands. Arms lifted her to her feet. Hands brushed her off, and familiar ones mingled with unfamiliar voices in a hundred different explanations of how the daughter of the good Rabbi Lubetkin—God forbid—almost was killed by the taxi that roared around the corner like a wild bull looking for someone innocent to mow down. And of course she was running away from her unhappy home because she could not stand the strain any longer of caring for . . .

No! No! No! She was on a mission of mercy, poor child! Taking items of charity to the soup kitchen when—God forbid—she was almost crushed beneath the wheels of this . . . But, the Eternal be praised! Jumping back just in time, she was snatched from the jaws of a horrible death!

The crowd looked ready to lynch the poor taxi driver.

Rachel was crying by this time. Her tears made matters much worse. Someone suggested that she be taken to a hospital to be checked in case anything was damaged.

"Please," Rachel said quietly, "the wagon just broke loose. It is nothing. I was taking this to the soup kitchen at the shul and the wagon broke away. Nothing. Just . . . I am fine."

The babble of excited voices drowned out her feeble voice. Rachel looked up in search of a reasonable face. Among the crowd of friends and strangers who now blocked traffic, Rachel saw the wry smile of the red-haired young man in the camel-hair coat. He was behind a three-deep line of neighbor women. His head and shoulders towered above their excitedly bobbing heads. He rolled his eyes, and shook his head, as if to say, *Who would believe this?*

He inched his way forward. "I saw it," he said to Rachel through the ruckus. "I'm afraid the wagon is done for, but we may yet save the cargo." He passed her a still-folded nightgown.

"They never listen!" Rachel said, looking down to where someone stood squarely in the middle of the butter. Yellow ooze was squishing out over the toes of scuffed shoes.

The red-haired boy fought his way down to rescue sacks of bread and buns and mismatched shoes. These he passed up to Rachel, who accepted them with a newfound composure as her crisis continued to be discussed by everyone at the same time.

An unbroken bag of sugar was retrieved. Matching shoes were found, rolled socks, shirts and dresses retrieved. Rachel's arms were full. She could carry nothing more. And then the young man rose to his feet. His arms were full as well.

"I was taking it to the soup kitchen," Rachel explained.

"Old shoes make good soup, I am told, if properly seasoned." The young man nudged past her and then began his escape through the press.

Rachel followed. No one noticed that the victim was leaving. Like the broken wagon, the butter and a few additional items were abandoned, left as evidence to the near tragedy.

On the other side of the square, Rachel and this young man with the rebellious red hair could see that the mob had grown to two hundred. The two walked quickly toward the soup kitchen at the end of the block.

"Rachel!" cried Herr Bilenki as he hurried past in the opposite direction. "What! What has happened over there, child, do you know?"

"Somebody—God forbid—is dead," Rachel replied as she kept on walking.

10

On the Beach

The crates were packed and ready for transport to the freighter in Tel Aviv. Orde was expecting the porters; instead, the door opened and a junior officer passed him a cable from London.

A reprieve from his disgrace, perhaps? Or word that he had been posted back to England to help sort out the problems of Palestine?

He tore open the envelope and scanned the brief paragraph. His hopes fell as quickly as they had risen. It was a telegram from John Murphy and the TENS office in London.

CAPTAIN ORDE
    REGRET TO HEAR OF YOUR POSTING BACK TO ENGLAND AND SUBSEQUENT DECISION TO RETIRE STOP TENS CURRENTLY IN NEED CORRESPONDENT IN POLAND STOP
    BOTH WRITING AND RADIO BROADCASTS REQUIRED STOP HOPEFUL YOU WILL APPLY FOR POSITION STOP
    SINCERELY JOHN MURPHY
BUREAU CHIEF TENS LONDON
    REPLY REQUESTED

The offer was kind, but Orde read it with a growing sense of despair. It was not at all the way he had envisioned spending the rest of his life. A journalist? No. Samuel Orde was a soldier from the ground up. The TENS proposal was one that he might think about on the trip back to England, but it was at the bottom of his list.

He folded the cable and stuck it in the pocket of his coat. Another knock sounded on the door.

"Yes?"

Hobbs poked his head in. "The messenger is still here, sar. Will y' be sendin' a reply?"

Orde answered with a curt nod and then scrawled out his message to Murphy on a torn sheet of note paper. It would be several weeks before he reached London, and Orde hoped the position would be filled by then so he would not have to even consider it. *THANKS FOR CONSIDERATION. WILL CONTACT YOU IN LONDON...*

There was much he needed to think about, to pray about. He had deceived himself into thinking that the Almighty had chosen him to help the cause of a Jewish homeland. And Orde had rather liked picturing himself in the role of a new Moses.

The thought of his arrogance made him wince. "That's the truth of it, old boy," he muttered to his reflection in the mirror. So here he was; not a Moses at all, but an Englishman punished by his own people because of that desire.

The knife of that reality cut deep into his heart. To work as a journalist meant reporting the history that other men made. Always before, Orde had considered himself a man who could make history happen.

That much of his life had come to an end, and now he had no personal life, no life at all to fill the void.

"Journalist," he muttered, clearly remembering something he had said before about members of the press. *Those who can, do. Those who can do nothing else, write what others have done.*

He wondered what sort of bloke this American John Murphy would be to work for. Probably insufferably arrogant and crude like most Yanks.

There was time enough to consider the proposal. Orde determined that he would discuss it with Winston Churchill when he got back to England. It was Winston, after all, whose infernal meddling had gotten him the assignment of Middle East correspondent.

Somehow Orde connected his own stories with this dismissal. Had he not been so vigorous in his reporting, he would not have drawn attention to himself and ... *No use thinking of that now.* It was too late. There was no reprieve, it seemed. He was going back to London no matter what.

―――――

The din of spoons against tin bowls was deafening.

Peter Wallich smoothed out the torn scrap of paper on the long trestle table in the community soup kitchen.

"Here it is, you see." He tapped it with his finger and ignored his bowl even though Rachel knew he must be very hungry. It seemed as though the fragment of yellow paper held all the hope for nourishment that Peter desired. The blue ink was water-stained, leaving only a small portion of the address legible. *"Niska Street,"* Peter said unhappily. "You see. That is all I have to go on."

"Niska is a very long street. It would be difficult these days to wander up and down knocking on the door of every flat to ask if someone had a relative in Vienna," Rachel frowned.

Peter moved his face closer to the paper as he attempted to decipher the water-smeared ink. "This could be an *A* or an *O*. And this maybe an *M* or an *N*. The last three letters are *SKI*. That is one certain thing."

Rachel looked up at him doubtfully. Poor boy. Did he not know that practically everyone in Warsaw had a relative with a last name ending in *SKI*? This was of little use, if any, in helping Peter Wallich locate the family he was searching for in Warsaw. Niska Street ran for miles. Thousands of mail slots were labeled with names ending with the only three legible letters in the name on the paper. "All the way from Vienna you have come for this," she murmured, her words lost beneath the clamor of the crowded dining room. She looked around at the gaunt faces of the diners. So far these tragic people had come, only to end up here!

"It was so absurd." Peter slammed his hand down on the paper.

"You should eat," Rachel urged.

"I was on my way here from Danzig, you see." He seemed to have lost his appetite. "On the train to Warsaw! Just walking through the corridor, and—you know how trains rock!"

Rachel shrugged. She had never been on a train. But in 1939, could she admit that she had never been on a train? *Too childish and provincial.* "I see," she said, using her imagination. *Like a tram, only worse.*

"So there I was, walking toward the third-class dining car," Peter continued. "I met this fellow carrying two cups of coffee. Just then the train hit a bad bump. The man fell into me!" He raised his hands and brought them down across the paper to show how the coffee had soaked him and the precious address to his destination. "And here, you see, is the result! The address in my pocket—all my hopes washed away in that moment."

Rachel sat silently, contemplating the terrible misfortune of Peter Wallich. She looked up to see Frau Sobrinski staring curiously at her from the door of the kitchen. The woman's eyebrows raised in disapproval. *So there was the rabbi's daughter talking to a total stranger of a boy in the soup kitchen! Oy!*

Rachel knew the yentas would talk. She did not care. She would go right home and tell her mother and father what had happened to this poor boy who had helped her carry the items for charity to the shul. Maybe Papa would have an idea what to do.

Frau Sobrinski still stared. Rachel smiled and waved, let the smile cool, and then turned away. The look plainly told Frau Sobrinski that she was being a yenta and she should tend her own soup! *Very good,*

Rachel thought. When she looked up again, the woman had scurried away.

"My father is the rabbi here," Rachel said to Peter as if that fact explained everything.

Peter looked alarmed. "I am not religious," he said sternly.

"Yes. I know. Baker Menkes told me you would not eat a meal here for that reason. Is that why you have not touched your soup?"

His expression grew more stern. "Soup is soup when one is hungry." He met her challenge by taking a bite.

"And a rabbi *IS* a rabbi when one needs help finding lost friends," she replied smugly. "So do not be so proud. My father knows everybody. And if he doesn't know *everybody,* he knows enough people who do." She folded her hands primly before her on the table. "So. Do you want help? Of course you do. Then you must tell me everything about your father in Vienna and the man who gave him this address, nu?"

———————

It took nearly an hour of explanation about the smashed wagon and spilled cargo before Rachel's parents allowed her to get on to the really important matters. By that time Papa's eyes looked very weary, and Mama was irritable. Mama was often irritable these days from the strain of Papa's illness and the terrible state of politics.

"But, Mama," Rachel protested when her mother told her the story could wait until later, "this is what I wanted to tell you! I just had to start with the wagon because that is where I met him."

"Etta," Papa wheezed, "we'll listen."

"Everyone in Warsaw has a story," Etta said. "And you need to rest, Aaron."

Papa raised his hand in a gesture that ordered no argument. Rachel had not meant to cause trouble. Now she wished she had waited until morning to tell the whole story.

"It is all right," Rachel replied. "Really. It can wait."

"Nonsense," Papa's brown eyes flashed. "I like a good story."

"Mama?" Rachel begged her mother's pardon.

"Your father is bored lying here," Mama sighed and shook her head. "One of the joys of being a rabbi is listening to everyone's troubles. As if we do not have enough of our own, Aaron." She managed a smile as she gently patted his arm. "So tell us the troubles of this red-haired boy who replaced the red wagon."

Rachel tried to strain out the unimportant parts, like the fact that Peter Wallich was not Orthodox. Not Conservative. Not religious at all. Starting with the spilled coffee, she traced back to the horrible Night of Broken Glass in Vienna and then Peter's escape to Danzig. By then,

Rachel could plainly see that her mother was indeed fascinated and sympathetic as well. *Such* a story!

"His mother and sister were supposed to meet him at the Danziger Hof Hotel in Danzig. They never came! He waited there for some time, hoping for a letter. Each week he went to the hotel and asked if maybe there was a message there for Peter Ruger, which is the name on his false passport. But they never wrote."

Mama clucked her tongue. So sad. Terrible. A son separated from his mother and sister. "And now he is in Warsaw?"

"With only this clue." Rachel passed Etta the yellow coffee-stained paper.

"There is nothing anyone can do with this." Mama passed it to Papa, who held it up to the light.

He shook his head. "Rachel." He sounded disapproving. "When there is no help, it is more harm than good to give someone hope. We can do nothing with this."

"But there is more," Rachel leaned forward. "He remembers things about the man in Vienna who gave his father this address!" She looked very pleased as she paused long enough for the suspense to build.

"Yes?"

"Well? So tell us."

Rachel nodded. "The man was from Warsaw, but very active against the Nazis in Austria. Like Peter's father, he tried to stop the Anschluss. He was killed just before Hitler took over Austria."

Once again Etta and Aaron exchanged looks. Many people were killed during that time. This was not news. "Is there more?" Papa asked, looking very tired indeed.

"Peter remembers something about him—though not his name. If he could remember his name, then Peter would not have such a problem." She paused. "He came to the Walliches' flat always very late at night. Peter says he carried a violin case and wore elegant clothes. Black dinner jacket and a fine overcoat. A musician. Not like the fellows who stand on the street corners and play their fiddles, but a *real* musician, like the men at the concert hall. And he was Jewish. Dark eyes and black hair. Handsome."

This description certainly matched no one in the congregation of Aaron Lubetkin. But maybe it *was* something. How many Jewish violinists had left Warsaw for Vienna and actually made a success in an orchestra there? It was the sort of thing a Jewish mother and father would talk about. *My son the concert violinist....* And then there was the matter of the son being killed. That would have made waves in the community somewhere.

"Good. This is good," Papa urged Rachel on. "There is more, maybe?"

Rachel nodded her head curtly. This was the really good part. "Peter saw this man's photograph in the newspaper. The headlines said he had murdered his mistress—"

At this, Mama looked suddenly disgusted. Rachel was not supposed to know about things like mistresses. That was the sort of terrible thing that happened on the *outside*.

"Finish," Papa said grimly.

"So Peter brought this newspaper to his father. His father got very white and said to Peter, 'This is no one I know. Do not speak of it again.' " Rachel shrugged to indicate that this was the last clue. "When the Nazis came, Peter's father was arrested and killed. His mother kept the address of the musician from Warsaw hidden. She gave it to him before they fled Vienna. And then . . . you know . . . the coffee spilled on it."

Well, this was certainly a story for the yentas of the block to talk about. But maybe not the sort of thing Mama was pleased had entered the ears of her daughter.

"It is enough." Aaron ran his hand across the stubble of his new beard. "It is something."

Hidden in the center of Karl Ibsen's ration of daily bread was a soft core. Not yet stale. Not yet shrouded with mold. This heart of the bread was the one taste of pleasure that Karl enjoyed each morning.

As always, he bowed his head and offered thanks for the bit of nourishment that kept him tied to this world. Then he glanced up toward the window and muttered something about the value of even one sparrow. And then in a voice his warders would have attributed to the madness of solitary confinement, the prisoner cried, "Whatever you do for the least of these, you have done for me."

With that, he rose from his knees and divided the precious heart of his bread into three fragments. Three one-inch squares of bread. Turning his water bucket upside down beneath the window, he stepped up on it. Straining every muscle, he reached up to boost the three small crumbs into the window ledge between the bars.

The bucket tipped and he fell with a clatter onto the filthy floor of his cell. He lay panting on his back for a while, never taking his eyes from the altar where he had laid his offering.

"You said you were hungry and we did not feed you," he said aloud when he found his breath again. "There is no man close enough for me to feed, Lord. And so I cannot share my bread with a person. But also . . . you said you know even when a sparrow falls. Even . . . a sparrow. So I will feed the sparrow in your name. Will a sparrow do? Will the bread crumbs work? I have nothing else to give. My prayers you have already. But while I am still here in this prison called earth, I will feed the sparrow because you said . . . if I feed the smallest, then I have fed you."

The sparrow had not returned for many days. Karl Ibsen sat on the floor of his cell and waited with perfect faith that it would come again.

———

There were certain places a woman like Lucy Strasburg would most likely patronize. Regardless of her low beginnings, Agent Hess had no doubt that her long association with Wolfgang von Fritschauer had honed her appreciation of the finer things in life. If Wolf had spoken truthfully and had indeed thrown her out, then no doubt she would still be frequenting the more elite of the Danzig clubs and restaurants in search of another male companion of Wolf's financial status. Such a woman could not survive long alone.

This afternoon Hess had chosen Cafe Passage as the location of his meeting with Gustav Ahlman, his assistant investigator in the matter of the Ibsen case. Situated along Dominiks Wall, in an old but elegant district of Danzig, the cafe served excellent wine and had tables on a patio overlooking a busy shopping area.

The sky was clear and blue above the red and white striped umbrellas of the cafe. Every table was crowded with women shoppers. Hess recognized the accents of nearly every country in the League of Nations. These were the wives of those diplomats who even now counseled together and worried helplessly about the future of the free port governed by their organization. Their women seemed oblivious to it all, unconcerned about anything but the rise in shoe prices since the fall of Czechoslovakia.

Hess did not look at the flowers of the Danzig parks. He did not gaze at the charming facades of the medieval buildings along Dominiks Wall. He sipped his schnapps, and from behind dark glasses, he scrutinized the elegant ladies of Danzig. There was only one among them all whom he wanted to see. *Tall. Shapely. Creamy smooth skin. Golden hair and the bearing of a princess with the heart of a back-street whore. This was Lucy Strasburg.* Even amid the elegance of Dominiks Wall shopping arcade, few could come close to such a description. Hess would find her. He was certain of that. After that he would devote his full attention to the matter of the Ibsen case.

Gustav Ahlman stepped from the tram across the square. Dodging traffic, he did not wait for the crossing signal, but headed straight to where Hess had been waiting for a quarter of an hour. The young man's thin face was pinched and harried. He was late. Hess did not like his junior officers to keep him waiting. Better to be hit by a bus while crossing against the signal than to be late.

He was panting as he took a seat. His fine brown hair fell across his high forehead. His eyes blinked rapidly as he looked nervously at his own reflection in Hess's dark glasses. He smoothed back his hair, cleared his throat, and looked nervously over his shoulder.

"Sorry I am late," he said.

Hess inclined his head to acknowledge the apology. He did not forgive the transgression, but he wanted Gustav to know that he had noticed.

"Well?" Hess sipped his schnapps and resumed his visual search of the ladies beyond the patio of Cafe Passage.

Gustav cleared his throat again. He was smiling as he wiped away sweat from his neck. "I have followed him as you instructed." The young voice was too excited. Hess squelched the enthusiasm with a withering look.

"And?"

Gustav Ahlman pulled out a small loose-leaf notebook and flipped it open. "I have it all here."

The waiter came, interrupting the report before it had begun. Gustav ordered tea and pastries. "Identical to those on the opposite table," he instructed like a schoolboy.

Hess eyed him briefly with disdain. Was this the best the Gestapo could come up with for his leg-man? Hess thought he could have hired an errand boy and accomplished the same thing. Ah well, everyone had to start somewhere. Gustav Ahlman had won the assignment of trailing Wolfgang von Fritschauer. He did not know why he was following Wolf, but he had dutifully recorded every move in this little book.

"What have you got for us?" Hess sounded bored already.

Again the intense brown eyes of the young man scanned the page. "Well, he has been to the doctor."

Not exactly earth-shattering news, Hess thought. "Is that all?"

"Actually, he has been to see a dozen different doctors around the city. As far away as the maternity clinic in Sopot."

Maternity? Hess turned his gaze on the eager young fellow. "You said—"

"Maternity." Gustav was triumphant. "I followed him into the waiting room of the last. Heard him talking to the doctor, and then the doctor talking to his receptionist. This Wolfgang von Fritschauer is also on the trail of someone. A woman. And she is . . . she is expecting a child, I heard him say."

This was unexpected news. Hess shook his head as he watched a shapely blond emerge from Neider's clothing store. Displays of the latest fashions and silk stockings mocked him from the showcase windows.

"So she is pregnant," he muttered. "The little slut is carrying a child for the Fatherland. And Wolf is the father, no doubt."

Suddenly it all made sense. The woman had not been thrown out by Wolf; she had left him. She had, like hundreds of willing unmarried S.S. mothers, suddenly become unwilling to give up her child.

"Good news, Agent Hess?" The young man was extremely proud of himself.

"Incomplete." Hess would not reward him with his favor. Not yet. "Find this woman for me. And then we will discuss good news. Stay with von Fritschauer. Report back to me any further developments."

Gustav leaned in close. "Is it a spy ring?" he asked in a whisper.

The tea and pastries came. Hess replied with a laconic shrug. He stared at the heaps of small cakes and eclairs and tried to imagine Lucy Strasburg slow and pregnant. An interesting thought, one which had completely evaded him over the long months of his recovery. Of course that did not alter his plans in any way. The woman would be silenced permanently regardless of her condition. Hopefully this would be accomplished before Wolf managed to find her and she had opportunity to talk about her escape.

In his pursuit of Lucy Strasburg, Agent Hess had not neglected his first duty to the Führer. He carried photographs of Jamie and Lori Ibsen in his briefcase. Sections of the city of Danzig had been marked out on the large detailed map on the wall of his hotel room. The search for Lucy had been combined with the hunt for the children until block by block he had checked all the cheap hotels and rooming houses and then crossed them off the list.

Like the loop of a snare, the broad circle of search was being drawn tighter. The outlying districts had been ruled out as possible places of refuge. Now, only the central market districts remained. Each remaining rooming house and block of cheap flats was identified with a red pin.

Hess was not only patient, he was thorough and exacting in the tedious work of tracking fugitives. One by one the red pins were plucked out and replaced by black pins, which now filled the map of Danzig like an ever-darkening shadow.

Lori insisted that it was not warm enough yet to lie on the beach at Sopot, but Jacob disagreed.

"It is now or never." He bowed with a flourish as Mark and Jamie and Alfie clustered around him to shout their agreement.

"This is a democracy," Jamie instructed his sister.

"Majority rules!" Mark added.

"Ja," Alfie said, a slow smile brightening his broad face. He held up the paw of Werner the cat to vote. "See? Werner also wants to go to the beach, Lori."

She shrugged in mock resignation. "You would think that once in a while Werner would vote with me on something. But we will take coats as well as swimming clothes."

Now the all-male majority of the Danzig Gang cheered little-mother Lori and danced an Indian dance around her as they had seen done in an American movie starring Rex the Wonder Horse last week.

"You're a good sport." Jacob thumped her on the arm as the others tumbled into the boys' quarters to gather their newly purchased swim gear and their heavy coats in case the Baltic breeze was cold at the beach.

"Another week and we will all be in foggy London," Lori said lightly. "And then when we tell people we spent almost five months on the Baltic, they will ask if we ever looked into the casino at Sopot or if the weather was as wonderful at the resort as everybody said. Terrible to admit we had not gone once to the beach." She blushed under Jacob's amused gaze, wondering if he would like the way she looked in her swimsuit. He had not seen her in a bathing suit since last summer, and she had grown up a lot since then. She pretended to busy herself gathering her own things, but he did not leave her room. "Well?" she asked at last. "Are you going? You'd better get your things."

In their excitement, the boys sounded like a growling, yelping pack of weaned puppies. Their squeals and protests penetrated Jacob's silence. He looked away from Lori. "They are killing each other in there," he said and left the room.

She closed the door and leaned against it, grateful for a moment to be alone, a moment without feeling the thoughtful gaze of Jacob Kalner warming her blood like a kettle on a slow fire. Maybe next week they would be in London! She and Jamie would be with Mama. *And where would Jacob and Mark and Alfie stay? Maybe one of the children's camps?* Lori frowned at the thought. She did not like the idea of such a separation. Maybe she could ask Uncle Theo . . . maybe there was some way, someplace where they could still live together in London! The Danzig Gang had been through too much together to be separated. Surely someone would see that. All the way from Berlin to here. They had lived by selling off the jewels Alfie had carried out in his pocket. Jacob had worked at the wharf. Lori took a job at the drugstore and Alfie had even found work as a janitor at Sprinter's ice cream parlor until the Hitler boys had roughed him up. Except for that reminder, life here had not been an ordeal at all, even though the adults in London had all sounded sympathetic and shocked that five children had been forced to survive on their own for six months. Lori had told her mother over the telephone that it was not *all* bad. What she should have said was that except for missing her parents, it was *not bad at all!*

She was the mama and Jacob was the papa. They had kept it all perfectly proper, however. He shared the big room with the boys. Lori slept in the tiny corner room alone, although there were times when she could almost feel his nearness through the door. On those nights she never slept well. On those nights she lay awake and stared into the darkness, grateful that she had *never* felt this way when they had shared sleeping quarters in the bellows room at New Church!

There were other moments when he brushed her hand by accident or looked at her when she had not expected it, and in those moments Lori felt as if she could hardly breathe. She had to make herself exhale and act as though everything were *not* spinning inside her.

Beyond the threats of Berlin, in the clean air of Danzig, something had happened to Lori. She wanted to talk to Mama about it. She would talk to her about it for hours—maybe next week.

"And we were standing in church together sharing the hymnbook, and his hand touched mine, and I thought I would faint. I did not hear the sermon. But he did not notice. He does not seem to be aware. We just ... you know ... take care of the boys like you and Papa would have. A regular little family, except..."

She slipped on her swimsuit and remembered how last year she had wished she filled out the top a little better. Now she filled it out nicely. The boys on the banks of the Spree back home would have looked at her. And looked again. *Indeed,* Lori thought, *something very nice has happened between last summer and now.* She had become a woman. She wondered if Jacob had noticed the change.

And she was also in love. At least she was practically certain that she was. She thought that probably Jacob would not notice that. And if he did, he would not care because she had been such a complete pain the entire time they had been locked up in New Church together.

He had teased her about being older and more mature when they celebrated their seventeenth birthdays in April. She was three days older than he was, and he said that he figured that was why she was always trying to tell him what to do. He had meant the comment as a joke, but still it stung. That meant he had not forgotten the Lori-of-New Church! Lori who cried often. Lori who complained. Lori who argued about everything! She did so want him to forget about all that!

She wanted him to see Lori-of-the-Danzig-Gang. Good sport. Capable. Happy. Willing to lose in a democratic vote! And now, she wanted him to see Lori-in-the-swimsuit. All grown up. Pretty. She wanted him to feel the same warmth that she felt when he looked at her. There was only one week left here if all went well! They could stand the agony of mutual attraction for one more week. After all, she had stood the agony of unspoken love for months!

She brushed her shoulder-length blond hair and tried it down, and then piled up on her head. She looked older with it up and so she pinned it up, leaving her shoulders bare. A touch of lipstick added to the effect. Satisfied, she pulled on her blouse and skirt, finishing just as the thumping of impatient fists on her door demanded her to hurry or be left behind!

"Come on! Hurry up! We'll miss the tram, Lori!"

And then the chuckle of Alfie and his thick, happy voice, "Meow! Werner says hurry up!"

It was only seven and a half miles from Kohlen Market in Danzig to the crisp white beaches of Sopot. Twenty-six minutes by tramway, including stops in the suburbs of Langfahr and Olivia.

The tram, powered by electricity, could have run very well on the excess energy being generated by the boys of the Danzig Gang. Lori sat at the far end of the bright yellow and green tram and tried to pretend she did not know who these noisy, rowdy, gawking travelers were.

All to no avail, of course. They whooped and pointed out the window and yelled down to her over the heads of other prim and disapproving passengers. *"Hey Lori! Lori! Lori! Look at that! Do you see that?"*

When the crescent curve of Danzig Bay appeared there was a sudden roar, the tumult of explorers seeing a new land for the first time and claiming that they really did *see it first*! Lori casually looked at the bright waters of the Baltic as though she had seen the bay a thousand times. She glanced away at the wooded hill sloping up from Sopot as if the new green of leaves were far more interesting. Jamie, Mark, Alfie, and Jacob pressed their faces against the tram windows like a group of caged orangutans reaching for a banana.

"There it is! Look at it! I won because I saw it first!"

"No! I saw it first!"

Just when it seemed there might be violence over who actually laid eyes on Danzig Bay first, Lori stood regally and pronounced, "I saw it first."

Silence descended, and then Alfie shook his head slowly. "No, you don't count . . . because you was not in on it." He seemed indignant over her intrusion in so great a matter. The other passengers looked at her curiously, wondering what she could say to satisfy this big fellow who was obviously not quite all there in the head.

She clutched at the leather strap and swayed for a moment as the tram rattled over the tracks. And then she spotted Werner-cat on Alfie's broad shoulder.

"Werner saw it first," she said. "Werner wins the ice cream, then."

Alfie liked the answer and congratulated his cat for seeing the bay first. The other boys groaned all together and told her to sit down and stay out of it. Then a new bet was born and the old one disregarded.

"First one into the water, then!"

"Not just touching it, but in!"

"Over the head! First one in over the head!"

Werner-cat would not be in this competition, they told Alfie. Cats did not like to swim even when the water was warm, so Werner would have to sit this one out.

"And you too, Lori," Jamie Ibsen warned his sister.

"Ah, you know girls," Mark added. "She won't get her hair wet anyway."

So went the conversation on the Danzig tram to Sopot. The line scooted along the seashore—iridescent blue sea on the right and the famous hotel and casino named Kurhaus right across from the pier. There was Northpark and Southpark where less brave bathers could play under the yew trees or ride a donkey cart. For those who preferred warm water to the real feel of the Baltic, there was the *Warmbad,* a heated pool complete with cabana and a brass oompah band on weekends.

Lori would have been quite happy with that luxury, but as the tram slipped by the wide awning of the building, the orangutans began to chant their cry about *the old lady pool, the pool for infants and convalescing arthritis patients.*

At that instant Lori spotted a jabbering tribe of flabby-thighed mothers being pulled into the entrance by their young children. Ah well, perhaps warm water was not everything.

Directly between Northpark and Southpark, where the courtyard of the Kurhaus Casino faced the Seesteg Pier, the tram grumbled and clanged and stopped.

Lori peered into the glittering entrance of the Kurhaus Casino and then back toward the Baltic. At this moment she remembered her father. This was the place Karl Ibsen had spoken of! Here it was! Why had she not remembered before this moment? *The Tram Ride to Temptation! The casino on one side and the ocean on the other! And there you are, caught between the devil and the deep blue sea!*

Papa had been here as a young man. To this *exact* place! He had told the story often of how he walked through the casino with its baccarat tables and roulette wheels. He had been the only one of his university friends who had not bet and had not gambled away all his funds for vacation.

"So this was the place," Lori whispered as the boys crammed through the tram doors all at the same moment and ran full bore toward the sparkling waters!

Lori simply savored the moment. She felt the nearness of the old story and wished that Papa were here to tell her all over again. She had not been heartsick for him for a long time, but the memory of his laughter and his warning about this very spot made her miss him fiercely!

She stepped off the tram and stood transfixed before the very door where Papa had entered as a young man. *Before he had even met Mama, he said!* She walked toward it, wishing very much to see this wilderness of sin where Papa had been tempted.

Suddenly Jacob spoke her name. "Are you coming, Lori?" He smiled at her. "Or do you want to see the casino?"

Her eyes widened. Did they dare go in? "Do you think. . . ?"

Jacob took her arm, propelling her past the red-coated doorman. "You know our fathers were here together." He hurried through the revolving door. "When they were at University."

"You mean *your* father?" The reek of stale tobacco greeted her. The clear voice of the croupier called out that bets must be placed. Then the whirl and the tick . . . tick . . . tick of the spinning roulette wheel.

"Yes. Our fathers." Jacob was grinning as he took in all the opulent splendor of this enormous gaming hall. "My father said a woman could walk through one of these casinos stark naked and probably nobody would look up . . . too busy losing their own shirts. Father lost all his money, he and the other fellows with him. Only Pastor Ibsen—except your father was not a pastor then, but quite a man about town—well, he was the only one who would not gamble. So everyone else lost their money and would have starved if Pastor Ibsen had not . . ."

Tears came to Lori's eyes. It was foolish of her. Embarrassing. But here she was hearing the other side of a story that was an Ibsen legend! And now . . . where were those two young men who had strolled through the Kurhaus? Where were the fathers of Jacob and Lori now?

A heavy foreboding for her own future came over Lori with that thought. And what was to become of *them* . . . the *Danzig Gang*? If there was a war? If their British visas did not come through? They were having such a lovely day, but all those worries came crashing down on her in the middle of it.

Jacob put his arm around her. "I . . . I'm sorry. I did not mean to. I thought you would think it was funny."

She nodded. "It is . . . or it *was* . . . but . . ." Her words trailed off. The thought that their fathers were both in a Nazi prison or worse . . . after so many wonderful years of friendship, somehow stole the laughter even from old memories. "I am, *really*, all right. I just . . . don't want to ever look back and wish for . . . all the good times *we* have had. All of us together, I mean. To be apart or . . ."

They inched their way through a crowd gathered around the roulette wheel. There was no need to say more. There were ghosts even here, in the laughter of the young men of Kurhaus. Jacob heard them, too. *The laughter of their fathers at age twenty, when they could not have known what the future held for them. Their wives. Their children . . .*

"Stupid of me," Jacob said as they emerged again into the bright clean air. "This is our day," he said gently. "We should make our own memories today, yes? And maybe one day tell our children?" He wiped away her only tear with his calloused thumb. Yet another tram arrived behind him and disgorged its passengers; some to the devil and some toward the deep blue sea.

Jacob sat beside Lori on the beach, but he never looked at her, never noticed the new swimsuit or the new Lori. His eyes were everywhere but on her—on the three boys splashing in the surf; on the little girl building sand castles; on the old couple walking their dog just out of reach of the waves. He studied the clouds that drifted across the sun, cutting off its warmth and then letting it loose again. But he did not notice the goose bumps on Lori's bare arms when the wind came up. He did not know why she did not at least wear her blouse over the swimsuit when bursts of cold breeze blew in from the Baltic.

Lori sighed. Could he really think she was enjoying this ordeal? Why did he not look at her once and *notice* that she was quite grown now? *A woman!* A half-frozen woman forcing a pleasant look on her face as she waited for him to glance her way just once! After that, she reasoned, she would ask to borrow his sweater like Garbo had done in . . . *what was the name of that film?*

Never mind. Jacob looked at the pier when she talked to him. When she asked him to rub suntan oil on her back, he said, "No thank you. I'm fine."

"Well *I'm* not. I could burn!"

He looked over her head at the heated swimming pool. "Then put your shirt on. Or go inside."

Instead, she turned over and let the sun beat down on her beet-red face. Even a sunburn could not outdo the flush of her embarrassment at his rebuff. She closed her eyes so he would not see how near to tears she was. A cool breeze swept across her skin, but suddenly she was very warm. She wished he would go swim with Alfie and the boys. She was sorry she ever bought this swimsuit, ashamed that she had thought of *Jacob* when she looked at her own reflection in the mirror.

Minutes passed. The dull crash of waves mingled with happy shrieks and dozens of voices. Lori could hear Alfie's deep, pleasant chuckle as he stammered some challenge to Mark and Jamie.

"Bet I . . . I . . . can hold my . . . breath longest . . ."

Jacob heard Alfie too, and now he spoke. "You were right, you know," Jacob said softly. "We could not have left Alfie in Berlin, and—"

She opened her eyes, certain of what he would say next. "We are *all* going together," she said almost angrily.

"But if they don't let him—"

"We have to believe! Papa would say . . . and I say now, God is in charge of even little sparrows. Why would He forsake Alfie?" She sat up and watched as big Alfie, fifteen-year-old Alfie, played contentedly with the little boys.

"But *if* . . . you know, Lori, I would have to stay with him. Find some way to get him out of here. He said it. They are here, the Nazis are. It's a matter of time. And—"

It was instinct. She rammed him hard in the ribs with her elbow and then drew back, as horrified by the blow as he was.

His breath came out with an *oof!*

"What?" He finally looked at her. "Why did you—?"

"Because. *Shut up!* Our *one* day at the beach, and you find *gloom* to talk about! And here I have been all day, wearing *this*. . . ."

At last! At last his eyes swept over her! She wanted to cheer! He looked at her for a moment, at least! Then he looked away quickly, back toward the boys.

"You didn't even notice," she finished quietly.

Jacob drew a deep breath, like a man inhaling the healthy sea air. He drew another breath and exhaled loudly. His eyes seemed glazed. His jaw muscle flexed.

"Are you . . . *all right?*" Now Lori thought perhaps she had hurt him with the jab to his ribs.

He sighed slowly, then put his head in his hands. "Oh," he moaned, "this is not doing any good at all!"

Now she knew she had hurt him! "Oh, Jacob! I'm so sorry!"

He stood, scattering sand on the blanket and on her. Stretching his neck, he squinted at the pier, the sea, the sky, the dog, the bath house. Then, as if he struggled against some powerful force, his face jerked around and he locked his gaze on her. Helpless resignation filled his eyes as he drank her in. Her eyes. Her throat. Shoulder. Arm. *Please, please, not the breasts*. . .Too late. Even as he battled himself, he took in every inch of her beautiful, incredible, too-perfect body.

"There!" He ran a hand through his hair. "All day I have been trying *not* to look—not to notice. And now look!"

It was the wrong thing to do, but Lori smiled up at him in his misery. "You have been the perfect gentleman," she said softly. "But I have not been a lady." She reached for her blouse.

Jacob knelt down beside her and put his hand on her arm. He shook his head slowly and moved nearer, his eyes never leaving hers.

Too late, Lori. Too late. You are beautiful; I knew that anyway, and now you are going to get kissed....

Waves still crashed against the sand. Children still laughed and shouted at the water's edge. Their voices carried far above Lori and Jacob like the hollow voices in a dream. The breeze was cool, but Lori did not notice anything but his lips against hers.

11

The Prodigal Sister

Wolf had left nothing to chance when he prepared for his first meeting with the priest at Marienkirche. He had called ahead and made an appointment, giving a brief summary of the situation. Posing as the worried and grief-stricken brother of Lucy, he had spoken of her as any brother might speak of a sister who had been deceived and abandoned by her lover.

Naturally, the priest had been most sympathetic and eager to help in any way.

Wolf had additional photos of Lucy copied. Along with the photograph of her on the steps of St. Stephan's, he included one with her in a red low-cut gown. In her raised hand was a glass of champagne. In this one, her face reflected the seductive look that was much more familiar to Wolf than what the doctor had described as Lucy's "innocence." In the mental script Wolf prepared for this interview, he labeled the two photos *before-he-seduced-her* and *after-he-took-her-from-her-family*. Wolf had dealt with these ecclesiastical types before; he was certain that he had only to say these words with the right touch of bitterness and sorrow, and the priest would move heaven and earth to help him locate his "prodigal sister." Even if he had not personally seen Lucy in his great cathedral, this priest would know who Wolf should contact within other Danzig parishes. Coupled with his own personal performance of sorrow, Wolf would offer a reward to the Catholic diocese in Danzig. A charitable contribution from his wealthy Prussian family in exchange for the return of his sister and her illegitimate child to the fold.

Well armed with this story, Wolf took a taxi to the massive Gothic cathedral that dominated the skyline of Danzig. Wolf considered the building not as one might look on a holy site, but as an example of pure German culture. Founded in the fourteenth century by Teutonic knights, Marienkirche was the mightiest example of German architecture in the Baltic. The massive west bell tower consisted of ancient brick rising to a summit 248 feet above the cobblestone street. Ten slender turrets reached heavenward from the gables. Inside, the beautiful grained vaulting was supported by twenty-eight pillars. The aisles and transepts were flanked with private chapels dedicated to German merchant burgomasters and their families. In the walls and floors between the buttresses, the proud and the rich descendants of those first Teutonic knights waited for eternity.

For Wolfgang von Fritschauer, the glory of Marienkirche had nothing to do with the Lord it claimed to glorify. In the gilded high altar, the woodcarvings, and stained-glass images of the apostles and Christ, Wolf did not see the Spirit of the living God—he saw the spirit of Aryan culture. He deified the stone carvers and the ancient painters, the builders of this place. They were his ancestors; those workers of this wonder—German, one and all. If the painted scene were not the image of Christ—if, instead, it were the face of Thor hurling thunderbolts to earth, it would have had equal meaning to Wolf. The great altarpiece depicting *The Last Judgment,* with its swirling smoke and rising flame and the angry face of a vengeful God, could just as easily have been made in the image of the Führer. The judgment of the German people was soon coming on the earth. The victory of German culture would be celebrated with new significance in this place. A new inferno was planned for those unworthy to enter the paradise of national socialism. And worthiness was, of course, determined by German law.

All these things flashed though Wolf's mind as he genuflected before the crucifix and extended his hand to the priest. He felt no awareness of blasphemy in his thoughts. His beliefs were as natural to him as breathing. The fact that he himself was worthy to be called pure of blood was owed to the wisdom of his ancestors. They had known the value of untainted race, and had practiced it long before the bricks of Marienkirche had risen as their monument.

The priest was short and swarthy—obviously of some mixed Slavic blood. He invited Wolf to follow him through a labyrinth of hallways to his office where they might speak privately about the man's sister. The priest could not guess the revulsion and disdain Wolf felt as he stared at the back of his too-round head and sloping shoulders.

"Won't you be seated, Herr von Fritschauer?" The priest kindly indicated a large tooled-leather chair beside his desk.

"Thank you, Father." Wolf opened his briefcase, displaying a stack of Lucy's photographs among his business papers. The priest sat opposite him and listened sympathetically to the story of Lucy Strasburg *before* and Lucy *after*. Not an unusual story these days in Germany. Young women in the *Bund Deutscher Mädel*, the "League of German Girls," were encouraged to have illegitimate children for the Reich.

Wolf brushed over the priest's obvious disapproval of the Nazi policies of rewarding immorality. He held fast to his story: "I am prepared to offer a reward to benefit the charity of your choice if you might help bring Lucy home." He fanned a dozen pictures out on the scarred desk. "Perhaps if you could make some phone calls on behalf of my family, put her picture into the hands of any who might have seen her here in Danzig."

And so it was as simple as that. A model of charity and kindness, the good Father promised to do all he could to return this wayward girl to her family.

The great bells of Marienkirche tolled high noon as Wolf strode confidently from the building.

————

With its bright yellow sides and lime-green roof, the Danzig tram No. 5 glided to a stop like a giant banana on rails. Danzig trams and taxis were the only things that seemed out of character in the medieval city.

Lucy considered the queue of passengers for only one moment of temptation. She fingered the few coins she carried in the deep pocket of her sweater. She had brought along these precious savings today for a special purpose. Although her ankles were swollen and her back ached terribly, she would not squander what little she had left on a tram ride out to shop.

Raising her chin slightly, she pretended that she simply preferred to walk. After all, walking was the best exercise for pregnant women. Women in this condition had been walking to market in Danzig long before these miracles of transportation were even imagined!

Peter had given up riding on the tram as well, but for a different reason. One day near the synagogue on Hunde Strasse the sign above the tram stop had been painted: *HUNDE STRASSE – HOUND STREET: DOGS ALLOWED – NO JEWS.*

Lucy had told him that she would not ride the public tram, either, if such signs were allowed to remain. It was a matter of honor.

But Peter was gone to Warsaw now, and if Lucy had only had money enough, she knew that today she would have gladly traded a bit of her newfound principle for even a few moments of luxury.

Never mind that, she told herself. *Hadn't Mama always gone out to milk the cows when she was expecting, even on the days the babies came? It was good for her, Mama said. Good for me, too.*

Lucy found herself thinking a lot about her mother these days—

missing her, longing to ask her a thousand questions. But there was no use trying to contact her parents. No doubt Wolf would have them watched. He wanted the child Lucy carried, and she did not doubt that her mother and father had already been questioned and warned. Probably once they learned of Lucy's condition they had gone to the priest and had the Mass read for her. They had mentally buried her in the plot reserved for sinners. She would not have been welcome in her father's house even if there had been some way to get home without being discovered by Wolf.

So there is no use thinking of Mama, except to remember what she did before each baby came.

She struck out along the waterfront known as Speicher-Insel. Here the ancient stucco and half-timbered grain elevators unloaded their freight onto cargo ships as they had done for centuries. Peter had found work here. Now that he was gone, there were a hundred men in line to take his job. The place was teeming with dock workers who would have stopped in their tracks to take a look at her only a few months before. Now not one head turned, Lucy noted in amusement. For the first time since she turned thirteen, men were not gawking at her, raising their eyebrows or winking.

She was just another pregnant Frau on her way to the green gate that led to Langer Market. Pregnancy had blessed her with a cloak of anonymity. She bore little resemblance to the stylish woman who had attended the opera in Vienna with the Nazi party officials. Nothing about her suggested that she had once sat beside the Führer and been admired by the most powerful men in the German Reich. All that was gone. With swollen ankles, swollen belly, and a puffy, weary-looking face, Lucy Strasburg was far from radiant. Perhaps that was the reason the Aryan mothers at the S.S. maternity homes were kept in strict confinement. No doubt the Nazi hierarchy did not wish to disillusion those potential mothers for the Reich who believed that carrying a child for the Führer gave young mothers the status and looks of a goddess.

Some goddess, Lucy thought as she caught her reflection in a shop window. She wondered what Wolf would say if he could see her now. Then she wondered what he would do to her if he ever found her here in Danzig.

Still, even with that remote possibility, she did not regret her decision not to go to Warsaw with Peter.

Lucy Strasburg saw the future of Danzig quite as clearly as Peter saw it. The howling threats of the Führer of Germany against Danzig and Poland were unmistakable. But the certainty of what was about to come made her adamant that she would never go to Warsaw. She had heard the German generals with her own ears as they spoke of the devastation their Air Force and tanks could bring to that place. All of

Poland could not stand for a week against the divisions of the Reich. Cavalry units and flashing sabres and suicide charges across the open fields would mean nothing against airplanes and panzer units. And now the giant Skoda armament factories of Czechoslovakia were in German control. Coal and steel mills and great deposits of iron had come into the orbit of *Mein Kampf*.

Lucy knew it. Maybe everyone knew it by now. Peter Wallich had run off to Warsaw, but it was only a matter of time.

And in spite of their promises, England would remain on its side of the Channel. They might declare war, but they would not come to help Poland until the Requiem Mass was read over all the dead of Warsaw. France would sit behind the great concrete wall known as the Maginot Line, and they, too, would wait.

It was not really a matter of language, Lucy thought as she walked through the bustling streets of Danzig. It was simply that one place on the Continent of Europe was no more safe than another. Just because there were no swastika flags replacing flower boxes in Warsaw did not mean that it would not soon be the case.

Not Warsaw for Lucy. Given any choice in the matter, she preferred to be somewhere else when the final bells of the Requiem tolled.

As if to reinforce her thoughts, the bells of Marienkirche boomed out over the city of Danzig. Lucy looked up toward the bell tower, remembering how she and Peter had climbed the steep stairs to watch the bell ringer on his wooden treadmill turning the green-tarnished gears that moved the bells. One strong man in that little squirrel cage caused all this commotion. Pigeons swirled skyward, people checked their watches and shuttered their shops for lunchtime. Danzig ordered its existence by the bells of Marienkirche.

Lucy knew that those bells would soon be ringing a life-shattering event for the Danzigers. *"One day,"* Hitler had shouted, *"the bells of Marienkirche will announce the reunification of German Danzig with the Reich!"*

When that day came, Lucy Strasburg hoped to be somewhere else. Not Warsaw. Not Paris. Not Brussels . . .

Lucy carried two books in the deep pockets of her smock. One book was an English-German dictionary. The other was a thin green volume she had found on the table of a used-book seller in the open market. This book she studied as though it contained the secrets of eternal life. *Her life. The life of her unborn baby. . . .*

WAITING AT TABLE
A Practical Guide
Including
PARLOURMAID'S WORK IN GENERAL
By
MRS. C.S. PEEL, O.B.E.

The bookseller did not know what the *O.B.E.* stood for after Mrs. Peel's name. However, he guaranteed that the former owner of this precious green volume had studied its contents and obtained a British visa, traveling to London, England, as a domestic servant. Lucy had heard of other such miracles. England did not want doctors or lawyers or skilled workers, but they were still in need of domestics—parlormaids who knew how to carve a leg of lamb properly!

Lucy had shelled out her few pennies and had purchased first the book, then the dictionary to help her decipher its secrets.

When the first drone of Luftwaffe engines was heard over Danzig and Warsaw, Lucy hoped to be practicing the fine art of carving loin of lamb, neck of veal, knuckle of veal, breast of veal, ham, hare, or rabbit. This was as far as she had gotten in her studies, and it was all difficult to remember since she had none of these things to actually practice carving. It had been a long time since she had eaten anything but the cheapest sausage and cheese. Reading about real food often made her mouth water. Dishing up such delicacies had filled her dreams. At night she closed her eyes and recited the catechism of carving: *chops should be cut off, beginning with the outer chop, unless these are too large, when slices should be cut the whole length of the joint. . . .*

As the baby kicked and thumped within her, she would drift off to mouth-watering dreams of steaming heaps of lamb on a plate before her. Nightmares about Wolf had long since faded, and the practical issues of food had filled his place nicely.

But in the clear light of day, when temptations beckoned her through the window of Haueisen Confectioners, she turned her face away from the eclair or heaping sandwich. Her fingers tightened around her coin purse. There were more important things to purchase than food. *Diapers. A basket for the baby to sleep in. Two glass baby bottles and spare nipples.*

Not that Lucy expected to need bottles. She would nurse her baby, as her own mother had nursed Lucy and her brothers and sisters.

Still, just in case, she bought canned milk. And it would be wonderful to find a christening robe with lace and little booties and a bonnet! The baby must be christened! Lucy had determined that this little one would be blessed by a priest, in spite of how it had come into being. Lucy was condemned, but she would not let that heartache touch this baby. She loved it, even unborn, and she yearned for it to have all the sweet little things a baby should have.

Lucy looked through the display window of the children's shop. Tiny shirts and gowns and little caps were draped over stuffed bears and a soft pink rabbit. Ruffled blankets and matching sheets adorned a hand-carved rosewood cradle.

She pulled out her list and studied it. *Diapers. Bottles. Alcohol for umbilical cord. Aspirin. Sanitary pads. Disinfectant.*

Lucy had attended two of her mother's deliveries. She had watched the milk cows give birth; seen kittens born. There was no money for a doctor. But the baby of Lucy Strasburg would have a christening gown. Silk and white lace. And matching booties. A bonnet over the velvety head.

This much, Lucy determined, she would do for her baby.

The prow of the White Star Line freighter rose and fell in a steady rhythm against the six-foot swells beyond the Tel Aviv sea wall.

Sam Orde did not look back toward the receding shoreline of Palestine. He stood braced in the windy bow of the ship and fixed his gaze on the gun-metal gray wall of clouds on the horizon. There was a squall up ahead, unusual for this time of year on the Mediterranean.

The cargo hold was filled with enormous flats of citrus fruit. Crates of oranges, lemons, limes, and grapefruits had been loaded by cranes. Fruit was placed in porcelain bowls in the otherwise sparsely provisioned passenger cabins. Fresh orange juice was promised for every breakfast. Lemonade was on hand at any hour. Limes were sliced and readily available for those passengers who preferred gin and tonic in the ship's salon. Orde was grateful the cargo was not onions or garlic.

Eleven other passengers traveled on board the *Lady of Avon*. Orde had boarded before any of them and had slept through their boarding and initial introductions. He dreaded polite conversation and inane questions that inevitably accompanied a small passenger list and a long voyage. The weight of the past few weeks was heavy on him. He hoped only to pass the voyage to England by long hours of sleep and as little human interaction as possible.

A number of the other passengers gathered on the stern of the ship. They strained their eyes for the last glimpse of the Holy Land. When Orde heard them pass by the porthole of his cabin, he emerged to stroll to the opposite end of the freighter. He braced himself in the bow and closed his eyes as he inhaled the cold, salty mist. A sea gull circled above his head, crying, and then wheeled away, back toward the land.

"Captain Orde, is it?" The voice of a young Englishman startled Orde.

No ship was large enough for anonymity, it seemed. He barely glanced at the smiling face of a man he had never met before. How did the fellow know his name?

"Yes. I don't believe I have had the pleasure . . ."

The fellow laughed. "Oh dear me, no. You don't know me. But I saw your picture in the newspaper. Right after that dreadful incident on the Temple Mount. An interview about the chap who was killed. Dreadful. Hard to forget such a thing. And I never forget a face."

"I see." Orde turned back to face the wind. He was being rude, but then so was this fellow, intruding on Orde's privacy.

"We heard you had resigned. Good heavens. A pity. A chap puts his whole life into the Army and then something like this happens." Perhaps the words were meant to be sympathetic, but an alarm bell sounded in Orde's brain.

Whitecaps topped the swells. The wind was cold, penetrating Orde's heavy cable-knit sweater and corduroy trousers. But he had claimed this spot in the bow and felt strangely unwilling to give up its solitude to anyone. Perhaps if he waited, the young man would grow bored and wander back with the other passengers.

The intruder buttoned his heavy coat and remained in place. He seemed unaware of Orde's melancholy reverie. Or if he knew, he was still determined to stand at the rail.

"Going back home to your wife and family, then are you?" He was oblivious to his own bad manners.

"No. Just going home to Mother England," Orde replied, unwilling to admit that a raw nerve had been struck.

"Well, what will you do with yourself?" He gripped the rail beside Orde. Uninvited. Unwelcome. "I mean, do you have some kind of job?"

Orde turned to face him with the same withering stare he might give a recruit whose gun was not properly cleaned. He raised his chin, exuding his military authority. He did not speak until the young man's exuberant curiosity wilted beneath the glare of rank. "You are just the sort of chap I enjoy getting under my command. A bit of cleaning up and discipline, and you might polish out half decent." Orde rose slightly on his toes with satisfaction at the horrified expression on the stunned face. "However, since I will not have opportunity to teach you manners, and I detest rudeness, I will retreat and leave you the forward position."

With a cold smile, Orde nodded his head and left the fellow staring after him.

Perhaps it was best not to mingle at all with the other passengers, Orde reasoned as he closed the door of his cabin. He could pay a bit more and take his meals in his room. *Wife and family ... Mother England ...* His wife was dead, and Mother England was angry with him. What did that leave him? What was he to do now?

Questions and self-doubt led to a wave of self-pity that threatened to drown him. He told himself that his faith in God had not wavered, only his faith that God had any use for him. This was the most devastating doubt of all. Orde had suffered losses before in his life. Katie had died in an auto accident near their home in Surrey. With her had perished their unborn child and all of Orde's hopes to live the normal life of a husband and father. He had raised his head and asked himself, *What now?* In that moment he found total dedication to the military was the only way to fill the empty hours. He embraced Mother England and believed that in fulfilling his duty to the English government in Palestine, he was also serving God. For years he had lived only for that purpose, that fulfillment.

Tonight, the chasm of uselessness opened before him. For the first time since she had gone, Orde allowed himself the luxury of longing for Katie once again. Yes, he had often thought of her; wondered what she would say about this event or that. He had imagined her tenderly in a thousand different ways. But tonight, he longed for her, ached for her, desired her once again.

He closed his eyes against the starlight that glistened through the porthole. Breathing in, he remembered the sweet fragrance of her skin. He reached his hand up into the emptiness above him as if to touch her face, to brush a finger across her lips and pull her down to kiss him.

He swallowed hard and opened his eyes again when the longing became unbearable. *So this was loneliness.* His eyes were moist, and now he questioned not himself, not England, but the God who had taken Katie from him and had cast him adrift.

He sat up and held his head in his hands in despair. Then he switched on the light and rummaged through his duffle bag for the well-worn Bible Katie had given him on their fourth anniversary. Almost desperate for comfort, he flipped open the cover to her delicate handwriting.

My Dearest Husband,

Four years of joy with you on earth makes me long for an eternity of joy with you. We will stand together before the Lord, and may He say to each of us, "Well done." Until then, it is your duty to serve Him in faraway and dangerous lands. It is mine to stay behind and bravely watch you go. To pray and believe that He goes with you always, even as He always stays by me in lonely times. Even when we do not see the answers we must pray and believe that our Lord knows all. This faith is all that He asks of us. It is the only real battle we fight. In the end this is why He will say, "Well done."

Your loving wife,
Katie.

Orde read her words as if seeing them for the first time. He wiped away tears with the back of his hand and whispered thanks to her. He had not dreamed that she would one day leave him behind. Nor had he imagined that he would ever face a moment so bleak in his life that he would be forced to say, *"I do not understand, and yet I trust in You, Lord!"*

Tonight, Orde said those words aloud. And for the first time he understood that the biggest battle was not fought against Muslim terrorists on the slopes of Zion, but against the doubt and despair that threatened to destroy true faith in God's love.

In the small dark hours as the ship steadily moved away from Palestine, Orde won that battle. As Jesus prayed in Gethsemane, Orde bowed his head and said, "Not my will, but yours be done."

The purple glow of dawn shone through the window of Karl Ibsen's cell. A single morning star was framed between the center bars to wink in at the sleeping prisoner. If he had opened his eyes, he would have felt the nearness of heaven by the light of that star. He would have smiled and imagined that the star was really an angel watching over him. But Karl did not awaken until the sky had ripened into morning and a beam of light penetrated his consciousness.

Far away he heard the song of birds in the forest that ringed Nameless camp, and then he heard the flutter of feathered wings above him. An angel? He did not open his eyes to see. Again the gentle rustle sounded, followed by a small, unmelodious chirp.

The lady sparrow had returned to the window ledge. Karl opened his eyes but did not move as he watched her peck curiously at the bread he had placed in the center of the bars.

Peck . . . peck . . . peck . . . and then a resounding "cheep!" With this exultant cry, she called another to join her at the feast. A darker-feathered sparrow whirred to her side. She deferred to him, hopping back a step and waiting politely until he plunged his orange beak first into one piece of bread and then into the next. Lady Sparrow cocked an eye toward Karl as if to remark that she knew where the bread had come from and how much she appreciated such an exorbitant gift in a place where starvation was so common. Karl nodded almost imperceptibly.

The big male sparrow hefted a morsel in his beak and then flew out of sight. Lady Sparrow waited a moment longer before she turned her attention away from Karl and likewise wrestled with a piece of bread, grasping it in her beak and hopping off the ledge.

One small square of Karl's offering remained. He knew the sparrows would come back for it. And if they came back once, they would come back a thousand times. They would return for as long as Karl continued to feed them. "Company," Karl whispered. "Thank you. Thank you, Jesus, for caring about sparrows. About me. About Lori and Jamie. . . ."

Father Kopecky arrived at the door of the Lubetkin home with a paper sack of plums and a package of fresh trout from the fish market. Unlike other friends and neighbors of the Lubetkin family, the priest did not bring food prepared in his own unkosher kitchen. For this sensitivity to the ways of a Jewish household, Etta was quietly grateful.

She led him down the hallway to Papa's room. "You see how well he looks!" Papa sat up in bed, waiting impatiently for Rachel to set up the chess board for their game, which was fast becoming a thrice weekly event.

"He looks like a scarecrow," Father Kopecky said with a grin on his impish face. "Today he will not beat me at chess like he did two days ago."

"Man looks at the outside," Papa declared, "while the Eternal knows what is in the mind of an accomplished chess player."

The priest took his seat beside Rachel. "Then God should tell me a few of your chess moves just to be fair about it." He winked at Rachel, which made her blush.

Sometimes she liked the priest. Other times he made her uncomfortable.

"Give it up, my friend," Papa said, rubbing his hands together in anticipation. "You do battle against a son of the covenant." He held up the black king in a threatening way. "Have you forgotten the words of the prophet Balaam? *He has blessed, and I cannot change it. . . . The shout of their King is among them. . . . Their king will be greater than Agag.*" He coughed as his own joke made him laugh. "Besides, you are a lousy chess player." He set his king back in place.

"Etta," cried the priest, "have I come here to be insulted?"

Mama smiled and shrugged. "Don't insult him, Aaron," she chided Papa. "He has brought us fresh plums and trout from the market. Let him win for once."

Then Mama jerked her head for Rachel to come out with her and leave the two friends to their game.

"He is good for your father," Mama said to Rachel as she unwrapped the fish.

"I like him," Rachel agreed. "But I do not trust him always." The headlines of the newspaper caught her attention. It was a Polish newspaper. A publication for the Saturday people who did not like Jews. In the house of Aaron Lubetkin, only Yiddish papers were read and studied. This newspaper was something quite different. It contained advertisements directed at Polish women for fashions from Paris. It held theater and cabaret listings. And today, it displayed a banner headline announcing that German Culture Week had been declared in Danzig! Smaller articles explained that for the occasion, a German battleship was scheduled to come into the port, and that Poland had forbidden such a thing. One thousand Gestapo and two thousand members of the S.A. were reported to be in Danzig. Jewish harassment there was being stepped up. Polish reservists had been called up, and German troops were playing war games across the border where Czechoslovakia used to be.

Etta noticed that even though she was talking to Rachel, her daughter had not heard a word for the last several minutes. She stood at Rachel's shoulder and read the news as seen through the eyes of an outraged Polish government. She looked from the newspaper to the fish and wondered out loud if the priest had wrapped his gift in this edition for any particular reason. Then she gathered it up just as Rachel was getting to the most frightening part of the story: *Poland has three hundred tanks, Germany has two thousand. . . .*

"Just the sort of thing suitable for wrapping fish," Mama said lightly as if the old black print did not send a shiver through her as it did through Rachel.

"It will be all right," Rachel agreed, turning to wash the plums. "Nothing will happen here, Mama. That is why people like Peter Wallich have come to Warsaw from Danzig, isn't it? The German Gestapo would not dare to come here. And as for the tanks, Papa says German tanks cannot outmaneuver the Polish cavalry. We are safe in Warsaw."

Mama heard her. She nodded, but did not reply other than that. German Culture Week in Danzig! Battleships in the harbor—over the Poles' dead bodies! Maybe it would come to that. Over their dead bodies. Maybe Hitler would also come to Warsaw and sleep in Pototzki Palace as he had slept in the castle in Prague.

All these fears were evident in Mama's eyes, although she did not say them to Rachel. And Rachel suddenly felt angry at the priest for wrapping the fish in such an ominous herald of the current events! Had he done such a thing on purpose, to frighten Mama into sending Rachel and David and Samuel and baby Yacov away? But where would they go? Was not one place the same as any other? At least here they had a roof over their heads. Why had the priest been so cruel?

Rachel could see that her mother was very pale. She looked ill. She looked afraid, just as she had the night Papa had been arrested.

"Go tell Frau Groshenki we are bringing the boys home now, tonight," she said, and Rachel saw that her hands were shaking.

"But what about our charade? No one will believe Papa has typhoid if we bring the boys home."

Mama looked at her sadly, as if the illusion did not matter anymore. "We should all be together," Mama said. "Here. Home. Under the same roof."

Rachel stared silently at her mother as the implication sunk in. *In times of trouble, in desperate hours, the family must stay together for as long ... as long as it remained possible.* Did Mama believe the Germans were coming to Warsaw, too?

Mama looked out the kitchen window as a bee buzzed and bumped against the glass pane. In that small hum, could she imagine the drone of airplanes overhead?

"Go on, Rachel," Mama said, wadding up the paper and throwing it angrily into the rubbish can. "Bring the boys home now. We have fine fish for supper. A feast."

Rachel left the house reluctantly, feeling as though the sky might tumble down before she got home with her brothers! Was the feast, in reality, about to end?

———

"It is not typhoid fever," Rachel told Frau Groshenki. "Rheumatic fever. Not catching, and so Mama wants us all to be home together."

With this simple statement of truth, Rachel felt a sudden relief. Perhaps the Poles were too busy now worrying about what the German hornet's nest was up to for one little rabbi to matter anymore. And why would they come again to arrest a man as sick as Papa? He would die if they took him. The doctor had said he must not be moved farther than from his bed to the bathroom. No physical exertion. Certainly the Polish police would know that they could not move the rabbi, because then the state would end up having to pay the cost of a burial and no purpose would be served by it.

And so the charade had ended. Frau Groshenki praised the mercy of the Eternal that the beloved Rabbi Lubetkin only had rheumatic fever instead of typhoid! "A miracle!" she exclaimed as she helped Rachel pack the boys' things.

This was the first time Rachel had heard of anyone praising the Eternal that someone had rheumatic fever! Ah well, it was the Jewish way of life, nu? *Things could always be worse....* And when things could not possibly get any worse, it was time to think of possibilities so terrible that one could still declare, "Things *could* always be worse." From there it was a short step to long recitations of how things were *much* worse for this cousin or that uncle. Such conversation made people feel better.

"You hear that, David?" Frau Groshenki said to David as he gratefully hefted his valise. "Your father the rabbi only has rheumatic fever. God be praised. Not typhoid. Or *worse,* like my cousin Mordechai, paralyzed from the neck down and living like the living dead! Oy! Now *that* is the worst."

Rachel gathered Little Yani in her arms. The baby nuzzled her face in slobbery kisses of infant gratitude, as if to tell her that nothing could be worse than being cooped up in Frau Groshenki's house!

David and Samuel thanked the Frau properly for her hospitality and then, when they were out of earshot, they railed on her for everything from her endless gossip to her piggish table manners.

"She talks with her mouth full of gefilte fish, Rachel!" David declared.

"She dips her pound cake in her teacup," Samuel added with five-year-old disgust. "And then she slurps up the soggy crumbs."

"Sometimes she brushes her teeth . . . but not usually." David wanted to be fair in his reporting.

"And she says the Nazis are going to come here to Warsaw and kill all who are Jews," said Samuel. "Even the *baby*!"

Rachel could tolerate the fact that Frau Groshenki ate like a pig and did not brush her teeth! *After all, things could be worse.* But this repetition of the worst fears in her own heart made her angry.

"She is a *nebech*!" Rachel declared angrily. "She is nothing!"

"What is rape?" David tugged his earlock thoughtfully.

Rachel stopped in the street and whirled to face the Groshenki house. She was furious. Did her brother see how that word angered her?

Little Samuel said in a serious voice, "Frau Groshenki says that when the Nazis come, they will rape the women."

David added, "She says she will die rather than be raped."

Rachel's eyes narrowed as she pictured the fat, wrinkled face of Frau Groshenki looking up at German soldiers and begging them to kill her rather than rape her. "She won't have to die," Rachel said in a haughty tone. "The Germans are not coming, and even if they did, I can promise that they would not be interested in Frau Groshenki!"

"But what if they come here?" Samuel asked as they walked slowly across the square.

Rachel looked up into the linden trees. She pointed to a nest of twigs where a family of sparrows lived. "The little birds would know if Nazis were coming. They fly everywhere, you see. And if they heard that the Nazis were coming to Muranow Square, would they build a nest and raise their children here?"

Samuel gazed somberly at the nest. He looked at the birds and listened to the persistent peep of the babies. "I suppose not."

Rachel gestured toward the big yellow house on the corner. "There is the nest our father built. Would he keep us here if he thought the Nazis would come?"

At this logical explanation, David and Samuel both seemed greatly relieved.

"So the worst will not come."

"Frau Groshenki is nothing but a yenta who sees a cloud around every silver lining, nu?" Rachel had heard this saying on the BBC radio.

The priest had explained it to her, and now she explained it to her brothers. By the time they reached the front steps, everyone was quite relieved. By the time they reached the embrace of their father, they had almost forgotten the terrible things Frau Groshenki had said.

12

The Warsaw Link

Allan regretted that he had insisted on having his bed linens changed once a week. The thought of a maid entering his room even for that was now a matter of concern and annoyance. What if she opened the bottom drawer of his bureau? And if she stumbled across his material, would she know what she was looking at?

That thought motivated Allan to travel to the luggage shop in Chelsea. Stacks of luggage took up nearly every square foot of floor space in the little shop. Steamer trunks formed the foundation on which skyscrapers of smaller cases and valises rose to the crown molding of the high ceiling. Allan wondered how those pieces on the bottom could ever be taken out without the whole pile coming down in an avalanche.

"And what size would you prefer, sir?" asked the pretty young shopkeeper.

"Personal size. For a cruise. Waterproof." Allan eyed a pyramid of hard-sided cases in the back of the store. "Like that. Fourth one from the top." A poster of a passenger ship was taped to the display.

It was perfect. Of medium size, the case was light aluminum covered with plain tan leather. The corners were protected by metal to match the lock. The sign on the stack read: *THE LATEST FOR YOUR CRUISE. WATERPROOF.*

"Ideal for ocean travels, sir. And for rainy weather, too." She moved the ladder and climbed up fearlessly. "No need to worry with the Deluxe World Traveler grip. If your ship goes down, you could simply paddle back to Southampton with all your things quite dry inside."

Allan did not bargain with her about the price. He would keep the receipt, and when everything was accomplished, he would present the bill to Colin for reimbursement.

In the meantime he would keep his things locked inside. With both keys around his neck, the hotel maid would not be able to get into it even if she were the curious sort.

The shopkeeper deftly removed the case from the stack like a magician pulling a tablecloth from beneath a set of dishes. A cloud of dust filtered down, causing Allan to cough convulsively. The young woman eyed him remorsefully. She should have dusted, she told him. By way of apology she lowered the price of the purchase by two shillings.

"Voyaging for your health, are you then?" she asked sympathetically. "With this model we will stamp your initials on the handle free of charge."

"Thank you. No time, I—"

"It will only take a few minutes."

"I may wish to sell it later," he replied, feeling pleased that he thought of an excuse so quickly.

"Well then," she whispered conspiratorially, "if you do, send the buyer back here. I'll stamp it for him all the same. Sometimes we have customers come in for initials, and they buy another piece of luggage from us." She winked and passed her card to Allan. "My name is on the back. Carol, you see?" She extended her hand. "You're American?"

"Allan Farrell," he answered, instantly sorry he had said his name. Could she guess what he really intended to do with the purchase? No, of course not. Still, he had a sense of intrigue he never would have had had he remained merely a sideline errand boy.

"Well, Mr. Farrell," she said, looking at his forehead and his mouth and his eyes, "if you change your mind and decide to keep the case, you know where I am. The offer will still be good."

She was speaking of things other than initials, Allan knew. Some other day he might have been flattered, might have made plans to drop in another time. Not now. Maybe never again.

———

Peter Wallich was early. Rachel watched him walk down the street with his shambling gait. He looked like a scarecrow that had jumped off a post and was now hurrying to escape over a furrowed field.

This morning Peter did not wear the heavy coat. The warm sun gleamed against his red hair, which was still partly wet from a shower. The hair which, already dry, had pulled up into a wild briar-bush curl to tower over the stuff that was too wet to stand up. The trousers Peter wore were too short at the cuffs, revealing brown socks that drooped around the tops of his worn shoes. The belt was pulled tight around his waist, gathering up both trousers and baggy shirt like a sack cinched in the middle. His long skinny arms protruded from short sleeves. He was very pale, and the freckles on his arms were a shade lighter than his hair. His mouth turned down slightly at the corners. His head and eyes were never still. He looked to the right and the left and back over his shoulder, like a little puppy turned loose in a garden.

All this taken together made Rachel think that Peter Wallich would have made a remarkably fine clown in the Imperial Warsaw Circus. Add a little makeup (very little), extend the length of the already big feet, give him a big stick with which he could swat rival clowns, and Peter would be quite at home in the center ring beneath a canvas tent. Only one thing did not fit into this comic appearance: his eyes seemed to contain all the sorrow in the world. Beyond the pale skin and the red hair and the long thin neck were those eyes—the reflection of a tragic life, a soul that had aged and hardened far beyond the gangly body in which it dwelt. Flashing at the perimeters of all that sorrow was the steel edge of bitterness and the glow of smoldering anger.

Those emotions could not be crammed into the resume of Peter's clownish appearance. There was no joy in him, no youth; nothing left behind those eyes that could enjoy laughter or a good prank.

Rachel had instinctively known all these things from their first conversation in the soup kitchen. This young man, not much older than Rachel herself, had seen firsthand in Vienna what the Saturday people could do to Jews once Hitler had declared Jews to be fair game. He had survived the first days of hunting season, but he bore the smell of death away with him. This frightened her, and yet she pitied him with her whole heart. Along with that pity, however, she carried the fear that he might hold up a mirror and show Rachel her own future. *What would I do without Mama and the boys? What if Papa had died in Warsaw prison instead of simply getting sick? What if I were left alone and lost like Peter Wallich? And what if the Nazis came here to Warsaw?*

Just seeing Peter brought all those terrible questions to the front of Rachel's consciousness.

She drew back from her place at the window, as if she did not want him to turn his sorrowing gaze upon her and pass the infection of tragedy to her life.

Peter, seeming to sense the fact that he was much too early for his appointment, stopped and leaned against the streetlamp on the corner of Muranow. He had no watch, but he stared a long time at the clock tower set at the far end of the square. He crossed his arms and waited for the minute hand to slide into place. It did not move fast enough to suit him, and so he turned impatiently and stared up at the big yellow house where the rabbi lived and where Rachel watched him from behind the screen of lace curtains.

She stepped back farther, half wishing she had not offered her father as counselor and adviser to this lost sheep. And then a rush of shame followed quickly as she considered that if she were in Peter Wallich's place, she would long for someone to advise her, to help her find a way back home.

With a shudder, she left the window of her bedroom and scurried downstairs, shouting her superstitious dread away.

"Papa! Peter Wallich is standing outside on the sidewalk! Mama! Should I let him in?"

"He is early." Mama poked her head out of the kitchen as Rachel reached the bottom of the stairs.

"He has nowhere else to go, I suppose," Rachel said.

"I suppose not." Etta looked toward the front door as though she also sensed something. Wiping her hands on her apron she said, "It is hot. I imagine the boy would like some apple juice. Your father is awake. So let your friend in, already."

————

Agent Hess poured himself yet another glass of schnapps as he decoded the dispatch from Berlin. He did not need to complete the work; he knew the message before he was halfway through the jumble of words.

LONDON AGENT REPORTS IBSEN CHILDREN IN CONTACT FROM DANZIG STOP ALL STEPS BEING TAKEN BY FAMILY IN LONDON TO OBTAIN VISAS FOR LORI AND JAMES IBSEN TO IMMIGRATE TO ENGLAND STOP NO DANZIG ADDRESS GIVEN THUS FAR STOP SUGGEST YOU PLACE AN AGENT AT BRITISH EMBASSY AND CHECK STEAMSHIP SCHEDULES STOP

Hess had already hired a man to watch the British Embassy. The fellow was a Jew, a former bank clerk from Bremmen who had managed to slip out of the Reich shortly after *Kristallnacht*. Hess had spent two days milling around outside the British compound as though he, too, were desperate to escape. He had struck up a conversation with the Bremen Jew, explained that his injuries had come as the result of a confrontation with the Gestapo, and won the fellow's confidence. It was only a short step from there to enlisting the Jew in his hunt for the Ibsen children. He presented himself as a member of the German resistance who was concerned for the welfare of a fallen comrade's family. That lie, combined with a promise of a room and regular food, was enough to win the Bremen banker's services as watchdog at the gates of the British Embassy. The fellow had only to keep his eyes open. When and if the lost children arrived, he was to observe them and then follow them back to their living quarters and report to Hess immediately at the Deutscher Hof.

Hess had learned early in his career that it was easy to enlist even the most ardent anti-Nazis on the payrolls of the Gestapo as long as they believed they were working for a righteous cause. Germany and the Western democracies were crowded with such unknowing betrayers. There were almost as many anti-Nazis on the payroll of the Reich Ministry of Information as there were Nazis. Hess had no doubt that if the children should arrive at the embassy, the banker from Bremen would follow his orders to the dot of the Nazi *i*.

———

Peter Wallich held his glass of apple juice in both hands as he sat in the straight-backed chair across from the bed of Rabbi Aaron Lubetkin.

Rachel thought how much her father looked the part of a great rabbi, in spite of the fact that his hair and beard had been shaved and now bristled at the same length on head and face. He was propped up among the pillows on his bed. The black skullcap was exactly in place, giving him an air of dignity that the unruly red locks on Peter's head did not have.

Here was wisdom advising the sad fool. Here was age and experience assisting the young and inexperienced. And yet . . . there was something in Papa's eyes that matched the sorrow behind the eyes of young Peter Wallich. In the comprehension of tragedy, both were equal. But Papa's expression held none of the bitterness the boy's displayed.

"And so your mother and sister simply vanished?" Papa asked gently.

"They never came to the Danziger Hof. Never sent word."

Papa considered what that meant and searched for some hope that might penetrate the bitterness in Peter's voice. "Your father was a prominent political prisoner. Your mother was also a suspect?"

"Yes. That is why we remained in hiding."

"Ah, well then." Papa's brown eyes flashed with confidence. "You know the Nazis announce the arrest of everyone they consider to be a prominent criminal. Did you ever see the name of your mother in the newspaper in Danzig?"

Something flickered in Peter's eyes. For a moment the black shadow of despair lifted. Here was some beam of hope! He slowly considered the question. "No. I did not. And I read the papers. I even read the Nazi edition of *Der Angriff* so I could have some idea of what they were up to."

Papa's voice was gentle. "They certainly would have made a great announcement about the apprehension of your mother. Don't you think so, Freund Wallich?"

Peter nodded. He looked at his hands for a moment and frowned as if he was afraid to look into the hopeful face of the rabbi. "I think so."

"Well then . . . *nu?*" By this, Papa meant that Peter had reason to be hopeful. Why should his eyes hold such despair when there was no evidence that the worst had indeed fallen upon his mother and sister?

"But . . . where?"

"They are somewhere," Papa said with a shrug. "We will try and find these people . . . the address on your paper. Just because the letters are washed away, this does not mean that the people are washed away. They, too, are somewhere, nu? Here in Warsaw, even. And since the fellow who fought beside your father against the Nazis in Vienna is a son of Warsaw, then we will find this fellow's family here. But it will take time." Papa raised his chin to instruct the young man. "And it will take *hope* on legs to find them. Do you understand?"

Peter shrugged; he tried to pretend that the rabbi had not glimpsed the depth of his sadness.

Rachel watched her father's eyes fill with compassion as he studied the boy's stony expression. She could see Peter resisting the tenderness, lest it once again allow him to feel hope.

"Maybe they are there. Maybe they are somewhere . . . maybe they are not." He was leaning toward the latter. It was easier to live with despair than with disappointed hopes.

"The Eternal knows such answers," Papa replied.

"I do not believe in the Eternal," Peter snapped. "This is not a religious call."

Papa smiled, unmoved by this new display of bitterness. "It does not matter if you believe, Peter. The Eternal does not need your belief in order to exist. That is why He is Eternal. And if your mother and sister are alive, they do not need your belief in order to remain alive. They eat and sleep and speak to each other. They certainly miss you." Papa paused as emotion filled Peter's hard eyes.

"It is better to expect the worst," Peter reasoned. "Then I will not be disappointed."

Papa shook his head from side to side. "No. Then you live in disappointment all the time. Then you are a slave to bitterness. Then, when good things happen you are only surprised by them. Much better to live on the other side of that mirror, nu? Hope in the survival of your mother and sister. Think of them laughing and talking; looking for you."

"But what if that is not true?"

"Then you can be surprised when you find out. There will be plenty of time then to grieve."

Ah, Rachel thought, *such a rabbi Papa is! So full of life, even thin and frail and weak from his own encounter with misery!* How proud she was of her father as he did battle on his sickbed with the very demon Rachel had seen in Peter's eyes and run from!

"Yes, I see," Peter said, and then he stiffened. "But I will not hope . . . believe in this Jewish God of yours."

"Much better in the end to find out you were wrong for believing, I always say. If I am wrong . . ." Papa shrugged. "Well then?" He lowered his chin. "But if you are wrong, Peter?"

"I did not come here to be made a religious Jew." Peter was stubborn. He would not be moved. "I came for advice. For help to find . . . if they are alive . . . my mother and sister."

"So." Papa rummaged through his papers on the bedside table. "Here is my letter of introduction. Everyone newly come to Warsaw needs something. This may move your case to the front of the queue. Here is also a list of people to speak with."

He passed the two letters to Peter, who took them in trembling hands and skimmed the contents as if he had at last found something to nourish his famished soul.

Rachel smiled a tight-lipped smile. There it was in the eyes of the mirthless clown . . . *hope* . . . alive in him again!

The Cliffs of Dover gleamed like a clean white wall off the starboard side of the freighter. Orde felt no joy at this view of England. While others among the small group of passengers chatted excitedly about home, Orde turned from the rail and retreated to his cabin.

Once there, he opened his scuffed leather letter case and pulled out the telegram from the London office of TENS. *Correspondent for Poland.* Beside that on his bunk, he placed the photographs of the Lubetkin family that old Rabbi Lebowitz had entrusted to his care.

Etta Lubetkin's clear blue eyes held a serene beauty even in the starkness of a black and white photo. Her eldest child, Rachel, was also lovely. She appeared much older to Orde than the birthdate on her certificate would indicate.

Orde sighed as he placed the photograph of Aaron Lubetkin beside that of his wife. He pitied the young, stern-looking rabbi; pitied him and envied him as well. How much easier it was for Orde to face the coming cataclysm than it must be for a man with a beautiful wife and such handsome children as these. Photographs of three little boys followed. Orde knew them by name. *David. Samuel. Baby Yacov, whom the family called Little Yani.* Lovingly the old rabbi had repeated the names of his grandchildren. How hopeful he had been when he placed the envelope with their rejected immigration papers in Orde's hands.

Orde touched each face with the same tenderness he had seen in the old man. Then, Orde once again picked up the telegram from John

Murphy which expressed the hope that Samuel Orde would consider a position in Warsaw. *Warsaw! Could such a thing be a coincidence?* Orde wondered. *Or is there a link between the job offer and something not yet understood about this family in Warsaw?*

"What is it you want of me?" Orde whispered. "What is it that you see, Lord, which I do not see?"

Such questions, of course, held no tangible answers for Orde. And yet, he felt some link between this telegram and this family. *Something . . . something . . . which he would know in time.*

The shoreline of his homeland loomed outside the porthole, yet Orde could not take his eyes from the faces of the Jewish family. *"It is Poland, isn't it?"* he questioned aloud. *"Warsaw for me?"*

Before the ship bumped against the docks of Southampton, Orde was confident of the answer.

13

Prelude to New Life

It was *enormous*, this unborn baby Murphy!

Lying back in the bathtub, Elisa looked at the bulging mound where a once-slender abdomen used to be. There was no hope of submersing everything in the warm water at once. Dipping a washcloth, she spread the soapy water on top of her belly. *Like a snowcap on Mont Blanc*, she thought.

Suddenly, without permission, the mound shifted to the right. Baby elbows and baby knees and baby rump bopped and gyrated to some unknown baby jazz tune.

This one would never grow up to be a classical musician! *He-she* took after Daddy Murphy! Ha! No doubt this baby would be born snapping its little baby fingers and whistling a tune from *D'Fat Lady Trio!* And Murphy would break into song in his irritating off-key voice, *Yessir, dat's my ba-by!*

And it *was* his baby, too. He ought to try carrying it for one night before he teased her so unmercifully! *"Gee, Elisa, I don't think this bed is big enough for the three of us anymore!"*

This comment came last night because of soda crackers. She did not crunch the crackers, but sucked on them very quietly while *Murphy's child* stoked up the fires of indigestion and warmed its little hands with glee.

"Then go sleep on the sofa!" Elisa ordered through her tears.

Murphy had rolled over and switched on the light, peering at her in astonished horror. *"You're crying!"*

"Insensitive! I . . . said . . . go . . ."

Tousled and hurt, he had taken pillow and blanket and shuffled out to the sofa. It really was for the best. Elisa had cried a little more, crunched her crackers loudly, then sprawled out for her first real night's sleep in a month.

She awakened in the morning with the worried face of Murphy hovering over her. "Anytime now, hon." There was sympathy in his voice. "Didn't the doc say so? Anytime." Then he kissed her and she forgave him for a minute until he patted her bulge and added, "Gotta go now. Let me rub your belly for luck . . ."

This rubbing-her-belly-for-luck was the final indignity. Just the memory of it made her eyes narrow and her lower lip extend in an injured pout. How could he be so calloused? How could he, who had put her in this condition in the first place, not see how much it hurt her when he made sophomoric jokes about the fact that she was no longer slender . . . no longer desirable. *Definitely resistible. Oversensitive. Edgy.* He certainly had not attempted to stay in bed with her last night when she ordered him out!

Not big enough for the three of us . . .

Tears of self-pity stung her eyelids once again. She was nearly two weeks past her due date. Two extra weeks in this purgatory of pregnancy, while the whole world flew by!

This afternoon she had yet another appointment with Dr. Howarth. No doubt he would thump her like a melon, declare her still unripe, and send her back to incubate and expand a few months more. *"So sorry, Mrs. Murphy. Sometimes in rare cases like yours, these things take several years to mature. Shall I call a freight truck to haul you home?"*

Elisa found herself unable to concentrate on anything but what was literally right in front of her. Like a hood ornament on a foggy day, baby Murphy was the clearest thing in sight.

Even though the flat of Anna and Theo Lindheim was packed wall to wall with refugee children in transit to foster homes, Anna had asked to take Charles and Louis for a few days so Elisa could relax. Frankly, the boys had seemed happy to go.

On top of that, Aunt Helen had gotten word from her children that they were safe in Danzig. But a battle was raging with immigration to have Lori and Jamie Ibsen and the others included on the last refugee transport ship scheduled to leave next week.

Elisa thought of Lori and Jamie every day, yet, she prayed for them with a strange sort of detachment. Every emotion, it seemed, was being expended on thinking about *the day*. Every prayer somehow started one place and made a big loop back to *this* baby; *her* child; its safe and healthy arrival.

She had gratefully taken her leave from the orchestra. It was undignified to waddle across the stage to her music stand. Her hours had been filled with packaging clothes for the children arriving on the refugee transport ships, acting as interpreter and counselor to the volunteer families taking children.

She casually mentioned her participation to Dr. Howarth, who had promptly hit the ceiling. He lectured her severely about exposing herself and her unborn child to possible communicable diseases brought to England by these children.

That had been the worst visit. She was also ten pounds overweight and had been warned about that, too. *Ah yes. The tears had flowed that day in Dr. Howarth's little office!*

Elisa had busied herself with painting and papering the nursery. The church and the women of the orchestra had teas for her and provided enough baby things for several babies. It was very nice, but all the same, Elisa longed for the day when she would no longer feel as though she were wearing a kettle drum around her middle!

Elisa hefted herself out of the tub and vowed to think about other things and people today. She braced herself against the sink and attempted to dry her legs as she whispered a guilty prayer for Aunt Helen and the arrival of Jamie and Lori and the others. And then, triggered by the thought of arriving children, she added a little something about baby Murphy once again. *How long, oh, Lord?*

Involuntarily, she imagined that Charles and Louis would probably be grown up before this stubborn baby arrived! If things happened on schedule, pregnancy would be endurable! *But two weeks late and big as a barn?*

Elisa had nightmares that she would be out crossing a busy intersection on Oxford Street or in church or shopping when her water broke. She had spent the day yesterday hiking up and down the apartment stairs in hopes of forcing the issue. *No use.* She would go to Dr. Howarth and he would say, *"So sorry!"* And one of these weeks her water would break and wash away the shoppers at Liberty.

She bent awkwardly to dry her right knee. It was down there somewhere. Maybe if she sat on the edge of the tub?

As she bent down, Elisa's water broke. *Yes! There in the bathroom!* Not shopping at Liberty as she had feared. Not out to tea with her mother. Not hiking up the stairs. But right here in her own bathroom.

There was none of the anticipated pain. Just a warm rush and a lovely release of pressure in her lower abdomen. She laughed and clapped her hands. There was time to clean up and dress. Time to make the bed and do the dishes.

And then those much-waited and longed-for contractions began with the syncopated rhythm of early labor. So much for vows of unselfish thoughts. It was a sure bet that today Elisa would be thinking of only one little person. . . .

This time Alfie had to leave Werner the cat at home. Each of the boys was dressed in his best Sunday suit and shoes. Jacob and Alfie wore trousers because they were older. Mark and Jamie wore knickers and long wool socks. Lori wore her prettiest dress, the one with pink and blue flowers that she had worn on Easter.

"But Werner stays home," Jacob warned. "The British Consulate would not take kindly to having Werner prowling over the desks of secretaries."

Once, Alfie had managed to sneak Werner into church in his pocket when Jacob told him not to. That morning during prayer time, Werner had skipped down the pew, then rushed past the legs of several old ladies and young ladies who screamed loudly one after the other. It had been very bad.

Werner had jumped onto the altar where the Communion plates were, and the whole service had been ruined. It did not matter that Alfie was very sorry and scolded his cat. Everyone was still angry at Alfie for bringing Werner. *Except maybe Jesus,* Alfie thought. He did not think that the Lord was angry. After all, it woke everyone up in what was a very dull church service.

The pastor had whispered too loudly to the choir director that he wished the *Dummkopf* would be left home with the cat. Everyone heard what he said. Alfie heard it and felt very sad. Jacob and Lori heard it and were angry.

After the service Jacob waited in the line to greet the pastor and his wife and Jacob told them both that if the cat and Alfie were not welcome, then none of them would be back because it was the deadest church he had ever been to. But he said it in a nice way, and then he shook the pastor's hand.

All the way back to the flat that day Lori had talked about her own papa, Pastor Ibsen. *"Remember what a sense of humor he had about such little disasters? Remember when Frau Meyer's baby threw up all over that mean old Herr Speer who had just fired his chauffeur in front of the church because he hadn't cleaned the pigeon droppings off the car?"*

Everyone remembered that great day, of course. Pastor Ibsen had tucked his notes away and preached about true humbleness. This memory led to the next. *"And remember when old Herr Speer died and the little dog fell into his grave sometime in the night and then started howling during the service?"*

These stories had made them all laugh again and forget how angry they felt about the preacher and his *Dummkopf* remark. Alfie had not been around when the dog started howling from Herr Speer's grave, but he liked the story a lot and laughed right along with everyone else. By the time they had gotten home, Alfie did not feel like a dummkopf anymore and no one was angry that Werner had frightened the old ladies in the church.

But today, going to the British Consulate was an entirely different matter. Jacob explained it again to Alfie. "They are the fellows who have our papers so we can go to England."

"Will they also have papers for Werner-cat to go to England?"

"No, Alfie, and we must not mention Werner to them."

"But if Werner can't go, I can't go."

"I know that. We will smuggle him on board with us. You must not worry about it." Jacob held up his finger. "But don't say anything at all. Lori and I will do all the talking. If anyone asks you a question you just say *yes* or *no*. And if they ask your name, well, then tell them. But don't say any more. Understand?"

Alfie ran it all through his mind. In a very serious tone he answered the way Jacob told him to. One word. "Yes."

"Good. All right then." Jacob looked very nervous. He straightened Alfie's blue bow tie. He double-checked Alfie's suspenders and tugged at the crease in his trousers. Then he placed a brand new fedora on Alfie's head. He pulled the brim down, stepped back and looked him over from top to toe.

Lori came in and laughed when she saw Alfie all dressed up in his new suit. "Why, Alfie! You look so handsome and adult!"

Alfie tried not to smile too big, tried to act as if it were really nothing at all. He turned to look at his reflection in the mirror. It was very nice. He remembered his own papa wearing a hat like this one and a blue serge suit with suspenders. "I . . . look . . . like Father. Uh-huh."

"Yes! You look *wonderful*! The Englishmen will think you look like a bank officer! The hat is perfect."

Alfie scratched his ear and ducked his head with embarrassment.

"Uh-huh. Englishmen don't like Dummkopfs. They will think I look smart, won't they?"

Lori and Jacob looked at each other in a way that made Alfie wish he had not said *the word*. Lori always said that the word *Dummkopf* made her heart hurt. Alfie had not meant to make her feel bad; he was only asking a question about how the Englishmen at the British Consulate might feel about people the Nazis said were Dummkopfs.

"Alfie," Lori said quietly. She put her hand on his arm. "You *are* smart. It is because of you that we are all alive now, because of you that I wrote Elisa in London. You have the smartest heart of anyone I know."

Alfie smiled down at her. She was very pretty and always so nice. He loved her very much. "Jacob is right," he said. "It would not be good to take Werner with us today to the English. He is just a cat and might say something he should not." Alfie meant that the cat might run against the legs of English women and make them scream like he had in church. Werner-cat could not *say* anything wrong . . . any

Dummkopf knew cats do not speak. "You know what I mean?" Alfie asked Lori.

"Yes." Lori patted him and straightened his tie again. "It is smart to leave him home today."

———————

The British Consulate was located in the most convenient section of Danzig. At 14 Stadtgraben, it was near the main train depot and the post office. The consulate occupied three stately baroque mansions that stood side by side on the main thoroughfare. The common walls had been opened up to join the buildings. Secretarial offices were housed in the smallest wing. In the center mansion, all the woodwork had been refurbished and the ballroom had been enlarged for official receptions. The portrait of the king smiled down regally from the wall where a wide mahogany staircase wound up to the offices of the British officials. The third wing had been made into the living quarters for the British staff. Paneled walls and thick wool carpets, paintings depicting idyllic English countryside and great British naval victories, all gave this wing of the consulate the air of an exclusive London club.

Each day at four o'clock precisely, work in the first two wings came to an abrupt halt while tea with sandwiches and pastries was served, just like at the Savoy in London. It was always a comfort to those members of the British Foreign Service that English culture could be satisfied with an assortment of teas and jams.

And so at 3:50 every afternoon, the gates of the consulate swung shut on the faces of the hundreds of refugees who made pilgrimage to this building as though it were a holy place where they might be healed of some terrible disease. They waited quietly in the street as the holy communion of high tea progressed within. They turned their gaunt faces up to the bright spotless windows, hoping that someone might look down and have pity.

But there was little pity at teatime. If diners chanced to look out at the silent masses, they saw people who did not comprehend the afternoon ritual. They saw hungry refugees who desired entry into England when they had not the slightest concept of British culture. This lack of understanding on the part of the hopeless thousands who filed past this building was indeed a sort of fatal disease. They could not share the holy rites of orange pekoe or Ceylon tea with scones and clotted cream. What did they care for orange marmalade?

Often the great decisions of life and death, escape or imprisonment in hostile Europe, boiled down to who would fit in at Piccadilly. Did the British want a steady diet of foreigners with foreign ways mucking up the tearooms of London's hotels?

Lori Ibsen had some idea of this principle, although she could not put it into words—not in German words, or English. But she looked at Alfie Halder with his blissful smile and clumsy gait and she trembled for him as they held their appointment notice through the iron bars of the consulate building. Even all dressed up and scrubbed until his skin was pink, Alfie did not fit. He carried his big head at a slight tilt to the side and down at the chin, his smile too broad, his eyes too wide and childlike.

He looked as though he could comprehend nothing, although Lori knew that Alfie Halder somehow understood everything all too well. Information ran through his mind like tea through a silver strainer, and in the end, it was all perfectly distilled within the cup of his great innocence.

Alfie's faith was what Lori's father had described as "that perfect faith which the Lord spoke of, the faith of a child. . . ." Even this great faith looked up at the windows of the British Consulate and asked, "Do they let . . . boys like me . . . inside, Lori?" He did not use *the word,* but indeed, he understood the issue.

Children like Alfie had been systematically euthanized by the Nazi government. If he were rejected by England because he was "not quite all right in the head," that rejection would be equal to a death sentence. And so many millions stood condemned for less cause than that!

"Lori?" Alfie asked quietly as the guard examined the official notice that these five young people were to come to the consulate at 3:45 exactly.

Lori held a finger to her lips to silence Alfie. The guard looked at his wristwatch and scowled. "You're late. Two minutes. We close at 3:50 for teatime, don't you know?"

Lori was the spokeswoman for the group. "Yes. We know all about four o'clock tea." Her English was quite good. The guard appraised her with a forgiving look, and yet . . .

"Well, you're late."

"These trams, you know," she replied as though public transportation in a foreign country was so very unreliable. "Anyway, shall I tell the official that we were kept waiting at the gate?"

Very good—in attitude as well as accent. "I see you are expected." His tone was apologetic. He glared back at the mob that pressed against the backs of the five visitors as though everyone might come in at once. Raising a hand he shouted, "Everyone back except these five! Back in your line! Only these five admitted!"

It was among the poorest of all the parishes in Danzig. The streets were so narrow beneath the overhang of the gables that a taxi could not drive there.

Wolf paid the cab driver and promised him extra if he would wait here at the end of *Heiliger Geist Strasse,* Holy Ghost Street. This narrow lane was named after the Catholic church where a young priest reported that he may have seen a woman matching the description of Lucy Strasburg. He could not remember if the woman had been expecting. *She was kneeling,* he said; *her face was childlike and glowed with an innocence rarely seen except among the very pious. Could this be the same fallen woman described by her brother? The same woman in the red dress holding the champagne glass?*

The priest was uncertain. He had called the office of the bishop and explained that the woman had left the church before he could retrieve the photograph from his study. Now the young priest carried the picture in the pocket of his cassock, but the woman had never returned. The office of the bishop contacted Wolf with this information. *Perhaps your sister lives in this district?*

There was a strong stench of sewage and rotting fish in the air as Wolf walked down the sloping lane. His eyes flitted from window to window of the dingy medieval rooming houses and cheap hotels. Beer cellars and secondhand shops lined the lower stories. Passing the dark entrance to a bar, Wolf could hear the shrill laughter of women mingled with the coarse voices of foreign sailors.

Yes. This is suitable for Lucy, he thought. *A sow gone to wallow with her own kind. A prostitute in search of a job. Up to the hotel room, and then to church in the morning to ask forgiveness.* This was just the sort of place he would expect to find her.

He felt his anger rising at the thought of how she would raise a baby in such a place. He would find her, take the baby to his own estate, and take Lucy back to the Reich for trial.

Staring up at the drawn shades of the windows, he imagined what she was doing; how she made her living selling herself for bargain prices to the ragged men of Heiliger Geist Strasse.

The ancient, soot-tarnished facade of the church loomed at the end of the curving lane. There was a workhouse across the small square where a line of destitute men and women waited for entry into a public soup kitchen. Their gray, hopeless faces reminded him of the disembodied souls in the painting of *The Last Judgment.* When Danzig was annexed to Germany again, such nests as this would be cleaned out.

At the core of his rage lay the realization that Lucy had chosen this life over him, over all he had offered her! Was that not proof of what she was? Proof enough for anyone with eyes to see.

Wolf entered the dark church building through a heavy wooden side door. This had been the instruction of the priest, lest Lucy see her brother if she was nearby, and not return to the church.

Wolf's jaw was set with anger as he descended the steep stone steps into the basement offices of Holy Ghost Church. One passageway led to the underground crypt and the other led to the library and robing room of the structure.

As arranged, the tall, worried young priest was in the library, hunched over a large volume of commentary. He jerked his head up and blinked at Wolf, as though he had forgotten the reason for his meeting here. Just as quickly, the confusion passed. He stood and nodded and extended his hand. When he spoke, his voice was a ridiculous whisper, as though Lucy might somehow hear him.

"You are the brother of the woman?"

Wolf had conducted secret meetings with agents in Danzig who bore less air of mystery than this priest.

"You have seen my sister?"

"Yes . . . that is, I think it was her. Blond. Pretty . . ." He said the word *pretty* as though it were a forbidden word. Wolf had wondered what thoughts had passed through the priest's hypocritical mind when he saw her.

"She was pregnant?"

He shrugged helplessly. "Kneeling at the altar. I could not tell. And when I turned away and looked back, she had gone."

"I suppose it is possible she has had the child."

The priest nodded. "She prayed before the Madonna and Child, as many women who are expecting do. And mothers come to pray for their children. I suppose—"

Wolf raised his hand to cut him off. "Why did you not try to speak with her? Detain her in some way?"

His voice accused the priest of neglecting his duty. "I was uncertain. And she was praying." He pulled her photograph from his pocket. It was the picture of Lucy on the steps of St. Stephan's. *Wide innocent eyes. Hopeful, slightly confused expression.*

"Is this the woman you saw then?"

"I am almost certain. But much older. Infinitely more . . . sad." His voice trailed off as he studied the picture again. "I carry the picture with me. She will not get away again. We thought you should know. In case she is the one. This neighborhood is quite—"

"I saw it . . . smelled it . . . myself. If my sister is here in such a place—and the baby—we must take her home. To think of her here is—"

"Yes. Heartbreaking. I know. I will do what I can. The bishop felt it wise that we meet. I will keep watch, Herr von Fritschauer. Such a lady as your sister has no place in the squalor of Heiliger Geist Strasse."

And so the chain of unwitting agents had found its final link on Wolf's behalf. Once again Wolf stressed that Lucy should be taken to some counseling office and detained without being made aware that her brother was searching for her. She must not be frightened away. A clever woman, she might slip the snare again, and time was running short.

———

Lucy's one-room flat was located in a tall narrow building in the Heiliger Giest district of Danzig not far from the ancient city wall. At one time it had been the spacious mansion of a wealthy coal merchant. Of course, that had been three hundred years earlier, before anyone had ever dreamed of indoor plumbing and electric lights.

In 1790, the place had been divided into a dozen flats on each of the first three stories. Much, much, later in its history, a sewer pipe had been installed on each floor, to be shared as communal toilet by the tenants. About that same time, gas lighting was added. A single cold water faucet in each room completed the latest in nineteenth-century conveniences to each flat.

Since that time there had been no improvements made. And so it remained as it had been for sixty years. Dock workers, poverty-stricken students, sailors without ships, and prostitutes in search of business lived here. Twelve flats to a floor, sometimes twelve tenants to a flat, they shared the toilet and accepted the fact that they were only a little better off than the rodents that used the groaning water pipes as thoroughfares from room to room.

But Lucy was on the fourth floor. Nestled in among hand-hewn rafters that might have served as the masts of an ancient galleon in a former life, she somehow felt above the squalor that packed the tenement. Her room had been the poorest room of all when this had been the house of a rich man. It had been his attic, the place he stored old furniture, the place his children played hide-and-seek. Tucked under the eaves at the back of the house, there was only one window, which faced another slate rooftop. Lucy could see the sky if she leaned out and craned her neck. She had pried open the sash and propped the window open with a stick. She did not need curtains; nor did it matter that the aged glass was caked with two hundred years of soot. There was no one to look in, and unless she cared to climb out on the roof to find a view, the window was only for ventilation.

This room was smaller than the others, she was told. It had a faucet and a basin, but she had to walk down one flight to empty her chamber pot. Peter had done that task when he was with her. Now the dreaded chore of entering the filthy closet that passed for a bathroom sickened her. She was grateful that her room was a floor above the stinking, teeming warren of the rest of the building.

She had to climb four steep flights of stairs, and her place was tiny, at best. But it was also cheaper than the rest. And isolated. She and

Peter had scrubbed and scraped and scoured every inch until now it was the cleanest flat in Altstadt. At night the rats chattered along the rafters and the pipes. She placed little piles of rat poison at every opening and Peter had nailed tin cans over the broadest rat tunnels to block their highways. Now only a few of the braver rodents skittered past and out again as quickly as possible. Peter had kept an axe handle by his bed. Lucy inherited it when he left. Usually a hard bang on the floor would frighten the midnight invaders away.

This afternoon, in honor of the imminent arrival of the baby, Lucy had once again scrubbed every inch of the room. From the rusty iron frame of her curtained bed, across every splintered plank of the bare wood floor, up the walls and along the rafters, the room was immaculate.

She moved the rickety table next to her bed and laid out everything she knew she would need. String to tie the cord. A sharp knife to cut it. A basin for water to wash. Another basin in which she would put bloodied sheets and towels. Antiseptic. Alcohol. Cotton gauze.

She sat on the edge of the sagging bed and studied her meager array of necessities. She stroked the child within her and looked up toward the shining silver crucifix that hung on the water-stained wall above the foot of her bed. She would be able to look up and see *Him* there. Of course she knew that Holy Christ would have no part of one like her, but the baby . . . *Would not Christ have mercy for the sake of this child?*

Just beneath the crucifix, Lucy laid out the soft satin christening gown, the matching cap and booties. Along with the silver filigree of the cross, they were the only bright and beautiful objects in the room. They were there, waiting to be filled by someone beautiful; someone tiny and perfect and innocent.

She fingered the soft hem of the christening gown. *White. Clean. Lacy. Like a wedding dress . . .*

Ah well, no use thinking of what will never be. Lucy fixed her imploring gaze on the silver Christ. "I . . . I know . . . you cannot hear me. I am too dark inside for you to hear." She mastered her tears, lest they stain the satin of the christening gown. "And so I will not ask you for myself. Nothing for me. But for this—" She touched the baby, who moved beneath her hand. "Sweet Christ? Please? Do you remember what it was to be . . . born in a stable? Your mother. Was she afraid? Were there rats there, too?" She searched the silver face, so full of agony, the hands, the fingers claw-like around the spikes. Had the mother of Jesus begged mercy for her child?

Lucy swallowed hard and did not look away. "For my baby, I ask— not for me, but for this little one. *I need help!* And I will give the baby to you if you help me. Not to Wolf. Or the Führer or Germany. This will be *your* child! I am past your mercy, not worthy. But—*Oh, God! I am afraid! Alone. Please . . . "*

Tears came, though her battle remained strong. What was the use? Why should she expect help? She stood and went to the window, breathing deeply the scent of the sea. She wanted to live. She wanted the baby to live and grow up to be someone better than she ever was. And she did not know how to do that alone.

The churchyard at Winchester had been the last place Orde had stopped before he left England for duty in Palestine. Today it was his first stop on his way back to London as well.

The churchyard gate groaned as Orde swung it open and entered. *Cemetery gates always groan,* Orde mused, swinging it back and forth again before pulling it closed. It was as though the rusty iron had captured the pain in Orde's heart and expressed it audibly for him.

He picked his way through the overgrown headstones to the far corner of the grounds. There, in shiny black granite lay the marker for his Katie:

KATHERINE JENNIFER ORDE
BELOVED WIFE OF . . .

Orde had wanted the stone to bear Katie's name, followed by the words *AND CHILD*. He was advised that since the baby had not been born, the sentiment would not be appropriate. But to Orde the child had been alive; it had been his, and he regretted that he had let them talk him out of it.

"Hullo, Love," he said quietly, laying the flowers at the base of the stone. "I must be the only one who remembers there are two of you here." He could see his own reflection in the stone. He looked much older. His image of Katie was still young; bright and beautiful as she had been the morning she left the house. "I remember," he said, "even though it's been a while. I remember clear as yesterday how it was. Our plans and such—baby things all put away in the nursery." He frowned and wrung his cap in his hands. "I gave it all away before I left. The house is the same, though. I'll be walking into the same house you walked out of when you went away." He looked up as a group of boys on bicycles rattled by outside the fence. "I'm not looking forward to going back there, I'll tell you. I feel more comfortable here, some-how. This is where I buried my heart. Where I think of myself." He frowned. "I won't be here long, Katie. I'm leaving for Poland, soon, if there's still a job for me." He ran his hand along the lapel of his jacket. "See, the whole world is going to war but me. I'm not a soldier any-more."

Orde sat down on the cool, moist soil beside the grave. He told Katie everything that had happened since he had last been here. And after that he wondered aloud what would happen between this hour and the next time he entered the groaning gate of Winchester where his heart was most at home.

————

Allan Farrell surveyed the materials spread out before him on the floor of his room. *One cutting board. Razors. Boxes of ordinary wooden kitchen matches. A hunk of steel pipe sealed at one end.* The simplicity of his design was ingenious. The fuse had been the most difficult problem, and now Allan had the solution to it quite clear in his mind.

This was the sort of weapon that sandbags and bomb shelters could not keep out. The pipe was small enough that it would fit easily up the sleeve of Allan's jacket. He could enter any public building, any hotel lobby or train station, and no one would know what he had up his sleeve. No one would even think to ask.

Carefully he razored the heads off the matches, dropping each round blue bead into the pipe. It was important that he not accidentally strike a match, he knew, or half of Mills University Hotel would go up in flames!

His hands were steady as he worked. He was not afraid even of the possibility that such a minor mistake could kill him before he had a chance to test his pipe bomb somewhere besides his own room. He had written a note to Uncle Colin, telling him to keep his ears open for unusual news about the IRA in London. If Allan died in his effort, he felt certain that his uncle would figure out what he had been up to. *He really was the son of Maureen Farrell, was he not?*

Allan hoped to live long enough to hear that glorious comment in person. Here was his own small proof that he was made of the same stuff as Colin and Kevin Fahey! More than just a messenger boy, Allan intended to deliver a message to the English that they would long remember!

He touched the scar beneath his eye. After tomorrow it would not matter how he acquired that scar. He would someday claim to have gotten it from the butt of an English soldier's gun, and his comrades would not question him! They would look at him with respect and ask his opinion of this action or that demonstration. The son of Maureen would at last have a name of his own.

14

Even Twigs Can Be Strong

Consulate Officer Brace was scowling down at his appointment book when the five members of the Danzig Gang entered his office. He looked up at them through his round wire-rimmed spectacles as though he wanted them to go away. It was, after all, five minutes until teatime. How could he settle all this in just five minutes?

"You're late," he said, cleaning his glasses.

"The trams, you know," Lori began. "And then all the people outside the consulate. Hard to get through to the gate."

Replacing his glasses on his hawkish nose, he blinked at the group as she made introductions. Bored and impatient, he thumbed through the applications that had been relayed through from London. So these were the children at the center of all the fuss. *Ibsen, Lori. Ibsen, James.* And these other three? Along for the ride. Holding to the coattails of these two Ibsen children. It was political favoritism, undoubtedly, to let these in when there were so many begging at the gates.

He checked his watch. Four minutes until teatime.

"So. You are Lori Ibsen." Out came the young woman's papers. "You look older than seventeen." She looked frightened by that, but she did not reply. "Student visa." He raised his visa stamp and thumped it down hard on her newly issued identity papers. She smiled broadly and exhaled with a burst of relief as she shoved her brother and the littlest Kalner boy forward.

The eyes of Officer Brace narrowed as he looked up at the two boys. "You look your ages." Out came the papers of James and Mark. "James Ibsen?" Jamie stepped forward. Down thumped the stamp. "Mark Kalner?" Mark squeezed in beside his friend. The third thump resounded joyfully, matching the beat of Lori's heart. The papers were shoved across the desk, snatched up and hugged tight to the hearts of the young ones.

Two and a half minutes until tea. "Right." Brace frowned slightly. "And now for the genius. Alfred Halder." Alfie stepped forward as had the others. He wrung his new fedora in his big hands. He blinked hopefully at the officer. *Did they take boys like Alfie?*

Brace stared at the papers and then at the young man in front of him. *Genius?* Ah well, had anyone taken a look at Einstein lately? Hair that looked like the scientist had been hit by lightning. A definite over-bite. Brace shook his head slightly. These genius types were all a bit on the imbecilic-looking side, weren't they?"

"So you are our genius?" Brace asked.

Alfie shrugged and smiled in a gesture that betrayed modesty. "Yes." He answered as Jacob had told him, even though he did not know what the officer had said.

"A linguist, eh?"

Alfie looked at Lori. Was he doing all right? She nodded and smiled, although she was very pale. "Yes," Alfie answered.

"Well, God knows we can use you in the Foreign Service." Brace thumped his rubber visa stamp across the proper square on Alfred Halder's papers. "No one seems to be able to understand a word any-one else is saying these days. Much easier if everyone spoke English."

"Yes," Alfie replied seriously. He took the document and bowed slightly.

"That's another thing. You Germans are much more polite than the French. Now, that is all."

Smiles vanished. Everyone looked at Jacob, who had been standing in the doorway of the tiny office. He had not been called forward. There had been no satisfying crash of the rubber stamp across his papers.

"Wait!" Lori's face grew pale.

Brace looked at his watch. He had been efficient. He deserved first selection on the pastry cart. His hand banged against his desk blotter. "What? What, what, what?"

Jacob broke through his companions. He smiled nervously and nodded. "Myself. I . . . am here the Bruder of Mark Kalner." Another timid smile from this very large young man. He was not a child at all—twenty years old if he was a day!

"Jacob Kalner," Jacob said.

Resentment filled the officer's eyes. "And what is it?"

"My Papiere, bitte. Papers?"

This one spoke rotten English. Besides, he did not look like the intellectual type. More like a rugby player who would take the job of some loyal Englishman as a dock worker.

"Ah, yes." Brace held up Jacob's documents and mumbled through them. "You claim to be seventeen?"

Lori moved to stand beside Jacob. She was frightened. "Yes," she blurted out. "He is. Seventeen."

"Young woman, you are not to interrupt." Brace was cold, official. The wheels of the pastry cart were no doubt in the tearoom by now. He studied the document a moment longer. "It says here you are of an exceptional intellect. How many years of school did you have, Mr. Kalner?" A muscle in his cheek twitched irritably.

"I . . . have . . . you know, the Nazis. They do not let . . . uh . . . non-Aryans stay in . . . the school."

"So? Yes? Well? How many years of schooling?"

Jacob could not remember the English pronunciation for the number ten. He held up his fingers. "This . . . and then I am made to . . . how do you say it?"

"Expelled." Brace helped him. "Rejected."

"Yes." Jacob did not look at the terrified face of Lori. It was going badly. He knew it. He wished he spoke English better!

"Well then. So this application is specious."

How was he to answer? He did not know that word. "I wish to England to go. With mein . . . Mark, ja?"

Consulate Officer Brace's expression turned to steel. He had enough of this nonsense. By now Phillip Smith had eaten the eclairs and all because of this . . . *imposter*! "I will tell you something, Mr. Kalner. This is obviously falsified." He tapped his finger on the application. "It is my duty to weed out the goats from the sheep in matters such as these and I think your performance is shameful. In the first place, you have no higher education, that is clear. Your mastery of the English language is rudimentary at best. You cannot be seventeen, certainly. And if you were seventeen that would still be above the cut-off date for the emergency child refugee provision." He raised his pointed chin as if to challenge Jacob. "Do you understand my meaning?"

Now Jacob looked painfully at Lori. Her hands were trembling. Tears hung in her eyes. "Please," she begged. "I know Jacob. He is *very* bright! The Nazis forced him from school. If he goes to England he can go to school again!"

"As what? Janitor?" Brace dug in his drawer for the other stamp. "This man is perfectly capable of taking care of himself here on the Continent. I could not live with myself if I let him take the place of . . . one of the children out there." He gestured angrily at the window. The shade was drawn, but he could sense the presence of so many others pressing against the gates.

Down came the rubber stamp with a loud bang. *REJECTED.*

"Please," Lori said again as she rushed forward to grasp the officer's hand.

The gesture was too much for him. He flung her hand away angrily and stood, calling for his secretary to escort these five people from the building.

By then it was three minutes after tea had begun. His day was quite ruined.

———

A furtive knock sounded on Agent Hess's door, betraying the identity of the visitor even before Hess turned the knob.

The Jewish banker from Bremen, perspiring heavily, leaned against the doorjamb. His labored breathing indicated he had run all the way from his post at the British Embassy gates.

Short, slope-shouldered and balding, the man was a stereotypical Jew. The face was pinched, the nose enormous, and on that nose perched spectacles so thick that the wearer's eyes looked unnaturally large and frightened.

This evening the eyes were even larger than usual. Hess stepped aside, allowing his exhausted accomplice to stumble past him into the room.

"I saw them!" he cried. But there was no victory in the declaration. Something had prevented the banker from fulfilling his entire duty.

"Well? Where are they?"

The Jew shrugged and shrank down onto the edge of the bed in defeat. "They entered just before four o'clock. Teatime at the British Embassy. Everything closes down, but they let these five children in all the same."

"Five children?"

"Yes. The two whom you are seeking were with three other boys. Well, maybe not children. Of late adolescence, I would judge."

Hess was not surprised that the Ibsen children had formed a company with others in their own predicament. That would simply mean that Hess would no doubt have more young charges to transport back to the Reich after their capture. "What about the two?"

The unwitting spy grimaced, giving his face a strangely rodent-like appearance. *Like a rat twitching his whiskers,* Hess thought. The fellow revolted him, yet he maintained his pleasant attitude in spite of it.

"Like I said, they all went in, escorted past the rest of us who had been waiting. Taken right into the building as if they had been invited for tea. Everyone was quite disgusted by such favoritism. We could tell they are not Jews like the rest of us. The British make no secret of their dislike of—"

Hess resisted the urge to slap the little weasel across the face. He let him grumble on about British favoritism and the injustice of Gentiles jumping line. "How long were they in there?"

"Half an hour. No more."

"And where did they go when they came out?"

The fellow looked almost angry. "The Englishmen took them to the side gate. I suppose it was so they would not be required to walk through such a large crowd of truly desperate people."

"You followed them?"

The huge eyes narrowed behind the lenses. "I attempted to follow them, comrade. They were a block ahead of me before I spotted them. Two blocks before I managed to make my way through the crowd. I tried not to look as though I was chasing them . . . as you instructed me. But then they turned onto a side street—"

"What street?" Although Hess knew the outcome of this tale of incompetence, perhaps something could be salvaged from it.

Once again the rat-like face screwed up in thought. The banker shoved his glasses up the thin bridge of his long nose. Hess had witnessed specimens of subhumans much less Jewish in appearance than this Jew being used as examples of all that was loathsome to the German people. It disgusted him that the Jew was sitting on his bed. Hess felt the muscle in his cheek twitch with suppressed fury as he stared hard at the Jew.

"Yes. Let me think. Hmmmm. I think. . . Tischler Strasse. Yes. Yes. It *was* Tischler Strasse. And then . . . the crowds. I did not see them. Could not find them."

Hess whirled to study his map. He traced his finger along the route the Ibsen children must have taken from the embassy. There were only red pins in the entire area. It amused him to think that the last district to be searched would indeed hide the fugitives.

Behind him, Hess could hear the Jew droning on in a high nasal voice about the difficulty of finding anyone with Danzig so full of refugees and everyone wanting to go anywhere else in the world but here. He congratulated himself that he had seen the children at all and that he had managed to follow them as far as he had. The worm would be expecting some sort of reward even though he had done only a fraction of what he had been hired to do. This recitation of difficulties was a prelude to asking for money. Hess could stand no more.

But the fellow was still of some possible use, and so Hess mastered the desire to shoot him between his close-set eyes. Instead, he dug into his pocket and pulled out a gulden, which he thrust into the fellow's hand. Then he grabbed him up by the collar of his jacket and whispered urgently, "We must find them before the Gestapo does, you understand? Stay at your post. No doubt they will be back. This time don't lose them!" With that, Hess jerked open the door and shoved the man out into the corridor.

Slamming the door, he returned to the map. Counting the pins within the last twenty-block area of Altstadt, he felt pleased that the resolution of this matter seemed so near.

It seemed almost providential to Hess that the last area of the hunt was likely to reveal that Lucy Strasburg and the children of Karl Ibsen had been living within a few blocks of one another.

He tapped his finger against the central landmark of the area. "Heiliger Geist Church," he muttered pleasantly.

————

The City of London Maternity Hospital at the corner of Old Street and City Road was the oldest institution of its kind in the kingdom. A green bronze plaque implanted in the cornerstone gave the date of establishment as 1750.

Antiquity was admirable in places like cathedrals and palaces, Murphy said, but a maternity hospital was a different matter—especially the hospital where his baby was about to be born.

The floor creaked as he paced the smoke-filled room where a dozen other expectant fathers waited. The more experienced hands played gin rummy or read the paper. Two fellows slept soundly on a cracked leather sofa—probably an original piece of furniture from bygone days of the hospital's glory.

Murphy felt sick. *Sick!* He wished they had checked out this listing old barn of a medical center before this. Elisa should be someplace with a decent waiting room and clean windows and nurses who had not been born in this very place in the last century.

The wheelchair they had taken Elisa away in was *wicker,* for goodness' sake! Probably willed to the institution by good old Queen Victoria! The electrical wires were all on the outside of the walls and had been painted over a half dozen times! Murphy had not seen round dial light switches of that vintage since he had visited the ancestral farm of the Murphy family as a five-year-old kid! Not exactly the kind of place he wanted to trust with the lives of his wife and child!

Did the terror show on his face? Why did they not let the fathers be with their wives? Anna could be in there. What was happening that they would not let him be with Elisa? And why was this taking so long?

A big man with a weather-beaten face and the clothes of a taxi driver whacked him on the back. "First time, eh?"

Murphy managed a miserable smile and a nod.

"Who's the Doc, then?"

"Howarth," Murphy replied.

"He's a good'n," said the big man. "A fine bloke, that Howarth."

Three other gin-rummy players agreed. *"Right. Good chap. He's taking care of my Maggie as well."*

Heads raised from newspapers. Two more bored-looking men nodded.

"My old lady as well."

In all, he figured that Dr. Howarth was delivering four babies besides Murphy's. That fresh and terrible revelation made him feel faint. He groped for a chair. His head was throbbing. This had been a moderately awful day to begin with, even before Elisa had called him and told him to meet her here. Now it definitely ranked right up there with the most horrible. How could one doctor deliver five babies all in the same day? *Impossible! Elisa would be left alone in some hallway somewhere! They would forget her there on the gurney and she would be calling his name, and* . . .

It was too terrible to contemplate. He hung his head and moaned. "We should have done this in the States."

"Ah, nothin' to it, mate!" growled someone. "Me wife's 'ad all of 'em 'ere!"

"How can he deliver five babies at once?" Murphy moaned.

"One at a time."

"Nothin' to it!"

" 'At's wha' we pay 'im for!"

Pay him. Whatever they paid him it was too much. This did not feel like a maternity hospital for women. It was a veterinary clinic!

Murphy had not paid attention when Elisa had told him that she had found a reasonable doctor. She should not have an unreasonable doctor at a time like this, he had quipped. Then she had said he was a doctor they could afford and hardly noticed the expense. *A specialist,* she said!

He wished he had walked through this place just one time and looked at the wiring. One of these days it was going to burn down. Probably tonight. He wished he had insisted that she have the baby back in America, where everyone spoke the same language and hospitals had not even been built in 1750. Benjamin Franklin had not even invented electricity when this place went up!

"America was still a colony when this place was built," he whispered hoarsely.

Someone laughed proudly. "Aye. We've been doin' this sort of thing a long time in England!"

"Somethin' new for you Yanks, then?"

Murphy stared at his hands. New for him, anyway. New for Elisa. Frightening and terrible and wonderful all at once. He wished he had thought all this through before. Last night she had called him insensitive and she was right. Any sensitive man would have made certain that the hospital his wife was in was at least newer than the Declaration of Independence!

He looked at his wrist and shook his head. His watch was broken, smashed when he tried to go through the door at the TENS office the wrong way. He hoped the man he knocked down was all right. He had not been moving when Murphy left. Maybe he was in a hospital, too. Not this one, though. Accident victims were probably treated better than women in labor.

Murphy did not want to ask what time it was. Daily life in London was tough enough trying to figure out the accent. Tonight he simply could not bear any more. He shook his broken watch. The crystal tinkled out on the floor.

"Break your watch?"

Murphy nodded at the voice. By now they all sounded alike, and he didn't care who said what anymore.

"Almost midnight." Someone answered, though no one had really asked.

Why did this take so long? Did these things always take so long?

"They'll be poppin' out soon enough!"

"Always in the wee hours."

As if on cue, a withered nurse poked her head through the door; she also looked to be of a pre-revolutionary war vintage. The gin-rummy game paused mid-gin. All eyes fixed on the face.

"Mr. Finsbury, please?"

One of the sleeping men shook himself awake. "Yes. Finsbury here."

"Good news! A baby boy."

The man stood and straightened his tie without a word, as if she had told him his car was in a tow zone.

"Jolly good," he commented, leaving his comrades without a second glance.

The card game resumed and then ended with the declaration of *gin*. It promptly began again. The men lit up fresh cigarettes and pipes, crossed their legs at a different angle. The slap of playing cards on the table was the only sound for half an hour more.

Murphy's mind played back every insensitive thing he had ever done or said. He then progressed into borderline insensitivity and onward into realms of guilt and self-recrimination he had never experienced before. He prayed and promised God that if everything came out okay— no pun intended—he would do better by Elisa and the kids. The world might be going nuts; Europe might be about to go up in flames; but Murphy would be a better father and husband!

"Twelve-twenty-six," muttered someone, breaking the silence.

Again the door opened and the prune face of a different nurse poked into the gray swirl of smoke.

"*Mr. Mur-pheeee?*"

"Yes! *Yes!* I *am* Murphy! That's *me!*" He was making a fool of himself, grabbing the arm of the old lady like that.

"*Yanks!*" someone grumbled from the gin table.

It was either very late at night or very early in the morning when the taxi pulled up beneath the window.

"He's home!" Charles cried, pouncing on the bed of his still-sleeping brother.

The announcement was something like saying Santa Claus had landed on the roof and was squeezing down the chimney. Louis sat bolt upright and the two scrambled to the window seat to peer down at the rattling black cab pulled to the curb of the little park opposite the house.

No sign of Murphy yet. The glow of gas lamps reflected against the hood of the vehicle. Beyond, the dark and deserted square seemed to be waiting for the arrival of a new baby in its perambulator. Murphy and Elisa had promised the boys they could give the baby rides around Red Lion Square. *Could we begin this morning?* Charles wondered.

The passenger door opened.

"There he is," Louis whispered, pressing his face against the glass.

"Where's Elisa?" Charles frowned when Murphy closed the door without sign of either Elisa or the new baby.

"Where's . . . the kid?" Louis echoed.

Charles thought for a moment. Murphy had said this was a very late kid. He had been saying that for weeks and had been growly more often these days. Elisa had been weepy. A normal thing, Murphy had told the boys man-to-man as they pretended to shave with him yesterday morning.

"Maybe the kid is still . . . late," Charles said.

This was a very disappointing homecoming. Charles and Louis had been forced to spend the evening with Hildy and Freddie. Trying to figure out what Hildy was talking about was a difficult proposition most of the time, but all evening her false teeth had clicked and clacked more than usual as she babbled on. She vacuumed twice and scolded Louis for getting cracker crumbs on the floor in front of the radio. It had been an unpleasant night, and now there was not even a baby to show for it. Would they have to do this *again*?

Murphy looked awful. His fedora was way back on his head. He needed a shave worse than usual. His tie was off; tucked into his coat pocket and hanging out nearly to his knees. He looked tired, *tired*. Worse than the nights when he came home from spending too many hours reporting on something terrible in the news. He walked slowly toward the house. The cab drove away.

Louis grimaced. "No kid."

"Rats."

Hildy was sound asleep on the sofa. Charles could hear her snoring. He wondered if she would someday suck in her false teeth and choke from such snoring. Not even Freddie snored like Hildy. He decided that next time they thought the baby was coming, he would ask if they could stay with Doc Grogan. He would have preferred Anna and Theo, of course, but they also would be at the hospital with Elisa because Elisa was their daughter. So, maybe they could stay with Doc Grogan who spoke real English instead of fractured, garbled stuff like Hildy. He said things like *rats, okay,* and other real American stuff like Murphy.

The boys turned away from the window and waited in the dark as the hollow sounds of Murphy's footsteps climbed the stairs.

Hildy heard him coming in her sleep. She snorted, and the snoring stopped. "Who ist dere, pleeze?"

Murphy replied in a muffled voice that it was he.

"Ach! Mein *Gott*! Mizter Murpheee! Und d' ba-bee ist. . . ?" The door banged back. Murphy's voice was low and quiet. Hildy's voice was loud and unintelligible. The pitch increased. Murphy, still tired, was talking all the same. Talking too quiet!

Something was up. The boys exchanged glances and padded quickly out to the landing where they could see Hildy's plump, wide body blocking Murphy from coming all the way in. If she caught them there she would shake her finger at them and scold them, so they stayed quiet and hoped she would go downstairs to her own place soon.

"Fine . . . fine, Hildy." Murphy managed to get in a word.

"Ach! Gott praise to be! Und danks to Gott, Mizter Mur-phee!"

Murphy's hands took the old woman by her shoulders. "The boys were good for you?" *Uh-oh. The question . . .*

"Like d'an-gels, dey ist! *Per*-fect! An-gels!"

Charles understood her. *Angels?* This was amazing. Murphy managed to switch places with Hildy so she was mostly outside. He was still speaking very low. She was very excited and loud. Crying. Were they happy tears or unhappy?

"You go . . . get some sleep now, Hildy. You must be tired. Thanks a lot . . . tell you all about it tomorrow."

She let out a big laugh and she slapped her hand against her legs like a German folk dancer. "Tomorrow ist already *here*!"

"So it is." Murphy looked at his wrist to check the time but he did not have his watch on. "Late. Early. G'night, Hildy." He shut the door. *Relief!* Murphy was better than anyone at getting Hildy out the door.

He sighed and looked up toward the landing. The tired look went away when he saw the boys waiting there in their pajamas. Something wonderful had happened. Charles could tell by the look on Murphy's face.

"It's okay, fellas," he called. "She's gone. You can come out now."

They clambered down the stairs to embrace him. He smelled like the ashtrays at the newsroom, but he was happy.

"Where's Elisa?"

"Where's the kid?" Louis asked. "Still late?"

Murphy laughed and hoisted them both up to touch the heavy rafters. "You've got a baby sister, boys," he cried. "As beautiful as her mother, too!"

———

Where the walls of his cell came together at the corner, Karl noticed a shadow just beneath the ceiling where one brick was missing. The sparrows saw it as a place to build their nest.

Karl's human logic could not understand why the sparrows would forsake the fragrant green boughs of a pine-tree home for the rank gloom of this prison cell. But such a miracle was beyond human logic. When Karl reasoned with his heart, he came to the conclusion that these tiny feathered creatures were sent to him as a gift. The sparrows did not belong to him. No. They were free to come and go as they pleased. They belonged to the Lord who cared for all creatures big and small, and God had loaned them to Karl to keep him company. How kind, how thoughtful, God was, Karl concluded. God had known about the missing brick. He had provided the bread. He had sent the sparrows and planted the desire in their hearts to build their home in the very walls that imprisoned Karl.

Twig by string by stem, the sparrows labored over their nest. As they twittered to each other, Karl's heart entered into their conversation. He understood the concerns of parenthood and marriage. Of building a safe place in which to bring up youngsters. All these concerns were acted out in miniature drama in the nitch above Karl's head. Lady Sparrow scolded and the male pouted. He tossed his head and she obeyed . . . but not without protest. Together they lined the nest with downy feathers, creating a soft place for their little ones through their own sacrifice.

Day by day Karl offered them the best morsels of his bread. In return, they sometimes brought him gifts. One day the leaf of an elm tree. The next a faintly fragrant pine needle, which he pressed between his fingers to inhale the scent. Twice, Lady Sparrow dropped the petals of a wild flower. By holding the fragile yellow fragment in his hand, Karl could imagine a whole field of yellow flowers sloping down toward the banks of a broad river.

They brought him pieces of the world. Little bits of beauty from which he could rebuild the memories of the things he had most enjoyed with his own family: Picnics by the River Spree. A hike through the fragrant forests of Bavaria. Late-night talks with Helen about their children. Their future. Their lives. Family . . .

The memories of long-ago things did not make Karl melancholy. Instead, he found comfort in replaying his life with Helen and Jamie and Lori. He had no regrets. Life had been good. Every day had been brushed with the colors of loving. Even the most ordinary routines now seemed somehow sacred and blessed, a holy sacrament.

Karl looked up at the nest. It was barely visible even though he knew where to look. If his jailors ever came into the cell, they would not see the little family high in the wall. He was grateful for this. The male had gone foraging this morning. Lady Sparrow was nestled in the downy feathers. A miracle was happening today, Karl knew. There would be eggs in the nest by the time her mate returned. This fact gave the cell the aura of a holy place. Karl bowed his head and worshiped the Lord of men and sparrows.

––––––––––

Only one thing did Rachel enjoy more than the weekly BBC concerts on the radio—the weekly live concerts performed at the Community Hall for free.

Tonight, Father Kopecky came to visit Papa. He had looked surprised that Rachel and Etta were not going to the concert.

"Why should the women stay home," he asked, "when a priest and a rabbi have so much to talk about?"

"And a game of chess to finish," Papa had added.

The boys were put to bed early. Etta French-braided Rachel's hair, giving her the appearance of a nearly adult young lady. Then they had changed into Shabbat clothes and joined the parade traipsing through Muranow Square toward the hall.

There were more strangers here than people who knew the Lubetkins. Fewer and fewer of the old friends and neighbors remained in Warsaw each day. The dress and dialects of the crowd verified that they had come here from everywhere.

Many looked just like the Poles whom Rachel had seen beyond the neighborhood. They would have fit in just as well at the Saxon Garden or on the sidewalks outside the Royal Palace where merchants with little carts cooked Polish sausages. Some wore clothing that once must have been as grand as anything that passed through the lobbies of the Bristol or the Europejski hotels. Others would have fit right in among the fish sellers on the docks of the Vistula.

One thing was certain; the newcomers did not look like Jews. They did not talk like Jews or act like Jews—at least not like the Jews of

Muranow Square! Rachel thought that maybe the Catholic priest would have fit into this assembly very well. The thought made her feel indignant and more than a bit uncomfortable. Across the aisle, in an entire row of wooden folding chairs, boys and girls sat all in a line, talking together, *holding hands*! The sight of such familiarity made her flush with embarrassment.

Rachel had heard Papa laughing about such things with the priest. His laughter had shocked her. His comment had sobered her, especially in the face of the terrible news from Germany these days.

"It seems impossible to me that Herr Hitler simply lumps all of us who are Jewish together," Papa had said. "I will give you the straight of it. You may preach a sermon on it, because it has not changed since Jesus walked in Jerusalem."

"Instruct me." The priest had moved his knight across the chess board and grinned at Papa's sour expression.

"Then be instructed." Papa swept a hand over the chessmen. "Our trouble in facing the Nazis is that we do not have one great army with one belief as they do. We are not even right or left. We are not even right, left, center. We are a spectrum." At that he began bumping his chess men from the table. "We are Orthodox, Karaites, Ashkenazim, General Zionists, Poale-Zion Right, Hasid, Mizrochi, Hashomer Hatsoir, Poale-Zion Left, and Communist."

All the little chess pieces lay in a pile, and Papa's king and queen were quite exposed to all the forces on the opposite side.

"I see," said Father Kopecky. "Check and checkmate." Then he said, "And you know why the Christians have been so utterly smashed in Germany as well? We are Catholic, Lutheran, Episcopal, Methodist, Baptist, Mennonite . . ." All his chessmen came crashing down as well. "Everyone with a different idea. All forgetting who God is as we cram Him into doctrinal boxes and squabble over this and that. Not so very different, after all, are we, Aaron?"

"Except that every Jew will die regardless of what he believes if the Nazis come here. If you Christians . . . renounce your faith, or simply alter it to conform . . . you will live."

"Not live, Aaron." He laid the two kings side by side as if they shared a mutual tomb. "Only survive. Breathe and walk in bodies that have lost their souls. And in the end, those who have betrayed their faith will be scraped off the shoe of God right along with the Nazis, I think."

Rachel had been called away from the rest of the discussion, but looking around her at all the different types gathered together under one roof, she recalled every word.

Just then she spotted the ragged form of Peter Wallich as he leaned forward at the foot of the stage and talked in serious tones to the violinist. She knew what Peter was asking about. And from the expression on his face, she knew that he had not found what he was looking for. He still was lost, still without the precious name he needed to find his way home to his mother and sister. That is, if they were really here in Warsaw.

She shuddered as she stared at his increasingly ragged clothes, his bushy, unkempt hair, and his face so thin that his bitter eyes were his most prominent feature.

And then a terrible thought came to her, a thought that made her want to leave the concert. *Peter Wallich is every Jew that was and will be. Lost and looking for home. This is what the enemy wishes to throw in the fire! Not an oak branch, but a bundle of twigs, an army to be defeated one lonely life at a time!*

She put her hand to her head and closed her eyes. Etta leaned close. "Are you all right? Do you have a headache?"

Rachel nodded. "A big one." She opened her eyes and Peter was gone, vanished from the place where she had seen him. She looked around but could not find him. He had simply blended into the crowd. Rich and poor, wise and foolish alike had simply absorbed Peter Wallich into themselves.

Where is home? Rachel wondered as she looked at each twig in the vast bundle and pitied them and herself. *Where is the home we are searching for?*

The spotlight flicked on behind the chairs. The audience applauded as the lights were turned off. The musicians began to play the Mozart Quintet K. 174, and for that moment all hearts listened as one heart, longing for the same home together. Once again Rachel closed her eyes and let her mind sing the words of the prophet Balaam:

How can I curse those whom God has not cursed?
How can I denounce
    those whom the Lord has not denounced?
From the rocky peaks I see them,
    from the heights I view them.
I see a people who live apart
    and do not consider themselves
    one of the nations.
Who can count the dust of Jacob
    or number the fourth part of Israel?
Let me die the death of the righteous,
    and may my end be like theirs!

The melody of those words filled her heart like the music. For a moment, at least, she felt peace. There was much she would have to ask Papa about that passage. Could it be that from heights God did not see a bundle of twigs in Israel, but a solid oak staff that would not bend beneath the weight of persecution, or break under the force of the stones that even now were hurled against this people called Israel?

God has made His walking stick out of brittle twigs, Rachel mused. *But in the hand of God, even twigs can be strong.*

15

The News Never Waits

"Where to, mate?" The taxi driver leaned his head far out the window and called to Samuel Orde. He seemed to be the only remaining taxi at London's Victoria Station tonight.

Orde touched his fingers to the brim of his Panama hat and then climbed into the back of the vehicle without answering the question.

"I say," tried the driver again, "where to?"

It had been a long time since Orde had given anyone the address of his London home. The last time, he had been with Katie. They had ordered a new sofa for delivery to the house. Now the sofa was covered with a sheet, as was all the rest of the furniture. Dusty sheets and lonely rooms. Orde was not anxious to enter that place again.

"I say—" The cabbie looked concerned. "Do you *parley* English?"

"Yes. Sorry. It's been some time since I've been here. For a moment the address—" He waved his hand as if he had forgotten. "Three Kings Yard—" *Katie had loved the name of their street.* "Between Claridge's and Grosvenor Square. Do you know it?"

The taxi had already lurched into motion. "Number?"

"Twelve." Orde looked out the window. All of London seemed asleep. There was hardly any traffic. He could see the reflection of the cab as it passed the showcase windows of the shops and hotels. Yes, London was asleep and Orde was dreaming. He had been dreaming since the day Katie died. Between that moment and this, it seemed that no time at all had passed. He would go home to their house—to the wallpaper she had hung, the furniture she had picked out. The paintings. The carpets. The china and crystal wine glasses they had gotten on their wedding day. And surely Katie would be there, too, waiting for him to wake up. *"Fresh strawberries and cream for breakfast, Sam.*

You've overslept. The sofa is coming today." And then she would lean
over to kiss him awake. She would tell him to shave and shower quickly
because . . . because . . .

Orde shook his head. He tapped on the glass partition separating
him from the driver. It had been a long time since he had seen the city,
Orde explained, and perhaps it would be better to have a look at it
while there was no traffic.

The cabbie shrugged in good-natured acquiescence. What did it
matter to him if this passenger wanted to rack up unnecessary miles
on the meter as long as he could pay for it? It did not occur to him to
ask why a man who had been away so long would not be eager to
arrive home. The real reason for Orde's sudden urge for this late-night
tour of the city was nothing Orde could have articulated even if someone had asked him.

Hyde Park. Marble Arch. Selfridge's Department Store where Katie
had loved to shop. Regent Street to Piccadilly Circus. Once around
Trafalgar Square and then back toward Buckingham Palace.

Everywhere Orde looked, sandbags piled like lumpy pillows against
the dark hulks of buildings. On the base of every monument, posted
signs proclaimed Britain's preparedness for whatever might come.
These ominous reminders of the daily headlines finally drew Orde out
of the melancholy memories of Katie and set him down squarely in
the present. When Katie had died, Spain had not yet erupted. Germany
had no army to speak of. Austria was still Austria and there was the
solid little democracy of Czechoslovakia in the heart of Europe.

There had been no sandbags in London when Katie left. . . .

Again Orde tapped on the window partition. "What is the date?" he
asked the cabbie. "The *year,* I mean?"

With a quick, concerned glance in the rearview mirror, the cabbie
answered, "1939."

Orde nodded. "Right. You may drive me home now, if you please.
Number 12. *Three Kings Yard."*

———

London seemed quite awake now. The din of traffic along Fleet
Street was deafening. Fumes of omnibuses and taxis threatened to
choke the two horses pulling hansom cabs to St. Paul's Cathedral.

Sam Orde double-checked his reflection in the window of a shop
next to the London office of Trump European News. He frowned and
smoothed the lapels of his ill-fitting tweed jacket. The shoulders were
cut too narrow. It had been a year since he last wore it, and he had
forgotten about the shoulders needing to be altered. The material of
his suit was definitely out of season for the warm month of May. But
he had nothing else suitable to wear with the possible exception of

his Royal Army uniform. And, of course, as of midnight last night, Orde was a private citizen again.

Ah well, perhaps Mr. Murphy would not notice the cut of Orde's clothes. And if he did, maybe it would not matter.

Orde drew a deep breath of exhaust-filled air. He pulled himself erect and walked—not marched—to the entrance of TENS. Hand on the door, he peered through the glass at the commotion within. Everyone seemed to be up and milling about. The young woman at the switchboard stood leaning against the counter and laughing. Orde could distinctly hear the shouts and laughter of men and women. Some sort of party—at eight-thirty in the morning? Orde wondered if he should have called Mr. Murphy. Of course, Orde had no telephone at the house. It had been disconnected for years. And if he was really going to accept this position as a member of the TENS staff, there was no reason to have it connected again, was there?

Taking another deep breath, Orde wondered if the Warsaw position had been filled. He pulled the door open. A buzzer rang, announcing his entrance, but no one even looked his way. The air inside was more rank than the exhaust fumes outside. *Cigar smoke!* Every man in the place was puffing away on enormous Cuban stogies. The women among them did not seem to mind. At least not much.

Someone shouted to the receptionist. "Hey, Marjorie! Open the door! Prop open the blasted door! We're all going to asphyxiate in here!"

Laughing, the receptionist brushed past Orde, who stood in the lobby. She did not notice him, did not speak to him as she propped the entry door open. Her face seemed perpetually frozen in a gleeful smile. Once the door was open, the noise of Fleet Street combined with the din of the group. The receptionist charged back past Orde as if he were a pillar rooted in the floor.

The swinging half door to her little cubicle slammed shut. She once again leaned against the counter to observe the celebration in the crowded newsroom beyond.

"I hope it doesn't look like you, Murph!" shouted a man who sat on a cluttered desk.

"Nope, looks just like Elisa!" remarked a fellow whose pockets seemed to be jammed with the offending cigars. "Beautiful."

"Ah come on, Murphy! I got three kids myself. Never saw one fresh out of the oven that didn't look like it needed to bake a while longer!" There was a great roar of approval at this truth.

"Nah!" said the cigar man again. "I'm telling you . . . really now . . ." His hands rose up in innocence. "Beautiful. All the rest of them in the nursery look squashed in the face, but not our girl! Just like her mother!"

Wolf whistles rang out in reply.

"Watchit! Watchit!" warned the cigar man. "I'm a father now. A little respect from you mugs, if you don't mind!"

Orde knew that he had walked into something wonderful. The rumpled-looking fellow thumped everyone on the back as he laughed, handed out cigars, and shouted back in joyful banter about his baby. His wife. Indeed, Orde had crashed a celebration; one which made his heart more than a little envious. *That might have been me.* He did not interrupt until someone spotted him hanging back.

"Hey, Murph! There's another one without a cee-gar!"

Three fellows charged through the swinging gate, and then Orde noticed that among the crowd was a policeman, a taxi driver, a chauffeur, and a man wearing a chef's hat.

"Come on! Come on!" They grabbed Orde by his tweed suit and propelled him into the newsroom until he stood face-to-face with the new father.

With a cigar clutched between his teeth, the father pulled another cigar from his jacket pocket. "Congratulate me, pardner. I am the proud father of a seven-pound, eight-ounce baby girl. Mother is doing swell." He handed Orde the cigar. "In honor of Katherine Anna Murphy!" He flicked the match with his thumb, sparking the flame to life and touching it to the top of the stogie.

So this is the boss, Orde thought, accepting the ritual offering. Not bad tobacco. Orde sized up the chap who might well be his employer. He liked him immediately. "Congratulations," he saluted lightly. "And may I ask if the father of Katherine Anna—"

"Katie! Katie, we decided. She's too little for all that Katherine. We just named her after my mother and Elisa's mother, but she looks like a Katie to me."

A slight twinge shot through Orde. A well-loved name: *Katie.* "Very well, then. Katie's father wouldn't happen to be John Murphy?"

"The same." Murphy raised his hands like a soccer player who had just made a goal. Great cheering rose up from the impromptu guests and regulars in attendance. "I'm not asking anyone's name," Murphy said through his cigar, "because I won't remember it."

"All the same, I am Samuel Orde." Orde presented the crumpled telegram to Murphy. "I believe you wished me to see you about a position?"

———

Like smoke after a Fourth of July fireworks display, a blue cigar haze still hung over the newsroom of London TENS. Heads were bowed over Olivetti keyboards. Crumpled paper overflowed metal trash cans beside each desk. The news could not wait just because John Murphy had become a father last night. And with the one exception of a baby girl named Katie, none of the news was good this morning.

Murphy's face still held a lopsided grin. For him the good news was too good to be tarnished by the latest horror story from Nazi-occupied Prague. Even as he explained to Sam Orde the gravity of the situation in Warsaw, the half smile did not vanish. The distant clatter of typewriters penetrated the glass-enclosed office like the faraway popping of rifle fire.

Murphy passed the latest wire dispatch across the desk. One thousand Czech citizens had been arrested and thrown into prison in retaliation for the killing of a Nazi policeman last night. German troops were reported on the move across Czech territory toward the border of Poland.

"I am convinced Warsaw is the next target," Murphy said. "And that you are the right man to have in place when it finally breaks." He paused, still smiling. "What I can't figure is which way Russia is going to jump in this." The grin finally wavered and faded. "There are a number of men in Parliament who have been trying to form an alliance with Stalin. Warsaw won't have any of it, of course."

"Certainly not. Warsaw dare not make an alliance with Russia for fear that an invasion by Germany would be an invitation for Russia to flood across Poland to fight the Germans. And maybe Stalin might take a liking to Warsaw and never leave."

Murphy seemed pleased by Orde's reply. He had grasped the essence of all Polish foreign policy: straddle a very high fence, and hope the Russians or the Germans did not climb over it. The fear that Murphy had shared with Winston Churchill was that Stalin and Hitler might simply advance to that center line through the heart of Poland, and divide the nation between them.

"Do you think Germany will attempt an alliance with Moscow?"

"In order to divide up Poland," Orde said flatly. Then he nodded. "Here in England the politicians say it cannot happen. And I am certain that the German people would be appalled by such a prospect. Hitler has built his support on a platform of fear about Communist Russia." He frowned and picked at the lint on his trouser leg. "But I cannot see any other way for Hitler to make good his threat about invading Poland. From a military point of view—"

Murphy leaned forward, urging Orde to continue. This was just the sort of insight he had hoped for from this man. "Go on. And once it happens, I'll print it."

"Hitler will not risk invading Poland if it means he must fight the West *and* Soviet Russia at once. Certainly Stalin will not sit back and allow the German divisions to sweep right up to his borders."

"And?"

"And so, Hitler must have some sort of . . . agreement . . . with Stalin. Perhaps a nonaggression pact of the sort he has with Italy. If that happens, then war is a certainty."

"What do you see standing in the way?"

"Hardly anything at all." He shrugged. "Prime Minister Chamberlain resists any alliance with the Russians. The Poles remain on their high wire, hoping that the breeze will not blow. And Hitler is looking eastward, considering how the devil may best make a pact with the bear."

"You have been paying attention while you were in Palestine, Captain Orde," Murphy said, genuinely impressed.

"What is happening in Palestine is very much linked to what is happening in Europe. Only a political moron would not see that." He paused. "Just call me Orde, if you please. Or Samuel."

"All right then. If you will call me Murphy." He reached across the desk to shake hands with a man he considered to be the finest TENS political reporter in all of Europe. Orde had recited the same political scenario that Murphy had heard from Winston Churchill over prime rib and Yorkshire pudding last month. Churchill was seldom wrong in his foresight of coming events.

"When do I begin?" Orde asked, looking around as though a steamer ticket had already been purchased.

"I thought, if you accepted the post, that you might want a bit of time in London to relax."

"I find after one night at home that I am more relaxed elsewhere. I will be ready to leave as soon as arrangements—"

At that moment, Harvey Terrill banged once on the glass door and then poked his head in the office. "Sorry, Boss. It's a trunk call all the way from Danzig. Some little girl . . . your cousin? Elisa's cousin? She speaks pretty good English. Says she tried to get through on the home lines and nobody answers. Collect call. I accepted."

Murphy nodded. The smile reappeared. It had to be Lori, reporting in on the news about their visas. "Sweet kid," Murphy said aloud and then, "Hullo?"

Today the sweet kid was anything but sweet. Anything but calm. Lori related to Murphy the sad tale of Jacob Kalner's rejection by the embassy official. She barely noticed when Murphy told her that the reason no one was home was because Elisa had just delivered a baby. She did not ask if the baby was a boy or girl.

"If Jacob does not come to England, then you must explain to my mother that I am not going either!"

"Wait a minute!"

"I mean what I am saying! He cannot be left in this place alone. Danzig is not a place where anyone should be alone. I will stay here with him until we can figure out another plan. But the boys will come

ahead. Tell my mother these things."

She rambled on, her voice betraying her emotional distress. She was not thinking clearly; not weighing the consequence of her turning down a visa. Likely there would be no more offered to her.

Murphy covered the mouthpiece as she talked. "Orde. We've got a situation here . . ." Lori's voice rose to a soprano of near-hysteria, and he simply spoke over her. "I'd like to give you an assistant. Put him on the payroll. He's seventeen. Jewish. In Danzig now. I can have him meet you. Messenger boy, valet, if you like. He speaks German almost exclusively, so the language might be a problem, but—"

Orde could hear every word of Lori Ibsen's long recitation. Within a moment he had a clear grasp of the desperate situation. "I have had seventeen-year-old recruits beside me in trenches before. Often they fight as well as men with ten years on them." He waved a hand. "Tell the girl . . . her chap will be well managed until we can get him to England." Orde smiled. He was still the captain of a very small troop.

———

Within thirty minutes Victoria Station would be packed with London commuters. It was still only half full when Allan Farrell passed through the main entrance.

Today he looked more like Maureen than himself, he thought as he caught his own reflection in the glass of the doors. He had shaved twice, put on the clothes and shoes of a woman and then a touch of lip rouge and powder to complete the effect. He covered his hair with a wide-brimmed hat and veil. His slim, small-boned structure lent itself well to such a disguise. He carried a large shopping basket and a handbag containing cigarettes and matches along with a handful of change.

His destination was neither ticket kiosk nor train. He moved rapidly across the echoing terminal to the ladies' lavatory. Without hesitation, he entered, walking quickly past a handful of women at the sinks. Two primped before the mirror, fixing their hair and makeup. Allan did not let himself think of their fate if they lingered too long in the ladies' room.

The stalls were mostly empty. He chose the one at the end of the row and locked the door behind him. Within moments the pipe bomb was placed on the water tank of the toilet. Allan fumbled in the handbag, taking out cigarette and matches and a spool of thread. He placed the matches against the cigarette, binding them to it with the thread. Once lit, the tobacco would burn down toward the match heads slowly enough for him to get away. Three minutes later, when the flame reached the matches, they would flare and ignite the contents of the pipe bomb. The result would be devastation.

One minute had passed since he entered the stall. He lit the cigarette fuse, blew on it until it glowed hot, and then placed it in position against the end of the pipe bomb.

With that, he dropped a towel into the toilet bowl and flushed. Instantly, the water filled and overflowed onto the floor, soaking his shoes and spreading rapidly as the ladies in the room squealed and grumbled and clamored to get out of the path of the flood.

"A toilet has broken! Everyone out! Hurry!" He had done his best. He could not think about those women who did not move fast enough to escape what followed. *Those who did not care about wet shoes would soon never have a care again.*

Five women went out the door with him. Two remained inside. They would die, Allan knew. He did not look back. He resisted the urge to run back and pull them from harm's way. Fixing his eyes on the telephone booth, he hurried toward it. One minute remained until the device exploded. He looked over his shoulder as one more disgusted-looking woman emerged.

With trembling hands he picked up the telephone and dialed the number he had memorized. He wanted to be certain the world knew . . .

"Hullo, Trump European News Service. How may I direct your—" Fifteen seconds.

"Shut up and listen. I am at Victoria Station. The explosion you are about to hear is courtesy of the IRA. Got it? IRA . . ."

He let the receiver fall. It was dangling there when the explosion rocked Victoria Station. When the shrieks and shouts of terror filled the chasm of the terminal, TENS was on the line. By the time the first wails of ambulances filled the streets, Allan Farrell was long gone. But they heard it all over the telephone at TENS. They heard everything from the name *IRA* until the moment the first reporters crowded through the police barriers.

Allan read about the incident in his morning issue of *The Times* as he sunned himself in Parliament Square and waited for his contact.

———

Visiting hours at the City of London Maternity Hospital were not long enough to suit Murphy. He stood for an hour in front of the glass partition of the nursery, tapping on the glass, talking to the little bundle named Katie who slept peacefully in her bassinet between two stout, bawling baby boys.

"An angel," Theo said of his granddaughter. He leaned his forehead against the glass, smiled and waved a tiny wave with the same adoration on his face as Murphy expressed.

"She looks like Elisa." Anna was anxious to hold her granddaughter, but it would be days before that was allowed. "Don't you think so, Helen?"

Helen Ibsen could only nod. The baby also looked like her own baby Lori had looked. She could not see anything behind the glass but the image of tiny Lori as she had been in her crib.

It was already seven o'clock according to the clock inside the nursery. Only one hour left to visit Elisa and then sneak back here for a final peek at Katie.

"Gotta git." Murphy kissed Anna lightly on the cheek. "Thanks," he said as he pumped Theo's hand. He wanted to thank them both for Elisa; their lives had resulted in his life being full to overflowing. But there were no words—just emotion enough to power the lights like a generator. And the sweeping second hand of that clock kept moving.

"Give her a kiss for me," Anna said.

"Kiss my baby girl and tell her I'm proud, ja?" Theo added.

Elisa was sitting up reading her Bible when Murphy walked in. A radio at the end of the ward played a Glenn Miller tune, but something in Elisa's eyes told him clearly that she had also heard the news about the bombing at Victoria Station.

He kissed her three times. "Once for your Mom. Once for Theo. And once for me." He grinned down at her, ignoring the worry in her eyes. "That's just for starters. We have an hour."

"She is so beautiful, isn't she, Murph?" Elisa said. There was more than pride in her voice; there was an edge of worry that they had brought something so perfect into an imperfect world. How could they shield this little one from the same terrible heartache they were seeing again and again among the children from the Reich?

Murphy felt it, too, but he did not speak of it. Instead, he took her hands. "You done good, kid," he said. "Real good. I called my mom. Good connection, too. I told her about the name, and she cried. Imagine! Calling all the way to Pennsylvania and then to have her bawl like that. Pop was pretty happy, too. He says we need to bring you all home soon, to teach Katie to ride a horse and milk cows." He was babbling, trying to pretend that he did not see what was in Elisa's eyes. He had heard the old saying before: *Any man with a baby in the cradle longs for peace in the world.* He had never understood it with his heart as he did now. "Anna and Theo say she looks just like you."

Elisa's brow furrowed with emotion. "And Aunt Helen? What does she say? I held Katie and thought how much she looks like little Lori looked. And then I remembered Lori and Jamie. Murphy, I haven't even asked you about them. Are they coming to London, Murphy? Did they make it through the paper mine field?"

Murphy patted her hand and nodded. She lay her head back on the pillows and sighed with relief. So much to think about . . . so many others to think about when this should be the happiest day of their lives. Murphy did not tell Elisa about Jacob Kalner except to explain that Jacob would be staying behind to work as the assistant of Samuel Orde in the new Warsaw branch of TENS. Putting the news in that light made it seem not at all terrible or threatening for the young man.

The second hand swept too swiftly around the clock face. Murphy did not say much about the Victoria Station bombing except that one toilet had blown up and an unfortunate woman was killed. He avoided mentioning that the woman had been only twenty-seven years old, or that she left behind two toddlers and a husband. Tonight the world should have been a perfect place, a safe place in which to raise some-one as precious as little Katie. Mothers should not have to worry about pipe bombs exploding in train stations or Nazis sweeping over half the world.

16

Kyrie

Along with the ordinary mail, two special letters whisked through the mail slot of the Lubetkin home in Warsaw, Poland. Rachel picked them up and scrutinized the postmarks and handwriting to see who had written, when the letters were mailed, and from where.

Mama had told Rachel a thousand times that she must not be so nosey. The mail was almost always addressed to Papa, and so it was not supposed to be any of Rachel's business who was writing.

But Rachel had gotten into the habit when Papa was in prison. No matter who had written, she and Mama had opened the letters and gone over them together. The experience made it difficult to wait patiently for Papa to scan his correspondence and decide which letter was for sharing with the family and which was for his eyes alone.

Rachel knew at a glance that one of the letters was for reading. Addressed to Papa in the spidery handwriting of Grandfather Lebowitz, the letter had been mailed from Jerusalem four weeks ago. This meant that it had arrived two weeks sooner than the usual time of six weeks. And so the news would be two weeks newer, provided Papa did not take his time about reading it!

The Jerusalem letters were always wonderfully long and entertaining. Grandfather wrote them on paper so thin that a person could see through it. He did this to save money on postage, Mama explained. And on this thin, practically transparent paper, he painted long and wonderful pictures of the Holy Land. He started with the weather, which was always six weeks out-of-date. He progressed to funny stories about the Old City neighborhood—what this yenta had said about that yenta and who was squabbling with whom. Or getting married. Or graduating from Yeshiva. Sometimes who had died.

With all of this, Mama's eyes were bright and her face happy or sad, as the occasion dictated. The best part was her running commentary about everything Grandfather wrote. She had grown up in the neighborhood, after all. So, shouldn't she know all the little extra details that made the story more interesting? Of course she should. And she did.

Over the last two years the weather reports and personal news also included a lot about the Muslim uprisings. Mama also commented on this, since she had lived in the Old City before the British had taken over the place and all of the Arabs had moved in from the neighboring countries. Always when Grandfather mentioned the Mufti of Jerusalem, she became indignant. *"So why did the British make the lunatic a Mufti, already? Haj Amin was born in Syria, and they make him Mufti in Jerusalem!"*

Things had been different when she was growing up, she said. Arab and Jew got along wonderfully well. Lately Papa had been saying that he was sure the British would work it all out, and wouldn't it be good to go back there?

Rachel was certain that Grandfather's letter would end on the same note. He would tell them that everything was wonderful and that they should come home as soon as the little details about their papers got sorted out. Grandfather said they could all live with him. Mama said he would have to rent a bigger flat, and then she always looked around wistfully at the pale yellow walls and the fine walnut furniture and the beveled-glass transom windows that made the sunlight into rainbows on the polished wood floor. Before this year, they had all thought it would be impossible to leave the wonderful house on Muranow Square. Rachel still considered the idea unthinkable. But something had changed in the way Mama and Papa talked about Jerusalem. Now there was something wistful in Mama's voice when she mentioned the shops on Julian's Way and the merchants in their stalls along David Street and the covered souks and ancient sites.

Rachel held the envelope up to a rainbow from the window. It was full of colors, sights, sounds, and even smells that Mama would describe for her. But Rachel did not want to go to Jerusalem to see it in person. A letter on onionskin paper to be recited lovingly in the house on Muranow Square was good enough for her. She did not want to end up like the vagabonds who stood in long lines for free soup. She did not want to leave her bedroom furniture for some other girl. Better to lie on her bed and dream about exotic places than to leave her bed behind and go there.

Mama called to her from the kitchen, "Rachel? Are you snooping through the mail again?"

"No, Mama." Rachel furtively examined the postmark on the second faraway correspondence. She gasped at what she saw. "Mama!" she cried. "A letter from Czechoslovakia! From *Turnau!*" She had given herself away. She had been snooping, but at this news about a letter from Uncle Maurice in what was now Nazi-controlled territory was something that drew Mama out from the kitchen in an instant. She did not even scold Rachel as she hurried the letter in to Papa.

"Aaron! Darling!" Mama never called him that if she thought anyone was listening. This was indeed an occasion. "Look, Aaron! A letter from Turnau! Maybe news about your brother!"

Rachel helped her father to sit. She plumped the pillows behind his back as he waited patiently for Mama to open the envelope. A letter from Czechoslovakia! They had been hoping for news from Uncle Maurice ever since the Germans had marched in and taken over. They had been waiting as stories had poured across the border like the desperate refugees. Papa had said a prayer each night for his older brother. He had hoped that Maurice and his sons would show up on the doorstep of the Muranow house unharmed.

"Well?" Papa asked as Mama looked at the signature.

"It is not from Maurice. It is from a friend," she answered, and Rachel could hear her voice tremble when she said the words. "Be patient," she said to Papa. Then she read on. Her face grew pale. Her eyes filled up with terrible visions that she would not read aloud. Then she looked at Rachel and said softly, "Leave the room, Rachel. . . ."

"But—"

Not harsh, but firm. "Leave us."

By this and the weary look on the face of her father, Rachel knew that something terrible indeed had happened in the little town of Turnau, Czechoslovakia. Uncle Maurice was prominent there. He was a Jew. The Nazi invaders no doubt found both of those factors to be distasteful.

———

The facts concerning the deaths of Maurice Lubetkin and his three sons had been written out in meticulous detail by a friend who had witnessed it all. The friend had taken his own life in his hands by recording their executions and sending the account to Aaron Lubetkin.

Distilled down to simple details, Aaron's brother and his teenaged boys had been chosen at random, lined up against a wall and shot in retaliation for the killing of a German policeman. In this way, according to German reasoning, the innocent learned an important lesson. Everyone paid for the rash act of one person. That same lesson had been taught during *Kristallnacht*.

Aaron Lubetkin was too ill to be allowed traditional mourning and fasting for the dead members of his family. So Etta and Rachel donned their black clothes. They tore the hems of their dresses. They fasted and mourned in silence except for prayers and the few words necessary for daily existence.

The priest came and expressed his dismay to Aaron. Rachel heard them speaking in low tones about the possibility of Nazis coming here to Warsaw. And if they came, the priest told Aaron, all his children should be dispersed among Catholic families of his parish.

Aaron did not argue with this unthinkable proposition. Rachel shuddered at the idea of actually living with the Saturday people who beat Jews on the head with their crucifixes and called them Christ-killers!

She decided that she would never go among them! Rachel would let them put her against a wall and shoot her full of holes, but she would not leave with Father Kopecky and go live with the Saturday people!

Why did her father not tell the priest that he would never consent to such a thing? How could he sit silently on his bed, knowing that the goyim had just murdered his brother and his nephews in Turnau!

Rachel waited in the hallway until the priest was finished talking to Papa. She leaned against the wall with her arms crossed defiantly and her eyes staring at the floor.

She looked up as Father Kopecky emerged. He was surprised to see her there. He knew she had heard.

"Rachel?" he questioned gently.

"I will never go with your kind," she said fiercely in a quiet voice. "Better to die than be with them."

He put out a hand to soothe her. "We were speaking only of the worst case." He shrugged. "It will not come to that."

"Papa would rather see us dead than live with the goyim."

The priest shook his head in disagreement. "You are wrong, I think. Not because your father would ever want you to forsake your people. But he knows, as you do not, that we are not all heartless and brutal. There are a few who see clearly what is good and what is evil. In case of the worst, Rachel, your father would say as a rabbi, *Baruch Hashem*. . . . For the sake of the Name of the Eternal, you must continue to live. It is easier sometimes to stand against the wall and let them shoot. But for the sake of the Name, we are called sometimes to suffer and go on living."

Rachel pushed past him and ran up the stairs to her room. She did not want to hear what he had to say! She did not want to think about suffering!

She stood at her window and looked out over the homeless who had pitched their shanty tents in the square. Had they left behind nice furniture? Fine clothes? Family meals around a big table in the dining room? For what? Were they really alive down there, or were they ghosts who had drifted in before her eyes to show her some grim vision of her future?

Rachel was afraid. Cold, sick fear climbed down her spine and settled in her stomach. She did not fear dying against a wall with her family falling with her. No. She feared the words of the priest much more . . . *Baruch Hashem!* Was God so cruel that He would require her to turn her back on everything just to go on suffering and living?

"Go away," she said to the homeless specters in the square. But they did not go away. And there, on the fringes, she saw the sunlight glint on the red hair of Peter Wallich. Still lost. Still homeless. He was the most frightening ghost of all! *"Go away!"* she said again, and then she pulled the window shade and turned away.

Bracing herself against the wall, Lucy descended the steep stairs from her apartment very slowly. At the bottom, she turned to look up, wondering how many more days it would be before she carried the baby in its christening gown down those same steps.

The time was very near. She sensed it in the same way the heavy-bellied animals on her farm at home had *known*. Feeling the thrill of that reality had frightened her this morning as she looked at the satin gown and wondered. The mix of excitement and dread had driven her from the little nest she had prepared. Never had she felt a more urgent need to walk the three winding blocks to Heilige Geist Church. She needed to close her eyes and listen to all the sounds that were so dear and familiar to her. She needed to pretend that she was home and her mother was close at hand, and that the priest would offer a prayer for her and for the child.

Maybe this was the last time she would carry the baby inside her to the Mass. Maybe next week his little head would turn to the sound of the great pipe organ and the voice of the choir. *Not heaven, little bird, but as close as we can get on earth. . . .*

The morning sun beamed down through the canyon of crooked gables overhead. Lucy inhaled deeply. It was early enough that the stink of rotting fish from the fish market did not yet pollute the clean Baltic air. The street was still quiet. Drunks and prostitutes slept off their hangovers behind drawn shades. Secondhand shops and beer cellars were not yet open. It was a good time to get out. The usual squalor of the neighborhood had not yet flooded out over the street.

Lucy knew that she would be one of only a handful at the early morning Mass, but it did not matter. She usually preferred the anonymity of crowds, but this morning she half hoped that a priest might notice her, speak to her kindly. How good it would be if someone would offer her a kind word today!

No one ever seemed to look her way anymore, except to wince at the sight of her ponderous waddle. Peter had teased her about it; said she had acquired the rolling gait of a drunken sailor and that now she fit in nicely on Heiliger Geist Strasse. She was secretly glad that he had identified her with a drunken sailor instead of with the painted women who lounged in open doorways and waited. The memory of his laugh gave her a twinge of loneliness. *If only he could have stayed in Danzig a few weeks more! No use thinking about that now. He was right. He could not stay here. Not the way things are going.*

She was out of breath by the time she reached the steps of Heilige Geist Church. Her ankles and feet were more swollen than usual and the heaviness of the baby seemed almost painful.

Entering the high arched portal, she touched her fingers in the holy water and crossed herself as she stole a look at the bulletin board on the back wall of a sanctuary. Sometimes there were offers of employment posted there. *Would it not be a miracle if some good Catholic family in England wanted a skilled parlormaid who knew all about carving?* Not likely in a parish like Heilige Geist.

There were new summer hours for the soup kitchen. An announcement about the departure of the refugee children's steamship to England. Boxes of used children's clothing were needed for them.

Lucy scrutinized the mimeographed sheet enviously. Some said it was the last children's transport. Departure time was seven o'clock Wednesday morning. How she wished she were a child again! *To go to England!*

Her hand went instinctively to the baby. The pipes of the organ bellowed the first notes, announcing that Mass was about to begin. She took her seat in the last row of chairs in the small side chapel where morning Mass was usually read.

Lucy stared at her clasped hands, then at the back of the empty seat in front of her. There were not more than a dozen worshipers scattered throughout the little chapel. She scanned her companions briefly. Nine old women and three old men. Their faces showed varying degrees of weathering, but all of them could have easily come from the same litter. The clothes were all ragged. The men all needed a shave; the women all carried the same ancient sorrow in their eyes. Lucy had seen these same people everywhere she had ever been, it seemed. Old. Tired. Waiting and preparing for death. They knelt on stiff knees. They prayed, silently beseeching, with lips that moved almost imperceptibly. Making the sign of the cross, they pulled themselves back into their seats and sat waiting as though the effort had exhausted them.

Lucy looked back at her hands and then toward the little altar where unlit candles waited for a flame. She wondered if she was the only one who had come here this morning in search of life? Had the faces around her ever been young? Ever known joy? Ever looked forward to anything other than that which was beyond the grave?

Her eyes darted to the crucifix again. To the dead Christ. *Are you Lord of the living, as well? Or only of the walking dead?*

The thought came involuntarily, and she blushed at her blasphemy. Who was she to ask such a question? After all, perhaps she was as near to death as these old ones around her. She let her eyes linger on her hands again. Her nails were clipped and unpolished, her fingers so swollen that she could no longer wear the cheap wedding band she had purchased for the illusion of propriety. This was the first time she had ventured into church without that ring. She had fooled shopkeeper and priest alike with it, but today she did not bring her disguise with her. Somehow, the absence of that ring made it seem as though she were seeing her own hands for the first time. *This is me. Just as I am. Today I do not want to hide from you. If you are the God of the living, then I want to know you. I want to live. I want my baby to live. If you can hear me—*

Her thoughts were interrupted as the priest and choir entered. Those in choir robes outnumbered the ragged worshipers.

The congregation all stood slowly as the priest prayed at the foot of the altar and the hymn was sung. Lucy studied the profile of the young priest. He could not have been much older than she was. She had seen hundreds of faces like his standing rank on rank before crowds of cheering Germans. She had toyed and flirted with men much older than this priest. It was a disquieting thought. Did she dare make confession to one so young?

She closed her eyes again as those around her read the Introit: *"When the just cry out, the Lord hears them, and from all their distress He rescues them."*

Could she trust even a priest, considering all she had fallen into? Would he urge her to give away the baby she had come to love? Or would he see her heart, and help her?

Her eyes opened, and she saw the priest looking intently at her, his gaze locked on her face. His eyes were agitated; anxious—as though he knew everything already.

He paused, too long, before beginning the Kyrie. There was no mistaking the fact that her presence at the service signified something to him . . . *something*. He spoke to a young man in the choir who also glanced at Lucy and then left the chapel.

"Lord have mercy," he began. His voice trembled.

"Lord have mercy," the congregation repeated in their cracked voices.

He looked away from her, then back again. "Christ have mercy."

Lucy could not make her lips move with the others. *"Christ have mercy...."* What had the priest said to the young man?

Like an electric shock, a charge of fear coursed through Lucy. *He knows something. Something, but not the truth. Not all the truth. Not my truth ... Wolf?*

She looked over her shoulder, feeling as though Wolf might stride through the door any moment. She could not think.

"Glory to God in the highest." It was obvious now that the priest held her captive in the corner of his vision.

"And on earth peace to men of good will."

The voices began a chanting echo in her brain.

"Lamb of God, You take away the sins of the world ... receive our prayer...."

Help me, Lucy breathed, unmoving. *Lord! Mercy! He knows!*

The priest turned to face the altar, breaking the spell that held her motionless. She gathered her little handbag and stood, bumping a chair noisily as she inched toward the aisle. The head of the priest moved at the sound. Was he listening for her escape as well as watching?

Her clumsy feet moved as if they belonged to someone besides Lucy. They slapped too loudly on the bare stone floor as she fled. Red and green votive candles became a blur of color as she ran through the main sanctuary. Then she heard footsteps behind her. *"Wait!"* a voice cried. "We will help you!"

She turned at the door to see the priest with his hand raised at the entrance of the chapel.

"Fraulein Strasburg!" he called.

Lucy gasped and threw herself hard against the massive wooden door of the Heilige Geist Church. Sunlight exploded into her eyes as she ran blindly into the street.

"Wait! Wait, Fraulein Strasburg ..."

The door boomed shut behind her, closing off the cries of the priest.

The street was awake—mercifully stinking, noisy, teeming with people. Lucy ran into the shelter of the crowds as she silently begged that they would hide her from anyone who might have followed.

———

Werner was a very handsome kitten. Everyone who saw him with Alfie in the fish market each morning stopped to scratch Werner's chin and tell him what a pretty kitten he was. Fishmongers in oilskin aprons and tall rubber boots offered Werner fish heads and fresh guts on newspapers. Alfie took Werner to a different stall each day so that he would not wear out their hospitality. Mama had told him, *"Fish and company stink in three days."*

Alfie knew that the saying meant that he should not stay too long in the same place, and since fish really started to stink in one day, he figured that he should not visit a fishmonger more than one day each week.

He explained this all very patiently to Werner, who blinked at him with wise kitten eyes. It did not matter to Werner where he got his daily fish head as long as he got it. One fishmonger was as good as another, and everyone along the wharf thought he was a superior cat anyway. Every day someone commented on how much Werner was growing. They congratulated Alfie in raising such a smart and polite cat. Werner was careful to clean his paws after every meal, and Alfie did not tell the men that Werner thought of it all by himself.

"Did you teach him such manners, Alfie?"

"Well . . . Werner . . . he is a smart kitten. He don't need . . . much teaching."

Alfie secretly thought that Werner was probably just licking the last of the fish flavor from his little toes. After all, Alfie always licked the jam from his fingers, so maybe that was how Werner learned it. All the same, it made Alfie feel good to put Werner on his shoulder and walk through the market. Werner was becoming handsomer every day. His black head and back were smooth and shiny. His white legs were always bright like Alfie's socks when Lori did the washing. He carried his tail proud and high like a main mast, and he rode on Alfie's shoulder like the captain on a bridge of a big ship. Alfie hoped very much that there would be a fish market like this in England.

England! For days Alfie had been happy when he thought about England, but today he was not happy. He was going. Lori and Jamie and Mark were going, but England did not want Jacob. Jacob was going to Warsaw to work on a newspaper, *unless* . . . Alfie was not worried about smuggling Werner onto the ship. Werner was small and would fit in a box. But Jacob was too big for a box. Too big even for a steamer trunk. How could they smuggle someone as big as Jacob onto the boat? And then off the boat in England? Couldn't Jacob work for the same newspaper in London instead of going all the way to Warsaw?

This was a problem they had talked about all night. Lori had cried and said she would not go unless Jacob went with her. Jacob had sounded angry and told her she must not talk so foolishly, that he could take care of himself well enough. Then she had run into her room and slammed the door. Lori was not happy about leaving Jacob even though he had a job. The boys had all sat very quietly staring at the floor for a long time.

"Well?" Jamie had said while his sister made muffled sobbing noises in her room.

"Well," Jacob said, *"we will call London tomorrow and tell them what's up. Maybe they will have some ideas."*

Last night had been a very sad night. But now it was tomorrow and Jacob and Lori were calling London to talk to Lori's family. Alfie did not want to go because he never got to talk on the telephone anyway, so here he was at *Herr Frankenmuth's Fresh Fish Daily* watching Werner finish off a herring on top of a newspaper with Hitler's greasy picture on it. Herr Frankenmuth enjoyed putting fish heads on top of the Führer. He told Alfie so. Herr Frankenmuth was a thin, frail-looking man with stooped shoulders and a sour face. He always had a black pipe hanging from his mouth. Alfie supposed it was because tobacco smelled better than fresh-fish-daily. Anyway, Herr Frankenmuth was a nice man who probably did not smile because his pipe might fall out if he did.

Today he noticed that Alfie was not cheerful. He wiped his hands on his fishy apron and looked at Werner. "What's the trouble today, Alfie?" he asked, sucking on his unlit pipe. "You have not smiled, even though today's front page shows Hitler with herring eyeballs and a fin for a mustache, eh? I arranged Werner's plate special today."

Alfie felt badly that he had not laughed at Herr Frankenmuth's cleverness. The fishmonger had gone to a lot of effort, after all. "Hitler looks better like that," Alfie said, but still he could not smile. "We are all going to England, except . . . except for Jacob. He cannot go. Lori cried a lot last night because I think she loves Jacob. Jacob is going to Warsaw to work for Lori's . . . well, I can't remember all of it. But Jacob is not going with us. He does seem too sad because he likes newspapers and radios. But the rest of us are sad all the same." It was a long story.

Herr Frankenmuth stared angrily at Hitler's fish eyes. He frowned at the news and shifted his pipe from one side of his mouth to the other. He stared at the trays of ice where the fish were laid out side by side; then he looked off beyond the gray canvas awning to where the smokestacks of the big freighters poked up over the warehouses.

"Every day somebody gets left behind," he mumbled. Then he asked, "This friend of yours, Jacob. A big boy, is he?"

"Big."

"Big as you?" His eyes measured Alfie's 5'9" frame as if he were measuring a fish.

"Bigger. Maybe. Yes. I think bigger."

Herr Frankenmuth frowned and squinted his eyes. "When are you all leaving?"

Alfie could not think of the day, but it was soon. "On the children's ship."

Herr Frankenmuth nodded his head. He knew when that was. He leaned down to scratch Werner's chin. "Are you taking Werner?"

Alfie nodded and glanced over his shoulder to make sure no one could overhear him. "In a box . . . Jacob made it. With a . . . a . . ." He could not remember the word.

"False bottom?" Herr Frankenmuth finished for him.

Yes. That was the word Alfie forgot. "False."

"Ah, good. A nice fellow, this friend of yours. Tell him, will you, if he needs anything, I could use a big strong lad around here to help out. Will you tell him that, Alfie?"

"Yes. I will." Alfie pointed to the newspaper. "Maybe you will cheer . . . cheer him up. If he is not too sad."

Herr Frankenmuth did not have time to say anything else because two women came under the awning to buy their supper. Alfie hoped he could come back to say goodbye before the children's ship left. He liked Herr Frankenmuth and wanted to show Lori what Hitler looked like with fish eyeballs on his face.

He picked up Werner and put him on his shoulder. Herr Frankenmuth nodded his head goodbye and Alfie turned back into the crowded alleyway of the market.

Faraway he heard the loud hooting of a ship horn. It sounded like saying goodbye. It reminded Alfie that his own papa had left on a ship and never came home again. When they left Danzig, would they ever see Jacob again? The thought troubled him and he did not smile at his waterfront friends when they called to him.

He was not watching where he was going. Mama always told him to pay attention to where he was going so he would not get lost. But today he was not doing that. He looked at the stacks and booms of the freight boats as he walked along, and then he smashed head-on into a lady who was running down the street.

Werner was knocked off balance and dug his claws through Alfie's shirt. The woman stumbled and managed to brace herself on the side of a market stall. She was young and had a pretty face and looked like the cat Joseph just before Joseph had kittens. Alfie could tell she was going to have a baby. He tried to say how sorry he was for smashing into her, but she never even looked at him. She looked back the way she had come and then pushed past Alfie as if she was running from something.

"Sorry," he called after her. She did not hear him. He stood and watched her because she did not act like everyone else in the fish market. She did not walk slowly through the stalls or stare at the trays of fish. She pushed and tumbled and bumped into a lot of other people besides Alfie.

Alfie looked all around to see who would be mean enough to chase after a woman so big from a baby? He could not see anyone running after her, and so he readjusted Werner on his shoulder and walked back through the market the way he had come.

Lucy's lungs felt seared by the time she stumbled up the stairs to her flat. She slammed the door and locked it, then leaned, panting, against it. Gazing wildly around the room she tried to think what she must do. Where could she go?

Warsaw! Peter! "You have a friend. . . . "

Expecting to hear the crash of boots ascending the steps, Lucy pulled her tattered valise from beneath the bed and began jamming her clothing into it. Forgetting how she had placed all the baby things neatly in a row and rearranged them hour after hour, she crammed them into the large basket she had purchased for the little one to sleep in and be carried in.

Bottles. Milk. Diapers. Pins. Talcum powder. Alcohol . . . She folded the satin gown with the cap and booties, then wrapped the bundle in thin paper and tucked the package beneath the blanket on the bottom of the basket.

At that moment, when panic and dread ruled every thought, the first contraction wrapped iron fingers around her.

"Not now!" she cried. *"Oh please, God! Not . . ."* A warm, liquid release of pressure told her that her water had broken. Looking at the crucifix over her bed, she groaned at this, the ultimate betrayal.

No use. No use. Where could she run to now? How could she hide?

The contraction slowly eased. She straightened and stood staring at her bed. Mechanically, she once again removed what she would need from the baby's basket. Without joy, without anticipation, she laid those things out in a neat row as they had been.

There was time enough to prepare the bed and undress before the next contraction came. And then there was time enough to brew a cup of tea and sit waiting by the window.

Minutes of hopelessness ticked into hours, and still no one came to pound against the thin door. Once again Lucy dared to hope. Perhaps no one had seen her. Perhaps she had eluded the priest. Perhaps he had not even attempted to follow her.

The pains came closer and stronger, driving every other thought from her mind at last. She lay down and curled into a ball facing the last light of day that seeped through the window. She was alone. Glad she was alone, and yet, wishing for her mother. Now it seemed there was no relief from the strength of the pain. She did not cry out, but felt certain that if anyone came for her in the morning they would find her dead.

Lord, have mercy! Christ . . . have mercy!

17

To Do What One Can Do

In spite of Doc Grogan's vow that he would never take more than one dozen children on the Thursday educational walk, this morning there were twenty standing in the ranks on the sidewalk outside Red Lion House.

Elisa and the new baby were coming home today, which meant that Anna and Aunt Helen would be busy at the house while Murphy brought wife and baby home from the hospital. Someone had to help out with the new refugee children who had not yet made the transfer to their new families. For most of them, this would be their only opportunity to see London.

Doc squared his shoulders and counted heads. "Eighteen, nineteen, twenty and *twenty-one*?" He scowled down at a fair-haired eight-year-old girl who scowled back at him. "Where did you come from?" he asked in German.

"You counted me twice," she replied, not much liking the attention.

"Then you must get in line only once," Doc chided, then turned to Murphy with a grin. "How about it if we trade places, eh? I will pick up Elisa and the baby, and you take the troops to the Houses of Parliament."

Hildy Frutschy broke her own rule about never speaking German. For the first time ever, Charles could clearly understand the plump little housekeeper as she shouted to the group, "Do you all have your lunch sacks?" Heads nodded in affirmative reply. *"Gut! Sehr gut, Kinder!"* But bobbing heads were not enough for Hildy. Again in German: "Raise your hand if you have your lunch." It appeared that all hands were up. *"Gut! Sehr gut!"* And then, one more check. "And if you do *not* have a lunch, *bitte,* now also raise your hand." No hands went up. *"Gut. Sehr gut!"* Her job was done. She wiped her hands on her apron and re-treated to the house to finish her work before the great arrival.

The adults had dwindled down to Murphy and Doc. Murphy was looking impatiently at his empty wrist. His watch was still broken, but he was sure the red double-decker bus was late—or at least it was not early as Murphy had hoped. He was staying on until the bus came. Doc needed the moral support until then. After that he would be on his own.

"We appreciate the help, Doc." He patted the weary-looking aca-demician on the shoulder.

"I am leaving with twenty," Doc replied. "I hope I will return with the same number." As if to emphasize his worry, he shouted to the standing group, "Stay together now! Remember! Everybody *stay to-gether!"*

"Keep away from the subways. No tube stations," Murphy warned. "There was another bomb scare yesterday. Nothing came of it. Probably nothing more afoot here in London after the Victoria bombing, but . . ." He looked over the heads of the children. "They have just come from that sort of thing. No use frightening them here in England."

"Parliament Square should be a safe enough place," Doc sighed. "I'm not so worried about IRA bombs as I am about having one of them wander off." He rubbed his chin thoughtfully. "More people were killed crossing the street last week than in the bombing."

"Only one out of millions in London," Murphy nodded. "Still, it's the idea of the thing. Not knowing where. Makes life a little shaky when you can't even go to the bathroom without wondering if the toilet is going to blow up."

Doc nodded. "Senseless."

"Not if you're a terrorist," Murphy disagreed. "Terror is a powerful weapon." He lowered his voice and looked at the haunted eyes of these mirthless children. "Take a look, Doc. This is the result of six years' worth of terror in Germany. Robbed the kids of their ability to laugh."

Doc nodded. He had indeed noticed and commented on the fact that every week these excursions with the refugee children were silent and somber. Unlike the babble of English school children that echoed in the great halls and museums, these children *marched!* Their little feet against the pavement echoed the tramp of the Nazi jackboots that had pursued them from their homes and smashed their families, scat-tering them throughout Europe.

"No laughter," Doc agreed. Then he reached out and mussed the hair of Charles. "Except for this one and his brother!" He chucked Louis under his chin. "Talk, talk, *talk!* And I enjoy hearing every word, too!"

The comment made Charles beam, showing the gap where his front teeth should have been. "I been . . . to Par-li-ment," he said proudly.

"We been every place," Louis added, bobbing up and down.

At first the boys had been disappointed that they would not be on hand when Elisa and their baby sister came home, but Doc and Murphy had explained that Doc needed them to "*ride herd*." Just like cowboys, keeping the group all together, Charles and Louis were assigned to bring up the rear, looking out for some children who were a lot older than they. The responsibility felt good.

"There is a triple duty police force on patrol, I'm told," Murphy said as the big red bus rounded the corner in a cloud of diesel smoke. "And Scotland Yard has plainclothesmen everywhere as well. Might be a help to the kids if you let them meet a bobby or two. Let them see the difference between here and the Reich. They still aren't going to get it for a while, I guess," Murphy added with a shrug. Then in a low voice he whispered, "You know, Charles is still having nightmares. After the Victoria bombing he slept in my bed. Poor kid."

Doc frowned at that news as though it made his heart hurt. He shook his head and patted his chest. But there was only a moment for reflection about what life in Germany could do to a child's dreams. The bus pulled up with a mighty belch. Doc counted heads as solemn faces piled into the bus. He realized that riding on a public bus was something many of these children had been forbidden to do in their homeland. All of them, without exception, headed straight to the fume-filled back of the vehicle and looked confused and nervous as they took their places.

"I'll bring them back a bit changed, I hope," Doc said to Murphy as he counted out the fares.

"Just bring them *back,* Doc," Murphy teased.

Doc did not seem to hear him. He shouted for everyone to move. "Top of the bus! Everyone up! Front seats, if you please!" It was good for a start.

Hildy opened the window and shouted down that there was a trunk call for Murphy, all the way from Danzig, no less!

Murphy looked impatiently at his wrist and then, muttering to himself about the fact that phone calls were more expensive than steamer fare, he ran up the stairs to face yet another bout with the pleading of Lori Ibsen.

"Can't you also give *me* a job in Warsaw?" she begged. "I do not want to leave Danzig unless we all leave together. *Please*. I am smart. I can work as a secretary! Please let me go to Warsaw with Jacob."

Murphy told her sternly that all positions were filled and that it would be good for Jacob Kalner to have experience as a news journalist's assistant through the rest of the summer. And certainly by autumn when it was time for him to be in school, the mix-up about his papers would be all straightened out. Murphy tried to assure the young woman, although he did not believe most of it. By autumn, Europe would be at war, and everyone who was getting out would be out. Or else.

It did not take a genius to figure out that Elisa's cousin was deeply in love with Jacob Kalner. Even Murphy caught on to that one two sentences into Lori's last long-distance try.

"His boss is a fellow named Sam Orde, just out of the British military. He'll run the Warsaw bureau like an army boot camp, Lori. It's no place for a young lady. But he'll take care of Jacob, that's for sure. He's arriving in Danzig the morning your ship leaves. Said he'd hang around the docks and meet up with Jacob. Okay?"

At last Murphy heard the resignation in her voice. No use trying. Staying was really impossible. She would be more trouble than anyone wanted to deal with if she tried to go to Warsaw.

"All right then," she replied quietly. "I suppose. If you promise he will be in school in the autumn."

Murphy looked at his wrist again. He would be late picking up Elisa and Katie. He hoped Lori would forgive him if, indeed, Jacob ended up being one of the unlucky ones left behind come September. "I will do all I can to make that happen," Murphy promised. What more could he do?

———

Allan Farrell stepped off the tube at the Westminster Station and bounded up the stairs into the bright sunlight of Parliament Square.

On the east, the square was bordered by the towers of Parliament. On the south was St. Margaret's Church, dwarfed in the shadow of Westminster Abbey. The square was ringed by statues of British statesmen whose heroic deeds were nearly forgotten now. Allan made his way across the area to the fountain that commemorated the abolition of slavery in the British dominions. Since Northern Ireland was still enslaved, Allan considered the symbolism of the fountain a sham; however, the water was cool. The spray dotted his forehead and eased the unrelenting heat. He dipped his handkerchief in the water and mopped his brow, then sat on a bench to wait for the arrival of his contact.

His first scanning of the heat-weary crowds of tourists and school children revealed that there was a disproportionately high number of policemen wandering about the square and standing in the shade of the towers and turrets of the surrounding buildings. Such vigilance on the part of Scotland Yard and the British authorities would be hard to penetrate during his next attack. He imagined that there was a plainclothes officer from Scotland Yard standing on duty at every urinal in the city of London.

The thought pleased him. The news accounts had called the Victoria Station bombing cowardly and depraved. Allan considered that it was just the opposite, and a tremendous success, judging from the visible evidence of so many blue-coated bobbies prowling around the place.

It was astounding how much damage one little pipe and a few match heads would do to the morale of the mighty British Empire. And words like *coward* held no meaning to Allan any longer. He had tasted blood, and like the newly tried hound of a hunt, he was eager for more.

Only this morning he had considered what his next job might be. A bomb right here? He looked at the spurting fountain, this monument to hypocrisy. Well, perhaps not this, he mused. He enjoyed it as his only refuge from the summer heat in his forays to pass information to the contact.

Maybe St. Margaret's Church? Or the abbey itself? That would certainly set all of England on its ear! A pipe bomb exploding in the organ of Westminster Abbey?

A matched pair of bobbies strolled past. They were greeted by yet another pair at the junction of the walkways in the square. Too much risk. It would be foolish to allow himself to be caught when he had only just begun his crusade.

St. Margaret's Street ran into the Old Palace Yard at the edge of the Houses of Parliament. The place was the scene of execution for a number of Catholic conspirators, led by one Guy Fawkes, who had attempted to blow up Parliament and King James I with all his lords as well. Bright fellows, those unfortunate men had been. They had rented a coal cellar that extended beneath the House of Lords and had crammed it full of gunpowder. They would have succeeded too, had it not been for an informer. The cellars were searched and the conspirators captured with a lantern ready to ignite the deadly fuse.

The course of history might have gone differently, Allan knew, if those Catholic dissenters had pulled it off. But half were executed in the Old Palace Yard and the others were killed near the entrance of London's great St. Paul's Cathedral. Protestant England still celebrated the failure of the Gunpowder Plot each year, and now it remained for someone else to carry the lantern and light the fuse beneath the city of London!

Allan had been raised on stories such as these. It was the dream of every brother in the IRA to pick up the tale where King James buried it. Those ideological forebears who had dreamed up the Gunpowder Plot in 1605 were perched on the pedestals of Allan Farrell's mind today as he gazed around the square. He was not so insane as to think that he could succeed where they had failed, but he longed to speak to England through the fire and smoke of terror as they had tried to do.

His sense of justice strengthened as he looked up into the cloudless sky. Pigeons fluttered past to roost in the shadowed cornices of the great facades. Perhaps, in this case, German bombers would one day finish the work of Guy Fawkes and his band of brave men. Allan imagined fire leaping through the roofs of Commons, devouring the great clock tower and turning Big Ben into molten metal.

The image reinforced his belief that all the evil the English had dished out would explode on their heads one day. But such dreams did little to satisfy his own sense of what he must do to hasten that certain day.

He must think; scout London for some unguarded relic, some fortress of well-being where the enemy would never imagine destruction could come upon them. A public lavatory at a train station was just a beginning, and a small beginning at that. But Allan fully intended to keep sleep from the eyes of Scotland Yard's best men. A small device, a small, tiny flash of destruction, would simply be his foretaste of something big yet to come. He would need help. He would need the proper materials.

When the German agents stepped from the red omnibus and walked slowly toward Allan, he remained where he was. Today he did not merely leave the information tucked into the pages of the London *Times*. Today Allan left a personal note stating that he wanted to extend his role beyond that of mere messenger boy.

Allan Farrell wanted to prove to the world and to himself that he was much more than just the son of Maureen; that he could outdo anything his mother had ever dreamed of! For Allan Farrell, all his life had come down to this moment.

———

"Well, Murphy, did you get mother and child home safely?"

"Both doing great, Winston."

"And what," inquired Winston Churchill, "was your impression of today's debate over the Prevention of Violence Act?"

"It must be gratifying to you, Winston, to finally see Parliament come to grips with an issue in such complete agreement," responded Murphy. "The government admits that terrorists are real and that special measures and deportations are in order."

Churchill shook his ponderous head slowly. "Don't give them too much credit, Murphy," he warned. "If I have seen a vicious dog bite four of my neighbors *already*, then my wisdom cannot receive a great deal of credit if I let the mongrel come into my yard and bite *me* before I decide that I need to do something about it!"

The great man paused to reflect before continuing. "What this government still does not see is the identity of the *master* of the dog named terrorism. Herr Hitler has done it with Arabs in Palestine, racial Germans in Austria and the Sudetenland and Danzig, and now with Irish extremists in London."

Murphy frowned thoughtfully. "I would have thought you'd be pleased with the home secretary's statement." The newsman paused and referred to a notebook. "Here it is: The terrorists are being actively stimulated by foreign organization."

"Bah," Churchill grumbled. "You'll note that he still does not accuse Nazis by name! I'm not entirely certain that he himself knows. He may be referring to the Irish Republican brotherhood in America! That group, the Clan da Gael, may buy some dog food, but it is still Herr Hitler who commands the dog to jump!

"No, Murphy," Churchill concluded sadly. "For all the rhetoric about expulsions, exclusions, and deportations, Chamberlain and his cronies still do not grasp the gravity of the situation."

———

Hitler listened as his interpreter, Dr. Schmidt, translated the text of the commons debate about IRA terrorism. The Führer nodded contentedly as Chamberlain's remarks were read. He seemed distracted, as if he were not really paying attention.

Then Schmidt began to translate the responses offered by Lloyd George and Anthony Eden. The Führer's face clouded over, and with each reference to Germany's instigation of the bombings, Hitler's countenance grew darker and darker.

Schmidt glanced up nervously, then back at the transcript, nearly losing his place. He could tell that the storm of Hitler's wrath was about to break.

When Schmidt reached Churchill's remarks, the interpreter was already braced for the explosion. "This English bulldog dares to snarl at us?" Hitler shouted. "This jowled species of British mongrel making watchdog noises!" Flecks of spittle flew from the lips of the leader of the Nazi Reich in his rage.

"Who is Churchill that anyone gives him room to speak?" Hitler demanded of the air. "He is discredited, a failure, a castoff wretch! The British want peace, peace, peace! Why do their papers still report the ravings of this warmongering cur?

"Schmidt!" Hitler snapped his fingers. "Enough! Stop reading! Tell Himmler I need to see him at once!"

———

Every piece of furniture in Orde's London home was shrouded in dusty sheets. Orde carefully removed the covering from a straight-backed petitpoint chair that he had never sat on before now. He left his favorite overstuffed chair out of sight as if one glimpse of the fabric would bring back too many memories. Better to view the room from this uncomfortable and unfamiliar angle. Katie had purchased the chair because she liked the needlework on the cushion. Now Orde sat firmly on it and thought what a frivolous purchase that had been. To buy a chair no one ever sat in simply because it was pretty.

That sort of impracticality had been out of character for Katie, and so Orde assumed she must have seen something extraordinary in the chair, some faraway purpose she imagined it would serve. *A mourning seat for Orde, so he would not have to take the covers from the really comfortable chairs. So he would not have to sit and remember and doze off to dream that the years without her were just a terrible dream!*

He resisted the insane urge to call for her to make him a cup of tea. He looked at the long dead ashes in the fireplace. He had not cleaned them out after she died. He had let the coals glow and watched the light pass from the embers, leaving his heart there in the ashes on the hearth.

He chided himself for not simply cleaning the place and renting it to some junior diplomat or a university professor on sabbatical. He had been foolish to simply let it sit and gather a coat of dust, while beneath the shroud the colors and pain of memories were as vivid as ever.

Sunlight leaked in through the slats of the shutters. Particles of dust stirred by his presence swirled in the shafts of light. Orde considered opening the windows to let the breeze in, but then he was seized by the thought that somewhere within this atmosphere was the breath of Katie.

He moaned and rested his head in his hands. What was he doing? And why was he making himself suffer like this? Why had he not mourned like a normal man instead of waiting until years later to walk in and be surprised by his own grief?

At that moment something else startled him. There was a soft rapping on the door and then the strident buzz of the doorbell.

A mistake, Orde thought. *Wrong address. Or perhaps a salesman. Who knows I am here? Worse yet, who cares that I am here?*

In spite of that, the bell continued to harass him. He resented this small interruption to his self-pity. Jerking open the door he glared down on the interloper who did not remove his finger from the button.

The handsome, sun-tanned face of Moshe Sachar grinned up at him. "Captain Orde!" Moshe exclaimed. "Glad to see you're really here! I was afraid I may have arrived too late!"

Orde had known that Moshe was about to take up his studies at

Oxford, but he had not expected to see him here in London. Maybe he had not expected to ever see the bright young Zionist again. He had not thought of him being anywhere at all besides Hanita, marching along with the other members of the Special Night Squad. Now he sat on the newly uncovered sofa.

Over tea, which Orde brewed after turning on the water and washing the kettle and the cups, the two men shared mutual stories about their trips. Orde was grateful for the distraction. They talked together like old friends, on a very different plane than that of commander and ordinary soldier.

Only after half an hour of small talk did Moshe finally come to the point of the visit.

"We heard you have accepted the position with TENS as Warsaw correspondent."

We? We heard? Orde knew who WE was, but he could not fathom that anyone of authority had sent a lad like Moshe to discuss anything important.

"How did you hear that?"

"Come on now, Captain—such a question, when you have so helped us to enlarge our understanding of the way the world operates." Moshe shrugged. "It doesn't matter anyway."

"Yes. I'm going to Poland. Hardly significant."

"That's where you're wrong." Moshe grinned, flashing the whiteness of his teeth in the gloomy room. "So. The British think with this last shipment of kids to England that we will give up?" He sipped his tea thoughtfully. "You know what I am about to say. You know what is coming to Poland—to the world. You have trained our young men after they arrive in Palestine. Can you not train them before they get there? Work with them at the Zionist youth camps near Warsaw. Pick the most able, and then . . ." His hand glided through the air like a bird. "Out the back door. Through Hungary to the seacoast of Yugoslavia."

Orde raised his eyebrows and inhaled deeply. "I have accepted a job. A time-consuming—"

"It need not interfere. In fact, it will be an excellent cover for you." Moshe shrugged. "Just train them. Pick a few at a time and send them on their way. The only difference is that they will know your military manual by heart before they ever set foot in Palestine, nu? Economy of resources, I call it. They get off the boat and they are ready to go to work. You've done the same job on the front end that you were doing on the back, and where are the Arabs to stop you? Who is going to call the English government and complain? It seems perfectly logical to us. We are not fools, Captain Orde. A Jew knows a good thing when he sees it. Everyone who has read your manual has commented—"

Orde nodded. He was flattered, but still strangely unmoved by the idea. It was like raising seedlings in a nursery instead of harvesting the crops. Still, it was something. "Yes. It is an excellent book." There was no false modesty about Samuel Orde. "But the Polish government might have something to say—"

"Nonsense! Warsaw is shaking in its boots. You think they will mind if an English Army officer trains a group of schoolboys in survival techniques?"

"If there is time for training even one group before the world explodes, I will be surprised," Orde added. "But how many can we take out?"

"There is talk of hiring a freighter in Ragusa. As many as a thousand children will be taken out if that comes through. Otherwise, we still have a number of fishing trawlers. Less risky, of course, but that cuts the number to three hundred."

Orde bit his lip as he considered the fate of the young man who had just been assigned to work with him in Warsaw. *Jacob Kalner.* Here was a way, if all else failed. And there was the Lubetkin family. "You are thinking only of young males with military potential?"

Moshe nodded. His face clouded slightly as he considered what that meant. *Making choices . . .* "Possibly a few able girls might be included. But they will be expected to march as far and fight as hard as the boys. That will have to be your ultimate selection."

No families. No small children. Few girls. Orde frowned. He nodded. He could hold classes in the Warsaw community centers. Bill it as *Instruction in Desert Survival.*

Moshe left the names and numbers of Zionist activists in Poland with Orde. He made only the promise that he would do what he could do in what he believed was an extremely short time. That satisfied Moshe Sachar, who pumped his hand and called him *Hayedid,* the Friend. Then he saluted and called Orde "Captain" one more time.

———

Anna straightened the tie of Theo's uniform, and kissed him lightly on the cheek. "You do not look like a grandfather," she smiled.

"Let's keep it at that." He rubbed the ache in his leg. "Don't ask me if I feel like one today, eh?"

Her eyes became solemn with understanding. Today a letter from Wilhelm and Dieter had arrived with the mail from America. Like their father, they had thrown themselves back into training as aviators . . . *"just in case the worst should come."*

An ominous reminder that Theo had served in a war on Germany's behalf only twenty years before, the boys had this news for him:

We located the American who saved your life at Belleau. He was at the address you gave us. But the most amazing thing, Father, is that his son, who is just nineteen, is also training as an aviator! If war breaks out and America remains neutral, then he plans to enlist in the Royal Canadian air force. He is a splendid fellow. A fine pilot. Perhaps we, the sons of former enemies, will soon fight together on the same side.

Such enthusiasm and eagerness in those words made Theo wince. "It takes twenty years to raise a son," he said, "and a moment of war to kill him." He embraced Anna. "The world has a way of coming around again, doesn't it, Anna. Was I spared twenty years ago so my sons could be born to fight? That wasn't the dream. No. When I lay in that ditch and saw the faces of the Americans, they were men like me. I knew they wanted the same for their sons as I wished for mine. *Peace.*"

Anna silently tucked the letter from Wilhelm and Dieter into the pocket of his tunic. "You should write your American friend. Perhaps it is important that two old enemies speak to one another about their sons. Yes. That is a good idea, Theo. Perhaps he feels as you do."

"It makes no difference how we feel now, Anna. It seems that we have come around to Belleau Wood once again."

18

In the Fullness of Time

Rachel pushed the black pram slowly beneath the shade trees of the square. The small, perfect hands of little Yacov, her *Yani*, reached up as blackbirds flew overhead. It was so good to have the boys all home again. Mama had been right—their happy laughter put a spark back in Papa's eyes.

Papa gathered them every day around his bed for lessons in the Torah. He instructed them and helped them with their Torah school studies. He piloted the minds and hearts of the household from his pillowed helm. Everything seemed almost normal. Very much better than it had before.

Baby Yani squealed with happiness at the birds that sat on the leafy branches of the linden trees. Like the birds, the baby had no awareness of anything unpleasant beyond the confines of the square.

Three blocks up Niska Street, the steady throbbing of diesel engines hummed as a convoy of Polish Legion vehicles moved equipment into place around the Umschlagplatz. There were anti-aircraft guns and machine guns already mounted on the roof of the train shed, Rachel knew. This was just one more reminder that all was not perfect in the world.

The second reminder approached Rachel from across the street. Peter Wallich was grinning like a mannequin in a shop window. His clothes flapped on his body. The sole of his right shoe flapped as he shambled toward her.

She tried to wheel the carriage around and go the other way. *Too late!*

"Rachel!" he called. "Rachel Lubetkin! Wait!"

Heads turned. They looked at her and then at the apparition that bumped to her side. Peter gaped down into the pram. He grinned at the baby and made baby noises in greeting.

"My brother Yani. Yacov. But I call him Yani," Rachel said coolly. She did not want Peter to pick up the baby, but he leaned down to scoop Yacov into his bony long arms anyway. The contrast between the healthy plumpness of Yacov and the lean, hungry-looking form of Peter was too much like seeing a skeleton caress her beloved brother. "Are you eating anything at all?" she blurted out.

His smile dimmed a bit. "I try. Sometimes it is difficult."

"The food at the kitchen is good," she reprimanded.

His sad eyes looked into hers. "Not like my mother's cooking, though."

She was ashamed of herself for dodging this lonely young man. He was telling her that he could not eat because he missed his mother. Understandable. Terrible. Tragic. "You will find her," she said more gently.

"Yes." He bounced Yacov, who laughed out loud. Then Peter laughed. "This is such a good age for babies, don't you think? I remember when my brother Willie was this age. I bounced him around so much that soon he wanted nothing but to be bounced." Again the sadness flicked through his eyes. "He is in America now. I was lucky enough to get him on one of the children's ships. He was placed with a family in America, last I heard. The British social worker wrote to tell me. . . ." A deeper sadness shadowed his face. "They thought he would get along better if all the ties were broken. He is young, they said. He will forget about me. It is better for him if he forgets, I suppose." Peter bounced Yacov one more time and then put him back into the carriage as if he were breakable, fragile porcelain, as if there were a sign on the pram that said: *OFF LIMITS TO PETER WALLICH!*

"Oh, Peter," Rachel said, feeling even more ashamed. "You can hold Yacov anytime you wish."

He shrugged. This was just a baby, after all. It was not his brother Willie who had so loved being bounced. "Well. Never mind." He drew a breath and exhaled loneliness. "I wanted to tell you that I came up with a brilliant idea!"

Now Rachel tried extra hard to make up for her coolness. "Papa said you are bright."

"Yes, well, not too bright or I would have thought of it before now," he grinned. "I have a friend in Danzig, you know."

Yes. Peter *had* told her about the pregnant former S.S. woman. A shocking story. It had made Rachel blush, even though she admired the woman for helping Peter get away. "Well?"

"I left the address with her."

"You mean *the* address?" This *was* news!

"Yes. Of course. So I wrote her a letter in Danzig, asking her to forward a copy to me at the soup kitchen box number." He snapped his fingers. "I only have to hang on a while. And then I will have it!"

She was genuinely happy for Peter. This tiny fragment of good fortune did a lot to wash away the feeling that Peter Wallich was the most unlucky person in the world. "Imagine! Solved so easily!"

"Yes." He drew himself up straight and smiled a crooked happy smile. Not bitter. Not a clenched-teeth smile like Rachel had seen before on his face. Here was hope.

"Mazel tov," she said.

"Thank you. Tell your father, will you?" With that he waved to another ragged-looking young man across the square and simply left.

Rachel was glad that he had told her his news. He was now telling the other fellow. He would doubtless tell everyone who would listen that his problem was about to be solved.

She watched him a moment. The sun gleamed dully on his hair. She wished that he would eat better and take another bath soon. In spite of that, she was happy for him as she returned to tell Papa his news.

Werner crouched and crept along the edge of the bed, keeping a hunter's eye on his shadow on the floor. Alfie watched the kitten pounce from bed to shadow and wrestle with the air for a moment. Usually Werner made Alfie smile when he played this way, but tonight Alfie could not smile. He wished that Werner would quit trying to make him feel happy. No one was happy tonight.

One suitcase was laid out for each of them—everyone but Jacob. He would travel on to Warsaw like Lori's relative Mr. Murphy told him. Once in Warsaw, Jacob would have a job with the Trump European News Service until some way could be found to get him to England, too.

Jacob was too cheerful. Just like Werner. He opened Alfie's valise to show him once again the false bottom where Werner would fit. Jacob had designed it and made it special himself. Somehow even that made Alfie feel badly. After all, if they were going to sneak Werner-kitten onto the ship, why could they not find some way to get Jacob on board as well?

Lori was not talking. She had hardly said anything since that terrible day in the British Consulate. Every day her eyes looked sadder. Alfie saw the way she looked at Jacob when Jacob was not looking. Alfie knew this was what it meant to love someone so much that it hurt. Alfie knew about such things, even though no one thought he knew.

"Bring Werner here," Jacob ordered brightly. "Let's test it out. See if it works."

Alfie reached for Werner, who reared up on his hind legs and batted Alfie's fingers playfully.

"Not now," Alfie said in an unhappy voice. "I don't want to play no more, Werner." The cat went limp and docile in his big hand, as though Werner finally understood that nobody felt like playing.

He meowed and Alfie put him in the bottom of the valise. Jacob fit the false bottom over the space. Werner meowed more unhappily. Now he was feeling badly too.

"He'll have to be quiet." Jacob frowned as the bag meowed on.

"Shhhh." Alfie patted the valise. "Don't talk, Werner."

But Werner did talk. His faint meow became a distinct howl, an alley-cat dirge, shrieking from the otherwise ordinary-looking piece of luggage.

"You think they'll notice?" Mark scoffed, looking up from the silent game of cards he had played all evening with Jamie.

"They'll notice," Lori said, no mirth in her voice.

Jacob straightened his back but continued to stare down at the racket. "We'll have to do something before you take him to the boat. They'll notice, and then Werner will end up here in Danzig with me!"

That was not a good thing to say. Everyone looked up at Jacob and stared at him. No one said anything until he nudged the suitcase with his toe.

"Hush up, Werner," Jacob instructed, but still the kitten did not hush. It was plain Werner did not take to this terrible imprisonment. He wanted out, and he would tell everyone in Danzig that he wanted out!

"I know," said Lori quietly. "I know what we can do!" For just a moment, she looked almost happy again. She glanced at Jamie who was studying his cards. "Remember the Wiedenbeck's cat?"

"Uh-huh."

"The way it wailed all night beneath Papa and Mama's window?"

Jamie smiled, but he did not look away from his cards. "Good idea," he said.

"What about it?" Jacob asked, grateful for this minor diversion from the heaviness in the apartment.

"Papa started feeding him beer every night in a saucer on the back step."

"And?"

"He got drunk. The cat, I mean. Every night he drank as much beer as his belly could hold and then he would stagger away home. Frau Wiedenbeck talked about her drunken cat to Mama. She could not understand who would be so terrible to give a cat beer. She was sure it was beer, because the cat smelled like a brewery and—"

"But did it get quiet?" Jacob asked, eyeing the moaning luggage.

"The perfect drunk, that cat was. Went home and curled up fast asleep every night. For a while it came to our house to wait for its pint, but then it quit coming. Mama said that Frau Wiedenbeck was feeding it beer to keep it home. A very good solution."

"Brilliant," Jacob said to her. "A great idea, Lori."

As soon as Jacob said her name, Lori's smile went away. Alfie could see that her eyes were bright and shining with tears even though she went out of the room to hide them. She cried whenever Jacob said her name. Alfie felt bad. He wished they could have thought about making Werner drunk without having to say Lori's name.

"Um . . . good. Good idea." Alfie did not say *Lori*. "Jacob can feed Werner beer like your papa."

From her room, a small sob leaked out. Then a bigger one. Werner yowled in the case and Lori cried in her room. It was a terrible night—the worst night they ever had since they came to Danzig.

Alfie supposed it was more fitting for Werner to be unhappy like everyone else. For a long time he did not take him out of his little secret case. He let Werner cry so no one would hear Lori as much.

————

Music from the cabaret drifted through the ghostly streets of Heiliger Geist District. Drunken sailors had gathered the prostitutes under their arms and staggered off to flea-bitten hotel rooms. Only a stubborn few remained in the cabaret now. Those women who were too old or homely to be chosen huddled at tables with men too broke or drunk to care. The barkeeper polished the last of the chipped glasses while the accordion player leaned against his groaning instrument and sipped cheap wine. The janitor up-ended chairs and mopped sour-smelling beer from beneath empty tables. It was like this every night. The Geist Cabaret would not lock its doors as long as there was even one customer buying drinks. It was the last outpost of the hopeless, a purgatory of desperation for men and women with nowhere else to go.

Tonight, Alexander Hess sat alone at a table, half a bottle of schnapps before him on the table. He had paid for the right to drink it all in this place, he told the accordion player, and therefore the music must continue!

He stood, bracing himself on the table as he gathered his cane in one hand and his bottle in the other. He swayed for a moment, then made his way cautiously to the open door of the cabaret. The music slowed, as if in hopes that Hess was leaving.

"*Play!* I *paid* for it! Play until *I say* you can stop!"

The barkeeper and the musician exchanged dubious looks. With a slight shrug, the barkeeper instructed the accordion to begin anew.

"That's more like it!" Hess shouted. He leaned against the door-frame and inhaled. His head cleared a bit as he looked up to scan the facades of the ragged buildings.

Hess imagined the notes of his vulgar song drifting through the ravines of Heiliger Geist's streets. He could almost see the tune and the words creeping up the bricks and through the rickety iron balconies into the rooms of those he sought. *"I am singing to you,"* he slurred. *"Listen! Whores and babies* . . . hear me? Through your windows and your locked doors my shadow comes . . . to pull you down . . . down into darkness."

────────

The distant sound of accordion music seemed a strange counter-point to the stillness of the room.

The pile of unwashed sheets lay on the floor where Lucy had thrown them. There was no strength left for her to make the bed, and so she lay down beside the baby on the bare mattress.

The light was dim in the room, and yet she could see that the still form beside her was beautiful. The gray, blood-streaked skin had turned a rosy pink. Ten perfect little toes. Ten perfect little fingers. The mouth was like her mother's; the eyes blue, hair blond and wispy. *Yes. Beautiful.* Just the sort of child a man like Wolf had desired.

She pulled back the fleecy towel. The spindly newborn's legs were drawn close to the rounded abdomen as though the little one still lay within her womb.

How she had prayed that the baby would be a girl! Wolf would have had less interest in taking a baby girl! But Lucy had a son, fine and healthy . . . beautiful. *Perfect!*

Lucy tucked her arm around him and pulled him close. He turned his face to her breast instinctively and she marveled at the miracle that one so new could claim her so immediately. As a girl on the farm she had witnessed the wonders of new life a hundred times. Puppies, calves, and kittens . . . mothers and babies, forgetting the trauma of birth as they settled into the sleepy tranquility of nursing.

Now that miracle was hers. She guided the tiny searching mouth to her breast, wincing slightly at the first hard tug. Stroking the velvet crown, she laid her fingers on the soft spot of his head and felt the steady rhythm of his heartbeat.

"And here you are," she whispered. "Hello." She kissed him lightly and smoothed his fine hair, curling it around her index finger. *Soft. So very soft.* Everything about him astonished her, filled her with joy be-yond measure!

Everything her mother had told her was true. She did not remember the pain of giving birth; it seemed like nothing more than a vague dream now. The nightmare reality that Wolf was probably close on her trail, however, lurked like a dark shadow in her consciousness. She closed her eyes, then opened them slowly as though her eyelids were weighted.

"Are you tired, little one?" Her eyes moved to the silver crucifix above her bed. *"For unto me a son is born. . . ."* She could not keep her eyes open any longer. "Thank you," she whispered. "Thank you that Wolf did not find me. Thank you . . . for helping . . . us." The child at her breast, Lucy drifted off to a dreamless sleep.

———————

They were playing music at the cabaret especially late tonight, Lori thought. She wondered if people were dancing together even now.

The door to her bedroom was open enough for the light and sounds from beyond the kitchen window to filter softly in. She could just distinguish the white outline of her blouse on the back of her chair and her sneakers on the dark floor beside her bed.

In odd harmony with the distant accordion music, she could hear the assorted wheezes and snorts of the four boys as they slept. She knew which boy belonged to each sound. Alfie snored soundly, like Papa used to after an especially long day. Mark wheezed in and rattled out. *Jamie?* That was easy. She had grown up listening to his asthmatic breathing. From the age of three she had gotten up in the middle of the night and padded down the hall behind her mother to stand quietly beside his bed and listen, to make certain he was properly tucked in.

Old habits were hard to break. Jamie was big enough that she did not need to check him while he slept. Still, from the beginning of their ordeal, Lori had gotten up each night, tiptoed to his bedside and straightened his blankets like Mama would have done. Big sister to little brother. Maybe she would never get over the urge to make certain Jamie's toes were not peeking out, or that his sheets were not kicked onto the floor.

She felt strangely like the character of Wendy in the novel *Peter Pan*—Mother of the Lost Boys. Lori had read the first German translation of the book when she was twelve. She had developed a terrible crush on the imaginary Peter Pan, and even in the cold months of Berlin autumn, she had left her window open in hopes the fairy tale might come true.

And so it had in a way. She and the boys were sailing off to London, while Jacob was doomed to remain in the terrible Never-Never Land of Europe. The weight of their imminent separation made her realize that what she felt for Jacob Kalner was much more than a childhood crush.

How she wished now that she had not let herself love him! This was no fairy tale; there was no promise of *happily-ever-after* in their future. And there was no calling back the love she felt for him. Every minute that passed was a reminder that there was one less moment she could see him; hear his voice; delight even in the simple pleasure of listening to him breathe as he slept.

Lori was awake—more awake than she had ever been; awake in ways she had never dreamed of. Her heart beat faster as she thought of Jacob's kiss, of kisses that had followed to stir up this hunger in her for more.

Her mind warned her that tonight she must not go into the other room to check her lost boys, or she, too, might be lost! She could feel his presence even at a distance. There was no use lying to herself about it, was there? She had left the door open tonight not so she could hear the sleeping boy, but in the hopes that Jacob would come to her. She looked at the vague light and wished that his shadow would block it out.

She prayed that she would fall asleep, that she would not dream of him again. But she did not wait for an answer to her prayer.

Slipping from her bed, she pulled on her robe like every other night. *Time to check the boys.* That was her excuse as she willed him to wake up. It was not Jamie or Mark or Alfie whom she slipped in to check. They could go on breathing without her! *But Jacob!* Would his breath stop once she left him? Would his heart cease to beat because she was not with him?

Lori wondered about the breaking of her own heart as well. How could she leave him? Was that not like leaving a part of herself for the vultures who swung low over Danzig? And if she had to leave her heart with him, could she not give him more than words to remember her by?

She blinked at the shadowed shapes in the room, hardly daring to believe the thoughts that filled her mind now. *Go back! You will hurt him more by this!*

But she did not want to return to her room. Every step away from her own bed was an act of defiance. She did not care! She would not go back to bed alone.

Alfie slept on a mattress on the floor, with Werner-kitten curled up on his chest. The two younger boys were tangled lumps among the sheets on the double bed beneath the window. She pretended she had come to tuck them in. She straightened the blankets and ran her hand across Jamie's tousled hair like always.

Jacob did not stir. He slept on a mattress at the foot of the bed. She wanted him to wake up and find her here, doing her duty as Mother to the Lost Boys. She brushed past him, resisting the desire to kneel and press her lips against his mouth; to stroke his cheek and wrap her arms around him in surrender before they had to say goodbye.

The strength of her emotion frightened her, warning the rational side of her that it was not safe to be so near him tonight.

As if he sensed her presence, Jacob drew a deep breath and shifted slightly on his mattress. She turned to stand over Jamie. *The Little Mother.* She told herself that she had come into the room to tuck Jamie in. *You are lying, Lori. You know why you came.*

The whole truth made her hands tremble as emotion swept through her with a power she had never felt before this moment. She tried to picture the face of her father. And then Mama. What would they say if they knew, *really* knew, what she was feeling?

God help me! She did not dare turn around to look at the shadowed place where Jacob slept. It would be too easy to join him there and be lost forever in another kind of darkness.

Gripping the cold iron headboard of the bed, she tried to pray, tried to steady herself and master her desire so she could walk calmly back to her own room and close the door behind her. *Escape!* Yet how she longed for him to open his eyes and see her there! How she ached to have him take her hand and pull her down to spend a night in his arms!

Only one touch. What would it hurt? She turned from pretense and stooped over him as if to brush his forehead with her fingertips.

From the darkness, his big hand reached up to grasp her painfully by the wrist. He held her there above him a moment and then pushed her back from him, sending her sprawling on the floor. The rough gesture made her gasp; startled her back to her senses.

She started to speak, to explain that she had only come in to—

He stopped her with a whisper. "No, Lori. Not like this. Not now. Go back to bed."

How had he known what she wanted? How had he read her intentions before she even touched his face the first time?

She drew her outstretched hand back and covered her eyes as desire for him was replaced by the hot flush of shame.

"I was just—" she tried to explain in a hoarse whisper. She knew whatever explanation she gave him would be a lie.

"Don't!" His voice was almost angry.

"I didn't mean . . . to wake you."

"Yes, you did," he challenged.

The steady breathing of the others changed to snorts and whistles of disturbed sleep.

"Tucking Jamie—" Tears of shame stung her eyes. The metal of the bedframe dug into her back.

"Go back to your room," he warned. "Lock the door! You hear me? *Lock it!*"

From Mark's side of the bed came a confused mumbling. "What? Is the door . . . huh?"

Jacob spoke in a loud voice, as though he wanted everyone in the room to wake up. *"Go to sleep, will you!"*

Lori stumbled back into her room. She slammed the door and locked it, although now there seemed to be no need for such precautions. Jacob had shamed her. He had good reason, too.

"Oh, God," Lori whispered miserably, "what have I . . . what was I *doing*?"

———

The morning light was another miracle for Lucy. She and the baby were still alone. The priest who had called out her name had not followed her, had not found her. Wolf had not come for the child. For all this, she raised her eyes to the sorrowing Christ and thanked Him. She could not let herself think any further than each moment of safety. The future was too uncertain, too frightening; and so she thought about the past, and she thought about now.

Lucy had seen the mother cows up and about the morning after giving birth. She had witnessed her own mother get up from the birthing bed after a few hours to respond to the cry of another child in the house. Why, then, should Lucy not sit up slowly and swing her legs over the edge of the bed?

The baby slept as Lucy washed herself and gathered the sheets to slip the bundle outside the window on the roof of the adjoining building. She shuffled to the stove and fixed herself a cup of tea and two pieces of toast.

At the soft cry of the baby, she felt milk fill her breasts. She bathed him, changed his diaper and doctored the stub of the umbilical cord before she made up the bed and lay down exhausted to feed him.

Like her mother, like the animals on the farm, Lucy was doing what she must do. She found there was at least strength enough for simple tasks.

Unbuttoning her cotton gown, she let him nuzzle her breast and settle into contented nursing once again. She stroked his head and whispered sweet things to him. She told him how lucky she was that he was her own, that she had not ever imagined such love or perfection. They grew drowsy together as the morning sun rose to heat the tiles of the roof just beyond the window, warming the room as well.

Lucy thought of small tasks she would perform when they awakened. To the gentle rhythm of the baby's breath, she sang the lullaby her mother had sung to her:

"I am small,
my heart is pure,
no one lives in it
but Jesus alone . . ."

And then, as if someone had sung the song to her, Lucy fell fast asleep.

———

"I am certain it was your sister." The young priest looked past Wolf as though he could still see the face of Lucy.

"Pregnant." Wolf clenched and unclenched his fist. He was furious at the ineptness of the priest, but he dared not show his anger. "Still pregnant?"

The priest nodded. "She could not have run far in such a condition."

"But the boy lost her."

"At the far end of the fish market. Philip was simply dwarfed in the crowd. He could not see over the heads of the people, you see. And so your sister escaped him." He frowned and spread his hands in a gesture of apology. "There are only two streets she could have taken. You see here." He passed the small square of the parish map across the desk. "The lad says he last saw her here." He pointed to a street corner and then slid his finger toward the two remaining streets where she might have turned. "That leaves you with three square blocks where you might inquire of her. Certainly someone will recognize her. Some shopkeeper or green grocer." He smiled a weak smile. "It is not so very hopeless any longer, Herr von Fritschauer. And I will pray for her that she might be restored to those who love her and the child."

Wolf's hands trembled with barely controlled rage, which the priest mistook as the emotion of a brother for his wayward sister. "I will not forget what you have done," Wolf said in a low voice. Indeed, he would never forget this show of incompetence—Lucy had been warned now! By now she could have packed up and moved out of the district! She could be halfway across Europe by this time! No, Wolf would not forget. He half-suspected that the priest had warned her himself! Perhaps the story of the chase through the fish market was all a deception as well.

He stepped out of the cool church into the hot sun high above Danzig. Replacing his white Panama hat, he stood for a moment on the steps of Heiliger Geist Church and scanned the square.

Setting his eyes toward the arched portal of the fish market, he retraced the steps she had taken as she fled. There was a small chance—very small—that she had not left the area. It was very near the time she was due to deliver, he knew. There was always that one chance that she had not made it out of the city.

19

The Most Precious Gift

The flowers that Father Kopecky brought to the home of Rabbi Lubetkin were picked, he explained, in the gardens of the great Warsaw cathedral. He presented them to Etta Lubetkin in thanks for the pound cake she had baked for him last week.

"Catholic flowers," Rachel said, eyeing them skeptically.

"They are as kosher as matzo balls," Mama scolded as she trimmed the stems and arranged them in a vase of water.

"Probably grown at the base of a graven idol," Rachel whispered.

Etta sniffed them. "All the same, they smell wonderful." She began to gather the leaves and stem pieces into the newspaper that the priest had wrapped around the bouquet. Etta stopped and peered at the headline. Then she looked at the date. She dropped the leaves into the rubbish container and, completely forgetting the vase of flowers, read the newspaper.

PEACE HOPES WANE
OUTLOOK BLACKEST SINCE 1914
DANZIG NAZI DECLARES "OUR HOUR IS COMING"

Black and white headlines had suddenly made the scent of the flowers unimportant.

"He brings us gifts wrapped in a prophecy of our death," Rachel said gloomily. "Why does he bring us fresh fish wrapped in such terrible news? Why not fish that is three days old? And why flowers that are pretty? More appropriate to pick dead flowers and give them to us. Is he trying to scare us into leaving, Mama?"

Etta shook her head. She did not know anything for sure anymore. Twice, the newspapers the priest had passed along in this unobtrusive manner had been German papers, Nazi publications with full stories of Jews fomenting rebellion in Czechoslovakia. According to the paper, Jews in Warsaw plotted to join Poland with Communist Russia and attack Germany!

And always he asked how progress was coming with the passports. *Would they soon have visas to leave Poland? What plans did they have if the visas did not come through? Would they travel under false documents? Had they prepared the children to talk the ordinary jargon of Polish Catholics in the countryside? Such things were important—as important as a warm coat in winter and a good pair of shoes and socks when one had to walk a long distance!*

Rachel crossed her arms and glared hard at the flowers. Mama did not look up from the heart-stopping news that stared up at her. "He ties up his gifts with a poisonous snake," Rachel said. "I would rather not think of any of it, since there is nothing to be done now. And Papa is sick anyway. How could we leave unless Papa is well?"

Etta raised her eyes slowly from the headlines. "Your father . . ." She frowned and looked at the flowers as if looking at something beautiful would help her say what was ugly and terrible. "Your father will not be leaving Warsaw, Rachel."

"Then none of us are leaving," Rachel replied with an uncharacteristic defiance. Her brilliant blue eyes flashed anger.

"Your father and I . . . are doing . . . everything we can to find a way out for you and your brothers."

"Mother!"

Etta held up a warning finger. "If what happened in Prague comes to Warsaw, then you are going!"

"Where?"

"Jerusalem. Grandfather Lebowitz."

"Not without you!"

"You have a responsibility, Rachel. You are the oldest! If your father and I cannot . . . will not . . . leave the congregation here in Warsaw, then you must take your brothers and . . ."

Rachel was furious at the priest for bringing the paper into their lives. It was better not to know what the Saturday people were doing! Better not to think about it! She turned away, hearing her mother's faraway voice, but letting none of the meaning penetrate her mind. She closed her eyes and buried her face in the bouquet of flowers. She inhaled the sweet fragrance as Etta talked and talked. *These flowers are only flowers. They grew in a garden and came wrapped in plain paper. There is no news. Warsaw is still Warsaw, a flower garden of Poles and Jews who grow side by side. No Nazis. No Danzig. No Hitler. No news today at all.*

Such mental games were like rearranging the flowers in the vase.

Tug a little on the stems of the red blossoms, and they show up better than the yellow ones. In the same way Rachel decided which news she would consider important. *Papa is home. Very important. The boys are home. We are all under the roof of this house together. If one is taken, all will be taken.* No matter what Mama said, she would not abandon her and Papa!

Each evening Karl scratched the passing day on his brick calendar. The marks were no longer simply a method of keeping track of lost freedom. Now Karl was counting the cycle until the eggs in the sparrows' nest would hatch. When he prayed for his own children, he prayed for the coming of the sparrow chicks as well.

As he placed the shared morsels of his bread on the window ledge, he whispered this reminder to himself: "What you have said in the dark will be heard in the daylight. What you have whispered in the ear in the inner rooms will be proclaimed from the rooftops." Karl paused and smiled up toward the concealed nest. "You must remember to tell them that," Karl said to Lady Sparrow. "Remember to tell them that Jesus cares for them. Will you tell them that?"

He stepped down from the bucket as the male sparrow fluttered past his ear and up to retrieve the bread crumbs. "When I am gone, little friends, you must preach this sermon to whoever comes into this place after me." He raised his hand. "Don't be afraid of those who kill the body and after that can do no more. . . .Will you tell them that, little sparrow? You see, Jesus spoke those words to fellows who had every right to be afraid. And right after that He mentioned you. . . . Are not five sparrows sold for two pennies? Yet not one of them is forgotten by God. . . ."

Karl stood in the center of the cell and closed his eyes. For a moment he stood beneath the spreading elm trees that surrounded New Church. Above his head the birds hatched their young. He was not afraid of what men could do to him. God cared even for the sparrows, did He not? And these sparrows raised their young in the branches of this tree of brick and bars. Karl looked forward to the moment when he would face his accusers for the last time. He was unafraid of what they would do to him. He was confident that the sparrows would preach his sermon after he was gone.

The inside of the Indian restaurant was a cool relief after the wave of heat that beat down on London. The atmosphere was heavy with spices, the decor straight from Bombay, India.

Sam Orde had not forgotten the promise he had made to old Rabbi

Lebowitz in Jerusalem. And so Orde hand-carried the passport photographs and rejected immigration applications of the Lubetkin family
to his lunch with Harry Norman at Veeraswamy's India Restaurant not
far from Piccadilly.

Harry was a former Eton classmate of Orde's. They had entered the
military on the same day and had served together in India. Harry had
lost his right arm and his army career in a motorcycle accident and
now was well-entrenched in government affairs at Whitehall.

The empty sleeve of his pin-striped suit was tucked under and sewn
up. "Like the clipped wing of a pet duck," he said to Orde with a grin.
"And as for you, old chap—" Harry tugged on a loose thread hanging
from Orde's tweed jacket. "You are as slovenly as ever." Harry's brown
eyes were bright with amusement as he appraised his old friend. "Now
don't tell me you've rung me up just to come down to Veeraswamy's
and reminisce. I know you better than that, Orde. I could tell from your
voice you want a favor." He sipped gingerly on his gin and tonic. "A
government position, right? Well, if you're going to work for the government, you'll have to do something about your clothes."

Behind their table the discordant twanging of a sitar played a perfect
background to the babble of Harry Norman. Orde savored the familiar
atmosphere of the place. Dark tapestry and the scent of curry brought
back a myriad of memories. Orde considered his old chum's receding
hairline and spreading paunch. One thing he had forgotten until now
was how much Harry talked. Years ago it had been one of the things
Orde enjoyed about him. It had been restful to sit back, enjoy his meal,
and let Harry Norman carry on all the conversation. Today, however,
the endless chatter was far from restful. First came a monologue about
the troubles in India. Then, of course, the current topic of the IRA
bombing bubbled up like a broken sewer line. Then on to trouble in
the Middle East. Never mind that Orde had been there; Harry Norman
had his own immutable opinion. Toward the end of an hour, he
rounded a conversational bend and pounced on the subject of the
refugees who were attempting to flood the free world in their drive to
escape Hitler.

The envelope containing the papers of the Lubetkin family seemed
useless baggage now as Harry railed against the admission of ten thousand refugee children into the United Kingdom.

Orde looked at Harry's empty plate. Not one kernel of rice remained,
although Orde's plate was still half full. When had Harry taken the time
to swallow?

Harry gulped his gin and tonic and looked at his watch. "Five minutes," he announced, "and I'll have to get back to the office. Now what
was it you wanted to talk to me about?"

Orde pushed his plate back, and with a sense of futility, pulled the

Lubetkin family papers out onto the table.

"Friends of mine." Orde placed each photograph in a line.

"Friends," Harry said flatly. "Jews. I heard you had gotten awfully chummy with the Jews. That's why you're back here Orde, old chap. Too chummy."

Orde pressed on. "The woman," he pointed to Etta, "was born in Jerusalem. Moved to Warsaw with her husband and would like reentry into the Mandate."

"With the rest of her family? Sorry. Not a chance. The quotas, you know."

"I was hoping you could pull some strings."

Harry wiped his mouth and tossed the napkin across his empty plate. "No strings left to pull. The White Paper has clipped them all, I'm afraid," he frowned. "Where are these people now?"

"Warsaw."

"Warsaw? How do you know them? *Warsaw?* A bit far from your last assignment."

"Etta's father is a rabbi in Jerusalem. He asked me to see what I could do here in London. I told him I would."

Harry smiled grimly. "He asked *you*? Good grief, Orde! That's like asking a leper to carry sheets into the hospital, isn't it? Does the rabbi know you're not the most popular fellow in government circles these days? Just having lunch with you is a bit risky, you know. I mean . . . but obviously there is nothing you can do to help anyone these days. Not even yourself."

A drop of tonic water spilled on the corner of Etta Lubetkin's application. Orde blotted it carefully lest the ink run. He shrugged and slipped the precious papers back into the envelope. He had forgotten what an unpleasant person Harry Norman could be. The curry formed a seething lump in his stomach. He regretted having brought up the matter with Harry. It was a mistake. Harry would carry the story back with him to the government offices and retell it with such a vengeance that everyone in London would know that Samuel Orde was prowling about, trying to get around the immigration quotas!

"Forget it. It's not important." Orde feigned indifference. "It's nothing at all. This old man simply asked me to see if there was anything to be done. I knew it was hopeless, but I wanted to keep my word to him." He checked the tab in the dim light. "Thanks, Harry. Marvelous to see you again."

There was nothing remotely marvelous about seeing Harry Norman. It was simply one more reminder to Orde that everything he held dear in England was buried in a small plot of earth in Winchester.

———

Allan Farrell was irritated that the London *Times* editorial called his pipe bomb attack "cowardly and amateurish." He read over the words for the hundredth time even as he set up the water glass and the double row of small aspirin bottles.

He forced himself to pay attention to his business when he removed the ground glass stopper from the acid container. The burned, yellow-stained tips of four fingers showed what happened when he did not pay enough attention.

He carefully stirred the mixture with a glass swizzle stick stolen from a bar near Piccadilly Circus. When the smelly concoction was adequately swirled together, he used the glass rod to guide the oily, amber liquid into each tiny bottle.

Allan delicately screwed the lid down on each vial. It would not do to have the acid mixture splash on the metal cap and start eating its way to a premature explosion. Two walnut pipe racks with rows of indentations for briars and protruding pegs for supporting meerschaums served very well to keep his little messages of terror upright and secure.

The Irish American rubbed his hands with satisfaction and inspected the surface of the tiled counter to be certain that no drop of the acid mixture remained. Convinced that it was clean, he proceeded to the next step: he retrieved the cotton garden gloves that had been drying on his windowsill and snipped off each of the fingers with a pair of scissors.

The common household substance that gave each glove finger a crystalline coating felt gritty in his hands. Allan doubted that anyone would notice through the envelopes.

But after he carried out this self-appointed mission, *he* would be noticed. He would not need to give another thought to the fact that the Germans had never bothered to respond to his note. After this, they would be coming to *him*. "Please, Mr. Farrell," they would say, "take charge of this operation for us. Won't you give us your assistance?"

He counted the aspirin bottles and the slipcovers of cotton fingers. Twenty of each, a perfect match. Allan gathered up the dismembered gloves and laid them aside.

Moving to his table, he took up the box of manila envelopes and the directory of Greater London. He had considered using only fictitious addresses, but he was not sure whether the stamps were canceled before or after being sorted. It would not do to have his pets collecting in some dead-letter office. Allan daydreamed for a moment about the vials being crushed and the acid bursting into flame on contact with the crystals.

He pondered the selection of names and addresses. It did not matter, not really, but he wanted at least the first address to have significance.

At last his eye lit on the perfect choice. In careful strokes of his fountain pen he inscribed, "O. Cromwell. 15 Sunset Lane."

————

The housekeeper at Winston Churchill's Chartwell estate came to the edge of the garden path with Murphy and Orde. Looking down toward the duck pond, she waved a dishtowel in the early morning sun to signal Churchill's bodyguard that these visitors were expected and approved.

The bodyguard's hand came off the revolver inside his jacket and acknowledged her signal. Behind the bodyguard, a portly mason in coveralls tapped a brick into place with his trowel handle and wiped his balding head with a handkerchief.

Murphy and Orde went directly up to the bricklayer. "Hullo, Winston," Orde acknowledged. "When I was here last you were working on that wall over there." Orde pointed toward a winding brick barricade on the other side of the pond.

"Hello, Orde, Murphy. No, you are wrong. The wall you saw me building was two before that one, on the other side of that clump of elms."

"What is this, Winston?" Murphy teased, "the Churchill Maginot Line? Tank traps to defend Chartwell from the Hun?"

"Bah," Churchill snorted. "This useful work is how I keep my sanity after listening to the drivel of useless and largely insane speeches. Besides," he continued, "my soul is not at ease unless I can claim an honorable profession to offset the corruption of politics and journalism." His voice leaned heavily on the last word. "Sit down," he offered, indicating a completed stretch of wall.

"I'm sorry to say that politics and journalism are both on the agenda for this visit," apologized Murphy. "You have heard that Orde is on his way to Warsaw, and . . ." A deep nod of Churchill's head indicated that he knew what the subject of their discussion was to be.

He wiped his brow again, then tucked the handkerchief away and laced his stubby fingers together. "What I share with you cannot be quoted," he warned. "There is one man in the foreign press department of Goebbels' Ministry of Propaganda. He likes newspapermen—though I can't for the life of me imagine why—and scotch whiskey. The combination seems to loosen his tongue."

"Are you certain he's not a plant?" asked Orde.

"We have tested his information against other sources, and so far, we have uncovered no inaccuracies. He admits that his department has been instructed to spread the message that the West will not go to war over Danzig."

Churchill picked up the trowel and waved it like a baton to silence the objections coming from Murphy and Orde. "We recognize the propaganda machine at work, but there is more. Recently this man was privy to the report of a conversation in which Hitler asked his generals for their predictions regarding the outcome of a general European war."

Murphy and Orde leaned forward attentively. "The consensus is that Germany would win if Russia does not join the conflict. Should Soviet Russia fight against the Nazis, General Keitel says that he is not optimistic, and Field Marshal Brauchitsch reportedly remarked that Germany would lose."

All three men were silent for a moment, letting the implications sink in. At last Orde spoke. "Then Danzig is not really the big question, nor is Poland even the key."

"Precisely," agreed Churchill. "The Führer does not want to fight a war on two fronts, but Poland is not the eastern front to him. He means Russia's three hundred divisions. So long as the Anglo-Soviet defense agreement is stalled, Hitler will do what he likes with tiny Danzig and indefensible Poland, and have no fears about the outcome."

Orde and Murphy exchanged looks. "Winston," Murphy wondered, "is Orde wasting his time going to Warsaw?"

Churchill shook his head emphatically. "The British government must be poked, prodded, and propelled into moving on an agreement with Russia. That instrument alone may save the peace when nothing else will. Captain Orde must report frankly and convincingly of how incapable the Poles are of defending themselves against the Nazis, while I do my humble best to nag Prime Minister Chamberlain from this end."

"Back before Hitler fortified the Rhine—" Churchill pointed to the brick wall across the small lake. "Before Czechoslovakia was betrayed and dismembered—" He gestured at the pond. "Europe had many places on which to stand and proclaim peace. Russia's assistance was not necessary. But now—" He patted the wall on which they sat. "Now I tell you frankly, we need the Russians on our side."

———

Something was up with Lori. Alfie knew something was up because she was not looking at anyone today. Especially not Jacob. She acted like Werner-kitten had acted when Alfie had let him out of his little cage in the satchel. Werner had shaken himself and gone off to lick his paws. He would not come to Alfie even when Alfie offered him a treat of sardines. It had taken a long time before Werner would let Alfie tickle his chin again. All the while, Alfie had fretted and wrung his hands and said he was very sorry for locking Werner in the cage. Werner did not forgive him until he had licked every paw twice.

Anyway, Alfie thought as he looked at Jacob looking at Lori, something like that was happening here. Lori fixed eggs. She did not sit down with everyone to eat. She fussed in the kitchen, scrubbing the burners on the stove.

"Come eat," Jacob worried.

She did not look at him, did not answer him. When the meal was over she cleared the table herself. Usually she made the boys do it and also wash the dishes. But not today.

Jacob was too cheerful, as he always was when something bothered him. When he was not cheerful, he looked very worried and unhappy. He sneaked looks at Lori. Worry. Worry. Then he whistled and said something bright about the weather or about what a fun time they had at the beach and wouldn't it be nice to go back to Sopot?

Lori never said anything at all. Soon everyone was casting worried looks at her. This was going on a lot longer than Werner licking his paws and feeling put upon!

So Alfie asked her as she washed the dishes herself, "How come you are . . . uh . . . are washing those?"

Lori looked at Alfie. He was the first person she had looked at all day, and it made him feel better. She almost smiled at him too. "Oh, Alf," she said. And then she washed some more.

"How uh . . . come you act like Werner did?"

Lori looked puzzled. "Werner?"

"When I let him out . . . uh . . . the cage. He thought I hurt him, locked him in on . . . uh, purpose." He drew a deep breath. "I would not hurt Werner, but he was mad all the same because I locked him in, because he got to get used to . . . so he don't get hurt. And you are acting like Werner when he licked his paws and don't talk to me because *he* thought . . ." Alfie's voice trailed off. It was a lot of talking, and he lost his place. He grimaced, hoping she knew he was not talking about Werner-kitten, but about her and the way she was acting about Jacob. "You understand, Lori?"

She shook her head. *No.* She had also lost her place. She kept washing the dishes. Not looking when Jacob whistled as he walked by one way and hummed back the other way.

"Can I dry those for you?" Jacob asked.

Lori acted as if she hadn't heard him. Jacob acted as if something was breaking inside him. Alfie watched them both. He did not know he was smiling until Jacob got angry at him.

"What are you looking at?" Jacob said in a loud voice to Alfie.

"Leave him alone!" Lori shouted.

"He's looking . . . smiling . . . this is not something to smile at!"

"He's not doing anything at all! He asked me if he could help! Leave him alone!" She was slinging the dishes into the water, pushing Jacob

out of the way while she scrubbed the counter top harder than she
had ever scrubbed it before.

"Alfie—" Jacob shook his head and Alfie could tell he was sorry
for yelling at him.

"It's . . . all right." Alfie made sure he did not smile now. This was
not *about* him. He patted Jacob on the shoulder, man-to-man, and then
he went into the other room.

Mark and Jamie had gone out. Alfie picked up Werner and thought
that he would also go out for a while. Something was up.

"I didn't mean to hurt you. . . ."

No answer as Alfie put his hand on the doorknob.

*"Please, Lori. Please understand. Last night I . . . I could have . . . if
I had not sent you away . . ."*

Alfie smiled. He slipped out the door. So this really was something
like Werner being put in his cage. Lori was nice. Lori was smart. Alfie
felt certain that she would see how much Jacob loved her, and then
she would quit licking her paws.

He reached up and scratched Werner under the chin. The kitten sat
on his shoulder as they swung out into the morning light. He leaned
hard against Alfie's big head and purred. Lori would be all right, just
like Werner-kitten.

———

Jacob ran his hand through his hair nervously. "It's a good thing
I'm not going with you, that's all."

Lori whirled to face him. "How can you say that? *How?* If you don't
feel the way I feel, then why did you tell me you loved me?"

"I do." Jacob stared down at the sink full of suds. Bubbles made
little rainbows in the sunlight. He groped for words. It had to be right,
what he was about to tell her. What words could he use? "I love you
. . . *permanently*. Last night, I was so afraid of hurting you. Hurting
us." He finished lamely with a shrug. "You see?"

Lori also stared at the bubbles. Her face reflected the long and
sleepless night. "I threw myself at you," she said miserably. "And you
threw me out. I . . . I'm so . . . *ashamed*." She covered her face with
her hands and leaned back against the counter.

Jacob looked at her. She was not a girl anymore. She was a woman.
The transformation had happened right before his eyes. Sunlight
glinted on her golden hair. He reached out and touched it. "You think
I don't know the value of the gift you offered me?" he said gently, pulling
her against his chest. She did not resist. "You're beautiful. Oh, *Lori*!
Like the best package under the Christmas tree. And I look at you and
wonder what it would be like to unwrap you. . . ." She let her arms
encircle his waist and she laid her cheek against his chest. He thought

for a moment he could not breathe. "But, Lori," he said. "It isn't Christmas yet. You can't unwrap the gift until Christmas, or the whole day is ruined. You *know*?"

She nodded. Her face moved up and down against him and her arms tightened around him. Her soft hands stroked his back. "Marry me," she whispered.

"Yes. Yes. When all this is over and we're—"

"No. Marry me today. Now. I want to spend Christmas with you."

He lifted her chin. "You think I could let you leave me if we. . . ?"

"I'm hoping you won't."

He shook his head, trying to make some sense of all this. "Then I won't . . . can't marry you now. Because, Lori, you've got to get out of here. I'll make it out someway. I'll find you again. But you have papers in order and a ticket to leave. You go to England, and—I promise—I'll find you by Christmas."

She was silent. Listening. Thinking. "Marry me before I leave. They'll let you join me if we're married!"

That made sense, but . . . "You know what our folks would say?"

"They would be glad we did things right. Glad we knew enough . . . glad and proud that you sent me away from you last night so we could talk it over by the light of day!" Her eyes were fierce as she looked up into his face. "And it *will* help you get to England if you have a wife there. It doesn't matter that we're young, does it? I'm sure. Sure that . . ." She leaned against him.

"You can't stay with me here," he warned, "even if we marry! You must promise not to ask that of me."

"I promise," she said in a small voice. "Oh, *please*. Let's not waste another minute. There are so few, Jacob. And time with you is my most precious gift. . . ."

Jacob closed his eyes, arguing silently with everything she said. In the end, he lost the argument.

———

"Does that mean you aren't coming to England, Lori?" Jamie looked worried as they all sat together around the table.

"*No!*" Jacob and Lori said at the same time. Then Jacob took over. "She is going. Just like we planned. I will come later."

Lori nodded and nodded as he explained. "You see, when there is a relative—like a mother or a wife already in England—it makes it easier for the person left behind to immigrate."

Mark scowled. "Well, I'm his brother! Aren't I enough?"

Alfie was smiling because Lori looked as if she were purring. Jacob held her hand and their fingers were woven together like a basket. "First you, Mark," Alfie said. "Then Lori will be the wife. And Jamie will be . . . something too. Related."

Jacob shifted in his chair and clapped Alfie on the back. Alfie got
it. Why were Mark and Jamie so reluctant to see the benefits of having
a wedding today?

Jamie scowled. "What will Mama say? She would want to be there.
And . . . and *Papa*! What about that? Walking down the aisle and all
that?" As the son of a pastor, Jamie had seen enough weddings that
he knew how real weddings were supposed to be conducted. This was
missing every possible ingredient for a successful occasion. Who
would play the organ? Where were their formal clothes? A wedding
dress? "What about the *ring*?" Jamie exploded. "You can't have a wedding without a ring!"

Alfie stood majestically and plopped Werner into Jamie's lap. He
hurried back into their room and pulled out a bureau drawer containing
his tin soldiers and his treasure sock. Dumping the sock out unceremo-
niously onto a line of cavalrymen, he found the answer to Jamie's
objection. It was a pretty ring, with green stones all around a large
diamond. He had been saving it for something special. This seemed
special enough.

"I got it!" Alfie cried, not bothering to put his other treasures back
into the sock. "The best one!"

He placed it in Jacob's hand and crossed his arms proudly. Mark
and Jamie looked at each other and shrugged. Well, they knew *absolutely* that their parents would not approve. They had done their best.
No one would blame them for this! Jamie gazed solemnly at the ring.
"Emeralds and diamonds," he said in a low, astonished tone. "Alfie,
you're a genius."

"A really smart fellow," Mark rephrased the comment. "I suppose
that we should forever hold our peace, then. There's no stopping them
if they have a ring."

"Papa won't think much of this." Jamie was still reluctant. "At least
you better do it in a church."

———

Lucy's legs trembled when she stood. Her hands shook as she fixed
her noonday meal of broth and crackers with a small slice of cheese
and apple. Her mother had taught her well that from the cows in the
barn to the hens in the coop, offspring fared better if the mothers were
well fed. Lucy had no appetite, but she ate for the sake of her baby.
She ate because she must be strong in order to leave Danzig soon.

But leave for where? Lucy pulled the chair close to the bed and sat
on a pillow to watch the baby sleep. How she wished she could go
home again! How she ached to see her mother, to hear words of advice
on caring for this precious little one. But there was no going back,

even if her parents had been willing to take her in. Wolf would find her there, and the end would be the same as if she had saved herself the trouble and stayed in Vienna!

Behind her through the open window, Lucy could clearly hear the persistent bellow of a ship's whistle. It would be wonderful, she thought as she looked at her little green book. *Waiting at Table . . . England!*

Before the priest had called out to her in the church, Lucy had imagined she had all the time in the world. Now she knew that the world had run out of time. Now, in this desperate moment, she must gather her wits and her strength for the sake of the baby. But she knew she did not have the strength to walk from here down the stairs. How, then, could she walk to the train station? Where would she find the stamina for that now?

Never had Lucy been so tired. Such weariness convinced her once again that if Wolf had not found her by now, perhaps he could not track her down at all.

She pulled back the sheet, revealing the baby's perfectly formed head. *So beautiful.* Lucy's mother would have commented on such a thing. She would have gathered her grandson into her arms and danced around the kitchen. She would have told everyone in the village that there never was a baby born with such a perfect head!

That thought somehow comforted Lucy as she looked down tenderly on the child whom she alone had admired. No doctor. No proud grandparents. No joyful neighbors bringing food. No priest . . .

But the lack of all that did not change the fact that her son was born; beautiful and sweet. He cried only when he was hungry, or when he needed changing. Did he somehow sense the sorrowing heart of his mother? Did an angel whisper in his little ear and tell him they were alone and without help, that he should be a quiet baby, a baby gentle and kind even in these first few hours of life?

It was the child who comforted Lucy, not she who comforted him. He was sleeping quietly, but she took him into her arms anyway. She pressed her cheek against his forehead as his eyes fluttered open and he considered her. She smiled down at him, and for that moment it did not matter that Lucy was alone. She felt no lack of mother or father or priest or doctor to gather in around her to admire this miracle.

Their absence did not change the fact that the miracle had happened. *"For unto me a son is born,"* Lucy whispered again. "And . . . his name shall be *wonderful!*"

She considered the little face as the baby's fist wobbled up to his toothless mouth. *Those eyes, so serious!* Yes. There was the matter of a name. Even the most wonderful baby could not be called *Wonderful!*

"I will sleep on it," Lucy said quietly as she tucked him close to nurse him back to sleep. "Something worthy of a little boy as good and thoughtful as you."

They lay together on the bed, and he comforted her as the ship's whistle sounded again and yet another ship slipped out of Danzig without Lucy and her son on board.

20

What God Has Joined Together

Concierge was an exalted word for the old man who lived at the foot of the stairs and collected the rent from the tenants of this building.

Hess presented his photographs to the dottering old fool. Crooked fingers clutched the edges awkwardly as dim eyes strained to see the images on the paper.

"Bitte. One moment." He looked up at a light socket where a bulb had been some years past. "The light is bad in here." He squinted and moved his arm back and forth like a trombone player as he attempted to find the proper focus for his eyes.

"A brother and a sister," Hess urged, tapping on the faces of Lori and Jamie Ibsen so the old man would not mistake Karl Ibsen and his wife as the ones Hess was looking for.

"A nice looking family," the concierge mumbled. "We do not have many of these sort let rooms here." The weathered face wrinkled in distaste as the shrill laughter of a woman drifted down from the upper floors. "In the old days this was a fine boardinghouse. Before the Great War, it was a reputable establishment," he said bitterly. "Now no one cares. No families like this come here anymore."

"I am not looking for the entire family," Hess repeated impatiently. "Just this boy and his sister. They would be with three other children. Not hard to spot. One among them is a Dummkopf, I am told. A big dimwitted boy."

At this the man's eyes sparked with recognition. He looked again at the photograph. "Yes. Not here in my block, but I think . . . the girl would be much older, you say?"

"Yes." Hess resisted the urge to shake the information out of the old man. "Two years older than the photograph, at least."

"Two small boys. Two older? One among them is the dimwit. A friendly fellow. Carries a little cat on his shoulder and has stopped to talk to me several times as I swept the steps." He smiled at the thought. "They are in the neighborhood. Yes. I cannot tell you exactly where, but one does not forget such a group on a street like this."

The old man could tell Hess nothing more. He did not know which direction they lived. Could not recall the names of the other children.

The gnarled hand stretched out, palm up, for a gratuity. Hess tossed a coin to him. It clattered on the chipped tile of the foyer, and he left the concierge groveling on the floor for his tip.

Orde had spent the better part of the week shuttling between the BBC and the TENS office on Fleet Street. He was getting acquainted with the mechanics of broadcasting live from the European Continent to the London studio, which would then relay the program to the United States.

Arrangements had already been made for Orde to have a small storefront office in the same block as the building housing Polski Radio. It would serve as his Warsaw broadcasting base.

On the surface, it appeared simple, like sending a message by radio back to GHQ from a forward position. The problem was making the timing of each live broadcast coincide with the tiny window of broadcast time allowed during radio programming.

"Suppose I am covering an important conference in Warsaw and I have nothing to report by airtime?" he asked Murphy and Harvey Terrill.

"Can you sing?" Harvey replied in a resentful tone.

"You'll just have to wing it," Murphy said with a grimace. Such things happened regularly in the new world of radio journalism. "Ask questions—plenty of questions. Get people wondering what's coming. Then they'll tune in when you have the answers." Murphy leveled a look at Orde. "Just remember, talk slow! Americans love the sound of an English accent, but—"

"Right, old chap," Orde replied. "I have heard it a million times from your Doc Grogan . . . *talk slowly and distinctly, please.*"

Murphy had put Dr. Patrick Grogan to work improving the rapid machine-gun dialect of Samuel Orde. The pleasant, round-faced elocution specialist had drilled Orde the way Professor Higgins had taught Eliza in *Pygmalion,* preparing him for every eventuality. With marbles in place in Orde's mouth, Grogan had dared to challenge Orde to heated political discussions. Grogan always took the opposite side of the argument and hammered away until Orde was red in the face with outrage and quite prepared to spit the marbles into the eye of his grinning teacher.

As if on cue, Doc Grogan entered the TENS office with Charles and Louis in tow. Grogan had kept the boys at his side during the day to help out with the arrival of the newest Murphy child. He waved broadly and puffed out his cheeks as a way of greeting Orde.

He did not knock, but entered the office with all the freedom of a TENS employee. "Well, well, it is Samuel Orde! I see you've lost your marbles at last. Here you are with Harv Terrill, and Terrill would kill to get the Warsaw assignment!" Grogan was smiling.

At this comment, Orde noticed the face of Harvey Terrill puckered with ill-suppressed dislike for Patrick Grogan.

Charles tugged Orde's sleeve and smiled at him with a toothless grin. "We will lith-en to the radio."

"Listen!" Louis corrected.

"Yeth. Er . . . *yes-s-s-s*. But talk slow."

Could I do otherwise with so many coaches? Orde wondered. "Even if bombs are exploding under me." He raised his hand in solemn promise.

Orde had never seen the harried night desk editor look anything but tired. Now, as the playful repartee was exchanged between Orde and Grogan, Terrill acted downright irritated. He flashed venomous looks in Grogan's direction. *What is that about?* Orde wondered. *Perhaps two junior officers competing for the approval of the boss?*

As the two boys boisterously clambered into Murphy's desk, Orde observed Terrill purposely bump a stack of papers beside them.

"Enough of this, Boss," Terrill said, as though the boys had knocked the papers over. "This is not some playground," he mumbled and stooped to retrieve and reorganize the documents.

Murphy shrugged apologetically. "I've been working you too hard, Harvey. Or you'd know this *is* a playground." Grogan and Orde laughed. Terrill grunted his disapproval of the interruption.

In deference to the sour mood of his second-in-command, Murphy escorted Grogan and the boys into the outer office. More laughs as Murphy swung Charles upside down until his face hung in front of the busy telephone receptionist. No one seemed surprised or concerned with Terrill's ill-humor. Only Terrill, Orde noted, did not give it up. He stared after Grogan and snapped. "He's in here with those kids at all hours snooping around. Doesn't even knock."

Then it was back to business. Orde had only an hour left to pick up his renewed passport, which now showed him as a civilian entering Poland on a six-month-renewable work permit. Murphy and Terrill went through the sheaf of documents required by the Polish government for broadcasting from Warsaw and Danzig. Frequencies and the names of contacts were rehearsed one final time, and then Murphy invited Orde to stop in at the Red Lion House before he left.

As Orde left the building, he caught a glimpse of Harvey Terrill's sullen face as the night desk editor sifted through the stacks of reports on his own desk. Was he simply overworked, as Murphy said, or did the man really resent the fact that Orde had taken the Warsaw assignment?

———————

Even though the London traffic was thick and particularly fumey today, Orde refused to take the underground train to the passport office. He preferred to ride behind the grumbling cab driver and see the city from above ground. Tube stations made marvelous air-raid shelters, Orde thought, but he had never enjoyed traveling like a mole tied to a Roman candle.

The passport office was located at 1 Queen Anne's Gate Building on Dartmouth Street. There were two doorways into the office. One had a long queue of people waiting to pass beneath the hooded arch of the entrance marked: *FOREIGN NATIONALS*. The line of weary-faced hopefuls stretched for an entire block. The question on every face was, *Will they renew my work permit? Or will I be instructed that my stay in England is at an end?*

Orde could hear the distinct, guttural conversation of those from Germany mingled with the language of the Poles. New among the lines today were the soft, fluid accents of the Irish who had been ordered to report for questioning at various government offices since the bombing. Orde easily spotted the Irish among the others—beautiful, ruddy-cheeked people with clear, worried eyes. Orde was quite certain that whoever had been planting the bombs would not be among those who answered the government summons to report here for questioning and registration.

Orde entered the office through the second door, labeled simply, *PASSPORTS—NEW AND RENEWAL*. There was no line to wait in. Perhaps no one in Great Britain was interested in traveling to the Continent of Europe these days. It was too much like hiking through a mine field.

One couple stood at the counter in front of him. They chatted amiably about traveling to New York to attend the World's Fair. The clerk listened patiently to their entire itinerary before bidding them farewell and wishing them a pleasant journey as if he were a travel agent.

He greeted Orde with the same enthusiasm. It was obvious that the clerk was relieved to be on this side of the office, rather than in the midst of all the unpleasantness on the other side.

He found the file containing Orde's new passport. "We could have sent it to you through the post if you were not in such a hurry," the man said apologetically. "This is not the best of times to have to come in to the office, is it?" As Orde grimaced at his dreadful passport picture, the clerk glanced down at the folder once again. "Why, Mr. Orde, is your wife not traveling with you?" He peered closely at a yellowed document.

Orde was mildly surprised at the question. So no one in the passport office had gotten word that Katie Orde had passed away over four years ago. "No," Orde said without explaining.

"All the same," said the clerk hopefully, "her passport is also due to expire. Let me see . . . just three months. You might wish to take care of it now so that if she should change her mind and join you in Warsaw, it would be in order." Without waiting for reply, he passed two renewal applications across the counter to Orde. "In case you make a mistake. Always good to have a practice sheet, I say. You would be surprised the number of people who mail these things in all scratched out, marked up. It goes much easier if you type it." He tapped the blank sheets. "Just like yours. And if you're not in such a hurry, mail it. Usually eight weeks is time enough for renewals. The ladies love having the new photographs made."

Orde smiled and listened to him babble. He accepted the applications without attempting to explain that Katie would definitely not be coming to Warsaw. No use getting into personal conversation with a chap who loved to hear himself talk.

"Enjoy your trip to Warsaw," he called after Orde.

Orde winced at the words. Maybe this fellow did not know what was happening in Warsaw these days, he mused.

Among all the little boys around Muranow Square and in the Torah school, the name of the great and magnificent *Hayedid,* Captain Samuel Orde, was already legend.

Who in the Jewish District did not know somebody—or at least know somebody who knew somebody—who had gone to Palestine? And if everyone knew of a somebody even twice removed in Jerusalem, then of course the daring and stupendous deeds of Captain Orde against the Arab gangs of the Mufti had been reported back to Warsaw. Thus the letter from Rabbi Lebowitz in Jerusalem caused a stir in the community when his aquaintance with the Hayedid was reported.

On the strength of one mention of Orde's name in a letter, David and Samuel Lubetkin announced that the very same courageous Englishman in all the news dispatches was coming to their very house! He was coming to hand deliver a note from their grandfather, they proclaimed. He was coming to discuss the situation with their father! And he was coming for a cup of tea as well, probably.

Such incredible news made both the Lubetkin brothers suspect among their classmates at Torah school. What they had said was something akin to claiming that Moses was coming for dinner. Not just somebody *named* Moses, but the very Moses who parted the Red Sea and brought other miracles to pass on behalf of the slaves in Egypt.

Some boys believed that it was the *real* Hayedid who was coming, but most others looked at one another and said, "There must be someone else with the name Captain Samuel Orde. Possibly it is a common name among the English, just as Moses is a common name among us."

Such logic insulted and angered David Lubetkin. It simply confused his younger brother Samuel. "There is only *one* brave and victorious Captain Orde," David announced outside the school. "It is the same captain who has conquered those who would curse Israel and drive the Jews into the sea!"

"And he is coming to have tea." Samuel's earlocks trembled with earnest excitement.

The doubters pushed their way to the front of the circle. A boy named Mordechai, two grades older than David, crossed his arms and glared down at him in accusation. "Why should the great Hayedid, of whom my uncle has written, come to visit you?"

"Because," ventured a smaller child who bristled with indignation at the doubt of something so tremendous, "the Hayedid is going to see Rabbi Lubetkin. Do not great warriors always hold conversations with holy men?"

Younger heads bobbed. Older heads, more experienced with huge rumors that never came true, raised their chins and lowered their eyelids as an expression of violent skepticism. And after a moment, the boy named Mordechai said *the word.* "Liars. David and Samuel are nothing but liars. Why should Captain Orde come to Warsaw for a conference when Jerusalem is jam-packed full of rabbis? I ask you—why?"

There was little doubt as to who threw the first punch. Actually, David threw more than a punch at Mordechai.

With a growl, David plowed into the belly of the startled boy, hurtling him backward into a wall of onlookers who stepped back with one astonished exclamation. *"A-H-H-H-H!"* they said in mutual approval and enjoyment of the spectacle. Such sights were rare among Torah school pupils, much more common among the other Jews who sent their children to nonreligious school. But here? Oy! Such a fight it was. Shouting and pounding and kicking and more shouting! It felt terrific! Books fell everywhere. A ring of short pants and knobby knees encircled the combatants, moving with them as they pummeled and kicked and rolled down the street!

The real reason of the argument was all but forgotten. The fists of every Torah-school boy were doubled up to punch and jab in vicarious battle!

It was all too wonderful for words until the cries of David's sister were heard. She fought her way through the crowd, elbows flying; she pushed back the startled spectators. For a girl, and a pretty girl at that, Rachel Lubetkin could hit pretty hard!

The presence of a member of the opposite sex put a different slant on the entire contest. Some of the older boys simply picked up their books and skull caps and hurried away. The younger crowd, those who believed in the coming of Captain Orde, were left to shout, all at the same time, that it was all the fault of the great bully Mordechai!

Rachel crossed her arms and stared down at Mordechai who lay on his back on the cobblestones. His nose was bleeding. His right eye was already swollen. David was rumpled and his school clothes were torn, but he seemed in better shape than his opponent.

Rachel was red-faced, furious that anyone had laid a hand on David. She waited until Mordechai sat up slowly and held his kerchief to his nose before she launched in.

"Well, Mordechai! Every time there is a fight, you are always in the middle of it!"

The last fight had been two years ago, and Mordechai had been hit with a rock. It was not his fault, but Rachel brought it up anyway.

"Ha!" said Mordechai behind his kerchief.

"And now you have taken to attacking small children," she continued. "You are twelve! David is ten! And yet here you are brawling in the street like any filthy Polish peasant!!" It was not a nice thing to say, but not dangerous right here in front of the synagogue. There were no Poles around.

"Who is bleeding? Nu!" He shook his kerchief at Rachel and clamped it back on his nose quickly.

"Whose clothes are torn?" Rachel put a protective arm around David's shoulders. David shrugged her arm away. He was doing just fine before she came; who needed an interfering sister, anyway?

Samuel stepped up and tugged her skirt. "Rachel, Mordechai says that Grandfather is a liar."

Her mouth and eyes widened at the same instant. She breathed in until some boys thought her lungs might pop. "*My* grandfather? The great Rabbi Lebowitz who prays each day beside the Western Wall? You say he is what?"

"I never said it," spat Mordechai, slowly climbing to his feet. "David and Samuel are liars and you, Rachel Lubetkin, are a contentious woman that we have just studied about in Proverbs."

Everyone stepped back at those words. Would Rachel follow the example of her brother David and hurl herself against Mordechai?

"I am a peacemaker!" she exclaimed haughtily. "Just because I am a woman I still can see injustice being done and put a stop to it! You think I would abandon my brother to a great bully in the street?"

The argument had veered off the subject. The audience exchanged looks. They did not want to hear who was right and who was wrong or who was winning and who got the worst of it! There was only one great issue today—was the real and authentic British hero for the Zionist cause actually coming to tea?

A deeper male voice called in from the back of the group. "Rachel Lubetkin!" It was Peter Wallich, the ragged lost gypsy of Muranow Square. "Are you all right, Rachel?"

"Fine. Here is a bully for you." She gestured toward Mordechai, whose nose bled on. "He attacked David in the street, called my grandfather a liar, and called me a contentious woman! May his mother hang him by his earlocks!"

"I said I did not believe it!" Mordechai defended. "I said the great and incredible hero of Zionism . . . the British Hayedid, Captain Samuel Orde . . . was not coming to their house for tea! And *then* . . . David Lubetkin attacked me!"

"So? Why shouldn't he hit you?" Peter seemed unimpressed by Mordechai's defense. "If you said I was lying, I might also hit you. Because they are not lying. I don't know about coming for tea, but I just heard from the leader of Zionist Youth that Captain Orde is coming to Warsaw. Muranow Square. He will teach the pioneers survival in the wilderness. A lecture class, he said."

The cheers rose up in a mighty roar. The Torah-school boys rushed in to thump David Lubetkin on his dirt-covered back. They shook his hand and fetched his yarmulke and his books. It was true! It was true! The great military leader was coming right here to take tea at the house of Rebbe Lubetkin! Oy! Such a moment! Moses comes marching into Egypt with his staff in hand!

"And he will teach us!" the little boys cried.

"Not *you*," Peter corrected. "Only boys who have had their Bar Mitzvah. Thirteen and older. *That* is who he will instruct."

Smiles faded almost as suddenly as they had come, and silence fell over the group. Mordechai brushed himself off. He was almost thirteen, he told Peter. Next week was his birthday. He would very much like to attend these lectures of the great and ferocious Hayedid, Captain Samuel Orde.

———

Orde arrived home in Three Kings Yard to find that all the personal belongings he had shipped from Jerusalem had finally arrived. Crates and boxes blocked the entrance to the house. With a shake of his head, Orde climbed over the heap and then began to wrestle it indoors. *Just in time to say goodbye,* he mused as he looked at the new mound of possessions in the center of the shrouded furniture. It would remain there until he returned from Warsaw.

Hands on hips, he gazed at it for a moment until he spotted the wooden box containing the old headstone from Gethsemane. Had it survived the trip? This one thing Orde set to work uncrating.

With a sigh of relief, he cleared away the packing paper and patted the old granite stone.

BY DYING I CONQUER LIFE.

Orde read the inscription again with bitter amusement. "Ah, Katie," he whispered, "if only it was just that easy. The trouble is, you see, in the meantime I have to keep *living* and conquering life."

He straightened slowly and pulled back the slipcover from Katie's writing desk. Opening the drawer, he found Katie's passport. Her birth certificate. Her certificate of death. He opened the passport and wished that she were here to travel with him; wished that she were one of the ladies so delighted to have a new passport picture taken. He smiled down at the gray, colorless picture. Katie had always been so full of life and color—her skin, her eyes, the sun highlighting bits of red and gold in her soft brown hair. *By dying I conquer life.*

Orde thought the ancient headstone had spoken aloud. Still holding the open passport, he turned and stared at the gray lifeless granite, the symbol of someone else's existence. There was something he was meant to understand from the inscription . . . *something!*

"What is it, Lord?" he prayed aloud.

At that moment his briefcase toppled off a crate. The plain manila envelope containing the Lubetkin family immigration material spilled out on the floor.

Without passports they are trapped in Poland. If the Nazis come, that family will be among the first singled out. Then Orde said aloud, "They are alive and cannot get passports. Katie has been dead for four years, and I can renew her papers by post!"

Orde knelt down and fanned out the photographs of the Lubetkin family on the floor—the boys with their earlocks; the rabbi with his beard; Etta in her severe dress—each of these bore the appearance of East European Jews. But the girl . . . *Rachel!* Her pretty young face would do well inside the stiff new cover of a British passport! It was a simple matter of matching her with some long-dead child in an English churchyard and writing in for a birth certificate.

"Can it be that simple?" he wondered aloud.

For a moment he considered sending in the photograph of Etta Lubetkin with Katie's passport renewal form. But Katie would have been much too young. The age discrepancy might be noticed. But there were other women in England who *would* have been the age of Etta had they lived! Perhaps there was a way for the dead to conquer life—at least to help conquer the obstacles of immigration for others to remain living for a while!

He stumbled to the telephone and dialed the number of the passport office. A clipped, officious voice answered.

"Hullo." Orde hoped she could not hear the excitement in his voice. He should sound irritated and unhappy, should he not? "I have lost my passport. All my identification, and I have a rather urgent trip abroad."

"A matter of obtaining your birth certificate and a new photo and bringing it to our office."

"Like a renewal then?"

"Yes. You will need to fill out the application. Nothing to it."

"I'm going north tonight."

"We can handle the matter by post if it is easier."

It was easy enough, Orde thought as he hung up and began to stuff his clothes into his baggage! Why had he not seen it before? A last glance at the headstone gave him courage as he left the house. Perhaps the next time he returned, he would open the shutters and take the dusty sheets off the furniture to see the colors once again!

———

Who would have guessed it would be so difficult to get married in Danzig? The tiny blue flowers woven into Lori's french-braided hair had wilted. Jacob's tie was loose and cocked off to the side. His collar was unbuttoned and he carried his jacket as the party trooped into the park around the corner from city hall in search of a shady bench on which to rest for a while.

Three churches of different Protestant denominations—three pastors, and none of them seemed to believe in holy matrimony, especially without *parental permission in addition to a marriage license!* When Jacob had explained that they could not obtain a license without parental permission, these men of the cloth had simply nodded and showed them the exit.

"Maybe we should give up," Mark said, wiping sweat from his brow.

Lori's eyes narrowed. "*You* give up! It's not your wedding anyhow."

Mark made a face. "Seems to me that a brother in England is as good a relative as a wife. I think you want to get married for some other reason."

"You're right," Jacob mumbled. "Now shut up."

Jamie lifted his chin in an arrogant fashion. "If Papa were here, he'd say that *God* is telling you not to get married."

Jacob scowled. "If your papa were here, we'd have parental permission and then God would be saying *yes!*"

Lori added, "If Papa were here, he'd perform the ceremony himself."

She cocked a superior eyebrow at Jamie.

Alfie leaned against a tree behind the bench. Werner jumped off his shoulder and perched on a branch. There was a sign warning that pets should be on a leash and that it was VERBOTEN to step on the grass, but Alfie was too hot to care. He decided not to read the sign even though it had words he knew, because then he could stand on the grass without knowing he broke the rules. It made sense in a roundabout way, Lori reasoned when she asked him to read the rules about standing on the grass.

Alfie sighed. "Does this mean I don't get to be the . . . best . . .best . . .uh . . ."

"Man," Jacob snapped. "Not yet. There is a church on nearly every corner in Danzig; we will find one *somewhere* willing to do a proper job of this."

"I think we should go back to Sopot and go swimming," Mark said sullenly.

"Yeah. It's too hot for us to get married today," Jamie agreed.

"I want to be . . . uh . . . best man." Alfie wiped his brow on the sleeve of his once-ironed shirt. "And Lori . . . can sleep in our room if her and Jacob is uh . . ."

At this, looks were exchanged all around. There would be no explaining this to Alfie.

Jamie tried. "Married people sleep in the same room."

"Uh-huh. I said that," Alfie nodded.

"Alone," Mark added.

"Why?" Alfie asked.

It was very warm. Jacob stood and tugged his collar open a bit more. "Maybe we should try the English Mariner's Church on the water-front," he suggested.

"You don't speak English," Jamie chided. "That's what got you into this mess."

All heads swiveled to pierce him through with black looks. Jamie shrugged and looked at the tram. Now he really wanted to go back to the beach!

"The English church then," Lori said. "I will translate."

"Just tell me when we're really married, will you?" Jacob tossed his jacket over his shoulder and struck out across the park. He did not care that Alfie had to climb the tree to fetch Werner and so almost got lost. Alfie told him it would have been an unlucky thing if the best cat was left in a tree somewhere.

The pastor of the English Mariner's Church was a burly Scot from Edinburgh. He had spent most of his life in the Merchant Marines, denting the walls of bars and assorted unholy places until his ship was torpedoed by Germans in the Great War in 1918. Four days drifting on scraps of lumber had been enough for Seaman Cecil Douglass to see the error of his ways. After several years in seminary he had taken up what he called a front-line position between the wharf and the brothels of the waterfront district.

The church building itself stood in the shadow of the half-timbered warehouses along the waterfront. It looked like any other little church from the English countryside. This fact pleased Pastor Douglass, who felt it stood as a beacon of hope, a reminder of home and family. These were matters of great importance to the pastor, and he preached often on the folly of unfaithful seafaring husbands who took no thought of the commandment against adultery.

All these things Jacob had heard from the fellows who worked with him on the docks. Pastor Douglass had taken his four days on a raft in the Mediterranean quite seriously, it seemed.

From this small bit of personal insight, Jacob and Lori formulated a strategy by which licenses and parental permission might be circumvented.

It was cool inside the little church, and everyone began feeling much better about the wedding. Lori and Jacob sat in the choir loft and spoke in low tones to the enormous pastor while the others stared gratefully at the cool white walls and stained-glass windows.

"Miss Ibsen," remarked the pastor, "I have heard of your father. Indeed I have. A giant of the faith. Suffering for the cause of the kingdom and Christ." He knit his bushy black brows together in consternation. "But without the permission of your father—" He spoke excellent German. There was no need for anyone to translate for Jacob.

"Since Lori's father is in prison, how can anyone expect us to get permission?"

Pastor Douglass smiled sympathetically. "But you are both underage."

"We are both Christians." Lori looked indignant. "We love each other."

The pastor wagged a thick finger at her. "And since Jacob is to be left behind, what sort of a marriage—"

"He will join us in England." Lori took Jacob's hand.

"Ah. Yes. And to do that, I suppose it would be convenient to have a marriage certificate." The frown deepened. "I will not make a mockery of God's holy ordinance of marriage."

Lori drew herself up. "Then when my father gets out of prison, I will tell him that the reason Jacob and I were forced to live in sin is because no Christian pastor would perform the ceremony." She tossed her braid, and wilted flowers tumbled out.

The pastor stared at the flowers and considered that no female puts such things in her hair if the wedding is only for a certificate of marriage to show the immigration officials. Perhaps this was indeed a matter of two hearts before the Lord. Here was this young man in a jacket and tie on such a hot day. Was it reasonable to think he would do that for any other reason than true love?

Pastor Douglass stuck out his lower lip. He scratched his cheek thoughtfully. Peering over the rail of the choir loft, he called, "Who's the best man?"

The big dimwitted chap with the kitten stood up and waved the cat in the air. "Me and Werner."

"And who will give the bride away?"

Jamie stood up and smiled weakly. He was taking Papa's place and was certain he could not do a good job. *"Me."*

"And is there a ring-bearer?"

"Me!" Mark jumped to his feet and dug deep into his pocket for the ring.

Pastor Douglass shrugged and stood. "Well, then. All we need is a bride and a groom."

21

Night Closes In

This was not at all what Alfie had meant when he suggested that Lori could share their bedroom.

While Jacob took his new bride for an ice cream soda at Sprinter's ice cream parlor, Mark, Jamie, and Alfie had hurried back to the flat to move mattresses from the big bedroom into Lori's tiny corner room. Jamie and Mark changed the sheets on the double bed and placed two bouquets of fresh flowers in quart canning jars on the night table and the chest of drawers.

It all looked very pretty, but Alfie had not meant that he and Jamie and Mark would have to move to the little room while Jacob and Lori got the big one. It did not take a smart person to see that three bodies crammed into Lori's small space did not fit as well as all five of them in the big room.

"What do you think?" Mark asked, stepping back and crossing his arms as they surveyed the honeymoon suite.

Jamie was not pleased. "I still say Papa will not like this when he finds out I helped." He stared sourly at the flowers. The yellow petals of the daisies had already begun to wilt and drop onto the night table.

"Jacob owes us for this." Mark nudged Jamie. "He said if we would make the place nice . . . romantic-like . . . that he would treat us three to lemon ice at Sprinter's when they got back."

Alfie licked his lips at the thought of lemon ice. His favorite. He looked at the flowers and imagined the bright colors of the umbrellas over the round tables at Sprinter's. He did not know why all five of them could not have gone there together, however. Instead, it was Jacob and Lori first and then the boys. Alfie thought it was sad that they could not all spend every minute together until the boat left for England.

"Well, I am going to have a double-double ice cream soda after this," Jamie scowled. "He owes us, all right! Some trade. I give my sister away today, and all I get is ice cream in return."

Mark seemed amused. "Like Esau giving Jacob his birthright for a mess of porridge."

Alfie winced in confusion. "Huh?"

"In the Bible," Mark answered.

Jamie sniffed. "A sister is worth more than a mess of porridge. More than a double-double soda." He scowled. "I was supposed to be the man of the family while Papa was gone. Now look what's happened." He gestured toward the perfectly made bed. Clean sheets and pillow cases. Not even a wrinkle.

Alfie was lost. "Your papa won't mind that you made the bed," he soothed.

Mark and Jamie exchanged *the look*. Alfie decided they knew more than they were telling. He scooped up Werner and went into Lori's old room to look at the pile of mattresses on the floor beside her iron cot. Not even a place to walk.

"I say we take the money and catch the train to Sopot," Jamie said. "Let's get out of here before they get back."

"I doubt Jacob would mind if we stayed out as late as ten." Mark sounded enthusiastic about the idea. "I'll write the note."

"Good thinking. Lori wouldn't like it at all if she knew I thought of it. With your handwriting . . . And Jacob will back us up, even if we slept all night on the beach."

"Worse and worse," Alfie mumbled to Werner. Sleep on the beach? Wasn't this tiny room bad enough? Now they had to sleep on the beach?

"Hurry up," Jamie hissed. "Tell him . . . them . . . in honor of their wedding night, we've decided to stay away for a while. How is that?"

No time to reply. A heavy knock sounded against the door. Jacob and Lori were back already. Alfie thought they must have swallowed their sodas in one gulp.

Mark and Jamie moaned. Too late. Jacob and Lori would never agree to let them stay on the beach in Sopot, no matter how hot the flat got tonight. No cool ocean breezes . . . no gentle drumming of the waves . . .

Again the knock sounded. "Open it, Alfie," Mark commanded.

Alfie put Werner on his shoulder and fixed a smile on his face even though he was not happy about the way everything was so confused. He pulled open the door.

"Hullo . . . uh . . . ." The smile went away. This was not Lori and Jacob after all.

A thin, frightened little man stood sweating in the corridor. His hatless head was drawn forward toward an enormous nose. Thick spectacles perched on his beak, making him look very much like a vulture. His wide eyes seemed to whirl behind the lenses. Alfie thought to himself that the stranger's eyes looked like bulging boiled eggs. He did not say that to the man, however, because that would have been rude.

"Hullo," Alfie said again. He shook the fellow's clammy hand. "I am Alfie."

The man looked over his shoulder, then at the number on the door. Alfie also looked at the number, then back at the man who seemed very nervous.

"Who is it?" Mark shouted from the bedroom.

"A man with egg-eyes who is sweating a lot," Alfie answered. Then he frowned because he had not meant to talk about the man's eyes, only his sweat. "He looks nice," he added.

"Please," the man said in a quiet voice. "I need to talk to someone . . . who is in charge. There is a young woman who lives here with you?"

"Lori is having a wedding . . . soda . . ." The man seemed very frightened. Alfie called Jamie. "Jamie, this man wants Lori."

His face set in a scowl, Jamie emerged. He looked past Alfie at the little man. The scowl melted into curiosity and then concern.

"Who do you want to see?" Jamie sounded adult as he challenged the stranger.

"Lori." The nervous glance over the stooped shoulder. "Her name is Lori? It is . . . about you. My business concerns you as well."

Jamie did not walk forward to the door. He hung back as though he was afraid the man might reach out and take him.

"Mark!" he called. Mark was already at his side. The two boys stared silently back at the man.

"Who are you?" Mark demanded.

The man wiped his brow with a yellowed handkerchief. "It does not matter who I am . . . I . . . have reason to believe . . ." He faltered, peering past Alfie who towered above him, blocking his entrance into the flat. "Please. I need to have a word with whoever is in charge."

"We are," Mark and Jamie said together.

"What do you want?" Mark drew himself up as he had seen Jacob do before a fight.

"I do not know who you are. Why you are here. But there is a man in Danzig who wants very much to find you." The stranger's voice was an urgent whisper. "I met him outside the British Embassy. He told me a story. He hired me to watch for you—" He pointed at Jamie. "And your sister. I followed you here, and went to report. He lives at the Deutscher Hof. In his room there was a map. Black pins and red pins.

He has searched every district, and now he knows you are here." He waved his hand back toward the stairs. "I did not tell him the name of the rooming house because I thought perhaps ... when I saw the map ... He seems not to be what he told me he was." The big eyes darted around the room. "Get out of here. I wanted to tell you. Get out of Danzig. Out of Heiliger Geist District. Stay clear of the Deutscher Hof."

Jamie, Mark, and Alfie stared silently at this prophet of doom. The silence drew out, long and heavy as the heat. Finally Werner moved, and the man looked at the kitten as though he was grateful for some response.

"Well," he shrugged and stepped back from the door. "I can do no more than warn you." And then he was gone. The clatter of his street shoes sounded on the long staircase to the lobby. Alfie stood in the doorway and listened until the footsteps disappeared.

———

"*What did he say?*" Jacob shouted as he pulled Mark up by his arms.

"We *told* you!" Jamie defended. "There was a map with pins in it in the man's room at the Deutscher Hof. Black pins where he had looked for us. Red pins where we might be!"

Alfie pointed at the floor. "Here is a red pin still."

"We can't stay here, Jacob!" Mark cried, responding to his brother's anger with equal feeling. "While we're standing here talking about this ... Don't you see? We have to get out of Danzig *now!*"

Lori bit her lip and looked toward the window as if she were afraid to get near it. *Could the unnamed pursuer be out there now? Looking toward this flat?* She remembered what Alfie had told her. *They are coming to Danzig....* He had known all along.

The boys gathered up all the packed luggage. It stood ready beside the door.

Jacob's face was ashen. He looked at the luggage and then at Lori. Had any wedding night ever been shadowed by such portent of disaster?

"They are right," Lori said with resignation. "We shouldn't waste any more time."

Jacob frowned and stared hard at the window. *He felt it, too!*

"The man said stay away from this district, away from the hotels." Jamie's brow furrowed with concern, an expression that made him look much older.

Lori turned away to look at the perfectly made double bed, the flowers in the quart jar vases. *Beautiful and sweet.* The gesture made her want to cry, but there was no time for that now. "Where should we go?" she asked Jacob.

Alfie looked up brightly. "It's hot here," he said. "Let's go . . . uh . . . Sopot is a good place to go!"

Six months ago Jacob might have scoffed at any suggestion Alfie made, but this evening he remembered that God seemed to whisper in Alfie's ear.

The light returned to the eyes of Jamie and Mark. *Sopot! The beach! The Kurhaus! The casino and hotel!*

Jacob raised his head as though he heard the same voice Alfie heard. "Sopot. Perfect. A resort. They would not think of looking for a gang of fugitives at Sopot!" He thumped Alfie on the back. "A very smart idea, Alfie."

"Uh-huh. Do . . . can kittens go in the casino?"

In reply, Jacob opened the false-bottomed valise and dropped Werner in. The racket of unhappy yowling began immediately. Alfie pressed his lips together with concern.

"They will not notice the noise," Lori reassured him. "Papa used to say someone could walk through naked and no one would look up."

That comment made Alfie blush. He could not think that Pastor Ibsen would ever say such a thing as that!

Allan Farrell rode from post office to post office by alternating cab and underground. At each location he nonchalantly removed one manila envelope from a scuffed leather briefcase. He deposited each in a mail slot and strolled unhurriedly back out to the street.

Sometimes he would make his drop at post offices that were close together. Other times he would deliberately ride past several or double back on his path so as to confuse his actual route.

The first of the envelopes blew up at 4:00 P.M. at the branch of the Royal Post Office not far from the British Museum. The eyesight of the postal worker who was operating the canceling machine was spared only because he wore glasses; the eruption of flames when the aspirin bottle was crushed burned the outline of his spectacles onto his face.

From there a string of nineteen more explosions rocked the London summer afternoon. At another post office in the city, no one was injured seriously, but two thousand business letters—banking and commerce, shipping and industry—were destroyed. How do you fight a fire of blazing paper except with water? But what does more damage; a flaming pile of envelopes or a two-inch stream of muddy Thames river water?

The most common injury among postal clerks was burns to their hands as they attempted to drag letters away from the bonfires. The more enterprising tried to smother the flames with canvas mail sacks, but unless they thought to soak the bags in water first, they only added fuel to the fires.

One envelope caused a particularly spectacular display. One of the bombs was addressed to an outlying district and so was loaded onto a mail car attached to the 6:15 train from Charing Cross Station. It had not even come near a canceling machine, but the length of time had been enough for the acid to eat through the thin metal cap on the bottle. The clerk later reported smelling a biting, acrid odor just before an entire sack of mail burst into flames!

Throwing open the sliding door and grabbing the canvas bag without regard to the vicious heat searing his hands and arms, the clerk pitched the blazing sack from the moving train. It arced through the air like a meteor streaking to earth, leaving a trail of gray smoke and flaming letters.

Its flight took it directly into the path of another train going the opposite direction. When the fireball was struck, it showered both sides of the railway carriages with burning debris.

Both engines ground to a halt and the tracks were soon swarming with passengers, crew, and curiosity seekers. Some were clutching smoldering fragments of envelopes as souvenirs. The injured mail clerk with blistered hands futilely tried to retrieve the letters from the ditches and the crowd.

By the time this happened, Allan Farrell had long since deposited the last of his weapons of terror and returned home to await results. The scream of sirens that began suddenly and increased rapidly gave him great satisfaction.

———

The distant sound of a siren pierced the evening air as Orde stepped onto the sidewalk. He raised his head to listen, then hurried inside.

Orde's bags were packed and loaded in the taxi that waited downstairs in front of the house on Red Lion Square. A broad-faced woman poked her head out to watch Orde suspiciously as he climbed the stairs to Murphy's residence. His step was light in anticipation of the plan he was about to present. *Precious British passports!*

"D'Mizzus Murphy, she has just home from the hospital got from the having of the baby!" The woman called after him to indicate he should not visit at such a time.

"I am invited," Orde said softly over his shoulder.

"Okay den, but you don't too long stay because all dis is wearing her out!" Then the door slammed shut. A moment later it opened again. "An' don't too loud on the door knock!" the indignant voice instructed him in a shouted whisper.

As per instructions, Orde rapped softly, doffed his cap, and ran his hand through his hair. Murphy's voice was a tiptoe beyond the door. "That you, Orde?"

He opened the door and stepped back, inviting Orde to enter with a finger placed over his lips. "She's sleeping," Murphy explained. Then Mrs. Murphy . . . Elisa . . . slipped into the room with two women following after. It was plain to see that they were all related. The physical resemblance was strong and impressive to Orde. Fine-looking women, all three of them. Elisa, her mother Anna, and Anna's sister Helen Ibsen.

Elisa Murphy did not look as though anything was wearing her out, Orde thought as he considered the warning of the woman in the stairwell. Dressed in a pale pink cotton skirt topped by a shirt that probably belonged to her husband, she looked as if she had just come in from a stroll on the beach at Brighton. Her short blond hair was swept back. She wore no makeup. Her skin looked fresh and scrubbed. Orde did not let himself look into the blueness of her eyes as he shook her hand. He envied Murphy in that moment. A new baby and a woman who would be a pleasure to wake up next to.

Anna and Helen were different, older versions of the same uncluttered attractiveness. Helen was younger and slightly taller than Anna and Elisa. And when he looked into Helen's eyes, he saw the sadness plainly.

Did she see something behind his face as well? Introductions were made all around; then it was Helen Ibsen who took charge of the meeting. She led Orde to the sofa, sat down, and indicated that he should sit beside her. Elisa and Anna slipped out to make coffee. Helen then told Orde the story of the young man with whom he was about to make contact. *Jacob Kalner, so in need of a passport!*

The story of Jacob Kalner was anything but happy. Reports were confirmed that Jacob's father had been executed in prison. His mother had died of typhus six weeks ago. They had not yet broken the news to Jacob. They had waited, hoping that he would be here in England among friends when he was told. "But he will ask," Helen said quietly. "It would be better if someone was there with him to tell him face-to-face."

Coffee was served, and Helen shared everything she could about him—much more than Orde cared to know. She finished by saying, "My daughter Lori is in love with him. She thinks I don't know, but . . . she is my daughter." Helen frowned. "There was a time when I promised Jacob's mother that we would care for him if something happened. Well, everything has happened. And Jacob is out of reach." She put a hand on Orde's arm. "I want to ask you to take good care of Jacob. He is like my own child. My children are coming home to me and Jacob is staying behind. Until we can find some way . . ." She paused, "He is a good boy, Captain Orde. And he will have no one but you for a while."

At first Helen Ibsen talked over and around the insistent wail of sirens that had begun moments after Orde entered. Then the increasing racket caused everyone to look at one another in concern.

Murphy stood up and went to the window as two more police cars screamed past and rounded the corner. "Excuse me," he mumbled, retreating to the office. "Ambulance chasing gets in the blood."

Murphy's voice could be heard as he telephoned the TENS office to see what news was coming over the police radio frequency. Before he emerged, the rapid stumbling of footsteps sounded on the stairs.

Charles and Louis burst into the room, their eyes wide and horrified. They were shouting a jumble of English and German words. Behind them, at a much slower pace, came Doc Grogan. He, too, looked pale and worried.

He did not say hello, did not seem to notice Orde, or Anna and Helen. "Where's Murphy?" he asked Elisa curtly.

"Here." Murphy stood framed in the doorway.

"Are the Nazis coming?" Charles clung, weeping to Elisa. There was no mistaking the terror in his eyes.

"Bombs." Doc began to talk in a rapid-fire voice that he had repeatedly warned Orde against using on the radio. "We took a taxi. I was afraid to take the underground with the boys." He shook his head. "Bombs all over London. Every district post office has been hit. I mean *every* post office we passed."

The hammering wail of sirens filled the air. Tomorrow the children of Helen Ibsen were leaving Danzig for the imagined safety of London. But apparently there was no safety. Not anywhere.

Orde looked toward his briefcase, which held the photographs of the Lubetkin family. He had not had a chance to explain his idea to Murphy. In an hour, Orde had to be on his ship, yet Murphy and Grogan were saying goodbye and rushing out the door. There was no use trying to pull Murphy into the office and explain his idea with all this going on.

Rocking on his heels, Orde stood at the window for a few minutes and watched fire trucks and ambulances speeding past. How best to approach these women with the plan for obtaining passports for Jacob Kalner and the others among the Lubetkin family?

The boys were crying. Baby Katie awoke unhappily as the noise grew louder. Over this confusion, Orde sat down and took a sip of tepid tea. What if they did not appreciate the logic of his plan? What if they. . . ? *Oh well,* he thought, *spill it.*

In the midst of this chaos, Orde displayed each photograph on the coffee table beside Katie's passport. No one noticed the sirens anymore as Orde explained his plan.

"I think the photograph of Rachel Lubetkin is good enough to pass easily for British. The pictures of the rest of her family will have to be retaken."

"What about Jacob?" asked Helen.

"It is only a matter of getting the passport pictures to you here in England. In the meantime, you should immediately begin looking in cemeteries."

The woman exchanged nervous glances. "We have been warned by certain British officials," Anna explained. "We are fairly certain they are watching us closely."

Orde had a ready reply. "Brass rubbing," he said. "A piece of paper, a crayon. Put it over the stone and rub. It is quite popular among the British. People studying genealogies. A pleasant summer pastime which no one will question."

"It looks as though we are back in business," Elisa said cheerfully as she took down the violin case from the cupboard. "Mother? How many do you think we can reasonably manage?"

Anna looked skyward. "It depends on how much time the politicians give us." Then to Orde, "This means you will have to make difficult choices. Appearance and mannerisms will be important. Language. It would not do to send someone on a steamer to Southampton who could not address the steward in English."

Orde was accustomed to difficult discussions. "Have the birth certificates ready to go. I am hoping to have the photographs in your hands within a fortnight of the time I arrive in Poland. I will send them by air courier among the regular news photographs. From there it will be a matter of submitting the passport applications and waiting a few weeks."

"And then smuggling the documents to you in Warsaw," Anna said.

Elisa looked at the battered violin case and remembered. "It cannot be half as hard in Poland as it was in the Reich."

"As long as Poland is not also the Reich," Orde added with a grimness that gave fulfillment of the plan a new desperation.

Hess knew from the first reply that he had at last found the right apartment building.

"So who wants to know about them?" asked the overweight middle-aged woman who owned the building and managed it herself.

"There is a reward," Hess remarked, sliding the photograph back into his packet as though time was short.

"A reward for what?" The woman eyed his black-gloved hand and the silver tip of his cane.

"Simply for locating them."

"They haven't broken the law, have they? They seem like good children. At first I did not wish to rent to them, but they seemed quite polite. They have been good tenants. Pay their rent on time. Quieter than most. No bother." She blew her nose noisily and scrutinized Hess with renewed suspicion. "So what have they done?"

"They are sought by their families."

"And what are you to them?"

"I am only the man hired to find them and bring them home."

The woman cleared her throat and looked both ways from hall to foyer. "You said something about a reward?"

"Fifty marks to the one who helps locate them."

"Fifty for me, or must I split it with you?"

"Have you keys to their flat?" Hess smiled and looked up the stairs. He had not doubted that he would find them. The surprise lay only in the fact that it had been so easy.

"For seventy-five marks I have keys." She laid her hand on the desk.

"I can knock on each door for nothing," Hess countered.

"They are not home." The hand remained unmoving and unintimidated on the desk.

Hess counted out the bills and then stepped back as she opened a cabinet with numbered keys hanging on the inside of the door. *Apartment 2-C.* She removed the brass keys and passed them to Hess.

"I can see myself up." He nodded his thanks.

She called after him, "It is only fair that I get seventy-five, you know, since you are taking my tenants and I will receive no more rent from them. It is only fair."

———

Hess did not turn on the light in the flat, although the gloom of twilight made it difficult for him to see well. He relocked the door and then stood in the center of the sparsely furnished front room, savoring his victory.

He could make out the shapes of dishes stacked on the shelf above the kitchen sink in the corner. *Clean. Neat.* Nothing seemed out of place. No wonder the landlady had demanded seventy-five marks for betraying such exemplary tenants.

He limped to the open door of a large bedroom. In the last ray of daylight he could see that the double bed was perfectly made up. Two vases of flowers filled the room with fragrance. He shoved the keys into his pocket and went to the window to look out on the narrow street below. From this vantage point he could just make out the corner window of the cabaret. He nodded, as if to congratulate himself on his superb instincts. They would have heard the music. Had they sensed their own peril?

He reached out with his uninjured hand to pluck a daisy from the bouquet on the chest of drawers. Tucking it into his buttonhole, he sat on the edge of the bed and swung his aching leg onto the mattress. Then he removed his pistol and placed it beside him on the pillow.

This would be as good a place to wait for them as any. The muzzle of a gun in the mouth of the first one through the door would hold them all prisoner. A simple matter.

Patting his flask, he considered celebrating with a swallow of schnapps. He thought better of it, and leaned his head back against the headboard as the room grew darker.

———

The Wilson Line steamer *East Sea* eased into the wharf. Though night had closed in around the port of Danzig, Orde could still make out the loading docks and cargo cranes.

Orde ran a practiced military eye over the scene, noting the spread of warehouses along the waterfront. *Journalist's eye,* he corrected himself, but he went on observing strong points and defensible positions just the same.

Danzig was supposed to be a place where war might break out. According to the ravings of Herr Hitler, Danzig must and would belong to the Reich. It was apparent to Orde that warlike preparations were taking place. A convoy of trucks, distinctly German in appearance but bearing Danzig license plates, streamed past the Wilson Line docks toward an isolated and dimly lit warehouse.

They are not transporting tea, thought Orde grimly. He declined the offer of a taxi to his hotel, deciding that he would walk the few blocks instead. From the pocket of his overcoat he retrieved a notebook with the address of the Ibsen children, but he replaced it unopened after realizing that it was too late to go there. He would see them at the docks tomorrow, anyway. Orde's luggage had been shipped ahead to Warsaw, except for the small valise he carried.

The area of Danzig adjacent to the harbor was gloomy and dismal. A trio of drunken sailors paused on wobbly legs, apparently searching their fuddled brains for directions. When the middle of the three men slid down to lie unconscious on the cobblestones, his companions dragged him out of the street, emptied his pockets of a few remaining coins, and left him propped against a warehouse wall.

Up ahead, one bright light in all the grimy dark beckoned to Orde. The polished globe of the lamp spoke of more care and concern than could be seen anywhere else in the quarter. Orde was drawn to the light to see what warranted such pride in the otherwise neglected surroundings.

The neatly lettered sign beside the door read ENGLISH MARINER'S CHURCH. The words were printed in English at the top, but repeated in German and in Polish below that. Orde thought how appropriate that seemed; here was Danzig caught between Germany and Poland with England trying to make sense of it all.

Orde knew that time was running short. If Danzig was a barrel of petrol, then the lighted match was very close indeed. He had heard the reports of how the Nazis were transporting arms and ammunition across the Nogat River from East Prussia by night. The Nazis in Danzig clearly wanted war, but then they had their sights set on a much larger target than just this port.

The rest of the German Danzigers expected to be reunited with the Reich, but without bloodshed, the way Hitler had demanded and gotten the Sudetenland. They wanted to be German, but not at the cost of war and the interruption of their trade with Poland. They were deluding themselves. The war that was most certainly coming would engulf them all.

———

Some time after dark a bank of storm clouds swept in from the Baltic and erupted over Danzig. Lucy awakened to the soft cry of her baby, tended to his needs first and then set out pots and pans to catch the drips from the leaking roof.

The dissonant clank of water drummed against the pots, and rain sluiced through the gutters. Lucy nursed the baby and then, lulled by the unwritten melody and the coolness of the air, she fell into a deep and untroubled sleep again.

The storm outside raged on, unabated through the long night. After a day of heat and profound exhaustion, Lucy was too weary to worry any longer that Wolf was somewhere in Danzig, perhaps very near. There was only one fundamental issue. She and the baby were both alive, both well. She had no strength to dwell on anything beyond that. Her sleep was dreamless and profound. If her baby had cried, Lucy would have awakened, but he did not cry. The child, too, simply slept on in the illusion of well-being beside the warmth of his mother's body.

The summer storm seemed to sing its lullaby to Lucy. She felt no foreboding at the drum of distant thunder. She never heard the sound of boots against the stairs. She did not stir at the rattle of the extra key that had been bought from the old concierge in the lobby. For these few hours, at least, Lucy was at peace beside her child. Merciful sleep. It shut the unthinkable disaster from her mind even as the lock clicked open and the hinge of the door groaned back.

22

One Moment of Joy

Werner seemed very happy with the large and elegant room at the Sopot casino. There were tabletops to explore and the fringe of a bed-spread with which he could do battle. The fixtures in the bathroom were shiny brass, and he could see a kitten reflection in the faucet. There was one big bed for Mark and Jamie to share and a very nice feather cushioned sofa for Alfie. A silver candy dish held perfect round chocolates. Mark poked his finger in the bottom of every one to see what was inside, but Alfie did not mind. He decided not to look at the bottom before he took a bite. He liked surprises as long as they were nice surprises. Butter creams, marshmallow, orange stuff, and cherries.

"This is much better than just going to Sprinter's for lemon ice and sleeping on the beach," Jamie said, finally looking happy.

"Jacob and Lori's room is not nearly so big as this." Mark sat back on the sofa and propped his feet on the coffee table. He punctured another chocolate, peered in, and popped it into his mouth. "You know if *they* were in here, we could not put our feet up or poke the choco-lates."

Alfie smiled. Now that they did not have to sleep all crammed into the little room where Lori had slept, he did not mind so much that they were not all together in the same room.

"They . . . won't have as much fun . . . as us," Alfie said confidently, biting into a cherry covered with light chocolate. He offered Werner-kitten a bite, but Werner was not interested. He hopped off the back of the satin sofa and ran to climb the pale yellow draperies.

"It has been a very good day," Jamie said with a contented sigh. He wiped his mouth on his sleeve and watched with admiration as Werner nearly made it to the top of the draperies before sliding down.

"We should fill the ice bucket with sand from the beach," Mark said. "Then Werner will have a toilet."

"Good idea," Alfie said. Then he called to Werner, "Plumbing inside, Werner!"

The cat meowed, much quieter than he had when he had been inside the despised hiding place in the valise. Lori had been right about nobody noticing the noise. Almost nobody had noticed except for the bell captain who sent men everywhere looking for the cat that had slipped into the lobby to hide somewhere. It had been fun to watch them on their knees, poking their heads into corners behind potted palms. They never imagined there was a kitten stashed in the luggage.

"It's a good thing your mother sent us money from England," Mark said. "We could stay here a whole week if we weren't leaving on the ship."

"And there would still be enough for Jacob to get to Warsaw." Jamie tossed a pillow at Werner, who jumped straight up and scampered across the mantel on the fireplace. "If I was him, I'd stay awhile after we leave. Who wants to go to Warsaw when you could stay in the Kurhaus Hotel and eat all the chocolates you want?"

"It wouldn't work," Mark interjected. "He told the man at the front desk that his papers were still in the luggage at the depot. So he didn't have to give our real names. But the clerk will want to see them, all right. He's got to be gone before then."

"Too bad." Alfie mumbled through a full mouth. "Sopot is . . ." He wanted to say that in his entire life he had never been anyplace as wonderful as Sopot and this hotel. This room had more space than three flats like theirs. The lights were bright and clean. The tub was big enough for him to play boats in—except that he had not owned any toy boats since Mama died. It did not matter. Soon he would be on a real boat. A big boat. And now that Jacob and Lori were really married, maybe Jacob could get on a boat to England much sooner.

"Probably it is better that Jacob has two relatives in England," Mark said. "A brother and a wife. I think so. Two of us will be able to make more of a fuss than one."

Jamie raised his head and looked all around the room. "My papa stayed here once, you know. He told us about it."

"My papa too," Mark added, not to be outdone.

"Maybe they stayed in this very room." Jamie smiled at the thought. "Papa will like it that Lori and Jacob had their honeymoon here, I think. Maybe it will make the rest all right. You think so?"

Alfie patted the sofa and Werner jumped up beside him. "They . . . they won't have as much fun . . . as our room." He scratched Werner's head and thought about filling the ice bucket with sand.

Mark and Jamie exchanged *the look*. Alfie wished he knew whatever secret they knew.

———————

Lucy's mother and father stood in the barnyard. The door to the barn was open. It was dark inside, but Lucy could see someone moving from stall to stall. Lucy's father smiled and tapped out the tobacco of his pipe. Then he reached his arms out to take the baby from her.

"What will we call him, Mother?" he asked of his wife.

Lucy's mother pulled the blanket back from the baby's face to study the serious blue eyes of the quiet infant. "He looks like Wolf, don't you think, Papa?" She smiled at Lucy. "Would you like to name him after his father, Lucy dear? He looks so much like Wolf. No mistaking he is the son of Wolfgang von Fritschauer."

In her sleep, those words were pleasing to Lucy. In her dream she could not remember everything that had gone on between Vienna and this arrival at her childhood home.

Lucy opened her mouth to speak, to agree that her son should be called Wolfgang; but the words would not come. She tried to say the name again and again. The word formed clearly in her mind. She could see the letters, suddenly inscribed in black on the red blanket in which the tiny form of innocence was wrapped: W-O-L-F.

"What is wrong, Lucy dear? You can't speak?" her mother asked her sympathetically. "Shall we call your son Wolf? Shall I say it for you?"

Lucy raised her hand to touch the head of the baby, but suddenly he was pulled away from her. The image of her mother's face faded and that of another woman took her place. The woman standing in front of her was the same one Lucy had seen among Wolf's photographs. Here was the wife of Wolfgang von Fritschauer! Her cold eyes glinted with pride as she took the baby from Lucy's father and cried, "Yes! Just like Wolf!"

At the same instant, Lucy's father stepped back, his face pale. "I have to tend to what is mine!" he shouted angrily as he hurried away into the barn. Lucy tried to follow, but she could not move. She tried to call out for her father to come back, but she could not speak.

Her hands hung heavily at her sides. She could not lift them to fight against the woman who smiled over the baby. As Lucy watched, the shadow from the barn stepped into the light. It was Wolf, tall and handsome in his black uniform. He looked at Lucy and smiled cruelly, as she had seen him do a thousand times before. Suddenly she remembered everything! Scenes from their life together replayed in a flash. She remembered the terror of her escape from him; the threat he had made to take her baby rang out clearly in her mind.

She looked at the blanket where her child lay. It was red, but a darker red than it had been before. The fabric seemed to dissolve and melt until it covered the arms of the woman with blood. The black letters of Wolf's name spun like pinwheels and moved together to form the shape of the Nazi swastika. Lucy tried to shout a warning to the woman; to tell her she must guard the baby; but still she made no sound.

Could they not see the blood that would drown the child? Why did they not take him out of the blanket before it suffocated him?

Lucy found the strength to step forward; she opened her mouth and willed herself to shout the warning. They did not hear her.

"What shall we name the Führer's child?" asked the woman.

"He looks like me," Wolf was pleased. "Just like all the rest. We will call him Wolf." Blood had pooled in the baby's eyes. Lucy could see her son open his little mouth and gasp for breath. She ran toward him, to wrench him from the unseeing woman, but as Lucy reached out, they floated just beyond her straining fingertips.

In the barn Lucy could hear the rattle of milk filling the metal pails. She could hear the cowbells banging against the stanchions where her father milked the cows. If she could reach her father, maybe he would help her! But the barn door, like the couple, swung lazily beyond her reach.

She tried to call out for her father, but he did not hear her. The clank of the milk pails grew louder; the baby coughed and cried and . . .

"I am dreaming."

Lucy opened her eyes as the slow drumming of rainwater in the pots on the floor reminded her of where she was. The rain had stopped. The world was silent except for the few stray drops that had not yet found their way off of the eaves. Lucy gathered her baby to her and stroked his face gently with her fingers. No blood. He was fine, breathing sweetly and evenly. Thank God!

She sighed and lay back down in the blackness with a shudder of relief. It had been so pleasant, at first—her dream; her sleep. And then what had happened?

Closing her eyes she tried to recapture the feeling of peace she had felt before the dream had changed so horribly. *A name. A name for the baby. Not Wolf.*

"What will I call you, little one?" she whispered softly, cradling the tiny fingers in her hand. "What name for my son?" Her own voice was drowsy and pleasant in the stillness of the night.

At that moment a match flared behind her. The room was suddenly illuminated with orange light.

Lucy cried out as she sat up on the bed. Wolf glared at her from the glow of his match. He was smiling—the cruel smile she knew so well. His raincoat was draped over the chair. His boots were still wet.

He stepped forward as though he might toss the match onto the bed; instead, he touched the flame to the wick of the gas lamp.

"His name is Wolf," he said with amusement. "Or have you forgotten whose child he is, Lucy dear?"

————

Morning had come, terrible and swift, to the Kurhaus Hotel at Sopot.

Lori had not slept at all, even though Jacob had slept and then awakened a dozen times throughout the night to her loving touch.

Only one night together, but it was enough to knit their hearts forever. Lori felt as if she had never been a child, never belonged to anyone but to Jacob.

She reached out and touched his muscled back. There was the scar he had gotten when he fell from his bicycle in fourth grade. She remembered that. He was brave even then; he had not cried even though his shoulder had been torn open. Any other boy in their class would have cried. Lori thought now that she had loved Jacob Kalner even then—and long before that day as well. He had tied her braids together in second grade, and she had been so angry. In first grade, he had told her to take a sniff of a jar with a rotten bird's egg, and she had run home crying. His mother had made him bring her flowers as an apology. He had doffed his hat and bowed and made her smile from behind the screen door. There were other memories—birthday cakes shared in Sunday school; family outings on the Spree when she publicly hated him and secretly loved him. And now all of that had come down to one night, the consummation of everything she had ever longed for. Jacob, her friend. Jacob, her hero. Jacob, her lover. Jacob, her husband.

They were not children any longer. After this one night of discovery and joy they were to be separated. For the first time in their lives, really, they would not be able to talk to each other or ignore each other; to tease or listen; to make wishes. Or to embrace again. *For how long, Lord?*

Lori moved closer to him, pressing herself against him and kissing the back of his neck. She did not want him to wake up. When he awoke he would turn and tell her it really was morning. *Don't wake up. Let me listen to your heart while you sleep.* She laid her cheek against his back and listened to the deep and steady beat of his heart. It was much slower than her own heartbeat. Strong and honest. He had loved her far more than she had loved herself. He had forced her to wait for this perfect night until it was right. How she adored him for that, for demanding only the best for her soul! Today at the docks he would demand that for her safety's sake as well.

Don't urge me to leave you or to turn back from you. Where you go I will go.

How could she let him go? How could she keep her promise not to beg him to let her stay at his side?

Hess had propped open the bedroom window to hear the cabaret accordion. One sip of schnapps had led to another until at last he had emptied the flask and dozed fitfully on the bed.

The first gray light of dawn illuminated the room. Hess opened his eyes as the memory of last night returned.

They had never come back to the flat! He sat straight up, sending the flask clattering to the floor. Had they been warned? He threw back the curtain and looked out on the still-sleeping street as though he might see them below. He groped toward the closet door and threw it open. *Empty!* Wooden hangers lay in a pile on the closet floor, one lone sock in the corner.

Hess cursed and then rushed to pull open the drawers of the chest. Each one *empty*! In his rage he threw the vase of flowers against the wall and overturned the night table, shattering the lamp.

Only then did it occur to him that perhaps his quarry had never ever been here! Had he been tricked? Seventy-five marks had yielded him nothing but a night's lodging in a vacant apartment.

Drawing his knife, he held the blade up to the just-breaking daylight. The landlady would spend twice as much as he had paid her in the repair of this flat. Plunging the knife into the mattress, he tugged the knife from the head of the bed to the foot.

Within five minutes, dishes were broken into shards, draperies and upholstery alike were shredded.

The thin, reedy voice of the newborn's cry covered the sound of blows as Wolfgang von Fritschauer unleashed the rage he had felt against Lucy for months.

She was too weak to resist when he grabbed her by the hair and slapped her again and again. Blood from her nose splattered across the clean white sheets, dotting the skin of the baby like a fulfillment of her worst nightmare. Wolf kicked the table over. He threw the basin against the wall.

"Beg me!" he hissed through clenched teeth as he threw her back on the bed. "I want to hear you beg me!"

"No, Wolf!" she cried. "Please, no more! The child. Please—" She held the sheet up to her face and tried to stop the bleeding. The sheet was soaked with red. "I *am* begging. . . ." She wept and held a hand up to restrain him as he unbuckled his belt and stepped toward her. Hooking his thumbs in his trouser pockets, he rocked upon his toes and glared down at her.

And the infant wailed on. The child's fair skin grew red with terror and outrage as his quiet world became a hell of confusion.

"You think I have forgotten you, eh?" he sneered. Then in a sarcastic voice he mimicked her. *"Oh please, Wolf! Don't make me go to the Lebensborn yet! We have such fun together still!"* He let his eyes linger on her gown where her milk dampened the fabric. He smiled cruelly, a smile she knew all too well.

She shook her head. "Please. The baby was only born last night. Oh, Wolf! Not even you could—" Her face was a mask of terror.

"That's right," he towered over her. *"Beg me."*

"I can make everything like it used to be," she pleaded. "I was just frightened! I did not want you to take my baby!"

"So all your efforts have come to this, eh?" Again he mocked, *"Oh Wolf, you must keep me pregnant!"* The muscles in his cheek twitched. "Why not start now?"

"Wolf!" she sobbed and pressed herself back against the iron bars of the bed where she was captive. "Don't do this thing!"

He threw his shirt across the room, then grabbed her gown at the neck and tore it from her. He laughed when he looked at her. "So this is what becomes of beauty . . . Not quite what you had before, Lucy. But it's been a long time—I do not mind."

She tried to scream, tried to fight him, but he clamped his hand over her mouth and pushed her beneath him.

Lucy's cries of pain were muffled and lost beneath the frantic wails of the baby born into a world gone terribly wrong.

———————

Cocking back the hammer of his pistol, Hess placed the barrel into the ear of the still-sleeping landlady. She awoke with a start and opened her mouth to scream as Hess clamped his hand down hard to silence her.

"Do not scream, dear Frau," he said quietly.

Her terrified eyes rolled wildly as if she would black out. He smiled down at her patronizingly. "So sorry to awaken you so early in the morning, but you see, you have something I want. Something I need."

From beneath his hand she begged him not to harm her.

"I do not like being made the butt of a joke," Hess explained as though he were telling a waitress his coffee was too cold. "You understand?"

She shook her head. She did not understand at all.

"Your tenants are quite sloppy," he continued in a whining voice.

"What a terrible mess they made of the flat before they left. Did you know?"

Again the head moved slowly. No. She did not know.

"If I remove my hand, you promise not to scream?"

She nodded, closing her eyes as if to pray. The hand was lifted slowly from her mouth. The gun remained at her ear.

"Please," she breathed. "Do not kill—"

"Kill you?" Hess jabbed the gun into her neck to make his point. "Only if you scream. Or lie. You will tell me everything, will you not?"

"Yes, only please . . ."

"I ask the questions and you answer. Right?"

"Yes. Anything." Tears streamed down her fat cheeks.

Hess gave her another sharp jab. "Shut up and listen. Your tenants in 2-C did not come back last night. Where are they?"

"I . . . I don't know," she stammered. "I am not their mother."

"Yes. Did you know the closet is empty? And their chest of drawers as well?"

"No! I swear! They were there! I saw them last . . . two days ago. They paid in advance until the end of the month. Still more than a week yet on their rent!"

"They are gone," Hess said. "And they left the flat—your lovely flat—a wreck, I'm afraid." He stepped back as the woman's face clouded with anger. At him and also at the children.

"They did not check out. Gave me no notice. Did not collect their cleaning deposit."

"Good. No doubt you will need it after what they have done." He waved the pistol in her face. "You do not know . . . have no idea . . . where they have gone?"

She lay very still on her back, staring past the gun toward the ceiling. "They had mentioned England. But I thought I would have noticed. I did not think they would just leave."

"England," Hess whispered. "How were they to travel?"

"How should I know?" the woman barked.

Once again he pressed the gun to her ear. A small cry escaped her lips. "Landladies know everything about their tenants."

"They said . . . by steamship . . . but if they left with their luggage, I would have seen them," she protested meekly. "Please. I have told you all I know."

"Not all." Hess leaned down very close to her face until the gray of his blind eye was all she could see. "Where is my money?" he growled. "My seventy-five marks!"

She pointed to her handbag. "There! In there! Take it and go! Please go! And do not hurt me!"

Hess smiled. His soulless eye mocked her terror as he pressed the steel of the pistol hard and steady against the side of her neck.

A sudden movement of his wrist was all Hess needed to slam the gun barrel into her head. Her eyes rolled back in unconsciousness. He dumped out her handbag and took back the cash he had given her; then he slipped out of the building without being seen.

Wolf buttoned his shirt slowly as he spoke to Lucy in a patronizing sing-song voice. He acted as though nothing had happened since she left him in Vienna, as though nothing at all had just happened in this garret room—no violence—no brutality.

"You are not hurt," he said lightly. "On the farm we breed back mares to stallions three days after they give birth." He managed a short laugh. "Probably you will be pregnant again from our little passion here."

Lucy did not reply. She lay very still beneath the red-spattered sheet. Her eyes were dull as she stared at the window. The baby nursed frantically. His breath trembled against her breast. Only now as she absently stroked his head was he quiet.

Wolf looked down at his clothes. Flecks of blood covered him. The morning light broke through a layer of clouds and streamed across the wood-plank floor covered with wreckage from Wolf's rage. "You are not going anywhere," he muttered, "until I take you."

"Where?" Her voice was barely audible.

"Back home. To the Reich. You would like to go home, wouldn't you?"

She did not reply.

Wolf's tone was still smooth. "There are questions which you must answer, you see. People who want to know . . ." He waited as if she would respond to his words. "Your friend, Otto Wattenbarger . . ."

"I do not know." And then she remembered it was Otto Wattenbarger who had hidden Peter Wallich's family in Vienna. A Gestapo agent himself, Otto had helped many political prisoners escape or die without talking. Otto had been arrested the night Peter and his mother had fled to Frau Singer's.

"You must remember him, eh? Maybe you were working together? Maybe you were in on the entire resistance plot in Vienna?"

"Oh, Wolf," she said wearily. *"Oh . . ."*

"You would like me to think you are too stupid and cow-like to be involved in such things. But you left Vienna with the family of Michael Wallich. Remember the Wallich case? Of course you do. Because you must be one of them as well. We would have had a confession from Otto, but he chose to launch himself out into eternity. Dead as a post in his cell. *Tragic.* And with so much he might have told us about the operation in Vienna." He put on his raincoat to cover the stains of her blood. "And so, my dear, I am afraid we will have to get our information from you."

"Let me sleep, Wolf. Please." She closed her eyes as tears crept from the corners.

"Yes. You are not going anywhere." She could hear his smile. "I have phone calls to make. But I will be back. And then you will come with me. You and the baby. A baby needs its mother—until someone else can be found to replace the nourishment."

Wolf was right. He had made certain she was too weak at this moment to move, too abused to do more than lie here until she could recover. By then, no doubt, he would be back. And then he would take her child. He would arrest her and give her to men who could, and would, match his own brutality. "By the way, I checked. The door can be locked from the outside. And I have both keys now. Just in case."

What was the use? What was left for her now? He was right. It had all been for nothing.

He stood over her bed and leaned close to her. "This morning's tryst may well be your last experience with physical pleasure. I hope it was unforgettable for you, dear Lucy."

With that, he slipped out of the room and locked the door from the outside, just to make certain she would still be here when he returned.

Lucy slept for what seemed like hours, yet when she opened her eyes the shadows on the rooftop were unchanged. It was as though the sun had not moved and no time at all had passed.

The bells of Marienkirche boomed out over the city. Lucy lay still and counted the tolling of the hours. *"Four . . . five . . . six . . . seven . . . eight . . ."* And then silence.

Could this be? Only eight o'clock? Wolf had just left the flat a few minutes before! His footsteps no doubt still echoed against the pavement of Heiliger Geist Strasse!

Lucy sat up slowly as if to test her fragile strength. She felt as though she had been asleep for days, as if the terror Wolf had brought into this room had happened days before.

She frowned, wondering if perhaps it really had been days ago that he had come to her. Perhaps something had happened to him and he had not been able to come back, she thought. Had she slept so long? Locked in some delirium of grief and pain had days instead of minutes passed? Had she cared for her baby without knowing what she was doing?

She touched his forehead. He was sleeping a deep, contented sleep. His diaper was dry. And yet, the blood—*her blood*—on the sheets was bright and fresh! She touched her nose. It was still bleeding slightly from Wolf's blows. Not broken, but tender and bruised, as was her right cheek.

Lucy ran her hands over her arms. The welts from Wolf's belt were bright red, *new*! There were the marks made by his fingers as he had held her down.

She swung her legs around and stood, gripping the iron bed for support. Her legs still trembled and her mind reeled, sending the room and the bright square of the window spinning until she sat down on the edge of the bed again.

She turned her head to the silver crucifix above the bed. "What day is this?" she asked aloud. "How long have I been sleeping?" With that, she stood once again, more slowly this time. The world did not spin. She kept her eyes fixed on the cross as she walked toward it and put her hand out to touch it. "You saw what he did," she moaned and began to weep silently. "Help me. Please . . ."

Taking the crucifix down from the nail, she clutched it to her. Wrapping herself in a sheet, she walked to the door and tried the knob. *Locked! From the outside!* Wolf had not returned. Only minutes had passed since he had left her! How much time did she have before he returned? And how could she get out?

Behind her through the partially open window, she heard the soft cooing of a pigeon. She turned to look as the bird walked along the ridgeline of the adjoining roof. Lucy frowned as she stared hard at it. She had never really looked at the roof before now. Always her eyes had swept up to the blue sky or the starlit night above the buildings.

But this was the only way.

Three brick chimneys protruded from the slate shingles, marking the division of houses. The structures all butted up against one another, providing a narrow tight-wire path along the high peak. Three buildings away was the smaller peak of a dormer window almost identical to the one where she stood now. She could not see inside. The angle obscured that view from her. She did not know if it was someone's apartment, or an office, or simply an empty garret room. *But if she could get to it!* If she could walk that narrow precipice, perhaps it was a way of escape!

She caught a glimpse of her reflection in the dingy glass. Even if she made it across the roof to the window, she could not walk three steps through the street without being noticed. Bruised face and matted hair. Ashen complexion and trembling hands. "Help me," she prayed as she turned to look with pity upon her baby. "Help me take him to safety. And then . . . it does not matter what happens to me. But for the baby! Sweet Christ Jesus! Have mercy on me!"

How long would Wolf's telephone calls take? There was no time to think about that now. Lucy found the washbasin and filled it with cold water. She bathed quickly and washed her hair. Dressing was more difficult. Each thing was done slowly, even though her mind rushed and her spirit shouted that she must *hurry!*

She donned a loose cotton dress. How strange it seemed to wear this dress now! She had bought it for a picnic by the Danube. Wolf had not liked it; he had ordered her never to wear it again. Clean and soft, it felt good against her skin. Somehow wearing it seemed to give her added strength to defy him. She braided her damp hair and then covered her head with a scarf. The finishing touch was a pair of dark glasses that she had worn on the ski slopes last fall. The glasses helped conceal the bruise beneath her eye. She powdered her nose to cover the redness, then added a touch of lipstick to give her deathly pale skin some color.

The bells of Marienkirche tolled the half hour. How long until Wolf ascended the stairs? She must be gone when he opened the door! No time to rest! No time to sit and let her trembling muscles gather new strength!

The basket of baby things was already packed, as was Lucy's own valise. But there was no hope that she could carry more than the basket and the baby across the roof. She stuffed some of her things into the basket. Underwear. One thin dress and a sweater. What was left of her money and the crucifix went on the bottom with her papers and the little green book, *Waiting at Table*.

The rest would remain for Wolf, proof that she had really been here—evidence, along with the blood-stained sheets, that Lucy Strasburg had been within his grasp.

The baby did not awaken when she gathered him up and placed him in the basket. "Let him sleep, dear God," she breathed. "And let him wake in heaven, or in safety somewhere. . . ."

With that, Lucy leaned her weight against the chest of drawers until it scraped a few inches across the floor to partially block the door. It would not hold Wolf up for long, but even seconds might make the difference.

The window jammed halfway open, making it difficult for Lucy to squeeze out onto the ridgeline. Wolf could not pass through the small space. Here again, he might be delayed.

The Baltic breeze blew hard against her, penetrating the fabric of the dress to awaken every nerve in her body. For just a moment she looked off down the steep slate precipice that fell away onto the shadowed street, and she doubted and feared what she was doing. But did she not fear Wolf more? And if she fell, and the baby fell with her, was not that end better than a future controlled by a man like Wolfgang von Fritschauer and his great Reich?

The thought gave her courage as the bells of Marienkirche tolled three quarters of an hour. Lucy could almost hear the tread of Wolf's returning footsteps resounding from the street below. She fixed her mind on the four-inch ridge along the peak of the roof and hooked her arm through the handle of the basket. She let go of the window sash and turned to put one foot in front of the other. *Like a child walking a rail fence,* she told herself. She did not look down. She did not think of the weakness of her legs or the momentary dizziness that threatened to draw her into the abyss. What was behind her was much more terrible than death. Her past *must not* become her future or the future of her baby! The cobblestones of Heiliger Geist Strasse were a gentler bed on which to sleep than the bed Lucy was running from. And so when the pigeons sailed past, she heard their wings and was unafraid. When the echo of traffic below filled her ears, she did not let herself dwell on those things.

Step followed step. She tottered toward the first chimney and then reached out to embrace it. *The first landmark of safety!* She paused there only long enough to catch her breath. Then fear crept up behind her and shouted that she was a fool, that she should go back to the room and find some other way! Lucy brushed the terror back and once again stepped away from the safety of the brick island to balance herself and launch out toward the next.

23

God Bless the Child

Hess limped into the lobby of the Deutscher Hof, only to be greeted by the eager face of Gustav Ahlman. Ahlman seemed as cheerful as Hess was grim.

"Herr Hess—" Ahlman motioned that his superior officer should join him for a short stroll outside.

"This had better be worth my time," Hess growled. "I have had a very difficult night and I am in no mood for—"

Ahlman seemed not to notice Hess's irritability. The news he had was too good to be short-circuited. "I was looking for you. Called the hotel three times last night from a public telephone in the Heiliger Geist District." He slowed his pace to match the halting step of Hess, who merely glared back at his exuberant expression.

"What of it?"

"I followed Major von Fritschauer as usual yesterday. He stopped at several of the derelict boardinghouses in the district."

Hess's eyes widened. Here it was, the evidence he had been expecting. Wolfgang von Fritschauer had been in the same district where the Ibsen children had lived. *So it was Wolf who warned them!* Hess stopped mid-stride. He shook his head angrily. He had been a fool. Why had he himself not followed Wolf? His throbbing leg held part of the answer to that question. "What did he do?" Hess demanded.

"He has found Lucy Strasburg for us, just as you predicted he would." Ahlman's voice grew tight with excitement. "He went up to her apartment and stayed several hours. I watched him from across the street."

"How do you know he was with the woman?"

Ahlman pulled out his dog-eared photograph of Lucy. "I showed this to the concierge of the building. Positive identification. He wanted to know if she was a criminal. Told me there was another fellow up there with her. I told him there was a reward for her capture, and that he must keep an eye out for her until I returned. And then I went to telephone you. Three times, as I said."

Hess paled with the realization that no doubt Wolf had warned Lucy of the danger of remaining in Danzig, just as he had warned the Ibsen children. "And you followed Wolf when he came out?" Hess was not pleased. "Why did you not stay at the boardinghouse to guard against the escape of the woman?"

Ahlman looked puzzled. "You ordered me to follow Major von Fritschauer. And so I did." He shrugged. "He is at his hotel. Two blocks from here. At least he was there a few minutes ago. I came straight here to tell you."

It was true that Hess had instructed the young agent to do nothing but follow and observe. Heinrich Himmler had given him this young, inexperienced agent from the Gestapo roll sheet. And now this was the result! Ahlman had followed the hounds and possibly let the fox go free!

Hess hailed a taxi. "Heiliger Geist District," he commanded; then he turned to the puzzled junior agent. "The name of her hotel?"

"Hanseatic. But what of von Fritschauer? Is he not the one we should apprehend?"

With a gesture, Hess ordered the underling to be silent. His patience had grown thin. The night had been long and unproductive. Hess could only hope that he was not too late.

———

Lucy dropped to her hands and knees as she neared the dormer. Holding tightly to the basket, she inched forward until the roof of the window was centered beneath her. Like a child descending a playground slide for the first time, she eased herself off the ridge and braced her feet as she scooted down onto the dormer peak to straddle it like a horse. But how to get through the window? She dared not get off the dormer roof. To do so would be to fall.

She crept forward and peered over the eaves and through the soot-caked glass into an attic storage room. The window was hinged to open at the center. Generations of pigeons roosting on the sill had pushed the right window in, leaving just enough of the edge exposed on the left side for Lucy to grasp and pull. "Please, God!" she cried out at the effort.

The hinges tore loose at the top, and with a groan, the window frame crashed forward to hang crazily from one corroded piece of hardware.

Lucy gauged how she might swing the basket and her baby safely through the opening and onto the attic floor from this position. With a sense of regret she looked back toward the window of her own apartment. There at the base of it were the sheets she had put out earlier. She wished she had thought to bring them. She might have made them into a rope by which she could lower the baby and herself to safety. But she had neither the strength nor the time to traverse back across the rooftops to retrieve them. Instead, she rummaged through the basket and pulled out her sweater.

Tying one sleeve around the handle of the basket, she lowered her baby out over the empty air; as her heart pounded in her ears, she swung the basket in a gentle arc passing it over the ledge into the attic. Twice it bumped against the broken window frame and then skittered across the glass to dangle above the courtyard four stories below. Lucy prayed. *Not for me. For the baby.* She tried again. The slowly swinging rope of yarn stretched beneath the weight as it swept out over the edge of the roof and then back toward the opening. The wicker passed through the narrow space and over the boards of the floor. At that instant, Lucy released her grip and let the weight of the basket carry it inside, where it thumped loudly to the floor.

The baby wailed as his cradle jarred him awake. At the sound of his cries, Lucy called out and forgot her own fears. In a moment she lowered herself off the dormer roof. Blindly, her foot groped for the solid feel of the windowsill. The broken window frame gave way beneath her weight as she probed the air. The cries of her child drove thoughts of the cobblestones from her mind! Was he injured? Had the basket fallen open and spilled him out on the dusty floor? "Oh, God!" she cried. "Help me!"

As if a hand touched her groping leg and guided it inward, the sole of her foot found the ledge. Bracing herself, she reached down first with one hand and then the other until she crouched half in and half out of the window. Staring into the dim room, she did not step down until she saw the basket, still closed, beneath her on the floor. Then Lucy tumbled forward, her energy all but expended as she tore open the hamper and picked up the child. He was frightened, wet, and hungry, but uninjured by the fall.

Lucy could not walk, not unless she rested here a while. But how long could she rest before Wolf made his way across the route of her escape and found her here?

Unbuttoning her dress, she reasoned that she could not go until the baby was nursed and at peace again. For the time being she decided that maybe God had taken an interest in this child, and so perhaps it would have to be God who kept Wolf at bay and helped her find her strength again. She closed her eyes as the baby nursed. She did not mean to fall asleep at such a time. It simply happened.

———

"Fourth floor." Ahlman raised his eyes to the steep staircase leading up to Lucy Strasburg's room.

"Go up. Wait there," Hess instructed. "I'll get the key from the concierge."

"What about Major von Fritschauer?"

"We will deal with him later." Hess knocked hard on the door of the concierge as Ahlman took the stairs two at a time.

The old concierge recognized Hess immediately. "Ah, but it was you who were looking for some wayward children yesterday. Why did you not show me the picture of the lady also then? She is right upstairs. She has been there for several months. A decent tenant, her and the boy, both." He turned down the radio and then began to paw through a drawer containing dozens of loose keys. "I gave the duplicate to the other gentleman last night." The old man showed off the small swastika pin that he wore openly on the collar of his frayed shirt. "You see where my loyalties lie," he smiled, revealing toothless gums beneath his drooping mustache. "Anything I can do to help, I told him. He paid me well also."

The boy. Certainly the tenant who lived with Lucy Strasburg was Peter Wallich. And so the entire nest would be cleaned out at once.

"If I had known she was a criminal," the old man babbled, "well, of course I would have notified the police. Soon enough we will have the criminals removed from Danzig, eh?" The man's accent was that of a Prussian. His sentiment was that of nearly every German who lived within the shadow of Poland. "A small key, it is. It was just the attic, you see, and so the key is different and—"

He held up a small, black iron key. "This is it. But I have no more for myself, and so you will have to pay me."

Hess slapped down a handful of loose change and snatched the key from the old man.

"Good luck," chuckled the concierge. "Bring back the key when you are finished. Heil Hitler, eh, brother?"

———

Wolf had showered and changed. He felt pleased with himself as he rounded the corner of Heiliger Geist Strasse. He looked up at the ornate baroque facades of the ancient buildings that housed thousands in this city. He congratulated himself. He had found the proverbial needle in the haystack.

This morning on the telephone to Berlin, he had noticed that the voice of Gestapo Chief Himmler had also sounded pleased at the news of Lucy's capture. Now, perhaps, the disapproval that Lucy had brought upon his head would finally disappear. He had sensed the suspicion of his superiors after the Wallich case went sour. Bringing Lucy back to Berlin to undergo interrogation would certainly dispel the last doubt anyone might have about Wolf's loyalty.

As for the child, a handsome baby boy, Wolf had already called his wife, asking her to meet him in Danzig tonight to pick up what he told her was the "motherless infant of an S.S. officer." No doubt she would see the resemblance the baby had to Wolf, but the woman was smart enough not to ask him too many questions. In these days women knew their place. If they presumed to step out of line, divorce was accomplished by a phone call to the Reich Ministry of Information. Only a phone call.

Wolf could not see the window to Lucy's room, but he imagined that the tiny garret was already hot and steamy from the humidity after the rainstorm. He had no desire to stay up there with her; instead, he would move her to his own hotel where he could watch her in some comfort until she recovered enough to travel back to the Reich.

There was no automobile traffic on Heiliger Geist because the street was too narrow. Even if she got away, she would have to walk three blocks in order for them to get a taxi. Judging from the condition she was in when he left her an hour before, it would probably take her most of the day to regain the strength for such a walk. His abuse had weakened her, but Wolf had no regrets. She had asked for it, and he had given her just what she deserved.

Wolf was humming as he swung into the lobby of the dilapidated hotel. Such cheerfulness was unusual for him. It lasted only until he reached the top of the stairs and saw that the door of Lucy's room was slightly open.

Alexander Hess and another man stood in the middle of the wreckage of the room. Hess's face was purple with rage as he turned his gun on Wolf. "Where is she?" Hess demanded. "You see! You will not get away with your treachery, Lieutenant von Fritschauer! You will tell us where she is, or you will take her place at the interrogations!"

It was hot in the attic. Stifling and miserable.

Lucy heard her name drift through the window. Distant shouting. The voice of Wolf. A second voice that she had heard before . . . somewhere.

Get up, she told herself. *A matter of seconds and they will be here!*

Mercifully, the baby slept again. She returned him to the wicker hamper and closed the lid. Staggering to her feet, she swayed in the center of the dark room as she searched the gloom for the way out.

Behind crates and old trunks, Lucy could just make out the outline of a door. She clambered over stacks of old books, sending them clattering to the floor. She prayed the door would be unlocked. Her fingers grasped the hot metal of the knob and . . . turned. The door squealed open. A narrow ladder led down to a landing. Every muscle in Lucy's body shook as she climbed down unsteadily. The air cooled as she descended. She was on the top floor of yet another warren of deteriorating apartments. Voices of tenants penetrated paper-thin walls. The rank odor of cooking grease and fried fish filled the air. Lucy grasped the loose banister and walked down the stairs. She tried to carry herself as though nothing were wrong, as if she belonged in the stinking place.

The doors of flats were all open for ventilation. No one seemed to look up as she walked down the long musty corridors and descended from one floor to the next. She could feel the presence of Wolf just behind her. The image of his face reminded her of the huge deer hounds she had seen as a child, their long legs gobbling up the field as the dogs pursued a doe and her fawn. Slowed by the progress of the baby, the doe had been dragged down and torn to pieces as the fawn screamed like a wounded eagle in the high, piercing voice of terror. And then, it too, had been killed.

Lucy clutched the basket tighter to her as she reached the foyer. The concierge of this building was playing solitaire at a table in the lobby. The woman did not look up as Lucy swept past and rushed toward the light that streamed through the glass in the door.

Once again she froze. *Voices behind her. But were there watchers in the street?*

"Looking for someone?" asked the concierge in a lazy voice.

"My friend is late," Lucy muttered and then she pushed out into the crowd of pedestrians wandering from shop to beer cellar up the sloping street.

Lucy wildly scanned the faces in the crowd. She resisted the urge to run. Like the doe in her memory, she did not want to attract the attention of the hounds. She did not want to be dragged down onto the cobblestones and watch her baby tumble out at the feet of men who would tear his soul to shreds!

She leaned briefly against a streetlamp as a fresh wave of dizziness threatened to knock her to her knees. And then, when the world slowed its lazy spin, she fixed her eyes on the bright scarf of a broad-backed woman and matched her pace.

Three blocks, and there were trams. Three blocks, and she could blend in with the bustle of thousands who traveled to Langer Market. For three blocks, Lucy lowered her head and looked neither to the right nor the left as she tramped behind the stranger whose width protected her from an oncoming view.

Not for me, her heart whispered. *For the child . . .*

Lucy could not let herself think what she must do after these three long blocks. She had come this far. There must be some place to run.

———

Lori was still in bed. She was very sad, Jacob explained, and probably would not come out until it was time to go. But there were important matters to attend to, so Jacob was up early.

Werner-kitten did not like the taste of beer. He would not drink it. Three of them together could not get more than a thimbleful of the stuff down his throat.

"Not enough to do any good," Jacob said, glaring at the indignant kitten who licked its chest and shook its head as if to spit out the vile-tasting brew.

Jacob went downstairs to the casino and ordered a glass of famous Goldwasser schnapps. Made in Danzig, the liqueur had tiny flecks of gold in it. But its potency, not its precious metal, had made it known throughout the world. Jacob looked plenty old enough to consume the schnapps if he wanted to, but the bartender looked twice at him because it was breakfast time. Only the most hardened drinkers could stand Goldwasser this early in the morning.

Claws out, ears back, Werner started his yowl in a low voice and ended it with a high shriek as Jacob and Alfie held him. Jamie opened his mouth, and Mark dribbled the potent schnapps down his throat.

"I'm sorry, Werner," Alfie said as tears of pity coursed down his broad face. He understood about terrible medicine that hung in his throat and made him want to throw up. But sometimes even kittens had to take medicine. "Don't hate me, Werner," Alfie pleaded as the kitten struggled to free himself.

"Hold his mouth open, will you?" shouted Mark as needle-sharp teeth tried to close around his finger.

"You see," Alfie explained to the kitten, "you have to be asleep and quiet in your box or they won't let you go to England. If you yowl, they will hear you and throw you off the boat." A terrible thought. Alfie thought of how his own papa had drowned in the water. It made him hold Werner a little tighter, but not too tight because the little bones were very small. Alfie did not want to crush Werner, only make him drunk. "Don't hurt him," Alfie said to Jacob. Jacob did not answer. He had a faraway sort of pain in his eyes. Alfie supposed that Jacob was wishing there were a secret box big enough to hold him, too.

"How much do I have to get down him?" Mark's face was flushed red from the effort, and he had the easiest job of anyone. Who would think that one little kitten could fight so hard?

"How much have you gotten down him?" Jacob leaned over and peered into the shot glass.

"Almost all," Mark said with relief.

"Well, three of those will lay a man under the table," Jacob replied with satisfaction. "Werner should be out for a while, I'd say."

But Werner was not out yet. He bit Jamie, who screeched. Then he turned to bite Alfie, who jumped back in hurt surprise. Werner had never behaved in such an angry way before. Jacob got claws down the arm as he turned loose too late to get back.

Then Werner began a wild dash around the room. He dashed across the back of the sofa, sending pillows flying. He swerved up the wall and back down again. He screamed up the curtains, turned, and jumped down to explode across the floor and into the bathroom. All the while he made a low sound like an electric motor whirring.

The boys looked at one another and held their wounds as the sound of Werner's claws across the marble bathroom counter told them he was not finished yet.

That instant a streak of black and white fur flashed across the floor and through their legs and up the wall beside the fireplace. Werner seemed to hang there in midair for an instant and then, claws still out, he slid down to the hearth.

Slowly, Werner turned around three times. He sat down and cocked his head quizzically to one side as he studied the traitors whom he had considered his friends. His wide cat eyes blinked lazily. He licked his paw and tried to clean his whiskers but instead, he fell down, curled up, and went to sleep.

A mighty cheer rose up from Alfie, Mark, and Jamie. Jacob did not cheer. Nothing could make him smile this morning, it seemed. Alfie felt very sorry for Jacob. Alfie knew what it was like to be left behind. He knew what it was like when friends went away and he had to stay.

Alfie wanted to hug Jacob, but he did not. That would not have made Jacob feel better. So Alfie said, "I wish you would be with us when Werner wakes up."

Jacob looked at the thin red claw marks. "Why? You scared to take him out of the box?" Jacob almost smiled. Alfie knew that Jacob did not understand what Alfie meant at all.

"He's going to be one mad cat," Jamie agreed. "We'll open it up and run for cover."

Mark added. "Too bad we can't turn him loose on a Nazi." He meowed and hissed to make his point.

Jacob still was not amused. "We've got an hour," he said. "Get your bags ready." And then Jacob left to go back and be with Lori again.

Rabbi Aaron Lubetkin was sitting in a chair by the window. Peter noticed how much stronger the great rabbi looked today—not so much the frail old man with one foot in the grave. There was some color on his cheeks. His beard filled out the hollowness of his face, and the hair on his head, though streaked with gray, was quite thick and healthy-looking.

Rabbi Lubetkin was dressed in a loose-fitting cotton caftan, belted at the waist over trousers that were much too big for his thin legs. Peter caught a glimpse of his own skinny reflection in the mirror. So why was he so concerned about the rabbi? Even after months in prison and a near-death joust with rheumatic fever, the rabbi looked healthier than Peter.

A copy of the book *Galilut Erez Yisroel,* by Halevi, was turned face-down on the table next to the water pitcher and a pair of reading glasses. The book was a good sign, Peter thought. Michael Wallich had loaned it to his son just days before the Nazis had arrested him in Vienna. Peter had read the book by flashlight under the covers after that. The book inspired men to long for a home in Israel. Yes, Peter thought, it was good to see that the rabbi was reading it. Such a book would make him listen to what Peter had to say.

The rabbi recited a blessing on Peter as he entered. Peter thanked him, even though he did not believe in such things. It was a matter of being polite, socially correct in a world that, to Peter, seemed centuries out of step with reality.

"I see you are reading the work of Gershon Halevi." Peter started there, with something they had in common.

"You know this book?" Rabbi Lubetkin seemed surprised.

"My father gave it to me before his death," Peter volunteered. "A fantastic book. But very deep." He paused. "Of course, when we fled Vienna it was something precious which I left behind. It would not do for me to carry such a book out under the noses of the Gestapo on the railway."

Rabbi Lubetkin passed the book to Peter. "I have read it through. Here. Take my copy. It is yours, Peter."

To this kindness, Peter responded bitterly, as though he could not see the depth of the rabbi's eyes. "You might as well keep it here. The Nazis will be in Warsaw soon enough, and then I will only have to run from them and leave the book behind to be burned once again."

The rabbi's kind smile did not waver, but the depth of those choc-olate-brown eyes reflected pity. He replaced the book on the table and folded his hands placidly on his lap. So much for Halevi's book. "So," said the rabbi, "Rachel tells us that you had an idea about how to find the address where your mother and sister might be staying here in Warsaw."

"I have heard nothing back from my friend in Danzig. I hope she will write me, but—" He shrugged a who-knows shrug.

"And none of the leads I gave you helped?"

"Half of them left Warsaw during the time you were in prison. The other half had no information."

"I am sorry," Rebbe Lubetkin said. It was clear by his expression that he truly was sorry for a lot of unspoken things in Peter's life. "I hope you find your way."

"That is why I am here, Rabbi Lubetkin." Peter scooted forward until he sat on the very edge of his chair. His eyes lingered on the spine of the Halevi book. "I have decided that I will find my way. No matter what else happens, I am going to Palestine!"

"Mazel tov, Peter!" Aaron Lubetkin seemed not only pleased but surprised. "You have gotten your papers then? Some miracle?" Everyone in the entire district knew that Rabbi Lubetkin was trying to procure papers for his children to go to Rabbi Lebowitz in Jerusalem. Every door had been closed to them. Curiosity sparked in the rabbi's face.

"I have come to offer you some help," Peter said with confidence—almost arrogance. "Because you helped me, I return the favor. Yes?"

The rabbi looked at his folded hands. Useless hands, helpless to remove his own children from the danger of Warsaw. "What is your plan, Peter?"

"You know that the British Captain Samuel Orde is coming here soon. He will be teaching the young people of Hashomer Hatsoir."

This was the Zionist youth movement where boys and girls worked together being trained as potential emigrants to Palestine. There was no mention of God in such training. It was a political movement to Aaron Lubetkin's way of thinking. There was much about it that he and others among the Orthodox disapproved of.

"I am happy for you," the rabbi said. "You will spend time on the Hachsharah." He spoke of the farm outside Warsaw that was used for summer training. "Maybe they will feed you and you will put on a little muscle, nu?"

"I am not going to the Hachsharah," Peter corrected. "There will be no time for such things. When the captain comes here, there is a rumor—or maybe it is the truth—but anyway, it is something I have heard whispered by someone who should know."

"And what is this whispered word?"

"The captain is not coming only to work on a newspaper! We all wondered how a man of such renown could resign his commission. Now it is said that he never resigned! He has come here to hand pick a few who will return with him to Palestine! Like Gideon, he will choose only a few." He inhaled deeply and stared straight ahead. "I will be among them."

"Mazel tov," the rabbi said wryly. His bearded cheek twitched as if to suppress a smile. "You have gotten your letter of acceptance to this school of Gideon's soldiers?"

"You are making fun of me, Rabbi Lubetkin. But I have come to tell you what I know."

"What you *think* you know—"

"What I know about the mission of Captain Orde." No arguments would stop Peter. He had thought it all through. "This great military genius, this brave and stalwart Englishman . . . he happens to be a friend of your father-in-law, Rabbi Lebowitz in Jerusalem. True?"

"True."

"And he is coming here to take tea with you, I have heard."

"I have never heard of an Englishman who will refuse tea if offered."

"Well, then . . ." Peter paused. "Now that you know the real reason he is coming to Warsaw, I thought maybe it would be a good thing if you would ask him to help you get Rachel out."

"Rachel? My little bird? Why, yes, the captain has offered to intervene with British authorities. We expect him to bring us good news from London. But, only Rachel?"

"If you cannot get your visas," Peter pushed ahead, "here is the plan. She should join Hashomer Hatsoir today. Come with me to a Zionist Youth meeting. That way when Captain Orde selects his few, no one will deny that Rachel should come with us to Palestine. You see? They will not say the captain is playing favorites, that he has chosen her over another girl or boy because she is the daughter of Rebbe Lubetkin and the granddaughter of Rabbi Lebowitz." He sat back and crossed his arms. "All fair, you see? Then over tea you can tell him she is a member, and that you wish her to go to Palestine."

Rabbi Lubetkin held up his finger to stop the flood of youthful excitement. "How did you think of all this?"

"I was thinking of her last night—" Peter blushed. "I mean . . . she handled herself bravely in the altercation between David and Mordechai. She is brave. And . . . worthy."

"And she has also taken an interest in your well-being." The rabbi did not speak of the fact that something about Peter made his daughter want to turn and run. "We have hoped you would find your way to your mother and sister. But Rachel is not the sort of girl for Hashomer Hatsoir." A soft smile. "She is betrothed to a young man named Reuven who lives in Lodz. The family would not—"

Peter leaped to his feet. "So what does it matter what his family thinks? Can't you see that there is no other way for us to get out of here now?"

"I am still praying for the visas. My children will go to be with their grandfather. In an Orthodox home. Not in the Hashomer to live on a kibbutz. You see, your way does not fit."

"You had better make my way fit, because pretty soon—" He picked up the Halevi book. "People who burn books, Rabbi Lubetkin, will also burn people. I have seen the wall of fire. It is not like the pillar of fire you say your God used against the Egyptians. No, this is a different kind of fire. It burns an impassable wall just at the border of Poland. I do not know what you will do with the rest of your children when it sweeps into Warsaw. But maybe you can help Rachel get out. Ask the captain about it!"

The boy's anger had receded into a hopeless desperation. By his tone, the rabbi knew that Peter Wallich cared for Rachel. *Hopeless*. Perhaps this outburst had been motivated by love, but even love was inappropriate in this instance.

Aaron Lubetkin tried to be gentle in his reply. But he did not let the boy hope for something so impossible. He simply nodded his head and said, "A good idea. We will see. Perhaps the captain will bring our travel documents with him, and then the problem will be solved."

24

Goodbyes Are Never Good

It was very early in the morning in the Red Lion House. Through the ceiling, Charles heard the groaning boards as Murphy got out of bed. Then the new baby cried a bit, and a second groaning of boards filtered down as Elisa got out of bed.

Other than that little bit of activity, the house and the world of London seemed very still this morning. Last night the sirens had wailed on and on, very late. Charles and Louis had finally gone to sleep in spite of the terrible sounds. But now everything was like a drowsy summer morning should be.

The scent of flowers drifted in from the roof garden and mingled with the rich aroma of coffee. Murphy always made coffee for Elisa in the morning. Charles liked the smell of the dark brew much better than that of tea. It was an aroma that reminded Charles of the long-ago days in Hamburg. The images were very distant, like a dream, but coffee brewing in the morning was something Charles remembered from that time when he and Louis had been with their mother and father.

Elisa opened the door a crack and called in, "Big day today, boys. You awake?"

Charles sat up slowly. "Big day?" Then he remembered that the last refugee children's ship was leaving Danzig this afternoon. There was shopping to do, Elisa had told them, and Charles and Louis could both help push baby Katie's pram through the market.

They did not leave for market immediately, however, even though Elisa usually liked to get vegetables before the day warmed them in the farmer's stalls.

This morning Charles and Louis pushed the new pram toward the little church at the opposite end of Red Lion Square. Murphy and Elisa held hands and walked slowly behind, as though they were just a family out for an early morning walk.

There was hardly any traffic. It was still too early for people to be going to work. This walk seemed unusual to Charles, but maybe babies, like vegetables, needed to be out in the early morning before the sun got high and wilted them.

The doors to the inside of the church were locked. But this did not seem to bother Murphy at all. He opened the gate of the churchyard and stepped aside, warning the boys that they must push the carriage carefully over the path between headstones, because it was rutted and they must not tip Katie out.

Then in a quiet voice, he said to Elisa, "The new area is over there." He gestured toward the newest headstones—shining marble without cracks. They did not lean or look as though they might crumble to dust.

"It does not matter when the date of death occurred," Elisa answered him. "Date of birth is what matters. I would think that something between 1919 and 1922 would do for him."

"That much range?"

"He was always such a big strapping child. His mother, Leona Kalner, said he outgrew his one-year clothes at six months."

And so this conversation went on as the happy family of five strolled leisurely through the cemetery of St. John the Evangelist Church.

Charles and Louis resisted the urge to roar along the path with the pram. They maintained a sedate pace as Elisa and Murphy peered down at names and dates of birth. Here was a date that was correct, but the name was a girl's name so it would not work. But Elisa wrote down the information anyway because she said it could be used for the Lubetkin girl in Warsaw.

At last, Murphy gave a happy exclamation. "Here it is! That Sam Orde is an absolute genius!" He explained. "Look! Look here! This is perfect."

Elisa stood at his side and frowned down at the tiny headstone of a baby boy.

WILLIAM HOWARD JOHNSON
BELOVED SON OF
HOWARD AND SUSAN JOHNSON
b. July 20, 1920
d. August 19, 1920

"Yes. It will work," Elisa said in a quiet voice. But her voice was not happy like Murphy's. She was seeing something besides the dates, and it made her sad.

Murphy scribbled down the names and dates. They began to walk back much faster now. Birds chirped above their heads. Elisa picked Katie up from the carriage once they were outside the churchyard and nuzzled her gently. Elisa looked as if she might cry, which seemed very strange indeed.

"What do we do now?" she asked Murphy.

"There is nothing to it." He tucked the paper into his pocket. He was smiling, looking around the square as the red omnibus stopped at the corner, then grumbled on its way. "I'll stop in at the birth registrar . . . No, better to just drop them a line, requesting a certified copy of the birth certificate. The department is down the hall from the death records. *Beautiful*. The right hand has no idea of what the left hand is doing. As far as birth records are concerned, William Howard Johnson is a big healthy nineteen-year-old Englishman. As far as passports are concerned, William Howard Johnson will be a big healthy Englishman about to take his first trip abroad."

"And Rachel Lubetkin?" Elisa looked at the name of the little girl who was about to lend her identity to someone in faraway Poland.

"Better have that birth certificate sent to your parents' address." Murphy frowned thoughtfully. "As a matter of fact, we should set up a number of different post boxes. That way the registrar will not be sending birth certificates to the same address." He grinned back over his shoulder toward the headstones in the sunlight. "A strange sort of resurrection, isn't it?" he muttered. "We'll have to be careful, but I think it can work."

Always before, Lori had acted the part of Mother to the Lost Boys. But this morning at the docks, Alfie could see that something had changed about her.

She made certain that each traveler had his identity tag properly tied to the center button of his shirt. Those tags matched the special travel permits and the luggage tags that were also properly attached. Very quietly, she spoke the names of Mark and Jamie and Alfie and gave them strict instructions about which line to stand in and how they absolutely must stay together so they were not separated.

But her attention was not really with the boys, Alfie noticed. Even as she spoke, she was looking mostly at Jacob. Touching his hand, leaning her head against his arm in between sentences. It was plain to see that Lori was not ready to be here. Her skin was very pale. Her blue eyes were bright with loving Jacob, with missing him terribly even before they were apart.

Jacob stood tall and very adult-looking in the suit he was wearing for the second day in a row. His hat was pulled down lower than usual over his forehead, making a shadow over his eyes. But Alfie could see all the same that Jacob was not ready for the parting, either. He looked at the ship. And then he looked so softly at Lori. He looked at the teeming crowds of children. Eight hundred tagged and ready. And then he looked at Lori. Her hair. Her hands. Her cheek. Her neck. His eyes wandered to a mother on the dock who cried and hugged her little girl goodbye. And then he looked back at Lori. He touched her hair without thinking about the fact that they were in the middle of hundreds of people. He breathed in so deeply that Alfie thought Jacob's lungs could not hold any more air. His eyes beneath the hat brim were sadder than any eyes Alfie had ever seen, except for the boys at the hospital. They all had eyes like that. Eyes that looked on and wished while other boys ran and played, eyes that lived in helpless bodies while minds were bright and *smart*.

Alfie saw all of this. It made his heart hurt for Jacob and for Lori. People with sad eyes like theirs hardly ever got well from whatever it was that made them sad, Alfie knew. He remembered what Herr Frankenmuth of Fresh Fish Daily had told him: *"Somebody is always being left behind these days."*

Only Werner-kitten seemed to be at peace in all this noise and confusion. Tucked into his secret compartment in the bottom of the valise, the kitten had not made even one peep since he had fallen asleep. Alfie thought it would have been easier if they had stuffed the Goldwasser down Lori and packed her away to sleep until England. As it was, she was barely holding on to her emotions. Everything was *right there,* on the edge, ready to break her into little pieces.

"John Murphy says you mustn't worry," Lori said above the din. "The fellow you are working for is here in Danzig right now. And do you remember where you are to meet him?"

Jacob nodded and pointed to the office of Hamburg-Amerika shipping just a few feet from where they were all standing. "Don't worry." Jacob touched her lips with his finger. "I will be lost without you, even though I will not be lost."

The emotion came again, glistening in her eyes. She kissed his finger, nodded, then looked away. Children were already walking up the gangway. She did not want to see that, so she stooped to flip the luggage tags, making certain that they were all as they should be.

The line inched forward for the luggage examination. English officials from the ship stood beside Polish customs men. The checks were not very complete. Sometimes a bag was opened, but mostly the children and their tiny parcels were simply waved through. Not like Germany. Not at all. This is what the Danzig Gang was counting on. Most likely the bag containing Werner would be looked at briefly and passed over the table, and then Alfie would carry it up into the ship.

"Murphy says we will be together again by the fall." Lori's voice grew more desperate as the line moved up again. Jacob held her hand. Their fingers were twined together, like Alfie's hands when he prayed.

"In the meantime this job . . ." The whistle of the ship boomed the warning that there was only half an hour to cram all these children onto the boat! Jacob's words were lost beneath the bellow of the horn.

"You can go to school in London and work part time at the newspaper office," Lori said.

"And we'll get a little place of our own."

"And I will plant a garden. . . ." Every word brought them a step nearer to the luggage table. Beyond that, the gangway and the ship waited.

"It will be fine for us, Lori. Wait and see." He put his hands on her shoulders, his eyes skimming the side of her face.

"This may be something you really enjoy doing. And . . . it will be all right. A lot of people . . . newly married . . . are . . . they have to be apart awhile." Tears welled up. Her chin trembled as she spoke.

Jacob lowered his head and looked her in the eye. "Don't. Or I will cry." He bit his lip. She brushed away the tears.

Lori did not let herself cry because she did not want to do that to Jacob. It was a very brave thing. Yes, Alfie thought, very brave.

Then they reached the luggage intersection. The bags were hefted onto the table, including Werner's secret hiding place.

"Well, what have we got?" the Polish inspector and the Englishman stood side by side. "Personal items?"

"Personal," Lori said in a very businesslike manner. "Clothing and such things as that."

The English inspector checked the luggage tags against the tags that were tied to their buttons. He took out his red pencil and began to check each bag.

At that moment Werner's bag let out the most mournful, terrible howl. The inspectors both jumped back and put their hands in the air. The yowl began again. Alfie knew they would find Werner now and not let him go, and he felt sick.

"Heavens!" exclaimed the Englishman. "What is in there?"

It was a most terrible calamity. All their bags were put to the side. They were told to stand over by the office, while others in line were checked right through. Werner continued his racket even then.

Jacob patted Alfie on the shoulder. "Sorry, old friend," he said. And Alfie knew that Jacob really was sorry. "We will have to let Werner out of the bag or they won't let you on the ship."

Alfie talked softly to Werner so he would not squirt out and run away when they opened his hiding place. Then Alfie lifted him out carefully. He was still drunk, Jacob said, but just awake enough to yell. So Alfie held Werner for the last time while they waited for the inspectors to come over and have a stern word with them. Alfie remembered how Lori did not cry, and so he did not either.

The line moved on. Two hundred remained. Lori and the boys would be last on board. Lori did not mind, she said. It gave her more time to spend beside Jacob. She drank him in, like Alfie drank the cool lemonade his mama had fixed on a hot day. That was a good way to think about how Lori and Jacob looked at each other. They were lemonade to each other on a hot day.

———

"You are an idiot!" Wolf glared at Hess and then looked at the gun in his hand with a careless disdain. "I had her here, and now you are letting her get away!" He gestured toward the window through which she had obviously escaped and the roof over which she had climbed.

Hess was unmoved by Wolf's pleas of innocence. "You warned the Ibsen children to abandon their flat," Hess snarled. "You have now warned Lucy Strasburg to leave this place."

Wolf paced, and the barrel of Hess's gun paced with him. He ran his hands through his hair in the frustration of encountering this moronic obstacle that even now kept him from tracking Lucy down. "She could not have gotten far." Wolf's eyes flashed angrily. "And if you will work with me in this matter, we will bring her in and settle once and for all who helped her escape. I, for one, believe it was *you*, Major Hess. And I shall not hesitate to report that you held me at gunpoint while the object of a massive manhunt slipped away through the streets of Danzig unhindered!"

Hess and Ahlman exchanged glances. "You were here with her last night, Wolfgang." Hess's voice was high and whining with perverse amusement. He wanted nothing more than to see this haughty Prussian aristocrat brought to trial. And Hess himself would deal with Lucy Strasburg—without assistance from Wolfgang von Fritschauer.

Wolf exploded with rage. "Look at the blood, Herr Hess! Does this look like I embraced her as comrade and fellow conspirator?" He gestured at the dried stains on the sheets, the dark splatters on the wall.

With this, the first doubt struck Hess. Yes. There was blood. Had von Fritschauer beaten the woman? If so, why? Seconds ticked by as he considered the implications of such a thing. Wolf would have beaten her only if . . . *if she had somehow betrayed him.*

Hess did not reply. He kept the weapon leveled at Wolf's gut, yet that unspoken doubt shouted to Wolf that perhaps he was getting through. "So. You think I have something to do with the Karl Ibsen case? Or perhaps that I am one of the conspirators with Michael Wallich and Otto Wattenbarger? You believe this insanity, even though it was I who arrested *both men*?"

"Wattenbarger took cyanide in his cell," Hess persisted. "Who provided it to him?"

"Would I arrest him only to kill him before he gave us names?" Wolf mocked everything in the dossier. "Someone else in the department made it easy for Otto—not me. And the woman we are both after betrayed me, just as she betrayed you and the Fatherland. Your own failure in this matter has made you suspicious of someone who might help you!" He whirled around to face Hess and he stared into the clouded eye. He was close enough to snatch the gun from him, but he did not. "You are looking for the Ibsen children? And for Lucy? I will tell you where they will be." Wolf could clearly see that he had gotten through to Hess at last. "Today is the day of the last children's refugee transport to England. Or have you forgotten such a minor point as that?"

———————

"I'll take care of Werner," Jacob said, thumping Alfie on the back. "Don't worry about that, Alfie."

Alfie was not worried. He was only sad. He cradled the kitten in his arms and stroked its head with his big finger. Werner breathed in and let every breath out with a low, unhappy growl. He looked very sick, even though Jacob said it was just the Goldwasser that had done this to him. Werner looked as sick as a cat could look, Alfie thought. He wished the kitten had stayed asleep in his hiding place.

Alfie looked at all the mothers kissing their children goodbye and it made his heart squeeze and his chest ache. He remembered how he had cried when Mama told him the Bible story about the mother of Moses putting her baby in a little boat and sending him away from the sword of the bad king. And now here were all these mothers, all these children. Their voices mixed together in one low groan. So many. So many. And certainly these mothers who were sending their children away felt even worse than Alfie, because they had their babies a lot longer than Alfie had Werner. And Werner was a kitten, not a human baby. Alfie felt terrible. It was hard to imagine how much worse these mothers and fathers felt seeing their babies walk up onto the ship.

Alfie had learned about goodbyes. There was nothing good about them.

Little faces peeked over the rail of the ship. Tearful eyes searched for familiar faces. Handkerchiefs fluttered at the tips of tiny hands. The air echoed with calls of *Mama! Mother! Mama! Mama!* And every woman there answered to that one name, as if no one had any other name but Mama and all the hearts became one huge broken heart. Hands raised up and hands reached down; love and sorrow bridged the gap between the children at the rail and the women on the dock.

But Alfie did not cry, even though he felt like it—for himself and for everyone else that day. He remembered how brave Jacob and Lori were and he did not cry.

Alfie turned to Jacob. "Will you write and tell me how Werner is?"

Jacob was touched by Alfie's question. "Sure. And you write me, too."

"I don't write so good," Alfie frowned.

"I'll help you," Lori said.

"I don't know where to write." Alfie noticed everyone else had addresses to write to.

"We will send our letters to TENS in Warsaw." Lori stroked Alfie's arm as tenderly as Alfie was stroking Werner's little head. "And Jacob will read your letters to Werner."

Well. That was something, anyway. *Letters.* But letters could not hug a kitten or a child.

He could not stand watching it anymore, so he turned and faced the other way. He looked at the giant loading cranes, at the crates and warehouses all along the waterfront. He looked at the dock workers, who were also standing with their arms crossed and watching the scene at the docks.

This was the last boat for children, Alfie knew. There would be no more after today. He thought of all the mothers who would like to put their children on such a ship and cry and wave farewell because they knew it would save their children. He remembered the long lines of mothers and children at the Jewish church in Berlin who had hoped they could get their little ones onto a ship like this. Not all of them made it, he knew. That was a different kind of sad.

And then he saw her.

Alfie recognized the woman right away, the same woman he had seen running through the fish market when he had taken Werner to eat at Herr Frankenmuth's Fresh Fish Daily. She had the same frightened look on her face then as she did now! On that day she had a baby in her stomach. But today, the lady held the baby in her arms.

She was standing in front of three people. One was the nurse from the ship, Alfie knew. The other two were men, both dressed like the other Englishmen who helped organize the children. The faces of the three were hopeless, wearing the kind of expressions that said they were sorry but they *could not . . .*

The woman held out the little bundle to the three. She begged them. Her face—such a sad and pretty face—seemed to have caught all the hurt from every heart on the dock that day. She looked over her shoulder. *Was someone still chasing her, like that day in the fish market?* Alfie remembered that she had been on the same train out of Germany. *Maybe she was being chased even on that night.*

Alfie looked where her eyes looked. He could not see anyone walking toward her. He could not find who was chasing her. Yet, like the mama of the baby named Moses, she was holding this brand-new baby out to three people who shook their heads and crossed their arms and would not take the baby no matter how she pleaded.

"Why don't they hold the baby?" Alfie asked out loud.

Lori asked Alfie if he had said something.

Alfie nodded. "Yes. Jacob," he asked politely, "would you hold Werner for a minute?"

Jacob took the kitten.

"Thanks," Alfie said. "I'll be right back."

They let him walk away. The toilets were just around the corner, and so no one thought anything about Alfie leaving just for a minute. He was glad no one followed.

He walked toward the woman and her baby and the three people with their arms crossed. Alfie stopped and watched and listened from the corner of the Hamburg-Amerika Line office.

"He is so small," the woman was crying. "You see? So small and helpless. *Oh, please!* He won't take up much room. And someone will want a baby. You see? Look how sweet, how beautiful . . . I have no place else to go. I am begging."

The nurse looked very sad. But she spoke first. "I have other things to attend to. You will handle this?" And then she left, hurrying back to her own table at the base of the gangway.

The two men looked at each other. Which one should do the talking? The short one shrugged and shook his head. "There is nothing we can do, madam." His German accent was very bad. "You see we are packing to the gills."

"But he is so tiny—"

"No room. One thousand children from the Continent. We have spent weeks choosing which children, documenting their need."

"But you see, this baby . . ." She lowered her voice until Alfie could barely hear her. "Nazis . . . take him . . . take my baby . . . raise him to be . . ."

The men glanced uneasily at each other and backed up a step. They put their hands out as though she were trying to hurt them instead of give them the bundle. Still, she begged. They backed up farther, shaking their heads. It was settled. No. They would not hold her baby, would not take the little one to safety.

Alfie frowned. Did they not know the story of Moses and the bad king and all the little ones who were killed by the soldiers? Could they not see that no mama made up such a thing, that only a very desperate mama wanted to give her baby away?

The men turned and walked away, each in a different direction, leaving the woman in the middle. She closed her eyes and held the baby close to her as she shook her head. Her lips still moved, but now she was not speaking to anyone. *Except maybe to God,* Alfie thought as he walked toward her. Her skin was very pale, like the delicate porcelain statues that Mama had kept on a special shelf so they would not get broken. This woman looked as if she might fall, as if she might break into pieces if she fell.

Alfie put out his hands to catch her. He did not think as he put his hands beneath her arms. She did not look at him as he guided her back through the crowds and the noise and helped her sit on a wooden crate.

Then he took the baby from her arms and sat down beside her. Did she notice? Her eyes were shut. Her hands were open on her lap.

Alfie looked at the baby that the others would not take. The baby, unlike its mother, was awake—wide awake, looking right up into Alfie's face and sucking on a little fist. Alfie's heart felt glad and sad at the same time when he smiled down at this very new human kitten. Such perfect hands. Fingers no bigger than . . . than what? Alfie had never seen such tiny little fingers before. The baby was squinting because the sun was so bright. Alfie held up his arm to shade it.

The woman still did not move. Alfie could see her face was bruised. Someone had hit her. He knew this because his own face had been bruised just the same way when the orderlies at the hospital had hit him. Alfie did not know if he should speak, because she seemed to be resting even though she was sitting up. But time was short. He looked at the baby. He put his finger out, and the tiny hand curled around it.

The ship's whistle blew. Fifteen minutes and everyone would have to be on board.

"You have a very nice baby, lady," Alfie said softly, as if he were waking someone up.

She opened her eyes and tears spilled out over the bruised place on her cheek. She looked at Alfie. Her eyes told him *thank you,* but she did not say anything. Maybe she could not talk anymore. Alfie knew about people who could not talk, because some of his best friends in the hospital could only talk with their eyes. But Alfie could see plainly what their souls were saying to him. Then he did most of the conversation, and they agreed.

"I saw you on the train to Danzig," Alfie said gently. "You were running from the Hitler-men."

She nodded. Only once. Her eyes lingered on the face of her child. *Such love.* Alfie saw it. He knew about that, too, even though people thought he did not.

"We ran away, too. We lived here in Danzig. And now they are letting us go to England."

She bit her lip and swallowed hard. Alfie could see that the woman wanted nothing in the world so much as for her baby to go to England.

"I saw you in the fish market when you were running," Alfie continued. "The Hitler-men are still chasing you?"

The nod said yes. The eyes said that they were very close behind her now, that they would hurt her and take the baby away. Alfie knew all of this in his heart, even though she did not speak it.

"They are not interested in me anymore, even though I am a Dumm-kopf. I am not in their country no more. So I do not think they will bother me."

At this, the woman looked surprised. Her face told Alfie that she did not think he was a Dummkopf, but a very kind gentleman to help her sit down and to take her baby in his arms until she could find the strength to hold him again.

And then her mouth opened and a voice croaked out, "What . . . is . . . your name?"

"Alfie Halder."

"Thank you, Alfie Halder. For helping." She was talking about helping her just for these few minutes because she knew there was no help beyond that very instant. It was all coming to an end for her, for this perfect little baby in Alfie's arms. There was no room on the ship. No room anywhere. She could not put this baby in his basket like the mother of Moses had done. The basket would not float. There was no one left to lift it from the water. The swords of the soldiers were drawn and the order had been given.

"What is the name of your baby?" he asked.

For just a moment he saw a twinge of something—*embarrassment?* Ah well, he understood. When someone has just had a baby and then had to run away, maybe there was not time to think about names. That was understandable. Names were things that needed lots of thinking.

"He hasn't a name yet," she whispered, and she looked at the baby's hand wrapped around Alfie's finger. "My name is Lucy."

"Lucy is a pretty name. Do you want to hold him again? The ship is leaving soon." He passed the baby back to her, although he hated giving up the feel of that little hand on his finger. His own fingers were so big and clumsy. He began to work on the tag that was tied around his button. Lori had knotted it so he would not lose it because, she explained, this was his ticket to get on the ship and get into England. It had his name on it and the official stamp saying that he was one of the specially chosen ones who got to leave this place and get away.

Alfie explained this to Lucy as he worked on the stubborn knot. Finally he jerked the button of his shirt off and held up the precious tag.

Lucy looked at him as if she did not know what he was up to. He held the tag for her to see clearly. "You see? There is my name. And I can spell it, too. *A-L-F-R-E-D H-A-L-D-E-R.* Except my friends call me Alfie. I am glad you like the name." He smiled big. He felt very glad inside for what he was doing.

The baby had a pretty blue gown on with little buttons down the front—very small buttons. Alfie chose the third button and began to tie the tag onto the baby's gown. What clumsy fingers!

"What are you doing?" Lucy asked in a frightened voice.

"There is not a lot of time to explain," Alfie answered. "Except I am going to stay behind with Jacob and Werner who they won't let go to England."

"But . . . your ticket . . . how—"

"There is no time to argue." Alfie had often heard Jacob say that when someone was wasting time. "We will call your baby Alfie. Lori will carry him on the ship to England like you want, and he will be safe."

Then Alfie remembered a very important thing. *Writing!* Every mother needed letters written to her. "Do you . . . have a place . . . an address? So Lori can write to you for the baby and you will know?"

Lucy was crying now. Crying very quietly, but also quite a lot. She gave the baby back to Alfie and stumbled toward a wicker hamper that she had left out in the middle of the concrete. Sitting down beside Alfie, she began to search through the basket. Her hands were shaking terribly. Tears drummed down on the things in the basket. She pulled out a little green book and opened it; then she took out a slip of paper with writing on it. She copied down the writing in her book and gave the address to Alfie. "Here," she said. "If I make it I will be at this place in Warsaw."

"We are going there, too. We will work in a news office called TENS." He frowned toward the place where he knew everyone would be waiting and worried about him. "Now you should go so Lori won't want to give the baby back."

She gathered up a few little things from the basket. "Take this. Diapers. Canned milk . . . bottles. It is his." And then her face filled with the pain, like the face of every other woman on the dock. Lucy took the baby back and held him for a moment. "Oh, God! Dear God! Help me let him go! Take care of him for me!" She laid her cheek against his forehead, her hand over his heart. One final kiss. Desperation laid the baby back in the arms of big Alfie Halder.

He stood in front of her with the baby in his arms and the basket in his hand. "We will see you in Warsaw," he said. He was certain of this because he had seen her three times already. Three important times. And God did not make such things happen for no reason. He knew that in his deepest heart. "Now," he said in a grown-up voice. "If they are looking for you, go back to my friend in the fish market. Herr Frankenmuth. He said he would help. And he does not like Hitler. He puts fish guts on Hitler's face in the newspaper. He will help you, Lucy. Tell him Alfie and Werner said so."

She nodded, reached up and touched the baby one last time, and then Alfie turned from her and hurried away. Goodbyes were never good, and she had to go away quickly. He was sure of that.

25

The Loving Heart of Jesus

From the high platform of a cargo crane, Orde had a clear view of the entire Danzig wharf. He scanned the face of the children who had already boarded the ship and then traced back the slowly moving line to the gangplank in search of Lori Ibsen and the boys.

His search was rewarded as he spotted the young people standing together in a worried little knot. They, too, seemed to be looking for someone.

The queue was growing shorter. Perhaps Lori would not board the ship until she had seen Jacob and Orde standing together. He started to climb down from his perch, when he noticed three men on the far end of the crowd. At first glance they were not there to see anyone off.

For a few seconds he traced their rough progress through the crush of people. At the point was a tall, aristocratic-looking man in a summer suit. His face was grim; his eyes never stopped moving. Behind him was a shorter, older man who pushed men and women from his path with a walking stick. The three fingers of his right hand were stiff beneath his gloves. *Gestapo*. Orde knew at once what he was seeing. The third man was young, probably not much older than Jacob Kalner. His brutish, muscular body seemed to enjoy shoving past those who were even remotely near him.

These three headed directly toward the line that shuffled toward the passenger gangway. They were moving toward the office where Jacob Kalner leaned down to gently kiss the lips of Lori Ibsen!

Orde clambered down the stairs and into the mob on the wharf. He had no illusions about whom the Gestapo agents were after.

The mother of baby Moses placed his basket into the water and then turned away, leaving her daughter to follow through the reeds to learn the fate of her son. But Lucy Strasburg could not turn away. She could not leave, as Alfie had warned her!

Lucy *had to know*! She had to see for herself what happened when Alfie presented the baby to his friends and told them what he had done. So Lucy followed along after him. She crouched behind crates, and peered through spaces between the cartons. She spotted a small group of young people who hailed Alfie and pointed to the last of the line moving up the gangway.

Lucy gritted her teeth as the grief of this distant parting tore through her. *There was the girl called Lori! Pretty. Fine-boned and delicate. A very young face. Seventeen, maybe eighteen years old.* Lori leveled her gaze on Alfie and scolded him with a look for being late and making them worry.

Lucy pressed her ear against the space and tried to hear her words, but the sound of a thousand other voices drowned out this one small drama.

Big Alfie was smiling happily as he stretched out his arms to present the baby to Lori. Lori's face registered disbelief, then outrage, then panic. She did not, *would not*, take the child. She shouted something at Alfie; then the ship's whistle exploded! Lori was shaking her head, denying that this could happen; refusing to accept the story that Alfie Halder explained patiently to her as he continued to hold the baby out to her.

Lori turned to a strong-looking young man for help. She clung to his arm, pleading for him to do something. The young man questioned Alfie, gestured as if to ask where the woman was who gave him the baby. Alfie shrugged. His smile did not diminish as he held up the tag on the baby's gown and then looked toward a little black-and-white kitten nestled in the arm of the young man.

Alfie shook his head slowly. *He was not going. He would not get on the ship!* Lori was ashen-faced, helpless. She could not grasp it! She, too, looked around through the mob. Lucy knew the girl was searching for her, that she would, indeed, give the baby back. Lucy fought the urge to run and snatch her baby from Alfie Halder's arms and find some other way. *Some other way!*

Looking from side to side along the wharf, she tried to think what she must do. This had been a terrible mistake! Several officials were gazing at the group of children, wondering what was going on. With a nervous glance, Lucy saw the nurse at her station checking papers. Would the woman recognize the baby that Lucy had begged her to take? Would she call out to the guards that a tiny imposter had stolen the identity of Alfie Halder and was trying to slip illegally into England?

Would they come and take the baby away to the Danzig Foundling Home? *"Please! Oh, dear God!"* Lucy prayed. And then, at the far end of the tearful crowd, Lucy glimpsed the sunlight on the head and shoulders of someone who looked like— *It was Wolf!* Lucy did not take her eyes from him as he moved through the press of bodies. He searched faces; he scanned across the tops of heads in search of Lucy, *in search of the child he claimed for the Führer!* Two other men trailed behind him, heading directly toward where the little band of travelers stood together absorbed in pitched debate!

Lucy bit her hand in an effort not to cry out. She felt the blood drain from her face. The world and the sky spun in opposite directions. "Take him!" Lucy cried silently. "Take my baby! Before Wolf comes to you! Get on the ship! Go *now*!"

Alfie held up the baby. He nudged the tiny form against Lori's body. A fragile little arm raised from the bundle. It waved below the girl's face for a moment as if to beg. *Take me!*

Wolf seemed to see the hand. *How could he know?* He called to his companions as the horn bellowed one last warning! They looked at Wolf and then at one another; then the three merged and pushed people out of their path in a frantic rush toward Lori and the tiny infant.

And then, a miracle! Before the swell of the whistle faded, Lori reluctantly took the baby from the arms of still-smiling Alfie. The gentle young man with the mind of a child patted his namesake and then retrieved the baby's basket for Lori.

Two dockhands stood at the base of the gangway to move it from the ship. Big Alfie raised his hands and stumbled forward to stop them. He pointed at Lori. At the baby. At the two other frantic-looking little boys with her. Then Alfie took the kitten from the other young man who pulled Lori to him in a final, careful embrace. A kiss, loving and desperate, passed between the two. All the while, Lucy's child was held by both of them.

The nurse at the table asked to see their tags as Wolf led his companions closer to the edge of the crowd. A wall of grieving mothers, ten deep, kept them back. They struggled and raged in their places while this final embrace took place. Then Lori, holding Lucy's baby, backed up the gangway. She waved and called back to the young man who loved her. She touched the fingertips of her right hand to her lips.

Wolf leaned hard against the human barricade. No one seemed to notice his roughness. He lunged past a man and a woman who simply turned their heads to look around him as they waved up to a little boy at the rail.

Lucy willed Lori to hurry up the gangway! Could she not see the dark and menacing looks on the faces of the three men who struggled to reach her and tear the baby from her?

Halfway up, Lori stopped. She gripped the rail for support as though she might run back down. *"Run!"* Lucy cried as Wolf reached the inner perimeter and at last broke through.

At that moment, the little boys with Lori nudged her along, pulling her with them up to the safety of the ship. The three disappeared with baby Alfie through the arch of a doorway and then emerged an instant later to take their places among the others at the rail.

Wolf moved forward toward the two young men who still gazed up at Lori. Then another man stepped from the crowd. He stood just behind Alfie and faced Wolf and his companions.

Strong, muscular arms crossed over a barrel chest. His sun-browned face was set, his eyes hard, yet he smiled at Wolf. It was the sort of smile that boys in the schoolyard smile before a fight. Lucy had not seen the stranger before this. She did not know where he came from, but now he stood as a tangible barrier between Wolf and the boys and the gangway where Lori had taken the baby. The newcomer looked British, Lucy thought, his sandy hair and mustache sun-bleached like that of a dock worker. He seemed unafraid of the odds of three to one. Perhaps he welcomed the chance to fight.

Wolf stopped mid-stride, pretending not to see the Englishman who had intervened with a look.

Lori and the others were not aware of the nearness of danger. Crouched behind her crate, Lucy watched the stand-off and wondered who the newcomer was.

Still the stranger grinned, daring Wolf to come near.

Wolf and his men also crossed their arms. They spoke quietly among themselves. *They were too late!*

Lucy could feel the air tremble from the power of their hatred. Their faces were set hard and ruthless against the young people who called out to one another in their grief. Wolf jerked his head, and the trio turned away from the unspoken challenge of the bodyguard at Alfie's back. For the moment it was over.

Lucy looked back to the bundle in Lori's arms. The final bellow of the ship's horn vibrated the air around her. Dock lines were cast away, and the first perceptible movement of the great liner caused the voices and shouts to grow even louder.

"Goodbye, Mama!"

"Don't forget to write!"

"Say your prayers!"

"I will think of you every hour!"

Lori reached her hand out over the slowly widening gulf. Alfie and his friend reached up as though they could touch her fingertips.

The bodyguard stood as a sentinel at their backs.

And in all the tumult the tiny hand of the baby reached up, fluttering for just one beautiful moment as if in poignant farewell to his mother.

No one else seemed to notice. Only Lucy, hiding at the edge of the water to see what fate awaited her child.

The massive brick spires of Danzig's Marienkirche receded in the distance, shrinking at last to tiny dark slivers against the late afternoon glare of the sky.

Lori sat beside Jamie on a thick mound of coiled rope and cradled newborn Alfie in her arms. A white crescent of sand framed the bright blue waters of the Bay of Danzig. Behind a thread of breakers, she could still make out the matchbox-size structure of the Kurhaus Casino and Hotel. The pier that had seemed to jut out so far into the bay was now only a dark stub of a pencil protruding from the land. Lori imagined children sitting with their mothers on the benches that looked out to sea. They would point at this black dot of a ship and wonder where it was going.

"We are going to England," Lori muttered in a joyless voice.

Jamie glared at her. "I know that." Her comment made him somehow indignant. Or perhaps he was just upset at the unhappy way events had unfolded today. "Who are you telling? The baby can't understand anything."

Lori could hear in Jamie's voice that her brother was angry at this helpless little one for taking the place of big Alfie. It was not what anyone had expected. Not what they had planned or prayed for.

She looked down into the face of innocence and knew that, given a choice, the mother of this baby would not have given him away. Lori held in her arms the most desperate evidence of love that could be demonstrated on earth. Here was love so strong that a mother had torn her heart out and sent it away, perhaps never to belong to her again.

Jamie scowled. "Alfie *is* a Dummkopf! Imagine, giving away his ticket to stay with a cat!"

Lori wanted to slap his face for uttering such blasphemy; she wanted to shake him and tell him to open his eyes! For months they had been living beside the purest heart, the wisest soul; yet Jamie still could not see what Alfie Halder was! But Lori did not hit Jamie. She did not scold him for thinking the obvious.

"Alfie knows much more than we give him credit for," Lori said as she touched the cheek of the infant. "He sees . . . things you and I do not see."

"Well, giving away a ticket to England is easy enough for anyone to do these days in Danzig," Jamie mocked. "Walk out on any street corner, hold up your ticket and your visa, and then watch out. A thousand people would mob you in thirty seconds." His eyes narrowed. He felt somehow betrayed. Jamie loved Alfie, and Alfie had chosen to stay behind. "Why would he do such a thing?" Jamie shook his head from side to side. "After all the trouble everyone went to get us here, and Jacob *wanting* to come, but Alfie gives his ticket to a complete stranger, and—"

Lori put a hand on Jamie's arm to stop the tirade. "Oh, Jamie, don't you see? *Alfie*—Alfie the Dummkopf, Alfie who was judged unworthy by the state to live, Alfie who can never be like other people—Alfie gave this little baby more than a ticket to England." She held up the tag for Jamie to see again. "Alfie gave the baby *his name*. His *life*! All new and bright in the Promised Land to start over!" She frowned at the bigness of what she knew was true. "It was what Jesus would do, Jamie. You see? Our Alfie is closer to heaven's heart than anyone I know!" Jamie grew pale and silent, wanting her to help him understand. "Today Alfie was the answer to some woman's prayer."

"Right!" Jamie scoffed. "*Help me give my baby away!* Some prayer!"

"No," Lori said. "You are wrong." She opened the basket at her feet and took out a delicate satin gown wrapped in paper and labeled with these words:

TO WHOM IT MAY CONCERN: PLEASE PLACE MY BABY IN A HOME WHERE CHRIST IS KNOWN. THIS GOWN IS FOR THE CHRISTENING. I WILL THINK OF HIM DRESSED IN THIS AND HOLD THE THOUGHT IN MY HEART LIKE A MOTHER'S MEMORY. MAY YOU BE BLESSED FOR SEEING TO THIS SMALL REQUEST. I WILL PRAY FOR YOU WHEN I PRAY FOR MY CHILD. THANK YOU. LUCY STRASBURG.

Jamie read and reread the words. He swallowed hard. He looked away and then back at the baby. *So new!* What darkness there was in the world when mothers wrote such notes and shipped their babies over the oceans in little baskets! Jamie resented having to contemplate such heartache. "I wish I was a baby again," he said softly. "When I see Mama I'm going to climb up in her lap and lay my head against her shoulder and . . ." His eyes clouded with emotion. He looked hard at this motherless child. "Can I hold him awhile, Lori?"

She carefully passed the sleeping infant to Jamie, showing him how to support the head and the back as he took the new Alfie into his arms. And then for the first time all day, Jamie smiled. He knew for himself what Lori had been trying to explain, and his resentment melted away. "Alfie's *heart* is a genius, isn't it, Lori?"

She nodded, wishing only that she could have been near enough to have given her ticket away to this child's mother. Lori's own heart had remained behind. With Jacob.

———

At the Danzig train station, Alfie and Jacob took turns making Werner jump for pieces of bologna out of a stale sandwich. Captain Orde stared out at them from the little square windows of the red telephone booth. He was talking long distance to London, Alfie knew, explaining to Lori's mother why a baby named Alfie was coming to England instead of a big Alfie.

Alfie also knew that everyone was blaming the whole thing on Werner because, as Captain Orde said, "The cat is a loud drunk, is he?"

This made Jacob laugh, and Alfie had laughed, too. Alfie decided that anyone who could make Jacob laugh on a day like today was worth liking. So Alfie liked Captain Orde. He even liked calling him *Captain*, because it made him feel as if he were in the army. A soldier, just like the little tin soldiers in his bag. It was exciting, and Alfie was very glad that he had decided to stay.

When Werner had eaten the last of the sandwich, Alfie looked all over the loading platforms to see if he could find Lucy. Captain Orde had told them about the three men who were coming after them, and Alfie had worried that maybe they had gotten Lucy. He was glad to know that the baby got away with Lori and Jamie and Mark. But he certainly was worried a lot about Lucy. He prayed for bright angels with swords to cover her. He also prayed that she would find Herr Frankenmuth of Fresh Fish Daily because sometimes he seemed like a gnarled-up old angel to Alfie. Herr Frankenmuth would see the bruises on her face and help her. If only she could find him.

The captain stepped out of the telephone booth and waved the phone at Jacob. "Come here, lad." He was smiling at Jacob. "Your *mother-in-law* wants a word with you."

Alfie laughed at the strange, nervous look that came over Jacob's face. Jacob looked very guilty at first; then as he walked up to the captain and took the phone, he straightened up and made a gruff and brave face.

But his voice was like a little boy. "Hello, uh . . . Frau Helen?" He shut the door behind him so that Alfie and the captain could not hear what he said. Captain Orde was enjoying the way Jacob was sweating and squirming in there, Alfie thought. It was fun to see Jacob look as if he had just knocked over a lamp in someone else's house.

Alfie picked up Werner and held him up to the glass pane of the booth so Jacob could see him. "Heh-heh, Jacob—" Alfie pretended that Werner was talking. "You should have thought about what Frau Helen would say before you married Lori! Heh-heh!"

Jacob was not amused. He put his big hand over the pane so Werner-kitten could not talk to him. The captain seemed very pleased by the whole thing. Jacob's face was very red, but when he slid the glass door open Alfie heard him say, "Give her a kiss for me. Tell her . . . I love her." And then as he hung up, his face seemed satisfied and relieved.

He looked straight past Alfie to the captain. "You warned them?"

Captain Orde nodded. "There will be an armed escort at the docks to meet the ship. Murphy says that his family is well protected. He was not surprised by the news, just surprised that they have just now caught up with you." The captain looked very serious. "If you had not been warned to leave your flat, well . . . things would not have turned out this nicely. Danzig is a powder keg." He looked toward some tough-looking young men at the entrance to the station. "And Herr Hitler has already lit the fuse. It is a good thing you contacted London when you did."

Jacob looked at Alfie, who pretended not to notice. "That was Alfie's idea, Captain Orde," he said quietly. "You'll see. Alfie *knows* things. Lori says angels speak to him."

Captain Orde did not make fun of Jacob. He put his hand on Alfie's shoulder and looked him straight in the eyes the way other people seldom did. "And a little child shall lead them," he whispered. Then in a louder voice he said, "Well, what shall we name you? You have given your name away. Who would you like to be?"

A slow smile spread across Alfie's face. This was probably the best thing anyone had ever said to him. "I gave my name to the baby," he repeated. "He will wear it good. He is a smart baby. I can tell."

Jacob joined in. "But now you have to pick a name! The name of a prophet, don't you think so, Captain Orde? Pick someone from a Sunday-school lesson, Alfie! Someone you like a lot."

Alfie frowned in deep thought. This was important stuff, the choosing of a name. He wished that he could have also spoken to Frau Helen on the telephone, because she had been his Sunday-school teacher and maybe she could help him.

"A prophet," Captain Orde said as the train whistle blew. "Exceptional idea. Very good."

It was a simple choice after Alfie ran all the stories through his mind. He did not want to be Jonah, because Alfie had seen the inside of fish bellies at Herr Frankenmuth's Fresh Fish Daily. The smell was most unpleasant. It would not be fun to be burped up by a fish.

He likewise did not want to be Jeremiah because the king's men had put him down a muddy well and left him for a long time. For a moment, Alfie considered Daniel; then he remembered how bad it felt when Werner nicked him with his little claws. A lion's den would be a scary place to spend the night.

There were others who had done good things, but Alfie did not especially like their names.

He smiled and held up Werner-kitten. Werner's mother had thought her baby kitten was dead, hadn't she? She had pushed tiny Werner with her nose and looked at Alfie for help. Then Alfie had worked and worked on Werner until his little kitten ribs had heaved up and down.

In a way it was like the story of Elisha, Alfie thought. Elisha was a good-hearted sort of prophet who did the same thing for a little boy that Alfie had done for the kitten. He had brought the boy back to life and given him back to his happy mother.

Alfie very much liked stories with such happy endings. It made him think of seeing his own mother alive in heaven. It made him imagine hugs and sitting together in the park to feed the ducks on the banks of the Spree River.

"Well?" Jacob asked impatiently. "What do we call you, Alfie? Now that you have given your name away."

"I like Elisha a lot. He was a very nice man. He watched his friend Elijah ride to heaven in a chariot with fiery horses. That is a good story too," he frowned. "And then Elisha did even better things than Elijah."

"Ha!" the captain exclaimed, as if the choice pleased him very much. Then he added, *"And as Elijah and Elisha were walking along and talking together, suddenly a chariot of fire and horses of fire appeared and separated the two of them. And Elijah went up in a whirlwind. Elisha saw this and cried out, My father! My father! The chariots and horsemen of Israel!"*

Jacob seemed surprised at the way this English captain could quote scripture as easily as Pastor Ibsen. But Alfie . . . or Elisha . . . was not at all surprised. "I like this," Alfie cried, thinking of his little tin soldiers on fiery horses that could fly through the air. "I like this a lot!"

Jacob looked doubtful. "An unusual name. This will take some getting used to." He looked mildly unhappy, as if maybe this was not such a good idea after all.

"A perfectly good name," said the captain.

Jacob disagreed. "You couldn't pick something simple. Like Daniel? or Samuel?"

"Samuel is taken," said the captain. "That is my name."

The announcement was made calling for passenger boarding on the Warsaw Express train.

"Elisha." Alfie repeated it slowly. He wanted to make sure.

"Come on, then," said the captain, putting an arm around Alfie's shoulder the way Alfie's papa used to do. "I will tell you the story of how I stood on the very spot where Elijah was taken to heaven in a whirlwind! The exact place where the fiery horses rode between Elijah and Elisha!"

"You were *there*? Did you get to see the horses?" This was better than anything, Alfie thought.

"Only the hoofprints on the rocks," the captain said as Jacob looked at him suspiciously.

Alfie walked toward the great locomotive and imagined smoke ris-

ing up from the chariots. He decided that he loved the English captain
very much. He was more happy than ever that he gave Lucy's little son
his ticket and his name.

"A clever woman, your Fräulein Strasburg." Hess rubbed his sight-
less eye as he appraised Wolf.

"Clever, ja, Agent Hess. You learned that on the train to Danzig, did
you not? But she is not my Fräulein."

"Somehow I have come to believe you in this matter," Hess said in
a patronizing tone, like a schoolmaster reluctant to discipline a tardy
pupil. "My assistant, Gustav Ahlman—" He swept a hand toward the
empty place where Ahlman would soon sit. "He has followed you
everywhere in Danzig. To the priests. And to the maternity wards." He
smiled as Wolf squirmed beneath his knowledge. "So. You made her
pregnant and she ran out on you. She made a fool of you, did she
not?"

Wolf inclined his head like a puppy who was watching his master
thoughtfully. "She and Peter Wallich also made a fool of you, Agent
Hess." He flicked his fingers toward Hess's right hand, where the
leather glove covered places where the fingers should have been. He
stared hard at the gray film across Hess's eye. "At least she only
wounded my dignity. And that, only as an insect might irritate a horse."

"We have one thing in common, von Fritschauer. The woman has
made fools of both of us, ja? Perhaps such commonalities are the stuff
great bonds are made from." He smiled at the thought that there could
be any bond at all between him and this haughty Prussian aristocrat.
"For some time I suspected that you were part of the escape of Peter
Wallich and Fräulein Strasburg. The boy described you as a great
friend. A brother and ally, really."

Wolf snorted at the thought. "But now you know the truth."

"Yes. Peter Wallich is also a clever boy, is he not?"

"I met him only once," Wolf said slowly, remembering the night he
and Lucy had gone to Otto Wattenbarger's flat in Vienna. Lucy had
argued with him about whether the Walliches were Jews or, in fact,
relatives of Otto Wattenbarger. All along she must have known the truth
and bought them time by convincing Wolf to delay his arrest. Clever.
Yes. And as for the boy? He had spoken of wanting to be an S.S. officer
like Wolf. He had admired the belt buckle of his uniform and the
inscription engraved on every S.S. dagger. And all the time the Jew had
been laughing up his sleeve at Wolf. Lucy had been laughing as well.
The memory brought a fresh rush of anger to Wolf. He clenched his
fists and stared out at the traffic rushing below the Deutscher Hof.

"I have no doubt that you will be given opportunity to deal appropriately with these clever people." Hess looked at his watch impatiently. Why was Gustav Ahlman not back? They had a plane to catch to London, after all. They had been on the Danzig wharf to see the Ibsen children off, and they would be there to greet them when they stepped off the ship tomorrow in England.

"She was not at the ship as I supposed," Wolf remarked darkly. "By now she could be anywhere."

Hess raised a finger to correct him. "But if the infant in the arms of Lori Ibsen was in fact the child of Fräulein Strasburg, well . . . there is no bond as strong as motherhood. Unless it is the bond of two fools who do not wish the rest of the world to know what fools they are." He shrugged. "Why did you not simply kill her?"

"I wanted to clear my name, wanted her to confess that I had nothing to do with her plots in Vienna," he blurted out. It was plain that he wished he had killed her. It would have been much simpler.

"I have already sent a wire to that effect to Berlin. In it I have stated that you carried out your duties here in an exemplary way." He grinned again at the surprise on Wolf's face. "So you see, I am not such a bad fellow. We must keep in touch, you and I. If the child is hers, some word will come from her sooner or later. And I know where to find the Ibsen family. As a matter of fact, I read the intelligence report from London on Monday, giving me the name of the man who was with the two boys at the docks."

Wolf leaned forward. "You have his name? But how?"

"He is Samuel Orde, a former army officer—now a journalist scheduled to begin work in Warsaw. This is of little importance to me, since I am going to England. Probably it makes no difference to your case, either." He spread his gloved hand as if to show he was giving Wolf everything. "I tell you this only to let you know that there is nothing which happens in London that does not find its way back to me. And if Fräulein Strasburg should attempt to make contact with the Ibsens in England, I will forward that on to you."

Gustav Ahlman appeared, interrupting Wolf's speech of cold gratitude in which he spoke of the comradeship of the Aryan soul. *It is just as well*, Hess thought. Such speeches bored him terribly.

Ahlman stood breathless in the center of the hotel room. "It is just as you predicted!" He directed his exuberant admiration to Hess alone. "The man and two boys got on the Warsaw Express train."

"Did anyone else approach them?" Hess queried.

"No one. But I was close enough to hear. The man placed a trunk call to London. He closed the door of the booth as I neared and shut out his conversation from me." Ahlman pulled a rumpled letter from his pocket. "I went back to her apartment, as you instructed. I broke open her letter box, and—" He passed the envelope to Hess with a broad smile. He had saved the best for last.

The envelope was addressed in a childish handwriting to Fräulein Lucy Strasburg. There was no return address on the outside, but the postmark was from the main post office in Warsaw.

Hess tore it open carefully, his three missing fingers causing some awkwardness. Wolf stared at him impatiently, then leaned forward with interest as Hess removed a single sheet of notebook paper.

Hess looked at it a moment, squinted in the dim light, then passed it to Wolf. "My vision is poor for reading. You will read it out loud."

A muscle in Wolf's cheek twitched as he read the words:

My dear Friend,

I have managed to arrive in Warsaw. That is the only thing that has gone as I expected. A clumsy oaf on the train spilled coffee on me, soaking my clothes and rendering the address of my destination undecipherable. I have managed to find my way to the Muranow Square Community Soup Kitchen for meals. I may use that address as a temporary mailbox, they tell me. I still have not found my dear mother or Marlene. I pray that you have not discarded the Warsaw address that I wrote out for you if you should decide to come and join me here. How fortunate it is that I left a copy there in Danzig with you. Perhaps I am not altogether lost. Only delayed.

Please send the address to me quickly. Or, if you have finally come to your senses and wish to have a safe haven for your baby, come join me here soon.

I think of you fondly and hope all is well with your baby.

A friend always,
Peter Wallich

Wolf scanned the note again as Hess clapped his hands together in deep satisfaction. He rose. "You have done well for us, Gustav." Then he bowed slightly to Wolf. "Peter Wallich. Delivered into our hands."

Wolf folded the note carefully. It was so easy! "Perhaps Providence has had pity on two fools, Agent Hess."

"There can be no doubt. Eventually Lucy will find her way to Peter Wallich. Or he to her." He gestured toward the still-grinning Gustav Ahlman. "I will need Gustav in London. My legs are not strong enough to run after children. However, there are several agents already in Warsaw who have been looking into various matters concerning fugitives who have fled the Reich. I will send a wire. Reichsführer Himmler has put an entire force at my disposal in this matter." He raised his hand like a priest reciting a blessing. "Peter Wallich has blazed our trail to Lucy, has he not? And every scrap of information that I receive in London will be immediately relayed to you." He indicated that Ahlman should make a note. "Your address?"

"Europejski Hotel. Warsaw."

"A fine establishment." Hess approved of his choice. "And I, in London, take more modest lodgings. In the Bloomsbury District, 107 Gower Street. Mills University Hotel."

Providence may have had pity on two fools, thought Hess as he watched Wolfgang von Fritschauer leave, *but I am no fool.*

He telephoned Berlin immediately and expressed his suspicion about Wolf. He was sending Gustav Ahlman to Warsaw to keep an eye on every movement of the Prussian officer. "He has allowed Lucy Strasburg to escape," Hess told Reichsführer Himmler with certainty. "And he thinks he is free simply to walk away. It is best if we let him do a little work on our behalf before we bring him in."

At that, Hess was ordered to stop in Berlin for a few hours before he continued on to London. A memorandum regarding this case had fired the imagination of the Führer. There were a few details to discuss in regard to timing the demonstration for the greatest effect against the arrogance of England.

Adolf Hitler had spent the day touring Germany's West Wall, the massive concrete structure that was the Reich's answer to the French Maginot Line. He praised the engineers and decorated several for conspicuous contributions to the Thousand-Year Reich. The Führer called the engineers "soldiers who fight with their intellects, but are no less brave because of that."

Hitler was in a jovial mood when he retired to his quarters for the night. The Siegfried Line was an impressive array of fortresses. Much propaganda mileage would be gained by focusing the attention of the democracies on the extreme defensive measures Germany was being forced to take. Goebbels' broadcasts would see to it that the British pacifist movement had plenty of ammunition (Hitler chuckled to himself at the play on words) with which to accuse the British government of pushing for a showdown against poor, abused Germany.

Hitler, Joseph Goebbels, and Gestapo Chief Himmler were meeting to review the slant in the program Goebbels was preparing. "Not only can we show the world to what great lengths we will go defensively," observed Goebbels, "but it will be well received by our own citizens to be reminded how well protected they are, and how invulnerable Germany's border is."

Hitler held up his hand in a familiar gesture that meant *Silence, I've thought of something.* Goebbels raised his eyebrows expectantly, and in a moment Hitler spoke.

"Invulnerable. Yes, that's it. Goebbels, you have reminded me of a dream I had last night."

The propaganda chief knew that Hitler put great stock in dreams and omens. "Something to do with the West Wall, mein Führer?" he asked.

"No," corrected Hitler, "about England. The British are so smugly superior because they feel secure on their tiny island. This quality allows them to meddle so confidently in the affairs of others. In my dream, I saw that smugness shattered as their invulnerability went up in flames! Stone monuments crashed down on the heads of the sanctimonious Britishers. Yes, I'm sure that's it!"

"But it cannot be an attack linked to us," protested Goebbels as he saw where this conversation was leading. "That would undo all our efforts to keep the appeasers in power."

"Not us directly," agreed Hitler, placing his hand on a concrete pillar as if testing its strength. "Himmler—" He beckoned to the bookish head of security. "Isn't it true that the IRA bombing campaign is going well?"

"Quite well, mein Führer. The Irish have successfully detonated over a hundred devices and disrupted transportation and communication."

"You see, Goebbels," said Hitler, "it need not be us who remind the British of the need to put their own house in order."

"Did you have a vision of a specific target?" questioned Himmler, since this operation would clearly fall into his domain.

Hitler closed his eyes and covered them with both hands. He stood that way long enough for Himmler and Goebbels to exchange a glance; then he replied.

"I see a dramatic moment when a revered British institution, a part of their cherished history, crashes to the ground. A bridge perhaps, or a famous building. And—" He held up an instructive finger. "If it should happen to fall on a political opponent of ours—if Mr. Winston Churchill, say, should have the misfortune to be killed—why, we would not shed many tears, would we, Goebbels?"

26

The Last Fortress of a Broken Heart

Herr Frankenmuth had made a bed for Lucy on the canvas tarp that lay in the bow of the twenty-foot fishing boat. She looked up at the myriad of stars passing overhead as the craft chugged against the slow current of the Vistula River. The thrumming of the small gas engine could not drown out the high whir of a million crickets that serenaded their passing from the riverbanks. A soft breeze carried the scent of new-mown hay from the broad green fields of the Polish countryside. Lucy scarcely smelled the heavy aroma of iced fish packed in crates for transport to the Polish markets.

The river cut through the heart of Poland on its lazy journey from Warsaw to Danzig and the Baltic Sea. Its summer mists were cool against Lucy's fevered skin. Several times, Herr Frankenmuth left the helm and came forward to touch her forehead with his rough hand.

"When we reach Warsaw," he promised, "you must see a doctor. I have friends there."

Lucy thanked him quietly. She had little strength left for more than that one word. She stared up at the spray of crystalline stars and considered the miracle of her escape aboard the fish monger's boat.

Twice a week Herr Frankenmuth and his son traveled the river from Danzig to Warsaw. Had Alfie remembered that small detail? she wondered. How had he known that at the mention of Alfie Halder and Werner, the fishseller would look at her bruised face and know somehow that she needed help?

When the refugee ship had gone, Lucy had stumbled into the marketplace and found the stall just as Alfie said she would. She had managed to mutter Alfie's name and then Herr Frankenmuth had gently guided her to a cot behind the stall, where she had collapsed and slept until evening.

He fed her supper as she told him only the barest details of what had happened to her—how she had met Alfie and given up the child. "And somehow I must get to Warsaw," she breathed the request.

And now the request was being granted. It seemed as though some other hand had guided Lucy, first to Alfie Halder and from him to Herr Frankenmuth.

It was a long journey up the Vistula to the Warsaw fish market, but the old man promised her that she would be out of reach of anyone who might harm her. As if to emphasize that assurance, he pulled a loaded shotgun out from between two crates of mackerel. The port of Danzig was crammed full of Nazi agents, he explained with a grin. And if it came to war, he would simply load and shoot into the blackshirted mob like shooting into a bait tank. Such a gun as this could drop an entire swarm of S.S. vermin, he claimed. He patted the stock of the ancient weapon and then patted Lucy on her arm. If a German battleship entered the harbor of Danzig, Herr Frankenmuth explained that he was well armed and ready to withdraw upriver to the fortress of Warsaw.

"The Nazis will never be in Warsaw," he declared. "There are a million and a half Polish soldiers and millions more just like me who will fight them if they try it." He swept his hand along the dark shadows of the riverbank. "In the daylight you can see Polish guns guarding the Vistula. This is our highway, and I tell you, the Nazis will not pass over it." He replaced his aging weapon in its hiding place. "You will be safe in Warsaw behind a wall of Polish gentlemen." Then, as an afterthought, he explained, "This German name of ours comes from a great-grandfather." He thumped his chest. "But we are Poles as sure as anything."

Lucy managed a smile of gratitude in reply. But she could not help wondering if all of Poland was equipped with such ancient guns. Pride and the courage to fight would mean nothing against new German tanks and modern aircraft. Lucy had heard Wolf say it a hundred times. She had listened while he laughed at the ill-equipped cavalry of Poland; while he had scoffed at the thought of Polish biplanes in combat against the new Heinkels being turned off the German assembly line.

She was too weary to think about it now. Perhaps all of Warsaw was safe from the designs of the Führer, perhaps not. All that mattered to Lucy was that her baby was safe. She was traveling to Warsaw so that there would be an address for her, a place where a letter might come to her from England with news about the child.

She raised her head slightly to look as the bright headlight of the express train to Warsaw washed over the berm beside the river.

"Look there," said Herr Frankenmuth proudly. "You can see our Polish guns along the tracks."

The old man was right. An artillery piece that had been new when Herr Frankenmuth was young now resumed its duty as a rusty sentinel between rail line and river. The silhouettes of soldiers waved up at the lighted windows of the passenger cars. Uniforms, helmets, and guns all seemed unchanged from photographs Lucy had seen of the Great War. A picket line of horses stamped and snorted a protest against the noise of the train.

Lucy laid her head down against the rough canvas and closed her eyes. It was not enough—horses and ancient artillery beside a river were nothing compared to what she had seen at every corner in the Reich. Tonight Lucy had no illusions about the security of great nations. Probably Warsaw was not the fortress that Herr Frankenmuth imagined it to be. But for the moment, none of that mattered to her. There was only one thing she cared about for herself now, that a letter would come for her in Warsaw and she would *know* where her baby was. She would hold it to her heart and imagine that the hand which had written it had just touched her child. That was all. That was enough. It was the last fortress for her broken heart.

Alfie Halder and Jacob Kalner slept soundly as the express train to Warsaw rattled over the rails. The black-and-white kitten that had disrupted the best-laid plans now curled peacefully on the lap of Samuel Orde.

The lights from the train reflected in the dark waters of the Vistula River. Houses and tiny villages huddled at the river's edge. Lanterns of ships and small boats glowed like fireflies in the night.

How peaceful the night is! Orde thought as he stroked the kitten. And yet, a Polish soldier had been shot and killed today on the frontier between Poland and Germany. Tonight, in answer to that, Warsaw had mobilized all Polish troops, moving their Army into the forward positions facing the Reich. Orde spotted evidence of this troop movement on the unpaved roads of the Polish countryside. He had noted the horse-drawn carts among outdated vehicles in the columns. What he knew about the German divisions on the opposite side of that unfortified border made him shudder inside.

Orde knew that Poland could not afford to remain mobilized for long. Unlike Germany, which directed every resource toward remaining on a war footing, Poland's Army was not equipped for months of standing on guard against aggressions.

What Orde had witnessed in Danzig convinced him that war here was inevitable. Certainly it must come before the first rains of autumn made the primitive highways of Poland impassible.

"September," he whispered, turning his gaze on his peacefully sleeping charges. He would have to find a way out for these boys and the Lubetkin family by then, or it would be too late. The fate of Poland would be their fate.

———

In the end it was not a coded report from a clandestine agent that caused Adolf Hitler to make up his mind. Nor was it a newspaper account of doings in Parliament that decided Hitler on his action against Winston Churchill.

Dr. Schmidt had been reading to the Führer from *The New York Times*. It was innocuous stuff—FDR's calm reassurances to some Chamber of Commerce about how the European situation would not damage the U.S. economic recovery. Roosevelt agreed with the businessmen's resolution that Americans should maintain strict neutrality, not getting entangled in foreign affairs that were of no concern to the U.S.

Hitler was relaxed and jovial, nodding pleasantly as he made a circuit of the great room at Berchtesgaden with its magnificent views of Alpine scenery. In Dr. Schmidt's view, it was the purest of bad fortune that Hitler's wanderings about the room took him past the hewn oak coffee table at the precise moment when Schmidt turned to page six of the first section.

There, opening directly under the Führer's gaze as if brought to his attention by some sinister force, was the abhorrent face of Winston Churchill. Hitler stopped in his tracks. He stared down at the page and his breath surged audibly through his nostrils.

It was an advertisement for an upcoming issue of *Collier's* magazine. With Churchill prominently displayed as the cover photo, the caption read: "HITLER IS ON THE RUN—THE INSIDE STORY FROM THE MAN WHO HAS BEEN WATCHING HIM SINCE 1933."

"Since 1933!" exclaimed the Führer. "Yes! In my way, hounding me, barking at me! But no longer . . . not one moment longer!"

Hitler practically ran to the telephone that stood on a small mahogany table in the corner of the room. "Himmler!" he demanded of the operator. "No, I'll wait!" His tone suggested that his wait had better not be a long one.

Dr. Schmidt heard the moment when Himmler must have come on the line. "No questions," ordered Hitler. "Commence Operation Edifice at once, exactly as planned."

———

Suddenly bread crumbs were not enough. As the hungry chirping of naked chicks filled the cell, mother and father sparrow embarked on a frenzy of journeys to and from the nest. They always carried morsels of food in their beaks, which they crammed into the wide-open throats of their offspring.

Four baby birds, as near as Karl could figure, maybe five. He could not see them, but he could hear them in their endless demand for nourishment. The bits of Karl's black bread were reserved for the adult sparrows, even though they no longer seemed to notice the meal Karl placed for them on the window ledge.

Caring for their children had driven every thought of self from their tiny minds. This fact made Karl smile to himself. Sparrows were not so unlike humans, after all, were they?

When moments of doubt and worry over the fate of Jamie and Lori came to Karl, he only had to look up at the sparrows laboring over their little ones. If the God who watched sparrows was aware of how the little birds loved their babies, then the God who loved him certainly understood the times when Karl Ibsen grieved for his own children.

And like the sparrows, Karl was prone to neglect nourishing his own soul when he worried so much about the nourishment of his children.

Today, once again, his feathered guests preached a sermon to him. "The Lord pities us as a father pities his children." If such a thing was true, then no doubt the Spirit of the living God hovered over Karl and Jamie and Lori. Like the sparrows, the Lord carried nourishment to them. He spread His wings to cover them and shield them from the danger that even now surrounded them.

Outside the window of his cell these days, the endless drone of aircraft could be heard skimming the tops of the trees, prowling along the border of Poland. Karl knew what this meant. He was certain of what was coming. The sky would not be safe for baby sparrows to learn to fly. The earth would not be safe for human children to walk to school. There was nothing he could do now to change that fact.

It was the last refugee children's transport ship. The last miracle. *The last chance!* Some said that it was easier for those who left than for the mothers who were left behind. After all, they reasoned, the children had a whole new world to learn about and exciting things to experience. The mothers, on the other hand, turned their faces from the last glimpse of the ship and returned to face empty rooms, scuffed little shoes left in the closet, a much-loved toy left behind.

And just beyond the horizon, the wall of fire loomed higher and brighter and swept ever nearer. Could those mothers dare to hope that they would ever see their little ones again?

A full twenty-four hours had passed since that last embrace. The ship arrived at Southampton. It was nothing like the arrival of a busload of children at summer camp. No smiles. No cheers. No little hands raised in greeting. Anxious, homesick faces looked down at the beginning of a new life. Anxious, hopeful adult faces looked back up at them from the quay. A small group of musicians played the bright music of Mozart. The music was nice. It was something familiar in this unfamiliar world.

Here and there among the waiting crowd, uncles and aunts, old family friends who had left Germany *in time,* called up to children whom they had not seen in years. Those children were considered the lucky ones by their companions. At least someone *knew* them, yes? This distant connection was better than nothing.

Exuberant joy, the tearful happy reunion of a mother with her two children was a miracle not expected on the docks of Southampton. Such a sight might have broken the little hearts who had no more mama to hold them; no more papa to lift them up and carry them away on top of broad shoulders.

For this reason, Helen Ibsen waited for her children in the privacy of a cluttered shipping office. She sat very still between Anna and Elisa while one thousand immigrant children were sorted between those who had *someone* and those who had *no one*. It was a lengthy process; an hour and a half that seemed as long and as terrible as all the months which had gone before. All the while doubts and fear hovered close and black in the little room.

When at last the door groaned open, Helen's heart hung in her throat. The grim face of a balding clergyman appeared.

"Mrs. Ibsen," he said in a soft voice. A sad and sympathetic voice. "We have a bit of a situation here. Something concerning one of the boys."

Helen, Elisa, and Anna stood together. They grasped each other's hands. As if their blood supply was linked, they grew pale at the same moment.

And then the clergyman stepped aside.

First Jamie ran to the arms of his mother with a shout! Then Mark entered—poor Mark, no mama among the three women. Had he guessed the fate of his mother and father? He looked hopefully at Anna and Elisa. He had been hoping for a surprise; hoping that his mother would be here. Like a gift that was expected, but not received, the absence of Mark's mother caused him to burst into tears. Helen reached out for him; pulled him close. She ran her fingers through his hair and touched the tears on his cheeks just as she did her own son.

And then came Lori, cradling the baby in her arms. Her eyes were red from crying. She looked exhausted from the ordeal of walking among so many little broken hearts.

She hung back, hesitant to run to her mother. Almost shyly she greeted Anna and Elisa. Four men and women wearing official identification tags crowded in behind Lori, interrupting the reunion with nervous coughs and uneasy looks.

"Mama?" Lori asked and then, she, too, fell into her mother's embrace.

It was well known and discussed openly among the older children on the refugee ship that in many cases infants were to be placed in British homes for permanent adoption.

Lori kept this in mind as she faced off with the tribunal of the immigration committee who questioned her about why this tiny baby was given Alfred Halder's identity when the records showed that Alfred Halder was quite a bit older, indeed.

When it was discussed that the infant should be placed immediately into the home of a loving British couple who had been longing for a newborn child, Lori wept with all the sincerity of that long-ago mother who stood before King Solomon to plead for the life of her baby.

She would not let anyone lay a hand on the baby. She claimed that the child was her own; that she and Jacob Kalner had conceived it in New Church, and that she had given birth to it prior to their hasty marriage.

Then, as a final touch, she presented her copy (one of two) of the certificate of legal and holy matrimony. It was dated, signed, and sealed by Pastor Douglass of the English Mariner's Church in Danzig.

A very shocking affair, indeed! The grandchild of the famous Pastor Karl Ibsen had been born out of wedlock! These words were whispered in urgent, barely audible voices by the committee.

However, they believed the story and enjoyed repeating it immensely in the coming days. The baby was allowed to stay with Lori. Papers were adjusted and the accounting showed that there was nothing irregular here as far as the correct number of children who passed through the line. One thousand ordered. One thousand delivered. And that was the end of that.

Even though Helen Ibsen knew the truth behind the story Lori had told, she did not mention it as she rode back to London with her arms around Lori. She cuddled the baby. She praised God for such a beautiful miracle as this!

Then Lori explained everything to Anna and Elisa and her mother. She told them how dear Alfie Halder had given his place to the baby—his life to save this life! She showed them the christening gown and the silver crucifix at the bottom of the basket. She laid the note before these women, *her family*; and they read it and wept for Lucy and circled around Lucy's baby like a herd of mother buffaloes protecting a calf!

Elisa knew as she held little Katie in her arms that the woman who had written such a note had love as strong as iron! Should the baby of Lucy Strasburg be given away and adopted and never be seen by her again?

Elisa, Anna, and Helen agreed with Lori. There was no arguing with the wisdom of Solomon that the mother who loved the child enough to give it up must be the woman who should ultimately raise the child.

Elisa decided that she had milk enough for two. Room enough for two. Clothes which she had not yet returned from baby showers intended for a baby boy. Lori would come and live with the Murphys and help out. And all of them together would begin to pray for Lucy Strasburg, whoever she was and whatever kind of trouble she was in that had driven her to such desperation. God paid wise attention to such prayers, Anna said, as she held the tiny baby boy in her arms.

And then, as if to shout His approval, the Lord himself saved a remarkable surprise for the last.

"She gave this address to Alfie." Lori took the torn page from her pocket. "She said she wants to know that the baby is well. She would like it if we could write."

Lori gave the paper to Elisa, who read the name and gasped and grew very pale. "Where did you. . . ? Where did she. . . ? *This name!* Lori? Can this be right?"

Anna took it from Elisa. She clamped her hand over her mouth and blinked in wonder at the hastily scrawled name and address.

FRÄULEIN LUCY STRASBURG %RUDOLF DORBRANSKY
2334 NISKA STREET APARTMENT 3A
WARSAW, POLAND

Rudy Dorbransky was dead, of course. He had died in Vienna, paid the ultimate penalty for moving Jewish children beyond the reach of the Reich. Elisa knew his family remained in Warsaw after Rudy had been killed. Somehow, seeing his name at this moment was a reminder of all that had gone on before; a verification that perhaps the children who had arrived on this *last ship* to the West *must not be the last*!

The train cars of Elisa's nightmares had been peopled with children guarded by Nazis and all had been headed *east*! *To Warsaw?* The children had dissolved into heaps of bones before her terrified eyes. But now, perhaps that dream had a different meaning than Elisa had imagined.

By carefully picking the identities of children long dead, they might give the children of Elisa's nightmares another chance at life. Alfie had given his own precious papers to this baby. It was the clearest sign to Elisa that they must not abandon hope of turning those eastbound trains back toward life and freedom!

The public house known as Lamb's Tavern looked out over the pleasant, tree-studded Red Lion Square. From the corner window overlooking Lamb's Conduit Road, the house of Elisa and John Murphy was in full view.

In this convenient perch, Alexander Hess and Allan Farrell shared a plain English midday meal of blandly flavored roast, mixed vegetables and cheese with a pint of Newcastle Brown Ale for each.

Hess inhaled the yeasty aroma of the dark brown ale. It reminded him of the smell of fresh baked bread. Although he carried the credentials identifying himself as a wine merchant, Hess would not touch the stuff. When quality schnapps was unavailable, there was nothing quite so welcoming as a glass of good beer.

It had been a hectic few days, but now everything seemed to be heading for a satisfactory conclusion. He relaxed, sipped his beer and listened as Allan Farrell filled him in on the progression of events that had occurred inside the Red Lion House.

"They were due home"—Farrel checked his watch—"over an hour ago."

It did not matter. Hess ordered another pint of Newcastle's. All the work and worry had been done in Danzig; now it was simply a matter of watching and waiting for the right moment. He was unconcerned by the late arrival of the Ibsen children. They would come. Helen Ibsen would be there. Anna Lindheim. Theo Lindheim was home on leave for the occasion. John and Elisa Murphy.

A scholarly-looking man holding the hands of two tow-headed boys swung around the far corner.

Farrell leaned forward and whispered urgently. "There he is. That is Grogan."

"And the children?" Hess asked, picking at his vegetables.

"German refugee brats. Being adopted by the Murphy family. Grogan uses them as a cover."

"Sensible," Hess remarked. "Who could suspect a man of anything sinister if he has won the hearts of children, eh?" Then he looked again at the harmlessness of the man's physical appearance.

Farrell smiled slightly and looked down at his hands. Who would look at Allan Farrell and imagine that he was any threat at all? And yet, he had turned England on its head. "His looks are deceiving," Farrell said in a matter-of-fact tone.

Hess watched Grogan and the boys stand and chat for a moment in the sunlight. Grogan leaned down and said something to one of the two children. Then he mussed the boy's hair affectionately and followed them up the stairs and into the upper story of the tall old house.

At the top of the steps, Grogan turned around and swept the square with his eyes. Satisfied, he disappeared into the house.

"Very good," Hess remarked. "But any man who knows would spot him as an agent. He has *the look*, you know. Like a very dull sentence with an exclamation mark at the end. It labels him like a sign."

"Murphy has a bodyguard, of course. An ex-prize fighter named Freddie Frutschy. You cannot miss him. He is not a young man, but he will be like the Maginot Line. Something to go around. Or over. You will not get through him, however. His wife is as protective as a hen. She squawks, but we shall wring her neck."

Hess smiled his old, patient smile. "When the time is right." Hess patted Farrell's arm. "You new fellows. Everything must be done yesterday." Hess shook his head. "We have opportunity here to change history if we do not rush. Yes? You must not forget which English statesman is the object of our mutual concern, the enemy of your people as well as mine, yes?"

"Churchill." Allan's eyes narrowed in unspoken hatred of the man. "He is responsible for the legislation against us. Thousands of Irish have left England."

"But not Irish Americans." Hess swallowed the last bit of ale. He was feeling very relaxed. "And that is the beauty of it. One of the reasons you have been so tremendously successful. Your work has not gone unnoticed. You may have heard the Führer's speech? We are all struggling against the same thing, are we not? The oppression of our respective races."

Allan's eyes flashed a moment of resentment. "No one has joined me in my struggle until now. I have gone it alone."

Hess laughed. "I assure you, your memorandum was personally approved by the Chancellor. You see, it is all a matter of timing. Perfect, impeccable timing. Surely you know about such things. The fuse must be lit at the right moment, you see. Now we are laying the groundwork together." His eyes flitted toward the heavy, old-fashioned black car that pulled to the curb in front of the Red Lion House.

Dressed in the summer uniform of a chauffeur, Freddie Frutschy got out and opened the door of the vehicle. A large man indeed. Formidable in a close situation. But perhaps he could be taken out at a distance. No doubt he carried a weapon and knew how to use it.

Out of the back compartment appeared faces that Hess knew well: Helen Ibsen. Lori Ibsen. James Ibsen. A dark-headed child of no importance. Then Anna Lindheim and Elisa Murphy, who was holding an infant.

Hess frowned as Grogan came out on the landing to greet them. The two blond boys flanked him and shouted their welcome. Grogan looked out over the square again. His eyes brushed over the corner window of Lamb's Tavern without stopping.

With the proper timing, Operation Edifice could be accomplished to the complete and total satisfaction of the Führer. Hess would watch, he would wait and listen, and then at the precise moment the fuse was lit in Poland, London would hear the deafening roar of the explosion in its own streets.

———

Rachel pretended not to notice the boys of Peter Wallich's little Zionist Youth brigade as they marched by with broomsticks over their shoulders.

Herr Menkes, the baker, came out from behind the counter. He dusted his powdered hands on his powdered apron and watched the *right, left, right, left* progress of the group. They did not march with the stiff-legged arrogance of the Nazis or the pomp of the Poles. This was the purposeful stride of the British soldier. Their arms swung in time, their broomstick rifles poised on their shoulders for action!

They were secretly called the Broomstick Brigade by the younger boys who were jealous and not allowed to drill with them. The oldest of the troop was nineteen. The youngest fourteen. There was a waiting list for those who wanted to join up.

Peter Wallich shouted his commands in English and was rewarded with precision responses from his soldiers.

"Why do you watch them?" Rachel asked irritably. Her purchase was left on the rack as the baker looked on with a big smile.

"They are quite good," said the baker with pride. "Look at the way the feet rise up and come down all together. An unusual accomplishment, for Jews to walk in step, nu?"

"Let the Germans march in step," she said scornfully. "And the Poles. Let them beat each other's brains out, and then maybe we Jews will have peace."

Menkes paid no attention to this clever daughter of the rabbi. "It is good for our boys. Good discipline."

"Why does Peter Wallich shout his orders in English?" she demanded. "No one speaks English in that whole bunch, but he calls out and they lift their sticks this way and that as though they understand."

Menkes watched them all the way to the base of the clock tower. They stood in straight rows while Peter walked up and down and pretended to inspect uniforms. Of course, there were no uniforms. Only ragged shirts tucked more neatly than usual into ragged trousers.

"I have spoken at length with this young mavin, Peter Wallich. He has good reasoning on the subject. He says that when the Germans attack Poland, the English will come in to fight against the Nazis. Now, everyone knows that the Poles do not think much of us Jews." He paused as the next command was given and the group whirled around in one splendid movement. "The Poles will not want us fighting with them, you see, but—" He held up a finger. "Since the Englishman is coming to visit, some say that the British government has sent him to train our boys."

"He is not a soldier anymore. England was unhappy because Captain Orde too much favored the Jews in Palestine. He was sent away because of that."

Menkes scoffed. "Just what they *want* the Germans to think. Just what they want the Mufti to think! England is not so foolish that they would turn out one of their best officers! Captain Orde saved the pipeline in Galilee and trained our fellows there to fight the Arab gangs! Would England punish him for such success?"

Rachel blinked in a puzzled way. It did not make sense. "But that was what my grandfather wrote us from Jerusalem."

"Well, I tell you, Peter Wallich has it figured out! So do some of the other people around here! This is just a *decoy*! The English want him to train our fellows to join them when they rush to the aid of Poland, you see? That is why Peter trains his boys in English. When the British come, the Poles will not know a British *right* from *left*." Menkes had learned the words by watching the daily parade through the square. "But *we* will know. We can fight with them right here in Warsaw."

"I don't think there will be a war," Rachel said. Maybe she did think there would be a war, but she did not want to think about it. "Everything will get worked out. All this is for nothing."

"We can hope." Menkes went back to his work. "It is a nice summer activity for them, anyway," he added paternally. "And if they don't fight here, maybe they can go to Palestine. Captain Orde, they say, plans to return and become the general of the Zionist Army one day."

"Quite an ambition for a Gentile," Rachel remarked dryly. "Especially since the newest British policy says there will not be a Jewish homeland and *nobody* can get into Palestine anymore. Not even us. I don't want to go anyway," she added. "Warsaw does not have buildings blowing up or Arabs slaughtering helpless settlers. Everyone is just all excited about this and that, and none of it means anything. They just want to march in step and beat their drums."

Menkes packaged the sugared rolls apart from the golden brown loaf of challah. "We can hope, nu?" he said, but his voice did not sound hopeful.

Rachel left the bakery feeling particularly irritated at Peter Wallich for parading around Muranow Square. There were Zionist Youth camps out in the countryside for such nonsense. Why did he have to show off right here? Who wanted to listen to the tramping of feet outside the window for hours at a time? *Unpleasant.* And David and Samuel were unhappy because they were not old enough for his little soldier games.

More terrible than all of that was the strange effect it had on Papa! He sat by the window and asked Rachel if perhaps *she* would not like to join the Zionist Youth movement?

"There are plenty of girls . . ." he had said in an off-handed way. It was as if he had lost his mind. *Those* girls were not from religious families, certainly not from the family of Rabbi Aaron Lubetkin!

She was indignant and she let him know by raising her nose slightly and becoming very silent. *Those* girls, she told Mama later, held hands with boys in public and smoked and even passed for Polish. Assimilationists! They were trying to forget who they were. Rachel asked Mama to ask Papa not to bring such a thing up because it was upsetting. She would not fit. She did not want to fit. Her life was here in Muranow Square with Mama and Papa and the boys until she was old enough to marry. She did not like to think of the world turned upside down. She did not like to think about the great Captain Samuel Orde coming into their home. He was an honored friend of Grandfather Lebowitz, perhaps, but he was also partly what inspired all this marching and saluting and looking so grim.

She wished it were last year. Or maybe the year before. Things had been even better the year before those years. Nobody thought about anything but who was getting married and who was being born and who was sick or who had gotten well. Nobody was running away from Warsaw. People weren't coming to Warsaw who had no business being here!

Rachel entered through the kitchen door. She could hear the voice of Father Kopecky in the other room. He was talking very quietly to Papa and Mama, but Rachel could hear every word.

"Not a pleasant thought," Papa said.

"Must be realistic," Mama added. "There is not a mother here who would not wish to send her child if it comes to that."

"The Nazis will be much harder on Jews than on ordinary Poles. I have compiled a list of a few trustworthy people in the church who will be willing. Small babies. Not yet speaking. Girls will be easier for us to manage. You should know that there are still a few good people willing to take them in."

"But the Polish Army?"

The priest did not sound hopeful. "Provided England and France come in on our side in time. But now it looks as though we may also have the Russians allied with the Nazis. If that is the case, men who know say that Germany will cut through Poland like butter, and England and France will wait on the sidelines. There is too much at stake not to have this little plan. Of course it involves only a handful of children. But . . . it is something."

Rachel had heard enough. She turned around and slammed the door loud as though she had just come in. Silence dropped like a curtain. Then Mama called, "Rachel? Is that you?"

She tried to sound cheerful. "Yes." She did not feel cheerful. She felt afraid. Why couldn't life just be ordinary again? Why must they think only of this? Why must they talk about Jewish mothers giving their babies away?

"Are you all right?" Mama heard it in her voice. Rachel was not all right.

"I have a headache," Rachel said. "Too much sun. *Too much...*"

27

Preparing the Way

Passport photos for Jacob Kalner and Alfie Halder arrived among a sheaf of photographs showing the Polish Army parading toward their frontiers with Germany. Harvey Terrill opened the envelope to scan through the material, his critical eye evaluating what could be cropped to fit in a number of different places in the paper.

He dumped the discarded photos in a basket and then presented the pictures of Jacob and Alfie to Murphy.

"Passport pictures?" he asked Murphy.

Murphy attempted to brush off the photographs as routine. "Just mug shots of the kids with Orde in Warsaw."

Terrill tossed another handful on the desk. A man, dark and very Jewish-looking. A pretty woman in her late thirties. Two little boys with very close-cut hair and serious eyes. "How about these?" he asked wryly. "Also employees?"

"I dunno. I'll ask him. He didn't send captions?"

"No. Nor immigration applications, either."

Murphy shrugged it off, scooted the mound of pictures to the side and pretended to be distracted by other things. He would warn Orde to send the photographs to Murphy's personal attention. There was no getting around the fact that Terrill had the cynical mind and the nose of a journalist. No use arousing his curiosity.

Twenty minutes later, Terrill was still smiling as if he had a secret. Smiles were rare on Terrill's face, and somehow Murphy liked him better sour.

———

Word came from the London agent soon after Wolf settled into his hotel in downtown Warsaw. A follow-up note from the Berlin office explained that the name of Lucy's Warsaw host was the father of the notorious Vienna resister, Rudolf Dorbransky.

Could there be any question left of her guilt? Any doubt that Lucy had been closely allied with the ring of anti-Nazis in Austria?

The Führer had been apprised of this, and was most anxious, therefore, that Wolf apprehend Lucy Strasburg and bring her back to Berlin.

At this news, Wolf had frowned. Hess had said it would be simpler just to eliminate her, but orders from the Führer were orders. Every traitor to the Führer and the Reich must be exposed. No doubt she knew much, Himmler wrote. Hitler believed completely that an appropriate interrogation of this woman would lead to an entire ring of disloyal army officers. With the plans in place for Case White against Poland, it seemed imperative that those traitors be rooted out.

At such a command, something stirred uneasily in Wolf. Certainly he was not still suspected? Had his association with Lucy Strasburg put his own life in jeopardy?

That possibility filled him with a fresh sense of anger toward her. He should have killed her in Danzig, and then there would not be this question remaining in anyone's mind.

He pressed the ammunition clip into place in his pistol and held his fingers out before his face to watch them tremble. Wolf was afraid. No doubt they were watching him even more closely now from the heights of Berlin's citadels of power. Nothing could go wrong this time in Warsaw.

"Why should it?" he reasoned aloud, staring down at the Dorbransky address. He had her cornered. It should be a simple matter of scooping her up.

———

The Bristol Hotel in Warsaw was the gathering place, a home-away-from-home for most of the English-speaking journalists assigned to cover the present chaotic politics of Poland. Not far from the government offices and the Royal Palace, motorcades containing every variety of diplomat streamed by. On the first day after Orde's arrival with the boys, the French foreign minister whisked past the uninterested residents of Warsaw. He met with the Polish foreign minister, Józef Beck, to urge Poland to *try a little harder* in negotiations with the German government.

Two hours after the French vehicle passed, Orde stood on the roof of the Bristol and reported the motorcade "live" to London through Polski Radio.

Murphy sent a telegram of congratulations. He did not guess that the French and Polish officials had already uttered frosty farewells.

On the second afternoon, a representative of the government of the Soviet Union also passed by. Polish policemen on horses lined the avenue in case there were demonstrations of any kind. They need not have bothered. Orde stood at his microphone and reported that spectators simply had not come.

He did not mention the one elderly man walking his dog. The mutt lifted his leg on the rear tire of the Russian limousine parked outside the great baroque government palace. Nor did Orde report that not one Polish policeman attempted to interfere with man or beast on this solemn occasion.

On the third day, there was a demonstration of a different sort. An emissary of the Pope arrived in Warsaw, and the square was packed curb to curb with cheering Poles. Now this was worth reporting! The Pope had sent a spokesman to plead for peace and restraint in this border dispute with Herr Hitler. The bells of the cathedrals rang out welcome.

Orde had to shout into the microphone to be heard above the tumult. Blue-coated policemen linked hands to restrain the crowds. What the French and the Russians and the British could not accomplish in Polish corridors of diplomacy, perhaps the prayers of the Pope could.

What passed between the Vatican spokesman and the Polish foreign minister was not reported. Later, a Mass was held at St. John's. The overflow crowd filled the streets for ten blocks around the cathedral.

The cardinal prayed for peace. The people prayed for peace. No doubt the Polish foreign minister prayed for peace right along with them.

That night there was a shooting incident at the border. Three Polish soldiers were killed by Germans. The frontier between Poland and Czechoslovakia was closed. The spokesman of the Pope went home, and another million Polish military reservists were ordered to report for duty.

All of this was dutifully discussed and reported by the Western journalists. The rumble of motorized and horse-drawn equipment echoed throughout Warsaw where the bells of St. John's had sounded.

It was decided by those exalted members of the press who had never seen military duty that this war would begin at dawn. *Wars were supposed to begin at dawn, weren't they?* A pool was formed for taking bets on the exact hour of the first shots. Then another pool for choosing the exact date, *and* the time of day! This was an American idea. For one buck a pop, the reporter who guessed the closest would win the entire jackpot.

The hat and the calendar were passed.

Orde looked at the hat full of money and IOU's. He looked at the list of guesses. Then he stood up and excused himself from the proceedings.

"Hey, where'ya goin', Orde?" called a fairly soused journalist from McCormick News in Chicago. "Come on, what's yer guess? When's the Blitzkrieg going to begin?"

Orde checked his watch and waved. "There's a new movie playing at the English theater. I'm treating my crew. So sorry."

"Whatcha say? Dawn? *What time is dawn?* This one gonna start at *dawn,* Orde?"

Orde continued to smile pleasantly, although making a game out of something so deadly and inevitable made him feel angered and sickened.

He had his opinion. He kept it to himself. He hoped he still had time enough to keep a promise to an old rabbi and, if he was lucky, to the Zionist Youth of Warsaw.

Upstairs in the hotel room, as Werner played with his shoelaces, Orde placed a telephone call to the home of Rabbi Aaron Lubetkin. In careful Yiddish he explained that he had been asked by Rabbi Lebowitz of Jerusalem to pay a call when he reached Warsaw. *Would Monday be acceptable?*

The voice was that of a young woman. She replied with polite dignity, but just before the receiver clattered into its cradle, he heard her shouting, *"MAMA! He's here in Warsaw!"*

Warsaw is lousy with Jews, thought Wolf as the taxi rolled to a stop in front of the Niska Street apartment building where Lucy imagined she was safe.

"Wait here," Wolf ordered in clear, unaccented Polish. His dialect was that of an aristocratic Pole. He managed to fit in quite well in *Gentile* Warsaw. But here in the Jewish District heads turned as he walked into the shabby foyer of the building.

He did not give the concierge time to ask his business or call ahead to warn the occupants of apartment 3A. Taking the steps two at a time, he reached the third floor before the antique elevator would have made it up one level.

Wolf fingered the gun in his pocket and fixed a smile on his face as he knocked on the chipped blue paint of the door.

"Who is it?" a woman's voice called through the thin wood panel.

"A friend," Wolf replied. He did not ask himself if the Jewess within would wonder who among their friends spoke with such refined accent. Indeed, her curiosity got the better of her. After a moment of hesitation, the door opened slightly. A chain was in place, intended to keep strangers out. She was not worried as she peered out at him.

"Who are you?" she asked. Her thin, serious face was still unafraid.

"I told you," Wolf lied. "I was a friend of Rudy Dorbransky in Vienna. The *younger* Dorbransky, I mean. Rudy was a great violinist. He spoke often of his family here in Warsaw. I thought I should look you up and—"

"They don't live here anymore," the woman replied quietly, but she did not slam the door on the handsome face of Wolf. She continued to look at him as if she hated to disappoint him.

"Oh yes." Wolf read the address aloud. He checked the number on the door. "This is the address."

"I am sorry." And she was. "But the Dorbransky family left some months ago."

"They are surely still in Warsaw?" Should he believe her? Behind her two small children chattered and played house.

"No. Not Warsaw." She looked skyward as though she could not remember. One of the children knocked something over with a clatter. She scolded in Yiddish, then turned back to Wolf in an embarrassed manner.

His smile was frozen on his face. He felt she was lying, and yet, he did not yet want to force the issue or the door. "You have a forwarding address?"

She shrugged. "No. Nothing. Some letters have come for them, but we send them back." She was reluctant to end the conversation, and yet . . . was there something behind that gaunt, mousy face?

"Why don't you open the door?" Wolf asked. "Maybe we can think of who might know how I can find my friends. I have come a long way."

The woman blushed. "My husband is not at home. I cannot . . . and I cannot help you in any way. We are from Cracow ourselves, you see. We were just very lucky to find this flat empty. They were just leaving. They sold us the furniture." She gestured at the furniture that Wolf could not see and shrugged. The children shouted and laughed, and at that moment, when she decided she was quite through, Wolf decided he was just beginning.

He braced his foot in the door as she attempted to close it. "Who was with Rudy's family?" He retained a pretense of friendliness even as he forced the door to remain open against the woman's wishes.

"I . . . please . . . don't remember. They were just leaving."

"A red-haired woman was with them, perhaps?" He remembered Peter Wallich's desperate note about his mother. This was the very place where Karin Wallich had fled from Vienna, Wolf sensed. And why not? It was Lucy's last refuge as well.

"Yes! A red-haired woman! A little girl! Also Viennese." She repeated this news with the hope that he would now go away.

Instead, powered by the awareness that Lucy also had this address, he shoved hard against the door, pulling the chain loose with a snap. The woman opened her mouth as if to scream. Wolf waved his weapon in front of her face and shook his head in a warning that she must remain silent.

The place was as thin on charm as the woman trembling before him. One severe square table and four chairs sat in the center of the room. A bookshelf stood against the wall. A few elegant pieces of porcelain sat upon the shelves as a stark reminder of how far these people must have fallen in society. The children played on, oblivious that anything was wrong.

"Where is Lucy?" Wolf asked with a smile, as if this was some sort of elaborate joke. Her joke on him? Or his on her?

Confusion mingled with terror in her eyes. "Lucy?"

Again he waved the gun beneath her nose. "You think I will not use this?"

"Please! Sir! I don't know anyone by that name! We are from Cracow! From Cracow, you see? They sold us the furniture and went away. I don't know where they went! No one named Lucy has come here!"

The fear was genuine. Wolf backed up a step in the tiny space that passed for the main room. He nudged open the bedroom door with the heel of his hand and then looked from the empty bed toward the rack that served as a closet. The bed was made up. From this one fact, he was satisfied that perhaps this living broomstick was telling him the truth.

At that, he pocketed the weapon, looked once more around the shabbiness of the flat and straightened his fingers for a small, unspoken Nazi salute. The woman did not recognize the gesture, Wolf knew, but soon enough it would be common in Warsaw. Perhaps then she would remember the man who entered her flat uninvited and know that the visit had been only a small foretaste of what was about to come upon the Jews of Warsaw.

Wolf could hear her crying as he descended the steps of the flat. He imagined what she would tell her husband when the man got home. Then he hurried to his hotel room to telephone Heinrich Himmler at Gestapo headquarters in Berlin with the news that the London agent had sent inaccurate information. Lucy was not there. But sooner or later, he knew she would contact the people in London who had the child. It was a matter of patience, Wolf told them. Of course, patience was not a virtue he possessed himself. He only asked that it be extended to him in this difficult situation.

Wolf apprised Berlin of his plans. He had Peter Wallich's address. He did not doubt that Lucy would eventually be in contact with the boy, he assured Himmler. When that moment came, Wolf would be on hand to arrest them both and bring them back to the Reich for the trial which the Führer desired so urgently.

The fact that Lucy Strasburg was not where the London agent said she would be was not Wolf's fault, was it? It certainly did not mean that she was not in Warsaw and within the reach of Nazi justice.

Wolf sensed that the impatience of Himmler was placated by his assurances. He only hoped that the Führer could also be soothed in the meantime.

———

"Six months' rent in advance," said the Polish landlord as Wolfgang von Fritschauer counted out the bills without argument. "And if you would like to pay for twelve months, of course there will be an additional discount."

"Six months will be sufficient," Wolf replied. The discount did not interest him as much as the location of the apartment.

Kowalski was a typical Polish landlord. Physically fat and soft, the man was nonetheless hard and shrewd in his dealings. He did not care what reason Wolf had for renting an upstairs flat on the corner of Niska Street and Muranow Square. The affairs of the tall, iron-jawed young man did not matter as long as the rent was paid. But Kowalski was *curious*!

Why should a well-groomed, well-educated businessman like *this* wish to rent a flat in the Jewish District of Warsaw? Certainly it was possible that the fellow had some business transactions with the Jews. Such a thing was quite common in Warsaw. After all, Kowalski conducted matters of a financial nature with the Jews on a daily basis. He owned several buildings in the Jewish District that were leased to the Jews. But Kowalski made the Jews come to his office in downtown Warsaw. He did not have an office anywhere near the noisy, medieval world in which they lived.

Well, then, was the business of this gentleman of a personal nature, perhaps? *A Jewish mistress?* At first Kowalski thought this was a logical explanation. Jewish women were known for their beauty. Polish wives were jealous. Polish men often discussed the desirability of the Jewesses. It was well known that certain members of the Polish nobility kept Jewish mistresses. Their fiery temperaments and lack of care for the proprieties of the church, it was said, made them excellent distractions for wealthy Poles. The joke was that a gentleman did not have to worry about his mistress making confession to his personal parish priest if she was Jewish. Such reasoning made sense, did it not?

But why would this fellow set his mistress up in the most religious sector of Jewish Warsaw? The Orthodox Jews had their own standards of moral behavior. They did not like their women running around with Polish men. In such an area, a Jewish mistress would have difficulty walking down the street without being reviled. Shops would be closed to her. Life would be unbearable.

This fellow could not have rented the flat for the keeping of a courtesan.

What was left, then?

Kowalski leaped to the only conclusion. Everyone knew that the Jewish District was a nest of Bolshevik dissension. The Polish government always worried about the Jews making plans with the Russians. Kowalski himself worried about such things. After all, if Poland was taken over by the Communists, he would lose his apartment buildings.

The Jews would form collectives and take over everything Kowalski owned. They would not pay him rent anymore. He would be poor—as poor as the people who now rented from him.

"You are a government man, are you not?" Kowalski asked.

Wolf looked up sharply. "I would not tell you if I was."

That reply was as good as a yes. "You are going to be keeping an eye on the Jews?"

A slight smile. "That is not your business, as long as I pay the rent."

Kowalski felt pleased. He had figured it out. "As I told you. A very prominent apartment. You can see the whole of Muranow Square all the way to the Community Center. There are so many Jews coming and going these days. Terrible times. We must be careful of the Jews or they will feed Poland to the Russian bear, eh, my friend?"

Wolf shrugged. He did not reply. But that was as good as a yes, was it not? Kowalski felt honored that his building was somehow in a very small way being used for the defense of Poland against the intrigues of the Jews. Everyone knew the Jews were plotting with the Communists. And now this government fellow was going to be right in Kowalski's own building, protecting the Polish state and Kowalski's property in the bargain.

For a moment, Kowalski considered giving this government agent a discount. He thought better of it. After all, Kowalski's taxes paid this fellow's salary and also paid the rent on the flat on Muranow Square.

Kowalski gave him the keys with a knowing smile. "Good luck then," he said. "You will enjoy the view very much."

———

The letter Elisa had sent to the Warsaw address of Lucy Strasburg returned to the London TENS office covered with large, angry-looking Polish words indicating that there was no one there by that name.

It lay open on Murphy's desk with the rest of the mail. The photograph of tiny baby Alfie at his christening poked out sadly from the torn envelope.

Murphy reread the letter Elisa and Lori had written. It was long and newsy, in the warm, friendly tones of someone who had lived among the outgoing people of Austria.

Harvey Terrill was just on his way home after what had been a very newsy night, but without any warmth of friendliness at all. Exhaustion reflected in Terrill's face.

"Thanks, Harvey," Murphy encouraged. Then he held up the letter. "When did this come in?"

"Yesterday," Harvey answered in a flat tone. "I opened it by mistake. Took me a while before I translated it and figured out it was talking about the baby." He frowned as if something just struck him. "I thought that baby was Lori Ibsen's kid."

"Long story," Murphy waved him off. "Go home and get some rest. The Nazis and the Russians are having a pow-wow tonight in Moscow. You'll have to be awake for that one."

Murphy waited until Harvey left the office before he picked up the letter again. He called Elisa and told her that the letter had been returned, and then he slipped it into the outgoing mail packet back to the Warsaw TENS office and Samuel Orde.

David and Samuel had blabbed the day and the time of Captain Samuel Orde's planned visit to the Lubetkin home.

Apparently, this time no one doubted their veracity. At 6:30 A.M., the first of the young men began to gather on the sidewalk outside the Muranow Square house. They chose their places along the curb, dusted off the pavement, and sat down to wait for the arrival of the great *Hayedid*!

After breakfast, Rachel looked out the window. The little knot of young men had grown to a crowd. Black coats mingled with the white, short-sleeved shirts of the nonreligious. The curb-sitters had multiplied to at least two hundred, with more coming from every direction like lines of ants on the march to the anthill!

"Mama!" Rachel shouted in alarm. "Hurry! Come look!"

There was no need for Etta to hurry. These men and boys were not going away. They had staked their claims on little parcels of pavement so they could see *him*! Like the Deliverer, he was! The one who had been in the newspapers and had trained the Special Night Squads *and so on and etcetera,* until he was practically a legend. *And so what if he was not a Jew? He probably really was a Jew, only nobody was telling it!*

Etta gasped in astonishment at the ever-spreading mass that began at her front door and moved outward into the square like an ink spill on a tablecloth! Among them near the front steps gleamed the red hair of Peter Wallich.

"Have they come to see the captain?" Etta breathed. "But how did they know he would be here today?"

At that, David and Samuel, dressed for Torah school, peeked their heads around the corner. If ever there were guilty faces, David and Samuel had them. Their eyes were wide with *who-me?* looks, their mouths clamped shut as if they had never opened to spill the news to friends and classmates.

Etta turned and glared at them. She put her hands on her hips and shook her head to let them know that they had better not pretend they had said nothing!

"Well? Nu? You should see what you have done! Next thing you know the Polish Secret Police will accuse us of hosting a riot!" She crooked her finger. *They should come see.*

Guilt made them tiptoe to the window. They gazed solemnly at a thousand below. More were coming. Brooms were being set aside and stoops were left dusty and untended. Now it was no longer just young men who flocked, but *everyone* was coming!

"We didn't tell," Samuel said in his sweetest voice.

Etta replied with a threatening look. *"Samuel!"*

"We just said . . . that is . . . *I* told *Mordechai* that—"

"Mordechai!" Rachel snarled the name. "You were showing off!"

"I told Mordechai that if he did not believe he should come here to our house at eleven o'clock." Samuel finished indignantly. "So?" He gestured toward the thousand and some Mordechais who had all come to *see*.

Etta's face reflected her puzzlement. "You think this many will show up when the Messiah comes?"

"If they do, then the Messiah will not be able to get through them all." Rachel glared at the smirking face of David. "What are you so happy about?"

"Mama?" David addressed his happy question to Etta and ignored his sister entirely. "How will Samuel and I get to Torah school this morning?"

Etta looked from the angelic face of her son to the teeming mob of spectators. "David, it would have been easier if you had told me you had a stomachache."

"You only told Mordechai?" Rachel challenged. "They must have sent out printed invitations to everyone in Warsaw so they would not have to go to school!"

"Not true." Samuel looked at her in a dangerous way. "Only Mordechai I told."

David never said *who* he had mentioned the event to. But everyone out there had heard from someone who had heard from *someone else* that the great and mighty English Zionist soldier, Captain Samuel Orde was coming to tea. Like the Messiah, he was coming. Like Gideon. Who in Jewish Warsaw could doubt such a marvelous tale? The Eternal always answered prayers during perilous times, did He not? Blessed be He! Was there even one Jewish male who was not in the square?

Maybe Mordechai was not there. Everyone knew that Mordechai was a poor loser.

28

The Deliverer Comes

Something was up with the Jews in Muranow Square. In all the days Wolf had been watching from his perch, he had never seen a gathering quite like this.

The clatter of milk bottles announced the arrival of the grocery delivery boy outside Wolf's door. He turned away from the window and fixed a smile on his face before he opened the door to the diffident youth who stood with his arms full of boxes.

A Polish language newspaper was folded and wedged between a small bottle of cream and another of milk. The boy looked red-faced and harried today.

"You are late," Wolf scolded in a friendly fashion. The building was without an elevator. The delivery boy was always later than promised.

"Did you see the mob in the square?" the boy blurted out, setting the boxes on the table and then going to peer out across the crowded square.

Wolf pretended that he had seen the demonstration but that it did not really interest him.

"Did someone die?" he asked, as he took the bottles of milk to the old-fashioned icebox. Always Wolf made the boy wait for his payment until the grocery boxes were empty. Jews talked too much for their own good, Wolf knew. This young fellow was like the others of his race in this way.

"No one died," he answered. It was not like him to leave the explanation incomplete.

"A wedding, perhaps," Wolf said knowingly and then he let the matter drop.

The boy stared distractedly down at the ever-expanding mob. It was plain he wanted to be among his people. He turned as if to leave. The tip seemed of little importance. "I have to go," he said, touching his hand to his cap. His voice betrayed excitement.

"The tip," Wolf replied. "Just a minute. Only a minute." He moved slowly toward the bedroom, where his wallet was. When he emerged, the boy stood rooted at the window. His eyes were wide with anticipation. Wolf stood unspeaking at his shoulder. "Will there be a riot?" Wolf asked.

The boy scoffed. "A holy man is coming," he said quietly. "No riot. You will be safe." He seemed amused by Wolf's question.

Wolf slipped him a few loose coins, then opened the door for him. *These Jews,* he thought with disgust. *A holy man, indeed!* At that, Wolf stretched out in his chair beside the window. He had just raised his field glasses to scan the crowd when the bright flash of the morning sun reflected off the windshield of a car with blinding intensity. The dull throb of a headache clamped across Wolf's skull like a vise.

He lowered his head for a moment and closed his eyes against the pain. It did not diminish. Instead, the dull throb became a roar in his ear. Small lights and shadows flickered at the edges of his vision.

He blinked rapidly and tried to focus his eyes. Lights shifted and danced, distorting his eyesight until he was unable to see even his hand clearly. He held his fingers up before his face. He could see only thumb and index finger. The agony in his skull gripped tighter. Wolf completely forgot the gathering in the square below. He groped toward the bathroom and felt for the aspirin bottle. His hand knocked the water glass to the floor with a crash. He gulped the aspirin without water and then stumbled to his bed and fell across it.

The light through the window seemed to focus down through the darkness that played across his vision. He struggled to sit up and draw the window shade, leaving the room in semidarkness. With a low moan, he lay back on his pillow and closed his eyes. Today was one day he would leave the Jews to their holy man. It did not matter anyway.

———

The gruff, unshaven Polish taxi driver grimaced and ran his hand over the stubble of his beard in concern.

"Something is up with the Jews," he said in a displeased voice.

Jacob and Alfie had been invited along so that they might explore the Jewish District while Orde made his call on the family of Rabbi Lubetkin. Both of them leaned forward to stare at the mass of black-coated backs blocking all traffic into Muranow Square.

A Polish traffic policeman was detouring all vehicles down Niska and away from the mob.

"What is it?" Orde muttered to himself.

"Oh, you know these Jews!" the driver scoffed. "Always something. A wedding or a funeral maybe. They always wear black, so who can tell?" He flicked his hand toward the crowd. Head out the window, he shouted profanities at them. Then with a shrug, he said, "Blocking traffic! *Troublemakers!*"

"Pull over," Orde commanded, "at *once!*" As he paid the man he asked pointedly, "Were you among the crowd at St. John's when the envoy of the Pope came?"

"Of course!" The man said.

"Then you blocked traffic as well, my friend."

"The Jews have cost me my full fare!" the Pole exclaimed.

"No! *You* have cost you the full fare! I do not ride with ill-mannered anti-Semites. At least not on purpose."

"No tip?"

"A tip? Yes, here is my tip to you. Keep your mouth shut if you are an ignorant bigot. And cut off your tongue before you ever curse the Jews again. Or have you not heard that *God himself will curse those who curse His chosen?*" Orde's eyes blazed like a fiery preacher during a revival meeting in a small country parish. The Pole had never seen anyone quite so crazy looking. A frightening thing to have hanging over the backseat while a mob of wild Jews blocked escape in the front of the taxi.

"Just get out!" he shouted. He made the sign of the cross as the hair on the back of his neck stood on end.

He had already shifted into reverse and was looking for his escape as Orde jumped from the vehicle.

"What did you say to him?" Jacob asked. Jacob did not understand the exchange that took place in Polish.

Orde grinned broadly as the wheels of the taxi squealed against the cobbles. "Discussing the prophet Balaam." Orde marched forward toward the mob, five to six thousand people filling the square.

Alfie was also smiling as he fell in line behind Jacob. With one backward glance, Orde could see that Alfie . . . *Elisha* . . . was looking upward toward the tops of the buildings. His eyes were bright with amusement. He raised his big hand and waved . . . a broad, signaling wave toward the Star of David that graced a synagogue poking up beyond the square. It was the sort of wave that said, "Yes, I see you!" But no one was there!

Orde too felt the hair on the back of his neck prickle. He stopped at the outermost perimeter of the crowd and turned to Alfie. In a quiet, certain voice, he asked, *"They* are here, aren't they?" Did Alfie understand the question?

Alfie nodded happily, swept his hand to the top of the Star; then upward to a line of buildings at the far end of Muranow, on to the peak of the clock tower, and finally to the big house that was their destination. Then, one more startling gesture; Alfie smiled at the empty air just above Orde. At that moment, the murmuring thousands grew strangely silent. A corridor of humans parted as though a hand had opened the way for Orde and Jacob and Alfie to walk through. The path led straight to the house of Rabbi Aaron Lubetkin.

There, on the sidewalk in front of the house, like soldiers waiting for the arrival of their general, a troop of fifty boys, from fourteen to nineteen, snapped to smart attention. Commands from a tall, gaunt red-headed boy were shouted in English.

"Ten-hut! Huh-bout-TURN!"

Five rows of ten ragged soldiers each saluted Orde as he approached them and smiled slightly with appreciation. Orde paused, responded in kind, and then prowled the line as if inspecting the readiness of his soldiers. Alfie and Jacob hung back and watched in amazement. The soldiers did not have guns, but they carried broomsticks as though they were rifles. At the barked commands of their red-haired leader, they progressed through a series of maneuvers as Captain Orde stood back and watched them with all the dignity he would have accorded the Highland Light Infantry.

A small pattering of applause rose up from those among the spectators who could see. When it was finished, Orde spoke quietly to the leader of the group.

"Captain Peter Wallich, First Warsaw Hashomer Platoon, reporting for duty!"

"Your English is excellent, Captain Wallich," Orde said. "And your men are well trained." He looked the stiff-backed rows up and down once more. "Where did you learn to drill?"

"Books, General Hayedid."

"Books?"

"Books. Rudyard Kipling, mostly. A lot of different books. And then there are movies. Errol Flynn."

"Ah." Orde nodded once and suppressed a smile. He knew the movie the boy was speaking of. *Charge of the Light Brigade.* That explained a number of peculiarities in the demonstration. But no matter. It was a tiny, unequipped and untrained bunch; yet as Orde looked up toward the metal outline of the Star on the synagogue, he felt the certain presence of other captains and other troops and the approving nod of their Commander here watching today. *God looks at the heart,* Orde thought. *And so must I.*

"Where are our headquarters, Captain Wallich?"

"The basement of the community soup kitchen." A pause. A moment of embarrassment. "There are more of us than this. These are the best."

"A well-disciplined group. Admirable. Well done." Orde did not let his gaze linger on the worn-out shoes or torn coats and trousers cinched with string or cracking leather. "I will have a word with your community leaders, and then we will begin immediately. You may dismiss the men."

At this, the crowd began to disperse. Had they come to meet Orde, or, like Alfie's angels, had they come to see the future army of Israel?

From the corner of his eye, Orde saw the scornful expression on the face of Jacob Kalner. Was it any wonder he was not impressed? He had seen a hundred thousand Hitler Youth dressed and polished, carrying real rifles over their shoulders! He had heard their voices raised in one song, to one Reich and one Führer! What was this pitiful little show compared to what Jacob had seen throughout Germany?

Jacob crossed his arms and watched as the Zionist Youth marched off in time. He looked with revulsion as the sole of one boy's shoe flapped an extra beat. The hands of many spectators reached out to tap the boys proudly on their shoulders as they passed through the square and on toward the synagogue.

"Pitiful," Jacob said.

"Very good," said Alfie, as if he wished he could line up so straight and march in step like that.

"Pathetic," Jacob said again.

Orde did not blame Jacob for his scorn. And yet he could not let it stand. "What is it?"

"Do they think they can make any difference against Nazi guns and tanks and planes?"

Orde smiled and turned to Alfie. "How many soldiers are on our side, Elisha?"

The light of admiration was bright on Alfie's face. He spread his arms wide and looked up into the sky where streaks of thin clouds passed above the earth like the trails of smoking chariots. "Look Jacob!" he cried.

Against his own volition, Jacob looked up. He stared hard at the vapors passing overhead on the wind until it felt as though the earth itself were moving, not the clouds. Were they just clouds?

Orde saw the goose bumps on Jacob's arms.

Alfie waved. *"Auf Wiedersehen."* Then he turned to Jacob. "They will be back. But don't worry. The General is still here." At that, Alfie pulled out the toy tin general he always carried in his pocket. The one he called *General Jesus.* "You want to put him in your pocket?" He tucked the toy soldier into Jacob's shirt pocket.

Orde smiled. "You are the one who told me he sees things."

Jacob nodded. He could not speak.

The door behind them opened. Etta Lubetkin stood framed in the doorway. Had she heard their discussion? She, too, was looking into the sky as the clouds dissipated above Warsaw.

Other men of importance were meeting with Rachel's father and the British Captain Orde. Two representatives of the Zionist community had come, as well as Father Kopecky and three other men whose positions Rachel did not know.

While Mama tended to full teacups and little sandwiches on a tray, David and Samuel were banished to play outdoors. Rachel sat beneath the shade of the elm tree in the garden and watched as baby Yacov struggled to pull himself into position to crawl.

Masculine voices drifted through the open window of Papa's study. Although Rachel could not understand all the words, the tone of the conversation was unmistakable. *Frightening.*

Rachel looked up into the green-leafed branches. Bits of blue shone through. Sunlight played against the leaves as they stirred in the slight breeze. Beneath the kitchen window, David and Samuel drilled with stick rifles over their shoulders in imitation of Peter Wallich's marching troops. Rachel missed the summers when play had involved which tree to climb and what book to read or how much blackberry jelly to make. The sounds of summer were the same. The aromas from the kitchen still drifted out. But along with those sweet things came the dark voices of the strangers who had come to Muranow Square all with the same concern.

"The children will be the first to suffer."

"The Nazis in Prague right now are making even children ..."

The grass was thick and soft beneath the blanket where baby Yacov lay. He lifted himself up on his pudgy arms and smiled a drooling smile at Rachel.

His eyes were bright and proud. Happy. He did not hear the droning voices speaking of threats against his innocence. His trusting confidence that all was right with the world and his patch of Warsaw made Rachel's heart ache.

"Mama says you are ready to crawl," she crooned to him, hiding her misery.

As if in reply, little Yani pulled one knee under his stomach and then the other. Crouched on all fours, he was in position to crawl, but he did not know what to do next. He rocked back and forth. He became very excited as he looked at his hands and then at Rachel.

She wriggled her fingers on the edge of the blanket. "Right here. Crawl over here and I will tickle your fat belly!"

"Evacuation seems to be ..."

"Evacuation to where?"

"The Catholic Poles may not be better off if . . ."

"Your opinion, Captain Orde?"

"Expect . . . siege against Warsaw . . . hold on until England . . ."

Yacov put out one tentative hand. Now what?

"Yes. That's it! And now the other! Move your other hand."

The baby moved a knee forward instead. It was effective. He was crawling! Another drooling, surprised grin. Rachel praised him loudly as if to shield him from this terrible talk of siege and hunger and bombing in Warsaw—*and the evacuation of babies!*

"The logistics of transporting little ones is . . ."

"Can we speak of logistics? These are the most helpless . . ."

"The smallest could be hidden among the Poles, as I have said before."

"Captain Orde, you have seen the corps of young boys who can be taken out on foot."

"Peter Wallich has been—"

"We are attempting to acquire papers for . . ."

And Little Yani crawled another step. He crept in unsteady excitement toward the sunlight that touched the edge of the blanket. Such an accomplishment would have given Rachel great pleasure some other time. She would have dashed in to summon her mother to witness the baby's little miracle.

Life had been that simple once. "So wonderful, Yani," Rachel praised her baby brother as she picked him up and walked into the house, wiping away tears with the edge of her apron.

Father Kopecky and Captain Orde left Papa's study together. *What else? The goyim!* They had made their plans together—made their lists and talked about how Jewish babies must be taken into Catholic homes if the worst really came to Warsaw!

Rachel was angry. She hoped they saw it on her face as they walked past her and Yacov and smiled their polite smiles! She wanted to shout at them, *You'll never have my brother! Nor any one of my family! We would rather die together than be separated!*

Instead, she smiled politely and saw them to the door with other members of the *Kehillot* who had come to talk to Papa about hospitals and the overflow of children at the orphanage.

Papa spotted her as she walked back toward the kitchen.

"Rachel?"

"Just going to help Mama in the kitchen." She felt angry at Papa, too. Was he actually thinking of sending Yacov off somewhere? Or David? Or Samuel? Or—God forbid—Rachel herself?

"Come here, daughter," Papa ordered in a businesslike way.

She sighed and entered the study without looking up at him.

"Yes, Papa," she said.

"You were impolite today."

She wanted to shout at him, but she did not. "I was nowhere close enough to anyone to—"

"Enough!" He really was angry. "It is as hot as the fires of Baal's altar today. So the window was open, and you sat beneath it purposely."

"Just under the elm tree, Papa. Because it *is* hot and I was watching Yacov. You should like me to sit in the sun?"

Papa was silent a moment. Drumming fingers on the big desk. "And singing your brother lullabies, were you?" He paused and then began to sing the words that Rachel had indeed been singing beneath the window as the meeting progressed.

Let's be joyous and tell our jokes,
We'll hold a wake when Hitler chokes.

She shrugged. A slight flush of shame crept to her cheeks, but not enough for her to admit. "Peter Wallich sings it with his Zionist Youth friends. They sing that and worse up and down the square all day. One cannot help but hear it."

"Yes. We all heard. The best men in the community. All trying to sort out major problems, and we all heard."

Her eyes flashed anger. She raised them in challenge to her father. "And *I* heard. You are planning to give us away if the Nazis come. Send us away to be Catholics, to live with the Saturday people! Well, I won't go! I won't leave Muranow Square or you and Mama and the boys."

"Enough!" Papa commanded in a tone he had not ever used with Rachel before. "While I was gone you developed an independent mind, I see."

"I won't go to Palestine!" She stamped her foot. "Or watch my brothers being taken away! This is my home and I will fight them and die before—"

Papa rose to his feet. He had never seen such defiance in Rachel before. "For now you will be silent and listen to me. For I will never speak to you on the matter again. Sit." She hesitated. *"Sit!"*

Rachel sat—primly and rigidly, to show her father she was not happy about sitting. He remained standing, as though this were the synagogue and he was in the bema and she was the congregation who *would* listen!

His voice moderated. "We have a saying, Rachel, that he who saves one life has saved the universe. You have heard this. An important thing, you will agree?"

She nodded. Of course. Everyone knew the saying.

"So." Papa stroked the beard that was only partly there now. "Perhaps the time is coming upon us when only one Jewish life will be saved. In the eyes of the Eternal the survival of only one Jew in all the world would be enough for Him to still perform every promise He made to Abraham. You will agree to this?"

Rachel shrugged and smoothed the folds of her skirt.

Papa continued. "God promised Abraham only *one* son from Sarah! *One son.* One miracle. And through that son a covenant was made. The Eternal promised the nation of Israel. Promised the Messiah. Promised the redemption of all mankind. It only takes *one!* Can you imagine how that fact must distress God's great enemy, Satan? For this reason, since that time the Evil One has sought actively to deceive and destroy every descendant of Abraham's promised son. And that means you, Rachel. And Yacov. And David and Samuel as well!"

Rachel raised her eyes. A congregation of one, her attention had been captured by the great Rabbi Lubetkin. She opened her mouth in a soundless *oh.*

Papa nodded. "Every Jew who survives openly sanctifies the covenant God made with Abraham. Now is the time for the sanctification of life. *Kiddush Hashem.* Once when our enemies demanded our souls, the Jew martyred his body. Today, Rachel, if the enemy demands that you die, it is your obligation to defend yourself and preserve your life so that God's covenant with Israel may be fulfilled at the coming of Messiah."

He waited as this sermon settled on her. She nodded. Meekly.

"Do you understand why our children must live? Who the true enemy of every Jew is, Rachel? Not the goyim. No. It is the *Evil One* who is God's enemy. It is *Satan* we must fight by remaining alive!"

Rachel did not like any of this. She wished she were wise enough to reply. "I know why I must stay alive. But if you were not . . . *alive,* it would be easier to die, Papa. Easier to die with us all together than to live alone like . . . like Peter Wallich!"

"But you are the daughter of Rabbi Aaron Lubetkin. The granddaughter of Rabbi Shlomo Lebowitz! It is important, *daughter of the seed of Abraham,* that you *live!* Even if it means going to Jerusalem without us."

She jumped to her feet. This was too blatant. It was no longer a discussion on living or dying and the obligations of being a Jew! Papa was talking about sending *her* away! Too much! "I will *live* wherever you and Mama are! I *won't* leave you! Or my brothers! Because . . . because . . . *Papa!* Can't you see my heart would no longer be alive in me without you? I would be sick for you all . . . I would."

It was a terrible thing. She was losing the argument and all she could do about it was run into Papa's arms and hold on tightly while she cried and cried.

After a moment he stroked her hair. He patted her back. "Well, now. It is not all that bad. You would never survive Yeshiva school if you cannot discuss a little thing like *Kiddush Hashem.* True? Of course true. Go on now. Wash your face. Stop this weeping. And no more singing of ditties beneath the window of important meetings."

It was dark when Wolf awoke from his deep sleep. His head still ached—as if he had a night of too much schnapps. But the agony of the morning was past.

He sat up carefully, slowly swinging his feet to the floor. He was still slightly nauseous and decided that he had experienced a touch of food poisoning. He raised the shade and peered out over the quiet square. Here and there lights shone in the windows of Jewish houses. The shops were closed tight. There was no sign at all that the Jewish holy man had come and gone—Muranow Square.

With a sigh, Wolf realized he had not eaten all day. He switched on the light and made his way to the kitchen. On the table was the open newspaper. The words emblazoned across the newspaper were the obituary for Poland: *GERMANY DENOUNCES POLISH MOBILIZA-TION.*

From the perspective of this Polish rag of a newspaper, this was called foolish propaganda. *Germany* had been rearming for years. No doubt London would also be crying foul as well. But for the Führer, Wolf knew, this was a necessary step. Now there would be opportunity to accuse *Poland* of aggression and increase Nazi demands.

Wolf read the accounts and then smiled down at the Jewish District of Warsaw. Soon there would be no holy man to stop what was coming on this place.

The Führer had set his sights on Poland. On Warsaw. On the Jews who took the living space that rightfully belonged to the German race.

Knowing this made his view of Jewish Warsaw seem like a very old silent motion picture. Wolf saw the movement of people in the square below him, but they seemed like gray apparitions of a people and a culture long dead. They did not know it, but the requiem had already been played for them. *They were no more!* The mind of the German Führer had decreed their end long ago. The headlines of today's news simply confirmed what was written against them.

As the reel spun out before Wolf's eyes, he watched the Jews with the fascination of one who knows the end of the story. Only the characters of this present scene seemed unaware that their destiny was already written.

The outlying English churchyards had been scoured for possible candidates for premature resurrection. Names were selected carefully for date of birth and gender. Lori joined her mother, Anna, and Elisa on these daily picnic excursions where identities were stolen from the dead so that they might save those condemned to die. Captain Orde had the new passport photos of Jacob and Alfie and Rachel Lubetkin. He had also chosen his own candidates for life from among those who had clamored to join his group of young Zionists. The criteria were simple: an Anglo-looking face and a passible grasp of the English language. Among the young men, only 157 fit those standards. At last word, the passport photos of that handful were on the way to London. If the photographs arrived before the powder keg exploded beneath Poland, then perhaps there was hope. But every day, it seemed, Germany and Poland moved more irrevocably toward confrontation.

The certainty of war struck terror in Lori's heart for two main reasons—along with a host of smaller reasons. If there was a war and England did indeed take sides with Poland, she would probably never see her father again. If there was a war before Jacob got his passport and got out of Poland—well, she could not let herself think about it.

She wrote Jacob every day and included little notes to Alfie and Werner as well. Three times a week the mail steamer brought Jacob's return letters to her. She read the newsy bits aloud to Mark and Jamie and her mother, but the other parts she saved for her own heart. She carried his love letters around in her pockets. When the day was too long or too slow or lonely, she would pull out a letter and read it over again until she felt that Jacob was right there with her.

If there was a war, the mail would stop. That realization evoked another kind of dread. She knew what it was like to live on without knowing the fate of the one you love more than your own life. She could see such brave grief in her mother. A hundred times a day Helen Ibsen looked off somewhere, and her eyes reflected the hope and memory of Karl Ibsen.

"Please, God," Lori prayed. For her father and now for her own husband, this little unfinished prayer helped her get through the hot summer days in London. *"Let them come home!"*

Then a miracle happened. Lori waited beside the mailbox and took the letters from the postman. At last, the passport of William Howard Johnson had arrived! Inside, the image of Jacob Kalner grinned out, daring anyone to challenge that he was a true Englishman!

Lori stood with one foot on the bottom step as she smiled back at Jacob. She wanted to shout for joy! She wanted to run into the little church across the way and blow kisses at the cross above the altar. She wanted to kneel on the weed-covered grave of the little boy who had lived only one short month in this life and say, "Thank you! Oh, thank you!"

In the midst of this miracle, Lori did not see the shadow of Doc Grogan at her elbow. She could not say how long he had been peering down at the passport before he finally spoke.

"William Howard Johnson. A good English name."

"Oh!" Lori snapped the new passport cover closed and put it behind her back. "I did not see you."

"I thought not," he said with a wry smile as he stepped around her. "I understood his name was Kalner?" He walked lightly up the stairs.

It was the day for the Thursday excursion with Doc Grogan. Most of the refugee children were settled in new homes. That left only Charles and Louis, Lori, Jamie, and Mark for today's outing.

From the beginning, Doc Grogan called Lori *Missus Kalner*! He peered over her shoulder when she held baby Alfie and said, "He looks just *exactly* like your husband, don't you think so, *Missus Kalner*!"

This usually made Lori blush, which was the purpose of the comment. He said he liked to see a little color on her wan and pale cheeks.

Wan was not a word Lori knew, so she looked it up in her English-German dictionary. It meant "pale." "So my cheeks are pale and pale?" She teased him. "I will not ever understand how English has so many words for the same thing!"

Then Jamie chimed in, "For instance, the word *Schwein* in Deutsch can be said *pig. Or swine. Or hog. Or pork. Or Nazi.*"

At this, everyone dissolved into laughter. Doc Grogan pointed out how wonderfully pink Missus Kalner's pale and pale cheeks were. And then how good it was to hear that she really could laugh. Mothers needed to laugh a lot, he admonished, so their babies could grow up hearing laughter. Then he made up a wild theory about how babies that don't hear a lot of laughter never quite know how to talk properly.

Lori had long ago decided that she liked Doc Grogan. He was chubby, round-faced and jolly. His skin was also *pale* and *pale*, but covered with a fine frosting of freckles. He was Bavarian in character, she decided, rather than austere and dry like someone from Prussia.

The bottom line was that he reminded her of her favorite history teacher who had left Germany for safer places in the middle of Lori's seventh-grade year. After that, school had been very dull.

On Thursdays Elisa shooed her out the door and told her to have fun. On this particular Thursday Anna and Helen took the babies while Elisa practiced her violin.

"Be sure you laugh a lot," Mark called as Helen and Anna pushed the pram the opposite direction. They did not need to be told. They prattled on about the babies like two grandmothers should do.

Moments later, through the open window they could hear the high, fine soprano voice of Elisa's violin as it played a Mozart rondo.

"There you have it." Doc Grogan walked backward and waved his arms as though he were conducting. "As good as laughter, is it not, Missus Kalner? Ah! How lovely to see you smile for a whole minute at a time! I feared you had forgotten how since you came to jolly old England and jolly good Red Lion Square."

"She is just Misses Jacob," Jamie teased.

Lori silenced him with a look. For these ten minutes she was doing just fine. Smiling. Feeling almost like breathing. Fine. She did not want to be reminded that there were moments when she missed Jacob so badly that she could barely speak, that at night she lay in bed and ached from missing him.

"My mother was married younger than you," said Grogan in a matter-of-fact tone. "Married ten days, and then he was off to the war. Spanish-American War. Teddy Roosevelt and the Rough Riders. He came home and *POP*, there was the first of eleven babies. Just that easy." They lined up to wait for the red bus. "Eleven children and imagine, none of them looked like him! Not like your little Alfie, eh, Missus Kalner."

Jamie and Mark howled at this because they knew the real story about the baby. How big Alfie had shoved him into Lori's arms and said, *Auf Wiedersehen!* Of course they were not permitted to tell the truth of it, or the immigration adoptions people would be standing on the doorstep demanding that the baby be given to some childless couple who ran a bee farm in Sussex or something. Murphy had warned them sternly. They could not even tell Doc Grogan the truth. Dangerous stuff, he said.

But they could laugh at Doc on Thursdays all the same. He took them here and there and made them speak like every educated Englishman should speak. Proper vowels and no making of W's into V's, like old Hildy Frutschy. *"Ve ist goinggg!"*

Today, like every Thursday, they joked and laughed as they waited for the bus. He sometimes withheld their true destination from them until they had already passed it once. This made them pay attention, he said—made them use their imaginations as they wondered which place was worth seeing and which was only mediocre.

The dome of St. Paul's Cathedral loomed ahead of them. Grogan did not bother to hide their destination from them.

"How would you like to see the place where the remembrance ceremony for your father will be held?" he asked Lori and Jamie.

Not even Charles and Louis had ever been inside St. Paul's with Doc. And to see anything in London without him was like not really seeing it.

A chorus of cheers arose. The wind on the top deck of the bus blew through Doc's thin hair. He looked hard at the dome in a very thoughtful way. "It will take us all day. You have your lunches?"

Five bagged lunches by Hildy were held up. She made wonderful bratwurst sandwiches, Hildy did—as long as the onions did not get warm. Then the bags made heads turn.

Grogan held up his own bag. "Good. We will eat at the top in the Golden Gallery. At one o'clock, so we can hear the ringing of Great Bell."

He made it sound so wonderful. For just a moment, Lori looked down at her photograph of Jacob. Could she help it if she missed him, wished beyond anything that he were here?

"We will begin in St. Dunstan's Chapel and then on to the crypt where they keep the old famous people in storage for posterity."

Charles and Louis exchanged puzzled looks. Should they tell him they did not understand this big English word *posterity*?

In predictable Doc-like fashion, he knew they did not know. Possibly that was why he used the word. "Future generations; children just like you, only fifty years from now, who will wander through history. Depending on the teacher, they will see nothing in the crypts but marble, chiseled and cold. Ah!" He held up a sausage finger. "But if their teacher is like me, then they will hear the voice of Lord Nelson shouting to his men! They will hear the tap-dancing step of those who once were and those who have yet to be!"

29

Requiem for Poland

Warsaw was a vast city spread out along the wide banks of the Vistula. It was a tangle of narrow streets and broad, proud avenues that expanded into wooded parks or cobbled squares, or erupted into the towering spires of the Cathedral of St. John and a very tall skyscraper on Napoleon Square.

To this large and beautiful city Lucy Strasburg awakened. She had a view from the room where she was carefully nursed to recovery by Herr Frankenmuth's widowed sister. At night the expanse of Warsaw seemed limitless. Lights spread like a carpet of jewels far into the late evening. Parts of the great city never slept. The heart of Warsaw glowed against the black sky, lighted by the neon marquees of theaters and clubs.

Lucy often lay awake with that view before her. She wondered about the fate of Peter Wallich. Had he found his mother Karin and sister Marlene? Had they then struck out for some safer, more distant place than Warsaw? Would they one day be reunited with baby Willie in America and then perhaps travel on to Jerusalem?

Such thoughts made her happy that she had stumbled on the Wallich family. How fortunate she was in this one instance that something good had managed to come out of the darkness of her life. She felt no pride for her help to the Wallich family; only a sort of humble gratitude that someone so worthless could be used. Beyond that, she only hoped that the Walliches would manage to slip from Warsaw before the next apocalypse descended on them. She held no such hope for herself.

Sensing the presence of Wolf, even here, she had no illusions about her own safety. Lucy longed for only one thing: to know the fate of her baby. She had put her son into the arms of a stranger. Where had the

child gone once he arrived in England? Did he have both mother *and*
father, as children should have? Was he loved? Had he been christened
in the satin gown as she dreamed a hundred times as the days passed?

These small details were the stuff that nourished Lucy's broken
heart. She could close her eyes and imagine her baby in a carriage
being pushed through a shady park in London. She awoke sometimes
to his cry. Her breasts filled again with milk as she reached out in the
darkness only to find that he was not there. And in those moments of
fierce longing, she did not ask God if she might hold him once again.
Such a prayer from one like her was doomed to go unheeded, she
believed. No. Lucy did not pray for her own longing. She prayed that
he was held when he cried. That he was fed when he was hungry. That
he was loved, all the time.

And then she asked that she might know that these small prayers
were answered on behalf of her son. She showed the address Peter
had given her to Frau Berson. Frau Berson had dug out a well-worn
city map and dragged her bony finger along Niska Street to where the
Jewish District of Warsaw began. It was the other side of the river, the
other side of Warsaw—a different world, Frau Berson warned her.

Lucy had nothing to pay the good woman for her care. Frau Berson
gestured toward the cross hanging above her corner table. The woman
took no more credit for helping Lucy than Lucy took for helping the
Wallich family. Instead, Frau Berson dipped into her coin purse and
presented Lucy with tram fare across Warsaw. She made her a lunch
and filled a canning jar with apple juice to drink because it was hot
today and Lucy might need something cool to drink.

"You intend to stay with these Jewish friends of yours?" Frau Berson
asked as though she doubted the wisdom of such mixing of cultures.

"Peter asked me to go with him to Warsaw. I should have done so."
That *should have* held all the regret she had ever felt. *If I had gone
with Peter, I would still have the baby. If I had gone with Peter, Wolf
would not have—*

She shuddered and stopped herself from thoughts that could not
change anything at all.

"You might be back." Frau Berson straightened her collar as though
Lucy were her daughter going off to school. "You have not seen the
way *they* live. It is not like the Jews in Berlin. Or the Jews in Danzig.
They are a different people than you or I. A world in which we do not
belong."

This warning clanged in Lucy's head like the bell of the tram. The
long tram car slid across the face of Warsaw mile after mile as Lucy
stared at the city and listened to the unfamiliar language of the Polish
passengers. Their tongues cracked against their palates in greeting and
in discussion of the terrible reports that were splashed across the front

pages of undecipherable newspapers.

The world of the Poles was strange enough to Lucy. Could the Jewish District possibly be more unfamiliar and frightening than this? She saw sandbag barricades and taped windows everywhere, yet downtown Warsaw was bustling with activity. Admiring women scanned shop windows. Lucy supposed that they could understand what the signs said and what the prices meant. The marquees of theaters displayed names that Lucy could not pronounce with letters turned oddly this way and that like the Russian alphabet.

Could it be that the Führer had not been lying when he said that Poland was near to being Russian in politics and culture? Is that why the German people feared and hated the Poles so desperately?

Lucy did not see people she need fear. She saw women holding the hands of their children as they walked down the streets. She saw ordinary shoppers passing in and out of the revolving doors of department stores. She saw men in uniform sitting in the parks beside pretty girls, an organ grinder with a monkey on a leash, a blind beggar standing beside a lamppost.

Ordinary people, except when they opened their mouths and gibberish flowed out in an incomprehensible torrent. Maybe that was the only difference between ordinary people here and anywhere.

An airplane passed overhead. All heads pivoted upward. Hands shielded against the sun. Anxious eyes wondered and then, a man in the uniform of an ordinary soldier announced, "Polski!"

People smiled and shrugged, sighing with relief. These people were also afraid. And Lucy pitied them because they had not seen anything yet. They had not even imagined what they were about to see. There would be no mistaking it when the German aircraft swooped down on Warsaw. No one would look up. Everyone would be too busy running for cover.

Wolf had told Lucy what the bombing was like in Spain. He said that when Warsaw had its turn, the Luftwaffe would be one hundred times more powerful.

She looked at the slip of paper with the address on it. She held it lightly between her fingers. Lucy knew that when the German bombers came to Warsaw, she would stand unmoving in the street. She would look up into the sky and welcome whatever fell on her.

There were only these little questions to clear up. She wanted to *know* that all was well with the baby. And then it did not matter any longer. She would not cause her own death, but she would not run from it, either. She did not think that welcoming death was a sin.

Wolf had reminded her of how little she was worth. That knowledge made living seem of little importance. And she prayed that perhaps there was some tiny attic room reserved for her in God's mansion.

She patted her pocket where she still carried the little green book with all the details of life as a parlormaid. She would never see the freedom of England or America. She would never hold her baby again, she knew. But she would be content to wait on tables and sweep up crumbs in heaven. This was the mercy Lucy Strasburg asked for.

The rumble of thousands of horses' hooves against the packed soil of the parade ground drowned out all conversation. Orde stood on the platform among dozens of other Western journalists to observe what was supposed to be a display of Polish prowess.

Dutiful to his newly acquired vocation, Orde snapped photographs with the cumbersome news camera, and took copious notes as to the state of readiness of the Polish Legion. To his right, Jacob Kalner watched with the wide-eyed admiration of one who could not conceive that *so many troops* could not stand up against the German divisions. On Orde's left, Alfie, the new Elisha, gazed over the scene with a strange smile on his lips, as if searching for legions of fiery angels. Sadly, he did not see them among the Poles.

At the front of the platform, Edward Smigly-Rydz, inspector general of the Polish Army, stood at attention. He had acquired the nickname of Smigly, meaning "nimble," as a young man fighting the Russian Bolsheviks in 1920. After an hour of conversation with the general, Orde had decided that he was more arrogant and shortsighted than nimble. The strength of the opposing German panzer divisions would require more than nimble cockiness to be defeated.

The endless sea of Polish cavalry spread out before the platform was crowned with old-style French helmets. Their weapons were lances, sabers, and rifles of the vintage of the last war.

Throughout the prancing troop were horses as white and glowing as neon signs in Piccadilly. For any man to ride a white horse into battle was certain suicide. Only a blind enemy could miss such a target. Such animals were meals on legs for the buzzards that now swooped low over Poland.

This display of tens of thousands of horses caused the Polish general to glow with pride. "You can see," he told Orde, "our cavalry is adapted for rapid movements over the Polish plain."

Orde knew that the plain was the flattest country of its size in all of Europe. This level vastness made Poland the least defensible of any nation on the Continent. Feeding horses would be a nightmarish logistical problem on the field. There was only one hope for Polish victory that Orde could see, although he did not express his pessimism aloud. The world must pray for an early rain to clog the dirt roads and turn the fields into mires that would suck down the German might. In such a case, horses might have some advantage against three thousand heavy German tanks. *Otherwise* ...

The Polish Army had six hundred light six-ton tanks, built on the English Vickers' design. These tin cans had been effective against the rifles of the Arabs in Palestine, Orde recalled. But crude land mines had taken out a number of the tanks easily even when wielded by primitive bands hiding among the rocks. Orde looked at Jacob's face beaming with envy. He would love to be a tank commander in such a force!

Orde shuddered involuntarily. He saw before him images of charred men in charred machines, of dead and bloated horses being scraped from the roads like so much manure from the floor of a barn.

Behind the tanks came horse-drawn light and medium artillery of the same manufacture as the world war.

The Polish general looked on proudly, his cruel face twisted into a perverse smile. Was he remembering, perhaps, how these same units swept across a portion of Czechoslovakia after the Munich Agreement last year? Was he under the illusion that Hitler's forces would simply lie down and roll over? General Smigly-Rydz had played the role of a scavenger when Czechoslovakia had been dismembered. Now, perhaps, the brutality of that action would come back on Poland. The general was more interested in nationhood than democracy. He was anti-Semitic; perhaps he was a man of courage, yet Orde had sensed great darkness in this man's soul.

Herr Hitler had been quite happy to send photographs of his weapons and troops out from the Reich for publication. He gloated in the fact that his army and air force were the most modern in the world. Had this Polish general not seen those photographs? Could he not hear the trembling of earth and sky as German divisions moved into place on three sides of the Polish border?

When war came to this place—and Orde did not doubt that inevitable occurrence—the Poles would be forced to fight a retreating action to hold back the Nazis from Prussia in the north, Czechoslovakia in the south, and Germany in the west. If they could cling to their plain until Britain and France arrived, then perhaps the rains would bring General Mud to their rescue.

The Reich surrounded all sides of Poland except one. Soviet Russia towered like a bear at their eastern back door. Here was one small reason to hope. England had sent an emissary to Moscow to attempt to form an alliance, a nonaggression pact which would guarantee that Russia would not tolerate any German aggression against Poland. That alone might cause the German Führer to rethink the million troops posed at Poland's front door. The horses of Poland's cavalry might be nothing to slice through, but did Hitler wish to face three hundred

Russian divisions on the other side?

The crack of rifles and the boom of field guns announced that this glorious display of might had come to an end. Men stood at attention as the Polish national anthem was played.

Tears stood in the eyes of general and troops alike. But to Orde as he listened respectfully, the anthem sounded like a requiem that resounded over the spires of Warsaw in the distance.

Lucy noted a perceptible change in the dress and language of the tram passengers at the edge of the Jewish District. Frau Berson had been correct in saying that this large, sprawling expanse of Warsaw was like stepping into a different world.

In the showcase windows of the shops, none of the latest Paris fashions were displayed. Hat makers displayed the newest Jewish headgear, which in fact had not changed in style for several hundred years. Marquees were written in Yiddish or in Hebrew, depending on the nature of the shop. The world of floral print dresses and pin-striped suits had vanished. Here were long severe dresses on the women; caftans of black that reached well below the knees of the men.

Lucy saw old men, white-bearded and stoop-shouldered, conversing animatedly with young men who dressed exactly the same. The only difference was the white hair and wrinkled skin.

Like rows of blackbirds on a wire, men crowded onto the tram. Women came along as well, but they sat in the back of the vehicle with their youngsters. Men and women alike stared at Lucy. *What are you doing here?* their looks asked. The tram moved slowly from stop to stop, and still Lucy did not get off. Two women looked at her curiously and then whispered behind their hands. *Maybe she is lost? Maybe she is blind? Maybe . . . who can say? Very strange, nu?*

Lucy had not imagined how different it could be. The neat rows of Hebrew letters on street signs and shop windows looked like little hands raised up in prayer. Words inscribed in that strange alphabet seemed like tongues of fire painted in a line.

Yet here, too, women stood chattering on street corners while their children ran around their legs or balanced to walk the curb. Delivery boys carried packages to doorsteps. Huge dray horses pulled wagon loads of cheese, vegetables, and ice through the streets.

A paper boy stood on the corner hocking his publications. The headlines, in large type, proclaimed only one word that Lucy recognized: *NAZI!*

Men young and old clustered around whoever had purchased a paper. They waved their arms and argued loudly. They gestured toward the east and then toward the west. Black eyebrows arched upward in concern.

What could these separate people possibly have in common with the world of the Poles that surrounded them?

Then Lucy saw it. The drone of a single airplane passed overhead. All faces peered skyward with ominous expectation. Hands shielded eyes from the glare, and then someone sighed and said, *POLSKI.*

So that was it. Fear was the common bond between Jew and Gentile Pole. But one thing was missing in the way that fear was dealt with. In Catholic Warsaw, everyone carried the obligatory gas masks. But here, as Niska Street grew ever more narrow and ever more crowded, there were no gas masks to be seen.

Mothers pushing baby carriages had no gas masks. Old men and young delivery boys carried no gas masks. Small, serious-faced scholars carried no gas masks.

Could it be that Jews did not believe in such a precaution? If that was the case, Lucy decided, they were foolish. Everyone knew about the mustard gas that had been used in the last war. Every day Frau Berson had talked of blistered skin and blind men and seared lungs. Just thinking of what Hitler might do with the gas made the old woman tremble. She had gone out on the first day the Polish government had issued them to all civilians, and after hours in long lines, she had returned with two. Lucy carried hers in a little cardboard box slung over her shoulder. Everyone in Gentile Warsaw had one. Lucy had seen them everywhere outside the borders of this district.

She frowned and looked at her own case; it must have been an obvious curiosity to the plump old woman sitting across from her.

"Polski?" the blue-eyed Jewess asked quietly. She was questioning Lucy's presence on the train.

"Nein," Lucy answered, surprised by the human voice addressing her.

"I see you are of *German* heritage," the old woman said with a twinge of sarcasm. Her eyes lingered on Lucy's gas-mask container. Other heads swiveled to look at Lucy.

"Ja. Deutsch," Lucy replied quietly.

"And you are wondering about our gas masks?" The woman's voice was heavily accented, but her German words were well chosen.

Again, a hesitant nod from Lucy.

The eyebrows of the woman rose slightly as though she knew some joke but was not sure if she should tell it. Then, she told.

"There are no gas masks for Jews, you see. Jews in Warsaw have no protection from the gas if the Führer should decide to use such a weapon against Poland." A shrug. "You see?"

The tram bell clanged loudly. This was Lucy's stop. She was grateful for the interruption. She inched through the other passengers, and as she stepped onto the sidewalk, she slipped her own gas mask into the large paper lunch sack Frau Berson had sent with her.

She looked unusual enough on this street, she reasoned. She did not want to flaunt that difference. *No protection for the Jews of Warsaw!*

She shuddered and lowered her eyes so she would not have to look into the faces that turned toward her and wondered. She took the scrap of notepaper from her pocket and looked at it again, although she knew the number well. *2334 Niska Street, Apartment 3A.* The name above the address was RUDOLF DORBRANSKY.

Lucy studied the row of mailboxes in the lobby of the gloomy building. Most had names above the numbers. Apartment 3A had an empty place behind the little glass window.

No matter. This was the correct address. The number Lucy had given to Alfie so that they could write her from England! She looked up the steep stairs, half expecting to see Peter Wallich and his sister appear on the landing above her!

Her mouth was dry with excitement. She hoped there had been time enough for a letter to get here about the baby. She dashed up the steps, using the banister to pull herself upward toward the answer she had come all this way to find. *No doubt the letter has come! Peter will know all about the news from England before me! Oh, won't it be good to see him again!*

Lucy was flushed and out of breath as she raised her hand and knocked on the door of Rudolf Dorbransky, Apartment 3A. She could hear the happy squeals of small children through the thin wood door. Had they heard her knock? She raised her hand again and then the door was opened just a crack. A timid slice of pale face peered out at her. Dark, frightened eyes filled with a freshly revived fear at the sight of her.

"Please, bitte—" Lucy leaned against the door to keep the woman from closing it on her face. "I am looking for—" She held out the address and managed to smile hopefully. She looked over the head of the woman, who glanced at the note and then pushed to close the door on Lucy's face.

"Not here!" the woman said in poor German.

"Please!" Lucy leaned harder on the door. "Peter!" she called. "Peter Wallich? Peter, *it is Lucy!* I have come here all the way from Danzig! Peter!"

"Wrong place!" The woman was angry. She pushed hard in an attempt to keep Lucy back.

"Please!" Lucy cried, unbelieving. "You are making a mistake! Ask Peter Wallich who I am! He will know me! *Lucy!* I am *Lucy Strasburg*!

A friend of Peter and Karin and Marlene Wallich! I was told to meet them here!"

The woman let out a garbled cry for help. Then a large hairy hand pulled the woman aside and Lucy tumbled forward into the tiny flat.

The faces of two ragged children gaped up at her in terror as a burly man stepped between Lucy and the rest. "You got the wrong place," he growled. He snatched the address from his thin, trembling wife and thrust it back at Lucy.

"But surely Peter Wallich can vouch for me."

He crossed his thick arms. His teeth were clenched between his black beard. His eyes smoldered. "No Peter Wallich here. No Rudolf Dorbransky. They move out. Who knows where to." He flung his hand up and Lucy winced as though he had struck her.

He had struck her, in a way. "But this is the address." Her voice was small and pitiful.

"I'm telling you." He was warning her as well.

Lucy backed up a step. "But did they come here? Peter? Marlene and Karin?"

The woman took pity. "A woman and a little girl?"

"Yes!" Lucy resisted the urge to grab the woman's hands. "Where did they go? Did they leave an address?"

"They left," the man said, "like everyone else. Now this is *our* place. Get out!"

"But were there letters?" Lucy directed this question to the brow-beaten woman who cringed beneath Lucy's pleading eyes.

The man stepped to the side, blocking Lucy's view of his wife. "No letters! We send the letters back! Nobody lives here by these names! Why should we keep letters when these people don't live here? Probably dead!"

He moved his bulk another step forward. He knew that Lucy was not *one of them,* and he hated her! He hated her as much as Wolf hated a Jew! Only he was not so cruel. He did not strike her physically. He simply slammed the door on her hopes and clicked the lock and snapped the chain into place.

"Not here," she muttered as she walked slowly down to the foyer. "How could that be?"

No Rudolf Dorbransky family. No Karin Wallich. No Peter Wallich. No letter from London. No hope.

Where can I go now? Lucy wondered. *What options are left to me?* She felt faint. She sat down on the bottom step and stared at the checkerboard tiles on the floor of the foyer. She cradled her head in her hands and tried to remember everything Alfie Halder had said to her in those last terrible moments of farewell on the Danzig wharf.

"See you in Warsaw ... newspaper ... TENS. See you in Warsaw!"

St. Paul's Cathedral was an immense building. Lori guessed that several churches the size of her father's church could have fit in it side by side. Probably another half dozen or so could have stacked up to fill the vast dome of the cupola.

The giant lantern on the top of the dome was easily seen from the Red Lion House, but Lori had not imagined that it could be so big or so high.

"It weighs seven hundred tons," explained Doc Grogan as he craned his neck back to look up into the misty heights of the cupola. "I do not speak of the weight of the dome itself," he warned. "Only the lantern and the cross on the tip top. An amazing feat of engineering."

That was the last thing Doc Grogan said for quite a while. He paid one shilling per head for the privilege of climbing 616 steps of a nearly vertical staircase that twisted upward between the walls of the inner dome and the outer shell. The views might have been awe-inspiring, but in this case, the trek was also breathtaking in a literal sense.

Allan Farrell stood staring out over the city of London from the vantage point of the Golden Gallery high atop St. Paul's Cathedral. Down the Thames in the middle distance was the arch of the Tower Bridge. Part of the great fortress called the Tower of London was visible as well.

Allan shook off the urge to take in the sights and forced his attention back to the slope of the roof that spread out its great bell-shaped curve just below where he stood. The lead-covered expanse fell away gently for the first few feet, then swooped abruptly downward. Anything sliding down that surface would shoot out into space with the acceleration of a meteor slamming to earth.

Allan's inspection turned upward toward the towering structure called the lantern that surmounted the dome. He looked up toward the cross on the very top, then over the railing again.

The terrorist circled the base of the lantern, pausing every so often as if gauging something in his mind. When he reached the west side of the gallery, he attempted to see the spot where the Gunpowder Plot conspirators had been executed, but even from that great height it was not visible. The bulk of the west facade of St. Paul's hid the exact location from view. "But I know it's there, just the same," he murmured to himself.

He was rounding the circuit of the Golden Gallery once more when he ran squarely into a line of children. A swirl of blond and brunette heads bobbed around him. Small necks craned to see everywhere at once, and fingers pointed a hundred different directions.

Allan waited impatiently for the children to move out of the way; then, the adult who was apparently their guide puffed and wheezed slowly out of the stairwell. "Children," he gasped, "stand aside and let this gentleman—"

The man's voice trailed off so abruptly that Allan looked to see what had caused the sudden change of tone. It was Grogan! Then these children must be . . . Allan ducked his head, then decided that his movement was suspicious, raised it again and found himself staring into Doc's direct gaze.

Grogan looked puzzled, then worried. He seemed about to speak, but Farrell roughly pushed through the knot of children and began a clattering descent of the stairs. Allan resisted the urge to run down the twisting iron corkscrew and forced himself to maintain a careful, deliberate pace.

All the way down the steps and up the aisle of the cathedral to the west entrance Allan thought about how this chance encounter could ruin things. Something would have to be done—and quickly.

No one had ever heard Doc Grogan so silent. He *was* gasping for breath, of course. But he was speechless, unable to utter one coherent syllable until long after they leaned against the stone railing of the parapet and looked over the sloping lead roof of the dome that slid off into the tiny London streets far below.

Lori snapped pictures of the shining ribbon of the Thames, of the boys crowded around the sweat-soaked, red-faced Doc; of the far distant landmarks of the Tower of London and the twisting lanes of the city.

They unpacked their lunches on this perch that seemed almost too high even for the pigeons. The ten-foot hands of the clock struck one, and the tolling of the Great Bell began.

30

The Scent of Death

It seemed as though the tolling of the bell of St. Paul's struck a discordant note in Doc Grogan. He stared out over the stone parapet and then looked up to the golden ball of the great lantern atop the dome.

Suddenly he barked, "That's it." In an angry-sounding voice, he ordered everyone down the stairs. He led the way, clattering down the iron steps almost at a run.

Jamie and Mark teased him about how much easier it was to go down the steps than up. He did not respond to their jokes, but instead glanced up at the inner brick shell of the dome and then back up to where the iron braces linked the interior cone to the lead-covered exterior roof.

Lori caught his sense of uneasiness. She felt a terrible sense of vertigo as she followed him down and down on the frail spiral of stairs. She wanted to shout for him to slow down. What if the little boys should slip? It was six hundred steps to the bottom, and as she peered over the railing, she could imagine falling straight to the stone floor below.

Jamie and Mark, however, enjoyed the rapid pace. They thought Doc Grogan was simply paying them back for the fact that they had left him in the dust on the way up. Lori let them go by. She was angry at Doc for this game. She hung back with Charles and Louis.

"Let them go," she said. "We don't have to hurry."

Grogan, Mark, and Jamie were already two twists of the spiral below them.

Louis and Charles seemed grateful for the fact that she slowed her pace to match their careful descent.

"Going up was easier," said Charles as he clutched the rail. " 'Cause we couldn't see down."

It took them ten minutes longer to reach the floor of the cathedral than it had taken Doc and the older boys. When Lori emerged from the exit, Jamie and Mark were sitting on a bench just to the side of the opening. Doc was nowhere to be seen.

They answered Lori's question before she asked.

"Doc said he had something really important to do. He told us we should all go back to Red Lion House and wait for him there."

Jacob paced the length of the small TENS office and back again. He was careful not to knock over the overflowing trash can or the stacks of military books beside Captain Orde's desk.

Werner sat on the windowsill, his head moving back and forth as he watched Jacob. Alfie thought Jacob's face looked as if he had found something he had always wanted. Alfie knew what that something was, too.

"All my life I have wanted to fight those arrogant, goose-stepping Nazis," Jacob said in an excited voice. "And now I can do it! There were plenty of soldiers marching in the legion today who are no older than I am! If war is coming, I want to join the Polish Army!"

The captain pressed his fingers together at the tips. Tap. Tap. Tap. Alfie could tell that Captain Orde did not like anything Jacob was saying. As a matter of fact, Alfie did not like it either. When the Nazi tanks came, they would kill Jacob in no time. Alfie frowned at the thought. He wanted to tell Jacob that, but it was better for the captain to talk about such things.

"You have a wife to think of," Orde said. He was not joking. Lori was a good thing to mention right now, because otherwise Jacob would run out the door and down to the recruiting office to enlist.

Jacob stopped pacing. He ran his fingers through his hair. Had he forgotten Lori was waiting in London? "She would expect me to be brave, expect me to fight the men who killed my parents and are keeping her father in prison!"

Alfie stuck out his lower lip. It was no wonder Jacob was ready to sign up with the Polish Army and go off to the border to wait until the shooting started! Jacob had not been thinking quite right since he found out about his father and mother. He had wanted to fight everyone since the captain had broken the terrible news. Mostly he wanted to take as many Germans with him as he could get hold of.

"Joining the Polish Army will not bring back your mother and father," the captain said above the tap, tap, tap of his fingers. "It will simply make certain that you join them much sooner than you would like to.

"Defeatist!" Jacob spat.

"Realist," the captain replied calmly. "Or have you forgotten the German counterpart to what we witnessed today?" He lowered his head and looked up at the still-pacing Jacob. "Have you forgotten that the Poles are driving pygmy tanks compared to the big ones you saw rolling through the streets of Berlin?"

"I saw them too," Alfie volunteered. "Much bigger. Lots more noisy, too."

Jacob glared at him unpleasantly. "Stay out of this, Elisha!" he cried. "Aren't you supposed to see angels all around? Fiery angels with drawn swords, protecting the righteous?"

Alfie shook his head. "Not today," he said slowly, trying to remember if he had missed something.

Captain Orde interrupted in a very captain-like way.

"If you want to fight the Nazis, I will help you. But not here. Not in Poland." He raised his head and sniffed the air. "What do you smell, Jacob?"

Jacob sniffed. "Polish sausages," he said in a flat tone.

Alfie knew that the captain was catching the scent of a dead dog out on the street. Alfie had just said how bad it smelled.

The captain narrowed his eyes. Tap. Tap. Tap. "That is death, Jacob," he said in a quiet voice. "Call it Polish sausages if you will, but I am telling you that unless there is a miracle, there will not be any place in Warsaw or all of Poland that does not stink like death."

"Then I will die bravely!"

Captain Orde stood and faced off with Jacob. "Better to live bravely. And sensibly!" He picked up a long narrow strip of paper from the teletype machine. Werner jumped down; he thought this would be a good thing to play with. The captain held it up for Jacob to see.

"I cannot read English," Jacob said in a proud and angry voice.

"Then I will translate." Orde began to read. "Today after failures in talks between Moscow and Great Britain to sign a mutual nonaggression pact, Moscow has announced that high German officials are flying to the Kremlin to discuss matters of mutual national interest." He stopped and looked at Jacob's blank face.

"So what?" Jacob snapped. "So Hitler is breaking every promise and finally climbing into bed with the Communists."

"You really do not know what this means, do you?" Captain Orde said.

Alfie thought that he might know, but he did not say it out loud. Stalin and Hitler hated each other a lot. Did this mean they were now going to be friends?

Captain Orde looked very pale. "The mutual bed on which Hitler and Stalin will lie is Poland." He swept his hand toward the lovely old buildings of Warsaw just outside the window. "Take a last look, Jacob. Then inhale deeply and remember the smell. The child these two monsters conceive is called Death. This will be its playground. Here. Warsaw." He sighed deeply and sat down on the squeaking desk chair. Then he looked at Alfie. "You understand, don't you, Elisha? There are no angels around Warsaw. No chariots of fire. No flaming swords or—" He placed the tape in a jumbled pile on his desk. "I promised Helen Ibsen I would do my best to get you out of here, Jacob. I intend to do that." He looked at Alfie, then back to Jacob. "Join the Zionist Youth organization. They train young men to travel to Palestine. To work there. To fight there if they must. The odds are not perfect, but much better than this. I have contacts. Several hundred young men were brought in illegally to the Mandate. There may still be time—"

"To run away," Jacob said bitterly.

"You have never seen running until you see what is about to happen here in Poland. They will run and they will be massacred. On all sides, I have no doubt. The Nazis will come in from the north, south, and west. The Russians will come in from the east. Both sides have been waiting twenty years to divide up Poland like a beef carcass."

All the fire left Jacob's eyes. He turned away and sat on the edge of a shipping crate that had not yet been unpacked since they arrived. Werner jumped up on his lap and Jacob scratched the kitten behind his ears. This was a good thing, Alfie thought. Jacob had remembered that Captain Orde was an honest man, a soldier who knew things just by looking.

"I want to fight them." Jacob's voice was sad more than angry.

"You will have your chance," Captain Orde said in a soldierly voice. "As a matter of fact, I have the hope that I might train you myself."

Jacob smiled a little. "You're retired."

"Temporary insanity on the part of the British High Command, I assure you." He squared his shoulders. "They will need me back soon enough. After what I saw today, I have no doubt of that." He raised his eyebrows and Alfie could tell that he was relieved. "Until then, you must promise me that you will not join the Polish Army."

A shrug. A nod from Jacob.

Captain Orde tapped his fingers in a happy way. "Good. A good strong lad like you will do well under my command. But you must learn to obey orders first." He looked over at the overflowing garbage can. "You will empty that, please. And then put the books on the shelf."

———

Alfie had been looking for Lucy Strasburg ever since they arrived in

Warsaw. He had not been wandering around *looking* for her, but rather he had been expecting to see her around every corner.

Today he swept the step and the broad sidewalk in front of the TENS office. Werner played tag with the broom, crouching and pouncing on the straw and then attacking wildly as Alfie pulled the broom across the pavement.

Busy people hurried past with gas masks hung from straps around their shoulders. Faces were grim. Alfie noticed that the eyes of everyone darted up to look into the sky every time an airplane rumbled over.

There were Polish uniforms everywhere. Long, shining sword scabbards dangled from wide belts and clattered noisily along the sidewalk. The swords made the sound of tin cans banging on the ground. The soldiers seemed not to notice the racket they made as they walked and talked to one another. But Alfie noticed. Along with the engines of automobiles and trams, Warsaw had become a very noisy place, indeed.

Like the Tin Man in the moving picture show that Captain Orde had taken them to last night, Warsaw rattled. Its old, rusty knees knocked together. Its jaw hinge groaned as it stood shaking in front of the Great and Terrible Oz of a Führer. Hitler's voice boomed out in a most terrifying way. Alfie replayed the scene in his mind.

"I AM THE GREAT AND TERRIBLE OZ!" This had been spoken in English with Polish subtitles and translated into German by Captain Orde.

Alfie looked down at Werner, a small version of the cowardly lion. Werner's ears went back when Alfie talked loud like the Wizard.

"You are supposed to try and run away, Werner," explained Alfie. "And then Dorothy and the Scarecrow and the Tin Man grab your tail and pull you back."

Alfie looked at his broom. He forgot his place in the story. The bad witch rode on the broom, didn't she? And then Dorothy threw water on her and she melted.

"Oh well," Alfie said. There would be no happy ending for the Tin Man this time. Captain Orde had said that England was the Cowardly Lion. It seemed to fit. He said that the French were like the Scarecrow— no brains. It made the moving picture show much better because in the end everything worked out. But Alfie thought it could have just as easily gone the other way. The heroes do not always win just because they are nice, Alfie knew. If that was true, then his friends at the hospital would not have been killed. The Hitler-men would not have put Pastor Ibsen in prison and killed Jacob's parents and burned down Jewish houses.

Alfie thought about this very hard as he swept. Countries like France had to be stuffed with more than straw in their heads. And a strong nation like England had to have more than just big muscles. England should have been brave, should have growled loud a lot sooner than it was doing now. *Cowardly Lion.*

One of the Polish Tin Men rattled past. He had a lot of bright medals on his chest. His boots were tall and shiny, and his uniform was just like one of Alfie's tin soldiers. He greeted a pretty lady in front of Cafe de Paris and they went in to eat lunch.

Alfie scratched his head and looked at Werner, who was chewing on the broom head ferociously. Alfie felt bad that he had called Werner the Cowardly Lion. He bent down and scooped the kitten up. He kissed Werner's nose and said, "Oh, I'm sorry, Werner. You are brave to attack something so big and unfeeling as a broom. I didn't mean *you* are a coward. I meant England."

Werner did not seem to mind. He purred when he smelled the tuna on Alfie's breath. It was good to have a friend.

The tram clanged by. There was a black hood over the headlight with a small slit in it. Only a tiny bit of light was allowed from trams and cars at night because everyone expected that the Nazis would soon bomb Warsaw.

Alfie looked up with everyone else as an airplane hummed over. *Just Polish.* Alfie looked down, then over at the people getting off the tram. Then he saw Lucy Strasburg, crossing the street behind the tram. Alfie was not at all surprised. He was just very happy to see her.

She looked much better than the day she gave the baby away. She was very thin, but her cheeks were not white like sheets. Her eyes looked serious, but bright and alive. She was checking a slip of paper with an address and then checking numbers on the fronts of the buildings. There was no sign yet for TENS, so Alfie raised up the broom like a flag on a stick and began to call her in his loudest voice.

"Lucy! Lucy *Strasss-burg*! Hey, Lucy! Lucy! LUCY!"

The effect was tremendous. Everyone looked at Alfie just the same way they looked at the planes. *Worried.*

"It's all right," Alfie said to a woman who walked far around the swinging broom. "The baby's mother—" He pointed the broom toward Lucy, who smiled wide at the very sight of Alfie. She was running now, dodging traffic to get to Alfie.

Alfie decided that he would have to tell her that he had gotten a new name and she would have to call him Elisha like everyone else. But first he wanted to know everything! He wanted to hear the whole story, because he was sure he had seen the bright ones follow her. Had she seen them, too? He squinted hard, but they weren't there. Well, they would be there when Lucy Strasburg needed them. He was sure of that.

She was out of breath and very happy. She took his hands and kissed them. "Oh! It is you! Oh! Alfie Halder! Bless you . . . *bless*! I thought I was lost. So afraid I had heard wrong and that I would not find you!"

"Why? I told you . . . we will be in Warsaw." He twisted his mouth around because he was embarrassed. Nobody had ever been so happy about seeing Alfie before—except maybe Werner when he was locked up a long time in the hotel room and they came home and turned on the light. Then Werner bounced all over the room.

"The address—" She held out a crumpled slip of paper. "The address Peter gave me was . . . the people have gone away, you see. So I . . . have you heard anything from England? Anything about my baby?" Her eyes held part of the sky in them, like the blue part with a heap of clouds moving in. She was worried. She was lonely. Alfie knew all about such eyes. He had seen them many times before.

"Baby Alfie is very well," Alfie said. "See?" He held up Werner as an example of how babies can do well even if they miss their mothers. Even if they have to go somewhere else to be safe.

Lucy bit her lip. "Tell me what you have heard."

"You want a letter?" he beamed. "Captain Orde has the letter. I can't read it . . . but I bet it is a good letter!"

Through the window of the TENS office in Warsaw, Orde, Jacob, and Alfie watched as Lucy opened the fat letter from Lori and Elisa. Pictures spilled out onto the park bench where Lucy sat.

She put her hand to her heart and then scrambled to retrieve them as if she feared some cruel wind would see and begin to blow out of the still air.

She held them like playing cards. Choosing one at a time, she gazed at them. Her face reflected joy and sorrow, then joy again. There were tears on her face. At this distance they could not see the tears, but she brushed her cheeks the way mothers do when they are happy about something wonderful.

Lucy went on this way for a long time. She did not open the letter until she tucked the edge of each photograph in a line beside her thigh. Then she read a little and looked down. She read a little more and then looked down once again at the pictures.

It was not as fine as it would have been if they could put that baby back in her arms, but it was a start, anyway, Orde told them in a gruff-sounding voice.

"Should we be looking at her like this?" Jacob asked. "Lori always hates it when I stand off and look at her and worry when she is . . . being . . . emotional."

"We should keep an eye on her," Orde said.

Alfie nodded. He wanted to go sit beside her. "Yes. We should. The man hurt her bad before she ran to the docks." Alfie put his hand to the place on his face where he remembered her terrible bruises.

Orde looked sharply at Alfie and then back at Lucy. Alfie's words made the captain nervous. Alfie could tell. Orde rose up on his toes and clasped his hands behind his back. He looked all around the square.

"I'll recognize him if he shows up," he muttered.

Jacob bumped his big fist into the palm of his hand. "A fellow like that. I almost wish he would try something."

"She shouldn't go away," Alfie warned with a frown.

"We can't stop her if she wants to go, Elisha," Jacob said. "Can we, Captain?" Was there a way to keep her from leaving?

Alfie looked at her, so bright and pretty in the sunlight. It was a terrible thing that somebody wanted to hurt someone so nice and pretty as Lucy. But Alfie was certain she should not go. He was as sure of that as he ever was about things. He bit his lip and felt scared inside. "How do we make her stay here, Captain?" Alfie said. "That man has hurt her bad. They will kill her if she goes. Maybe kill her if she stays. But for sure if she is not with us."

Orde and Jacob looked at each other around Alfie. "No angels around her, Elisha?" Jacob asked. He was not making fun.

Alfie frowned and looked everywhere. "No. No angels. Just us."

The letter from London. The photographs of her baby. It was all so much more than Lucy had hoped for. If she never heard another word, maybe she could manage now that he was safe.

A thousand times Lucy had replayed the escape of her baby from Wolf on the docks of Danzig harbor. Time and again she had seen it in her mind. *Lori carrying the child onto the ship. And then Wolf appearing with Hess and the other man, only to be stopped by the grim smile of the sun-browned stranger who stepped between them and the gangway to block their path.*

Lucy sat across from Sam Orde and repeated the story as it had happened to her. She did not tell everything, of course, but she knew from the way he looked at her that he guessed the details she left out. He had the eyes of a priest, full and kind, yet also wondering how Lucy had come to such a condition.

He did not question her about her relationship with Wolf. It was enough to say that Wolf was S.S. and that he had fathered the child with the intention of taking it from Lucy. At that, Orde merely frowned more deeply, his eyes reflecting both pity and perhaps a fleeting moment of revulsion. *Ah well,* Lucy thought, *this Englishman with the eyes of a holy man was only human, after all.* Should she blame him if his disgust for her was revealed for an unguarded instant?

She sat erect in her chair and looked straight ahead at the wall as she had done as a child in trouble at the convent school. No doubt Mother Superior would have looked at her more harshly than this fellow did!

Lucy deliberately passed over her days and nights of anguish as she had grieved and wondered about the baby. Best to stick to cold facts.

"So you see, Wolfgang von Fritschauer was not in pursuit of the children. He wished only to take the baby away." She bit her lip. "And I am certain he saw the baby in Lori's arms." She turned her eyes on Orde's face. The emotion she saw there surprised her. *Sadness?*

He exhaled loudly as though letting out a pain, deep in his chest. "And the address you gave Alfie?"

"My friends—the people I expected to be there—have moved away. No forwarding address. Apparently the address is months out of date." She could not stand the intensity of his sympathetic gaze, and so she focused her eyes on the wall again.

"I am glad you remembered us. The letter only arrived yesterday. I was hoping you would come. Your baby is beautiful."

Do not be so gentle or I will cry, Lucy thought as she stood to go. "Danke. Thank you," she said in English, which made him smile for the first time.

"You are learning English. Good. Planning to join your child in England?"

Planning was too strong a word for a dream that was only a prayer. Lucy pulled her green book from her handbag and passed it to him, hoping for a sign of approval.

"Ah." He smiled more broadly, but there was a doubt in his eyes. "Studying to be a parlormaid. Good. Yes." A long pause—too long. "But where are you going now?"

Lucy pointed toward the park across the street. She held up her sack lunch. She stepped back and extended her hand for the precious little volume. "I will not keep you from your work." She swept a hand over the cluttered mess of the office. "I have my lunch, as you see."

"But do you have a place to stay in Warsaw?"

"I will go back to the home of the woman who took care of me. I was unwell, you see." This was one of the details she had not mentioned in her recitation. "Until I can find a place of my own and work."

"Ah." Orde held up his finger. *"Work!* The very thing I was getting at, Fräulein." He looked embarrassed as he stepped around an open crate of books. "Work. You see, I have been in need of . . . here in Warsaw . . . a secretary. You were a secretary in Vienna, you said?"

"Only German." Lucy tried not to look too disappointed. *Work as a secretary until she could get to England! Oh, God! But certainly he needed someone who spoke Polish and English!*

Orde indicated that her parlormaid instruction book was in English. "German is what I need. Partly, at least. You do take shorthand? The office is in need of someone who can take down the various speeches of the German government, then transcribe them. You do type as well?"

Her hopes began to rise. She resisted the urge to clap her hands together in joy. "Yes. I was fastest in the typing pool. I can . . . but my English is very poor," she concluded doubtfully.

"Good enough," Orde said in a businesslike manner. He inhaled and exhaled. A great concern had been lifted from him. "Other office work is required, of course." He frowned down at the jumble of files left by his predecessor, a Pole who was addicted to vodka as the drink of choice for breakfast, lunch, and dinner. Orde opened the dusty file drawer full of empty vodka bottles. "Not mine," Orde said. "But, as you see, more than anything we are in need of organizational skills. Typing. Clerical things." His lower lip protruded with concern. "And if this fellow, von Fritschauer, should come around, I should not like for you to meet him . . ." Orde's gaze lingered on the remaining trace of a bruise on the side of her nose. "If he has followed you here, as he followed you to Danzig . . ."

And so, he said the very thing that Lucy sensed. *The thing she feared!* She looked through the office window to the sidewalk, where Alfie and Jacob stood talking to a Polish gendarme as they waited for Orde and Lucy to complete their interview.

Maybe she should go away, Lucy reasoned—simply melt away and call Samuel Orde later when he had more news of the baby. She had come only for news, not expecting sympathy or a job. "Wolf has never let anyone stand in the way of what he wants."

"He did not get past me on the Danzig quay," Orde responded. "I was in his way then." He smiled the schoolyard brawl kind of smile she had seen that day. "Frankly, this chap is just the sort I enjoy standing in the way of, Fräulein Strasburg. No need to speak further of it. You will need a room in which to stay. Appropriate clothing for work. TENS will assist in this. An advance of perhaps two weeks' salary? Yes? Good. Then it is all settled. Have your lunch here and then—well, start where you wish."

Doc Grogan crouched behind an ivy-covered wall on the corner of the street opposite Mills University Hotel. Twice he had pretended to be tying his shoe for the benefit of a passerby, but fortunately there was very little traffic to wonder about why the man remained in one spot for so long.

At last the only pedestrian Grogan cared about appeared at the top of the steps of the hotel. Allan Farrell looked up and down the quiet street repeatedly before proceeding, as if he were trying to cross Piccadilly without using the subway.

Farrell apparently satisfied himself that no one was observing him, and he strode purposefully down the steps carrying a small leather satchel. Grogan waited until the young man was out of sight around the far corner before leaving his place of concealment and rushing into the hotel.

Grogan mentally reviewed what it was he was seeking, even while another part of his mind was complaining about having still more stairs to climb! He was panting again when he reached Allan's door. He started to try the knob, then decided to knock first instead.

After a moment's delay brought no response, he tried the door and found it locked. After a quick glance up and down the hall, Grogan's hand extracted a small ring of oddly shaped keys from his pocket. He squinted at the lock, then at the keys.

Selecting one, he inserted it in the lock and was rewarded with a satisfying click. The door swung open, and Grogan stepped inside quickly and locked the door behind him.

A glance around the room showed very little that was out of the ordinary. The table had an untidy look, with bits of paper and twine lying about, as if something had been hastily wrapped.

Grogan's inspection of the closet revealed a curiosity: nine small leather cases, twins to the one Farrel had been carrying. They were all empty, but identical in description.

The language professor ran his fingers over the walls and floor of the closet and soon found what he was seeking. The edge of one board protruded past the others just enough for Grogan's fingers to grasp it and pull it free. He reached through the opening into a recessed compartment, and his hand closed around a small glass bottle.

Extracting the bottle very carefully from its hiding place, Grogan gently unscrewed the lid. One whiff of the contents told him all he needed to know. He was even more careful as he replaced it.

He was about to reinstall the board when his fingers brushed something else inside the cubicle. Grogan brought a leather-bound book out into the room with him and carried it to the window to inspect it.

It was a small red volume entitled *BAEDEKER'S LONDON AND ITS ENVIRONS*. The book fell open in Doc's hand to the place marked by a red ribbon. The indicated section was labeled "St. Paul's Cathedral— The Dome."

A terrible suspicion forced itself to Doc Grogan's attention. He cursed at the cabbie for driving too slowly and shoved pedestrians out of his way after he jumped from the traffic-jammed taxi.

Grogan's face was distracted, nervous as he appeared in the doorway of Red Lion House. He was sweating ferociously.

"Come on!" he called to the little boys.

"Where?" Charles wondered in a puzzled voice.

"Get out here!" Grogan insisted; then he hefted the twins and hauled them downstairs.

"What?" Lori insisted. "Why are we—?"

"Take the children over there," Grogan demanded. There was no arguing with his tone of voice. He left her on the sidewalk and ran back up into the house with more urgency. She heard him shout now, angrily, for the other boys to get out.

Moments later, puzzled and irritated, Jamie and Mark emerged and at Grogan's urging, hurried into the square to join Lori.

"Wait for me," he said. Then he pointed to the bench at the farthest end of Red Lion Square, "Over there."

"What's wrong?" Lori asked him as a cold knot of fear formed in her stomach. She had felt this way at New Church when the Nazis had come in to search and Jacob had pushed them into the bellows. It was the sense of panic, thinly veiled beneath a calm exterior.

Grogan did not reply. He jogged across the grass of the square as though he did not hear her question. Then, not waiting until the street was clear, he dodged traffic and recrossed the street in front of the house.

He knocked on the door of the downstairs flat where Freddie and Hildy lived.

"They aren't home!" Lori shouted. Did he hear her? "Gone shopping! And to pick up Elisa!"

He turned the knob cautiously, hesitated a moment, then gave the door a shove. It opened. It was not locked. Had extra-careful Hildy ever left the door unlocked before?

"What's he doing?" Jamie asked with alarm.

Grogan reached inside the pocket of his tan linen jacket, and then with a glance over his shoulder toward the children, slipped into the flat.

"What's wrong?" Mark echoed. Charles and Louis, who stood apart holding hands, unexplainably began to cry. They had never seen their beloved Doc act so strangely before!

Suddenly the crash of broken glass sounded from the lower flat. Windows were broken one after another as Doc Grogan threw pieces of furniture out into the street. And then, as if pursued by someone or *something*, he dashed out the door!

In that instant there was a great flash of light behind him! A rolling pillar of fire lifted him off the ground and spun him over and over into the air like a bird.

It seemed to happen in slow motion. Doc Grogan floated above the shrieking cars as the children screamed in horror from the far side of the square. Windows from neighboring houses trembled and shattered inward with the blast. The leaves and limbs of the trees moved as if a giant wind had smashed against them.

Lori covered Charles and Louis with her body as debris swirled in the sky and clattered down with the same slow motion as the rag-doll body of Doc Grogan.

And then everything was very quiet. *So quiet!* Traffic completely still. No birds chirping. No voices calling. Seconds ticked by. The hiss of a car radiator erupted. The crackle of the fire that had flashed and devoured the inside of the downstairs vanished. From far away there came the faint wail of a siren. The boys looked up from where they had fallen. They knew Doc Grogan was dead. The house did not matter. Doc was dead. He had gotten them out, and now he lay in the rubble beside the curb in front of the lovely old Red Lion House.

People began to shout. A woman holding her bloody forehead stumbled from the house next door. A dazed man climbed from his wrecked car and walked carefully over the broken glass to where Doc Grogan lay. He stooped and peered at the body. He leaned closer, then jumped to his feet and shouted, "He is breathing! He is alive!"

31

In the Balance

Hildy Frutschy was hysterical. She sobbed and trembled as the Scotland Yard detectives interviewed her. She blamed herself for everything while big Freddie sat forlornly beside her and wrung his cap in his enormous hands.

Had she left the gas on after brewing her tea? She had worried about that after she was gone. She frequently worried about such horrible things, and now it had come true, hadn't it? Her very worst nightmare had come true, just as she had always worried about it. The children were almost killed. And now poor Doc Grogan lay on the very threshold of death and . . . oh! It was the absolute fault of her own carelessness, wasn't it?

Anna and Helen and Theo comforted the boys in a private sitting room at the hospital. Elisa and Murphy sat with Lori as Scotland Yard Detective Thompson asked her to replay the incident once again from the beginning.

The ordeal had lasted for hours. Lori's brow furrowed as she repeated the story once more. "He seemed agitated . . . No, I did not smell gas from the house. He ran up the stairs and got the boys out . . . ran back, smashing windows and then—" At last Lori began to weep. She leaned her head against Elisa's shoulder and cried very softly.

If it was an accident, why go through this again? Why put Lori through the horror of reliving it over and over?

Yet another detective opened the door and motioned to Detective Thompson with a crook of his finger. "Grogan died a few minutes ago."

Murphy and Elisa exchanged sorrowing looks. Doc Grogan *dead*! Lori covered her ears and buried her face deeper in Elisa's shoulder.

Elisa held her as if she were a little girl.

"Do you want your mother?" Elisa asked gently; then she shot a withering look at Detective Thompson. Why was he pressing so hard? "She needs her mother," Elisa said to Murphy in a voice loud and indignant enough that Thompson could hear her. "And then she needs to sleep!"

Murphy stood and crossed his arms across his chest in a defiant way. He waited until the second agent slipped out, leaving Thompson to glance at his watch apologetically. Yes. It had been going on a long time.

"I suppose you overheard?" He looked at the door. "I am sorry. I was hopeful Grogan would survive this. Shed some light."

"The girl is worn out." Murphy indicated that there was to be no more questioning.

The agent nodded and swept his hands toward the door where the others waited. Then as Elisa and Lori moved out, he put a hand up to stop Murphy. Waiting until the two women were out of earshot he said quietly, "There is someone here you should talk to."

Murphy was convinced that there was nothing more to the headline than *CARELESS HOUSEKEEPER LEAVES GAS STOVE ON—BLOWS UP HOUSE—ONE KILLED.* This continued probing seemed needlessly cruel, and he was angered by it. Murphy sighed and nodded. It was ten minutes more before anyone came.

The door swung back, revealing the bulk of the man Murphy recognized immediately as Mr. Tedrick, of the British Secret Service. It had been over a year since Tedrick had arranged for Murphy and Elisa to meet together in the cottage of New Forest. This was one man Murphy had hoped never to have to see again.

"Hullo there, Murphy." Tedrick extended his meaty hand. He was too cheerful for a time like this. His smile was too broad, his voice too eager to spill the bad news.

"What are you doing here?" Murphy did not shake his hand. He was finished for the time being, and he wanted to gather up his family and find a nice quiet hotel to sleep in for a while.

Tedrick would not be put off. He sat down heavily in the one comfortable chair and indicated that perhaps Murphy should sit somewhere as well. Murphy continued standing.

"Suit yourself," Tedrick said. "I suppose you've already written the story. Let me guess—something about a careless housekeeper? A gas burner left on? Household accident?"

"Something like that."

"Print whatever you like. Probably that is the best story to circulate in a case like this."

"What case?" Murphy asked in an unmistakably angry tone.

"What was Patrick Grogan to you?"

"Dr. Grogan . . . Doc . . . was a speech therapist. One of our boys—" He ran his hand through his hair. The effort of telling even this small detail seemed too great. Murphy could not believe that Doc was gone. He needed to think about that. Digest it. Try to understand the loss. Instead, Murphy was standing in a little room across from an arrogant government man who manipulated personal lives like a game of chess. "What difference does it make?" Murphy finished and sat down.

"Grogan was more than that." Tedrick looked at his nails and then back to gauge Murphy's response. "He was an agent."

Murphy shook his head. He looked toward the stony face of Detective Thompson. "Yours? Or theirs?"

"Actually," Tedrick said with a half smile, "yours. American."

"Well, well," Murphy said with disgust. "Is that for publication, Tedrick? Remember who you're talking to. My profession." His voice was thick with sarcasm.

"Suit yourself." Tedrick was not threatened. "Your government might not be too happy about it, though."

"Listen," Murphy growled. "It's late. The bottom of my house blew up today, just about taking my kids up with it, killing a man we were all genuinely fond of. I don't much like you, Tedrick. Never have. So if you've got something to say, just get to it, because I'm taking my family someplace quiet in about three minutes."

Tedrick's amused expression did not change. "Well, then. You always were a rather direct chap."

"That's what makes me a newsman and you a professional sneak. So? What's up?"

"Grogan was an American agent, working closely with us on the link between the Nazis and the American Clan de Gael. Recognize the name?"

"The American version of the IRA. Yes." Still angry, he showed little interest in the news, as though nothing surprised him. Maybe nothing did anymore.

Tedrick continued as if he were talking about the weather or a motoring trip to Blackpool. "We have known for some time that information about you . . . your family . . . has been of great interest to the other side. The Nazis. With your wife's former activities and personal associations—"

Murphy narrowed his eyes threateningly. If this clown brought up the fact that Elisa made a mistake once a long time ago with a former Nazi, Murphy decided he would knock him cold. Patience was gone. Tedrick seemed to sense that and backed off a bit.

"Her connection, for instance, with Pastor Karl Ibsen, on the one hand. And on the other, her activities in Vienna. Smuggling children out of the Reich. Children like . . . your boys, for instance. Charles and Louis Kronenberger. Such things are all an active irritant to the sensitive stomach lining of the German Führer, we are certain. For this reason we thought it best if your . . . bodyguard—" He was openly amused at Freddie Frutschy. "Well, Grogan was a healthy backup, as you can see from today's incident."

"Not an accident? Then what?"

"Grogan lost his life. The bomb—"

"Bomb?"

A slow nod replied. The irritating smile remained as if to say, *What else, you idiot?* "Bomb. Yes. We are ninety percent certain. It was a botched attempt on the lives of the Ibsen children. On your children. No doubt your wife and the babies were supposed to be there for the event as well. If Grogan had not broken out the windows, the whole block might have been lifted up and sent elsewhere."

Murphy's stomach lurched. He felt cold and then hot. Beads of sweat formed on his forehead. There was no room left for defiance, no matter what he felt for Tedrick.

"Okay. *Why?*" he pleaded.

Tedrick studied his nails again; then rubbed his hands together thoughtfully. "Have you ever heard the name Paul Golden?"

Murphy played the name over in his mind a few times. "Golden? Paul Golden?" He sighed and scratched his head in confusion. "No," he shrugged.

Now Tedrick looked concerned. "Grogan said the name. Three times before he died. *Paul Golden* and *light wells.*"

"He spoke?"

"Paul Golden. Light wells. Ibsen. Churchill," Tedrick replied. "He was on to something big. Told me last week—"

"Told you?"

"Yes. Grogan was not hostile to me, as you are. We did have a bit in common. Like rooting out the scum from London's gutters before someone innocent slipped and—" He waved his hand. That was all beside the point. No use discussing political ideologies in the face of cold, brutal murder. "So, he told me there was someone in your organization bleeding you dry for information. The leak is from a stationary agent in your house, possibly at the TENS office. From there it is passed to the IRA and then on to the Nazis." He paused, letting the implications sink in.

"You mean someone close to us?"

"I was hoping Paul Golden worked for you," Tedrick said in a distracted way. "Have you noticed things missing? Or maybe out of place?"

"Come to think of it," Murphy shrugged, "I thought it was just me." He frowned as he considered the times he had misplaced things. The postcards warning Elisa that she might still be in danger had vanished completely. There were plenty of other things as well. But Paul Golden? The name meant nothing to Murphy.

"I just had a word with the ladies about it." He held up his hand to stop Murphy's reaction. "No one knows Paul Golden." The smile was gone. "Where would you like to stay? Savoy, perhaps? You will need a round-the-clock bodyguard. I'll get my best man on it right away. Freddie Frutschy and his wife are leaving for Wales tonight. They have a son there. Freddie told me the Missus needs to get away." Tedrick talked rapidly. "This is beyond him anyway," Tedrick said grimly. "I am making arrangements for Mrs. Lindheim and her sister to leave London with the boys before the first public orders for evacuation are announced tomorrow."

"Evacuation?" Tedrick had said the word in such an offhanded way that it sounded as though the event were common knowledge. He left no room for argument. Decisions had been made.

"Yes. School children. They are being evacuated out of the areas most likely to be targeted by the Luftwaffe." He cleared his throat. Evacuation was the final admission by the British government that things had become hopeless. "There is a cottage in Evesham near the Avon. Charles and Louis Kronenberger, Jamie Ibsen, and Mark Kalner will be happy there until you can make arrangements to get them back to the States. I suggested that Elisa leave as well. She refuses to consider it until after the memorial concert at St. Paul's. She says now, more than ever, it must go on. Lori Kalner is adamant that she will stay until Elisa leaves London."

"You've already talked this over with them?" Murphy challenged. His weary brain replayed the news of mass evacuation of English school children. Again and again he rolled the news over until the implications of it made him feel a little light-headed. And Tedrick had already spoken with Anna and Elisa about it!

Evacuation! Refugees here in England? First in Germany, then in Austria. The Sudetenland had followed. Prague in March. Danzig. And now that Poland was certain to be swallowed, the evacuation order was finally to be given right here in London!

"So it has come to this," Murphy replied in a hoarse voice. "I hoped it wouldn't."

"But it has. And now we will make the best of it."

———

"It is hard to believe that there could be any good news on a day like this." Anna gently put her hand on Murphy's arm.

He looked up at her, barely able to comprehend what she was saying. She pulled two envelopes out of her handbag. The return address was the passport office. The passports of Alfie Halder and Rachel Lubetkin had arrived in the mail today.

Lori carried Jacob's document in her handbag. But 157 birth certificates had gone up in the flames of the Red Lion House. Destroyed with them were the hopes that they might be used to obtain additional passports for the boys in Orde's Zionist Youth brigade.

A number of applications were pending, however. Twenty-nine were currently being processed. But the political situation deteriorated by the hour. Should Murphy take these three passports to Warsaw? Or should they wait until more arrived?

Murphy gazed at the solemn faces inside the slick blue folders. Rachel Lubetkin. Jacob Kalner. Alfie Halder. Their safety seemed to hang in the balance with that decision.

———

Peter Wallich was taller, it seemed to Lucy, when she first spotted him at the long table in the Community Center soup kitchen. He was definitely thinner and more tattered. She recognized the plaid shirt he wore—the same shirt he had on the day he left her in Danzig.

The center of attention among a group of young people his own age, Peter gestured broadly as he related some story to his audience.

Lucy looked around for some sign of Peter's mother and sister. Where was Karin Wallich amidst the clamor? Where was Marlene, with her dark and sullen face?

No one had yet noticed Orde's entrance into the enormous room, or spoons would have been silent against bowls, and conversations would have fallen away. Orde had deliberately come early. The photographer was scheduled to arrive at seven o'clock to begin the arduous task of taking several hundred passport photos. Orde had not explained that he was sending them back to England a few at a time in hopes that they would come back inside shiny new British folders. Lucy had heard Orde gruffly inform the photographer that what happened to the photos was of no concern as long as he was paid.

"What is it?" Orde leaned in to Lucy as he noticed her gazing with mild wonder in the direction of Peter Wallich.

"Peter," she answered.

"Yes. A member of the Zionist Youth. How do you know him?"

"I know him," Lucy said as the boy happened to look up and see her.

He gaped at her a bare moment before he leaped to his feet and dashed through the narrow aisles between tables to where she stood.

"Lucy!" he shouted, loudly enough that his cries of joy turned heads. "Lucy! It's *you!*"

Suddenly everyone noticed that the woman Peter Wallich was shouting at happened to be in the company of the great and magnificent British Zionist, Samuel Orde. So who was this Lucy, anyway? And how did Peter happen to know her?

All propriety was thrown to the wind. Peter charged up and embraced her, laughing and shouting her name! A small group of his companions made a curious semicircle around him as he and Lucy embraced and looked at each other with delight.

"Last I saw you, you were not so thin!" Peter exclaimed.

"And I could say the same for you," she replied.

"You got my letter?"

"No."

"Where is the baby?"

"In England."

A moment of dark comprehension flashed in his eyes; then he brushed it away. "But you had to get the letter—you found me here. I lost the address where mother and Marlene—"

"They are not there anymore," Lucy said in a rush.

And so the reunion stumbled from one revelation to the next as members of the Zionist Youth lined up to have their pictures taken in the basement.

Peter and Lucy talked for three hours in a quiet corner of the now-deserted dining room of the soup kitchen. When Orde and Jacob and Alfie emerged from the evening's instruction, the red-haired youth leader's countenance had changed from one of joy to somber concern.

The conclusion of their rambling conversation had come to a frightening possibility that Peter shared with Orde.

"So you see, when I lost my address, I wrote to Lucy in Danzig inquiring of her to send the information to me. I gave this place as my return address."

"I never got his letter," Lucy added.

"It is possible that the man who pursued her in Danzig could have intercepted that letter," Peter finished. "He would have this address, you see. He arrested the man who helped my family in Vienna, and I do not doubt that he is still—"

Orde nodded and looked at Lucy with a new concern. "Yes. It is best that you remain with me. He will show up, sooner or later." The prospect seemed to please him. "In the meantime, the photographer is still waiting downstairs. Both of you . . . if you please."

———

Allan Farrell coupled the wires of a small black device to a bundle of explosives on his kitchen table. Another of the leather satchels stood open on the floor beside him. There was a sharp rap on his door.

Farrell started to sweep all his material off the table and into the case when he heard two more knocks, followed by a pause, and then two more. He continued putting everything out of sight, but in an unhurried manner. Then he went over to the door and admitted Hess.

"Ah, Mr. Farrell," said Hess. "Sorry to interrupt you." He tugged on the glove covering his crippled hand. "Is all proceeding as planned?"

Allan nodded. "Soon everything will be in place."

"What a great pity that the explosion that removed the man Grogan did not eliminate a few more nuisances as well."

Farrell stiffened, expecting a rebuke for his rash act.

Hess noted the worried expression that crossed Allan's face. "Don't be alarmed, Mr. Farrell. You did very well in removing a potentially troublesome opponent, and as for the rest—well, they will not be around to bother us much longer, will they? But I have come to say goodbye. Other important events are going forward that demand my presence elsewhere, so I leave you to the completion of your mission. Do you have all that you require?"

"Everything."

"Good. If you find the need for additional supplies, just leave your request in the usual way. Between our technology and your courage and resourcefulness, I am certain you cannot fail." Hess straightened his necktie. "That's it, then. I'll be listening for the sound of your success. The echo will undoubtedly be heard throughout Europe."

———

Two days later, Hess stood in the bowels of Gestapo headquarters in Berlin, reviewing Allan Farrell's progress.

"You are certain that Operation Edifice is positioned and will take place as planned?" demanded Himmler.

"Quite sure, Reichsführer," responded Hess. "And there will be no way to link the activity to anyone but the IRA."

"And will all the principal targets be in place?"

Hess nodded a contented agreement. "The Murphys, the Ibsens, and the Lindheims will all be attending to hear Winston Churchill deliver an address on what is sure to be a memorable occasion."

Both men chuckled slightly. "You have done well, Agent Hess. Your reward will be participation in another event of great significance."

"Thank you, Reichsführer," Hess nodded modestly. "And the nature of my new assignment?"

"It is the opening scene of what is called Case White," explained Himmler, waving a handkerchief of that color which he was using to polish his spectacles. "The Führer was very taken with an American radio production called, I believe, *The War of the Worlds*. In it a race of beings from the planet Mars attacks the earth. This is, however, beside the point. The night that the broadcast occurred, a great many

Americans believed such a ludicrous invasion was actually taking place! There was widespread panic, and armed citizens fortified their homes against the threat from Mars." Himmler paused and smiled at the puzzled look on the face of Hess.

"You understand that Poland must make a move of aggression against the Reich. The Poles have so far not cooperated, but we will see to it that they attack a radio station in the border town of Gleiwitz. We have arranged that some political prisoners and some traitorous officers are going to be the Poles for this attack. They are even going to be dressed in Polish uniforms."

Agent Hess nodded his understanding. "And my role in this little stage play?" he asked.

"You are to select the participants and see that they are equipped and in position on the morning of September 1."

"And may I ask for your guidance in regard to the selection?" requested Hess.

"I believe that you are acquainted with the prison compound near the Polish border crossing where your unfortunate injuries took place. You should make your selections there."

Hess rose and saluted, then paused. "One additional thought, Reichsführer. May I suggest adding Major von Fritschauer to the list?"

Himmler paused in thought, then agreed. "I will send word that he is needed back here in Berlin. It does not appear that anything useful is to be gained by following him, and most recently he has attempted to hide himself among the Jewish community of Warsaw." Himmler shook his head sadly that a young officer could have fallen so far.

"Shocking," agreed Hess, and he saluted again before leaving.

————

Rachel extended her hand shyly to the beautiful woman who had saved Peter Wallich and was even now, according to Peter, being pursued by Nazi agents.

It was like meeting the heroine of a very exciting story in person. Rachel considered the details of the dramatic escape from Vienna, the chance meeting with Adolf Hitler, the long and terrible ride with the Gestapo agent in the rail car! How much more exciting did a story have to be in order for this Lucy Strasburg to really be a heroine? Peter had recited the harrowing tale a hundred times. And now *here* was the very Lucy!

"Is she Jewish?" asked the old yentas in the soup kitchen.

"She must be."

"Probably raised in an assimilated family. Ignorant of Jewish ways, you can tell."

"So what? That is what helped her save Peter Wallich! I'd like to see how you would handle meeting the German Führer, God forbid! Oy! Makes my head ache to think about it!"

Thus everyone *knew* the secret that Lucy Strasburg was really Jewish, even though it did not show. Just like they knew that Captain Samuel Orde was also really secretly Jewish. Peter had not mentioned the part about the baby, which might have caused the yentas to view her with less kindly eyes. That part of the adventure being left out created room for speculation about what a lovely couple Captain Samuel Orde and Lucy Strasburg would make standing together beneath a chuppa! *Nu?*

All the talk among the women in the soup kitchen made Rachel blush deeply when she finally got to meet Lucy. *A real heroine. Oy! And maybe even a little romance in her future as well.*

For the moment at least, with the spark of her imagination ignited, Rachel thought about something besides the turmoil that had turned her peaceful existence upside down. Only much later in the night, when she lay on her bed and contemplated the past of such a beautiful woman as Lucy, did it occur to her that Lucy was not in Warsaw because she wanted to be. Like all the rest, she was running, running, running away!

———

"I am in love with her," Peter blurted out to Lucy, nodding absently at Rachel Lubetkin as she carried yet another stack of pillowcases down to the basement.

Lucy smiled slightly. "Then I envy you both. First love." She dried the tin bowls as they spoke.

Peter looked miserably at the empty doorway where Rachel had just disappeared. "She hates me. At least I think she does. Just my luck, huh? To fall in love with the prettiest girl in the district, who also happens to be the rabbi's daughter."

"She will come around." Lucy tried to console Peter.

He shook his head in disagreement. "She is already engaged. To a boy named Reuven in Lodz whom she has never met."

"Hmmm," Lucy said with surprise. "They are still doing that sort of thing?"

"And I am not religious. Obviously. But . . . I have spoken with her father."

"Courageous, Peter."

"I told him she should leave Poland with us." He looked at Lucy. "Already Hayedid has sent out ten groups of twelve to go to Yugoslavia. Soon enough they'll be in Palestine, papers or no papers."

"And will your Rachel leave her family?" Lucy thought it might be the family of Rachel Lubetkin that tied her to Poland, not this Reuven fellow in Lodz.

"If her father orders her," Peter said hopefully. "And he might if—" So here came the point.

"Just say it, Peter."

"All right then. If you use your influence and speak with the captain, then he will speak to the rabbi, and—"

"And your Rachel will go with you to live on a kibbutz."

"Yes."

Lucy nodded. "I have no influence with the captain," she said softly. "He is a kind man who has employed me. That is all."

Peter looked at her in disbelief. "Everyone talks about the way he looks at you."

Lucy frowned and looked away. She did not want to hear this. She knew how men looked at her. She hoped the captain was not like other men. "It is your imagination."

Peter took her wet hand in his. "Tell me you will speak with him about Rachel. She is too pretty to stay here." His eyes were desperate. "And you know what I am talking about. If the Nazis come here . . . Well, there is no use saying they don't do whatever they want to women, is there?"

His comment had not been intended to hurt Lucy, but it did. "Yes. No use denying it. And I will speak to him about her. Although I think you could get further with him than I can."

Peter kissed her hand in gratitude and then stumbled clumsily off down the stairs after Rachel.

———

TENS Warsaw acquired the last two-bedroom suite available at the Bristol Hotel. Perhaps they rented the last suite available anywhere in Warsaw. With the enormous influx of Western journalists crowding into the city to follow the shuttling politicians, every hotel was packed, and no one seemed to be checking out.

Alfie knew that this fact was a relief to Captain Orde, because it had settled the issue of where Lucy would be staying.

"Of course you must stay with the TENS staff at the Bristol," he told Lucy in a very businesslike tone. "Elisha and Jacob will move into my room with me. You may have the other room. You *must* have the other room until things in Warsaw settle down a bit."

Alfie knew that the captain did not really believe anything in Warsaw would settle down. As a matter of fact, he had made a tour of the basement of the Bristol Hotel, which had been converted into a bomb shelter. The captain had told Alfie that when the siren blew, he must very quickly put the kitten in his hiding place in the valise and carry it with him down to the basement.

The captain did not say *if* the siren blows, but *when* it blows. The people in charge of the bomb shelter would not let a kitten in if they knew it was a kitten. But if they thought it was just a piece of baggage, they would not make a fuss about it. For this reason, Alfie had kept a few extra cans of sardines in Werner's valise. That way, if they were in the basement shelter a long time, Alfie could feed Werner and maybe Werner would not yowl so loud and upset the other people in the shelter.

All of this had been discussed long before Lucy arrived at the TENS office, and also a long time before Warsaw filled up with so many people. The point was, Jacob explained to Alfie, the captain most likely was very pleased to give up his room to Lucy. He did not seem to want to let her out of his sight.

Jacob was right about that. When Lucy went down to the delicatessen to pick up sandwiches which Captain Orde ordered, the captain paced nervously in the office and stopped at every turn to look out over the street. He muttered, "Shouldn't let her go." Then he rocked back and forth on his toes and looked almost angry.

Jacob nodded at Alfie as if to show how right he was. Alfie shrugged and nodded, then said to the captain, "Why didn't you go with her?"

At this, the face of Captain Orde brightened. "I'll just go see what's keeping her." Then he dashed out the door.

Jacob looked smug. He put his feet up on the desk. "Don Quixote," he remarked with a grin. "And he has met his Dulcinea at last."

Alfie did not understand what Jacob meant and he did not want to ask because Jacob might think he was a Dummkopf. "Yes," Alfie said as though he understood perfectly. This made Jacob look at him with surprise.

Maybe Alfie did not know about Don Quixote, but he could tell easily that the captain was very worried about Lucy Strasburg. Captain Orde would fight for her. He would very much enjoy smashing the face of the man who had hurt Lucy.

"Look at this." Jacob grinned and took his feet off the desk as Orde and Lucy walked together toward the office. Orde was carrying the paper bags with sandwiches. He was talking to her in a pleasant way. A kindly way. Alfie could not tell what they were talking about, but Lucy Strasburg had the same misty smile she had on her face as when she saw the pictures of her baby.

"The protective instinct of the chivalrous British knight." Jacob pretended to read a newspaper, but he was watching all the while. "King Arthur and Guinevere," he said under his breath.

"Yes," Alfie agreed. He did not understand this either, but it made him very happy to see the way their lonely captain worried over Lucy, who was also a very lonely person. Alfie knew about lonely people. He knew all about that even if he did not understand what Jacob was talking about exactly.

The captain did not talk to Lucy in the same gruff manner in which he discussed things with Jacob and Alfie. That evening at the hotel, he told her about the complete safety of the bomb shelter beneath the hotel. He said that the sirens would no doubt blow, but that she must not be frightened by such an event. Even if there were some sort of German aggression against Poland, he told her, she was not to worry. The British Army was pledged to protect and defend, the captain said confidently.

Alfie had heard the captain talk about the way he felt the war would go. Poland would not be able to hold on until England and France came to help. Warsaw might come under siege. If that happened, they would have to get out any way they could.

What Orde told Lucy sounded different from what he had told them. Alfie did not think that the captain was lying to her. Maybe he was just putting the best face on what was really a very, *very* bad future for Poland.

And what did the captain mean when he told Lucy that the British Army was pledged to protect and defend? Alfie figured it out when Werner knocked over Lucy's water glass at supper. Orde had scooped up the kitten and locked him in the bathroom, then had come back to the table with towels.

"In the British Army we call this mopping-up operations."

Lucy's face had gotten very soft as she watched him blot the spill, as if she had never seen a man clean up anything before. It was a very gentle thing to see, Alfie thought. It made him feel good inside. And then he knew that Samuel Orde was her own personal English army to protect and defend.

Maybe later, Alfie decided, he would ask someone about King Arthur and the other fellow, Don Quixote. If they were like the captain and Lucy Strasburg, they must be very good stories.

Alfie hoped they had happy endings.

32

New Orders

Captain Orde was a kind man—perhaps the only really kind man Lucy had ever met. Why then did she fear his look? Why could she not lift her gaze to meet his? Was it because she knew he would see how broken she was inside, and knowing that would give him power over her?

She approached his desk with a neatly typed list of provisions for the Torah school air-raid shelter. He was poring over other lists; names of young men he had slated to slip out of Poland and across the borders of Hungary and Yugoslavia, then on to Palestine. The TENS office of Warsaw was barely a news office. Samuel Orde's primary mission was to rescue as many young Jewish men as could be saved. Lucy found this amazing. Incomprehensible. So very different from Wolf, whose mission it was to kill the same young men.

She waited for him to finish. He looked up, and she gazed at the corner of his desk rather than chance a look into the depth of his eyes.

"Peter Wallich asked me to speak with you," she said almost shyly.

"Peter? My future general of Israel? He can't speak for himself?"

"We are old friends. This is a matter of the heart. A very tender heart, Peter has."

"A heart you know well, I do not doubt." He sat back in his squeaking chair and smiled up at her.

She raised her eyes only briefly and let her gaze take in the smile lines at the edge of his sun-browned face. Even his skin, rough and weathered, was different from Wolf's cool, smooth complexion.

"We were together a long time," she said briskly, wanting to get past that.

"Yes. He has told me about it."

She felt her color rise. *What had Peter told him?* Had he spoken of the way she looked when she carried the baby? The silly songs she had sung as she sat in the chair beside the window and dreamed of holding the little one? Had every vulnerable expression and word been shared with Captain Orde?

"He told me you were someone to be trusted," Orde added. "Utterly and completely."

She let her breath out with relief and tried to organize her thoughts. "He has asked me . . . well, it is foolish that he asked me at all, but it is a matter of his personal . . ." She faltered.

"Yes?" He thumbed the edge of a sheaf of papers impatiently.

"He is in love, you see." She lowered her voice, aware that Alfie was looking at her quite openly. "With the rabbi's daughter. With Rachel Lubetkin."

"Ah, yes." Orde seemed amused. "So is every young male in the Zionist Youth brigade. Rachel is a pretty girl."

"And Peter is concerned about her staying here in Warsaw, you see. There is such danger. Especially for . . . young girls who are pretty." The words came out like a shrouded confession of her own past, her own involvement with a man who had won her over by making her feel desired. All because she was attractive. But of course her life was nothing like Rachel's. "You see?" she asked lamely.

Orde hung on her words for a moment. She could feel him looking at her, wondering if being pretty had made her own life hard in some way. Better to be homely than to live as she had lived. But that was not what they were discussing here.

"Peter is anxious to get her out of Warsaw. Is that it?"

"Out of Poland. Yes. To Palestine."

"I have seen what the Arab gangs do to pretty Jewish girls in Palestine," Orde said under his breath.

She looked up at him with surprise. "What?"

He waved away the thought. It was nothing he wanted to get into now. The issue was Rachel Lubetkin. Lovely. Innocent. A girl any boy could fall in love with. And here she was with a million other girls just like herself. Some more attractive. Some less. But all of them Jewish and all in the path of a Nazi steamroller that crushed all women and children equally to serve its purpose.

Orde inhaled deeply. "Her father has spoken to me already of his concern. And her grandfather in Jerusalem before that. There are people in London working on getting a passport for her. So, you see—" He smiled and shrugged. "Peter Wallich is not the only one who loves her. The question is whether the girl wants to be loved away from her home here in Warsaw. She is not at all happy with the suggestion, I can tell you. And I don't imagine she would return Peter's affection if he tried to get her to leave with the Zionist Youth brigade."

"I'll tell him then. Tell him that other ways are being explored to help her leave. He will be relieved." Lucy backed away, nodded her thanks, and managed to slip back to her desk without ever once having to look the captain full in his face.

Even after she returned to her typing she could feel his thoughtful gaze hot on her back. She did not need to look up to know he was wondering about her. Her shame made her clumsy and slow in her work.

––––––

After breakfast, Rabbi Aaron Lubetkin announced that he would get out of bed and go see for himself the work being done on the shelter in the basement of the Community Center.

Etta helped him bathe, then made him rest before he dressed. After he dressed in his finest Shabbat clothes, she made him rest again and eat.

Word had gotten out, no doubt through young David and Samuel again, that their father was coming to see the defense efforts, and so in anticipation, the efforts were doubled.

Far beneath the floor of the soup kitchen, salvaged timbers were hoisted in place to reinforce the walls and ceiling of the basement. Outside the structure and within, pillowcases and flour sacks alike now held earth from every flower pot and garden plot in the district.

Menkes the baker recruited a number of refugees who had in far-away lives been bakers themselves. Mounds of golden-crusted loaves grew like heaps of sandbags to defend against hunger in the quarter should the Nazi threats prove real.

Older men from among the Zionists directed the younger men from the Yeshiva schools. The English Captain Orde moved among them all, indicating which barricade should be strengthened and how best to brace walls and ceilings against shelling. Groups within groups coalesced around him, then scattered in a dozen different directions as others moved in for new orders. *Water to be stored. Canned goods. Flashlights or candles. Blankets and bandages.* These supplies were gathered and then distributed to the shelters of the Community Center, the Torah school, and a dozen smaller buildings around the district.

Into this beehive came the word that Rabbi Lubetkin was coming to inspect the work of his congregation, coming to bless the work that had been done and that which was being done.

Groups of bearded Hasidim came first, as if to prepare the way. Their black caftans flapped like the glossy wings of crows in the sunlight as they moved steadily toward the soup kitchen to form a welcoming committee.

––––––

Wolf's view of Muranow Square from the window of Kowalski's apartment reminded him of a swarm of insects. Since dawn the square had been attracting Jews by the hundreds. More continued to come, and none ever seemed to leave until the area was filled with milling bodies.

They seemed to be doing nothing more than talking. The Jews created knots of conversation that unraveled and formed anew as different speakers approached and earlier members broke away to join other groups.

What was all the discussion about? Wolf raised his field glasses and tried to discover the topic by examining newspaper headlines over the shoulders of black-coated gesticulating speakers.

At last one front page remained still long enough for him to make it out. In Yiddish phrases the paper announced an obituary for Poland: *GERMANY AND RUSSIA SIGN NONAGGRESSION PACT.*

Wolf was exhilarated by the announcement of the event. The three hundred Russian divisions would be kept on the sidelines! It was still important that the Nazis not fire the first shot, but a Polish response to provocation would undoubtedly happen soon, and then the attack on Poland would begin.

But it also meant that Wolf would have to hurry. He would have to locate Lucy and return her to Germany quickly. He again raised the field glasses to his eyes.

On the far side of the square, directly in front of the Community Center building, a double line of marchers appeared. The twin ranks, providing the only orderliness in the whole chaotic scene, instantly attracted Wolf's attention. One quick glance and Wolf snorted in derision. These were not soldiers at all, but the ragged boys who played at being soldiers.

As Wolf watched, the rows of broomstick warriors marched and counter-marched as if oblivious to the surging crowd that surrounded them. When they halted, they were facing Wolf. He noted the scarecrow-thin figure, his too-short trousers flapping against his bony shanks, walking up and down the ranks with his back toward the Kowalski building.

Wolf snorted again at the ludicrous figure of the boy playing officer; then his snort turned into a strangled cough. The officer-boy had turned to salute a sandy-haired man who had stepped out from the crowd.

The features of the man seemed to leap through the field glasses directly into Wolf's apartment. It was the Britisher who had interfered on the dock in Danzig! Wolf swung his gaze back to the thin, pinched face of the boy. Peter Wallich! Lucy must be close at hand!

———

As the word of Rabbi Lubetkin's imminent arrival leaped from the parapets and ricocheted from the buildings of Muranow Square, Peter

Wallich laid aside his shovel and called his troop together in front of the community building.

Lucy left her work in the kitchen and joined the throngs outside in the square who gathered to welcome back their beloved rabbi from his long convalescence.

From her place beside Alfie, she could see Orde talking seriously with Peter. The boy had dust in his hair, giving it the appearance of tarnished copper.

Everyone had heard the unveiled threats that the German Führer had hurled at the Jewish population of Poland last night, and then this morning came the terrible news about Russia. Without equivocation, Hitler promised to wipe the Jews from the face of the earth. The Jews of Poland, he claimed, wanted to plunge Germany into war, and he would retaliate if they continued their agitation against the Reich!

Lucy had transcribed the speech for Orde. He had rewritten his daily story and focused on the pillowcase sandbags that formed the pitiful bulwarks of the Warsaw Jewish community. He had compared them to the concrete bunkers in Germany that had been under construction for years.

Lucy watched Peter Wallich and his little band as they performed their drills as the ragged honor guard for the rabbi. She could not help but compare them with the hundred thousand Hitler Youth she had seen at the Nuremberg rally last September. They had marched with burnished shovels over their shoulders. Lines had been straight. Voices had roared.

Behind Lucy, the baker Menkes blustered about the preparedness of the Polish Army and about the readiness of the Jews of Warsaw! "If the Germans come here, we will show them a fist! Fight the rats!"

Just then a small boy darted past and climbed the brick wall beside the Community Center. Poised on the top of the wall like a bird on a wire, he reached deep into his pocket, whipped out a piece of chalk, and with five bold strokes drew a picture on the bricks.

Then he flapped off the wall and disappeared into the crowd, leaving behind him the likeness of Hitler scraped upon the gray bricks! There was no doubt about the identity of the face in the cartoon. The oval shape of the face; one definite stroke curving down over the forehead in the Führer's cowlick; that tiny brush of a mustache! And over the entire face was drawn an insulting, dismissing, enormous *X*!

A small ripple of laughter rose, then the pattering of applause. Lucy smiled with the rest, but her heart grew heavy with a sense of uneasiness for these people and this place.

Involuntarily she looked up and remembered that Wolf had told her about the German Führer's plans for Poland. *The bombs will fall here first.* Hitler had said as much in the broadcast last night. No matter how many times he changed his policies; no matter even that he had now signed a pact with Stalin, the one thing that never changed in Hitler's rhetoric was his hatred of the Jews. He had drawn their caricature in his mind and crossed them out with the vengeance that the little urchin had used when marking on the brick facade of the Community Center.

Attention returned to matters of real importance to the people of Muranow.

"Here comes Rabbi Lubetkin!"

"See how pale he is!"

"He is walking without help! The Eternal be praised!"

Wolf hurriedly scanned the ebb and flow of the crowd around the sandy-haired man and Peter Wallich. Lucy must be nearby, she must be! He sensed her presence even before he saw her, then lined up the field glasses on the back of a woman he knew was Lucy, even before she turned.

At last! A feeling of urgency filled Wolf. He would not wait a single minute longer. He would follow her, capture her, and take her back to Germany.

A last quick glance through the field glasses confirmed that Lucy was not leaving. She and the Britisher were watching Peter Wallich drill his pitiful troop. Wolf tossed the glasses down and turned to the door to go.

Halfway down the stairs, someone was coming up. The figure called out to him, "Herr von Fritschauer. Good! I have news."

Gustav Ahlman! What was he doing in Warsaw? "Not now, Ahlman," said Wolf, starting to push past. "I've spotted her at last."

Ahlman moved in front of Wolf, blocking the stairs. "Important news," he repeated. "New orders."

An angry sweep of Wolf's arm caught Gustav off balance, shoving him against the banister. "Get out of my way," Wolf shouted, and he ran down the stairs.

Wolf scarcely heard the echo of Gustav Ahlman's voice calling out, "New orders!" In Wolf's mind there was only one objective, one focus of all his attention: to capture Lucy.

It was indeed time for Wolf to return to Berlin. Great things were happening, events in which he had the duty, the right, to participate. But Wolf knew that he could not go until this duty was accomplished. He could not leave Warsaw having failed to erase the shadow on his reputation.

How could he have been so deceived? A mystery surrounded Lucy Strasburg. The woman he had believed to be an ignorant peasant was standing by the side of a military Britisher. She was obviously connected somehow with the largest community of Jews in all of Europe.

Wolf dodged a knot of black-coated men standing in a circle. Their beards and earlocks bobbed in rhythm as they gestured gnarled fingers toward newspaper headlines. A babble of voices rose from the square and assaulted Wolf's ears; Yiddish, Polish, German, even Slavic tongues for which he had no names. It was as if all the Jews from all of Europe had been poured into Warsaw and stirred together.

Wolf darted to one side of the crowd of men and bumped into two short plump women walking with linked elbows. With heavily laden shopping bags hanging from their arms, they revolved slowly around like a gate swinging on rusty hinges and blocked Wolf's path. Wolf tried to pass by them, only to have them pivot in front of him and bar his way again.

He bounced up on his toes, trying to see over the crowd. Lucy had seemed so near through the field glasses! Up close, the square was both expansively broad and packed with bodies! It was almost as if they were deliberately preventing Wolf from reaching her!

He pushed between the elderly women and a group of schoolgirls. The girls, a flock of twittering birds in dark blue jumpers, braids and freckles, pointed at him and giggled. What could this Saturday person be so anxious to find in Muranow Square?

Wolf hopped up on a low brick wall and scanned the crowd in the direction of the Community Center. He thought he had lost his way completely until he spotted again a file of broomsticks marking time to the marching steps of their bearers. There she was! Lucy's glowing blond hair was unmistakable. She was still where he had seen her last.

Wolf started to jump down from the wall, but found the crowd pressed in around him. He turned, looked down into faces that stared back at him. Jewish faces, every one. He turned again and saw a completely solid ring of people watching him with anticipation.

They think I'm going to speak, he thought with confusion. *They must believe I have a message to deliver.* Indeed, those in the ring nearest Wolf were asking for silence, shushing the others around them.

"Husband!" a voice cried out. "It's him! The man I told you about." Wolf tried to see whom the words came from. He located an arm pointing at him and followed it back to the mousy face of the woman from the Dorbransky apartment.

Wolf was confronted by a powerfully built man whose curly black hair seemed to spill off his head and flow over his brawny arms and out the collar of his shirt. Cracow, the woman had said . . . no doubt her husband was a steel worker!

Wolf attempted to stride past. "What do you mean, breaking into my home? Scaring my family?" demanded the man.

Wolf touched the pistol in his pocket, but saw how awash he was in a sea of angry, questioning eyes and left it undrawn. "Must be some mistake," he argued. "I don't know you."

"We'll see whose mistake it was," said the man, reaching out for Wolf.

"Von Fritschauer, wait!" called Gustav Ahlman from just behind Wolf.

Ahlman lunged through the ring of people, clutching for Wolf's sleeve. Wolf jerked aside, and Gustav's rush carried him into the face of the steel worker.

"What's this, another one?" shouted the man. He drew back a fist the size of a pipe wrench and crashed it against Ahlman's nose. Gustav's nostrils exploded in spurts of crimson and an audible crunch of cartilage and bone.

Wolf seized on the distraction as an opportunity to shove two on-lookers out of the way and plunge on in pursuit of Lucy. He must not lose her now!

———

Allan Farrell skirted the rim of the Whispering Gallery that over-looked the rotunda of the cathedral floor without even glancing at the paintings or the statues. He had many other things to think about, and his mind had long since ceased to contemplate the art work.

When this operation had first begun, Allan had worried that making so many trips up the hundreds of steps might attract unfortunate at-tention. But none of the priests or lay attendants paid the slightest attention to one more tourist amid the crowds of sightseers.

In the satchel he carried was another, smaller leather bag. This inner bag was actually one of the packages Allan was making the repeated trips to deposit. Eight packages meant eight deliveries to the Golden Gallery high atop the outside of the dome.

When Allan reached the last of the spiraled iron stairs and emerged into the breezy London afternoon, he congratulated himself on his timing: he was alone on the platform. This simple fact meant that he would not have to wait for an opportunity to make another deposit.

Allan listened at the top of the stairs for the clatter of footsteps that would give away the approach of more sightseers. When he heard nothing but the soft sighing of the wind, he immediately opened the satchel and removed the inner bag with its already attached length of light rope.

A quick check showed that the wires connecting the radio receiver and the explosives were firmly attached. Allan counted stone pillars around to the right from the stairwell. When he reached the fourth one he stopped and lowered the bag over the railing and into the opening in the lead-sheathed curve of the roof.

When the bag had gently come to rest at the bottom of the opening, Allan dropped the end of the cord in after. Out of habit he leaned over the rail to see if any trace of his handiwork could be seen, but nothing was visible. Perhaps if someone had hung by their toes over the parapet and dangled headfirst they could spot the little bag, but not otherwise.

Allan picked up the outer carrying case with a great sense of satisfaction. *Six eggs in the nest,* he thought. *Almost home.*

The linking of Rachel Lubetkin's arm through her own startled Lucy. Cradling her baby brother on her hip, Rachel led Lucy into the packed gathering that had assembled to hear Rabbi Lubetkin speak publicly for the first time since his arrest in November.

The synagogue itself was not large enough to hold the numbers of men and women coming into the auditorium. The enormous hall was filled to standing room only and still the crowds trailed out the double doors and into the square.

Yet room was made for Lucy Strasburg. *A heroine, was she not? One who saved the life of one Jewish boy?* And now she stood beside the rabbi's daughter.

Wolf had escaped from the clutches of the steel worker from Cracow and from the pursuit of Gustav Ahlman, but neither of these successes amounted to anything. Lucy was gone! By the time Wolf had reached the far corner of the square, she had vanished as surely as if the earth had swallowed her up.

The Britisher had also disappeared, and the last definite connection with Lucy, Peter Wallich, was marching out of Muranow Square at the head of his ragged band of play soldiers.

Wolf revolved slowly around in place. In his mind he cursed Ahlman for delaying him, cursed the couple from Cracow for interfering, cursed all the Jews of Muranow Square and his own excruciatingly bad luck.

What to do now? He could only think that if he had once spotted Lucy from the window of his rented apartment, he could do it again. He went back to the Kowalski flat, this time skirting the edge of the square instead of forcing his way through the middle. He was careful to turn up a side street in order to avoid the spot where he had encountered the woman and her husband.

Deep in thought, he ascended the stairs toward his apartment. Perhaps it was time to enlist additional aid from Berlin. If he could reach Himmler, and explain how close he was to success, next time he would have a ring of operatives around the square. That was the answer, no doubt of it. Perhaps Reichsführer Himmler would shed some light on what the new orders involved—in code, of course.

Wolf pushed open the door of his room. It had been stupid of him to rush out and leave it unlocked, but he had been in a hurry: Ahlman's interruption had delayed him, and the result had been failure instead of success. Wolf decided that he would give Ahlman the cursing of his life when next they met; he might even denounce the oaf to Himmler.

Two strides into the living room, Wolf saw the oaf already present to be cursed and denounced. Ahlman was seated in a chair with his back toward the view of Muranow Square and a Luger semiautomatic pistol pointed at Wolf's midsection. His eyes were surrounded by saucer-sized purple rings, and where his nose had been was an ungainly mass of tape and sticking plaster.

"Major von Fritschauer," Ahlman said flatly, "your new orders are that you will accompany me back to Berlin at once."

Have you selected a headquarters for the Gleiwitz operation, Agent Hess?"

"Yes, Reichsführer. There is a schoolhouse in a nearby village that is suitable," answered Hess. "My assistant has already made the necessary arrangements."

"Excellent. And have the participants been identified?"

"Yes, Reichsführer, we have selected thirteen, including Wolfgang von Fritschauer. I trust you approve the selection of Karl Ibsen as well?"

"Considering the timing," commented Himmler with a thoughtful look in his eyes, "it is absolutely poetic."

"And the code name that has been assigned?" inquired Hess as he stood to leave.

"I am certain you will appreciate the subtlety," smiled Himmler. "Your code is *Konserven*—Operation Canned Goods."

The entire block of solitary cells groaned aloud as morning came with muggy regularity. Karl opened his eyes to the insistent peeping of the young sparrows. A few moments of just-breaking sunlight slid across the bricks and illuminated the nest where four feathered heads with bright button eyes poked up from the lip of the nest.

On the window ledge, mother and father sparrow looked at their offspring with a kind of dare in their expression. It was nearly the last of August. Karl knew this from the marks on his brick calendar. It was time the young sparrows learn to fly. Already they had hopped up on the edge of the nest and flapped their stubby wings in imitation of their parents. But today was different. For some reason Karl could not understand, this was the day when they would fly.

He did not make a move to sit up even when the clatter of the meal tray sounded outside in the corridor. The steel trap slid back and the bread and porridge were shoved through. The black water that passed as coffee was already cold. The mush was cold as well. It would not matter if Karl ate now or waited awhile. He dared not disturb the small drama being played out above him.

Lady Sparrow leaped from her perch and flew toward the nest. With a flurry, she brushed her children firmly, urging them up. Pushing them toward the edge. Then just as abruptly the big male rushed toward the nest, pushing his mate aside. She resumed her place on the window ledge while he took over. He was much rougher with his children. Today they would fly. He would not accept excuses. If they did not fly, then they would go hungry. They might die. No exceptions. He beat the inside of the nest with his wings. The down lining flew up and floated down to land on Karl's bed. Welcome to the real world.

All four young birds beat their wings frantically. The big male shoved them one after another from the nest. And one after another, they flew clumsily to where their mother sat beside the bread crumbs on the ledge.

Karl wanted to cheer! This was the first time he had seen them all at once. But he lay very still as the young birds were lectured and then directed to fly back to their little home. The largest of the young sparrows spread his wings and flapped, raising himself off the ledge a few inches. Then, his father's stern feathers at his back, he leaped up into space and hovered a moment, sank down, and then with his father at his side, he weaved back to the nitch in the bricks.

His three siblings followed after, each with a different degree of skill. All of them made it home and only then were they fed. By this event, Karl marked the end of summer. The end of a sermon that God had been whispering in his ear for months.

When the door to his cell crashed open, revealing the grim faces of the prison warden and four armed S.S. guards, Karl was not surprised.

The sparrows watched silently from their nest.

"Prisoner Ibsen," said the warden, "your stay here with us is at an end, I'm afraid."

Karl managed to stand. His clothes hung in tattered rags from his thin frame.

"He will need a bath. *Mein Gott!* This one stinks! Come on, pig! Out of your filth!"

Karl did not look up at the family of sparrows as he tottered from the cell. He did not want to reveal their hiding place to these men. The butt of a rifle would easily crush the nest and the sparrows. Such men would take pleasure in destroying in a moment the miracle that had come to Karl in his cell. He wanted to look over his shoulder. He wanted to whisper goodbye. And thanks. But he did not.

The rifle urged him hard from this nest. The door slammed shut behind Karl and the family of sparrows was safe.

"Where are you taking me?" Karl asked. His voice was strong and untroubled.

"The Führer has arranged a little party for you at the border," sneered an S.S. guard.

"Silence," ordered the warden, then, "For now, Prisoner Ibsen, a shower. Clean clothes. A meal perhaps?"

Karl did not need further explanation. Was this not the kindness offered a condemned man? Maybe this was the day when Karl Ibsen would finally be nudged from the nest. No longer bound by earth, he hoped that soon, like the young sparrows, he would fly.

———

From high atop the fifteen-story platform of Warsaw's Prudential building, Orde broadcast the scene of imminent war by shortwave to Belgium and then to London. In the morning sunlight, anti-aircraft batteries were clearly visible. Like the nests of storks, machine guns perched among the red brick chimneys of buildings overlooking the main highways.

A cloud of dust rose up like smoke from a convoy of antiquated military vehicles. Private automobiles, commandeered in the last week by the Polish Army, were blanketed with soldiers on hoods and roofs and trunks and running boards.

From the high perspective, it looked more like an army in retreat than an army moving forward to face the massive German Wehrmacht.

As the military traffic rolled out from Warsaw in creeping black columns, thousands of people struggled against the tide as they oozed into Warsaw from the threatened battlefields of western Poland. On the other side of the city, thousands more were leaving Warsaw on highways headed east.

Every road and rutted lane was crammed with human flotsam drifting from the shipwreck of failed politics. There seemed to be no beginning of the mass, and no end.

Orde spotted the massive traffic jams at the Warsaw aerodrome and at various rail terminals throughout the city. Even as he spoke, he scanned the horizon for the way he would take out of Warsaw in order to lead his little group to safety. His broadcast was an unspoken plea that somehow the passports be sent. He was certain that Murphy was listening in London.

33

The Pain of Not Being Good Enough

Lori knew what the Warsaw broadcast meant before Murphy explained it to her. Stalin and Hitler had signed a mutual nonaggression pact. Hitler had annexed Danzig.

Poland had not yet officially declared war, but it was coming. Why should anyone try to raise her hopes? There was going to be a war, and Jacob was still in Warsaw with Alfie!

In England, a general mobilization had been announced. Soldiers home on leave had been called back to ships and army bases. Tonight London was to be in complete blackout in anticipation of German bombing.

All of this was reality, yet still the precious passports of Alfie and Jacob had not been sent to them in Warsaw! *Why?*

Three passports were laid out on the bed of their Savoy Hotel room—one for Jacob, one for Alfie, one for the Jewish girl named Rachel.

Lori held them in trembling hands. "I will go to Warsaw myself if you are afraid," she challenged Murphy angrily.

"Fear has nothing to do with it." Elisa tried to calm her. "In the first place, it is practically impossible to get a flight to Warsaw."

"Can you honestly think it will be easier when the war begins?" Lori asked. "Or are you hoping this will all go away? *Look!* Three of them—three passports to get them out! And here we are waiting for dozens more that might not come until the whole of Warsaw is up in smoke! And these three will go up in smoke with it when we might have saved them!"

"We were hoping more would come, Lori," Murphy said gently. "There are passports in process. One for Lucy Strasburg, others for kids your age, and younger, trapped in Warsaw. There will not be a second chance to get them out. When I take the passports to them, there may not be another opportunity to go back with the documents that arrive a day or two later in the mail!"

"In a day or two, maybe it will be too late for these. Then what about Jacob? What about Alfie?" She was pleading. "Go now," she begged. "I know there is no time left!" She pulled back the curtains and looked down at the sandbagged buildings all along the Strand. Shop windows were boarded up. Helmeted members of the Home Guard talked together on the street corner outside the theater. Taxi drivers at the curbs covered their headlamps with black cloth.

"What more proof do you need? The government has announced that every English citizen should come out of Poland," Lori cried distractedly. "Look at these!" She held up the passports. "These make Jacob a British subject! And the same for Alfie. But if England goes to war with Germany, then *they* and their passports are no longer neutral, are they? Then the Nazis can march right in and arrest them for being British, just the same as they arrest someone for being a Jew or a German Christian like my father!"

She ran her hands through her hair and paced back and forth in front of the window. "Tomorrow, Elisa, you are playing a concert to remember my father in a Nazi prison. And Churchill is speaking. The bells will ring, and everyone will remember what could have been done to stop Hitler! Please . . . I don't want to sit there and have to remember that there was a chance to get Jacob out of Poland! I don't want to think about him running through Warsaw streets while *German bombers—*"

Suddenly she grew silent and sank down beside Elisa on the bed. Elisa wrapped her arms around Lori as she finished her tirade with tears of frustration.

Murphy leaned against the mantel of the fireplace and rubbed his hands nervously across his lips. The girl had a point. She had several points. He could not argue with even one of them.

———

The twelve men in the back of the transport truck from Nameless camp had no idea where they were being taken. The truck's canvas flap was tied shut securely, and the prisoners were told that even to loosen the fabric to get some air in the stifling interior meant severe punishment for all the occupants.

The one positive result of this demand for a cloak of concealment was the opportunity it provided for the men to talk. They shared names, stories, and the crimes against the state that had brought them to this place. The discussion soon turned to speculation about the mysterious exercise. Some claimed that they were going to be exchanged for German spies who had been captured by the Poles. Others said flatly that they were going to be executed. Neither argument made much sense; either release or execution could have been accomplished without all the secrecy.

Soon the atmosphere was so suffocatingly hot that even the will to speculate about their destination or fate required too great an effort. At last all discussion ground to a halt, while the truck continued to grind onward.

In a final effort at conversation, one of the prisoners asked, "Does anyone know what the date is?"

Karl consulted his memory of the scratches on his cell wall. "Near the end of August," he said. "I think it is the thirty-first."

Orde's Zionist Youth brigade was out in force—but, then, so was all of Jewish Warsaw. Orde stood on the brick wall in the center of the square dispatching orders to the various corners with Peter Wallich's troops as messengers.

"Take Jacob and Elisha and three others and deliver this load of lumber," Orde directed Peter. "You and your men stay and aid the residents in boarding up their ground-floor windows."

"At once, Hayedid," agreed Peter, and he gave a snappy salute.

Three men and a woman appeared in the square behind Orde and arranged a group of chairs and music stands. "Is this where you want us?" one called out.

"Quite right," returned Orde. "Please remember to keep it light and cheerful." A few moments later the sounds of a string quartet mingled with the hammering and sawing noises of Muranow Square.

Orde watched a group of men filling pillowcases with earth from the flower beds. A fine layer of dust settled on their black hats and in their beards. It coated their faces with a pallor that reminded Orde of corpses. But the eyes of these men were lively, interested, and pleased to be doing something in defense of their homes.

The Hayedid stepped down off the wall and approached an aged rabbi whose frame was nearly bent in two by the weight of his years even before he started filling sandbags. "Rabbi," said Orde respectfully, "it is not necessary for you to do this labor. There are plenty of younger men."

"So," replied the rabbi, "where is it written that a man becomes too old to work with his hands?"

"Ah, but, Rabbi," countered Orde, "I have other important duties for you. Soil we have in adequate supply and laborers also, but we will soon experience a shortage of pillowcases. Will you please take personal charge of collecting more?"

The string quartet soared into a breezy composition, a waltz-tempo piece that Orde could not name. He went over to the Community Center, where the women of Muranow Square were preparing to feed the workers. From the doorway the delicious smell of freshly baked bread mingled with the aroma of potato soup.

Orde spotted Lucy standing with Rachel Lubetkin, stacking bowls next to the cauldrons of soup. He thought how fine Lucy looked, even dressed in a plain blue skirt and white blouse, with her hair pulled back under a scarf. She felt his approving glance and looked up, then smiled shyly and looked away again.

A voice at Orde's elbow caused him to turn. "Excuse me, Hayedid," said a young man named Avriel. The scholarly-looking youth wore round spectacles and had prematurely thinning hair. "You are wanted at the barricade."

At the main street leading out of Muranow Square, Orde found a Polish army staff car. Its exhaust was churning out a foul cloud of bluish smoke, but at Orde's appearance, the engine was shut off and a pear-shaped man in the uniform of a brigadier general appeared.

"Captain Orde," said the officer, "I am General Wojoski."

"I am not military," corrected Orde. "I am a correspondent with TENS news service, and today I am here helping my friends."

The general waved off Orde's protest. "We know who you are really, Captain Orde, and it is about your help that I have come. We could use your expertise in planning the defenses of Warsaw proper. Not," he added hastily, "that they will be necessary. Strictly as a precautionary measure."

Those nearest the barricade stopped shoveling and hammering to listen to Orde's reply, but it came without any hesitation. "I am sorry, General," he returned, "but as you can see, we have more than enough to keep busy with here. However," added Orde thoughtfully, "I wonder if you could look into something for us? It seems that by an unfortunate oversight there have been no gas masks distributed in this quarter."

The general swelled up slightly as if about to respond to the thinly veiled accusation, then abruptly changed his mind. "I'll see what I can find out," he said gruffly, and returned to his car.

"Bravo, Captain," said Avriel. From the center of the square, the string quartet continued to play.

———

Only three passports out of dozens. Murphy paced the length of the bedroom and back again. He looked out the French doors to the balcony. Block by block, London was evacuating school children. Lori was right: tomorrow might be too late.

Elisa spread the precious passports out on the bed. One each for Jacob, Alfie, and Rachel Lubetkin.

"Orde will not leave Poland unless they leave with him." Murphy shrugged. "But that includes Lucy Strasburg, obviously. He's a good man." Murphy sat beside her and took her hands in his hands. "I was hoping we could . . . that there would be more passports to smuggle in."

Elisa's face reflected the disappointment. There had just not been enough time. "So close," she managed. "Oh, Murphy." She looked at the three new folders. "But *these*! You'll have to take them to Warsaw. To wait even one more day will mean that they are lost as well. And Sam Orde lost with them."

"It should not be this hard. Just a few more days. I was hoping—"

Elisa opened her violin case, took the blue silk scarf from the Guarnerius, and removed the violin from its velvet nest. With practiced fingers she found the hidden panel and lifted it. Then, as she had done a dozen times before, she placed the precious passports into their hiding place and sealed it securely once again. Then, she replaced Rudy's violin. "There are still jewels behind the tuning peg that may be useful," she said.

Murphy telephoned three airlines. KLM was the only one still with service to Warsaw. "You'll touch down in Vilnyus, Lithuania, tonight," explained the agent. "We Dutch are neutral, so, if it is possible to fly through German and Polish air space—" He laughed nervously. "Well, then, we will get you to Warsaw." There was a long pause. "I assume you are leaving Warsaw again shortly?"

"Yes. The next flight. And I will be traveling with companions."

"I will have to wire ahead, sir. We cannot guarantee any seats on flights leaving Warsaw unless we wire ahead. If you will stop at the ticket counter before you depart, I should have an answer for you."

The agent asked a few mundane questions about the weight of each of the passengers. Murphy guessed at the weight of Rachel from Elisa's weight. For Orde, Jacob, and Alfie, he placed their weight within a pound or two of his own.

The agent gave Murphy a stern warning about the luggage allowance. One case per passenger. Murphy signaled Elisa to stop packing. The violin case was all he would be taking on this trip. He rolled up clean socks and underwear and stuffed them into his pockets. He took his overcoat out of the closet and folded one clean shirt into a minute square, which he likewise stuffed into the deep pocket.

Then he took Elisa's face in his hands. "I hope this is right. There won't be a second chance to get in. Not if the war breaks."

Elisa nodded. She laid her head against Murphy's chest for a moment. Could he feel how frightened she was to have him leave today? She did not speak of fear. She did not ask him to wait until more passports arrived, until this whole terrible thing blew over. She knew, as he did, that there was no more time.

"I'll get Lori," Elisa said softly. Then she opened the door to the adjoining room. Lori sat beside the open window overlooking the city and the hulk of St. Paul's.

"Tonight they are turning off the lights," Lori said bleakly. "They finally believe us, don't they, Elisa?" The voice was so small and sad that Elisa almost forgot that Lori was not the tiny girl she had played dolls with in the backyard of the old Wilhelmstrasse mansion.

"Murphy is going to Warsaw," Elisa answered—a practical answer that shouted all was not yet lost!

Silence. Lori stood up. *"When?"*

"Today."

"Oh, Elisa!" she cried, running to embrace her.

"He is leaving in an hour. Tonight he lands in Warsaw. If God is willing, Murphy will take them the passports and bring your Jacob back with him on the next plane."

"Oh, Elisa!" Lori broke into tears. "I am so afraid. So very afraid! My father is still . . . even if Jacob is free and with me, my mother will be alone. With the war there will be no more hope for Father. No more . . . all of them. So many. Has God forgotten them, Elisa? And all the children? All the birth certificates we collected. Useless." Silence. "It is so dark, isn't it, Elisa?" She was not speaking of the fact that the lights would be blacked out throughout London.

"It is dark. But God can see, even in the darkness." As she said it, Elisa regretted the trite, simplistic sound of the words. But the words were true. God had eyes that could pierce the blackest night and illuminate the darkest heart.

The gentle drumming of rain sounded on the awning over the window ledge. "Yes," Lori said, reaching out to touch the drops. "He is crying, too."

Murphy stood in the doorway behind them. "I'm leaving now. I called down for a taxi. Stay here with Lori and the babies." Then, to Lori, "Don't worry, Missus Kalner. We'll do our best."

––––––––––

Gustav Ahlman was standing outside the schoolhouse when the truck arrived from Nameless camp. He stood by with an air of importance as the flap was untied and the parched prisoners tumbled out, blinking in the afternoon sunlight.

"Bring them some water," he ordered. A bucket and a dipper made the rounds of the twelve men. It had to be refilled four times before all were satisfied.

In a stupor induced by the long airless ride, and now waterlogged as well, the men stumbled into the schoolroom as indicated by Ahlman. In a heap on the floor was a pile of jackets, trousers and boots. "First, new clothing," announced Ahlman cheerfully, "then supper."

"What are these jackets?" asked one man as he hunted for a size that would fit him.

"They look like army uniforms—Polish, I think," offered another as he searched for a matching pair of boots.

"No talking," said Ahlman. "Anyone who breaks this rule will not be fed."

The men got dressed in silence.

———

Wolfgang von Fritschauer arrived at the schoolhouse headquarters in a staff car with Agent Hess. "When can you tell me what this mission involves?" he asked.

"I see no reason not to inform you right now," offered Hess. "You are about to meet those who will also be part of this operation, so it is time for you to understand the plan.

"You are aware," he continued, "that the Führer has promised Russia and Italy that we will take no military action against Poland unless the Poles act as aggressors first."

Wolf waved his hand to indicate that he was as aware of international politics as Hess.

"This operation is designed to furnish that instance of aggression." Hess continued. "You will be involved in a mock attack on the radio transmitter located in Gleiwitz. We will seize the station, broadcast a message of contempt for the forces of the Reich, and retire, having given the Führer ample reason to retaliate."

"Simplicity itself," nodded Wolf. "I am grateful for the chance to prove myself again to Reichsführer Himmler. Was it he who suggested my participation?"

"Actually, I asked for you personally," said Hess, "with Herr Himmler's wholehearted agreement."

———

"These men are not soldiers," protested Wolf to Hess after they had entered the schoolhouse. "They are not Gestapo, either. What is going on here, Hess?"

Hess pulled Wolf into an adjoining room. On a schoolteacher's wooden revolving chair lay the uniform of a Polish officer. "Get dressed, and I will explain," said Hess, gesturing toward the clothing. "It is necessary to furnish some bodies as proof of the validity of the attack. All these men were political prisoners. They have been promised a reduction in their sentences for their participation. After we are through here, no one will question what has happened to them."

"Ingenious," complimented Wolf. "But how can we prevent them from escaping before it is time for them to become casualties?"

"That is your first duty to this mission," said Hess. "As you can see, you are dressed the same as they, so they will trust you. They will be told that they are to receive a standard military inoculation. They will not protest the administration of the narcotic because they will see you receive an injection of a harmless saline solution first."

"Now everything is clear to me," agreed Wolf. "You will find that I am eager to cooperate."

―――――

It was very late. Warsaw was entirely dark because of the blackout. Jacob was asleep beside Alfie. Werner-kitten was also asleep, curled up in a warm ball on Alfie's pillow. His soft kitten breath fanned Alfie's cheek. The night seemed very peaceful. All the darkness of a big city without lights also seemed peaceful, but Alfie knew that it was not. Not really.

Captain Orde was awake, his chair pulled up beside the window. The curtains were open wide because all the lamps were off. This was so a Nazi airplane would not see the light in their hotel room and drop a bomb on the Bristol.

There was just enough starlight that Alfie could see the serious look on the captain's face. His eyes were lost in the shadow of his frown. He tapped a pencil on the arm of the chair. The tapping was like the sound of a drum. One little drum for the one-man army who had pledged to protect and defend Lucy.

Lucy was in bed in the other room. Alfie did not know if she was asleep or awake like the captain. Alfie smiled quietly. It would be funny if he asked if anyone was awake and everyone answered *yes* at the same time.

Alfie considered asking. He decided against it because he was sure that the British Army was thinking very serious thoughts about the one-woman nation he pledged to protect.

All evening long, Orde had looked at Lucy when she was not looking. Then, when she raised her eyes toward him, the captain would look away quickly. And then it would be Lucy's turn to look at the captain—until he looked up. It had gone on like this, both of them trying not to look at the other when the other was looking.

Once when their eyes had accidentally bumped, Lucy had gotten red and Orde had looked very embarrassed.

Alfie had noticed this, and it reminded him a lot of the way Jacob had looked at Lori and then had tried *not* to look at Lori. It seemed to be very painful. Alfie wondered why Orde did not just hold Lucy's pretty face in his hands and look and look and look. Like having all the ice cream a person could eat, only free.

Captain Orde sighed loudly. A lonely sigh. Alfie had heard their captain make that sort of sound before. "Why don't you help him, Jesus?" Alfie prayed. He had not meant to say the words aloud, but sometimes thoughts came out on their own.

"Hmmm?" asked Orde. "Did you say something, Elisha?"

"Not to you," Alfie answered truthfully. "Just *about* you."

"What about me?" The captain talked to Alfie as though he really mattered. Alfie liked that.

"Jesus should help . . . you."

Silence. "Yes. I hope He will."

Silence. "Her eyes are sad," Alfie said.

His comment startled the captain. "Her . . . what are you saying?"

How could Alfie tell the captain what he had seen in Lucy Strasburg's eyes? Alfie had not been afraid to look at her. Not at all. He had looked at her face all evening long when the captain was trying not to. In her eyes, Alfie had seen so many friends who had all gone away to the Promised Land . . . dead. All dead on the night that the Hitler-men had burned Berlin. When he looked at Lucy, he could easily remember the way his friend Werner had looked when other children walked by and he could not walk. Alfie remembered Dieter, who could not feed himself. Heinz, who could not move his legs or arms without shaking. And there were others.

They had all worn their hearts in their eyes. The terrible ache was the same. It was not pain that came from being crippled; it was pain that came from not being loved. Not believing that anyone would ever love them because they were not straight and tall or strong or smart. When the Nazi orderlies were cruel to them, they thought somehow it was their fault. Sometimes Alfie had felt that way, too. Yes, sometimes Alfie had the ache of his heart in his eyes, too. Because Alfie was not smart. But then Alfie remembered that he did not have to be smart to be loved. He knew that Jesus loved him and that made the hurt of being *not good enough* go away.

Lucy was broken inside, just like Alfie's friends had been broken on the outside. It kept her from playing, it kept her from speaking, and in a way, it made her helpless even to feed her own soul.

What Lucy needed was somebody to love her, like Alfie had loved his friends at the Sisters of Mercy Hospital before the Hitler-men killed them.

But who would carry Lucy until she was strong enough inside? And how would she get strong unless someone loved her enough to feed her soul? If there was nobody to do that for her, then Lucy with the sad heart would die inside. The darkness would steal her too, just as surely as it had stolen the lives of the boys in the ward.

How could Alfie tell all of this to a man so smart as Captain Samuel Orde? "How can I, Jesus?" he asked out loud again.

Orde turned away from the window as though he wanted to hear Alfie's heart tell him all about Lucy and himself, too.

"What do you see, Elisha?" Orde whispered. "What is it?"

Alfie reached up and touched Werner-kitten on his pillow. The soft rumble of a purr erupted like a laugh, and then Alfie knew how he could say it.

"My kitten was almost . . . *dead*. His mother Joseph did not want him. But I took care of him. Just like Werner . . ." He tried not to confuse Werner the kitten with Werner the boy, even though the stories were a lot alike. "I took care of him because he needed more than the other kittens, or his heart would have died." Alfie smiled as Werner purred louder. "And now . . . you hear him? He loves me a lot, too." Werner got up and moved against Alfie's head. "Lucy is like Werner was. You should take her face and hold it."

At that, the captain laughed a small, nervous laugh. "I . . . don't know her, Elisha. Not at all. How can I?"

"Just look at her eyes. She don't have to tell you anything. Her heart . . . just barely hanging on. Somebody's got to love her back to life."

"What have I got to give her?" Orde asked in a truly puzzled way, the sort of voice that *wanted* to do something right, but did not know how.

"Oh, Captain." Alfie thought maybe he had forgotten. "You know . . . Jesus. He made lame people walk and blind people see. He loved them before they were well . . . loves me, even if I'm . . . not smart. You tell Lucy. You can say it . . . in a smart way. Huh?"

Captain Orde sat a long time in the dark. He did not move. He just looked into the dark place where Alfie's voice had come from. And then he got up and came to the side of the bed. He reached out and touched Alfie's forehead. He smoothed Alfie's hair back like Mama used to do. And then he kissed Alfie on the forehead and went back to sit in his chair beside the window.

And now the night was peaceful. Alfie went to sleep.

34

The Ant and the Cricket

"What will happen to us now, Papa?" Rachel sat at the feet of her father in the dark study. The baby was asleep on Etta's lap, and David and Samuel rested on pillows nearest the open window.

Somehow, tonight, on what was possibly the last night of peace, they all wanted to stay together in this room. The walls were filled with Papa's books—wisdom from floor to ceiling. The books were old friends, like relatives, in a way, to the family of Rabbi Aaron Lubetkin. Who could say what would become of those leather-bound friends if the war began tonight and the Nazis came tomorrow?

Papa was silent in his big leather chair. He turned his face toward the sound of crickets chirping in the garden.

Why did he not answer?

"I am afraid, Papa," David said from his pillow.

Then little Samuel began to cry softly.

"Listen!" Papa said with a smile in his voice. "I will tell you a story. Listen now, Samuel. David. Rachel. A story you must remember. It is a story about an arrogant cricket and an ant."

He cleared his throat, still rusty from his months of illness. But his voice was very strong as he began.

"Once there was an ant who was carrying a very large bread crumb home to his family. He was very proud of himself because the crumb was ten times bigger than he was. All of a sudden he heard the loud whining voice of a cricket high above him. 'Tsk-tsk! You are a tiny fellow to be carrying such a load. Let me help you.' "

Here he paused to let them imagine the voice of the cricket.

" 'Thank you,' said the ant in a squeaky voice. 'You are very kind.' At that, the cricket picked up the bread crumb and gulped it down in one enormous bite. A very cruel and unfriendly act, don't you think, David?"

At this David replied indignantly that it was, indeed.

"The ant thought so too, and told the cricket just that! The cricket said, 'Hold your tongue and feelers. I see you are a strong ant! I have work that you must do, or I will eat you, too!' "

By now Rachel noticed that little Samuel was no longer crying. He sat up and glared at the imaginary cricket as Papa continued.

"At that, the cricket stated he wanted to travel, and the ant must drag along the cricket's things, which were wrapped in a birch-leaf case. The bundle was even larger than the bread crumb. The ant obeyed as the cricket hopped a big hop, then lay down to snooze and wait for the ant to drag the case after him. The poor ant got no rest and was very worried about his family."

The evening air seemed cool and pleasant now as Papa spoke about the ant and the cricket. The terrible chirping of the German Führer did not seem so threatening.

"One day the cricket came to a puddle," Papa continued. "The ant said, 'I'll wager a year of my servitude that you cannot jump across that puddle!' The cricket stretched his leapers and hopped across in one hop. 'I did not think you could do it,' cried the ant.

"The cricket mocked him when the ant caught up at last. 'Now you owe me a year of servitude!' "

"This is not such a good story," David said grimly.

"But wait!" Papa said knowingly. "The ant was a smart little fellow. Day after day as he dragged the bundle along he challenged the cricket to jump over this and that. A path. A wall. A stream. And each time the ant doubled the wager. Every time the cricket leaped easily over the obstacle and won the bet."

"Why is this good?" David asked Papa again.

The rabbi waved his hand in the dark. He was getting to the point. " 'You will notice,' said the ant, 'that I am betting double or nothing every time. I am sure there is nothing you cannot do, Herr Cricket!' The day after that, the cricket and the ant came to the sea. 'I will wager you 16,384 years of service that you cannot jump across the sea.' "

David listened with renewed respect for the ant. The crickets in the garden chirped on brashly as Papa finished his tale.

"The cricket stood up. He stretched his leapers. He had a wild look in his eyes and he cried, 'There is nothing I cannot do!' With that, he bent his leapers double. Beads of sweat formed on his forehead. Then he gave a mighty jump into the sea, where he drowned. The ant smiled. He picked up the cricket's belongings and started for home."

Samuel laughed a high, happy laugh. Satisfied, David sat against the wall. Rachel smiled at the bookshelves and wondered if their printed pages were jealous of her papa.

"When you wonder what will happen to us, you must never forget. We are the ants. One day Herr Hitler will leap once too often. Perhaps he will leap into Poland and be surprised, nu?"

"It is a nice night, Papa," Samuel said. "Tell us another story."

———

Lori was not asleep when the telephone rang. The insistent bell was a jarring interruption to thoughts and prayers. Lori could hear Murphy's cheerful voice on the telephone as she joined Elisa.

"We're refueling. KLM has seats for all of us leaving Warsaw tonight at 11:30," he babbled happily. "I've been trying to reach Orde in Warsaw. No luck. Nothing getting through."

"What should we do?"

"Orde is going to have to meet me at Warsaw airport. The plane turns right around and leaves fifty minutes after I get off. There's no time for me to chase them down in Warsaw." He sounded mildly distracted. "Maybe a direct wire from London TENS to Orde at Warsaw TENS. I talked to Harvey Terrill and told him I was off to Warsaw, but now I can't reach him. Hope the phone isn't out."

"I'll take care of it," she promised. Certainly tickets on a plane leaving what was soon to be a battle zone was a small miracle!

After quick goodbyes, Elisa dialed the number of London TENS. No answer. Where was Harvey Terrill?

"What is it?" Lori sat on the bed beside her.

"Murphy got the tickets out of Warsaw, but Orde has to have everyone ready to leave at the airport when Murphy gets there." The TENS phone continued to ring. "Murphy can't reach Orde. The telephones in Poland are not taking long distance." She let the telephone clatter into the cradle. "I'll have to go to the office. Send the wire on our equipment."

Lori looked out at the blackout. "Now?"

"It's two blocks." She waved her hand as if to say how safe she would be.

"Take the Secret Service agent then," Lori warned.

Elisa frowned and bit her thumb. How could she take this government man into the TENS office and send a wire to Orde telling that Murphy was bringing passports and then naming the recipients of the prized illegal documents? She half suspected that the agents had been put in place less to protect them than to keep an eye on everything they did. This would ruin everything!

Elisa explained briefly to Lori and then they considered how she could get around them.

"Lori," she instructed. "Open your door. Talk to them about . . .

anything. The blackout. Tell them you are frightened. Keep them talking for a few minutes, and I'll slip out my door, down the stairs, and to the office. I'll be back before they even notice I've been gone."

Lori really was frightened. She clasped Elisa's hands. "Are you sure you should go?" Lori had seen what a bomb could do. She knew how really terrible things could get. "Isn't there some other way?"

Elisa rang up the TENS number once again. Still no answer. *Where was Harvey?* Twenty rings and no reply. "I can send the wire," Elisa said lightly.

Lori agreed reluctantly. At that instant, baby Katie wailed a hungry protest.

The two women exchanged glances. This was one thing Lori could not attend to.

"I can go," Lori said with a grin. "I can run faster than you, anyway."

Katie woke baby Alfie. His lusty cry filled the room as Elisa printed out a message for Harvey Terrill to transmit to Warsaw.

"Harvey can't have gone far," Elisa said. "Not on a night like tonight. Wait for him at the office. Tell him I tried to reach him by telephone, and that this message needs to be sent to Orde immediately in Warsaw."

Lori opened the paper. ORDE: MURPHY DUE TO ARRIVE 4:30 P.M. WARSAW AIRFIELD TOMORROW. BE THERE WITH . . ." The names followed as though there were nothing unusual about such a message at all. Would Harvey be curious about the required immigration papers for Alfie and Jacob?

"If he asks, tell him you think it's all straightened out," Elisa answered. "He's just nosey. Don't let him intimidate you." Elisa always got along with Harvey Terrill. Lori preferred to give the sullen man a wide berth.

What else was there to do? The airline would sell the tickets to someone else if Jacob and the rest were not there to claim them! That thought was more terrifying than the blackout!

It was simple for Lori to slip out of her room and down the hall; she trembled at the thought that it might also be simple for someone to enter the Savoy Hotel and make his way up to the suite. Elisa talked to the kind and patronizing agents who assured her that everything was quite under control.

At the far end of the hall, Lori sneaked into the stairwell and disappeared. *Round little Hildy Frutschy at the bottom of the stairs at the Red Lion House had made a far better watchdog than these two fellows,* Lori thought. They droned on about the closeness of air-raid shelters and the vigilance of the anti-aircraft crews who even now watched the skies above England.

Lori did not have any sense of danger from German planes tonight.

She remembered too clearly that the explosion which had taken Doc's life did not come from a Nazi bomber.

———

Lori made her way quickly through the blue-lit lobby of the Savoy Hotel. A strange, confused atmosphere pervaded London. Among some small cliques of citizens, the voices were low and serious as the reality of the crisis was discussed. Among others, the laughter and the conversation were especially loud and bright. *Those Londoners are whistling in the dark,* Lori thought, pushing her way through the revolving doors into the still night air.

Thin slits of light from covered headlights were all that was visible of the automobiles that crept up the street. There had already been a number of traffic accidents, Lori had heard.

Passing groups of people along the way, she listened to snatches of conversation. *"Parachutists . . . that's most likely what the Nazis will do. They'll send in parachutists first and saboteurs to blow the bridges, and . . ."*

"They've set up thousands more beds at the hospitals. They're digging an underground passage from the railway to the hospital."

"What good are sandbags gonna do, I ask you, if a bomb falls on your house?"

Word had just come over the BBC that a million and a half children were being evacuated from London.

Lori was relieved that the younger children were already safely tucked into bed in a farmhouse in western England. After everything that had gone before, what would scenes of mass evacuation have done to the emotions of the boys?

Lori tried to read her wristwatch by the starlight. Surely Murphy's plane would have taken off again by now. She looked skyward and prayed for him as she rounded the corner and half jogged down the alley to the side entrance of the TENS building. She prayed for Jacob! She prayed that she would be able to reach Sam Orde in Warsaw, to warn him to be at the airport with Jacob and Alfie in plenty of time!

The glass of the transom window was covered with black paper. Lori could hear muffled voices within. She heaved a sigh of relief! *So Harvey Terrill was there! Probably overwhelmed with business,* she reasoned as she slipped Elisa's key into the lock. *Maybe in a meeting or on the phone?* It would be best to simply send the message to Warsaw and slip out without interrupting him. The harried night editor was seldom pleasant these days. She did not want to get underfoot on a night like tonight.

Conscious that she must not let interior light spill out, she squeezed quickly through the door into the coffee room of the TENS office. Terrill's voice in the adjoining office was tense, almost angry. Lori stood for a moment, not wanting to interrupt what was obviously an important conference.

"He's gone to Warsaw, I tell you. Out of the way."

Lori had a sense of indignation at Terrill's obvious pleasure over Murphy's absence! She stiffened and stood silently in the anteroom as her eyes adjusted to the scene through the door in front of her.

The newly installed blackout curtains were pulled tightly across the windows. A single bank of lights was burning, creating a pool of dim illumination in the center of the room while leaving the corners in shadow.

Underneath the light and bent over the conference table were the figures of Harvey Terrill to one side, and a small, thin man with his back to Lori. Some sort of blueprint was unrolled on the tabletop and weighted in place at the corners with two dictionaries and two telephone books.

The night editor jabbed his finger toward the plans. "You can drop the dome with just eight charges?"

What was he saying? Lori backed up a step deeper into the shadow. *Drop what dome? What was he talking about?* Her heart hung in her throat and a feeling of cold fear welled up in her.

The man across from Harvey answered in a youthful, excited rush. "See now, this is the way it works. Not the whole dome. We don't need the whole dome, you see? The lantern tower is plenty." He sounded pleased, like a little boy showing off some grand scheme. "The lantern tower is eighty-five feet tall. Seven hundred tons."

Lantern tower? The tower of St. Paul's? She tried to silence her breathing, which suddenly seemed unnaturally loud.

Harvey peered at the plans. "You've put the charges in the light wells?"

"Right. You see here." The small man slid his finger in a tight circle. "Wells through the roof to catch the light at the top of the Golden Gallery. The lantern tower rests right there on the top of the inner cone. Nothing but brick supporting seven hundred tons! When we blow that, the lantern will drop through the dome three hundred feet to the pavement of the church! It won't stop there. It will carry the floor of the rotunda and everyone right down with it into the crypt."

There was a heart-stopping silence as Harvey Terrill digested everything that was before him. Lori felt the ground sway beneath her in one terrible moment of realization. This was what Doc Grogan had been trying to tell them!

Paul Golden. Light wells.

Not a name! It was a place! St. Paul's! The Golden Gallery! The light wells at the base of the lantern tower were set with explosives!

The young man paused in blissful contemplation as Harvey Terrill smiled grimly with understanding. "Your mother would be proud of you, boy," he said softly in appreciation. "Blowing up the parish church of the British Empire."

A pleased chuckle sounded. "If we time this right, old Nelson and all the moldering British corpses will have a host of new neighbors joining them. Including Winston Churchill."

"You're sure these little satchels will do the job?"

"The eight 'little satchels,' as you call them, are sitting right on the brick. They'll all go at once when I send the radio signal. I'll be in the bell tower at the front of the west facade with the transmitter. When Churchill climbs the pulpit and begins to speak, you walk out of the building. That will be all the signal I need to press the button. And—"

Enough! Lori stood with her back pressed hard against the counter. She inched her way back toward the door. *Paul ... Golden ... light wells ... Churchill ... Papa!*

All of this had been planned for the special service at St. Paul's for her father and the other pastors. But *why?* Why had Harvey Terrill done this?

Her hand dripped with perspiration as she groped for the doorknob. The slippery metal resisted her grasp. She whirled like an animal trapped in a corner, and Elisa's message fluttered away. Her elbow caught a coffee cup and sent it crashing to the floor!

A cry of alarm pursued her as she threw the door back. In only an instant she would have been free, but the strong grasp of angry hands slammed against her, pulling her back from those few steps into the alley!

A vise-like ring of arms clamped around her, wrestling her through the open door, then slammed her down hard against the counter and onto the floor.

Lori tried to cry out, but a hand pressed down over her mouth.

Terrill swore angrily. "It's Lori Ibsen!" He grabbed her hair and held her head close to his scowling face. "Little snoop. How much did you hear?" His eyes were blazing even in the dim light.

The other man sat squarely on her. "However much she heard, it's too much, Harvey. She knows too much."

Karl Ibsen was the last to receive the injection. By then there were vacant stares on some of the faces of the men who had preceded him, and he knew what was being done. In a few moments several of the others were completely unconscious and passed out on the floor, including the man dressed as a Polish officer who had not come with the prisoners from Nameless camp.

Karl looked knowingly into the eyes of the doctor as he received his shot. "We were told that we might win our freedom today," he said.

The doctor looked away uncomfortably. "I am sorry for the prison that you are in," Karl said.

"*I* am not a prisoner," remarked the doctor in a startled tone.

———

"There is no answer at that number," said the Savoy Hotel operator impatiently.

"Please," Elisa argued. "Let it ring. I know someone is there."

"I am sorry, Mrs. Murphy. We cannot keep the lines tied up. If you would like to ring the number later—"

Elisa had already telephoned the TENS office six times in the last hour. Why did Harvey not pick up the receiver? Where was Lori?

Elisa paced the room nervously. She stopped to lean against the rail of the crib where Katie and Alfie lay peacefully sleeping at opposite ends. Her head throbbed. She regretted that she had let Lori go alone on a night like this. Murphy had warned her to be careful of going out during the blackout. People would be running down pedestrians like chickens crossing a highway, he said. Headlamps were all but blacked out. Streetlights were out entirely. Pickpockets were no doubt out in droves!

Lori had only two blocks to walk to the office. Where had she gone? Why did she not telephone Elisa at the hotel? Had she been hit by a car? Or thumped over the head by some back-street Artful Dodger taking advantage of the new blackout regulations? Elisa felt as though *she* had been hit on the head. Her temples throbbed. She opened the French doors and stepped out onto the balcony. The noise of traffic emanated up from the dark canyons of the streets stretching out from the Savoy. Far across the city, Elisa could hear the howl of a siren. She could easily spot the black mountain of St. Paul's Cathedral silhouetted against the starlit sky.

———

It was dark, and so Allan Farrell did not bother to conceal the pistol. His right arm held Lori's shoulders as they walked from Fleet Street to Ludgate Hill, directly toward the dark hulk of St. Paul's. He held the barrel of the weapon in her left side. "I will blow your heart out," he explained softly, "if you make one wrong move. You understand?"

She answered with a nod. She could not speak.

Impatient with her, he jabbed her harder with the pistol. "Don't think I won't do it," he whispered in her ear as they passed the dark forms of a group of people standing on the corner of New Bridge Street and Ludgate.

"It's saboteurs they're worried about, luv. They've put extra men patrolling every bridge across the Thames...."

Lori heard the soft, knowing chuckle of her captor as the nervous conversation of men and women mingled with laughter and jokes. No faces. Just shadows with voices.

The shadow that held her whispered, "No one would even see you fall if I shot. Just the sound of a gun and there you would be with your guts hanging out all over the sidewalk. I would just walk away."

Lori was trembling all over. Her legs felt as though they would not support her. She believed this man. She was certain he would do what he threatened, and so she stumbled on beside him up the gentle slope toward the cathedral.

Framed against the starry sky were the two bell towers flanking the entrance. The dark mound of the dome loomed from the center.

Lori lifted her eyes to the pinnacle of the lantern tower high atop the dome. She tried to make out the cross that crowned the lightless lantern. Always before it had been easily discernible, but not now. The hour of darkness had enveloped even that one fragment of hope and comfort.

She phrased her question carefully. "Where are we going?"

He did not reply. A harsh squeeze to her shoulder warned her that she must not speak. She knew the answer anyway. He was taking her to St. Paul's, which would soon enough be one vast crypt. Lori had no doubt that he intended her to be entombed there as well.

Should she scream and try to break away? Get it over with? *Oh, God!* Life was so precious that she clung tenaciously even to these few terrifying minutes! Her thoughts flew to Jacob and to Papa! She prayed for courage, and prayed somehow to survive! She fought the urge to beg this man to let her go. If she spoke, if she begged or wept, he would simply shoot her and be done with it!

Why doesn't he shoot? she wondered as they passed the statue of Queen Anne in front of the cathedral. She looked up at the edifice of St. Paul's. Soon it would be tons of rubble. It would collapse in upon itself by the will of this man, and Lori would vanish with it in a roar of light!

Involuntarily she croaked, *"Why?"*

She winced, expecting the utterance to be answered with a rough jerk or a painful jab of the pistol in her ribs. Instead, he stopped and craned his head upward. A quiet, almost inaudible whisper rasped in her ear. "This war is very old." The voice was strangely detached, inhuman, escaping like steam from his throat. "Like the tide, it rises and recedes, but always it is here. Millions drown. Millions more will die before we are finished." He tightened his grip on her flesh. "You are nothing compared to that. We cannot let you live to fight us. You

know too much for us to ignore you. You know enough to stop us."
And then, a shove forward and a calm, patronizing voice, "You see?"

At that, he prodded her on through the gate of the churchyard on
the south side of the structure. There were workmen everywhere, filling
sandbags, stacking them against the outside of the church for protection against bombs. They could not guess that the devastation was
already planted within the structure. They did not see that the fire
waited within the walls to collapse the great cathedral inward and take
them with it into the crypt!

No one looked up as Allan Farrell led his captive through the wide
open doors. No one stopped them as they passed, or challenged their
purpose there. By the pale glow of candles, some prayed silently at the
altar for peace, for salvation, for the tide of darkness to be turned! *But
it was too late!* Too late they were shoring up the walls of their church,
too late the workers climbed their ladders and built frames to protect
the windows!

Eight little satchels had been placed in the light wells. One man
would walk out and raise his hand in signal, and all the prayers, all
the fortifications, all the work would come crashing down on the heads
of the Christians in this place!

The destruction comes from within! Look among you! Lori wanted
to shout as they walked easily past a group of parishioners who had
come to help.

They walked past the baptismal font and then past Lord Nelson's
monument. Along the wall, Lori could see two men carefully removing
the painting of Christ holding His lantern and knocking on the door.

Tor Auf! her heart cried. *Open the gate! Open your eyes!*

Allan nudged her toward the door that led to the honeycomb of
stairs within the walls. "To the top," he whispered. "Climb."

Twice on the spiral stairs they met men coming down. They talked
and laughed over their shoulders. They nodded greetings to Allan and
Lori as if to say they were grateful they had come to help. Allan seemed
undisturbed by the presence of people on his killing grounds. He was
certain of himself. Certain of his purpose.

From the dim glow of a blue lantern, Lori could see the expression
on his face. He gloried in the fact that even in these final hours people
worked to shore up what he, one man, would soon destroy!

Allan was right. She was nothing compared to this, and yet she was
everything because she knew enough to stop it! *But how?*

He forced her to the top of the edifice, to the Golden Gallery at the
base of the lantern tower. No one else was there. Buckets of sand and
water had been carried up by workers as protection against incendiary
bombs, but the platform was deserted. The others had descended to
bring up more little buckets. Over the edge of the parapet, Lori could

see the dark wells in the roof that were meant to catch the sunlight and channel it into the interior of the dome.

Allan twisted her arm and dragged her to the door that led into the forbidden interior of the lantern tower. Deftly, he manipulated the ancient iron lock and pushed the door back on its groaning hinges. Then he forced her up an almost vertical set of steps and into a tiny sealed room in the interior of the tower.

Once there, he gagged her and tied her to a large winch-like machine in the center of the space. She lay in dust that had been undisturbed for years.

"Don't waste your time," he said, touching the gag as a warning that what little noise she might make would go unheard. "You are insulated by seven hundred tons of stone in this tower. No one will hear you."

He stood over her for a moment. The rough corduroy of his trousers brushed her face. "It will not hurt," he said gently, as though talking to a child. "You will not feel anything at all."

Stepping back, he waited a moment more, then descended the steps, closing a massive trapdoor after him.

Lori could not hear the door at the base of the pinnacle as he slipped out. She could not hear anything at all except her own breathing.

"She might have gotten lost," offered the burly Scotland Yard detective, replacing the receiver of the telephone. "No one answering her description has been taken to the area hospitals."

The blackout curtains were drawn tightly in the hotel room. Elisa sat on the edge of a striped chair and stared at the telephone. Something had happened. She was certain of it now. Something had happened to Lori!

The second agent had called only moments before from the TENS office. Harvey Terrill said that he had not seen Lori at the office tonight. He had been out for a few minutes when he found that the telephones were out of order, but other than that short time, he had been right there all evening long.

"I gave her my key to the office," Elisa managed to whisper. "She could have let herself in. Waited for Harvey."

The agent's tone implied a reprimand. "It was nonsense for her to sneak out alone. That is why we are here. Either Tom or I could have accompanied her." He frowned at the bowl of fruit on the table. "Absurd for a young woman to be out alone with the blackout in full effect." He looked at Elisa resentfully. This incident would no doubt reflect on his performance, and it was Elisa Murphy's fault. "What was the nature of her business at such an hour?"

"My husband telephoned. He wanted a message delivered to the news office. The telephones—" She waved a hand helplessly in the air. Tears stung her eyes. *Lori!*

"Probably took a wrong turn," said the agent again doubtfully. "Probably got on the tube and ended up in Kent or someplace."

It was the most hopeful scenario. But why had she not called?

"She is a thoughtful person," Elisa said softly. She bit her lip at the certainty of what she was about to say. "If she could, Lori would call me here. No. Something . . . something has happened to her."

35

Judas Kiss

Tedrick arrived at the Savoy half an hour later with a cadre of agents in tow. Two were sent immediately to the London TENS office, where Harvey Terrill was found hard at work. He had not seen Lori. Except for a small break for a quick meal, Harvey claimed that he had been in the office all night. "The telephone exchange was apparently out of commission," he explained when asked why he had not answered repeated calls.

Elisa's head was throbbing. She ached with exhaustion and worry. Tedrick placed one more call to the little cottage near Evesham where Helen Ibsen and Anna had taken the boys.

If Tedrick had known Lori, he would not have bothered to place the call. Lori had slipped out of the hotel this evening, he explained in an unconcerned-sounding voice. Probably just missing her mother. Probably sick of all the fuss in London. No doubt she would show up on their doorstep soon enough. The train service was drastically curtailed because of all this, and no doubt the impetuous young lady would be arriving later today.

It was nonsense. They all knew it. Still, Tedrick maintained this charade of mild concern until he put down the receiver.

His angry voice penetrated the door to Elisa's room as he took apart the agents for negligence. Tedrick's harsh reprimand pierced her with shame. *How had she been so foolish to let Lori go out alone?* She had never made it to the office. The message had still not been sent to Orde in Warsaw, and Lori had vanished! Lori had gone out for nothing!

Within hours, Murphy would arrive at the Warsaw aerodrome and Orde would not be there to meet him! The realization of that doubled the sense of futility in Elisa.

Alone in her room with the babies, she paced like a caged lion as Tedrick's rage reached a crescendo in the next room. Elisa looked at the telephone and decided that probably Tedrick had it tapped. *But what else was there to do?*

For the last time, Elisa telephoned the London TENS office. In an uncharacteristically friendly voice, Harvey Terrill answered on the second ring.

"Ah, Elisa! Did the lost sheep come home yet?"

The too-cheerful words were like a knife. "No. Now listen," she said in an urgent whisper. "She was coming to tell you to contact Orde in Warsaw. Tell him to have Jacob and Alfie and Rachel Lubetkin ready to go at the Warsaw airport at eleven o'clock tonight."

"That's it? You could have called."

She almost choked. "I tried . . . please, Harvey! It's urgent! Just send the wire."

"Murphy got the passports for them, does he? You think the immigration officers aren't wise to phoney passports?"

Tedrick's fury slowed to a dull roar. The muffled replies of the recalcitrant agents were punctuated by Tedrick's mocking replies.

"Send the message, Harvey. That is all she was coming to tell you."

"You know kids. She got distracted by something . . . or someone, maybe. Some bloke in a uniform."

Elisa closed her eyes in frustration. Harvey Terrill did not seem to comprehend what was happening here. "Harvey, Jacob Kalner is Lori's husband. She did not wander off like a stray on a side street. *Tell me you'll wire the message to Warsaw!*"

Harvey sounded slightly wounded. "Sure. Right away."

Elisa placed the telephone easily back into the cradle as Tedrick's voice rose one last time. *"You're through! Finished! Done! Back to pounding a beat in Soho!"*

Moments later he emerged, beads of sweat lining his brow. Behind him the two chastised agents stood staring dully at the floor.

"Listen," he said to Elisa, "if there's something you're not telling me about this, the girl's life could depend on it."

Elisa sat silently in the chair and looked out over the city toward the blacked-out dome of St. Paul's. What could she tell him? Lori was delivering a simple message to Harvey Terrill at TENS. She never arrived. The content of the message did not matter. It had nothing to do with anything. How could it? She had told the truth about everything but the passports. "Murphy wanted the Warsaw correspondent to meet him at the airport. It is that simple."

Tedrick crossed his massive arms. "The girl was with Grogan the day he was killed. She saw something . . . *someone* . . . who did not want to be seen."

"She would have told us."

"Not if she didn't know what it was."

———

Harvey Terrill hummed to himself as he flipped through his file in search of the emergency telephone number for the Polish Embassy in London.

He dialed and let it ring as he edited the front-page story Orde had wired in from Warsaw. *The Polish government has given up all hopes for a peaceful solution to the annexation of Danzig by the Germans. In Warsaw, small children and old men are filling sandbags. Even in the Jewish District of the city, rabbis and Yeshiva students are digging slit trenches in city squares. The basements of synagogues are being fortified for use as air-raid shelters. Meanwhile, citizens of Warsaw carry on. The cafes are still filled. Theaters are crowded. In the English movie house, the motion picture "Stagecoach" is playing with Polish subtitles to a packed house.*

It was an interesting study in contrasts, Harvey mused. Slit trenches and bomb shelters on one hand; cafes and American movies on the other.

Life went on. Like ants moving in an orderly line beneath the shadow of a raised boot, Poland marched along.

Tonight the embassy took a little longer to answer the telephone, but Harvey's call was eventually put through.

"I have information you may wish to relay to your authorities in Warsaw."

"Your name, please?"

"There is a gentleman arriving tonight at 11:30 in Warsaw on the KLM flight from Vilnyus. He is an American newsman named John Murphy."

"Murphy?"

"John *M-U-R-P-H-Y*. Yes. I have learned from a reliable source that Mr. Murphy is carrying forged passports into Poland. I am not certain if they are American or British passports, but they are intended for two members of the staff of Trump European News Service. Something you will want to follow up."

———

The KLM flight touched down in Warsaw a few minutes after midnight. The atmosphere of the place was thick and humid.

"Mr. Murphy? Mr. John Murphy?" The thin man in the dark blue uniform of a Polish customs officer was polite but firm. Murphy was asked to accompany him to an office for questioning that was clearly not routine.

Murphy felt as if the violin case tucked under his arm had suddenly turned bright orange and sprouted a sign that read "Look here for contraband!" He decided that his best approach was wounded innocence.

"What's the reason for this delay? I'm here on business for Trump European News, and I have only a short time before I need to catch a return flight to London." Waving his passport, he added, "I'm an American, as you can plainly see."

"Yes, Mr. Murphy, we know all about who you are, and there is no problem with *your* passport."

Murphy's blood begin to pound in his ears at the significantly emphasized word. "Well, then," he said with all the brass he could manage, "I'll just be on my way," and he started to stand.

The customs officer gave a brief shake of his head and waved Murphy back to his seat. "A moment more, if you please. Regulations permit us to search for suspected smuggled items. Would you be so kind as to tell me what is in the case you are carrying?"

Murphy did his best to act unconcerned. "This is a violin that belongs to my wife, who is a professional musician. Since I was making this trip to Warsaw, she asked if I would deliver it to a friend here who has asked to borrow it."

"And the name of this friend in Warsaw?"

Stupid, stupid, stupid! Murphy had no ready answer and anything he might make up would sound suspicious. At the obvious delay in replying the officer continued, "Perhaps I should examine the case, then?"

Murphy held on to the case. "Say," he said calmly, "I'm sure we can work this out. Isn't it customary to offer a little gratuity for good service? After all, I am in a terrible hurry, and my internationally known firm would be grateful for any assistance you can provide."

"Bribery, Mr. Murphy?" the man said grimly. "At this point, I really must insist on seeing the instrument." A thin, bony arm snaked out of the uniform sleeve and a hand extended expectantly toward the violin. Reluctantly, Murphy handed it over.

The American was surprised when the officer raised the lid of the case and removed the violin. Setting the case aside, the Polish official studied the violin with great care, even holding it at an angle so that the light from his desk lamp would shine inside.

There was a long, uncomfortable delay. Murphy tried not to look at the case, tried not to rub his sweaty hands together, tried not to think about what he knew of Polish prisons. When the officer at last gave a long sigh, Murphy almost jumped out of his chair. He fought down an insane urge to yell at the man to stop playing and get it over with.

"It is a genuine Guarnerius," the customs officer commented.

"What? Oh, right. Absolutely genuine. So?"

"Mr. Murphy," said the man, folding his hands in an attitude of sincerity and gazing at Murphy with the demeanor of a doctor about to inform a patient of a terminal illness, "smuggling is an extremely serious offense, particularly in these tense times."

Murphy nodded his understanding, but made no comment.

"What would you say," the man continued, "if I told you that this violin is very suspect and must be confiscated?"

For a moment Murphy acted as if he did not understand, and then for another instant, he thought of protesting. How could he give up Elisa's violin? Then he thought of Lori Ibsen. *Kalner,* he corrected himself. He thought of the terror that was certainly coming to Warsaw, and that the next KLM flight was the last one out. All this went through his mind in the space of one deep breath. "All right," he said. "You keep the violin, and I'll keep the case."

———

Cradling the empty violin case, Murphy emerged from the Polish customs office into the airport waiting area.

The room was stifling and crammed with desperate people. The noise of competing voices gave the area the frantic atmosphere of the stock exchange on a hectic day of trading. While some people waited anxiously for a flight to be announced, others argued loudly with clerks of customs officials, or with one another. Some waved wads of money and offered to buy tickets to anywhere, as long as it was away from Poland and nowhere near Germany. Polish money was scorned. French francs and British pounds were considered by the more cool-headed of the ticket holders. American cash was looked on with some interest, and here and there a few precious passages from Warsaw were purchased.

Murphy stood on a bench and scanned the crowd in search of Sam Orde and his little group of travelers. Were they here? Had they already checked in at the KLM counter and picked up their tickets?

He worked his way through the jostling crowd to the long line for KLM Air Service. Precious minutes slid away as Murphy moved forward too slowly.

If Orde had received the message from London TENS, he would be here by now, Murphy knew. He continued to scan the mob expectantly.

Holding tightly to the case that had contained Elisa's violin, he thought how much more valuable the passports were. *But where was Orde? Where were the faces that matched the photos on these priceless documents?* Jacob. Alfie. Rachel. They would not be able to pick up their tickets without the passports.

At the head of the line, a florid-faced man was shouting that there must be more tickets available. The man looked as though he might have a stroke as his color grew redder and redder and his voice shriller and shriller. At last the man seemed to believe the clerk that there were no more tickets to be had, and he deflated like a punctured balloon. From loud and demanding, the man shrank in on himself till he meekly moved aside and went to sit forlornly on a bench next to a woman and two small children.

"Next!" the harried clerk shouted and pointed at Murphy impatiently.

Murphy produced his return ticket. "I expect to be joined by some business associates," he said. "Has anyone been here asking for John Murphy? Trump European News. Four reservations out of Warsaw were confirmed for them in London." He gave the names slowly. She scanned the list with an air of indifference. Could Mr. Murphy not see that there was near panic here? Could she keep track of all the people looking for someone?

"No," the girl replied, "not yet. What's more, your friends should already be here and checked in. Don't you know that this is the last flight out of Warsaw? There are lots of others waiting to use those tickets."

"Can you give me a little more time?" Murphy asked. "I'm sure they are on the way."

The clerk consulted a clock on the wall behind her, "Five more minutes! The plane leaves in fifteen."

The head of TENS walked rapidly out the front doors of the airport and looked frantically for Orde and the boys. On the street corner he waved off some taxis; there was not enough time for him to reach the news service office and return to catch the plane.

Murphy went back inside the airport to a bank of pay phones. Every telephone was dead!

When the American turned away from the phone, he found the ticket clerk waving at him. "Has the rest of your party arrived yet?" she asked. "Your time is up."

"No," he said, "but they are on the way. Any chance of holding the flight?"

The woman looked shocked. "Absolutely not," she replied. "Do you see this case?" she asked, pulling a small bag out from under the counter. "This is my bag, and this is my flight. If your friends aren't here, it's just too bad." She waved to the florid-faced man, who jumped up eagerly. "There are now three seats available," she said.

Murphy ran back outside. Up the sidewalk a block in one direction, then back past the terminal building and a block down the other way. No Orde! Murphy heard the engines of the KLM plane turn over with a roar.

He came to a sudden decision and hurried over to the first cab in the taxi stand. "Do you know the office of Trump European News?" he asked, and he gave the address of TENS, Warsaw. "I want you to take this case to the man in charge there. His name is Samuel Orde. Have you got that? Samuel Orde." He thrust the violin case into the man's hands, along with twice the requested fare. "Take it right now," he directed.

One glance over his shoulder at the departing taxi, then he ran straight out to the tarmac. "Hurry!" called the KLM clerk from the bottom of the boarding stairs.

As the last KLM flight out of Warsaw taxied away from the gate, Murphy's final view was of a large man waving bravely over the fence. He could not hear the man's sobs, but Murphy had no doubt that they echoed the ones coming from the seats beside him and across the aisle.

Pastor Karl was unable to move his legs or his arms, but he was perfectly awake. He watched the burly S.S. guards come into the room where the prisoners had been drugged and sling the men over their shoulders like sacks of potatoes.

When it came his turn, Karl had the odd sensation of being swept up high in the air. It brought back long-forgotten memories of Karl's own childhood, occasions when a toddler named Karl Ibsen had been lifted high by his father and swung through space.

He had no ability to feel the hands that roughly reached around his thin frame, or of the brawny shoulders over which he was tossed. If he closed his eyes, he could imagine that a completely invisible force was carrying him.

Karl opened his eyes in time to see the truck into which they were being loaded. The prisoners were stacked carefully, face up, so they would not suffocate, but otherwise they rested all over each other like sacks of grain in the back of a wagon.

After a short ride in the truck, the human cargo was unloaded again and carried through a shady, wooded area. Karl enjoyed the sweet breeze that played on his eyelids. He liked the sounds of crickets chirping along a stream, and when he was at last dumped without ceremony against a tree trunk, Karl was grateful that he was propped upright and could look around him.

Alfie knew he was dreaming, and yet it was not a dream.

He could smell the scents of the woods. Crickets fiddled and bull-frogs boasted on the banks of the Vistula River. It was very dark every-

where except for fireflies that bobbed drunkenly in the branches of the bushes.

Alfie was walking in a line of men. He lifted his feet high like a soldier marching. He did not stumble when he walked, even though the path was dark. Werner-kitten rode on his shoulder and rumbled in his ear. Ahead of him, Alfie could see the forms of the boys from Sisters of Mercy Hospital. They, too, were being carried. Slung over the shoulders of strong men, they were being taken some place . . . someplace. But where?

His friend Werner looked up at him. Alfie was glad to see his face.

"I thought they killed you," Alfie said to Werner the boy.

"Yes," Werner replied. His eyes looked worried.

"Where are they taking us?" Alfie asked. He hoped that Werner would answer him. Werner was smart. He always knew the answers.

Werner could not point. His hands dangled over the shoulders of the man who carried him. Werner moved his eyes to show Alfie where they were marching to. Alfie looked up to a high hill with a big metal tower on top. There was a square cement building on the hill as well. Alfie thought that the tower looked very much like the radio tower on top of the Polski Radio broadcasting studio where the captain had gone to send his report to London. But it was not the same. There were crickets and bullfrogs. This seemed a very lonely place.

"What is this place?" Alfie asked Werner.

"Look behind you," Werner said.

Alfie looked over his shoulder. The kitten stopped purring. Marching along behind Alfie was a Hitler-man in his uniform. Over his big shoulder was Pastor Ibsen. Pastor Ibsen was also wearing a uniform, but it was like the ones Alfie saw on all the Polish soldiers.

"Are you awake?" Alfie asked Pastor Karl, who had his eyes closed.

Pastor Karl opened his eyes. "Hello, Alfie," said the pastor just like always. "I like your kitten."

Alfie wanted to hug Pastor Karl, but he could not stop marching. "Where are we going?" Alfie asked.

"There." Pastor Karl's eyes pointed to the tower.

"Why is the Hitler-man carrying you?" Alfie asked.

"I cannot walk," Pastor Karl replied.

The bullfrogs bellowed loudly, almost drowning out pastor's voice.

"Why?" Alfie asked, but the sound of bullfrogs became so loud that he was certain the pastor could not hear him.

Then the pastor looked up into the starry sky. There were lights moving above them, bright lights. Suddenly Alfie knew that the sound he was hearing was not bullfrogs, but the rumble of airplane engines.

"You must run!" shouted Pastor Ibsen. "Run and tell them!"

Alfie could not run. His feet kept marching in the line with all the

*rest. He looked down at his clothes and saw that he was also dressed
in the uniform of a Polish soldier. Why was he marching between these
Nazi soldiers?*

*"I can't run!" he cried to Pastor Karl. His heart was pounding. He
was sweating because he was afraid. Something terrible was ahead
on the path. He knew it, and yet he could not make his legs stop marching forward.*

*Pastor Karl raised his arm to the tower. "Tell them." Small spouts
of flame erupted in the blackness. A popping sound rattled all around
the ground where Alfie marched! There was a great explosion beside
the tower. The light from it made the metal frame glow like a skeleton
against the sky.*

*Alfie looked at the face of his friend Werner. "RUN, Alfie!" Werner
shouted. "It has begun!"*

*"I can't run!" Alfie cried. His legs marched on toward the fire and
the spurting lights that Alfie now knew were guns firing down on them.
"Help me!" Alfie cried to Pastor Karl.*

*"Step aside," replied the pastor in a kind voice. "One step to the
side, Elisha. Tell them. Tell your captain."*

*Alfie stepped one step to the side, and now he was no longer march-
ing with the rest. He backed up as other Hitler-men, carrying men on
their shoulders, marched on without seeing him.*

*"Where do I run to, Pastor Karl?" Alfie shouted after him as fire
began to fall from the sky in sheets like a waterfall.*

*There was no answer. In the glow of the fire, Alfie saw the Nazi
soldiers lay their burdens down in the grass of the hillside.*

Hess brought a staggering Wolfgang von Fritschauer to the grassy
knoll on which the transmitter stood. "Now," he observed in a friendly
fashion, "now is your opportunity to prove your loyalty to the Führer."

"Yes, I see," slurred Wolf. "Now we can strike at Poland after such
pro . . . what's the word?"

"Provocation. Exactly," agreed Hess.

"And my part?" asked Wolf. "Do I lead . . . attack the town, or stay
here and broadcast?" he mumbled.

"Neither," said Hess quietly.

"Then do I lead the prisoners so we can be seen retreating?"

"Nothing as involved as that," corrected Hess.

"What am I expected to do, then?"

"Why, Wolf," said Hess in a kind voice, "you are expected to die."
He shot Wolf through the neck with a Polish army-issue pistol.

Wolf's body was laid out on the grass. Hess placed the pistol in
Wolf's outstretched hand. It would be clear to any observer that the

man had been killed while directing a Polish attack on the German radio transmitter.

Operation Canned Goods continued in the woods between Gleiwitz and the Polish border. Karl Ibsen was wide awake when he was placed against a tree trunk, but he had no strength to escape. To Gustav Ahlman, he remarked, "What will you say to the Judge of the Universe? You know this war is going to bring great destruction and sorrow on Germany. Is that what you want?"

"It will bring your destruction first," Ahlman said, pressing the muzzle of his pistol against Karl's head.

"Oh, God," Karl cried, "receive my spirit!"

Then Ahlman pulled the trigger.

"Where do I run to, Pastor Karl?" Alfie whispered the question once again as a wide gulf of water separated him from the pastor. Would he find no answer? "Where should we go?"

Silence. No crickets. No bullfrogs. No explosions or thrumming engines. Only silence and a very bright light all around Alfie, as if a silver cocoon had suddenly surrounded him and made him safe. Alfie was not afraid any longer. But still he asked the question.

"Where?"

The voice of Pastor Karl was soft and happy. "The Promised Land."

"A good idea," Alfie replied.

The light began to fade. "More with you . . . than are with them."

"Very good," Alfie said, feeling happy. He reached up and stroked Werner-kitten, who purred in a sleepy way on the pillow.

Alfie knew he was dreaming. Werner was on Alfie's pillow. Jacob was fast asleep in the bed beside him. There were no crickets chirping. No fire or explosions. But something was coming to Warsaw. Alfie was sure of that when he opened his eyes and sat up.

"Are you awake?" Alfie shook Jacob's shoulder.

"Huh?"

"Wake up." Alfie shook Jacob again.

"What?" Jacob sounded angry. He fumbled for the clock and held it close to his face. "Elisha, it's 4:30 in the morning. Go back to sleep."

"No." Alfie said, feeling very sure that he must not go back to sleep. "We have to tell the captain. The planes are coming."

Jacob lay very still with the clock in front of his nose. It ticked loudly. There was another sound. Alfie knew that Jacob was now awake. The sound was the terrible buzzing of engines.

"Planes."

"Coming to Warsaw."

"Now? Luftwaffe?"

"Yes," Alfie said, climbing out of bed and looking for his trousers. "We should tell the captain. And then we should go to the Promised Land."

———

Hess was inside the radio station and on the air. In excellent Polish he announced that the forces of the Polish Army had liberated Gleiwitz from German oppression. Hess called on Poles working nearby to rise up in revolt.

He ordered machine guns to open up on the concrete building. Moments later, all the windows were shattered and there were convincing pock-marked walls to prove the reality of the attack. The gunners were extremely careful not to damage the antenna or the transmitter.

36

The Promised Land

Friday, September 1, 1939
Warsaw

Orde awoke suddenly. Something terrible had happened. The air was filled with the unending rage of a beehive buzzing full blast. Without realizing what was on his face, he brushed plaster and glass from his cheeks and groped for the lamp that had been on the table beside the couch. It was not there. Plaster was on the table, strewn on the floor of the hotel suite.

There were planes overhead, planes so near that they seemed to be in the room! Double-engine planes. *Luftwaffe!*

He put his feet on the floor and cut his right foot on glass from the broken lamp. Outside, not far from the Bristol, another bomb crashed down. The floor shook. Then another boom! And another, moving closer in a perfect rhythm. The whole building shuddered. Another huge chunk of ceiling crumbled down, filling the room with choking plaster dust.

Orde coughed. He tried to call out to Alfie and Jacob in one room and then to Lucy in the other! Their names caught in his throat. He gasped for breath and wondered why it was so dark. The blackout curtains hung crazily from a broken rod. The glass of the windowpanes was gone. Orde could see fires in the distance, the eruption of flame like a waterspout in the direction of the airport!

Orde remembered the light switch in the bathroom. Maybe it still worked. But he could not walk across the floor because of the litter of glass shards. Orde groped in the darkness for his slippers, miraculously finding them where he had left them by the sofa. They were full of rubble. He shook them out and slipped them on the wrong feet.

"Jacob!" he cried, shuffling toward Lucy's room in confusion. He tripped over an upturned chair. "Lucy!" he shouted.

Behind him he heard the voice of Alfie in a sing-song cadence above the incessant droning of the motors. "We have to go now, Captain! Get dressed, Lucy!"

Alfie emerged from the room, the kitten tucked into his shirt. The little black and white face peered out at the neck just beneath Alfie's chin. A second head.

"We're all right, Captain," Alfie said.

Then, behind Orde, Lucy came to the other door in her nightgown, her hair falling over her face. By the light of yet another explosion, Orde could see that she had a cut above her right eye that was bleeding. She held her hand to it, then looked at the black liquid that was her own blood. "I'm not hurt," she muttered.

"Get dressed," Alfie said. "We have to go. Pastor Ibsen said it's time to go to the Promised Land."

———————

There was no traffic in Muranow Square. No taxis. No trams running. Peter Wallich slept on an iron cot in a long line of other iron cots in the dormitory of the Community Center.

He opened his eyes to the sound of distant motors and a thumping, like a paper bag filled with air being popped. He sat up and listened. Other men and boys in the room snored and wheezed on as though nothing were out of place in the sounds of early morning.

Peter got up and pulled his trousers over his nightshirt. He found his shoes and undarned socks and stumbled through the unfriendly iron frames of the cots.

It was hot, even though it was not yet light. The thumping sound grew louder. Not nearer. Just *louder*.

He pushed through the swinging door out into the dining room. It was deserted, dark. He threaded his way through the long wooden tables and benches to the entrance, then out through the doors, where the buzzing sound increased in volume.

Peter searched the vaguely lightening sky. It seemed empty, except for bright morning stars. Daylight was coming, slowly turning the deep purple of the eastern sky to hues of violet. Pastel shades reflected in the taped and boarded windows of houses and shops all around the square. The gold of newly stenciled letters on baker Menkes' shop caught a ray of light. But it was not sunlight!

Far across the rooftops, in the direction of the angry whirring sound of a buzz saw, a flash of light exploded like lightning. *The airport? Had a plane gone down?* Several seconds later the resounding *boom* of that explosion reached Peter's ears.

Several others joined him on the steps. "What is it?" asked a boy of about twelve.

No one wanted to answer what they *thought* it was. What they *feared* it to be!

Peter looked toward the open window of Rabbi Lubetkin. Why was that window open? No tape. No boards. Did the rabbi not believe that *they* could come here?

The distant humming of the bee swarm was suddenly accompanied by a *slap! slap! slap!*

Bombs?

Across the square, Peter could just make out the form of Rabbi Lubetkin as he ran out on his front steps, his wife at his side.

Had they left their windows open so they could clearly hear this terrible moment?

Pulling her robe around her shoulders, Rachel followed her father and mother out into the tepid morning air. The scents of the river drifted around her.

Papa walked slowly down the steps and then out into the street so he could see better. He held his hand up like a scout looking for a trail or shading his eyes against the sun. But there was no sun—only distant fire and the sound of airplane engines. So it had begun! He stared to a faraway place on the horizon, where puffs of smoke erupted like little mushrooms.

"The airport," he said. "It is true." He turned. "Downtown Warsaw. There." He pointed to a spiraling purple plume of smoke. "Polski Radio, maybe."

"But will they bomb us, Aaron?" Mama's voice trembled.

"No." He sounded so certain. So *confident*! Why, then, was Rachel still so afraid?

Across the square, Dolek's horse-drawn milk wagon plodded up the street. Ludicrous, because it was so ordinary on such a morning, it turned lazily into Niska to continue its regular route.

Rachel watched it with astonishment, and then she remembered that the old milkman was mostly deaf. Probably his horse was deaf, as well.

"What do we do now, Aaron?" Mama's voice was still shaking.

"No air-raid sirens," Papa said in that same confident tone. "No doubt the Polish Air Force is giving them a beating." He turned away and walked back up the steps. Then he gathered Rachel and Mama into his outstretched arms and urged them inside.

Once in the foyer, Rachel felt almost normal. Nearly unafraid. This was her house. Everything was just the same. No matter if a little something was going on at the airport, nu? Even so, her heart was pumping hard.

Papa looked around him. He looked at the ceiling and at the walls. His gaze was not friendly. "Maybe the Poles have fallen asleep. Maybe the sirens do not work. Make a call, Etta," he instructed. "Get the telephone chain up and busy. Sirens or not, have morning prayers in the air-raid shelter, I think."

———————

A hint of daylight pushed back the darkness, creeping over the broken windowpane, then through the torn black-out curtain. Outside the hotel room, women wept noisily in the corridor, while others shouted. Someone was yelling for everyone to get down to the air-raid shelter. Still there were no sirens wailing over the city.

Lucy bandaged Orde's foot while Alfie stood beside the window and peered out across the rooftops. Jacob sat quietly in the chair beside him. His eyes were closed, his lips moving silently. Orde knew the boy was praying and he was glad for it. His own thoughts were laced with prayers, but his mind was jumping like a bullfrog from puddle to puddle.

The corner of the ceiling was down. Lucy was on her knees, worrying over his foot as though there were nothing else. *Dear God, where to take them? How to get them out? I waited too long.*

Two walls were cracked with diagonal fissures running top to bottom. *How was the outside masonry holding up?* The sound of engines was almost gone. Very far away he heard the sound of feeble anti-aircraft fire. Probably this one raid over downtown Warsaw was nothing more than the Germans leaving a little calling card, a brief memo that the real stuff would soon be arriving. Right now the battle was far to the west. Some impatient Luftwaffe pilot had not been able to resist the urge to wake up Warsaw and then scoot back to business.

Still no sirens. Yet the cry came, *"Get to the shelters!"*

Orde made a sudden decision. He looked at Lucy's face, at the cut over her eye. The sad resignation and worry on her expression. "I'm going to the office," he said. "You all go down to the shelter until—"

Alfie turned. He was not smiling anymore. "Not the shelter, Captain," he said without doubt.

"I'm going to get to the shortwave radio. Try to find out what's happening," Orde replied quietly. "It's a long way to the office, and the shelter here is—"

"We should stay together, Captain," Alfie said. He turned back to the window.

Lucy looked into Orde's face as if to beg him to listen. Alfie had seen something. Orde frowned, considering what it would be like for the four of them to be caught out in the street in the open if the bombers came back.

Lucy put a hand on his arm. She bit her lip, and her eyes held the silent entreaty, *Do not leave without me.*

Jacob looked up as the distant popping sounded in the morning air. "I don't want to go to the shelter," he said. "If a bomb falls on me, I want it to be just a bomb. Not a whole building along with it."

Outvoted, Orde nodded agreement. The voice in the hall was still shouting for everyone to get to the shelter. The weeping women had been led away down the stairs.

"We should hurry," Alfie said. "They will be waiting."

Orde slipped his shoe over his bandaged foot. Then he reached down to help Lucy to her feet. It was a strange time to tell her what he wanted to tell her, and yet, maybe there would not be another time.

Jacob and Alfie looked on as he took her face in his hands. This time, for the first time, she did not turn her eyes away from his. He did not speak for a moment as they stood there in the dust and rubble. Alfie was right. He could clearly see the beauty of her broken heart and he knew. *Orde knew!* He *loved* this woman!

"I will not leave you," he whispered. "The Lord has never stopped loving you. He has let me see you, Lucy. *Come with me.*"

She nodded, still searching his eyes and believing him. She was no longer afraid. No longer ashamed. In that moment she laid her heart in his hands to carry.

The hall outside had grown silent, as had the street below. Orde took her hand in his.

"We should hurry," Orde said.

"Yes." Alfie agreed. He was smiling again, that knowing smile. "A long way to go."

————

Everyone was moving too slowly. David and Samuel got up at their mother's urging, but they were cranky and belligerent from a long night with little sleep.

Rachel dressed more quickly than her brothers. She took over the job of phoning friends and neighbors with the news that Papa thought it would be better if everyone went ahead to their assigned shelters.

Yes. Yes. The battles seemed very far away. Why should anyone waste time or bombs on the Jewish District? But all the same, send the children on. Gather up your belongings. It was only the first day. Just the first day. A good day to practice in case the conflict should develop into something serious. School could start early for the young ones. It could be held just as easily in the basement of Torah school, where there were sandbags and canned food and water—just in case a bomber should get lost.

David and Samuel, wide awake, were excited by the prospect of a real war. After all, they had been practicing marching in the shade of the elm tree. Now they would really see something!

They dressed as though it were a regular school day. Mama gave them their haversacks and asked Rachel to escort them to the corner, to watch them all the way to the school. There were still phone calls for Mama to make. Things to do. No doubt by the evening more refugees would be coming into Muranow Square.

"We'll be along in a bit." Mama kissed the boys lightly. She seemed not at all afraid, and yet her eyes held something in them that cut a cold knife of fear through Rachel's own heart.

For David and Samuel, walking out into the newly breaking day was an adventure. School chums from all over the district emerged onto Muranow on their way to early school in the air-raid shelter. They hailed one another. They pointed to distant sounds of guns whumping. Such small sounds, they were; it was difficult to believe that they were more than sounds, that men were dying, being blown to little pieces every time a gun cleared its throat.

Rachel was glad nothing had come so close to Muranow! Glad and relieved that all the children were going into the shelter. She was not anxious to join them, because she wanted to look, to watch the fly-sized airplanes climbing high and then falling off to drop their deadly little eggs on some unknown target.

Six-thirty in the morning. Hundreds of children surged around her. She waved goodbye to her brothers on the corner. The excitement was like some sort of game. She was smiling. David and Samuel did not turn around to wave. "I'll bet the Polish Air Force is giving them a beating!" David said to his brother.

There was pride in that statement. The Polish Air Force at that moment was *their* air force, protecting the Jewish community.

Rachel turned to go back home. She took three steps and then stopped. Suddenly the air filled with the high, undulating wail of the Warsaw sirens!

What?

All conversation ceased in that instant. Little faces turned upward in confusion. Could this wail be meant for them? For the Jewish Quarter of Warsaw?

Suddenly, as if drawn by the screaming of the sirens, a formation of German planes appeared just at the level of the housetops! How many? Ten? Or maybe fifty? Or a hundred? No! It was only three, but the terrible crooked cross of the swastika was plainly visible on their tail rudders!

Hundreds of screams, the shrill screams of children, rose up, only to be lost in the spinning props of the planes. The roar of engines was deafening!

Rachel stood, rooted with fear on the sidewalk. She could plainly see the features of the pilots. They flew unopposed, no Polish planes pursued them! And they were smiling as they flew overhead.

Then the screams were drowned out by the terrible shriek of the bombs. The children all began to run at once as spouts of pavement erupted behind them and in front of them and beneath them. The bigger ones outran their little brothers and sisters. Rachel screamed and fell to her knees as little Samuel was knocked to the ground. David threw himself over Samuel, kicking back the others who stumbled on in blind terror toward the school. Then little ones struggled to follow the bigger ones, and all of them reached the steps just as the entire building exploded outward, tumbling down on top of the children to betray their belief that someplace was safe for them.

Rachel screamed at the sight of cart-wheeling bodies and tumbling bricks. The dust, the noise, the horror of it made the whole world shake. Sandbags were nothing. Boarded windows simply disintegrated behind the protective covering. Rachel covered her head as a shower of debris rained down and the drone of the engines sped away in search of other targets.

Then came the silence, eerie and dark in its implication. Silence where laughter and excited voices had been a moment before. Silence covering prostrate bodies like the masonry dust. No birds. No more sirens. Rachel heard her own sobs as she peered up through the cloud that covered what had been Muranow Square.

No more children. No more childhood. It vanished forever in that terrible moment.

"God!" she called. Had the bombs also silenced the Almighty? Could three men, three planes, do this? Only *three*?

Rachel pulled herself to her knees. She raised her hands, imploring the silent heavens to help her stand. To walk forward to look for her brothers.

At that moment, she saw them. They walked . . . stumbled . . . out from the gray cloud of fire and destruction. Hats off. Clothes askew. Their knees and hands were bloody, their faces streaked with tears, but they were alive!

Behind her, Rachel heard other voices. Mothers. Fathers. Running toward the scene, calling out the names of their children!

And then the high, terrible wail of the siren began again, calling those who were left to the shelter of the Community Center.

————

Orde and the others were only five blocks from the Bristol Hotel when the Heinkel raiders struck. The bombs dropped in four install-ments, lifting the hotel from its foundations. When it came down again, the roof collapsed from the center as the walls puffed out in a weird orange glow of fire and rolling black smoke.

Orde shielded Lucy as debris rained down all around them. He raised his eyes to watch the retreating tails of the planes. No one could have survived the bombing in the shelter of the Bristol. The threatening hiss of escaping gas from the mains made Orde jump to his feet.

Alfie and Jacob were already steps ahead of him. Lucy stumbled after, her head turned back in horror to gape at the remains of the Bristol.

As they ran up the deserted street, Orde could see smoke billowing up from the Jewish District near Muranow Square. Three German bombers scooted away unopposed just above the level of the rooftops.

Telephone lines had been installed in Elisa's suite at the Savoy Hotel. The hope was that Lori's abductors would ring with ransom terms.

With Tedrick towering in the background, he raised his hand in signal for Elisa to answer when the telephone rang. At the same moment he picked up the extension.

No sinister voice replied to Elisa's tentative "hello."

It was Winston Churchill, growling over the lines from Chartwell. "They've started, Elisa," he said gruffly. "The Nazis are bombing Warsaw and Cracow right now."

Tedrick replied with an unexpected expletive. "Great heavens, Winston! Are you *certain*?"

"That you, Tedrick? Yes. Certain. Straight from the Polish ambassador a few minutes ago."

Elisa felt faint. She lowered herself onto the sofa. *Bombing Warsaw!* Had Murphy made it out? Had he managed to connect up with Orde and the kids?

Winston asked the question that showed that nothing escaped his attention, even as she framed it in her mind. "Have you had word from Murphy in Warsaw?"

"Not yet," Elisa said in a faltering voice.

"You do not know if he was able to meet Orde?"

"We are praying so."

"Yes," the voice drawled in a kindly way. "And as for the young lady? Your cousin Lori?"

Tedrick replied. "No word. No ransom demands. I fully expected that some demands would be linked to the service at St. Paul's this morning. Perhaps some note, a political statement to be read from the pulpit—possibly by you, Winston."

"The world, it seems, is run by blackmail and extortion these days," he replied in a gloomy voice.

"Shall we go ahead with the service, Winston?" Elisa asked painfully.

The answer was definitive. "Yes! By all means in our power! As Hitler explodes his bombs on the churches of Poland, we shall gather to pray before the righteous throne! Can the God of heaven ignore the difference in the way we begin a conflict and the Nazi disregard for heaven? Yes! By all means we shall continue with our plans." He paused. "I suppose that your father will be on alert, unable to come. But your mother? And Helen Ibsen?"

Tedrick replied again. "We will send a car for them. If there is some demand made, some political statement to be read, perhaps Mrs. Ibsen should be on hand." He frowned, deep in thought. "The Nazis have not been able to break her husband. It seems logical that this might be a ploy to extract some statement from her. Especially now with the Polish war."

"Well then—" Churchill sounded satisfied. "Elisa, perhaps you should also consider bringing the boys along. They are young, but not too young to remember the prayers of England on a day such as this. I would like them in the front row as I speak."

It was a kind thought, made from a great heart. Elisa hung up and immediately telephoned Anna and Helen with the request.

Allan Farrell paused beside the statue of Queen Anne that stood just below the steps leading to the grand entrance of St. Paul's Cathedral. Allan knew very little about the reign of the real Queen Anne, but he hated her memory just the same. After all, was she not depicted as standing above a prostrate Ireland? In the terrorist's twisted mind, the queen seemed to be smiling spitefully down at the spot where the Gunpowder Plot conspirators had been executed. He vowed to wipe the smile off her face.

He was several hours early for the Remembrance Service, well before the dignitaries and the crowd were due to assemble, but already well into his plan. Allan reached into the leather satchel and extracted a camera that he hung around his neck. Among the contents of the bag were another camera, a light meter, and the radio transmitter, which Allan believed he could pass off as one more piece of camera gear.

Allan had been prepared to find a cordon of policemen surrounding the church in response to the news that Poland and Germany were finally at war. The fragile and deceptive calm of the day before had been shown for what it really was: the collectively held breath of all of

Europe. Now that wishful thinking was shattered.

But there were no policemen surrounding St. Paul's, no special security measures, no troops patrolling the streets. Despite the fact that the early editions of the papers had announced the start of the war and the mobilization of British troops, it was clear that Britain was still not prepared to have the war on its doorstep. Allan was anxious to prove just how wrong the British were.

Once inside the building, Allan wandered up to the spot directly beneath the dome where the two arms of the great edifice crossed. He noted with particular interest the placement of the chairs for VIPs in the very front row, just below the pulpit. He also saw the provision of chairs for the musicians, to one side of the south transept. And his thoughts went to the girl tied up high above his head.

"Excuse me, sir," inquired a wizened little man. "Do you need assistance?"

"I'm a photographer," announced Allan, holding up the camera. "I'm looking for the best spots from which to take pictures of the proceedings. Sort of scouting the ground before the crowds arrive."

"Right you are too, sir. Just you let me know if there's anything you need. We certainly want to have a fine record of the doings here today."

"We certainly do," agreed Allan. "Say, there is one thing. I suppose that the dignitaries will be brought in the grand entrance, won't they?" At the man's agreement, Allan continued. "Then where would be the best place to get a view of their arrivals? I mean, I'm sure the steps in front will be crowded with onlookers."

"I've got just the thing," said the old man. "Leave it to me. What you want is the bell tower, just above the entrance. I'll take you there myself."

The KLM plane refueled in Amsterdam for the return flight to London. Murphy telephoned Elisa with his own list of bad news and was met with a catastrophic roster from her end.

Lori was missing. Elisa had managed to phone Harvey Terrill to send Orde the wire in Warsaw. But Harvey had obviously not gotten through. Now the violin was gone, the passports sent off across war-torn Warsaw in a taxi. Who could tell what was coming in the next few hours?

One bright spot remained. The prayer service at St. Paul's would continue as planned. *If ever the world needs prayer, this is the moment,* Murphy thought as he dashed back to the waiting plane.

The horse stood a little way apart from the overturned milk wagon and the crumpled body of Dolek the milkman. Cans were upended, mingling milk with the blood of the old man and others. The liquid ran in a pink stream in the gutters as the family of Rabbi Aaron Lubetkin ran with hundreds to the safety of the large shelter under the Community Center.

Rachel hung back just a moment as the wail of the useless Warsaw sirens kicked in again. She looked back over her shoulder at the devastation of the square. The linden tree where the birds had built their nests was now an uprooted, shattered mass lying across the churned grass.

Beyond its broken branches, Rachel spotted Peter Wallich's red hair glistening in the sunlight as he leaped a barricade with a dozen other boys from the Zionist Youth brigade.

One by one they vanished up Niska Street. They did not look back. Rachel knew they were getting out of Warsaw. *Warsaw,* where they had all come for refuge, was not a safe place to be.

It was hot even though the sun was only barely up. Alfie had sweated through his shirt, and Werner was soggy and unhappy against Alfie's belly as they ran the last two blocks to the TENS office.

The entire building was untouched. For blocks around, the city seemed as perfect and unharmed as it had last week, and for years before that. Except for the distant sounds of exploding shells and the smell of the smoke, it was impossible to tell that there was a war on.

Peter Wallich stood impatient in the sun, his red hair was covered with plaster dust. His clothes were a uniform shade of gray. There were a dozen other boys his age with him, also coated with dust. Their appearance indicated that they had been near the explosions in the Jewish District.

Peter stared up anxiously into the sky. One of his companions spotted Orde and the others approaching and tugged his sleeve. Peter looked at them and then, as if all powered by the same thought, they ran in a bunch to surround Orde and Lucy, Jacob and Alfie.

Talking at once, they recited where they had been when the first bombs fell.

Then the questions tumbled out from every mouth. "What is happening?"

"Are the Poles fighting?"

"Should we stay and fight?"

"Should we leave Warsaw?"

These were the young men scheduled to slip out of Poland in two days. The diving of the Heinkels may have moved their schedule up somewhat.

Orde pushed through them, his hands raised in an attempt to silence the chatter. Did they see the plaster dust on his hair, the cut above Lucy's eye?

Orde dug into his pocket for his keys. He patted each pocket. No keys anywhere. No matter. He gave the glass pane in the door a little kick and let the glass tinkle to the ground and then he reached in and opened the door. As the group bunched up behind him in the entrance, he halted, stooped, and picked up something.

Beneath the broken glass lay a violin case. A strange thing, indeed, to find resting on the doormat of a news office. Left by an itinerant musician in panic, perhaps, as he fled the roaring of the bombs?

The address of the TENS office was tucked into the battered handle. Orde shook the case. He smiled and entered the office.

———

By the time Murphy's KLM flight landed in England, both his clothes and his thoughts were rumpled, and he was in need of a shave. His mouth felt as if the soles of Wehrmacht boots had tramped through it.

Just as they are tramping through Poland right now, he reflected. Somewhere over the English Channel the KLM pilot had picked up a BBC broadcast and relayed it to his passengers. Since before dawn, German planes had been bombing Polish towns, and German tanks were advancing on four fronts into Polish territory.

It had all apparently started with some action involving an unknown village named Gleiwitz, but that fact seemed unimportant. The war, long expected and feared, had begun.

Murphy struggled with deciding what to do first. He desperately wanted to go home to Elisa, but knew that he should go to the TENS office and start gathering the threads of the breaking stories.

Glancing at his new watch, Murphy realized that there was not time to do both. If he went directly to TENS, he could change clothes there and meet Elisa at the Remembrance Service. Maybe he could get through to TENS Warsaw. Then he could at least reassure Elisa about Jacob Kalner. But what to do about Lori?

37

Passport to Life

The harsh voice of the German Führer emanated clearly over the radio from the Kroll Opera House in Berlin, where he now met with his rubber-stamp Reichstag.

Everything inside the London TENS office had been put on hold as staffers gathered around the shortwave to listen to the Führer rasp out his reasons for attacking Poland.

Murphy entered and stood for a moment, unnoticed at the back of the tense and angry group.

The voice cried in fury, *"I should like to say this to the world. I alone was in the position to make such proposals.... For two whole days I sat with my Government and waited.... I can no longer find any willingness on the part of the Polish Government to conduct serious negotiations with us.... I have therefore resolved to speak to Poland in the same language that Poland for months past has used toward us."*

Staff members exchanged disgusted looks. "Bombs," said James Samuels dryly. Then he noticed Murphy. "Hi, Boss." Back to the radio.

The applause of the Reichstag slowed. *"This night for the first time Polish regular soldiers fired on our own territory.... We have been returning the fire, and from now on bombs will be met with bombs!"* The roar of approval was tremendous.

Murphy imagined Timmons observing this farce from the press gallery as the heroic voice of the German leader rallied his people to his call to die:

"I am from now on just the first soldier of the German Reich. I have once more put on that coat that was most sacred and dear to me. I will not take it off again until victory is secured, or I will not survive the outcome!"

The familiar chant of *Sieg Heil! Sieg Heil!* erupted from the receiver.
"Well, I guess that is that."

"You heard the man. Victory or death."

"Gives us something to aim for." Nervous laughter followed.

"No," Murphy added. "Gives us something to shoot at." More laughter. Faces turned to see him, recognizing him in a surprised sort of way.

"Thought you were in Warsaw, Boss. Harvey said—"

"Did you get Orde out in time? And the kids?"

Murphy shook his head. "No dice."

All faces were glum at the news. The radio was switched off. Reporters moved like sleepwalkers back to their desks. There was plenty to write about, but nothing to talk about. No one felt like gabbing.

Murphy caught his grimy reflection in the glass of his office. A quick glance at the clock told him he had only minutes to get to St. Paul's to hear what Winston Churchill would say in reply to the lies and distortions of Adolf Hitler.

There had been no further word on Lori Kalner, his secretary informed him. Murphy felt sick. Had there ever been a day so tragic in its portent of the future?

"Where's Harvey?" he asked. To his surprise, the night desk editor, who always seemed to be present when bad news hit, had left for home. "Said he had to change for the service at St. Paul's," a secretary remembered.

Murphy reflected that he had not even known that Terrill cared enough to attend the Remembrance Service. Murphy chided himself for unreasonably wishing that Harvey had stayed at the office to track war stories.

After a quick change and a washroom shave that caused only two small nicks, Murphy went into the conference room. The bulletin boards there were plastered with maps of Poland. Strands of red yarn were already creeping across Polish territory like the spreading tentacles of an octopus.

Murphy picked up the conference-room phone. "Try to get me Orde in Warsaw," he said to the operator. Then he turned back to studying the maps. The floor was littered with reports and dispatches. The head of TENS picked up a handful and flipped through them, comparing village names with map locations.

About halfway down the pile he came to a note in Elisa's handwriting. It requested Harvey to contact Orde about meeting the plane. The phone rang. "I'm sorry, sir," the operator said. "I can't get through to Warsaw. Shall I keep ringing?" Murphy stuffed the note in his pocket.

"No. Send a wire telling Orde to contact us, although I'll bet he's already trying. By the way, I'm leaving now for St. Paul's. I'll be back in a couple of hours."

Allan Farrell watched from his perch in the bell tower as the cars began to arrive at St. Paul's Cathedral. Pastors in clerical collars, musicians lugging instrument cases, and politicians in formal dress arrived in anxious little knots.

Soon after these recognizable professions came the common folks. Some looked sad, others frightened. A cabbie brought a group of people, then parked and joined the crowd now thronging into the church. "Need to teach that Hitler bloke a lesson, we does." He spoke so loudly that Allan could hear every word.

The words "teach a lesson" reminded Allan of his mission, and he checked the transmitter for the hundredth time. He fretted briefly about the lack of opportunity to test the device, then relaxed when he reminded himself of the previous successes of German technology.

He turned his attention back to the front steps. When the terrorist spotted three women arriving together and noted the resemblance to Lori Ibsen, he was certain that he was watching the Lindheim-Murphy-Ibsen family.

The discordant sounds of the orchestra tuning up floated out of the church and drifted up to the bell tower. Allan tried to imagine the noises that would come from the centuries-old building as the lantern tower came crashing through the dome and floor. He compared the kettledrum sound to the thunder of falling masonry and the plaintive strings to the wail of human voices. Excitement gripped him as he anticipated his symphony of terror.

But where was Churchill? Where was the greatest stroke of all?

As if saving the best for last, a car bearing Churchill and Anthony Eden arrived. The two men, grim-faced and deep in discussion, were obviously hurrying between meetings. It was Allan's intention that they would never hurry anywhere again.

Three passports lay in the secret compartment of the violin case. *Only three?*

Orde's face was pained as he looked at the folders. He had hoped for so many more. He opened each one. As the boys of the Zionist Youth brigade looked on like starving children, he gave Jacob his identity. Then he smiled and handed Alfie his folder.

As he gazed down at the photograph on the third folder, his face was troubled. *Rachel Lubetkin! And not one for Lucy!*

The thin, dirt-streaked arm of Peter Wallich snaked in over the shoulders of the circle. His fingers clamped around the passport and he pulled it back to stare at it.

"She will be saved," he said.

Behind him, as if to emphasize his thought, the radio announced: *ALL CITIZENS OF GREAT BRITAIN ARE URGED TO REPORT TO THEIR EMBASSY AT ONCE. A STATE OF WAR HAS NOT YET BEEN DECLARED BETWEEN GREAT BRITAIN AND GERMANY. . . .*

The group exchanged horrified looks. *Where was England?* Polish cavalry in the west was being overrun by German panzer divisions. Even now tons of dynamite were exploding on fourteen Polish cities. Where was England? Were they not coming? Would England and France arrive in time to save Poland?

Peter's hands trembled. He held up the passport. "With this she can get out?"

Jacob looked down at his own folder. His passport to life, a ticket past the German lines. British citizenship! As long as war was still undeclared, he could walk up to any German officer, flash this passport, and be let through the lines all the way to England.

Did Alfie understand? Alfie looked at his own photograph. He was listening to the devastation being reported over the shortwave. His eyes were sad.

"Where is England?" asked Peter.

Alfie patted Orde on his shoulder. "Right here."

"But . . . where is *England*?" asked another boy, his voice filled with a sense of betrayal. "Who will save us?"

Alfie answered again in the uncomfortable silence. "Here is the captain. He will save us."

Peter whirled on Alfie angrily, "Idiot! Don't you hear what I'm asking? England! *An army!* Will they come to fight for us?"

Alfie was unoffended. He still smiled. "We should stay together," he said. "And see the Promised Land."

Orde had turned away to fiddle with the radio in a preoccupied way. The Poles were taking a beating in the west. New formations of Luftwaffe had passed over the city, bombing indiscriminately.

"Elisha," Orde said. "At nightfall you and Jacob will go to the embassy compound. You will be taken out. You will be safe there. Lucy and the rest of us will—"

"No!" Alfie said. "We stay together! Me and you and him and him and Lucy and—"

"Dummkopf!" Peter shouted.

"Shut up!" Jacob stepped between Peter and Alfie, and for a moment it seemed as though another sort of battle would explode right here. Orde pushed both boys aside as the shortwave continued to blare the bad news of the German Blitzkrieg rolling over Polish defenses.

Sweating and panting in the small space, Jacob and Peter stared at each other around Orde.

"That's enough!" Orde menaced. "Or I will beat both of you! Now is not the time or the place!"

Alfie was still smiling. He gave Werner-kitten to Lucy. He shrugged and shuffled his feet self-consciously. He had not meant to make anyone angry, but he knew how they would get out and he also knew that they *must* stay together. "Today is Friday," Alfie said. Angry, resentful eyes looked at him, but he pressed on. "I know how we can get out of Warsaw on Friday."

Peter snapped Rachel's passport folder down. "I am going back to the Jewish District," he said, as though Alfie were only rambling. "I'm going to find Rachel and get her to the British Embassy." He backed up a step.

Alfie continued to talk. "On Friday all the Catholics in Warsaw eat fish. Herr Frankenmuth told me—"

"The Germans are bombing that quarter worse than anywhere else, Peter," Orde warned. "You might make it in, but—"

Alfie pressed on. "Werner is very hungry. He has not had any breakfast. None at all."

The kitten yowled at the mention of his name.

Peter looked down at the picture of Rachel. "I know a way, if I can get this to her. Britain is not yet at war. That's bad for Poland, but good for whoever has one of these." He held it up. He was going. Orde could not stop him. Peter looked at Lucy, whose eyes reflected her love for him. Her admiration.

Alfie said loudly, *"Peter!"*

"I'm sorry," Peter said softly to Alfie as the buzz of bomber engines grew louder again.

"Don't miss the boat!" Alfie stepped forward and pumped his hand. "We are going to Herr Frankenmuth at the fish market, you see? He sells fish to the Catholics in Warsaw every Friday, and he will take us on his boat! The fish market! Hurry!"

The planes had returned again over the Jewish District of Warsaw. This time they were serious. Why, after all, bomb a military target when there were so many Jews down below to exterminate?

Rachel finally understood the meaning of the meetings, the discussions of how to protect the Jewish children of Warsaw—where to take them, how to get them out of here if the worst should come. Well, the worst had arrived. It *had* come! And this was only the first morning of the war!

Rachel held baby Yacov, his eyes wide and troubled by the rhythmic thumping noise and the trembling of the earth. Women in the shelter wept for their lost children. Men prayed.

At last Rachel understood why Mama had talked of sending her children away. Rachel would gladly give up Yacov, give up David and Samuel forever, if only they could escape this terror!

Papa stood, his face lost in the shadow of the strange light of carbide lamps.

All eyes turned to the great Rabbi of Muranow. They looked to him for hope, for comfort. He raised his hands and gradually the weeping died away, except for one woman who huddled by the door and called the name of two children who had fallen on the steps of the Torah school. Her quiet sobs accompanied his prayers like the counter-melody of a sad symphony.

"For the sake of heaven, Jews, don't despair! The salvation from God appears in an instant!"

And then he began to sing this summons to believe, this cry for salvation found in a Yiddish melody as old as the hope for the coming Messiah:

> O look down from heaven and behold,
> Look down from the skies and see!
> For we have become as a derision,
> A derision among the nations. . . .

Hundreds in the packed shelter joined in. Papa closed his eyes as he sang. The song was heard in heaven, Rachel knew, but how would God answer it? Would He save them all in one miraculous sweep of His hand? Or, as Papa had explained to her, would He save only one? For God's plan, even one Jew would be enough to keep His covenant! Because of this He cared for every Jew as though each was the only one! Rachel felt the presence of the Eternal One among them. He came to them in the calling of their hearts. One to one, the Lord of heaven was very near.

> Therefore we plead with you ever:
> Now help us Guardian of Israel,
> Take notice of our tears. . . .

The bereaved mother wept on. Only one woman crying, and yet she cried for everyone, every Jewish mother who had ever lost a child. Rachel knew this as she sang.

> Now take notice of our tears,
> For still do we cry aloud, "Hear O Israel."
> Show all the peoples that you are our God,
> We have indeed none other, just you alone,
> Whose name is ONE.

Papa prayed again, and even the weeping mother, the one woman, raised her head and was comforted.

———————

The orchestra assembled to remember the plight of the imprisoned pastors soared into their contribution. It was the *Elijah* by Mendelssohn.

Fret not thyself because of evildoers . . . the words of Psalm 37 reminded the listeners, *For they shall soon be cut down like the grass.*

In the front row of the congregation, three women joined hands and hearts. They prayed for the missing Lori, for absent Jacob, for Theo who was even now flying patrol missions with trainee pilots along the English coastline, for thousands of children represented by those sitting bravely beside them.

The Lord knoweth the days of the upright: and their inheritance shall be for ever.

They prayed for the Poles, for the free nations to resist Nazi aggression, for the Jewish people trapped in the middle.

The wicked watcheth the righteous, and seeketh to slay him.

They prayed for the righteous men of honor and courage who stood up to evil when they could easily have saved themselves instead. For Karl Isben: pastor, husband, father. They prayed for courage for themselves to be as strong.

The salvation of the righteous is of the Lord: he is their strength in time of trouble.

The melodic strains floated up and up into the shining bright dome where the soft glow was like looking into heaven. Lifted by the prayers of hundreds of anxious hearts, the sounds and thoughts reached past the galleries of stone to the ears of the frightened girl imprisoned overhead.

"Oh, Papa," she whispered. "Mama, Jacob. I'm here."

———————

Charles remembered that the last time they had been with Doc Grogan on their Thursday excursion, they had been right here—St. Paul's Cathedral, in this very place. It was a peaceful place. A happy memory, as long as he did not think past the time they spent here in St. Paul's.

Today rows and rows of chairs filled the space just beneath the dome. There had been no chairs here on the day they had climbed high up into the Whispering Gallery and then on to the Golden Gallery. The polished marble floor had been empty that day. Louis had leaned far over the rail and considered spitting, but Jamie had reminded him that this was a church, a holy place. Although it would have been fun to watch his spit fall so far, it would not have been a nice thing to do.

So here they were, all in a row far below the place from where they had looked down. Mr. Winston Churchill had asked for them to be here today, and Charles was glad for that. Although it had hardly been any time at all since he had been with Elisa, he had missed her terribly and wished she was with them all in the little cottage. Elisa had stayed in London to practice for today's performance. Lori had stayed to help with the babies. *Now where was Lori?*

Little Katie and baby Alfie were parked in their carriage next to Elisa at the end of the aisle. Charles could see them sleeping. He could make out the box that contained the little tent which served as a covering for little ones in case of a chemical gas attack by the Nazis.

Charles supposed that now everyone throughout England would carry their gas masks all the time. He looked over his shoulder at the worried faces of the grown-ups. All of them, indeed, had their gas masks with them.

Charles, Louis, Jamie, and Mark seemed to be the only children in the whole vast gathering. Already half the children in London had been evacuated because everyone knew what was coming. And here it was. A war, just like Mr. Churchill said would come if someone did not stop Herr Hitler. Charles was very glad that Mr. Churchill was going to speak today. It would be a terrible thing if everyone in England was quiet on a day when Germany was dropping tons of bombs on Poland.

That thought made him remember the long talks Murphy and Doc Grogan had about that very thing. Charles looked far up into the misty heights of the dome, where shafts of light beamed through from the light wells in the Golden Gallery. Louis also looked up. Then Mark and Jamie leaned their heads back and stared at the golden glow so many hundreds of feet above them.

The music swirled—very pretty music. Charles touched Elisa's arm. "Look," he whispered. "It looks like heaven."

She nodded. Her face was sad and worried. She looked over her shoulder at the entrance in hopes that Murphy would come soon. Harvey Terrill stood to one side, beside the stairs that led up through the interior of the dome.

Charles smiled and thought how tired Doc had been when they climbed all the way up, how long it had taken him to tell them all the stuff he knew about St. Paul's because he could hardly breathe.

He leaned his head back on his chair again. "We were up there with Doc." He pointed up and up. "Golden Gallery."

Elisa looked at him strangely, as if she were thinking about Doc again. She craned her neck back with the boys as the pretty music drifted on the light beams.

Then she leaned down and put her lips against Charles's ear. "Doc climbed up there?" She also remembered that it had been his last day.

Charles nodded. Her head went back again. "No windows," she whispered to herself.

"Light wells." Charles was pleased that he remembered what Doc had showed them. He pointed up toward the highest gallery just beneath the lantern tower. He would tell her more if she wanted to know. But after the service. It was almost time for Elisa to play. She was using her Steiner fiddle today. It was out across her lap. She had practiced here with it a dozen times, and—

Elisa's face grew very white. She was looking up into the dome. Even though the time for her to play was very near, she was searching the light beams of the dome as though she could see something there. *Something*. Maybe Charles would take her up there after the service. Maybe they could all climb up inside together and sit on the stone benches and remember good times with Doc. Maybe Jamie and Lori and Aunt Helen would also want to remember good times with Pastor Ibsen. A picnic on the Golden Gallery would be as good a memorial as this, Charles reasoned. He would tell them his plan after this was all over and everyone else went home.

Looking up and listening to the music, Charles could almost imagine that there were angels playing on the beams from the light wells. He did not even have to close his eyes to imagine such a thing.

It was perfect, except that Theo was gone in a plane. Lori was not here. And where was Murphy? Well, it was almost perfect. Just about everyone was here today.

———

Jacob Kalner tucked his passport into his pocket and then said firmly, "I am sticking with you, Elisha." He had a peculiar smile on his face as the other boys looked at him with amusement.

Who among them would not have jumped at the chance to flash that precious document in the face of a British Embassy official and simply slip in behind the high metal gates to be taken out of Poland in safety? But here was this *meshugge* actually choosing to go with them into the Warsaw fish market as if nothing at all might fall on his head and kill him! *Oy!* They could understand the confusion of this big oaf called Elisha—after all, he was not all there. He acted as though something had already hit him on the head and knocked a few brains loose, nu? But Jacob Kalner had always seemed a sensible fellow. Why, then, did he refuse to go to the British Embassy? And why did Captain Orde, who also could go to the embassy, insist that everyone was leaving together or no one was leaving?

It was an amazing thing to see. The one called Elisha marched on one side of Lucy Strasburg and the captain on the other. The kitten poked his head out of the neck of Elisha's shirt in front. Lucy, who knew just exactly where Herr Frankenmuth should be, was giving directions. *Turn here. Then go left here. His boat was moored halfway down the quay.*

All the while as they tramped down the streets, the German Heinkels buzzed persistently above. Their shadows brushed the cobblestones behind and in front of where they ran. Why then, did they not run faster?

"Herr Frankenmuth will be there," Alfie assured them. "He is waiting for us to come."

A haze of smoke from burning buildings drifted across the sky above Peter. He could hear the sounds of pitched battle not far away. The engines of the airplanes seemed always the same, neither far nor near, only sometimes louder and softer. He knew when they climbed because the pitch changed, and he knew when they came down against their targets because the roar turned into an angry scream, followed by dull explosions. Peter did not look up as he ran through the deserted streets of the Jewish District. He did not stop to look at the lifeless faces of the children who had died there this morning.

He ran on toward the cavernous doorway on Kozhla Street, the winding little lane where the animal market was. He passed beneath the archway and there, in the smoke, he saw something enormous moving toward him! It moved quietly and took shape. Yes! It was the great horse of Dolek the milkman! Its reins hung down from the bridle. It took a step and stepped on the end of a rein and stopped. Its enormous hoof held the leather fast against the cobblestones, and so the horse did not move when Peter walked to him. The horse's liquid brown eyes were watering—probably from the smoke, and yet, for a moment it looked to Peter as though the beast were weeping silently.

He crooned to the animal and stroked his thick neck. He took the leather rein, lifted the foot, and then led the horse to a heap of rubble. Peter climbed the rubble nervously and then slid his leg across the broad, sweating back. Grabbing a handful of mane, Peter turned the animal back toward the square and nudged him forward.

The hollow *clop, clop, clop* of iron horse shoes against the pavement beat a rhythm in time with the explosions of Nazi bombs on the train stations and warehouses on the outskirts of town.

Every newspaper in London had a special edition already on the streets. War news was already being shouted from the news kiosks that lined Fleet Street.

Cars and taxis pulled to curbs or hailed the newsboys who ran through slowly moving traffic selling their papers. Murphy took one look at the traffic jam and headed up the street toward St. Paul's on foot.

His brain was dull from lack of sleep and the unending onslaught of events over the last twenty-four hours. He looked at the clock tower of the cathedral. Still a few minutes before Elisa was scheduled to play. How he regretted the loss of her violin—the beautiful Guarnerius, given over to a crooked customs inspector who seemed to know very well the quality of the instrument.

Murphy's head ached. He brushed past pedestrians on the packed sidewalks and began the ascent up Ludgate Hill to St. Paul's. He was angry at himself for his failure. No Orde. No Jacob or Alfie or Rachel Lubetkin. And the violin, gone, for nothing.

He bit his lip and paused mid-stride for one instant. How had the Polish customs' inspector known to challenge Murphy about *passports*? "Not *your* passport," the man had said.

Murphy turned the incident over in his thoughts once again. It seemed that the inspector had come looking specifically for Murphy.

Elisa had told Murphy that she had managed to sneak a call to Harvey Terrill. That she had asked him to send the cable to TENS Warsaw.

Murphy reached into his pocket and pulled out the note he had found in the office just a few minutes before. Elisa's handwriting: a note to Harvey.

Murphy stopped walking. He frowned down at the message. He looked up at St. Paul's. People pushed past him, but he did not notice.

He knew without a doubt that he held the note that Elisa had sent Lori to deliver to Harvey last night at the TENS office! *The message— and Lori—had reached TENS!*

He began jogging rapidly up Ludgate Hill toward the cathedral. Why had Harvey lied? Why would he lie about seeing Lori? And how had Polish customs gotten the tip to detain Murphy?

Harvey Terrill!

Allan Farrell watched a flock of pigeons swirl in a figure-eight pattern around the clock tower and the bell tower of St. Paul's. He was growing impatient for the time to push the button.

He toyed with the idea of pushing the button without waiting for the signal. After all, everyone was inside already, weren't they? Did it matter whether Churchill died while speaking or while sitting in the audience? How much longer was the orchestra going to play, anyway?

Igniting the charges right now, however, would kill his accomplice as well. He wondered how much trouble he would get into for that. Of course, he could always explain that it was a mistake. He doubted that anyone really liked Harvey Terrill enough to care very much anyway.

The transmitter lay on top of the satchel. A flick of one switch turned it on, then a long push on the button, and . . . Allan's eyes again sought the top of the dome. Would the tower drop straight into the inside like a candle being pushed down into a cake? Or would part of the fabric of the dome collapse, too? Allan was eager to find out.

38

Live and Be Well

Outside the packed shelter, the steady *whump! whump! whump!* of falling bombs penetrated the thick walls of sandbags.

Rachel huddled close to her mother. She was frightened but not terrified as many others seemed to be. Everywhere the sounds of sobbing could be heard—mothers who had lost children, sisters who had lost brothers.

Rachel looked at the dust-covered forms of David and Samuel. There was blood on the knees of David's torn knickers. Samuel had a trickle of dried blood on his right cheek. How had they survived? It was a miracle when so many had perished this morning!

But how long would this go on? Would the Germans run out of bombs soon? Would they be shot out of the skies by the Polish Air Force—or by the English?

"Where is England?" someone muttered. "They will surely come and stop this!"

As if in reply, a desperate pounding sounded against the barricaded door of the shelter.

"You think that is England, already?" A ripple of nervous laughter filled the room.

"Maybe Hitler got lost and wants in." More laughter.

It was an odd thing to have someone knocking on the door with destruction raining down outside. And then everyone realized at once that it was not odd—someone had found his or her way to the shelter!

"Let them in!" cried a dozen voices in unison.

First the question was shouted, "Who is it?"

"Peter Wallich" came the muffled reply. "Please! Let me in! Is Rabbi Lubetkin inside? I have an urgent message!"

Heads swiveled to look at the rabbi. "Let the boy in," he urged.

Rachel shuddered at the thought of the door swinging back. She did not want the terrible noise of the explosions to fill the shelter. She snuggled closer to her mother and leaned her face against Etta's arm.

———

"*Please!* No, Papa!" Rachel begged. In the small storage room of the shelter, she wrapped her arms around her father's waist and clung to him.

Mama held the British passport in her hands as though it contained her every hope.

"Rachel," Mama said gently. "God has heard my prayers and answered." She put a hand on Rachel's shoulders, and the girl turned and buried her face against her mother.

"Mama! I don't want to leave you! Don't make me go with Peter! Oh, Mama! Let me stay with you!"

Aaron Lubetkin swallowed hard and stepped back. He could not bear to look at the misery of his only daughter. It would be easier for her to stay right here with them. Much easier for Rachel. Maybe even easier for him to allow her to stay.

"You must *choose life,* Rachel," he managed to say. His voice did not carry the authority of the spiritual leader of his community. Instead, there was only the grief of a father who must now bid his daughter farewell, possibly for the last time.

Peter Wallich waited outside the metal door. He had warned them that they did not have long. He had risked his life to come for Rachel. He would be risking his life to take her to the gates of the British Embassy to safety. And then he still had a journey to make.

How much longer did they dare take in this parting? Mama held Rachel close and stroked her hair. She kissed her daughter on the head as she perched on the crate and begged with an embrace that they not be parted.

Then Etta reached behind her and grasped Rachel's clasped hands. Finger by finger she pried them loose; all the while she whispered Rachel's name gently, as if she were trying to wake her from a nightmare. "Rachel? Rachel? Sweet Rachel? It is time. It is time to go now. We will meet again. Please. Rachel? You must go now. *You must.*"

Rachel sat back in a daze on the crate. So it was true. It was harder to choose life. Much harder.

"May I say goodbye to David and Samuel? To the baby?"

Papa opened the door slightly. David entered, carrying the baby. Samuel followed. Samuel was also crying, although he did not know why. The door clicked shut. Only one moment more . . .

Rachel embraced little Samuel first. She took his face in her hands.

"What's the matter, sister?"

"I have to leave," Rachel managed to say bravely.

"Will you come back?" His eyes were puzzled, frightened that she would leave the shelter and never come back. The streets were littered with friends who were not coming back.

Rachel looked to her mother for help.

Etta stepped forward and pulled Samuel into her embrace. "Rachel is going to be with Grandfather Lebowitz. To live at his house. She is going to the Promised Land."

"And you will come later," Rachel said. But the tears did not stop flowing; she did not truly believe in this dark hour that anyone would ever be in Jerusalem with Grandfather!

David stepped up and hugged her in a manly way as Papa held the baby. "The Eternal go with you," he said gruffly.

"And give you . . . peace . . ." Rachel broke. Only for a moment. Then she caught herself and took Yacov from Papa. The baby, not understanding anything, only felt Rachel's sorrow. He nuzzled her damp cheek with a sloppy kiss.

Then Mama took him from her and opened the door. Peter stood before her. She gave the passport to Peter, as if the passport were Rachel herself. Rachel's life.

Shalom. . . .

Rachel did not look at the faces of the people in the shelter who watched her leave. She followed Peter out into the smoke-shrouded sunlight. The sun was a red ball in the sky glaring down on Muranow Square.

The big horse of Dolek the milkman was tied to a broken branch on the great fallen tree in the square. Peter held her hand as if she were a small child. He led her through the rubble and helped her stand on the horizontal trunk of the tree and then boosted her onto the back of the animal. He jumped on behind her as the constant boom of bombs and artillery fire pushed against the hot air around the broken city of Warsaw.

Harvey Terrill leaned nervously against the wall of the south aisle of the cathedral. Directly behind him were the circular stone stairs, the first part of the ascent to the dome. Harvey had chosen to stand in that spot so he could see if anyone went up to the galleries. Now he was not at all sure why he did it.

What was he going to do, anyway? Tackle someone to prevent him from climbing the steps? Argue with the person?

Harvey could not take his eyes from the hazy hollow globe of the dome over his head. It seemed so vast and so high and so permanent.

It was hard to imagine that in minutes, both peace and permanence would be shattered right here in the heart of London.

The enormity of it made Harvey nervous. He thought of how much stone and lead-covered timber was over his head, and he wondered how impatient his partner with the trigger was getting. He wished this service would speed up. Didn't Churchill have more important things waiting? How long before the man would speak?

Elisa Murphy was shifting in her chair. That meant she was getting ready to play, and Harvey knew she was on the program right before Churchill.

Then Harvey noticed—she, too, was looking upward at the blue shimmer of the dome! Terrill's head snapped back. Was there something up there that gave the plot away? Had she gotten some clue to what was about to happen?

Harvey looked anxiously to see if any of the others were stirring. Had Churchill been warned? No; there he sat next to David Lloyd George and Anthony Eden and others of similar politics. Harvey forced himself to calm down, to think about what a blow would be struck here today. All of the anti-Hitler, anti-appeasement crowd were gathered in this one place.

Still, he wished it would hurry up and get over with. Even if this event was going to be bigger news than the Führer's speech, Terrill wished it would happen soon!

Besides, the two adopted brats of the Murphys' were staring up at the dome as if they knew something. How much longer?

———

Elisa trembled as she looked down at the reddish hues of the old Steiner violin. What had been Doc Grogan's last words? *Paul.* She raised her eyes to scan the majestic creation of Sir Christopher Wren. St. Paul's Cathedral. Could Grogan have meant. . . ?

Golden. She craned her neck to search up into the heights of the Golden Gallery, where Doc Grogan had spent his last hours with the children. *Paul Golden? A man?* Or St. Paul's? *Golden* . . . Golden Gallery! *Light wells!*

She listened as the last strains of Karl Ibsen's favorite symphony built to a crescendo. *Ibsen!* She looked to where Winston Churchill studied his notes in preparation for his coming speech! *Churchill!*

She let her eyes linger on the violin. Not the Guarnerius. Why had Murphy been intercepted by Polish customs and asked about passports? Illegal passports?

One more look to her far right told her she was not wrong. Harvey Terrill was staring up into the dome of the cathedral as though something was terribly wrong above his head. He glanced at his watch, shifted his weight from one foot to the other as if he wanted to run from this place.

Harvey. St. Paul's. Golden Gallery. Light Wells. Ibsen and Churchill.

Elisa leaned forward and looked around the sides of the sanctuary in search of Mr. Tedrick. Where was he, now that she needed him? Where was Tedrick? Whom should she tell, if not Tedrick? And what, exactly, should she tell? Could she be wrong? Had her imagination simply swirled away into the heights of absurdity?

"What is it, Elisa?" Anna whispered with concern. "Are you all right?"

Elisa nodded, and sat back. She continued to search the gathering for the enormous bulk of Tedrick.

Once again she followed the gaze of Harvey Terrill skyward. Was someone on the gallery, planning to shoot Churchill?

There was no more time to delay. Elisa stood and passed the violin to her mother. She did not know what she intended to do. She hoped that Tedrick would see her, that he would watch her walking toward Harvey Terrill. That he would see how pale she was, and *know*.

Harvey nodded, with nervous pleasantness, strained at every muscle in his face and eyes. He glanced at his watch. Looking down at the floor and ignoring her approach, he began to walk slowly, *too calmly* back toward the grand entrance.

He then saw Elisa start toward him. This was not right. He did not know what she knew, or guessed, or had figured out, but she was coming toward him instead of going up to play her violin. Something was wrong!

The only thing Terrill could think of doing was to give the signal early. Now, in fact!

He started for the west entrance along the south aisle, walking deliberately at first, then faster and faster as panic took hold. What if she signaled someone? What if she called to him to stop, shouted out for the crowd to run out of the church?

Behind him, he heard Churchill being introduced. Speaker and showman that he was, Churchill was covering for any awkwardness at the change in program, going on smoothly, moving into his talk. "In this solemn hour it is a consolation to recall our repeated efforts for peace. Outside, the storms of war may blow and the lands may be lashed with the fury of its gales, but in our hearts this morning there is peace."

Not for long would there be peace! Just the time it took for Harvey to run out the door and down the steps to the statue of Queen Anne. Then there would be no peace in this place—in this whole nation— except the peace of the grave!

———

"Close your eyes!" Peter shouted to Rachel as the horse picked its way through the rubble of a residential area.

She saw a child's broken doll. A hat beneath a brick. A photo in a broken frame. The scattered pages of a book. And, aware that this was the death of something . . . someone . . . she closed her eyes and pressed back against Peter's bony chest.

She held on to the mane tightly as the horse picked up its feet in a more steady rhythm once again.

"All right," Peter instructed. "We are past it. Open your eyes."

She did so, and saw a miracle. They trotted down an ordinary street, lined on either side with regular apartment buildings. The windows were taped, but not broken. There were even a few red geraniums in window boxes. A few cars remained parked along the straight, unbroken street that stretched out before them. *The cars must not run,* Rachel thought, *or they would be with the Polish Army right now being blown to pieces!*

She and Peter seemed to be the only living souls on all that long expanse of city street. It was the street that led to the British Embassy, Peter explained. He would make sure she was taken care of, and then he would meet up with Captain Orde on the wharf of the Vistula. From there, he said, they would escape upriver.

This is all like a story in a storybook, Rachel thought. Some other day she might like to sit and read such an exciting fairy tale. But this was a *real* story—her own story—and so for now she wanted somehow to step out of the pages of this living hell and find a quiet place to sleep, to lay her head on Mama's lap and pretend it was not happening!

"Only three blocks," Peter said, nudging the old horse to a faster trot.

Rachel did not reply. She felt no joy, no sense of relief at being so near to safety. She simply clung tighter to the horse's mane. She raised her head only slightly as the deafening drone of Hienkel's engine approached behind them. The horse did not quicken his step until the black shadow swooped down over them.

Peter cried out with alarm as the plane banked low over the housetops and rolled to circle back over them for an easy kill!

––––––––

The orchestra had stopped. Some part of the program was now complete. Allan did not know exactly what the order of the service was, but he knew they were one step closer to Churchill's speech.

He picked up the transmitter and set it on the balustrade on the side facing the dome. Just as quickly he took it down again. What if he should accidentally knock it off with his excited, agitated movements? Perhaps the impact with the ground would send the signal to the explosives; perhaps not. Allan did not want to take any chances—not now, not when he was so close.

He would go down in history! His name, *his* name, would ring down through time as the one who dealt oppression one of the greatest blows ever struck. Children would ask their grandparents where they were the day St. Paul's was blasted!

Allan's hymn of self-praise was interrupted by the sight of someone running toward the cathedral. The man sprinted up the hill, dodging around other people on the sidewalk and darting in front of a bus when one side of the street became too crowded. People don't run like that without a purpose. If this were simply a late arrival who did not want to miss Churchill's speech, he would not be running this desperately, this doggedly.

Allan pivoted sharply and grabbed the transmitter. He flicked the power switch on and was rewarded with an answering gleam from a small bulb lighting a dial that masked the device's real purpose. Should he press the button now? Should he wait for Harvey's signal?

There was a clatter on the steps of the cathedral. Even before Harvey Terrill had appeared beside the statue, Allan knew who it was. He braced himself for the blast. Strange how he had never thought about how loud the explosion would be. He wondered if he should have brought some earplugs. Well, it was too late to worry about it now. With deliberately applied firmness, Allan pressed the transmitter button.

———

Peter kicked the clumsy horse hard and pulled the one rein to the left. Urging the animal up three stone steps, he leaped from its back and grabbed Rachel to dash back into the archway of a small church. Peter slapped the big horse hard on the neck. There was no room to shelter it here. Its broad rump was sticking out as if to point to a target for the German airplane!

"Get!" Peter roared at the horse. He flapped his arms as Rachel crouched down beside the door and covered her head. "Run! Stupid horse! Run!"

The horse spun on its heels and trotted off down the road. The rein dragged along beside it. The booming roar of the double-engine plane filled every corner of the street. The burst of machine-gun fire popped a staccato dance as bullets sparked against the cobblestones at the heels of the animal.

Rachel screamed as the roar echoed and the plane climbed up above the city again. But the pilot had other things to do, apparently. He did not come back. The horse trotted a ways and then stepped on his rein again.

Peter grabbed Rachel by her blouse and pulled her down the steps. He ran to the horse, took the leather strap of the rein, but did not bother to climb back on the animal.

There, in front of the British Embassy, stood a small knot of desperate people clinging to the gates as a man in an English army uniform checked documents.

Peter stopped across the street, removed Rachel's blue folder from his pocket and gave it to her.

"There," he said. "Go and be well."

She did not thank him, because she did not feel thankful. She nodded, fingering the folder. "Goodbye, then," she said softly.

"I can't miss the boat." Peter had already led the horse to stand beside a banister. He climbed the banister and leaped onto the back of his mount. "Now get going!" he shouted at her angrily. *"Live!"*

Rachel nodded and turned toward the frantic people at the embassy gate. Peter did not wait to watch her enter. There was not enough time. She stopped in the middle of the street and watched him as he retreated back down the empty street.

The big, slow horse did not vary his gait even though Peter kicked and flapped his arms wildly. *"Get! Get going!"* She could hear him shouting at the deaf animal. "Stupid horse! Hurry! Hurry!" The sun glinted briefly on his hair. He was like a clown—the high comedy of panic. Rachel smiled at his appearance in spite of herself. He looked as if he were trying to fly. Trying to make the aged horse of Dolek the milkman lift off and soar to safety above the dying city of Warsaw.

"Live," Rachel repeated the admonition to Peter. "Live and be well. Find your Promised Land, Peter Wallich."

One Jew! Would that one Jew who lived be someone like Peter? *Ah, the Eternal must have a sense of humor if it is Peter alone among us who lives,* she thought.

Peter turned up a distant street on his way to the river and the fish market. Only then did Rachel pivot and walk slowly toward the desperate people who begged at the gates of Great Britain.

She stood apart and looked at her own likeness on the page of the passport—black hair, serious blue eyes, unsmiling lips.

Rachel scanned the crowd. Maybe three hundred were there. Surely someone among them—some girl or young woman. . . .

Face after face, she studied those who pressed in and shouted for refuge. And then she saw her—a woman of perhaps twenty. She wore a white broad-brimmed hat that shielded her face. Her clothes were modern, stylish. She was shouting loudly, waving a Czech passport in the air. Her face was desperate. Czech passports meant nothing any longer, not since the Nazis had taken over in March.

Rachel smiled and remembered what Papa had told her: *"He who saves a life, saves the universe."*

Yes. This woman might pass for her sister, even without the hat. Ah, but *with the hat*, she could pass for the girl in this precious British passport that Rachel held.

Rachel walked quickly to her, and she pulled her to one side. "This is yours." Rachel extended the passport to her.

"No," said the woman. *She is very pretty,* Rachel thought.

"Yes. It is yours. I saw you drop it. Now go in. Live and be well." Rachel shoved it into her hands, then turned and ran back down the street, back through the broken city of Warsaw. She ran and ran. She would not look back until she reached the smashed square of Mura-now.

———

The sense of urgency that drove Murphy up Ludgate Hill was greater than the war, greater than the death of Doc Grogan, greater than the missing Lori. Elisa was at St. Paul's and Harvey Terrill was at St. Paul's! That seemingly innocuous information filled him with a nameless dread he could not explain.

He zigzagged across Fleet Street to miss a stretch of sidewalk blocked by a man unloading stacks of newspapers. Newspapers! *GERMAN ARMY ATTACKS POLAND,* the headlines screamed. *CITIES BOMBED, PORT BLOCKADED!*

Almost there. The bulk of St. Paul's dominated his path. From under the shadow of the west facade, the great dome itself was hardly visible. Only the lantern tower surmounted by the ball and cross could be seen from this low angle. Closer at hand, the bell and clock towers seemed to lean over the statue of Queen Anne.

From the doors at the top of the steps, Harvey Terrill burst into view and ran down toward the statue. He spotted Murphy at the same instant and skidded to a halt. A hideous caricature of a smile played over his features; the grin of a corpse. "Murphy," he said, and ran out of words.

"Harvey," Murphy demanded, "Lori was at TENS last night, wasn't she? What's going on here, Harvey? Who tipped off the Polish customs? Who's Paul Golden?"

"Not *who*, Murphy, *what*!" Elisa burst out with this exclamation as she dashed down the steps behind Terrill. "St. *Paul*'s. *Golden* Gallery. *Light Wells*. It's *there*, Murphy!" she shouted, pointing up at the lantern. "Whatever it was Grogan died trying to tell us, it's up there!"

Murphy grabbed Terrill's forearm and spun him around with his hand twisted up beneath his shoulder blades. "Let me go!" Terrill cried. "It's too late now. Too late!"

"Too late for what?" Murphy demanded. "What is it, Harvey? Where's Lori?"

Nothing happened! Allan pressed his finger against the button again and again! He switched the power switch off and pushed the trigger button again. Still no result—no satisfying roar, no crashing bricks.

He flicked the power switch back and forth. Maybe it was jammed! With each blink of the tiny light he pressed the firing button over and over. No screams of panic, no rush of smoke, no place in history!

Allan began to tear the back off the transmitter. Maybe a loose wire? There was still time . . . if only . . . He tore off one fingernail, then another. No tools! Why hadn't he brought tools?

With bloody fingers, he raised the device over his head and smashed it down on the stones. No explosion agreed with his anger. Allan stamped on the radio with his heel, but the only destruction he caused was to the device itself.

Wait! Perhaps there was another way. He dug into the satchel, tossing out film, light meter, camera strap. Under the false bottom was a pistol.

There was still a chance. No alarm had yet been given. No sirens, no rush of people for exits. To be a living hero would have been nice, but to become famous as a freedom fighter—even martyrdom was not too high a price.

"What's too late?" demanded Murphy again.

Terrill grew strangely silent. He looked intently at the bell tower, then the clock tower, as if he was confused. He stretched up on his toes to look at the lantern, standing as a sentinel against the peaceful sky. "I can't understand it," he mumbled.

"Come on then," said a grim-faced Murphy, dragging Terrill up the steps. "We'll figure it out together."

Once inside the south aisle, Churchill's voice was heard ringing into the thrust of his speech: "This is not a question of fighting for Poland. We must fight to save the whole world from the pestilence of Nazi tyranny. We must accept the challenge laid before us all by those who have so ably and courageously carried the torch of freedom. 'Lift it high,' their examples say. 'Let no tyrant extinguish it.' "

Tedrick met Murphy at the rear of the nave. "What's all this?" he asked in a dark whisper. Terrill was almost limp in Murphy's grasp, but he continued to shoot fearful and shuddering looks up at the dome.

"Harvey knows something about what Grogan was trying to tell us.

It has to do with the dome and the Golden Gallery . . . maybe Lori, too."

"And it's about today," broke in Elisa. "He said *Ibsen* and *Churchill* too."

A young man came out of the doorway that connected with the clock tower. He started to cross the nave directly toward Tedrick, then spotted the small group standing in the shadows and pivoted to walk rapidly down the north aisle.

When he reached a point opposite the stairway to the galleries, he increased his pace to jog toward the opening. Terrill seemed to come out of his stupor at the sight. "Take me back outside," he pleaded. "I don't feel well, that's all—I need air."

Elisa was the first to see the connection. "That man," she said, pointing. "He's going up into the dome!"

———

Alarmed by the disturbance at the rear of the service, a policeman moved to block Murphy's path to the stairs. No time to explain! With a move that would have done credit to a Penn State running back, Murphy faked the policeman out of position and dashed up the steps.

The left-hand spiral of the shallow steps cork-screwed upward. Above him Murphy could hear the clattering feet of his unknown quarry. Churchill's voice continued to follow him upward: "Our war is not for material gain. It is a war for the rights of the individual, championed by individuals of the highest, most resolute character. Shall we do less than they?"

The painted, glossy black treads curled up and up around a central support pillar marred by centuries-old graffiti. *T.S. 1776* was carved into the stone. *G.C. 1815.*

The footsteps tapping over his head now retreated in volume. Finally, out onto a landing, Murphy found himself at the base of the dome, where the huge half-globe rested on arches above the rotunda. Churchill's voice, echoing up from a hundred feet below, threatened to drown out the sounds of the other man's passage. "We must not underrate the gravity of our task . . ."

There he was! On the far side of the Whispering Gallery, beneath the watchful gaze of a painted St. Paul, the small, delicate-looking man disappeared into another doorway. He threw a look over his shoulder and caught a glimpse of Murphy's pursuit, then increased the tempo of his flight.

The audience reacted to the clattering footsteps overhead with annoyance rather than alarm. Churchill was saying, "We must expect dangers and disappointments . . ." Murphy ran past a scene of St. Paul's shipwreck, around the gallery, and through the exit door. The stone steps grew steep, the passage narrow. He ran ten steps upward to a wider tread for a landing; every few landings a crude wooden bench. But there was no time to rest. Murphy panted with the exertion, and his leg muscles burned.

———

One hundred eighteen steps upward from the Whispering Gallery, Allan Farrell burst into the outside air. He rushed around the circular walkway with its enclosing stone parapet. He no longer concealed his pistol, but carried it in his hand as he ran.

His plan was simple: he would ascend to the Golden Gallery, climb over the rail to where he could see a satchel of explosives concealed in a light well, and detonate the bomb by shooting the blasting cap.

In the instant of his martyrdom, twenty pounds of explosives would erupt three hundred feet above the floor of the church. Maybe the other charges would go off from the concussion, or perhaps just the sudden loss of support on one side of the tower would make it collapse anyway.

Regardless of how great the destruction, debris would shower down inside the cathedral. People would be killed; terror would reign. Allan felt a kind of exaltation at the prospect.

As he circled the gallery, he reflected that with the pistol in his hand he could have run directly at Churchill and fired. Allan was shocked at the thought. He was no common murderer, no assassin! Where was the drama, where was the glory in shooting a man with a pistol?

———

The Stone Gallery opened in front of Murphy's last step with an expanse of gleaming white railing set against a brilliant blue sky. Which way to turn now? Still another hundred feet to the Golden Gallery, where something waited.

Murphy vaulted up on a block of stone just as the man he was chasing reached another flight of marble steps leading back inside the dome. A small hand holding a large revolver swung upward, waved in Murphy's direction. A shot boomed and the bullet smashed into the stone balustrade with a crack of flying masonry as Murphy threw himself to the side.

Cautiously peering over the marble block, Murphy saw that the man had gone inside, into the space between the outer dome and the brick cone that supported it.

Clanging footsteps rang overhead, telling Murphy that his quarry was still racing up. The stairs here were made of iron, and rattled with every jarring step. A clockwise spiral of metal curved up another twenty feet.

When Murphy looked up, he could see the retreating form of the other man two spirals above him. Allan chose that moment to look down and spotted Murphy crossing a walkway. The gun boomed in the narrow, walled space and the echoes reverberated throughout the dome.

The bullet flashed against the iron frame of the stairs, showering sparks from the ricochet. Another shot followed, making Murphy lunge to get directly beneath Allan, hoping to spoil his aim.

The terrorist returned to fleeing upward. At the last curve of the staircase below the Golden Gallery, he caught his toe on a protruding iron bolt. Allan fell, sprawling across the platform, the pistol jarred from his hand by the impact.

The revolver spun across the grill and teetered on the edge. Allan jumped for it. The swollen and clumsy fingers he had torn on the transmitter case brushed it, knocking if off the stairs.

With an angry cry, Allan watched it tumble to the next level down and bounce on the steps. When the pistol hit, it loosed another shot, this time directly into the bricks of the interior cone. A flattened lead slug zigzagged between the walls before dropping, spent, into the darkness below.

Both men, gasping for breath, stared stupidly at the revolver lying on the platform between them. Their eyes met, locked, challenged. They sprang for the steps. Allan hopped down awkwardly, the ankle that was twisted in his fall buckling beneath his weight. Murphy pounded upward, his legs on fire and his breath ragged in his chest.

Allan reached the landing first and bent to retrieve the pistol. Murphy, from behind, crashed into him, smashing him against the rail. They grappled for the gun. Murphy's greater strength twisted the revolver in Allan's grasp.

Allan's fingers, slipping from the grip, sought and found the trigger. He tried to squeeze off a shot into Murphy's face. Murphy's hands locked around the barrel and pushed it aside just as another round exploded. Powder flashed, burning Murphy's eyes. He threw up his hands.

Allan had the gun; he leveled it at Murphy's head. Murphy's eyes, streaming tears, watched the trigger finger tighten, the hammer start back. Then Farrell stopped.

Only one shot left! Allan needed it to detonate the explosives! He shoved hard against the dazed Murphy, trying to throw him over the railing. Murphy clutched desperately at the iron bar, hanging on. Allan hit him on the side of the head with the pistol, a weak, ineffectual blow.

Others had reached the spiral stairs and were coming up. Allan spun away from Murphy and clambered back toward the Golden Gallery. Outside at last, he hoisted himself up to the rail, preparing to jump down into the light well. At the moment of springing he was hit from behind; Murphy, grabbing for his ankles.

Allan leaped away, kicking back hard—too hard. He missed the opening; he had overshot the light well. He hung suspended from its lip, clumsily supporting his weight with his one free hand and two fingers of the hand still grasping the gun.

Murphy, staggering, appeared above the rail. "Give it up," he said. "It's over." Above him, he heard a muffled cry.

Allan gritted his teeth and tried to drag himself up and over the rim of the light well. If he could reach the edge and drop inside . . . But his strength failed. His feet could find no hold on the slick lead surface. He could hang there, but he could climb no higher.

Murphy watched, horrified, as Allan tried to aim the pistol over the rim and fire into the satchel. But his injured hand could not steady the revolver.

Allan Farrell had one chance left: if he hung from his elbows, he could use both hands to aim. One shot! One chance! "Don't!" Murphy shouted.

The blast recoiled the gun backward, jerked Allan's elbows loose, and sent him sliding down the dome. His face scraped against the curve of the dome he had sought to destroy. Slower at first, then faster, as the angle of the slope increased.

His body parted company with the dome and hurtled into space. He had an instant of thought, a momentary gleam of comprehension, just before his body struck the rail of the Stone Gallery. He knew he had failed; his last shot had missed.

———

The German Luftwaffe had smashed dozens of vessels, large and small, tied to the docks along the Vistula River.

The small fishing boat of Herr Frankenmuth was moored beneath a wooden roof beside a garbage scow. Hardly a worthy target for a crack Nazi pilot.

In this unlikely place, Lucy found the fish merchant working desperately on the petulant engine of his boat. Wrenches and screwdrivers were spread everywhere. The old man was covered with grease from head to foot. His son looked very worn out from the ordeal, although it was plain to see that perhaps the broken engine had saved them from disaster. The waters were littered with half-submerged boats that had attempted to flee the gun sights of the German planes.

Herr Frankenmuth barely looked up when a fighter buzzed overhead. This engine was his enemy now!

He wiped his rough hands on a rag that seemed less soiled than his clothes, then he looked up at the sound of approaching feet and chattering voices.

"Hans," he called to his son, "it is Werner the kitten!"

The son poked his head up from the belly of the boat.

Alfie was smiling and waving. He held Werner high over his head in greeting. "Hello, Herr Frankenmuth! Me and Werner have brought some friends."

"Huh?" said the son and the old man in unison. Near and far, the booming of guns accompanied the reunion. Father and son exchanged amazed looks. Should they be surprised?

"No fish today." Herr Frankenmuth stepped out onto the dock and into the center of a circle of sweating, grimy boys. "We have not been able to fish." He waved a hand into the air as a plane passed low over the shed. Its shadow flickered through the cracks between the slats of the roof. "And so far the Luftwaffe has not got our little fish in the barrel either."

Except for Herr Frankenmuth, the docks were empty. A fire was raging at the far end of the wharf.

Orde stepped forward, wiped sweat from his brow, and extended his hand. "Can I help?"

"Engine trouble," said Herr Frankenmuth. "We cannot find what is wrong. Tried all day." He nodded at Lucy. There was no time or inclination to talk. He turned to his son, who sat beside the starter. "All right, Hans, give it a try."

The younger man flipped the starter switch. There was a long pause. Nothing. He flipped it once again, and the motor sputtered and then rumbled to life. The old man's eyes widened. He looked at Alfie and then at Lucy. He reached up and scratched the ears of the kitten. "Well, well," he said, "I should have known you were on the way." Then, to Alfie, "Where are we going?"

"The Promised Land," Alfie answered.

"Ah, I should have known."

Behind them came the hollow clopping of a horse's hooves against the pavement, then a rhythmic *thunk, thunk, thunk,* as the horse came onto the wood of the dock.

It was Peter Wallich, looking very pained and tired but very relieved to see his companions.

The blue smoke of the motor rose up in the little shed. It was getting dark.

"The Germans should be heading back soon," Orde said. "They have had a successful first day. They'll be here with more in the morning."

Herr Frankenmuth frowned slightly and looked out toward the wreckage on the river. "Do you think it is safe to travel by night?"

Alfie put the kitten on his shoulder. "Look, Werner." He pointed to the far side of the riverbank, where wooden piers had been smashed and burned. "Do you see them, Werner?" He took the paw of the kitten and raised it up in a little kitten wave. Then he waved his big hand and called, "Hello! Yes! I see you!"

The boys beside the boat looked at one another strangely. There was no one over on the other bank. No one at all.

"Who is he talking to?" asked one under his breath.

"Who is over there, Elisha?" asked Peter as he came up to the group.

Alfie smiled. He knew that Werner saw them. After all, they had been following them all day. They had walked before and behind. They had hovered above and sheltered them with their shining wings when the German planes had swept over. How could the other boys not see them?

"Oh," said Alfie. "There are lots more with us than with the Nazis. We don't have to be afraid. They are going with us to the Promised Land, see?" He waved again—a close wave, just above the heads of Samuel Orde and Lucy Strasburg.

Epilogue

November 13, 1939

The sharp prow of the fishing trawler rose and fell in cadence with the rhythmic beat of the diesel engine. The Mediterranean was mercifully calm tonight. Even so, nearly half of the passengers on board the *Ave Maria* were seasick. The air below deck was rank with the sour odor of vomit and diesel fumes.

Sam Orde and Lucy made their way to the bow of the trawler. The cold wind and stinging salt spray against their faces were a welcome relief. Lucy shuddered from the chill. Orde put his arm around her and gripped the slick rail for support. His keen eyes scanned the midnight darkness for some sign of the British and German ships that prowled these waters.

The refugees on board the *Ave Maria* had been fortunate in their journey. Twice they had spotted the plumes of great naval ships on the far horizons of the sea, but the little trawler had slipped away undetected. Now, only hours away from the end of a long and desperate flight, Orde prayed that the tiny vessel might run the final blockade of British gunboats patrolling the coast. It seemed strange to contemplate that they must escape both Nazi and British ships to win their freedom. Either navy would gladly blow a shipload of Jewish refugees out of the water with never a pause to ask questions.

Sensing the apprehension of her new husband, Lucy leaned her head against Orde's chest. "We are so close now, Sam," she said, "and not one of us lost in all the weeks since we left Warsaw. We are almost home."

"Hmmm," he replied, sweeping his eyes over the star-dusted skies to where the darkness marked the rim of the world. "The coast is thick with patrols. It was true before the war. It is doubly true now."

"Spoken like a military man." She brushed his cheek with her fingertips and tucked herself closer against him. "The Lord would not bring us so far only to let us die within sight of our goal."

Her faith made him smile. He kissed her forehead and then turned his eyes back to the horizon. He believed that her words were true, and yet, this was the hour for vigilance. Alfie, Jacob, Peter, and the others had become the sons of his heart, his own dear family. He would not relax until they all stood together on safe and solid ground, until Lucy held her baby in her arms again.

As if drawn by the drama of these final hours, Alfie stumbled to find Lucy and Orde at the bow. Jacob and Peter followed on his heels, silent with apprehension. They, too, felt the peril of these last few miles.

Alfie cleared his throat and stroked the head of Werner, who was tucked into the boy's shirt. "Werner don't like the ocean," said Alfie. "I told him about crossing the Red Sea and God opening up the water so we could get through, but he still isn't happy."

"Everyone is sick," Jacob said.

"Except us," Peter added. Then, "How much longer, Captain?"

Orde raised a hand to a point where the constellation Orion rose over the black horizon. "Keep your eyes there, boys. You'll see it soon enough. A light. No bigger than a star from this distance, but shining from the darkness. That will mark the place we land."

Heads pivoted to stare hard at the lowest star in Orion's belt. Were they as close as that?

"Any sign of gunboats? Patrols?" Jacob asked. He was a soldier at heart, just like the captain. He believed in the angels that Alfie spoke of, yet still he watched.

"Nothing yet," Orde replied quietly.

Alfie was smiling broadly. The starlight illuminated his broad face with joy. Or perhaps it was his joy that lit the night. "There it is." Alfie pointed as a single beam of light winked on and off. "Look, Captain! Lucy! Look, Werner! Just like they said . . ."

"I didn't see it," chided Peter.

"Me either," added Jacob.

Neither Orde nor Lucy had seen Alfie's light.

"Oh yes!" Alfie insisted. "Look!" he cried, pointing toward where the shoreline certainly lay. "Me and Werner can see it! They are there! Right there where they are supposed to be! Can't you see?"

Still nothing but the stars and the darkness. The group exchanged looks. And then, right where Alfie pointed, a bright light for just an instant did indeed gleam.

"There it is! Look!" They shouted and clung to one another at the miracle of their beacon.

Alfie pulled little Werner from the protected covering and held him high over his head. "Look, Werner! Just like you always said it would be! Werner! It's the Promised Land!"

Authors' Note

The events following the Nazi invasion of Poland in September 1939 pursued a chaotic course, but one foreseen by Winston Churchill. England and France continued to vacillate about going to the aid of embattled Poland. Prime Minister Chamberlain sent threatening diplomatic communiques to the Führer, who was at the front lines in Poland within days of the invasion. No British or French troops, however, were deployed to Poland.

By the time the Allies committed to war, Poland had already been partitioned between Germany and Russia. Stalin used the opportunity provided by his pact with Adolf Hitler to swallow up the Baltic States of Estonia, Latvia, and Lithuania as well. The conflict and turmoil in present-day Europe are deeply rooted in that terrible era.

Where was the United States in all this? Why was the nation with such power to tip the scales on the side of justice simply a spectator from across a wide ocean? And what were the results of American neutrality?

In the research and creation of The Zion Chronicles and The Zion Covenant Series, these were questions we asked ourselves again and again, questions that we feel are worthy of further exploration.

The story of America is the story of our parents and grandparents . . . and yours as well. Eventually, the war raging in Europe would touch us even here. The sons of men who had fought in the Great War now would be called on to fight again in a much more terrible conflict. Ordinary beginnings on farms and in cities led to great bravery and memorable deeds. Boys who might have been considered average by everyone but their loved ones went on to turn the tide of victory against the Nazi darkness that engulfed the world. Wives, mothers, sweethearts remained behind to work in the factories and run the machinery while maintaining the homes that are the heart of a nation.

The gates of history swing on small hinges. The course of all the world can indeed be changed by the life of one man; by the prayers and faith of one woman.

It is the story of these folks that should be told next—ordinary men and women who lived through hard times and kept their faith intact until that moment when their lives became inexorably linked with those whom we have come to know in The Zion Covenant and The Zion Chronicles Series.

The Shiloh Legacy Series begins right here at home with the people we know best of all. . . .

Brock and Bodie Thoene
September 1, 1991
In My Father's House

---

*If you would like to contact the authors,
you may write to them at the following address:*

Bodie and Brock Thoene
P.O. Box 542
Glenbrook, NV 89413

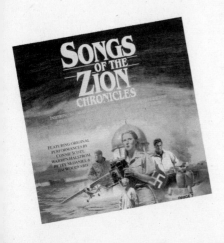